Biochemical Basis of Pediatric Disease

THIRD EDITION

EDITED BY

Steven J. Soldin

Nader Rifai

Jocelyn M. Hicks

AACC Press 2101 L Street, N.W. Washington, DC 20037-1526

Library of Congress Cataloging-in-Publication Data

Biochemical basis of pediatric disease / edited by Steven J. Soldin,
Nader Rifai, Jocelyn M. Hicks. – 3rd ed.
p. cm.
Includes bibliographical references and index.
ISBN 1-890883-01-08
1. Pediatric pathology. 2. Physiology, Pathological. 3 Clinical
biochemistry. I. Soldin, Steven J. II. Rifai, Nader. III. Hicks,
Jocelyn M.
[DNLM: 1. Clinical Chemistry Tests—in infancy & childhood.
2. Pediatrics. 3. Pathology. WS 141B615 1998]
RJ49.4.B56 1998
618.92´007—dc21
DNLM/DLC
for Library of Congress 98-19476
CIP

Production and editorial services by Evalyn Schoppet, Sterling Publishing Services
Typography by Business Graphics, Inc.
Cover design by Gate Roth Watts, Paper Graffiti

ISBN 1-890883-01-08

Printed in the United States of America.

Contents

Preface xiii

Philip A. Pizzo, M.D.
Physician-in-Chief
Chair, Department of Medicine
Children's Hospital
Thomas Morgan Rotch Professor of Pediatrics
Harvard Medical School
Boston, MA

1 *Pediatric Clinical Biochemistry: Why Is It Different?* 1

Jocelyn M. Hicks, Ph.D., F.A.C.B., F.R.C. Path.
Professor, Departments of Pediatrics and Pathology
The George Washington University Medical Center
Chief, Laboratory Medicine and Pathology
Children's National Medical Center
Washington, DC

2 *Respiratory Disorders* 17

Michele C. Walsh-Sukys, M.D.
Assistant Professor, Department of Pediatrics
Case Western Reserve University School of Medicine
Associate Director, ECMO Center, and Co-Director,
Neonatal Intensive Care Unit
Rainbow Babies' & Children's Hospital
Cleveland, OH

L. Kyle Walker, M.D.
Assistant Professor, Department of Anesthesiology
and Critical Care Medicine
The Johns Hopkins Medical Institutions
Director, ECMO Program
The Johns Hopkins University Hospital
Baltimore, MD

Billie Lou Short, M.D.
Professor, Department of Pediatrics
George Washington University School of Medicine
Director, ECMO Program
Children's National Medical Center
Washington, DC

3 *Kidney and Urinary Tract Disorders* 45

Elizabeth A. Harvey, M.D., F.R.C.P.(C)
Assistant Professor, Pediatrics
University of Toronto
Staff Nephrologist, Division of Nephrology
The Hospital for Sick Children
Toronto, Ontario, Canada

John Williamson Balfe, M.D., F.R.C.P.(C)
Professor, Department of Pediatrics
University of Toronto
Clinical Director, Division of Nephrology
The Hospital for Sick Children
Toronto, Ontario, Canada

4 *Biochemical Tests of Hepatic and Intestinal Disorders* 81

J. Calvin, Ph.D., M.C.B., F.R.C. Path.
Principal Grade Biochemist
Department of Clinical Biochemistry
Addenbrooke's Hospital
Cambridge, United Kingdom

G. A. Maguire, Ph.D., M.C.B., F.R.C. Path.
Consultant Biochemist
Department of Clinical Biochemistry
Addenbrooke's Hospital
Cambridge, United Kingdom

5 *Cardiovascular Disorders* 127

Ronald V. Lacro, M.D.
Associate in Cardiology
Children's Hospital
Assistant Professor of Clinical Pediatrics
Harvard Medical School
Boston, MS

6 *Growth Disorders* 157

Raphaël Rappaport, M.D.
Professor of Developmental Biology
University René Descartes, Paris
Head of Pediatric Endocrinology
Groupe Hospitalier Necker-Enfants Malades
Paris, France

Jean-Claude Souberbielle, Ph.D.
Assistant Director, Radioimmunology Laboratory
Department of Physiology
University René Descartes, Paris
Groupe Hospitalier Necker-Enfants Malades
Paris, France

7 *The Diagnosis of Pediatric Reproductive Disorders* 181

Claude J. Migeon, M.D.
Professor, Department of Pediatrics
The Johns Hopkins University School of Medicine
Director, Pediatric Endocrine Clinic
Johns Hopkins Hospital
Baltimore, MD

Gary D. Berkovitz, M.D.
Associate Professor, Department of Pediatrics
Division of Pediatric Endocrinology
The Johns Hopkins University School of Medicine
Johns Hopkins Hospital
Baltimore, MD

Patricia Y. Fechner, M.D.
Fellow, Department of Pediatrics
Division of Pediatric Endocrinology
The Johns Hopkins University School of Medicine
Baltimore, MD

8 *Disorders of the Thyroid Gland* 207

Wellington Hung, M.D., Ph.D. F.A.A.P., F.A.C.P.
Professor, Department of Pediatrics
The Georgetown University School of Medicine
Washington, DC
Senior Clinical Investigator, Developmental Endocrinology Branch
National Institute of Child Health and Human Development
National Institutes of Health
Bethesda, MD

9 *Disorders of the Adrenal Gland* 225

G. Michael Addison, M.A., M.B., B.Chir., M.Sc., Ph.D.
Consultant, Department of Chemical Pathology
Royal Manchester Children's Hospital
(University of Manchester School of Medicine)
Manchester, United Kingdom

10 *Disorders of Calcium and Phosphorus Metabolism in Infants and Children* 253

Ran Namgung, M.D., Ph.D.
Associate Professor, Department of Pediatrics
Yonsei University College of Medicine
Seoul, Korea

Ronald Bainbridge, M.D.
Maimonides Medical Center
Child's Center, Department of Pediatrics
Assistant Professor, Department of Pediatrics
State University of New York
Brooklyn, NY

Maria Lourdes A. Cruz, M.D.
Assistant Professor, Pediatrics
University of the Philippines
Manila, Philippines

Reginald C. Tsang, M.D.
Professor, Pediatrics, Obstetrics and Gynecology
University of Cincinnati College of Medicine
Executive Director, Perinatal Research Center
Children's Hospital Medical Center
Cincinnati, OH

11 *Disorders of Carbohydrate Metabolism in Infants and Children* 273

Denis Daneman, M.B., B.Ch., F.R.C.P.(C)
Professor, Department of Pediatrics
University of Toronto
Chief, Division of Endocrinology
The Hospital for Sick Children
Toronto, Ontario, Canada

12 *Neurologic and Psychiatric Disorders* 303

Roger J. Packer, M.D.
Professor of Neurology and Pediatrics
The George Washington University School of Medicine
Chairman, Department of Neurology
Children's National Medical Center
Washington, DC

Stephen I. Deutsch, M.D., Ph.D.
Professor of Psychiatry
Associate Chairman for Clinical Neurosciences
Department of Psychiatry
Georgetown University School of Medicine
Chief, Psychiatry Service
Department of Veteran Affairs Medical Center
Washington, DC

13 *Primary Immunodeficiency Diseases* 339

Maria M. Chan, Ph.D.
Director, Immunology
Department of Laboratory Medicine
Associate Professor, Pediatrics and Pathology
The George Washington University School of Medicine
Children's National Medical Center
Washington, DC

Brett J. Loechelt, M.D.
Attending Physician
Special Immunology Service
Assistant Professor of Pediatrics
The George Washington University School of Medicine
Washington, DC

14 *Autoimmune Disorders of Childhood* 363

Robert N. Lipnick, M.D., F.A.A.P., F.A.C.R.
Associate Professor
Department of Pediatrics
University of Virginia
Charlottesville, VA

15 *The Laboratory and Adolescent Medicine* 377

John T. Repke, M.D.
The Chris J. and Marie A. Olson Professor of
Obstetrics and Gynecology
Chairman, Department of Obstetrics and Gynecology
University of Nebraska Medical Center
Omaha, NE

Sue Ellen Carpenter, M.D.
Assistant Professor, Department of Gynecology and Obstetrics
Emory University School of Medicine
Atlanta, GA

Michele D. Wilson, M.D.
Assistant Professor, Department of Pediatrics
The Johns Hopkins University School of Medicine
Baltimore, MD

16 *Clinical and Laboratory Approach to the Diagnosis of Inherited Genetic Disorders* 397

Harvey J. Stern, M.D., Ph.D.
Genetics & IVF Institute
Fairfax, VA
Clinical Associate Professor of Human Genetics
Virginia Commonwealth University
Medical College of Virginia
Richmond, VA

17 *Genetic Metabolic Disorders* 419

Lawrence Sweetman, Ph.D.
Director, Mass Spectrometry Laboratory
Institute of Metabolic Disease
Baylor University Medical Center
Dallas, TX

Julian C. Williams, M.D., Ph.D.
Associate Professor, Department of Pediatrics
University of Southern California School of Medicine
Head, Division of Medical Genetics
Children's Hospital Los Angeles
Los Angeles, CA

18 *Disorders of Lipid and Lipoprotein Metabolism in Children and Adolescents* 457

Nader Rifai, Ph.D., F.A.C.B.
Associate Professor of Pediatrics and Pathology
Harvard Medical School
Director, Clinical Chemistry
Children's Hospital
Boston, MA

Peter O. Kwiterovich, Jr., M.D.
Professor of Pediatrics and Medicine
Director of the Lipid Research-Atherosclerosis Unit
The Johns Hopkins University School of Medicine
Baltimore, MD

19 *Diagnosis and Management of Pediatric Tumors* 489

Guy Young, M.D.
Clinical Instructor of Pediatrics
The George Washington University School of Medicine
Washington, DC
Senior Fellow
Department of Hematology-Oncology
Children's National Medical Center

Karen L. Kaucic, M.D.
Assistant Professor, Department of Pediatrics
The George Washington University School of Medicine
Children's National Medical Center
Washington, DC

Gregory H. Reaman, M.D.
Professor, Department of Pediatrics
The George Washington University School of Medicine
Chairman, Department of Hematology/Oncology
Children's National Medical Center
Washington, DC

20 *Disorders of Porphyrin Metabolism* 515

George H. Elder, B.A., M.D., F.R.C. Path., F.R.C.P.
Professor and Head of Department
Department of Medical Biochemistry
University of Wales College of Medicine
Cardiff, United Kingdom

21 *Therapeutic Drug Monitoring and Clinical Toxicology in a Pediatric Hospital* 533

Steven J. Soldin, Ph.D., F.A.C.B., F.C.A.C.B.
Professor, Departments of Pediatrics and Pathology
George Washington University School of Medicine
Director, Clinical Chemistry
Department of Laboratory Medicine
Children's National Medical Center
Washington, DC

Tai C. Kwong, Ph.D., F.A.C.B.
Professor, Department of Pathology and Laboratory Medicine
University of Rochester
Director Toxicology and Associate Director Clinical Chemistry
Strong Memorial Hospital
Rochester, NY

22 *Assessment of Nutritional Status: The Role of the Laboratory* 571

Clodagh M. Loughrey, M.D., M.R.C.P.(U.K.), Dip. R.C. Path.
Fellow in Clinical Chemistry
Harvard Medical School
Department of Laboratory Medicine
Children's Hospital
Boston, MA

Christopher Duggan, M.D., M.P.H.
Assistant Professor of Clinical Pediatrics
Harvard Medical School
Director, Clinical Nutrition Service
Children's Hospital
Boston, MA

23 *The Biochemical Basis for Red Blood Cell Disorders* 599

Jeanne A. Lumadue, M.D., Ph.D.
Assistant Professor, Pediatrics and Pathology
George Washington University
Director, Hematology/Stem Cell Laboratory
Children's National Medical Center
Washington, DC

Carlo Brugnara, M.D.
Associate Professor of Pathology
Harvard University
Boston, MA
Department of Laboratory Medicine
Children's Hospital
Washington, DC

Index 637

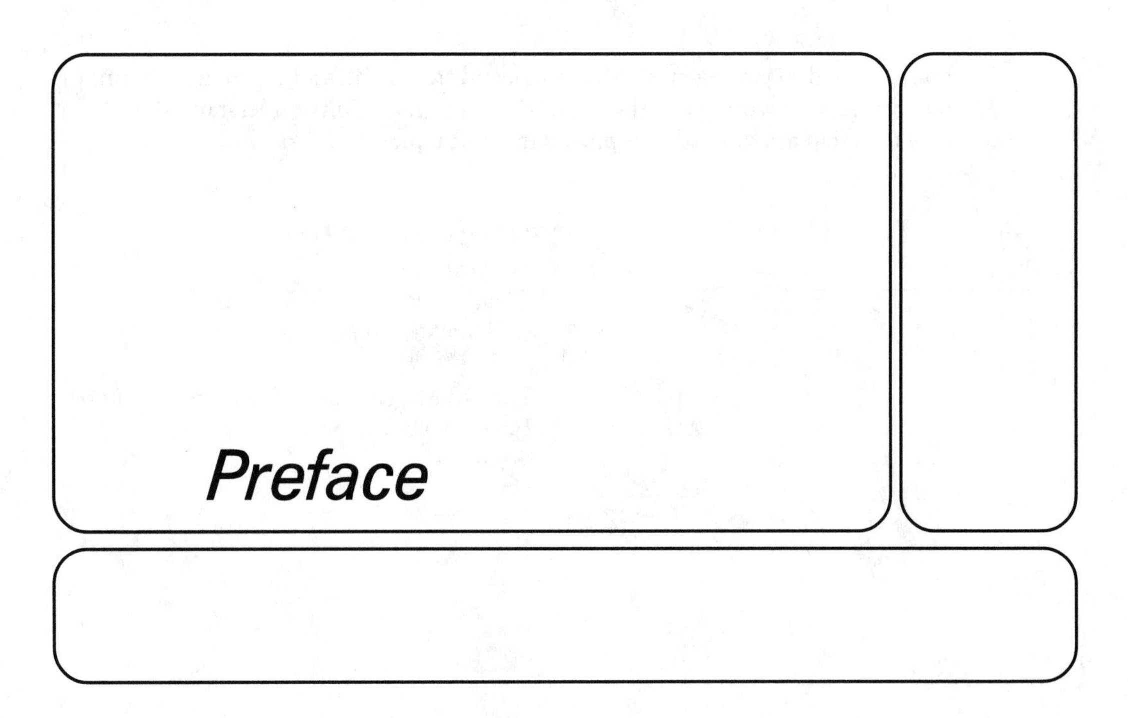

Preface

During the last several decades, the diagnosis and management of children have become increasingly sophisticated and dependent on an ever-increasing array of imaging and laboratory testing. Although a careful and well considered history and physical examination still stands as the starting point for all diagnostic and therapeutic interventions, modern medicine simply could not be practiced without the support of highly sophisticated and increasingly specific laboratory tests. Although the use of laboratory testing has become integrally related to modern pediatric practice, the depth of knowledge of most pediatricians about what they are measuring, and what the results truly mean, is less than most would desire. Indeed, the basis for current laboratory monitoring is insufficiently taught and incompletely understood by many pediatricians who utilize this information in the care of their patients.

Thankfully, with the Third Edition of *Biochemical Basis of Pediatric Disease,* edited by Drs. Soldin, Rifai, and Hicks, pediatricians have a wonderful companion to guide them through the evaluation and understanding of the laboratory studies that they use to guide patient care. The Third Edition, like its predecessors, begins with a general overview of pediatric clinical biochemistry, followed by a comprehensive review of the biochemical tests that are used to monitor and guide the diagnosis and management of children with virtually every form of illness. This is an extremely impressive compendium that provides information not available in even the most comprehensive pediatric text. For that reason, it can be synergistic with books related to pathogenesis, diagnosis, and treatment, and it provides an important foundation with which the pediatrician can more fully understand the laboratory tests that are routinely employed in clinical practice.

Philip A. Pizzo, M.D.
Physician-in-Chief
Chair, Department of Medicine
Children's Hospital
and
Thomas Morgan Rotch Professor of Pediatrics
Harvard Medical School
Boston, MA

CHAPTER 1

Pediatric Clinical Chemistry: Why Is It Different?

Jocelyn M. Hicks, Ph.D., F.A.C.B., F.R.C. Path.

INTRODUCTION

The big difference between a pediatric hospital laboratory and a general hospital is in the type of service provided. In the general hospital, the patient population is relatively similar, with a typical mix of surgical, medical, and critical care cases. The pediatric hospital has, in addition to the same types of cases that are found in an adult facility, a patient population that includes premature infants, newborns, and children at all stages of development, including adolescents and young adults. In fact, pediatrics is characterized by infant growth and development, upon which disease entities are superimposed. Issues that are of particular concern in a pediatric laboratory include the correct collection of specimens and the choice of appropriate instrumentation and methods whereby only a small volume of sample is used. The methods should not be subject to common interferences such as bilirubin, hemoglobin, and lipids. It is also important to have a knowledge of reference ranges by age. The diagnosis of metabolic diseases and an understanding of the pharmacokinetics of therapeutic drugs are a must for the pediatric laboratory. Other important aspects of pediatric laboratory practice include rapid turnaround time for results and a good performance improvement program.

BLOOD COLLECTION

Blood drawing is a major problem in pediatric medicine, especially from premature infants and neonates. In the Middle Ages, bloodletting using blood cups or leeches was considered as a cure for patients. Today, the collection of blood or other body fluids is used as a key to the diagnosis and therapy of disease.

Skin Puncture

Although venipuncture is practical and even preferred for older children, finger or heel sticks are better and less traumatic for young children and neonates. Other possible, although less desirable, sites are the great toe or the ear lobe. The lateral or medial portion of the plantar surface of the heel is the preferred site in neonates, but the finger is preferable for infants and young children.

Blumenfeld et al. first described the preferred way of collecting skin puncture specimens.[1] A possible complication of heel punctures is the development of calcaneal osteomyelitis. In his article, Blumenfeld showed that this can be avoided if the calcaneus is not penetrated during blood collection. The risk of puncturing the calcaneus is greater in premature infants because the distance between the dermal subcutaneous junction and the periosteum increases as the infant gains weight. If the puncture is less deep than 2.4 mm, there is no risk of puncturing the perichondrium, even in tiny premature infants. Since the distance from skin surface to the perichondrium is least at the posterior curvative of the heel, it is strongly advised not to use this position to draw blood. Figure 1–1 illustrates the best area from which to obtain blood from an infant's heel.

Procedure

In 1986, the National Committee for Clinical Laboratory Standards (NCCLS) published *Procedures for the Collection of Diagnostic Blood Specimens by Skin Puncture.*[2] Since skin-puncture blood is a mixture of blood from arterioles, venules, and capillaries and contains interstitial and intracellular fluids, it is important that the skin site be warmed prior to puncture, especially for specimens for blood gas analyses. The most practical approach is to use a washcloth or towel that has been soaked in hot

FIGURE 1–1. Sites of Collection from an Infant's Heel

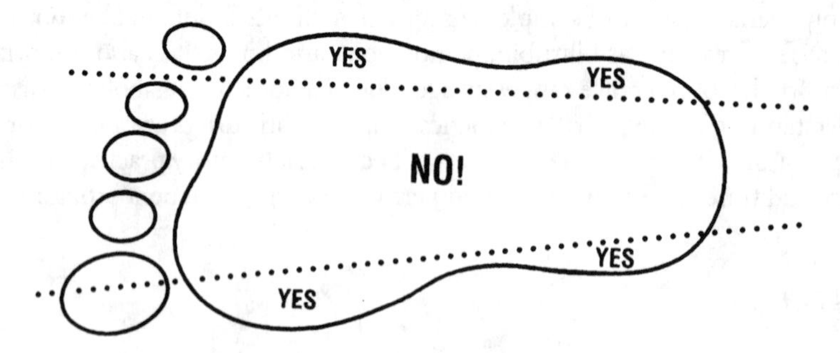

From: Blumenfeld TA, Turi GK, Blanc WA. Recommended site and depth of newborn heel skin punctures based on anatomical measurements and histopathology. Lancet 1979;1:231. Reprinted with permission.

running water (38–42° C). It has been demonstrated that warming the skin puncture site can increase blood flow sevenfold, and that it primarily increases the arterial blood flow.[3]

To prevent nosocomial infections, the person drawing the blood should remove all jewelry, wash his or her hands and forearms thoroughly up to the elbows, and put on a new, unused pair of latex gloves. After the infant's skin has been warmed, the site should be cleaned with a 75% aqueous solution of isopropanol (75% w/v). The site should then be thoroughly dried with a sterile gauze pad so that residual alcohol does not cause hemolysis. Betadine should not be used, as it can increase concentrations of potassium, phosphorus, or uric acid.[4]

A short-tipped, sterile lancet or an automated device that does not cause a puncture of more than 2.4 mm should be used. After the site has been chosen and punctured, the first drop of blood should be wiped away, since it is most likely to contain excess tissue fluid.

After blood has been collected from an infant's heel or finger, the limb should be raised above the level of the heart and a sterile gauze pad pressed against the puncture site until the bleeding stops. It is not advisable to use adhesive bandages for small infants, as their skin is sensitive. Also, there is a danger with infants that the bandage will be pulled off, placed in the mouth, and aspirated.

The Pediatric Committee of the American Association for Clinical Chemistry made recommendations regarding the actual technique for obtaining blood.[5] The infant's heel should be grasped with a moderately firm grip, placing one's forefinger at the arch of the foot and one's thumb well below the puncture site, at the ankle. The puncture should be made in a continuous, deliberate motion, in a direction perpendicular to the puncture site. The pressure with the thumb should be eased and reapplied as drops of blood form and flow into the collection device. Strong massage or "milking" should be avoided, since this can cause hemolysis or introduce interstitial fluid into the specimen, which could cause falsely increased values for analytes such as potassium and magnesium. There are also differences between skin puncture values and venipuncture values for certain analytes, such as glucose, where the skin puncture value can be up to 10% higher than the venipuncture value.

Venipuncture

This is the technique of choice with older children, as they have larger and firmer veins and are less likely to be psychologically affected by the sight of a needle. Generally speaking, the median cubital vein is used for obtaining blood. A tourniquet should be applied midway between the child's elbow and shoulder, with enough pressure to compress the vein but not the artery. A syringe with a needle attached or a vacutainer system may be used. In our experience, however, the needle of a 23-gauge butterfly works extremely well. This should be inserted in line with the vein at a 15° angle to the skin. Once the blood is flowing through the butterfly tubing, the tourniquet should be removed. The blood is then put into the collection tube. When the needle has been removed, a sterile cotton gauze should be applied with pressure until the bleeding has stopped (about three minutes) and then an adhesive bandage applied.

The recent introduction of EMLA (Astra, Westborough, MA) cream has been very helpful in alleviating the pain of blood drawing from pediatric patients. Its only drawback is that it takes approximately half an hour to anesthetize the site. EMLA contains lidocaine (2–5%) and prilocaine (2–5%) in a eutectic mixture.

Arterial Puncture

This is the technique of choice for blood-gas analyses. It should be done by an experienced physician.

SPECIMEN CONSIDERATIONS

Specimen Volume

Even though much modern instrumentation uses small volumes of specimens, specimen size remains of prime concern to the pediatric laboratory. This is because the number of very premature babies cared for in neonatal nurseries increases year by year. In our nursery, the number of babies under 1000 g ten years ago was approximately 9–10 per year; now there are more than 50.

Although the total blood volume of a healthy newborn is approximately 85 μL, that of a premature infant can be much less. Figure 1–2 shows how total blood volume can be estimated according to the age and size of the infant. Since the hematocrit in a newborn infant can be 60% or more, the yield of serum or plasma is often less than can be expected from the volume of blood collected.[2] Table 1–1 shows hematocrit by age. An infant's hematocrit reaches adult values by approximately three months of age.

In the premature infant, good planning of required laboratory tests should be done to avoid excessive blood drawing. The blood hematocrit and hemoglobin should be monitored and a replacement blood transfusion should be given if essential.

Evaporation

Specimen evaporation can be a major problem with small specimens. Rifai[6] has shown the effects of leaving serum samples uncovered for a period of 30–240 min (see Figure 1–3). It can be seen that in an hour, values can change by as much as 10% if the sample is 0.1 mL in size, whereas it is much less if the sample is larger, i.e., 5 mL (see Figure 1–4).

Interferences

Hemolysis

Several analytes in serum or plasma will yield erroneous results if they are measured in hemolyzed specimens. Potassium, magnesium, lactate dehydrogenase, and other constituents are present in higher concentrations in red blood cells than in extracellular fluid. Hemolysis will therefore cause increased concentrations of these analytes

FIGURE 1–2. Infant Blood Volume

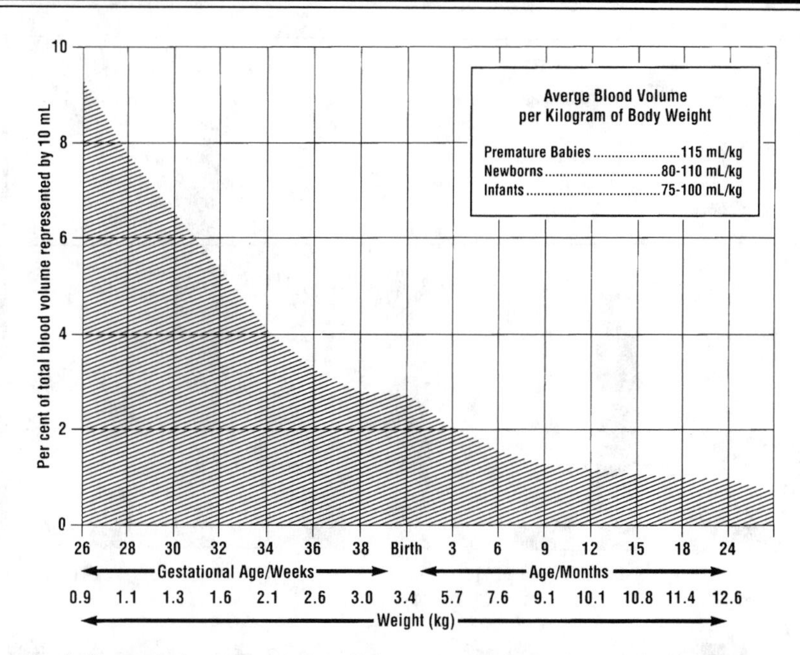

From: Werner M, ed. Microtechniques for the clinical laboratory. New York: Wiley, 1976:2. Reprinted with permission.

TABLE 1–1. Hematocrit By Age

Age	Hct (%) + S.D.
1d	61 ± 7.4
2d	60 ± 6.4
3d	62 ± 9.3
4d	57 ± 8.1
5d	57 ± 7.3
6d	54 ± 7.2
7d	56 ± 9.4
1–2w	54 ± 7.3
2–3w	43 ± 5.7
3–4w	36 ± 4.8
4–5w	36 ± 6.2
5–6w	36 ± 5.8
6–7w	36 ± 4.8
7–8w	33 ± 3.7
8–9w	31 ± 2.5
9–10w	32 ± 2.7
10–11w	34 ± 2.1
11–12w	33 ± 3.3

From: Matoth Y, Zaizov R, Varsaro I. Acta Paed. Scand 1971;60:318. Reproduced with permission.

FIGURE 1–3. Evaporation Effects on Serum Samples (sample volume 0.1 mL)

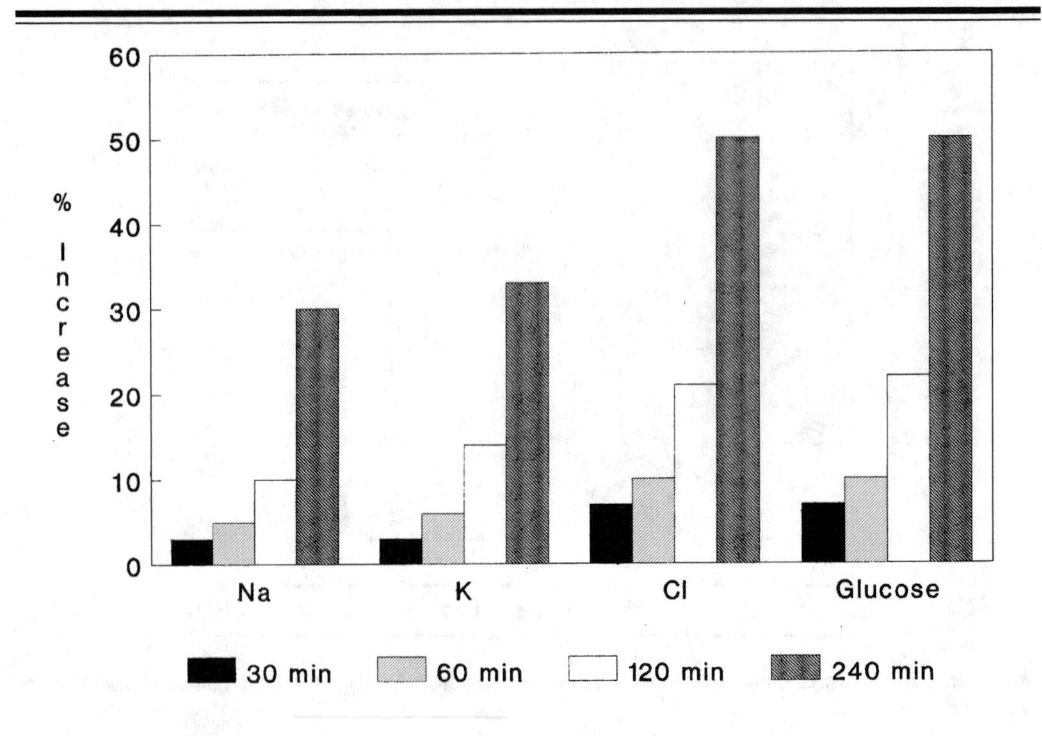

FIGURE 1–4. Evaporation Effects on Serum Samples (sample volume 5 mL)

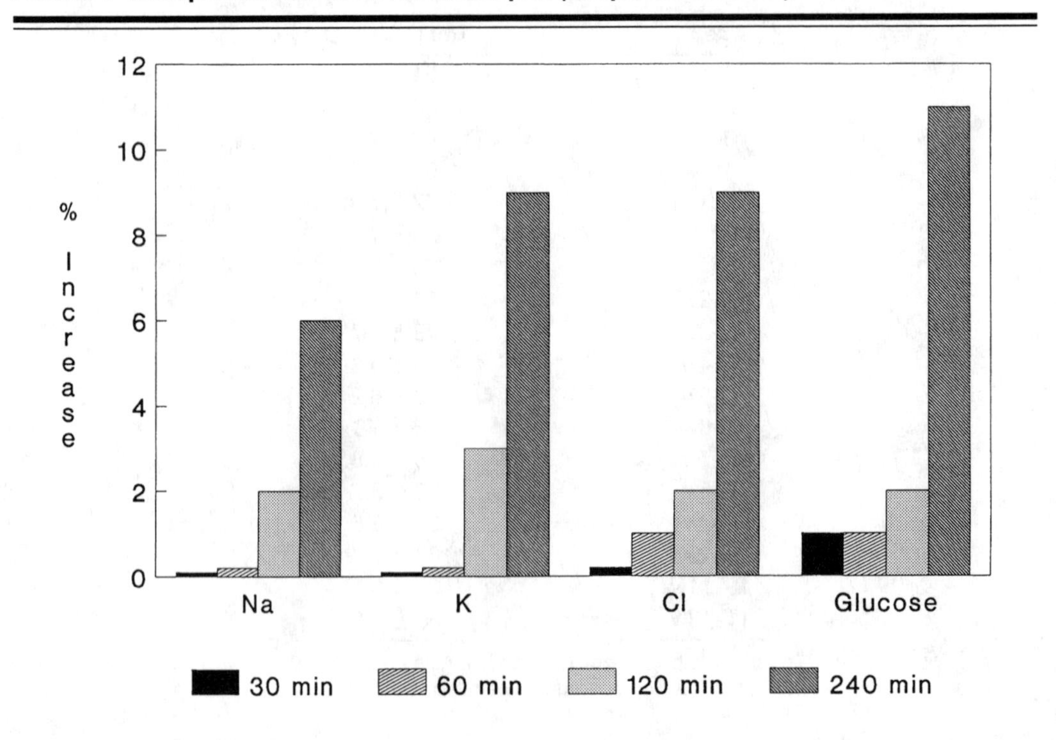

in serum or plasma (see Table 1–2). Hemoglobin can also interfere in the technical procedure; for example, the presence of hemolysis can cause a decrease in the measured bilirubin concentration. It is therefore important to avoid hemolysis when drawing specimens.

Lipemia

Premature infants receiving Intralipid (Kabi Vitrum Inc., Alameda, CA) may sometimes have lipemic blood specimens. Lipemia, especially if severe, can interfere with any analysis performed by spectrophotometric techniques or with sodium and potassium measurements using a flame photometer.

Bilirubinemia

Many premature and some term infants will exhibit bilirubinemia in the first few days of life. Bilirubin may interfere with certain analyses using particular instrumentation. For example, bilirubin will produce spuriously low cholesterol values when using the Cobas Mira (One Sunset Avenue, Montclair, NJ), and will also significantly lower the creatinine values obtained using the Hitachi instruments (Boehringer-Mannheim Diagnostics, Inc., Indianapolis IN). The Cobas Mira using Roche creatinine reagents employs a kinetic modification of the Jaffe reaction, with creatinine and picric acid at alkaline pH forming a red complex measured at 520 nm. The Hitachi instruments also use a modified Jaffe method using picric acid in alkaline medium. The color intensity is measured photometrically at 505 and 507 nm. The Vitros systems (Johnson and Johnson, Rochester, NY), which show no interference of bilirubin with the creatinine method, measure creatinine by its enzymatic hydrolysis to produce ammonia. The reflectance is measured at 600 nm. An

TABLE 1–2. The Effect of Hemolysis on Some Commonly Measured Analytes (↑ = increased, ↓ = decreased)

Analyte	Result
Acid Phosphatase	↑
Amino Acids	↑
Ammonia	↑
Aspartate aminotransferase	↑
Alanine aminotransferase	↑
Bilirubin	↓
Creatinine Kinase	↑
Iron	↑
Lactate dehydrogenase	↑
Magnesium	↑
Phosphorus	↑
Potassium	↑
Total Protein	↑

excellent guide to interferences in clinical chemistry instruments was published in 1987 by Glick and Ryder.[7]

Labelling the Specimen

Small tubes can be very difficult to label adequately. It is, however, essential to include the last and first name of the patient, the hospital identification number, the location of the patient (floor or clinic), and the date the specimen was obtained. The tube label should also be signed by the person obtaining the specimen. Since micro tubes are so small, it has been difficult to take advantage of the patient identification bar coding that can be read by certain equipment, but it is possible to find appropriate bar coding labels for the Becton-Dickinson Microtainers® (Becton-Dickinson, Rutherford, NJ). These labels can be printed on label printers made by MedPlus, Inc. (Cincinnati, OH). For primary tube sampling on the Vitros Instruments and the Immuno I (Miles Diagnostics, Inc., Tarrytown, NY) we currently use Becton-Dickinson 2.5 mL 100 × 16 mm vacutainer tubes containing a serum separator.

Collection Devices

Capillary tubes are needed for the collection of blood gases. These can hold up to 140° L blood (Ciba-Corning, Medfield, MA). These are heparinized with $Na^+/Li^+/Ca^{++}$ heparin. Specimens for blood gases should be mixed using "metal fleas." All blood-gas analyses should be performed immediately after the blood is obtained. The specimens should be received on ice.

Although somewhat expensive, the Microtainers or similar tubes are preferred for serum or plasma collection for neonates. These tubes have a serum separator and hold 600 μL blood. The tubes are easy to label and separation of the serum from the cells occurs after a single short centrifugation. In addition, the serum separator does not affect the values of most common analytes.[8] Plasma may be obtained by using a green topped (lithium heparin) microtainer tube. Common practice in our institution is to draw the blood using a Butterfly (Abbott Diagnostics, N. Chicago, IL) attached to a syringe. If larger volumes of blood are required for certain assays, such as hormones, the 2.5 mL vacutainers (Becton-Dickinson) may be used as collection devices. We do not use the Vacutainer® method of drawing, since the veins collapse easily in young children.

Choice of Anticoagulant

Although most laboratories in the United States use serum for the majority of clinical chemistry analyses, we recommend the use of plasma. This is because it speeds up the turnaround time, since one does not have to wait for clotting to occur, and there is generally less hemolysis. For most routine analyses, there is no difference in the results whether using serum or plasma.[8] Also, there is good evidence that plasma should be used for the measurement of potassium.[9] This is particularly the case in those patients who have high platelet or white blood cell counts. It is important to ensure that the anticoagulant used does not directly influence the analyte to be measured.

Heparin

The ammonium, sodium, or lithium salts of heparin may be used. We generally prefer the sodium salt. Sodium values are not increased with the measurement of sodium using sodium heparin tubes, because the concentration of sodium is very small compared to the concentration in serum or plasma.

Sodium Fluoride

This is the preservative of choice for glucose analyses. The fluoride prevents glycolysis and therefore stops the usual decrease in glucose that occurs if the specimen is left unseparated for a period of time. If the serum is not separated from the red cells immediately after collection, one sees a decrease of serum glucose of 7% in the first hour.[10]

Ethylenediamine Tetraacetic Acid (EDTA)

EDTA is used for the collection of whole blood for lead analysis. It is also used for the collection of hematologic specimens, as it does not destroy the cellular components of blood. The ratio of EDTA to blood is important for hematologic specimens. It is imperative that the tube be filled with blood. We recommend the use of the Microtainer tube or a similar-size tube.

Centrifugation of Microspecimens

Any small table-top centrifuge that can attain speeds of 10,000 to 13,000 ×g may be used. Serum or plasma separation can then be effected in 1–2 minutes.

Environment

When drawing specimens from children, it is important to have a pleasant atmosphere. It is advisable that phlebotomists wear colored uniforms rather than white. The rooms should be colorful as well. The phlebotomist should have a positive, pleasant attitude and should spend the time to put the patient at ease and gain his or her confidence. The child should be told what is going to happen, that it is going to hurt a little, and that it will soon be finished. It is very important to identify the patient correctly. With an inpatient, the armband should be checked carefully. With an outpatient, the parent, or the child, if old enough, should be asked for his or her name. Our performance standard for children is that venipunctures should be successful on the first attempt at least 90% of the time. This has been part of our performance improvement efforts, which has greatly improved compliance with this standard.

Collection of Cerebrospinal Fluid (CSF)

CSF should be collected by lumbar puncture by an experienced and qualified physician. Four separate sterile tubes are used for collecting the specimens. The first tube should be saved for future studies; the second tube should be used for microbiology and virology studies, the third tube for clinical chemistry studies, and the fourth tube for hematology studies. Protein analysis should not be done on a bloody specimen, because the contribution of protein from lysed blood cells and plasma cannot be assessed accurately. Specimens for glucose should be refrigerated.

Collection of Other Specimens

Fluids such as knee-joint aspirates and peritoneal, pericardial, and ascitic fluids should be collected into plain, sterile tubes by a qualified physician.

Urine Collection

It is frequently preferable to collect a 24-hour specimen, since urine specimens can be more or less concentrated at different times of the day. There can also be significant diurnal variation in the excretion of certain analytes. To collect a good 24-hour specimen, the bladder should be emptied and the specimen discarded, the time noted, and all urine specimens in the following 24 hours should be collected, including one at the same time of day as when the collection was started. The specimens should be pooled and mixed thoroughly. The laboratory should provide the appropriate container. Table 1–3 shows the correct preservatives to use. It is very difficult to collect specimens from neonates and young babies. It is recommended to collect specimens using a plastic bag designed for the purpose (U bag, Hollister Inc., Chicago, IL).

Since 24-hour urinary collections can be notoriously inaccurate, it is of value to know the expected urine volume from children of different ages so as to have some idea of the appropriate volume. Figure 1–5 shows expected urine volumes in the normal pediatric population. Specimens for urinalysis should be kept refrigerated. Early-morning specimens are also the specimens of choice for pregnancy testing and screening for metabolic disorders.

Fecal Collection

It is sometimes necessary to collect fecal specimens for specialized tests, such as fecal fat determinations for the diagnosis of pancreatic insufficiency, fecal trypsin for the diagnosis of cystic fibrosis, reducing substances for the diagnosis of sucrose intolerance, and fecal electrolytes to assess severe electrolyte losses. Stools may also be examined for the presence of occult blood. When collecting fecal specimens, the patient should be told not to contaminate the specimen with urine. A well-cleaned and boiled glass container or a plastic container may be used.

Specimen Transport

A general rule is that all specimens should be transported to the laboratory as soon as possible. This is particularly important for some analyses, such as blood gases and ammonia; these specimens should be transported on ice. Blood for a complete blood count and differential and urines should also be transported quickly, since cellular elements can disintegrate.

TABLE 1–3. Preservation of Urine

Test	Instructions	Preservative and Amount to be Used		
		< 6 mo.	*6 mo to 5 y*	*5 to 18 y*
Aminolevulinic acid	Protect from light	8 mL 6N HCl	15mL 6N HCl	30mL 6N HCl
Aldosterone	Add boric acid	2–5g H_3BO_3	5g H_3BO_3	10g H3BO$_3$
Arylsulfatase A	Freeze			
Calcium	Verify pH is < 7	8 mL 6N HCl	15 mL 6N HCl	30 mL 6N HCl
Catecholamines		1–3g Na_2CO_3	2–5g Na_2C0_3	5g Na_2C0_3
Coproporphyrin	Protect from light	—	—	—
Cortisol (free)	1g boric acid per 100 mL urine	—	—	—
Heavy metals	Adjust pH	8 mL 6N HCl	15 mL 6N HCl	30 mL 6N HCl
5-HIAAA	Adjust pH	8 mL 6N HCl	8 mL 6N HCl	30 mL 6N HCl
HVA		5 mL 50% HAC*	12 mL 50% HAC*	25 mL 50% HAC*
17-OH-Corticosteroid	Add 1 g boric acid per 100 mL urine	—	—	—
17-Ketosteroids	Adjust pH	8 mL 6N HCl	15 mL 6N HCl	30 mL 6N HCl
Lead	Lead-free container	—	—	—
Metanephrines		8 mL 6N HCl	12 mL 6N HCl	30 mL 6N HCl
Oxalate	Adjust pH	8 mL 6N HCl	15 mL 6N HCl	30 mL 6N HCl
Phosphorus	Adjust pH	8 mL 6N HCl	15 mL 6N HCl	30 mL 6N HCl
Porphobilinogen	Protect from light; *freeze*	—	—	—
Porphyrins	Protect from light; refrigerate	1–3 g Na_2C0_3	2–5 g Na2C0$_3$	5 g Na2C0$_3$
Pregnanetriol	No preservative	—	—	—
Urea nitrogen	Refigerate; no preservative	—	—	—
Uric Acid	No preservative	—	—	—
Urobilinogen	2 h timed specimen; *freeze* immediately; protect from light	1–3 g Na_2C0_3	2–5 g Na2C0$_3$	5 g Na2C0$_3$

FIGURE 1–5. Expected Urine Volumes in the Normal Pediatric Population

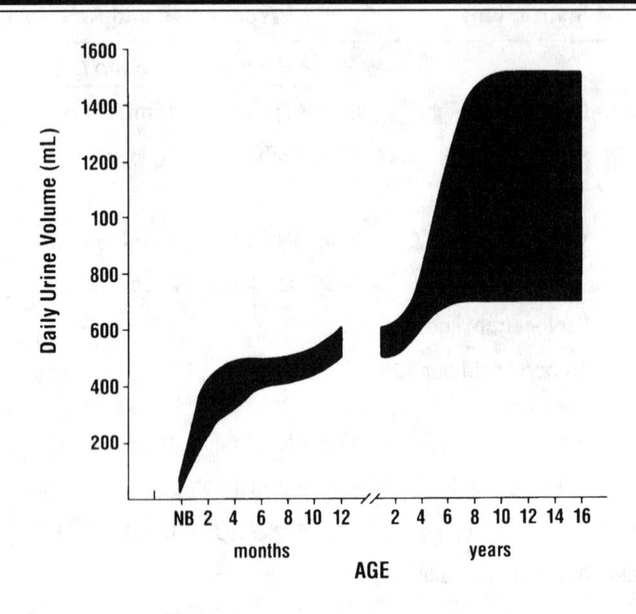

UNIVERSAL PRECAUTIONS

Because the potential *infectivity* of any patient's blood or body fluids cannot be known with certainty, it is important that the blood and body fluid precautions recommended by the CDC[11] be followed for all patients. NCCLS recommends that gloves be worn at all times when handling laboratory specimens.[12] It is also important for phlebotomists to wear gloves when drawing blood or obtaining specimens from patients. Laboratory coats should not be worn outside of the laboratory, but should be removed before going home, out for lunch, etc.

REFERENCE RANGES

Correct interpretation of laboratory data depends on the availability of appropriate reference ranges (normal values) for the age and development of the child. Laboratory data obtained from cord blood serum are often close to those of the mother's serum. Thereafter, they may change rapidly. For example, cord blood T_4 was reported by Walfish to be 85–225 nmol/L (6.6–17.5 ng/dL) and to rise at 1–3 days of age to 142–278 nmol/L (10.0–21.5 ng/dL).[13] Serum proteins, especially immunoglobulins, also undergo changes during the maturation of the neonate to an adolescent. The analyte that shows marked changes with age is alkaline phosphatase. During the growth spurts in infancy and adolescence, the serum alkaline phosphatase increases greatly to values which would be considered pathological in an adult. For example, the reference range on the Vitros equipment for a female aged 12–13 y is

105–420 U/L and at age 16–19 y is 50–130 U/L.[14] These reference ranges are also different for males and females. For example, at the same ages, the reference ranges for males are 200–495 U/L and 65–260 U/L, respectively. A recent publication by Soldin, Brugnara, Gunter, and Hicks[15] gives detailed pediatric reference ranges for clinical chemistry and hematology tests by age and sex for approximately 240 analytes. It outlines the methods, both technical and statistical, to obtain these ranges.

LABORATORY INSTRUMENTATION AND METHODOLOGY

In the pediatric laboratory, both methods and instruments should be chosen with the sample size in mind. For automated equipment, the sample size should probably be no bigger than 10 μL. Methods should be chosen that are not subject to interference from endogenous or exogenous substances. In particular, the common interferents bilirubin, hemoglobin, and lipids should not affect the results. As mentioned earlier, there is an excellent monograph by Glick[7] which shows the effect of common interferents on analyses using a variety of clinical chemistry analyzers.

Certain requirements are basic in the pediatric laboratory:

1. Care must be taken to minimize the evaporation of the sample, which can be considerable if specimens and samples are not kept covered at all times. The use of narrow, deep containers is recommended to reduce the area from which evaporation can occur.
2. Precise pipetting of small-volume specimens is essential.
3. A well-defined list of those tests which can be ordered on a stat basis should be developed in conjunction with the medical staff.

An important consideration that is often overlooked is the dead volume, i.e., the amount of sample that must remain in the sample cup after the samples are aspirated for analysis. There is no point to having a 5 μL sample requirement if the dead volume is 300 μL (see Table 1–4).

TABLE 1–4. Dead Volume Requirement for Certain Analyzers

Analyzer	Sample Volume (μL)	Dead Volume (μL)
Vitros (Johnson & Johnson)	10	30
TDx (Abbott)	50	10–20
ADx (Abbott)	50	10–20
Immuno I (Miles)	2–50	75
IMx (Abbott)	150	50
System 6300 (Beckman)	100	250 (Extraction)
HPLC (Hewlett-Packard)	100	N/A
BGS 288 (Corning)	140	N/A
SpectrAA (Varian)	200	N/A

N/A = not applicable

SERVICES OFFERED

In a comprehensive pediatric clinical chemistry laboratory, a wide variety of services and a large armamentarium of tests should be offered. It is necessary to provide services in the following areas: routine clinical chemistry tests, endocrinology, trace metals, therapeutic drug monitoring, toxicology, biochemical and molecular genetics, urinalysis, and immunology. In the area of biochemical and molecular genetics, the pediatric laboratory should be able to offer tests such as urinary metabolic screens, organic acids, amino acids, Tay-Sachs, Gaucher's, and fragile X on site. More esoteric genetic tests should be sent out. The laboratory director must keep a comprehensive list of such tests and the laboratories performing them. In today's environment of cost cutting to remain competitive in the managed care marketplace, reorganization of the clinical laboratory may become essential.

In our institution, we have reduced the number of sections of the laboratory to three: Rapid Response, Specialty Testing, and Transfusion Medicine. The Rapid Response Laboratory incorporates any test which is automated, whether chemistry, hematology, microbiology, virology, or immunology. In addition, any manual tests for which results could be required in less than one hour are performed in this laboratory. The turnaround time must be no longer than one hour and preferably 30 minutes or less. In this laboratory, we use a preponderance of technicians.

The Specialty Laboratory is an open, flexible laboratory which incorporates special chemistry, special hematology, virology, microbiology, molecular diagnostics, genetic/metabolic testing, and immunology. In this laboratory, we use mostly technologists.

The key to the success of the previously described two laboratories is cross-training. Each technologist or technician must be able to perform *at least* two types of testing, e.g., chemistry and hematology or microbiology and virology. The third section of the laboratory is Transfusion Medicine, which incorporates preparation of blood components for transfusion, the blood donor center for blood donations, platelet pheresis, and therapeutic pheresis and the hematopoetic (stem cell) laboratory.

Point-of-care testing in our institution has grown at a logarithmic rate over the last few years, from some random urinalyses and blood glucose tests to approximately one-third of our basic testing. This revolution in point-of-care testing is due to several factors, which include innovative and reliable technology, the demand for quicker results, changes in reimbursement strategies, emphasis on decreased labor costs, and better quality as well as service to the patients.

Most of the point-of-care testing performed in our hospital is done in critical care units such as the Intensive Care Unit, the Neonatal Unit, and the Emergency Room. In addition, some testing is done on the clinical units, the Operating Room, and satellite clinics located approximately 20 miles or more from the hospital. In the Emergency Room we offer testing for drugs of abuse, pregnancy testing, blood gases, electrolytes, blood urea nitrogen, and glucose. In the Cardiac Catherization Laboratory and Operating Rooms we offer activated clotting times and blood gases. In the Intensive Care Units we rely on the i-STAT (Princeton, NJ) technology for blood gases, blood urea nitrogen, ionized calcium, electrolytes, and hemoglobin. A nurse or other health care professionals can easily use these instruments. The test results and quality control values can be downloaded into the main laboratory information system.[2]

By moving to i-STAT testing at the bedside, we have been able to cut out the salaries of five technologists because existing nursing and respiratory therapy personnel now perform the testing. Although the cartridges make i-STAT technology more expensive than conventional testing in the central laboratory, a modest overall cost savings has been realized due to the labor savings in the central laboratory, elimination of transport charges, and much reduced costs for quality control and calibration. In recent months, this cost savings has improved as i-STAT's prices have been reduced significantly.

If a hospital central laboratory is to embrace point-of-care testing, several steps must be taken: One of the laboratory directors must be assigned the responsibility of overseeing the testing, a point-of-care coordinator must be hired, and a Coordinating Committee must be established. The coordinator is responsible for monitoring errors, training, and evaluating new point-of-care testing. This person should be a well-trained, experienced Medical Technologist. The Director is responsible for reviewing all the quality control, choosing the technology to use, responding to physician inquiries, and chairing the Coordinating Committee. The training component of point-of-care testing is extremely important, as is retraining on a yearly basis. With the turnover of nursing staff, the training can be a very time consuming and demanding task.

Choice of technology should focus not only on the obvious, such as the accuracy or precision of the tests, but also on the ease of use of the device and the ability for test results to be downloaded into the central laboratory computer. The Coordinating Committee should include the designated Laboratory Director (in our case, the Director of Clinical Chemistry), the Point-of-Care Coordinator, the QC Coordinator, Nursing Educators, Nursing Administrators, Respiratory Therapists, and a clinician. Sometimes it might be necessary to invite attendees from Medical Records, Information Systems, and Materials Management.

The benefits of point-of-care testing include quicker turnaround time; more responsive medical management; less testing; greater physician, nurse, and patient satisfaction; and reduced costs. It has not been well established whether medical outcomes are better as a result of testing at the bedside, and it is essential that these types of studies be conducted.

As we move even more into an era of decreased reimbursement and increased competition between hospitals, it is important that the clinical laboratory of a pediatric hospital make testing easier and more patient-friendly. As the costs of point-of-care technology decrease, this is clearly an attractive way to provide laboratory testing, especially in critical care areas.

Given that the diagnosis and therapy of disease is the *raison d'être* of the clinical pathology laboratory, it is essential to staff the laboratory with a skilled technical staff and directors at the M.D. and Ph.D. level. These directors must be available 24 hours a day, seven days a week, through an "on-call" system. In addition, the laboratory physician and scientist should offer consultation services, particularly in the areas of therapeutic drug monitoring and the diagnosis of genetic and metabolic diseases. It is through good planning and goal setting that an excellent service can be provided to allow the laboratory to assist the physician in his or her task of patient care. The quality of the work must be assessed constantly through good quality-control, quality-assurance, and continuous quality-improvement programs.

Some of this text is taken from Hicks JM, Boeckx, RL, in Pediatric Clinical Chemistry, W. B. Saunders Company, Philadelphia, PA, with permission from the publisher.

REFERENCES

1. Blumenfeld TA, Turi GK, Blanc WA. Recommended site and depth of newborn heel skin punctures based on anatomical measurements and histopathology. Lancet 1979;1:230–33.
2. Procedures for the collection of diagnostic blood specimens by skin puncture, 2nd ed. NCCLS Approved Standard, 1986.
3. Wilkinson RH. Chemical micromethods in clinical medicine. Springfield, IL: Charles C Thomas, 1960:19–25.
4. Van Steirteghem AC, Young DS. Povidone-iodine (betadine) disinfectant as a source of error. Clin Chem 1977;23:1512–6.
5. Meites S, Levitt MJ. Skin puncture and blood collecting techniques for infants. Clin Chem 1979;25:183–89.
6. Rifai N. Personal communication.
7. Glick MR, Ryder K. Interferographs: User's guide to interferences in clinical chemistry instruments. Indianapolis: Science Enterprises, Inc., 1987.
8. Hicks JM, Rowland GL, Buffone GJ. Evaluation of a new blood collecting device ("Microtainer") that is suited for pediatric use. Clin Chem 1976;22:2034–6.
9. Oski FA. Hematological problems in neonatology. In: Neonatology: Pathophysiology and management of the of the newborn, 2nd ed. GB Avery, Ed. Philadelphia: J.B. Lippincott Co., 1994.
10. Weissman M, Klein B. Evaluation of glucose determinations in untreated serum samples. Clin Chem 1958;4:420–4.
11. CDC update: Universal precautions for prevention of transmission of human immunodeficiency virus, hepatitis B virus, and other bloodborne pathogens in health-care settings. MMWR 37:377–87, 1988.
12. Protection of laboratory workers from infectious disease transmitted by blood, body fluids and tissue. NCCLS Document M29-T, 1989:18.
13. Walfish PG. Thyroid function in pediatrics. In: Hicks JM, Boeckx RL., eds., Pediatric clinical chemistry. Philadelphia: Saunders, 1984:170–239.
14. Lockitch G, Halstead AC In: Meites S, Ed., Pediatric clinical chemistry: Reference (normal) values, Washington, DC: AACC Press, 1988:209.
15. Soldin SJ, Brugnara C, Gunter KC, Hicks, JM. Pediatric reference ranges. Washington, DC: AACC Press, 1997.

CHAPTER 2

Respiratory Disorders

Michele C. Walsh-Sukys, M.D., L. Kyle Walker, M.D., Billie Lou Short, M.D.

INTRODUCTION

This chapter describes the clinical picture of the most common pediatric respiratory disorders seen in the neonatal and pediatric intensive care setting. By far, the most common disorder encountered in the neonatal intensive care unit is respiratory distress syndrome. This single entity is associated with 30% of all neonatal deaths and 50–70% of premature deaths in the United States. This disorder is primarily seen in the preterm infant; disorders such as persistent pulmonary hypertension, pneumonia, and meconium aspiration are diseases of the term infant and are far less common than respiratory distress syndrome. Another common finding in premature infants who have resolved their pulmonary disease is apnea of prematurity, which can be so severe that mechanical ventilation is needed. Infants who require ventilator or oxygen support may sustain lung injury from such therapies, called "bronchopulmonary dysplasia." This disorder is more commonly seen in the very immature infant (< 28 w gestation).

The older child's respiratory diseases are much less homogenous when compared to the newborn, but in general can be grouped into upper and lower airway diseases. Although upper airway diseases can be emergent, life-threatening disorders, they represent only a small number of the admissions to a pediatric intensive care unit as compared to the lower respiratory disorders.

Lower airway disease can be divided into disorders of the bronchi and conducting airways and diseases of the alveoli. Each is discussed in detail in this chapter.

NEONATAL RESPIRATORY DISORDERS

Respiratory Distress Syndrome

Respiratory Distress Syndrome (RDS), formerly called hyaline membrane disease, is due to pulmonary surfactant deficiency. Surfactant deficiency is usually a developmental condition related to immaturity of the neonatal lung, but any number of insults may perturb the complex and delicate enzymatic systems responsible for surfactant synthesis and produce a picture indistinguishable from that seen in the preterm infant. Thus, RDS has been described in term infants and in older children as well as adults.[1] However, prematurity remains the single most important risk factor for RDS. The incidence and severity of RDS decreases with increasing gestational age, with fully 70% of those infants born at 28–30 w gestation manifesting full-blown RDS.

In the classical presentation of RDS, a premature infant may appear well initially, but shortly after birth may develop tachypnea, signs of compromised respiration, and use of the accessory muscles of ventilation (grunting, nasal flaring, and intercostal retractions). Hypoxemia is the presenting feature on arterial blood gas analysis, but increases of carbon dioxide are seen as the disease progresses. Radiographic study of the chest reveals a hazy ground-glass appearance in mild RDS, while complete opacification of the lung fields may be seen in more severe disease. Clinical symptoms worsen over the first 3–5 d of life and then begin to subside slowly. Clinical improvement is frequently heralded by a urinary diuresis.[2]

The primary biochemical defect in RDS is a deficiency of pulmonary surfactant. The molecular biology of surfactant synthesis has been well described by Weaver and Whitsett.[3] Pulmonary surfactant is composed of 80–90% phospholipid and 10% protein. In human surfactant, phosphatidylcholine represents 80% of the total phospholipid and is enriched in desaturated forms of phosphatidylcholine. The phospholipid fraction is the primary surface tension lowering component of pulmonary surfactant. Four distinct surfactant-associated proteins have been described. SP-A is the most abundant lipid-associated protein in pulmonary surfactant. It is synthesized by respiratory epithelial cells in the fetal lung, with increasing expression in late gestation. The functions of SP-A have not been fully elucidated, but *in vitro* work has confirmed its ability to aggregate phospholipids in a calcium-dependent manner and, together with SP-B, to generate tubular myelin-like structures. *In vitro* SP-A binds to Type II epithelial cells and to macrophages. Data from this work suggest that SP-A plays an important regulatory role in surfactant synthesis.

The other major surfactant-associated proteins—B, C, and D—are small hydrophobic molecules. Their function is less well defined, but evidence suggests that they play an important role in maintaining phospholipid components in an alignment that optimally reduces surface tension.

Nogee and others have described several cases of congenital surfactant protein B deficiency.[4–6] These infants were all full term and presented with severe respiratory distress shortly after birth. The respiratory disease was progressive and frequently led to treatment with extracorporeal membrane oxygenation

(ECMO), which was unsuccessful. In one family, three siblings were affected, and all had a fatal outcome. All of the affected children had SP-B absent in alveolar fluid and 70% shared a common gene defect: a 2 base pair deletion in codon 121 of the SP-B gene on chromosome 2. It is perplexing that treatment with high doses of bovine surfactant, which is rich in surfactant B, failed to improve lung function. Lung transplant is currently the only available therapy. Further study of inborn errors of surfactants will enhance our understanding of the biochemistry and physiology of surfactant function.

Prevention of RDS is possible when women threatened with preterm birth are treated with corticosteroids antenatally to augment lung maturity. Currently this therapy is underutilized by obstetricians, in part because early studies lacked the power to demonstrate a convincing benefit. However, recent meta-analyses have definitively demonstrated the benefit of this therapy, and it therefore may enjoy more widespread dissemination.[7]

Numerous controlled trials of exogenous surfactant administration have produced conflicting results (Table 2–1).[1, 8–19] Overall, these studies have shown that the severity of RDS has been reduced, but the impact on chronic lung disease and mortality has been more variable. In the largest study to date, the National Institute of Child Health and Human Development Neonatal Research Network evaluated the impact of surfactant therapy in 2780 very-low-birthweight (< 1500 grams) neonates and demonstrated a reduction in mortality from 28% to 20%.[20] In a subsequent study, the NICHD network compared the efficacy of the two major commercially available surfactants, one a natural lung surfactant that contains surfactant-associated proteins and the other a protein-free synthetic surfactant. In 617 neonates randomized to treatment, the infants who received the natural surfactant had lower inspired oxygen and pressure in the 72 hours following treatment. Despite this, there were no statistical differences in the incidence of chronic lung disease or in mortality.[21] This suggests that there are differences in physiologic response to natural surfactants. Symptomatic support of the infant with RDS using supplemental oxygen and mechanical ventilation remains the mainstay of therapy.

The dawn of the era of surfactant replacement therapy has brought the need for a rapid postnatal test for surfactant deficiency. It is likely that these tests will be derived from those currently in use for *in utero* assessment of fetal lung maturity using amniotic fluid. The large number of tests currently in use suggests that none is entirely satisfactory. Physical measurements of surfactant do not measure individual phospholipids, but instead test non-chemical properties such as optical density, microviscosity, and foam stability. These all have the advantage of simplicity and speed, but have not been well correlated with clinical outcome. Biochemical assays of maturity are more widely used.

Measurement of the ratio of lecithin to sphingomyelin is the most common assay employed. Sphingomyelin content is constant in amniotic fluid during the third trimester, while the concentrations of all phospholipids rise dramatically after 35 weeks. Thus, sphingomyelin serves as a convenient reference phospholipid against which changes in lecithin can be compared. A second biochemical technique involves direct assay of the major phospholipid components of surfactant, with

TABLE 2–1. Results of Controlled Trials of Exogenous Surfactant Administration in the Treatment of Respiratory Distress Syndrome (RDS)

Investigators	Preparation*	Time of Administration	Number of Doses	Beneficial Effect
Chu et al., 1967	DDPC	After first breath	One	None
Morley et al., 1981	Dry DPPC:PG	At birth	One	Reduced mortality
Fujiwara et al., 1984	Surfactant TA	After ventilation	One	Reduced mortality
Halliday et al., 1984	DPPC	After ventilation	One	None
Wilkinson et al., 1985	Dry DPDC:PG	Trial 1: Before ventilation	One	None
		Trial 2: After ventilation	One	None
Hallman et al., 1985	Human surfactant from amniotic fluid	After ventilation	One	Reduced mortality and severity of RDS
Enhorning et al., 1985	Cow lung surfactant extract	Before ventilation	One	Reduced mortality and severity of RDS
Kwong et al., 1985	Calf lung surfactant extract	Before ventilation	One	Reduced severity of RDS; no change in mortality or BPD**
Shapiro et al., 1985	Calf lung surfactant extract	Before ventilation	One	Reduced severity of RDS; no change in mortality or BPD
Merritt et al., 1986	Human surfactant from amniotic fluid	At birth and later	Multiple	Reduced mortality and bronchopulmonary dysplasia
Gitlin et al., 1987	Surfactant TA	After ventilation	One	Reduced severity of RDS; no change in mortality or BPD
Kendig et al., 1991	Calf lung surfactant extract	At birth vs. later	Multiple	Reduced in those treated at birth
Dunn et al., 1991	Calf lung surfactant extract	At birth vs. later	Multiple	Reduced severity of RDS and BPD

Adapted from: Notler RH, Shapiro DL. Clin Perinatol 1987; 14:433.

*DPPC, Dipalmitoyl phosphatidylcholine; dry DPPC:PG, a dry powder of egg phosphatidylglycerol; surfactant TA, a surfactant extracted from minced cow lungs and enriched with DPPC and other additives.

**BPD, Bronchopulmonary dysplasia

phosphatidylglycerol (PG) the most common component utilized. Kulovich and co-workers assayed PG in the amniotic fluid of women with diabetes mellitus and found the presence of PG to be predictive of lung maturity. The application of these prenatal technologies to delivered infants has not become commonplace. In the research setting, measurement of surfactant protein-A concentration by either ELISA or RIA techniques has been used successfully.

Persistent Pulmonary Hypertension of the Newborn

Persistent Pulmonary Hypertension of the Newborn (PPHN) is a pathophysiologic state related to sustained postnatal increase of pulmonary vascular resistance. This frequently leads to increased pulmonary artery pressure and a right-to-left shunt at the patent ductus arteriosus and/or the foramen ovale. The shunt is a dynamic event and may improve or worsen in response to therapeutic maneuvers or environmental stimuli. Profound and refractory hypoxemia is the ultimate consequence of PPHN.

PPHN is generally seen in post-mature infants, but also may be seen in near-term and term babies. Many different neonatal and perinatal factors may predispose to the development of PPHN (see Table 2–2), but it is seen most commonly with Meconium Aspiration Syndrome (MAS). Whatever the original insult, asphyxia and hypoxemia combine to promote pulmonary vasoconstriction.[22] If the condition persists over a long period of time, medial hypertrophy can occur, with extension of muscle into the normally nonmuscularized small pulmonary arteries. Once muscular proliferation occurs, the hypertension is usually irreversible and fatal.[23]

PPHN should be considered in newborns with or without respiratory compromise and with refractory hypoxemia.[24] Arterial blood gases will confirm hypoxemia. Simultaneous preductal (right radial artery) and postductal (usually umbilical artery) gases are useful to document a right-to-left shunt at the ductal level. It must be remembered that a shunt at the atrial level will equalize the preductal and postductal gases. A hyperoxia test may be both diagnostic and therapeutic. Supplemental oxygen is increased to 100% and a blood gas obtained after 20 min. Hypoxemia will improve if due to pulmonary parenchymal disease, but will remain if related to either PPHN or cyanotic heart disease. If hypoxemia is not relieved by supplemental oxygen, a two-dimensional echocardiogram should be obtained to assess for PPHN and to exclude cyanotic heart disease. Echocardiographic systolic time intervals have been used to assess pulmonary vascular resistance noninvasively. The right ventricular pre-ejection period is prolonged in PPHN (> 0.37), presumably due to increased pulmonary vascular resistance. Doppler-aided two-dimensional echocardiography is another modality which is very useful in assessing the level and direction of shunts as well as in quantifying tricuspid and pulmonic regurgitation.

Much work has been directed toward identifying the biochemical mediators of PPHN.[25–27] There is now considerable evidence that the regulation of vascular muscle tone at the cellular level occurs via nitric oxide (NO), which is identical to the previously described endothelium-derived relaxing factor.[28–30] Nitric oxide is generated enzymatically by one of several NO synthases from L-arginine.[31] NO activates guanyl cyclase by binding to its heme component, leading to production of cyclic GMP. The mechanism by which cyclic GMP produces vascular relaxation is

TABLE 2–2. Conditions Associated with Persistent Pulmonary Hypertension of the Newborn (PPHN)

Prenatal and Perinatal Conditions	Postnatal Conditions
Prolonged maternal aspirin or indomethacin therapy	Neonatal asphyxia
Maternal pregnancy-induced or chronic hypertension	Meconium aspiration syndrome
Maternal intravenous drug use	Sepsis neonatorum
Oligohydramnios	Pulmonary hypoplasia
Placental insufficiency and intrauterine hypoxia	Congenital diaphragmatic hernia
Postmaturity	Respiratory distress syndrome
Meconium-stained amniotic fluid	Cold stress
Perinatal asphyxia	Hypoglycemia
	Hypocalcemia
	Systemic hypotension
	Myocardial dysfunction
	Polycythemia and hyperviscosity

not clear, but may involve limitation of cytosolic calcium concentration.[32, 33] From studies of animals it is becoming clear that derangements of NO synthesis probably play a key role in PPHN. NO has been shown to modulate resting pulmonary vascular tone in the newborn lamb[34] and to mediate the increase in pulmonary blood flow induced by an increase in oxygen tension.[35] Abman and colleagues have shown in a late-gestation bovine model that inhibition of NO production produces fetal pulmonary and systemic hypertension, which was reversible with inhalation of NO.[36]

In addition to NO, or interacting with NO, disorders of arachidonic acid metabolites may contribute to PPHN (Figure 2–1). Hammerman measured plasma thromboxane B_2 levels in 14 human neonates with PPHN and 6 control infants and found marked elevations in 13 of the 14 infants with PPHN and none in the controls.[37] Stenmark and colleagues found elevated leukotriene concentrations in the tracheal effluent in 5 neonates with PPHN and found elevated levels of leukotriene D_4, with minimal levels detected in control infants.[38]

Although two decades have passed since its first description, the treatment of PPHN remains controversial. Hyperventilation was introduced as a treatment for PPHN in 1980 and has since been widely adopted.[39, 40] However, no large, prospective trial has validated its efficacy, and uncontrolled reports cite mortality ranging from 30–50%. The use of hyperventilation induces alkalosis, which in turn triggers vasodilation, but the cost paid in barotrauma and oxygen toxicity are considerable. In addition, cerebral blood flow is impaired at extremes of alkalosis, which may account for the high rate of neurodevelopmental impairment seen in survivors of this therapy.[41–44] In 1985, Wung and James reported on their experience with a conservative ventilation regime with excellent survival.[45]

Clearly, a well-controlled randomized trial is critically needed to determine the most efficacious therapy for PPHN. Some infants fail to respond to conventional ventilation, regardless of the technique used. In these infants, selective pul-

FIGURE 2–1. Metabolites of Arachidonic Acid

Byproducts illustrated are vasoactive agents.

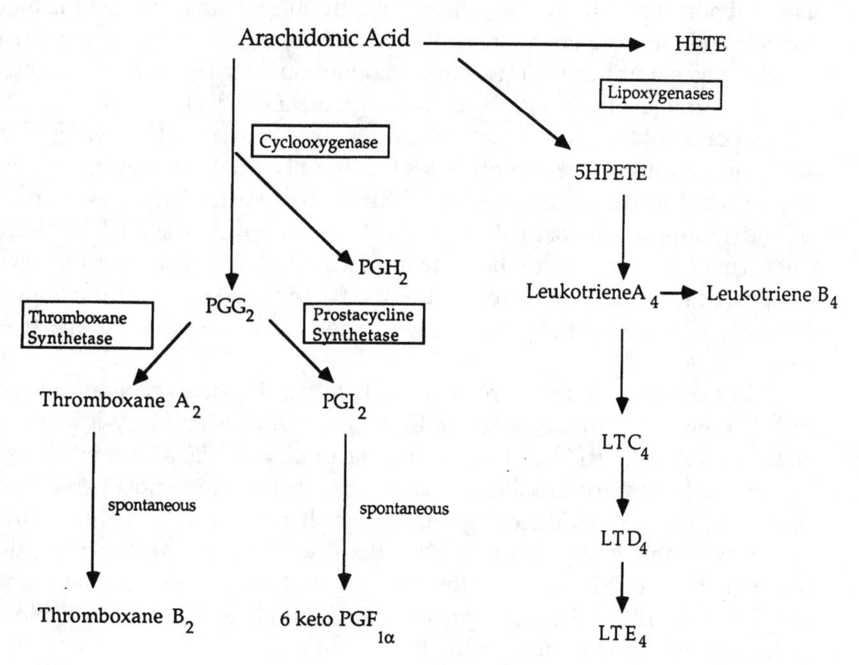

monary vasodilation is attempted.[46–49] Unfortunately, no intravenous vasodilator is specific to the pulmonary vascular bed; systemic hypotension is a frequent result of treatment. Inhaled nitric oxide (iNO) appears to be a selective pulmonary vasodilator. In three published trials, iNO was able to improve oxygenation sufficiently to avoid the use of ECMO treatments.[50–52] While these results are encouraging, caution is still required. In high-oxygen environments, nitric oxide generates reactive species including nitrogen dioxide and peroxynitrite, both of which are potent oxidizing agents capable of damaging lipids and proteins in the biological membranes of the lung and in surfactant.[53–56]

No long-term data are available on the safety of iNO in human infants. Furthermore, only limited data are available on the pulmonary outcomes of infants who improve on iNO, avoid ECMO, and thus are potentially exposed to longer duration of hyperoxia and mechanical ventilation. Rosenberg and colleagues[57] have reported favorable outcomes at 1 year of age in a group of 58 term infants treated with iNO and high-frequency ventilation. For infants in whom all other therapies have failed, support with ECMO may be life saving[58] (see discussion below).

ECMO Therapy for PPHN

ECMO is the use of extracorporeal circulation and gas exchange to provide temporary life support in patients with cardiac or pulmonary failure.[59] The key component of ECMO is the transport of oxygen into blood across a semi-permeable membrane, which is achieved with the use of a silicone membrane lung (Avecor, Inc., Minneapolis, MN) and a modified cardiopulmonary bypass system.[60] Long-term (5–21 days) support is possible because the membrane lung separates oxygen and blood components and therefore does not result in hemolysis over time, as was the case with the bubble oxygenators that were used in cardiopulmonary bypass surgery. Gas exchange is through a simple diffusion process across a gradient (see Figure 2–2).

Because of the invasive nature and systemic heparinization required, there are many limitations to the use of ECMO in the neonatal population. If a neonate's respiratory disorder can be reversed within a 21-day period, it is feasible that ECMO will safely support the patient. After this time, complications such as bleeding and clot formation in the circuit become more difficult to control. For this reason, it is not practical to use ECMO to treat a disease process such as bronchopulmonary dysplasia, which would require a longer period on the system to reverse the chronic lung damage.

The common causes of respiratory failure in neonates generally are reversible within a few days; average time on ECMO is 5 days. Many very-low-birth-weight infants have severe RDS and would appear to be good ECMO candidates, but the heparinization and/or the alterations in pulsatility of blood flow created by ECMO cause a significant incidence of intracranial hemorrhage, and thus a prohibitive mortality in this group of infants.[61, 62] Because of the above concerns, the infant considered for ECMO are usually ≥ 34 w gestation, have reversible lung disease, have less than 10–14 d of assisted ventilation, and lack an uncontrollable coagulopathy or major intracranial hemorrhage.

FIGURE 2–2. Schematic of the Silicone Membrane Lung Used in ECMO

Oxygen and carbon dioxide transfer because of simple diffusion across a concentration gradient. The silicone membrane separates the blood and gas phases, thus decreasing the risk for hemolysis.

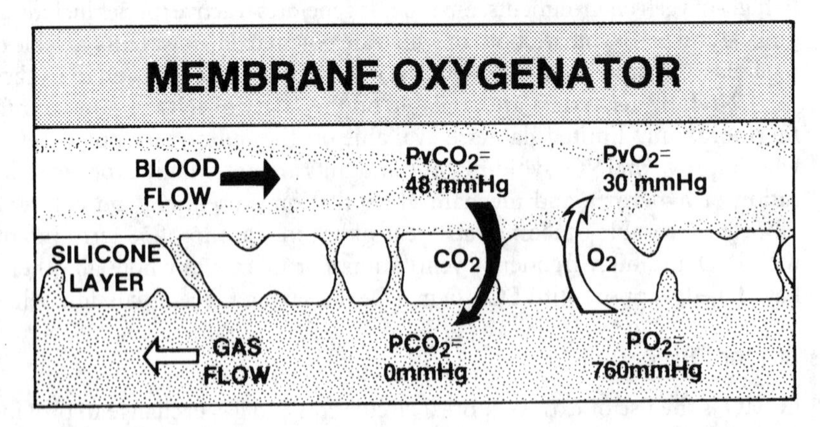

From: Fox W, Polin R (Eds.), Fetal and neonatal physiology. W.B. Saunders, 1991. Reprinted with permission.

Institutional criteria predicting a high mortality without ECMO[63, 64] should be used to determine when to institute ECMO therapy. The majority of the pulmonary diseases treated with ECMO are those with underlying persistent pulmonary hypertension resulting in significant right-to-left shunting through the ductus arteriosus and/or foramen ovale, and include meconium aspiration syndrome, severe respiratory distress syndrome, sepsis and/or pneumonia, and congenital diaphragmatic hernia (CDH). Idiopathic persistent pulmonary hypertension represents almost 20% of ECMO cases.[59, 60]

In venoarterial (VA) bypass, blood is drained from the right atrium through a catheter placed in the *right internal jugular vein* with the tip of the catheter in the right atrium, into a venous reservoir bag, pumped through a membrane oxygenator where gas exchange occurs, passed through a heat exchanger to warm to body temperature, and returned to the patient through the *right common carotid artery* (see Figure 2–3). This mode of bypass provides excellent support for the heart and lungs. If myocardial ischemia and dysfunction are major components in the patient's pathology, VA bypass will provide excellent cardiac support.

FIGURE 2–3. Venoarterial ECMO Circuit

Blood is drained from the right atrium into the venous reservoir bag and is pumped into the membrane lung, where oxygenation occurs. It is then warmed to body temperature by the heat exchanger and returned to the arch of the aorta via the carotid artery catheter.

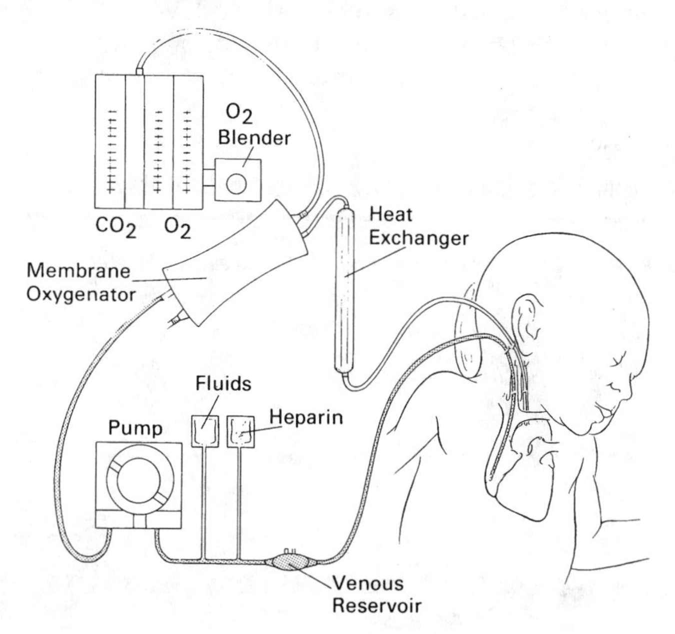

From: Fox W, Polin R (Eds.), Fetal and neonatal physiology. W.B. Saunders Co., 1991. Reprinted with permission.

Advantages and disadvantages of VA bypass are as follows:

Advantages

- Excellent support of the heart and lungs
- Only one surgical site
- Excellent oxygenation at low flows
- Not dependent on cardiac function

Disadvantages

- Any particles, bubbles, or emboli in the circuit could be infused into the patient's arterial system and hence to the brain
- Carotid ligation
- Potential hyperoxia of blood supplying the brain

Venovenous (VV) bypass (Figure 2–4) is now being used in infants, using a single double-lumen venous catheter (The Kendall Co., Mansfield, MA).[65] The inflow and outflow ports of this catheter hook into the circuit as if there were two catheters, and therefore the circuit design is the same as with VA ECMO. Infants treated with VV ECMO must have intact cardiac function, for the heart pumps the blood and not the ECMO pump. Those who cannot tolerate VV ECMO can easily be converted to VA ECMO by placing an arterial catheter in the carotid artery, while using the double-lumen VV catheter as the venous catheter.

ECMO supplies pulmonary support so that the lungs can rest, thereby allowing time for injured lungs to heal. Although VA ECMO can mechanically decrease pulmonary artery pressure by diverting blood flow from the right atrium through the ECMO circuit, the exact mechanism involved in reversal of pulmonary hyper-

FIGURE 2–4. Schematic of the Venovenous Catheter in the Right Atrium

Shown are return and outflow portions of the double-lumen single catheter.

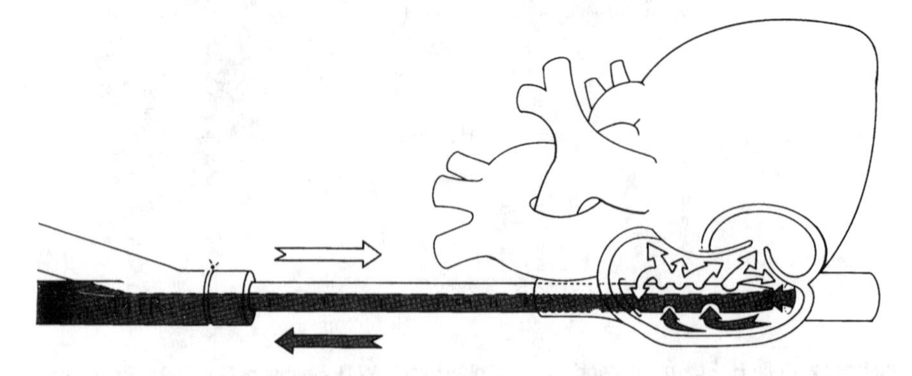

From: Short BL (Ed.), The CNMC ECMO training manual. CNMC, 1991.Reprinted with permission.

tension and/or the underlying pulmonary pathology is unknown. In the first days on ECMO, 60% of the cardiac output (120 mL/kg/min) must flow through the circuit and thus through the membrane lung. As the lungs improve, the infant's arterial blood gases will improve and the ECMO circuit blood flow rates can be gradually decreased. This gradual decrease continues until only 10% of the cardiac output is going through the ECMO circuit, at which time the patient can usually be taken off ECMO successfully.

Laboratory requirements for the patient on ECMO are extensive, and are discussed in a later section entitled "Special Needs of a Newborn Intensive Care Unit."

Apnea of Prematurity

Apnea of prematurity results from developmental immaturity of the respiratory control centers which improves as the infant matures.[66] Apnea is defined as a cessation of respiration which lasts at least 15 s. It is frequently accompanied by cyanosis, hypotonia, and bradycardia. The incidence and severity of apnea varies inversely with gestational age; the least mature infants are the most affected. Approximately 50% of all infants with birth weights < 1500 g require intervention for apnea. An understanding of the pathophysiology of apnea may allow rational therapeutic intervention.

Respiratory neurons are located on the ventrolateral surface of the medulla and the pons. Von Euler proposed that the center receives input from both chemoreceptors and mechanoreceptors and then alters rhythmic discharges of the medullary centers responsible for sending efferent impulses to the respiratory musculature.[67] Immaturity appears to adversely influence the rhythmic firing of the brainstem neurons. Peripheral stimuli may influence respirations through chemical receptors that monitor PaO_2, $PaCO_2$, and pH. These chemoreceptors are located both centrally and peripherally. The normal response to hypercarbia in term neonates and in adults is to increase minute ventilation. The response to hypercarbia is blunted in preterm infants. Gerhardt and Bancalari found that apneic infants did not increase minute ventilation as effectively as nonapneic infants.[68] This is believed to reflect a low sensitivity of the respiratory center to hypercarbia and seems again to be a function of immaturity.

Hypoxemia is the other major chemical mediator of respiration. Older children and adults show an immediate increase in ventilation when placed in a hypoxic environment and suppress ventilation when placed in an oxygen-enriched environment. However, when challenged with a low inspired oxygen concentration, both term and preterm newborns briefly increase ventilation and then return to their resting level. Once the infant is 2–3 w old, hyperventilation in response to hypoxia is sustained, just as it is in older children. The mechanism responsible for this inappropriate response to hypoxia remains controversial. Traditionally the response is attributed to initial chemoreceptor stimulation, followed by hypoxic depression of the respiratory centers. Other proposed mechanisms include modulation of respiratory center response by endorphins, fatigue of the respiratory muscles, and hypoxia-induced increases in cerebral blood flow, which then lead to cerebral hypocapnia and respiratory depression.

Apnea may occur when the central drive to respiratory muscle fails, leading to a simultaneous cessation of both chest wall movement and airflow. This mechanism is termed "central apnea." In the past, central apnea was believed to be the exclusive mechanism responsible for apnea in the preterm infant. However, by measuring chest wall movements simultaneously with nasal air flow, investigators have demonstrated a cessation of air flow despite continued respiratory muscle activity. This has been termed "obstructive apnea." Although obstruction may be the exclusive mechanism responsible for apnea in a given infant, the most common pattern observed is a central respiratory pause either preceded by or followed by an obstruction. This pattern has been termed "mixed apnea" and represents the predominant form of apnea in 50% of infants. Brief episodes of apnea are more likely to be centrally mediated, whereas episodes longer than 15 s frequently have an obstructive component.

The upper airway of the preterm infant is susceptible to obstruction at the pharyngeal and hypopharyngeal levels. This obstruction may be aggravated by passive flexion of the neck and conversely may be relieved by passive extension.[69, 70] Pharyngeal tone is diminished in preterm infants. During inspiration, negative pressure generated by contraction of the diaphragm may collapse the pharyngeal musculature. For the collapsed airway to open, the infant must generate sufficient pressure by activation of the upper airway muscles such as the genioglossus to overcome surface adhesive forces (Figure 2–5). Infants with apnea fail to activate the genioglossus in response to induced end-expiratory airway occlusion, whereas preterm infants without apnea prolong the action and the intensity of genioglossus activity.[71, 72] Thus, infants with apnea appear to lack an important mechanism for resolving the apneic episode.

FIGURE 2–5. Obstructive Apnea

Obstructive apnea may result when forces that initiate collapse of the upper airway are not adequately balanced by dilating forces of the upper airway muscles.

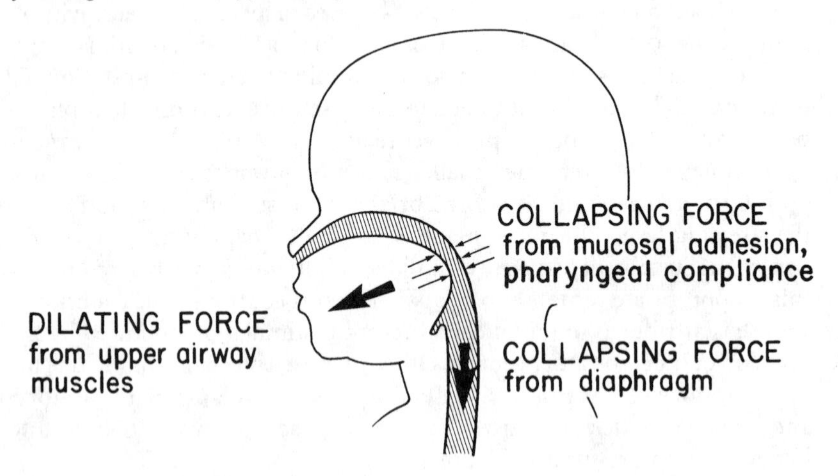

From: Martin RJ, Miller MJ, Carlo WA. Neonatal-perinatal medicine: Diseases of the fetus and newborn. J Pediatr 1986:109;733. Reprinted with permission.

Apnea as the final common response of immature respiratory regulatory centers may be associated with a large number of diverse factors in susceptible preterm infants (Figure 2–6). The diagnosis of apnea of prematurity can only be made after other potentially triggering events have been evaluated and excluded. All preterm infants less than 34 w gestation should be monitored continuously with a cardiorespiratory monitor until they are greater than 34 w gestation and free of apnea events for at least a week.[73] The goal of immediate management of an apneic episode is to restore adequate ventilation and to relieve hypoxemia. Gentle stimulation is frequently sufficient to arouse the infant and resolve the apneic episode. If stimulation is unsuccessful, artificial ventilation with bag and mask must be initiated. The infant's neck may be gently extended to overcome pharyngeal obstruction. Continuous positive airway pressure (CPAP) administered by nasal prongs at 2–5 cm H_2O may reduce obstructive and mixed apnea by stinting open the upper airway.[70] CPAP is ineffective in central apnea. Methylxanthines such as caffeine and theophylline may be effective in the treatment of refractory apnea regardless of the mechanism.[74] Infants are free of toxicity at plasma concentrations of theophylline of 5–10 mg/L and caffeine of 8–20 mg/L.

Bronchopulmonary Dysplasia

Low-birth-weight infants who have required support with oxygen and mechanical ventilation may have persistent chronic pulmonary dysfunction, which was termed

FIGURE 2–6. Contributors to Apnea

Apnea may rise in response to a staggering number of insults which perturb the immature respiratory system.

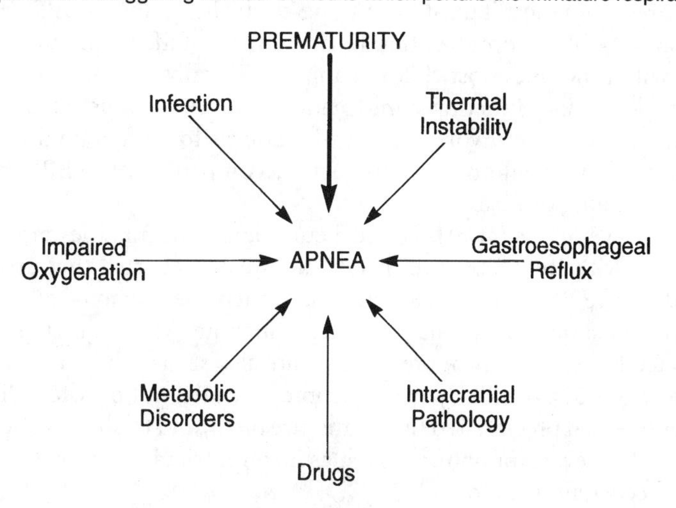

From: Martin RJ, Miller MJ, Carlo WA. Neonatal-perinatal medicine: Diseases of the fetus and newborn. J Pediatr 1986:109;733. Reprinted with permission.

Bronchopulmonary Dysplasia (BPD) by Northway and co-workers.[75] Some authors have labeled BPD as an iatrogenic disease, which implies some degree of therapeutic misadventure. An alternative view is that BPD is the inevitable consequence of exposure of the developing bronchopulmonary tree to oxygen and ventilation, spontaneous or mechanical, many weeks "too soon" in terms of biologic maturity.

There is no universally accepted definition of BPD. One of the most commonly used is that proposed by Bancalari:

1. a requirement for positive-pressure ventilation for greater than 3 days in the first week of life;
2. respiratory symptoms for greater than 28 days;
3. a need for supplemental oxygen for greater than 28 days to maintain a PaO_2 over 50 mmHg; and
4. a chest roentgenogram showing persistent infiltrates alternating with normal or cystic changes.[76]

The risk of BPD is greatest among the most immature infants. In one study of infants who received mechanical ventilation, 72% of infants weighing less than 1000 g developed BPD, compared to 22% of infants between 1250–1500 g. The incidence of BPD varies dramatically between centers and is influenced not only by the definition used within each center, but also by treatment approaches within each center.[77]

The natural history of BPD is not completely understood. Mortality varies from 11% to 73% in different reports. Most patients who die do so within the first year of life. The incidence of sudden death is increased sevenfold over that seen in normal infants.[78]

Infants who survive BPD frequently have residual cardiopulmonary dysfunction.[79] Minor respiratory illnesses may unmask limited cardiopulmonary reserve and require rehospitalization. In one study, infants with BPD were rehospitalized an average of five times within the first 2 years of life. Pulmonary symptoms diminish with time, and most children appear clinically well by 3–4 y of age.[80] Nevertheless, pulmonary function abnormalities can be demonstrated in both school-age and adolescent survivors of BPD who appear to be functioning normally in every other way. Cor pulmonale, a frequent accompaniment to BPD, resolves in parallel with the lung disease.

Developmental delays and neurologic abnormalities are seen frequently in infants with BPD.[81] Several investigators have reported that up to 80% of infants with severe BPD had developmental quotients less than 80 at 2–5 y of age. Infants with less severe disease have a better outcome. Severe hearing loss and blindness related to retinopathy of prematurity are also seen with increased frequency in survivors of BPD. It is likely that outcome is related not only to BPD, but to perinatal events which precipitated the premature birth, and to all the concomitant problems related to severe immaturity, such as intraventricular hemorrhage, delayed growth, and recurrent infection.

Our understanding of the pathophysiology of BPD is still in its infancy. Goetzman has proposed that a susceptible host, with an immature lung, asphyxia, or a genetic predisposition suffers acute pulmonary injury because of surfactant deficiency, oxygen toxicity, and/or barotrauma.[82] The initial injury leads to release of oxidants and proteolytic enzymes which cause further lung injury. The lung then heals in an abnormal manner, perhaps aggravated by inadequate nutrition and vitamin deficiencies.[83] The need for continued therapy with oxygen or mechanical ventilation may generate new injury and inhibit healing of prior injury. Superimposed infection may lead to proliferation of inflammatory mediators and cellular cytokines, which create a chronic inflammatory response and prevent normal healing.

The management of the infant with BPD is controversial and fraught with frustration, since the need for continued life-supporting therapies implies continuation of treatments that contributed to the pathogenesis of the disease. The key to eventual recovery is growth. Infants frequently must consume 120–150 kcal/kg/d to meet the increased caloric requirements of breathing and tissue repair and still allow growth. Supplemental oxygen and/or mechanical ventilation may be needed for prolonged periods, which may exceed one year in severely affected infants. Bronchodilators have been demonstrated in short-term studies to improve compliance and reduce airway resistance. Diuretics may also improve compliance.

The use of corticosteroids early in the course of respiratory illness (14–28 d of age) in an attempt to limit inflammatory injury and therefore prevent BPD has been a recent advance in the care of ventilator dependent low-birth-weight infants. In small, short-term studies, infants treated with steroids demonstrated improved lung compliance and an enhanced ability to wean from mechanical ventilation.[84] Treatment was not without side effects, however; hypertension, hyperglycemia, and sepsis were all seen at increased rates. Two large, randomized trials on the use of postnatal steroids have been published.[85, 86] In both trials, infants treated with postnatal steroids showed earlier extubation from mechanical ventilation, but no difference in duration of oxygen therapy or hospital stay. The same side effects noted in the earlier, small studies were again found. Sepsis was also significantly more likely. These data suggest that dexamethasone is associated with significant side effects without dramatic improvements. Hence, routine use of dexamethasone is not recommended.

Special Needs of the Newborn Intensive Care Unit: Laboratory Tests and Blood Gas Monitoring

State-of-the-art care of preterm infants requires a laboratory capable of the collection and rapid processing of samples using microtechniques. It is imperative that phlebotomists are trained thoroughly to obtain specimens by capillary sampling from the heel to ensure both minimal trauma to the infant as well as accurate laboratory results. Laboratories must provide a 24-h service for electrolyte, complete blood count, bilirubin, coagulation, microbiology, and blood gas monitoring. Ideally, blood gas measurements should be done in the NICU. Blood gas values should be available within 10–15 mins. Results of emergent studies should be available within 60 min, and of routine studies within 4–6 h. Consultation with a clinical pathologist or laboratory scientist skilled in the problems of newborn infants must also be available around the clock. The microbiology laboratory must be familiar with the unique problems of premature infants with regard to infection, including the pathogenicity of organisms such as *Staphylococcus epidermidis* which might otherwise be dismissed as contaminants.

Bedside monitoring including pulse oximetry and, to a lesser extent, transcutaneous pO_2 and pCO_2 monitoring have allowed the care-taking team to make changes in F_iO_2 without the need for an arterial or capillary blood gas, thus decreasing the workload of blood gas laboratories.

Most critically ill newborns will require arterial blood gases every 1–2 h and complete blood count, electrolytes, and calcium concentrations every 12–24 h. Also of importance to the newborn, and especially the preterm infant, is total, direct, and indirect serum bilirubin, which may be needed every 8 h in the first few days of life, and the serum glucose values which are needed to confirm bedside dextrometer measurements. Drug monitoring is also a needed item in the NICU, including serum aminoglycoside, vancomycin, caffeine, and theophylline concentrations. When starting a new drug, concentrations will need to be monitored daily until therapeutic measurements are achieved. Nutritional monitoring must be undertaken if an infant is on hyperalimentation, including serum phosphorus, magnesium, liver function studies, triglycerides, and the routine tests listed above. If a coagulopathy is suspected, coagulation profiles must be available, include platelet counts, prothrombin time, partial thromboplastin time, fibrinogen, D-dimer, and fibrin degradation products.

The infant on ECMO requires a significant amount of laboratory support. Arterial blood gas measurements will need to be taken often (1–2h); these can be decreased to 2–4 h if an in-line venous saturation monitor is used. Membrane blood gas measurements should be taken every 8 h as a minimum, and more often if clinically indicated. The membrane lung blood gases will have an extremely high PO_2 (350–500 torr) due to the efficiency of the membrane lung. Laboratory tests needed every 8–12 h include hemoglobin, hematocrit, calcium, sodium, potassium, chloride, and CO_2. The membrane lung binds platelets, and therefore values will need to be determined every 8 h.[87, 88] Platelet counts are kept between 60,000 and 200,000 mm^3 depending on the bleeding complications of the patient, resulting in 1–2 units of platelets transfused per day. Daily laboratory tests should include phosphorus, magnesium, serum osmolality, BUN, creatinine, and total, direct, and indirect bilirubin. Infants on ECMO require very little sodium replacement (1–2 mEq/kg/ d), high potassium replacement (4–5 mEq/kg/d), and relatively high calcium replacement (40–50 mg of elemental calcium/kg/d). Reasons for these requirements are not fully understood.

Prolonged heparinization of the infant requires the use of a bedside test to determine activated clotting times (ACT). Centers use various systems, with the Hemachron (International Technidyne, Edison, NJ), which uses only 0.25 mL per sample, being the most popular. ACTs are kept between 180–250 seconds depending on the bleeding complications in the patient. When disseminated intravascular coagulation is thought to be a problem in an ECMO patient, PT/PTT values using the heptasorb methodology will need to be available. Other clotting tests that should be available are antithrombin III, fibrin degradation products, fibrinogen, and D-dimer. Plasma free hemoglobin levels are also needed on a daily basis in the venovenous patients because the high resistance in the VV catheter can cause significant hemolysis.

Laboratory and hematologic support is critical for patients on ECMO who require surgery, such as the patient with congenital diaphragmatic hernia. ACT values are kept very low at 180–190 seconds, with platelets > 200,000mm^3 and fibrinogen levels > 150 mg/dL. Bleeding can be catastrophic, requiring removal from ECMO, and can result in death. Blood products including packed cells, platelets, fresh frozen plasma, and cryoprecipitate must be available on an emergency basis. Protocols for transfusion of products on ECMO should be developed.

PEDIATRIC RESPIRATORY DISORDERS

A respiratory disorder can be defined as any pathophysiologic disorder that impairs the ability of the airways to maintain adequate avenues for exchange of respiratory gases (i.e., oxygen and carbon dioxide). Gas travels through the nasopharynx into the larynx, through the trachea, and through conducting airways into the alveoli, where the exchange of oxygen and carbon dioxide is carried out by passive diffusion and driven by diffusion gradients. The movement of gas into and out of the airways is dependent on the structure of the airways themselves and on the normal function of the diaphragm and intercostal muscles, which create negative and positive changes in intrathoracic pressure and thereby cause flow. In addition, adequate central nervous system respiratory drive must be present. The anatomic level of the lesion is a useful way to analyze the different causes of impaired ability, as the symptoms and pathophysiology can be quite different. The most common classification scheme calls for division into upper and lower airway disease. There are also disorders of respiratory drive, although these are not discussed in this chapter.

Upper Airway Disease

Upper airway disease is more prominent in children than in adults due to anatomical differences in the growing and developing airway. At birth, the larynx and epiglottis are located much higher in the neck. The placement is more anterior and closer to the nasopharynx. This positioning renders the infant an obligate nose-breather until 2–6 m of age.[89] With growth, the larynx descends caudally and posteriorly until it reaches the adult positioning at approximately age 10 y. Other differences in the pediatric airway include increased prominence of the tongue and arytenoids, a softer and more elastic larynx and trachea, and, most importantly, a much smaller diameter. Since resistance to flow is related inversely to the fourth power of the radius, decreased diameter causes enormous increases in resistance.

The causes of upper airway disease can be broken down into two categories: congenital anomalies or acquired lesions. Table 2–3 lists some of the more common causes. The symptoms of upper airway obstruction are more indicative of the anatomic level of the lesion rather than the cause. A common symptom is stridor or "noisy" breathing caused by rapid, turbulent flow through an obstructed or nar-

TABLE 2–3. Causes of Upper Airway Obstruction

Congenital Lesions	Acquired Lesions
Intrinsic lesions	Infections
Subglottic stenosis	Retropharyngeal abscess
Web	Ludwig's angina
Cyst	Laryngotracheobronchitis
Laryngocele	Supraglottitis
Tumor	Fungal infection
Laryngomalacia	Peritonsillar abscess
Laryngotracheoesophageal cleft	Diphtheria
Tracheomalacia	Bacterial tracheitis
Tracheoesophageal fistula	Trauma—internal
Extrinsic lesions	Postextubation croup
Vascular ring	Post-tracheostomy removal
Cystic hygroma	Trauma—external
Birth Trauma	Burns—thermal, chemical
Neurologic lesion	Foreign body aspiration
Craniofacial anomalies	Systemic disorders
Metabolic disorders—Hypocalcemia	Neoplasms—internal, external
	Neurologic lesions
	Chronic upper airway obstruction
	Hypertrophic tonsils, adenoids
	Tight surgical neck dressing

From: Rogers MC, ed. Textbook of pediatric intensive care. Williams and Wilkins, 1987. Reprinted with permission.

rowed portion of the airway.[89] Inspiratory stridor is common with lesions above or at the level of the larynx, while expiratory stridor is more often seen with lesions below the level of the vocal cords. Stridor with inspiration and expiration often indicates a fixed lesion, such as subglottic stenosis. Other symptoms include a weak or muffled cry, a "barking cough," feeding difficulties, retractions, tachypnea, and tachycardia. Hypoventilation with a rising CO_2 is seen before cyanosis, but both are late findings and signify a need for rapid action.

The most common presentation of upper airway disease is respiratory distress and noisy breathing. Congenital lesions may not be symptomatic at birth, with the exception of choanal atresia, as the children may compensate until a critical degree of obstruction occurs. This decompensation often occurs with an upper respiratory infection. Stridor at or near birth does require evaluation, as it is often an indicator of a congenital problem, the most common being laryngomalacia.

The differential diagnosis until recent years has revolved around distinguishing croup from epiglottitis (Table 2–4). With the widespread availability of H. influenza B vaccines in recent years, the incidence of epiglottitis has dropped dramatically. The differentiation is important because epiglottitis can cause such swelling and

TABLE 2–4. Clinical Characteristics Differentiating Laryngotracheobronchitis (LTB) from Supraglottitis

Characteristic	LTB	Supraglottitis
Age	6 m to 3 y	2 to 6 y
Onset	Gradual	Rapid
Etiology	Viral	Bacterial
Swelling site	Subglottic	Supraglottic
Symptoms		
Cough/voice	Hoarse cough	No cough; muffled voice
Posture	Any position	Sitting
Mouth	Closed; nasal flaring	Open—chin forward, drooling
Fever	Absent to high	High
Appearance	Often not acutely ill	Anxious; acutely ill
X-ray	Narrow subglottic area	Swollen epiglottis and supraglottic structures
Palpation larynx	Nontender	Tender
Recurrence	May recur	Rarely recurs
Seasonal incidence	Winter	None

From: Rogers MC, ed. Textbook of pediatric intensive care. Williams and Wilkins, 1987. Reprinted with permission.

distortion of the supraglottic structures that laryngoscopy is difficult and sometimes impossible. Control of the airway by a skilled pediatric airway specialist, usually in the operating room under inhalational anesthesia, is most often recommended.[89]

Assessment of the pediatric patient with upper airway disease is made primarily by clinical observations dealing with the degree of respiratory failure. Clinical scoring systems utilize respiratory rate, cyanosis, and the use of accessory respiratory muscles, as well as mental status. The most helpful laboratory evaluations are arterial blood gases. The patient with respiratory acidosis in this situation is in grave danger. The white blood cell count can be helpful, as it is usually more elevated with bacterial infections and has a larger component of polymorphonuclear cells with juvenile forms.

Lower Airway Disease

Lower airway disease can be divided into disorders of the bronchi and conducting airways and diseases of the alveoli. The two most common diseases of the conducting airways include bronchiolitis and asthma, and there is evidence of overlap between the two processes. Acute respiratory failure after injury to the alveolar capillary unit may occur after a variety of insults.[90] These can include infectious pneumonias, inhalational injuries, sepsis, or shock. A list of common causes is presented in Table 2–5.[90] Injury to the alveolar capillary unit results in a common group of pathophysiologic findings currently referred to in the literature as adult respiratory distress syndrome (ARDS).

TABLE 2–5. Disorders Associated with (Causing) Adult Respiratory Distress Syndrome (ARDS)

Common	Uncommon
Trauma	Drug overdose (e.g., narcotic—idiosyncratic reaction)
Sepsis	Cardiopulmonary bypass
Near drowning	Hemodialysis
Shock	Fat embolism
Surface burns	High altitude
Smoke inhalation	Strangulation
Infectious pneumonia	Toxic gas inhalation
Gram-negative bacteria	Pancreatitis
Viral	Massive transfusion
Pneumocystis	
Aspiration pneumonia	
Disseminated intravascular coagulopathy	

From: Rogers MC, ed. Textbook of pediatric intensive care. Williams and Wilkins, 1987. Reprinted with permission.

Bronchiolitis

Bronchiolitis is an acute inflammatory disease of the lower respiratory tract which results in obstruction of the small airways.[91] It is most commonly seen in infants 1–2 y of age. The reported incidence of 11.4 cases per 100 children per year in the first year of life falls to 6 per 100 children per year in the second year of life.[92] Viral agents are the cause and include respiratory syncytial virus (the most common identified cause), parainfluenza, rhinovirus, adenovirus, influenza, and occasionally mumps.[91]

Histopathologically, there is an inflammatory lesion of the respiratory epithelium which leads to small airway obstruction. There is necrosis of the ciliated epithelium with proliferation of non-ciliated cells and edema. In addition to the edema, debris builds up in the bronchioles due to lack of cilia, and they become partially or completely obstructed. A chest radiograph will typically show air trapping and peribronchial thickening, with occasional lobar consolidation or collapse. The alveoli may also be involved in the inflammatory process, with infiltrates of lymphocytes and edema seen in the alveolar lining cells.[91]

Clinically, the infants present with expiratory wheezing, tachypnea, retractions, and irritability. There is often a low-grade fever, cyanosis, and feeding difficulties. Auscultation reveals diffuse wheezing, prolonged expiration, and rales. Younger infants have a significant risk of apnea.[93] At one time it was commonly thought that bronchiolitis was the cause of all wheezing in children under age 2 y, and that asthma did not appear until a later age. This is clearly not true. Reversible airway obstruction can occur in infants as well as children, and there are questions about an association between severe bronchiolitis as an infant and an increased incidence of asthma in the childhood years.

TABLE 2–6. Some Factors that Precipitate Bronchoconstriction in Asthma

Allergy (mediator release)	**Infections**
Histamine	Viral respiratory tract infection
SRS-A	
Prostaglandins	**Pharmacologic Agents**
Thromboxane	β-adrenergic blockade (propranolol)
Other	Prostaglandin inhibitors (aspirin and nonsteroidal anti-inflammatory drugs)
Autonomic Imbalance	
Excessive cholinergic response	
Reduced β-adrenergic responsiveness	**Exercise Induced**
Nonspecific irritant	Psychogenic

From: Rogers MC, ed. Textbook of pediatric intensive care. Williams and Wilkins, 1987. Reprinted with permission.

Asthma

The hallmark of asthma is a reversible diffuse obstruction to airflow caused by narrowing of hyperreactive airways. This obstruction is intermittent and may reverse with or without treatment. Periods between attacks are usually symptom free, although some abnormalities may be detected with pulmonary function testing.[91] The bronchoconstriction can be precipitated by a variety of stimuli, including allergens, infectious agents, exercise, emotional stress, or the administration of certain drugs (see Table 2–6).

Autopsy findings in a patient who dies from status asthmaticus show hypertrophy of smooth muscle in the bronchial wall, associated submucosal and mucosal edema, and mucous plugging of the airways.[92] There are several proposed schemata to explain the pathophysiology of asthma, including:

1. allergens and mast cell/histamine/mediator derangements;[94, 95]
2. derangements of the autonomic nervous system with reduced β-adrenergic responsiveness;[96] and
3. aberrant bronchial smooth muscle.[97]

Clinically, patients present with gradual or sudden onset of respiratory distress, which is characterized by diffuse wheezing, a prolonged expiratory phase, tachypnea, tachycardia, and cyanosis. This bronchospasm or acute airway obstruction is often responsive to acute administration of β-adrenergic agonists. Progressive, severe airflow obstruction that is unresponsive to therapy with adrenergic drugs and theophylline is defined as status asthmaticus. Current acute therapy includes administration of β-adrenergic agonists such as epinephrine or terbutaline subcutaneously, or metaproterenol (alupent) or salbutamol (albuterol) by aerosol; intravenous theophylline; intravenous corticosteroids; and aerosolized anti-cholinergic agents such as atropine or ipratropium bromide. Patients should have humidified oxygen administered as needed, as they may be dehydrated because of decreased fluid intake and increased, insensible loss. Ventilatory support with intubation and mechanical ventilation may be necessary in face of progressive tiring and hypoventilation, but carries significant risk of mechanical barotrauma. Chronic therapy includes oral theophylline, inhaled cromolyn sodium, inhaled β-adrenergic agonists, and steroids and oral steroids.

Assessment of the infant or child with obstruction to gas flow in the conducting airways involves both physiologic laboratory support as well as biochemical laboratory support. Pulmonary function tests documenting the physiologic degree of airway obstruction are correlated with arterial blood gases and the patient's clinical history and appearance.

In the evaluation of a patient with acute exacerbation of asthma, severe airway obstruction and a rising $PaCO_2$ signals a need for urgent intervention. Long-term outpatient management involves the monitoring of theophylline levels if that medication is used, as well as repetitive pulmonary function monitoring. Evaluation of an allergic component with skin testing and desensitization can be important in certain cases.

Adult Respiratory Distress Syndrome (ARDS)

The term ARDS was introduced by Ashbaugh et al.[98] in 1967 and its definition now includes the following points:[99]

1. a catastrophic pulmonary or non-pulmonary event in the patient with previously normal lungs;
2. respiratory distress with hypoxemia, decreased pulmonary compliance, and increased shunt (Qs/Qt) fraction;
3. radiologic evidence of diffuse pulmonary infiltrates; and
4. exclusion of left heart disease and congestive heart failure.

The common microscopic findings include degeneration of alveolar epithelial cells and evidence of injury to the pulmonary capillary endothelium with disruption of the alveolar-capillary membrane.[90] There also may be clots and microemboli that extend from the subendothelial space into the capillary lumen.[100] There is development of proteinaceous hemorrhagic edema in the interstitium, alveolar wall, and alveolus because of the loss of alveolar capillary membrane integrity. This proteinaceous fluid can coalesce and form hyaline membranes. Effort to repair this injury results in proliferation of cuboidal type II pneumocytes, migration of white cells, and formation of fibrous tissue which increases the interstitial volume and destroys acinar architecture. If the destruction is great enough, there is life-threatening loss of surface area available for gas exchange.[90] Functionally, there is loss of compliance and reduced lung volumes with severe arterial hypoxemia and a large venous admixture. The hypoxemia is explained by both right-to-left intrapulmonary shunting and ventilation/perfusion mismatch. There is often an increase in pulmonary vascular resistance.

The clinical presentation is usually characterized by a latent period of minimal symptoms, except that of hyperventilation, and then the gradual onset of respiratory distress. There is profound hypoxemia which is unresponsive to supplemental oxygen by face mask or nasal prongs. The chest X-ray is relatively nonspecific, being normal initially and then showing evidence of pulmonary edema without cardiomegaly and an evolving interstitial pattern.[101] Standard therapy includes tracheal intubation and mechanical ventilation in the face of worsening lung disease when the patient is hypoxemic on > 0.5 F_iO_2.[90] Different mechanical ventilatory maneuvers are used, but the most common involves the use of increased positive end-expiratory pressure (PEEP) to increase and maintain alveolar patency and lung volume. This also improves ventilation and perfusion matching.[90] PEEP itself has many side effects, including barotrauma, increased lung water, and a fall in cardiac output. Therefore, measurements of cardiac output and oxygen delivery obtained with various methods are often used to guide therapy if a PEEP of ≥ 15 cmH_2O is used. Other therapy involves treating inciting disorders if possible, careful fluid balance, inotropic agents, and meticulous monitoring of vital signs, blood pressure, and arterial blood gases. There is no specific therapy available, as the actual mode of injury is multifactorial and is still being investigated.

In spite of careful monitoring and aggressive support, the mortality for ARDS remains quite high. Pediatric mortality in the literature ranges from 28% to 90%, with an average of 52%.[61] Most often, death is not from refractory respiratory failure but secondary to sepsis and failure of other major organs.

The assessment and care of these children requires a plethora of laboratory-based support services. In the early stage of the disease, when oxygen administration alone is necessary, the most important point of evaluation involves identifying the cause of the alveolar disease. Current clinical care of the pathophysiologic process is supportive, so early treatment of the causal factor is imperative. This necessitates full bacteriologic evaluation and the ability to obtain and rapidly process bronchoscopic and biopsy specimens. Any injury to the body that causes shock or a systemic inflammatory response can result in ARDS; once again, the rapid evaluation and treatment of the inciting injury is essential.

Once the patient requires intubation and mechanical ventilation, the requirements for close monitoring of serum electrolytes, frequent blood gases, and monitoring of other organ functions is essential, as the appearance of multi-organ system failure has dire prognostic significance and often requires further intervention. The course is often complicated by sepsis from secondary organisms. Nutritional evaluation and support is imperative.

The impact of bedside devices that provide on-line measures of respiratory function, such as pulse oximetry and end tidal CO_2 monitoring, is still being evaluated. These monitors should improve the speed of response to changes in clinical status, and may result in lowering the frequency of measuring arterial blood gases. The new generation of blood chemistry machines that require smaller samples of blood for analysis should also have significant impact on the management of these patients. At this time, even adult patients often require transfusion because of the amounts of blood drawn for evaluation. Avoiding transfusion would conserve resources and reduce patient risk.

SUMMARY

The respiratory diseases treated in the newborn and pediatric patient are diverse and often life-threatening. These cases require an intensive approach to laboratory monitoring, and thus centers that care for these infants must maintain a laboratory capable of microtechniques and "stat-lab" response times, to ensure proper care of the patient.

REFERENCES

1. Chu J, Clements JA, Cotton EK, et al. Neonatal pulmonary ischemia: clinical and physiologic studies. Pediatrics 1967;40:709–66.
2. Green TP, Thompson TR, Johnson DE, Lock JE. Diuresis and pulmonary function in premature infants with respiratory distress syndrome. J Pediatr 1983;103:618–23.
3. Weaver TE, Whitsett JA. Function and regulation of expression of pulmonary surfactant associated proteins. Biochem J 1991;273:249–55.
4. Nogee LM, deMello DE, Dehner LP, Colten HR. Brief report: deficiency of pulmonary surfactant protein B in congenital alveolar proteinosis. N Engl J Med 1993;328:406–10.
5. Nogee LM, Garnier G, Dietz HC, et al. A mutation in the surfactant protein B gene responsible for fatal neonatal respiratory disease in multiple kindreds. J Clin Invest 1994;93:1860–63.
6. Hamvas A, Cole FS, deMello DE, et al. Surfactant protein B deficiency: antenatal diagnosis and prospective treatment with surfactant replacement. J Pediatr 1994;125:356–61.
7. NIH Consensus Development Conference on the Effect of Corticosteroids for Fetal Maturation on Perinatal Outcomes, February 28–March 2, 1994.
8. Morley CJ, Mangham AD, Miller N, et al. Dry artificial lung surfactant and its effect on very premature babies. Lancet 1981;1:64–68.
9. Fujiwara T. Surfactant replacement in neonatal RDS. In: Robertson B, van Golde LMG, Batenburg JJ, eds. Pulmonary surfactant. Amsterdam: Elsevier, 1984:479–504.
10. Halliday HL, McClure G, Reid M, et al. Controlled trial of artificial surfactant to prevent respiratory distress syndrome. Lancet 1984;1:476–78.
11. Wilkinson A, Jenkins PA, Jeffrey JA. Two controlled trials of artificial surfactant: early effects and later outcome in babies with surfactant deficiency. Lancet 1985;2:287–91.
12. Hallman M, Merritt TA, Jarvenpaa A-L, et al. Exogenous human surfactant for treatment of severe respiratory distress syndrome: a randomized, prospective clinical trial. J Pediatr 1985;106:963–69.
13. Enhorning GE, Shennan A, Possmayer F, et al. Prevention of neonatal respiratory distress syndrome by tracheal instillation of surfactant: a randomized clinical trial. Pediatrics 1985;76:145–53.
14. Kwong MS, Egan EA, Notter RH, et al. A double-blind clinical trial of calf lung lipid for the prevention of hyaline membrane disease in extremely premature infants. Pediatrics 1985;76:585–92.
15. Shapiro DL, Notter RH, Monh FC, et al. A double-blind, randomized trial of a calf lung surfactant extract administered at birth to very premature infants for prevention of the respiratory distress syndrome. Pediatrics 1985;76:593–99.
16. Merritt TA, Hallman M, Bloom BT, et al. Prophylactic treatment of very premature infants with human surfactant. N Engl J Med 1986;315:785–90.
17. Gitlin JD, Sou CF, Parad RB, et al. Randomized controlled trial of exogenous surfactant for the treatment of hyaline membrane disease. Pediatrics 1987;79:31–37.
18. Kendig JW, Notter RH, Cox C, et al. A comparison of surfactant as immediate prophylaxis and as rescue therapy in newborns of less than 30 weeks gestation. N Engl J Med 1991;324:865–71.

19. Dunn MS, et al. Bovine surfactant replacement therapy in neonates of less than 30 weeks gestation: a randomized controlled trial of prophylaxis versus treatment. Pediatrics 1991;87:377.
20. Horbar JD, Wright EC, Onstad L, and the members of the NICHD Neonatal Research Network. Decreasing mortality associated with the introduction of surfactant therapy: an observational study of neonates weighing 601–1300 grams at birth. Pediatrics 1993;92:191–96.
21. Horbar JD, Wright LL, Soll RF, et al. A multicenter randomized trial comparing two surfactants for the treatment of neonatal respiratory distress syndrome. J Pediatr 1993;123:757–66.
22. Peckham GJ, Fox WW. Physiologic factors affecting pulmonary artery pressure in infants with persistent pulmonary hypertension. J Pediatr 1978;93:1005–10.
23. Murphy JE, Rabinovitch M, Goldstein JD, Reid LM. The structural basis of persistent pulmonary hypertension of the newborn infant. J Pediatr 1981;98:962–67.
24. Geggel RL, Reid LM. The structural basis of PPHN. Clin Perinatol 1984;11:525–45.
25. Heymann MA, le Biodis J, Soifer SJ, Clyman RI. Leukotriene synthesis inhibition increases pulmonary blood flow in fetal lambs. Chest 1988;93:117S.
26. Murphy JD, Freed MD, Lang P, et al. Prostaglandin-E_1 in neonatal persistent pulmonary hypertension. Pediatr Res 1980;14:606.
27. Levin DL, Fixler DE, Morriss FC, et al. Morphologic analysis of the pulmonary vascular bed in infants exposed in utero to prostaglandin synthetase inhibitors. J Pediatr 1978;92:478–83.
28. Ignarro LJ, Buga GM, Wood KS, et al. Endothelium derived relaxing factor produced and released from artery and vein is nitric oxide. Proc Natl Acad Sci USA 1987;84:9265–69.
29. Ignarro LJ. Biological actions and properties of endothelium derived nitric oxide formed and released from the artery and vein. Circ Res 1989;65:1–2.
30. Archer SI, Rist K, Nelson DP, et al. Comparison of the hemodynamic effects of nitric oxide and endothelium dependent vasodilators in intact lungs. J App Physiol 1990;68:735–47.
31. Palmer RMJ, Ferrige AG, Ashton DS, Moncada S. L-arginine is the physiologic precursor for the formation of nitric oxide in endothelium derived relaxing factor. Biochem Biophys Res Commun 1988;153:1251–56.
32. Ignarro LJ, Adams JB, Horwitz PM, Wood KS. Activation of soluble guanylate cyclase by NO-hemoproteins involves NO-heme exchange. J Biol Chem 1986;261:4997–5002.
33. Burke-Wolin T, Abate CJ, Wolin MS, Gurtner GH. Hydrogen peroxide induced pulmonary vasodilation: role of guanosine 3′, 5′-cyclic monophosphate. Am J Physiol 1991;261:393–98.
34. Fineman JR, Heymann MA, Soifer SJ. N-nitro-L arginine attenuates endothelium dependent pulmonary vasodilation in lambs. Am J Physiol 1991;260:H1299–1306.
35. Shaul PW, Farrar MA, Zellers TM. Oxygen modulates endothelium derived relaxing factor production in fetal pulmonary arteries. Am J Physio 1992;262:H355–64.
36. Abman SH, Chatfield BA, Hall SL, McMurty IF. Role of endothelium derived relaxing factor during transition of the pulmonary circulation at birth. Am J Physiol 1990;259:H1921–27.
37. Hammerman C, Lass N, Strales E, et al. Prostanoids in neonates with pulmonary hypertension. J Pediatr 1987;110:470–72.
38. Stenmark K, Janes S, Voekel N. Leukotriene C4 and D4 in neonates with hypoxemia and pulmonary hypertension. N Engl J Med 1983;309:77–80.
39. Drummond WH, Gregory GA, Heymann MA, Phibbs RA. The independent effect of hyperventilation, tolazoline and dopamine on infants with persistent pulmonary hypertension. J Pediatr 1981;98:603–11.
40. Duara S, Gewitz MH, Fox WW. Use of mechanical ventilation for clinical management of persistent pulmonary hypertension of the newborn. Clin Perinatol 1984;11:641–52.
41. Gleason CA, Short BL, Jones MD Jr. Cerebral blood flow and metabolism during and after prolonged hypocapnia in newborn lambs. J Pediatr 1989;115:309–11.
42. Bifano EM, Pfannenstiel N. Duration of hyperventilation and outcome in infants with persistent pulmonary hypertension. Pediatrics 1988;81:657–60.
43. Ferrara B, Johnson DE, Chong P-N, Thompson TR. Efficacy and neurologic outcome of profound hypocapneic alkalosis for the treatment of persistent pulmonary hypertension in infancy. J Pediatr 1984;105:457–61.

44. Hendricks-Munoz KD, Walton JP. Hearing loss in infants with persistent fetal circulation. Pediatrics 1988;81:650–56.
45. Wung J-T, Jones LS, Kilchevsky E, James E. Management of infants with severe respiratory failure and persistence of the fetal circulation, without hyperventilation. Pediatrics 1985;76:488–94.
46. Goetzman BW, Milstein JM. Pulmonary vasodilator action of tolazoline. Pediatr Res 1979;13:942–46.
47. Hageman JR, Farrell EE. Intravenous nitroglycerin (NTG) in the treatment of persistent pulmonary hypertension of the newborn (PPHN). Pediatr Res 1985;19:345A.
48. Klinke WP, Gilbert JAL. Diazoxide in primary pulmonary hypertension. N Engl J Med 1989;302:91–92.
49. Stevenson DK, Kastings DS, Darrall RA Jr, et al. Refractory hypoxemia associated with neonatal pulmonary disease: the use and limitations of tolazoline. J Pediatr 1979;95:595–99.
50. The Neonatal Inhaled Nitric Oxide Study Group. Inhaled nitric oxide in full-term and nearly full-term infants with hypoxic respiratory failure. N Engl J Med 1997;336:597–604.
51. Roberts JD, Fineman JR, Morin FC, et al. Inhaled nitric oxide and persistent pulmonary hypertension of the newborn. N Engl J Med 1997;336:605–10.
52. Wessel DL, Adatia I, VanMarter LJ, et al. Improved oxygenation in a randomized trial of inhaled nitric oxide for PPHN. Pediatrics 1997;100:888 (e7).
53. Schedin U, Norman M, Gustafsson LE, et al. Endogenous nitric oxide in the upper airways of premature and term infants. Acta Paediatr 1997;86:1229–35.
54. Haddad IY, Ischiropouls H, Holm BA, et al. Mechanisms of peroxynitric-induced injury to pulmonary surfactants. Am J Physiol 1993;265:L555–64.
55. Haddad IY, Zhu S, Crow J, Barefield E, et al. Inhibition of alveolar type II cell ATP and surfactant synthesis by nitric oxide. Am J Physiol 1996;270:L898–906.
56. Hallman M, Bry K. Nitric oxide and lung surfactant. Semin Perinatal 1996;20:173–85.
57. Rosenberg AA, Kennaugh JM, Moreland SG, et al. Longitudinal follow-up of a cohort of infants treated with inhaled nitric oxide for PPHN. J Pediatrics 1997;131:70–75.
58. Andrews AF, Roloff DW, Bartlett RH. Use of extracorporeal membrane oxygenators in persistent pulmonary hypertension of the newborn. Clin Perinatol 1984;11:729–36.
59. Stolar CJH, Snedecor SM, Bartlett RH. Extracorporeal membrane oxygenation and neonatal respiratory failure: experience from the extracorporeal life support organization. J of Pediatr Surg 1991;26:563–71.
60. Short BL, Miller MK, Anderson KD. Extracorporeal membrane oxygenation in the management of respiratory failure in the newborn. Clin Perinatol 1987;14:737–48.
61. Cilley RE, Zwischenberger JB, Andrews A, et al. Intracranial hemorrhage during extracorporeal membrane oxygenation in neonates. AJDC 1988;142:1320–24.
62. Revenis ME, Glass P, Short BL. Mortality and morbidity rates among lower birth weight infants (2000 to 2500 grams) treated with extracorporeal membrane oxygenation. J Pediatr 1992;121:452–58.
63. Beck R, Anderson D, Pearson GD, et al. Criteria for extracorporeal membrane oxygenation in a population of infants with PPHN. J Pediatr Surg 1986;21:297–302.
64. Marsh TD, Wilkerson SA, Cook LN. Extracorporeal membrane oxygenation selection criteria: partial pressure of arterial oxygen versus alveolar-arterial oxygen gradient. Pediatr 1988;82:162–66.
65. Anderson HL, Otsu T, Chapman RA, et al. Venovenous extracorporeal life support in neonates using a double lumen catheter. ASAIO Trans 1989;35:659–53.
66. Henderson-Smart DJ, Pettigrew AG, Campbell DJ. Clinical apnea and brain-stem neural function in preterm infants. N Engl J Med 1983;308:353–57.
67. Von Euler C. On the central pattern generator for the basic breathing rhythmicity. J Appli Physiol 1983;55:1647–59.
68. Gerhardt T, Bancalari E. Apnea of prematurity. I. Lung function and regulation of breathing. Pediatrics 1984;74:58–62.
69. Thach BT, Stark AR. Spontaneous neck flexion and airway obstruction during apneic spells in preterm infants. J Pediatr 1979;94:275–81.

70. Miller MJ, Carlo WA, Martin RJ. Continuous positive pressure selectively reduces obstructive apnea in preterm infants. J Pediatr 1985;106:91–94.
71. Carlo WA, Miller MJ, Martin RJ. Differential response of upper airway diaphragmatic activities to airway occlusion in infants. J Appl Physiol 1985;59:847–52.
72. Gauda EB, Miller MJ, Carlo WA, et al. Genioglossus response to airway occlusion in apneic vs. nonapneic infants. Pediatr Res 1987;22:683–87.
73. National Institutes of Health Consensus Panel. Development conference of infantile apnea and home monitoring, Sept. 29 to Oct. 1, 1986. Pediatrics 1987;79:292–99.
74. Gerhardt T, McCarthy J, Bancalari E. Effect of aminophylline on respiratory center activity and metabolic rate in premature infants with idiopathic apnea. Pediatrics 1979;63:537–42.
75. Northway NR Jr, Rosan RC, Porter DY. Pulmonary disease following respiratory therapy of hyaline membrane disease. N Engl J Med 1967;276:357–62.
76. Bancalari E, Abdenour GE, Feller R, Gannon J. Bronchopulmonary dysplasia: a clinical presentation. J Pediatr 1979;95:819–23.
77. Avery ME, Todey WA, Keller JB, et al. Is chronic lung disease in low birth weight infants preventable? A survey of eight centers. Pediatrics 1987;79:26–30.
78. Werthanner J, Brown ER, Neff EK, Taeusch HW. Sudden infant death syndrome in infants with bronchopulmonary dysplasia. Pediatrics 1982;69:301–4.
79. Smyth JA, Jabachnik E, Duncan WJ, et al. Pulmonary function and bronchial hyperreactivity in long-term survivors of bronchopulmonary dysplasia. Pediatrics 1981;68:336–40.
80. Yu VYH, Orgill AA, Lim SB, et al. Growth and development of VLBW infants recovering from bronchopulmonary dysplasia. Arch Dis Child 1983;58:791–94.
81. Vohr BR, Bell EF, Oh W. Infants with BPD-growth pattern and neurologic and developmental outcome. Am J Dis Child 1982;136:443–47.
82. Goetzman BW. Understanding bronchopulmonary dysplasia. Am J Dis Child 1986; 140:332–34.
83. Frank L, Sosenko IR. Undernutrition as a major contributing factor in the pathogenesis of bronchopulmonary dysplasia. Am Rev Respir Dis 1988;138:725–29.
84. Avery GB, Fletcher AB, Kaplan M, et al. Controlled trial of dexamethasone in respiratory-dependent infants with BPD. Pediatrics 1985;75:106–11.
85. Yeh TF, Lin YJ, Hsien WS, et al. Early postnatal dexamethasone therapy for the prevention of chronic lung disease in preterm infants with respiratory distress syndrome: a multi-center clinical trial. Pediatrics 1997;100:715–16 (e3).
86. Papile L, Tyson JE, Stoll BJ, et al. A multicenter trial of two dexamethasone regimens in ventilator-dependent premature infants. N Engl J Med 1998;338:1112–8.
87. Anderson JM, Kottke-Marchant K. Platelet interactions with biomaterials and artificial devices. In: Williams DF, ed. Blood compatibility, Vol. I. Boca Raton, FL: CRC Press, 1987:103–34.
88. Turitto VT, Weiss HJ, Baumgartner HR, et al. Cells and aggregates at surfaces. In: Leonard EF, Turitto VT, Vroman L, eds. Blood in contact with natural and artificial surfaces. New York: The New York Academy of Sciences, 1987:453–67.
89. Backofen JE, Rogers MC. Upper airway disease. In: Rogers MC, ed. Textbook of pediatric intensive care. Baltimore: Williams and Wilkins, 1987:171–97.
90. Nichols DG, Rogers MC. Adult respiratory distress syndrome. In: Rogers MC, ed. Textbook of pediatric intensive care. Baltimore: Williams and Wilkins, 1987:237–71.
91. Chantarojanasiri T, Nichols DG, Rogers MC. Lower airway disease: bronchiolitis and asthma. In: Rogers MC, ed. Textbook of pediatric intensive care. Baltimore: Williams and Wilkins, 1987:199–235.
92. Henderson FW, Clyde WA, Collier AM, et al. The etiologic and epidemiologic spectrum of bronchiolitis in pediatric practice. J Pediatr 1979;95:183–190.
93. Church NR, Anas NG, Hall CB, et al. Respiratory syncytial virus related apnea in infants. Am J Dis Child 1984;138:247–51.
94. Dunnill MS. Pathology of asthma. In: Porter R, Birch J, eds. Identification of asthma (Ciba Foundation Symposium Study Group #38). London: Churchill Livingstone, 1971:35–50.
95. Kay AB. Basic mechanism in allergic asthma. Eur J Resp Dis 1982;122(Suppl):9–16.

96. Leff A. Pathogenesis of asthma: neurophysiology and pharmacology of bronchospasm. Chest 1982;81:224–29.
97. Daniel EE, Davis C, Jones T. Control of airway smooth muscle. In: Hargrave E, ed. Airway hyperactivity, mechanisms and clinical relevance. Proceedings of a symposium, McMaster University. Hamilton, Ontario: Astra Pharmaceuticals, June 1975.
98. Ashbaugh DG, Bigelow DB, Petty TL, et al. Acute respiratory distress in adults. Lancet 1967;2:319–23.
99. Petty TL. Adult respiratory distress syndrome: definition and historical perspective. Clin Chest Med 1982;3:3–15.
100. Backofen M, Weible ER. Alterations of the gas exchange apparatus in adult respiratory insufficiency associated with septicemia. Am Rev Respir Dis 1977;116:589–615.
101. Joffe N. The adult respiratory distress syndrome. Am J Roentgen 1974;122:719–32.

CHAPTER 3

Kidney and Urinary Tract Disorders

Elizabeth A. Harvey, M.D., F.R.C.P.(C)
John Williamson Balfe, M.D., F.R.C.P.(C)

INTRODUCTION

The role of the healthy kidney is to maintain the fluid and electrolyte composition of the body within a narrow range of normal despite wide fluctuations in dietary intake of fluid and solute. This is accomplished by a complex process of filtration, reabsorption, and secretion of electrolytes, solutes, and water, mediated by various hormonal systems. Approximately 20% of the cardiac output is delivered to the filtering units of the kidney, the glomeruli, of which there are 1.2 million in each kidney. Passage of water through the glomeruli occurs freely, while passage of electrolytes and solutes is determined by their size and charge. As water and solute travel along the tubular system of the nephron, varying amounts are reabsorbed and secreted to maintain homeostasis. Disruption of this complex process results in clinical disease.

METHODS OF EVALUATION

Evaluation of the child for kidney disease can range from simple screening as part of a routine physical examination to a detailed, specific evaluation based on suggestive clinical features. Children are frightened by hospitals and procedures, especially blood tests. Therefore, blood tests should be kept to a minimum, and only the smallest specimen necessary taken. Timed urine specimens are particularly difficult to obtain and are often inaccurate, and therefore short timed or spot collections should be done, with results expressed as a concentration ratio to a plasma value or relationship to urinary creatinine. Laboratory results are interpreted in relation to normal children of similar age and size. Functional tests or excretion rates should be related to body weight, surface area, or caloric expenditure. A recent listing of reference laboratory ranges is available.[1] However, reference values are method dependent. Values quoted in this text are for methods currently employed at the Hospital for Sick Children in Toronto, Canada.

Electrolytes

Sodium

The reference range for a child's sodium (Na) is 135–143 mmol/L (mEq/L). The range for infants is lower, at 132–142 mmol/L (mEq/L). The healthy kidney can maintain a normal plasma sodium in spite of a large variation in sodium intake, i.e., 2–1000 mmol/d. The tolerance limits are reduced in renal insufficiency.

Hyponatremia (Na < 130 mmol/L [mEq/L]) implies a dilution of body solute, either as a result of sodium loss and extracellular fluid (ECF) volume contraction or water retention and ECF volume expansion. Pseudohyponatremia may result from hyperlipidemia, hyperglycemia, or hyperproteinemia, but is rare in children since the aberration must be large. Ion-specific electrodes are free of the effect caused by lipid and protein and are therefore preferred to flame photometry for the measurement of sodium and potassium. For every 3.4 mmol/L (62 mg/dL) increment in the plasma glucose concentration, water will be drawn out of the cells to reduce the plasma Na concentration by 1 mmol/L (mEq/L).[2]

Hypernatremia (Na > 150 mmol/L [mEq/L]) is usually secondary to a water deficit and is seen in some cases of diarrhea and in infants with diabetes insipidus of pituitary or renal origin. Salt-poisoning is a rare cause of hypernatremia.

Potassium

The reference range for a child's plasma potassium (K) is 3.5–5.0 mmol/L (mEq/L), but it is higher in the premature and term infant, at 4.5–6.5 mmol/L (mEq/L). Maintenance of the ECF potassium concentration is related to hormone control, drugs, disease, and, to a lesser extent, dietary intake.[3]

Hyperkalemia (K > 5.0 mmol/L [mEq/L]) can be the result of excessive potassium intake in patients with renal failure or hypoaldosteronism. Spurious hyperkalemia can occur with thrombocytosis and hemolysis.

Hypokalemia (K < 3.5 mmol/L [mEq/L]) is seen in renal tubular disorders such as Fanconi syndrome and in hyperaldosteronism, which may occur in hypertension secondary to renal artery stenosis. It also occurs with diuretic use.

Calcium

The reference range for total plasma calcium in a child is 2.25–2.62 mmol/L (9.0–10.5 mg/dL) and for ionized calcium is 1.14–1.29 mmol/L (4.6–5.2 mg/dL). The range for total calcium for a premature infant is 1.8–2.5 mmol/L (7.2–10 mg/dL) and for a term infant is 2.0–2.75 mmol/L (8–11 mg/dL). The range for ionized calcium in infants is 1.10–1.5 mmol/L (4.4–6.0 mg/dL). Much of the plasma calcium is bound to protein (40%) and the remainder exists as free or ionized calcium (50%) or in complex with ions (10%). The ionized calcium is physiologically active. In hypoalbuminemic states, the total calcium is reduced, and if measurement of ionized calcium is not available, one can adjust the result by adding 0.023 mmol/L (0.09 mg/dL) for every 1 g/L (0.1 g/dL) that the albumin is < 46 g/L (4.6 g/dL). An alternate formula is:

$$\text{Corrected Calcium (Ca)} = [\text{Ca} - (\text{alb} \div 40)] + 1$$

where albumin is in g/L.

Hypocalcemia may present with tetany and occurs with hypoparathyroidism and vitamin D deficiency rickets. Hypercalcemia occurs with vitamin D toxicity, hyperparathyroidism, and some malignancies.

Magnesium

The reference range for plasma magnesium is 0.75–1.15 mmol/L (1.5–2.3 mEq/L) for the newborn,0.70–0.95 mmol/L (1.4–1.19 mEq/L) for children, and 0.65–1.00 mmol/L (1.3–2.0 mEq/L) for adults. Hypomagnesemia is seen in neonatal tetany, diseases with increased gastrointestinal fluid loss, and diuretic therapy. Renal magnesium wasting can occur with Gitelman syndrome, a renal tubular disorder where there is also urinary potassium wasting, and can be associated with the use of drugs such as aminoglycosides and cis-platinum.

Urea

The reference range for plasma urea is 2–10 mmol/L (5.6–28 mg/dL) for the newborn, 1.8–5.4 mmol/L (5–15 mg/dL) at 1 to 2 years of age, and 2.9–7.1 mmol/L (8–20 mg/dL) at 2 to 16 years. Urea is the main nitrogen-containing metabolite of protein catabolism. It is synthesized in the liver from ammonia by hepatic enzymes of the urea cycle. Over 90% is excreted by the kidney. Because of tubular reabsorption of urea, especially in the presence of oliguria, urea clearance underestimates glomerular filtration rate (GFR). Although plasma urea does not give a good reflection of GFR, it does give important metabolic data. It is increased in babies who are fed excessive protein or insufficient water, and in states of acute reversible renal failure from dehydration. Assessment of the diet of patients with chronic renal failure is aided by knowing the plasma urea value. Each gram of protein leads to the excretion of 0.3 grams of urea.

Creatinine

Creatinine is an endogenous product of muscle metabolism. Its rate of production is proportional to muscle mass and it is excreted predominantly by glomerular filtration (90%), with a small and varying component via renal tubular secretion (10%). Under normal circumstances, the rates of production and excretion are fairly con-

TABLE 3–1. Plasma Creatinine Values for Children

Age (yrs)	μmol/L	mg/dL
< 5	< 44	< 0.5
5-<6	< 53	< 0.6
6-<7	< 62	< 0.7
7-<8	< 71	< 0.8
8-<9	< 80	< 0.9
9-<10	< 88	< 1.0
≥ 10	< 106	< 1.2

stant. The repeated measurement of plasma creatinine concentration is a useful and simple test of GFR for clinical practice. However, in small children or elderly adults with reduced muscle mass, the plasma creatinine may be misleading as it may be in the normal range and not reflect a reduced GFR. It should be noted that the GFR may be reduced as much as 50% without a detectable change in the plasma creatinine concentration. The reference ranges are listed in Table 3–1.

Glomerular Filtration Rate

The clearance of endogenous creatinine (Ccr) can be used as a measure of GFR, even though it overestimates the result because there is some tubular secretion.

$$Ccr = UcrV/Pcr$$

where:
Ucr = urine creatinine concentration
V = urine volume in mL per minute
Pcr = plasma creatinine concentration

In children of normal body habitus and in a steady state, there are formulae to estimate the Ccr from the plasma creatinine concentration and the patient's height.[4]

$$Ccr = kL/Pcr$$

where:
L = height (cm)
Pcr = plasma creatinine
k = 29 μmol/L (.33 mg/dL) for pre-term infants
= 40 μmol/L (.45 mg/dL) for full-term infants and toddlers
= 49 μmol/L (.55 mg/dL) for children and adolescent females
= 62 μmol/L (.70 mg/dL) for adolescent males

It should be appreciated that this formula only estimates GFR and should not replace a formal measurement of GFR when accuracy is needed.[5] There is considerable experience using a single intravenous bolus injection of isotopic markers, such as ^{125}I iothalamate and ^{99m}Tc diethylenetriamine pentacetic acid (DTPA). The rate of disappearance of the isotope from the plasma estimates GFR without the need for urine collection. If one assumes a single compartment, fewer blood specimens are required. To improve accuracy, a two-compartment model may be assumed using double rather than single exponential analysis. An even more accurate method can be applied by using the area under the plasma disappearance curve for the GFR agent and dividing this into the quantity of isotope injected.[6] The practical disadvantage is the need for six to nine blood specimens. A constant infusion technique is another accurate method and has pediatric appeal since only one or two blood samples are required.

Tubular Function Tests

The fluid which enters the tubules is a plasma ultrafiltrate devoid of large plasma proteins. The role of the proximal tubule is to reclaim appropriate amounts of filtered glucose, amino acids, electrolytes, phosphate, and bicarbonate. In disease states affecting proximal tubular function, excess amounts of these solutes may be lost in the urine, with subsequent abnormalities of the blood chemistries. Analysis of the urine will assist in diagnosis.[7, 8]

Proximal Tubule

Sodium

The most common test of tubular function is the ability to conserve sodium appropriately to preserve the ECF volume. There is no "normal" value for sodium excretion. In the steady state, the urinary sodium excretion reflects dietary intake. In disease states, the urinary sodium concentration should be interpreted in light of the expected normal renal response. With hyponatremic ECF volume contraction, the expected response is excretion of concentrated urine with a sodium concentration < 10 mmol/L (mEq/L). In this situation, high urine sodium (> 20 mmol/L [mEq/L]) may be related to proximal tubular defects, diuretics, vomiting, or aldosterone deficiency. Measurement of urinary potassium and chloride concentrations will help clarify the cause. With hyponatremia secondary to water gain (ECF volume expansion), the urine should have a low sodium concentration and be maximally dilute. Failure of this expected response may be seen in the syndrome of inappropriate antidiuretic hormone secretion, or with low effective circulating volume such as occurs with congestive heart failure or hypoalbuminemia. In hypernatremia, usually secondary to water loss with ECF volume contraction, the expected response is excretion of a minimal volume of maximally concentrated urine with a low sodium concentration.

An extremely low urine osmolality will be seen with diabetes insipidus, while a mildly hypertonic urine may occur with an osmotic diuresis or diuretic use.

Potassium

Assessment of potassium excretion is essential in the investigation of hyper-and hypokalemia. Potassium is filtered and completely reabsorbed in the proximal nephron. Urinary potassium excretion is the result of secretion in the late distal convoluted tubule and cortical collecting duct. Since urinary potassium excretion should equal dietary intake, there is no "normal" value. In the face of hypokalemia, a urinary potassium > 20 mmol/L (mEq/L) or a daily potassium excretion > 0.5 mmol(mEq)/kg/d (> 30 mmol(mEq)/d in adults) suggests a renal cause for the hypokalemia.

The transtubular potassium gradient (TTKG) is an approximation of potassium concentration at the end of the cortical distal nephron, prior to (and corrected for) water reabsorption in the medullary collecting duct. It provides an assessment of aldosterone activity in vivo and is calculated as follows:

$$\text{TTKG} = \frac{[\text{K}]\ \text{urine}}{[\text{U}/\text{P}]\ \text{osmol}} \div [\text{K}]\ \text{Plasma}$$

where (urine/plasma) osmolality > 1 and urine sodium > 25 mmol/L (mEq/L).

When the TTKG exceeds 7, mineralocorticoid is present, while a TTKG of less than 4 implies no activity.

Bicarbonate

Normally 80–90% of filtered bicarbonate is reabsorbed in the proximal tubule. A further 15–20% is reabsorbed distally so that very little bicarbonate escapes into the urine (fractional excretion < 5%). In proximal renal tubular acidosis (RTA), bicarbonate reabsorption is impaired, resulting in an increased fractional excretion of bicarbonate, above 10–15%. Proximal RTA most often occurs in conjunction with a generalized proximal tubular disorder. The bicarbonate loading test measures bicarbonate excretion and reabsorption at different filtered loads of bicarbonate. During bicarbonate infusion, plasma and urine bicarbonate and creatinine concentrations are measured and plotted against the plasma bicarbonate to determine the bicarbonate threshold.

Glucose

The proximal tubular glucose concentration is the same as that of plasma, as glucose is freely filtered. Ninety percent of filtered glucose is reabsorbed against a concentration gradient in the proximal tubule via a sodium-coupled active transport mechanism. The glucose receptors are "saturable." As blood glucose rises, so does the glucose concentration in the tubular fluid. Proximal glucose reabsorption increases linearly until the receptors are saturated, at which point a maximum value of glucose transport is reached, i.e., the tubular maximum (Tm). The Tm for adults, children, and infants is 16 mmol/min/1.73m^2 (300 mg/min/1.73m^2) and occurs at a plasma glucose of 10 mmol/L (180 mg/dL). The normal 24 h excretion of glucose should be < 2.8 mmol/d (0.5 g/d). When glucosuria is present, it is important to rule out hyperglycemia. Glucosuria without hyperglycemia may be due to isolated renal glucosuria. It may also be secondary to multiple proximal tubular defects (renal Fanconi syndrome). Reagent strips for testing glucose are based on the use of the enzyme glucose oxidase.

Phosphate

Eighty-five to ninety-five percent of filtered phosphate is reabsorbed by the proximal tubule via an active transport system. The 24 h excretion of phosphate is diet dependent, but averages 10–15% of the filtered load. Thus, a normal tubular reabsorption of phosphate (TRP) is greater than 85% and is calculated as follows:

$$TRP\% = 1 - \left(\frac{U_{PO_4}}{P_{PO_4}} \times \frac{P_{cr}}{U_{cr}} \right) \times 100$$

where U = urine, P = plasma, PO_4 = phosphate, Cr = creatinine.

It is generally agreed, however, that the renal threshold phosphate excretion (TP/GFR) best represents the renal tubular handling of phosphate. In adults, the TP/GFR is equivalent to the tubular maximum phosphate reabsorption per GFR (TmP/GFR), measured during phosphate loading. A nomogram exists which allows calculation of the TmP/GFR using a spot urine and a fasting serum phosphate and creatinine value.[9] The tubular reabsorption of phosphate is calculated from the above and plotted along with the serum phosphate to derive the TmP/GFR.

In children, values of TmP/GFR are very similar to TP/GFR without phosphate loading. TP/GFR is calculated by the following formula, with GFR represented by creatinine clearance:

$$TP\,/\,GFR\,(Ccr) = Sp - \left(\frac{U_p \times S_{cr}}{U_{cr}} \right)$$

where:

S_p = serum phosphate
U_p = urine phosphate
S_{cr} = serum creatinine
U_{cr} = urine creatinine

Use of the TmP/GFR nomogram is not recommended in children as it tends to overestimate TP/GFR due to the higher threshold values in children compared to adults.[10] Published normal values are not standardized as they depend on the method used.

An abnormally low TRP or TP/GFR results in hypophosphatemia and is associated with the renal Fanconi syndrome, tubulo-interstitial diseases, hyperparathyroidism, or Vitamin D resistant rickets.

Amino Acids

Normally, 95% of filtered amino acids are reabsorbed in the proximal tubule. Fractional clearances for most amino acids are less than 1%, with the exception of aspartate, serine, glycine, histidine, and taurine, which range from 2–9%. Thus, amounts in excess of 5% of the filtered load are abnormal. Aminoaciduria may be generalized and associated with the renal Fanconi syndrome. Alternately, it may be due to abnormalities in the transport of neutral amino acids (Hartnup disease), acidic amino acids (benign condition), or cystine (cystinuria) and the basic amino acids (ornithine, arginine, and lysine), which predisposes to urolithiasis. Cystine causes a positive urinary cyanide nitroprusside test.

Chloride

The urinary excretion of chloride is dependent on dietary intake and the state of hydration. With ECF volume contraction, the urinary chloride will be low (< 10 mmol/L [mEq/L]) unless the volume contraction is secondary to diarrhea. With acute diuretic use, the chloride will be high in the presence of ECF volume contraction, as is the case in Bartter syndrome.

Titratable Acid

The major urine buffers are phosphate and ammonium. Hydrogen ions buffered with phosphate are referred to as titratable acid. The buffering capacity of phosphate is limited to 20–50 mmol/d, even in severe acidosis. Ammonium provides the extra buffering capacity in sustained acidosis. Net acid excretion equals titratable acid plus ammonium minus bicarbonate.

Urine pH

The major value of urinary pH measurement is in the detection of bicarbonaturia (pH > 7). It is not a reliable indicator of distal ammonium excretion. However, once a low distal ammonium excretion is suggested by a positive urine net charge (see discussion below), the urine pH will help differentiate low ammonium generation (acid pH) from low distal hydrogen ion secretion (alkaline pH). Urine pH must be measured from a fresh, anaerobically collected sample. This may require urinary catheterization in infants.

Distal Tubule

Urine Net Charge

The urine net charge is an indirect measurement of ammonium production by the distal nephron and is a useful test for assessment of normal anion gap metabolic acidosis. When ammonium is present in the urine, it is usually in the form of ammonium chloride. The urine net charge is calculated as:

$$\text{Urine net charge} = [\text{Cl} - (\text{Na} + \text{K})] \text{ in mmol/L}$$

When urinary chloride concentration exceeds the sum of sodium and potassium (negative net charge), ammonium is present. When chloride is less than the sum of sodium and potassium (positive net charge), little ammonium is present in the urine.

In metabolic acidosis, ammonium is the major route for excretion of hydrogen (see titratable acid). Thus, ammonium excretion should be maximal. When the net charge is positive, the urine $pC0_2$ should be measured in an alkaline urine (see discussion below). Excretion of ammonium with an anion other than chloride may mimic a distal renal tubular acidosis (e.g., toluene inhalation). Calculation of the urinary osmolal gap (see discussion below) will reveal an unmeasured anion.

Urine $pC0_2$

Measurement of the urinary $pC0_2$ is useful in the assessment of normal anion gap acidosis with a positive urine net charge (low ammonium excretion). It differentiates between failure of distal hydrogen secretion and deficient ammonium production. The $pC0_2$ must be measured in an alkaline urine ($pH > 7$), which is achieved by loading the patient with sodium bicarbonate. With normal distal hydrogen secretion, the urine $pC0_2$ will be > 70 mmHg, whereas with defective hydrogen secretion it is < 55 mmHg.

Urine Osmolal Gap

The urine osmolal gap, defined as measured osmolality minus calculated osmolality, is useful for the detection of unmeasured anions. The urine osmolality is calculated as follows:

$$[2 \times (\text{Na} + \text{K}) + \text{glucose} + \text{urea}] \text{ in mmol/L}$$

When the osmolal gap is > 100 mOsm/L, an unmeasured anion, such as hippurate in cases of glue (toluene) sniffing, should be suspected.

Renal Tubular Acidosis

Renal tubular acidosis (RTA) is characterized by a normal anion gap, hyperchloremic metabolic acidosis. It may be due to an increased fractional excretion of bicarbonate (Type 2 [proximal] RTA), failure of distal hydrogen excretion or ammonium generation (Type 1 [distal] RTA), or associated with hyperkalemia (Type 4 RTA). Kamel et al. have recently reviewed this disease.[11]

Table 3–2 summarizes the results of the above tests in differentiating the type of renal tubular acidosis.[12] Other tests such as the ammonium chloride loading test or furosemide test may be useful in assessing a urinary acidification defect.

URINARY TRACT INFECTION

Urinary tract infection (UTI) is common, affecting 3% of females and 1% of males in the pediatric age group. The risk of recurrence is 30% following the first UTI and

TABLE 3–2. Renal Tubular Acidosis

Test	Proximal	Distal	Hyperkalemic
During Acidosis:			
Urine net charge	negative	positive	positive
Urine pH	< 5.5	> 5.5	< 5.5
Alkali Loading:			
$FeHCO_3$ (%)	> 10–15%	< 5%	> 5–10%
Urine pCO_2 (mmHg)	> 70	< 55	≥ 70
Associated defects of tubular function	present	absent	absent
Hypercalciuria/nephrocalcinosis	absent	present	absent

$FeHCO_3$ = fractional excretion of bicarbonate = [(U/P) HCO_3 ÷ (U/P) creatinine] × 100

increases to 75% following subsequent infections. The majority of UTIs occur in the absence of an anatomical urinary tract abnormality. However, the occurrence of an infection in the presence of urinary obstruction or vesicoureteric reflux may predispose to renal scarring. Thus, the detection of obstruction (incidence of 1–10%) and vesicoureteric reflux is important.

UTIs may be classified on the basis of symptoms, the presence of an underlying anatomic or functional abnormality, or the site of infection. Symptoms of cystitis include dysuria, frequency, and urgency and may be accompanied by foul-smelling or cloudy urine. Pyelonephritis may manifest as flank or abdominal pain, fever, and rigors. In infants, UTI is often accompanied by septicemia and potentially life-threatening metabolic abnormalities.

The approach to UTI in the pediatric age group incorporates diagnosis, localization of infection, treatment, investigation and follow-up.[13–19]

Diagnosis of UTI

The diagnosis of UTI is based on finding significant numbers of microorganisms on urine culture.

Significant Bacteriuria

The term "significant bacteriuria" differentiates true infection from bacterial contamination. Its definition varies with the method of urine collection, as outlined below. Indicators of contamination include low bacterial colony counts, multiple organisms, different organisms on serial culture, or the detection of nonpathogenic organisms. False-negative cultures may occur in dilute urine from a patient with a urinary concentrating defect.

Collection Methods

Various methods of obtaining urine for culture in children have evolved because of the difficulty in obtaining voided specimens in infants and non-toilet-trained toddlers.

Suprapubic Aspiration

This procedure, considered the "gold standard" for diagnosing bacteriuria, is most suited to infants in whom the bladder is an intra-abdominal organ. Any growth is significant.

Catheter Specimen

Controversy exists over the use of catheterization to obtain urine samples for culture. Introduction of bacteria into the bladder and trauma to the urethra may occur at the time of catheterization. Careful adherence to aseptic technique is essential. Bacterial growth of $\geq 10^3$ colony forming units per mL (CFU/mL) (1×10^6 CFU/L) has traditionally been accepted as significant. However, investigations in children suggest that colony counts $\geq 5 \times 10^4$ CFU/mL (50×10^6 CFU/L) associated with pyuria ≥ 10 WBC/mm^3 (10×10^6 WBC/L) better discriminates true infection from contamination.[19]

Bag Sample

Urine is obtained by affixing a sterile bag following cleansing of the genitalia. Contamination frequently occurs, and a bag sample is most useful when it is negative for significant bacterial growth. A pure growth of the same organism with colony counts $\geq 10^5$ CFU/mL (100×10^6 CFU/L) on two or more occasions suggests infection, especially when associated with pyuria or symptoms.

Mid-Stream Urine (MSU)

An MSU is obtained by cleansing the genitalia and collecting the mid-portion of the urinary stream to reduce contamination from urethral or prostatic secretions. Significant bacteriuria is $\geq 10^5$ CFU/mL (100×10^6 CFU/L) as correlated with bladder aspiration and catheterized samples.

Bacterial Culture

Once obtained, urine for bacterial culture should be plated immediately, using a calibrated loop, onto 5% sheep blood agar and a medium selective for gram-negative bacilli such as MacConkey agar. The culture is incubated for 24 h to obtain a colony count, and a further 12–24 h are necessary for in vitro antibiotic sensitivity testing. If immediate plating is not possible, refrigeration at 4° C will maintain stable colony counts for 24 h.

Bacterial culture is expensive and time consuming, and automated, rapid culture methods have been developed. However, they have low sensitivity, especially for low colony counts and slow-growing organisms, making them inappropriate for nosocomial infections and for patients with low-grade bacteriuria.

Ancillary Tests

Tests are available to assist in diagnosis of significant bacteriuria, but are not diagnostic by themselves.

Pyuria

Pyuria is defined clinically as ≥ 10 WBC/mm^3 (10×10^6 WBC/L) of uncentrifuged urine, counted with a hemocytometer, or > 10 WBC per high-power field of centrifuged urine. The presence of pyuria is suggestive of, but not diagnostic for, UTI. In infants, the presence of ≥ 10 WBC/mm^3 (10×10^6 WBC/L) on a catheter urine specimen has been shown to be 91% sensitive in detecting colony counts of $\geq 5 \times 10^4$ CFU/mL (50×10^6 CFU/L).[19]

Bacteria

Microscopy for bacteria may assist in the diagnosis of UTI. The presence of ≥ 1 organism per oil immersion field on an uncentrifuged, gram-stained urine correlates with $\geq 10^5$ CFU/mL (100×10^6 CFU/L) organisms on culture. In infants, ≥ 1 organism per 10 oil immersion fields on a Gram-stained, uncentrifuged, catheter urine is 93% sensitive in detecting colony counts of $\geq 5 \times 10^4$ CFU/mL ($\geq 50 \times 10^6$ CFU/L). The combination of pyuria and bacteriuria on microscopy has an 88% positive predictive value for significant infection as defined above.[19]

Urinary Nitrite

Urinary nitrite is produced by the reduction of dietary nitrate by certain bacteria. It can be detected using an amine-impregnated dipstick, which produces a pink color reaction when positive. False negatives occur in the presence of dilute urine, inadequate dietary nitrates, and non-nitrate reducing bacteria such as Staphylococcus and Enterococcus. The test is insensitive at colony counts of $< 10^5$ CFU/mL (100×10^6 CFU/L). One pediatric study on primarily MSU samples has documented a specificity and positive predictive value for infection of 100%, with a sensitivity of only 37%.[19, 20]

Leucocyte Esterase

Leucocyte esterase, an enzyme found in neutrophils, can be detected by the dipstick method. It correlates best with pyuria rather than UTI.[19, 20] Leucocyte esterase and nitrite assays should not be a substitute for direct microscopy or culture in the detection of UTI.

Localization of Infection

Upper tract infection requires initial treatment with intravenous antibiotics and carries a risk of renal scarring. Thus, early diagnosis and treatment is important. Fever, flank pain, and systemic illness points to a diagnosis of pyelonephritis, but infants may have only non-specific symptoms.

A variety of tests have been used in an attempt to diagnose pyelonephritis, but have not gained widespread clinical use. The tests include antibody coated bacteria, β2-microglobulin measurement, and urinary total LDH and isoenzyme 5 determination.[13, 14] The most useful clinical test for detection of renal parenchymal infection during a febrile UTI is ^{99m}Technetium-dimercaptosuccinic acid (^{99m}Tc-DMSA).

Radio-labelled DMSA is taken up by proximal tubular cells, thereby providing a functional image of cortical mass. DMSA scintigraphy is the most sensitive technique for detecting established renal scarring. However, acute pyelonephritis is also associated with decreased cortical uptake of the isotope, so that DMSA scanning has become the clinically recommended method for detection of pyelonephritis in febrile UTI.[15, 21–23]

Persistence of an abnormal DMSA scan beyond 3–6 months after a UTI likely represents permanent scarring. Stokland et al. demonstrated a tenfold risk of renal scarring at 1 y, as demonstrated by renal cortical scintigraphy, when children presented with a high C-reactive protein, high fever, and dilating vesicoureteric reflux.[24]

Treatment, Investigation, and Follow-up

These aspects of urinary tract infection are beyond the scope of this chapter. Reviews are available.[15–18, 23]

PROTEINURIA

The presence of an abnormal quantity of protein in the urine is a most reliable marker of renal parenchymal disease. Normal individuals should excrete < 100–150 mg (60 mg/m^2) of protein per day. The newborn may transiently have proteinuria up to 1 g/d.

The dipstick test primarily detects albuminuria. It is based on the tetrabromophenol blue colorimetric test. The turbidimetric test, which uses 10% sulfosalicylic acid, is useful for detecting low-molecular-weight protein. The acid precipitates as little as 0.05–0.1 g/L of low-molecular-weight protein. The precipitate will disappear when brought to a boil and reappear on cooling.

Low-Grade Proteinuria

Low-grade proteinuria (< 1 g/d) is fairly common and can occur with a number of renal problems:

Asymptomatic Persistent Proteinuria

This is defined as constant proteinuria > 250 mg/d in infants and > 500 mg/d in children. The long-term prognosis for such children is not known, so they should be carefully followed every 3–6 m, measuring the blood pressure and plasma creatinine. A renal biopsy is not necessary as long as the patient is stable. If hematuria is present, the prognosis is guarded.

Functional Proteinuria

This occurs with fever, exercise, and congestive heart failure. The urine sediment is normal. The proteinuria should resolve with treatment of the primary problem.

Tubular Proteinuria

This type of proteinuria is found in renal tubular acidosis, Fanconi syndrome, and Lowe syndrome. The identifying characteristic of tubular proteinuria is the presence of 25–60% of proteins of low molecular weight. It is generally held that this proteinuria results from failure of tubular reabsorption of plasma proteins.

The measurement of β2-microglobulin (MW = 11,815 daltons) is sometimes used as an index of tubular proteinuria. The ratio of urine albumin to β2-microglobulin is < 15 in tubular proteinuria, whereas in glomerular proteinuria the ratio is > 1000.

Retinol-binding protein (MW = 21,200 daltons) has been suggested as a better measurement of low molecular weight proteinuria, because, unlike β2-microglobulin, it is stable in acid urine. The high molecular weight lysosomal enzyme N-acetyl-β-D-glucosaminidase (NAG) is not specifically a renal protein but is highly active in proximal tubular cells. In states of proximal tubular injury from disease or nephrotoxins, urinary NAG is increased. NAG is measured colorimetrically, although dietary substances can interfere with the assay.

Renal Proteins

Tamm-Horsfall glycoprotein (THG) is the main protein constituent of normal urine. Changes in THG excretion unfortunately do not correlate with renal pathology. In the future, various urinary proteins and renal cell proteins potentially will be measured using monoclonal antibodies to specific renal antigens.

Nephronophthisis

This disease is characterized by polyuria and polydypsia, anemia, and failure to thrive. The proteinuria may be a tubular pattern with a predominance of β2-microglobulin. There is a tendency to renal salt-wasting. The urine sediment is unremarkable. Renal failure occurs in early adolescence. Tapetoretinal degeneration is the most common association.

Chronic Tubulo-Interstitial Nephritis

This may be secondary to chronic analgesic abuse, toxins such as lead, cadmium, or oxalate, hyperuricemia, hypercalcemia, and hypokalemia. The proteinuria is mild.

Orthostatic Proteinuria

This type of proteinuria is frequent in children, especially adolescents. It is the presence of increased amounts of protein in urine formed when the patient is in the upright position, but not in urine formed when the patient is recumbent. If the proteinuria is orthostatic and < 1 g/d without sediment abnormalities, serious renal disease is unlikely and a good outcome is predicted.

To quantify protein excretion, a split 24 h urine collection is done, one sample at night while the patient is in the recumbent position and one sample during the day while the patient is ambulatory. An alternative qualitative test is to dipstick the urine for protein on the first void of the day and 2 hours later, which can be done each day for three days.

Heavy Proteinuria (Nephrotic Syndrome)

Nephrotic syndrome is defined as heavy proteinuria (> 3.0 g/1.73 m^2/d or > 50–100 mg/kg/d) with hypoalbuminemia (plasma albumin < 2.5 g/dL; < 25 g/L), edema, and hyperlipidemia. The incidence in children of all forms of the syndrome is 2–4 new cases per 100,000 population per year, with a prevalenceof 16 per 100,000, making it the most prevalent glomerular disease in children. There is a male preponderance in early childhood, with 80% of cases being minimal lesion nephrotic syndrome, compared to only 20% in adults.

Ninety percent of children respond to prednisone, compared to 60% of adults. Cyclophosphamide may produce a permanent remission in frequent relapsers, i.e., patients who experience two relapses in six months or three relapses in one year. Non-responsiveness to prednisone may suggest focal segmental glomerulosclerosis, which may progress to chronic renal failure. A renal biopsy is performed on prednisone-resistant cases.

Rarer causes of nephrotic syndrome are (1) membranoproliferative glomerulonephritis (MPGN), which is usually associated with an active urine sediment and hypocomplementemia, and (2) membranous nephropathy.

Although primary nephrotic syndrome is the most common type, it is necessary to exclude other events or diseases associated with nephrotic syndrome such as:

1. Medications (penicillamine, NSAIDs, gold)
2. Allergens (bee sting, poison ivy)
3. Infections (post-streptococcal glomerulonephritis, infective endocarditis, syphilis, hepatitis B)
4. Neoplasia (carcinoma, lymphoma)
5. Multisystem disease [lupus, Henoch-Schönlein purpura (HSP)]
6. Metabolic (diabetes mellitus, amyloidosis, Fabry's disease)

It is usual to admit new cases to hospital, especially if the edema is significant. Fluids and sodium are restricted and diuretics such as hydrochlorothiazide and spironolactone are prescribed. For severe edema, intravenous albumin (1 g/kg over 4 h) plus furosemide (1 mg/kg) at mid-infusion are given. Prednisone is the main therapy directed towards the proteinuria, and many different regimens exist. Our center uses 60 mg/m^2/d in three divided doses (maximum 75 mg/d) for 4 weeks. If a remission is achieved during this time, prednisone is tapered to 40 mg/m^2 on alternate days for 4 weeks, 20 mg/m^2 on alternate days for 8 days, 10 mg/m^2 on alternate days for 8 days, and then discontinued. Relapses are common and require retreatment with prednisone. For relapses, tapering commences after the urine is free of protein for 3 consecutive days and tapering occurs over 48 days.

MICROALBUMINURIA

The usual routine urinalysis dipstick for protein (albumin) cannot detect microalbuminuria. Laboratory methods such as radioimmunoassay and nephelometry are able to measure very low concentrations of urinary albumin. Normoalbuminuria is defined as a urine albumin excretion (UAE) rate of < 15 μg/min, and microalbuminuria as a raised UAE of 15–200 μg/min. To screen for microalbuminuria, a short timed (e.g., 1 h) urine collection can be used. This has been validated in many studies, including our own. False-negative results are extremely low; the predictive value of a negative test is 96% and its specificity is 81%.[25] Positive test results (UAE > 15 μg/min) need to be confirmed with at least two of three 24-h urine collections. Exercise must be avoided during the collection period.

Microalbuminuria is the earliest sign of diabetic nephropathy.[26] The prevalence in children and adolescents with insulin dependent diabetes mellitus is 15-20%, and mostly occurs in post-pubertal patients.

HEMATURIA

Hematuria is defined as > 5–10 red blood cells per high-power field in centrifuged urine or dipstick-positive hematuria on qualitative testing. Unlike proteinuria, which usually signifies glomerular disease, hematuria may arise anywhere along the urinary tract.

One of the clinician's great challenges is differentiating glomerular from nonglomerular bleeding. A correct diagnosis may obviate the need for multiple investigations and save the patient much discomfort. The presence of red blood cell casts is pathognomonic of glomerular origin, while brown or smoky urine is highly suggestive. Morphological examination of the urine for "dysmorphic" erythrocytes as a means of distinguishing glomerular from nonglomerular hematuria has been advocated. Phase contrast microscopy improves the specificity, but there is a need for standardization of what constitutes a "dysmorphic RBC," and for the percentage of dysmorphic cells compatible with glomerular hematuria.[27] Using a definition of > 3 different dysmorphic shapes, Crompton et al. documented a 93–95% sensitivity and 95–100% specificity for predicting glomerular hematuria in children.[28]

In 1992, Tomita et al. described a doughnut-shaped RBC with bulbous projections or vesicles, termed the G1-cell, which had a high degree of sensitivity and specificity for glomerular hematuria.[29] Subsequent studies in both adults and children have found the presence of ≥ 5% G1-cells in acidic (pH ≤ 6.4) and concentrated urine (osmolality ≥ 400 mOsm/kg) to be 99.5–100 % sensitive and 100% specific for glomerular bleeding.[30, 31]

Measurement of urinary red cell volume distribution using a cell counter has been shown in both adults and children to successfully differentiate glomerular from nonglomerular hematuria, but is unreliable with small amounts of hematuria.[32, 33] The use of automated flow cytometry has also been shown to discriminate glomerular from non-glomerular hematuria, with the former demonstrating smaller size. In practice, both microscopy and volumetric analysis of RBCs are complementary.

Coexistence of hematuria and proteinuria implies a glomerular etiology for the hematuria. Immunocytochemical staining of urinary erythrocytes for Tamm-Horsfall protein also appears to predict glomerular hematuria.[34] The pattern of excretion of urinary proteins (albumin, total protein, IgG, and α-2 macroglobulin) and tubular enzymes (α-1 microglobulin, NAG) may also be used to localize the source of bleeding.[35,36] None of these techniques has yet gained widespread clinical use, and none has been validated in children.

Blood clots do not occur with glomerular bleeding and suggest a lower urinary tract cause, as does terminal hematuria. Red urine does not always signify blood in the urine; it may be caused by drugs (e.g., rifampin and pyridium), pigmented foods (e.g., beets), urates, porphyrins, or myoglobin and hemoglobin.

To diagnose true hematuria, a combination of urine dipstick analysis and microscopy is essential. The current dipsticks, based on the peroxidase activity of the heme portion of the hemoglobin molecule, detect heme pigment, not red cells themselves, and are positive with hemoglobinuria, myoglobinuria, and hematuria. A positive dipstick in the absence of red cells on examination of a fresh sediment suggests hemoglobinuria or myoglobinuria. The former is confirmed by finding pink serum and the latter can be measured directly using radial immunodiffusion.

The history is invaluable in determining the cause of hematuria. Dysuria and frequency suggest urinary tract infection; colicky flank pain occurs with renal calculi; a recent upper respiratory tract infection is common in IgA nephropathy; and with postinfectious nephritis, a sore throat occurs 1–2 w previously. Terminal hematuria suggests a lesion in the bladder trigone, initial hematuria occurs with urethral lesions, and blood throughout the stream occurs with bleeding from other sites. A history of trauma, drug ingestion, or bleeding diathesis and a family history of renal disease should be elicited.

Hematuria may be microscopic or macroscopic, and the two may coexist in the same disease entity. Microscopic hematuria occurs with a frequency of 0.5–1.0% in children. The frequency of macroscopic hematuria is 0.13%. Common causes include UTI, trauma, stones, coagulopathy, glomerular diseases, structural abnormalities, and tumors. The causes of hematuria vary with the age of the child. In the newborn, common causes include renal vein thrombosis, birth asphyxia with subsequent acute tubular necrosis, obstruction, and coagulopathies. In infants, hemolytic uremic syndrome, renal vein thrombosis, and Wilms tumor predominate. In older children, various forms of glomerulonephritis, including HSP, tumors, foreign bodies, trauma, and cystitis are most common.[37]

Investigation

Investigation of hematuria begins with a careful history and physical exam, followed by dipstick examination of the urine, microscopy, and urine culture. Renal imaging studies (e.g., ultrasound [U/S], intravenous urogram [IVU], or computerized tomography [CAT] scan) are indicated with a history of trauma or colicky pain suggestive of urolithiasis. Other tests which may be indicated include renal function tests, electrolytes, calcium, phosphorus, hemoglobin, platelets and coagulation parameters, sickle test, serum complements (see discussion below), antinuclear factor, antistreptolysin titre, and antineutrophil cytoplasmic antibody (ANCA; see discussion below). Ancillary tests may include audiology and ophthalmology assessments.

Glomerulonephritis (GN)

The acute nephritic syndrome is characterized by hematuria, azotemia, oliguria, edema, and hypertension caused by salt and water retention secondary to a reduced glomerular filtration rate. The presence of red cell casts with or without proteinuria is usual. To diagnose the particular type of GN, the third component of the complement system, C3, used in conjunction with C4 and total hemolytic complement (C′H50), is useful. Activation of the classical pathway will result in low concentrations of C3 and C4, whereas with activation of the alternate pathway, only low C3 values occur. Deficiencies of other complement components will give a normal C3 and C4, but a low C′H50. The glomerulonephritides commonly associated with low C3 concentrations include systemic lupus erythematosus (SLE), MPGN, GN caused by chronic infections such as bacterial endocarditis or infected ventriculoperitoneal shunts, postinfectious nephritis (usually streptococcal), and inherited abnormalities of the complement system. Diseases usually associated with normal C3 concentrations include HSP, Berger's disease (IgA nephropathy), epidemic hemolytic uremic syndrome, Goodpasture disease, and hereditary nephritis.[38] Normal values are:

C3: age 0–5 d: 0.39–1.56 g/L (39–156 mg/dL)
> 5 d: 0.77–1.43 g/L (77–143 mg/dL)
C4: age 0–5 d: 0.05–0.33 g/L (5–33 mg/dL)
> 5 d: 0.07–0.40 g/L (7–40 mg/dL)
C′H50: 1:24 (serial dilution bioassay)

A useful approach to classifying a patient into one of the above categories utilizes the serum complement and the clinical assessment of the patient, namely whether the disease process involves multiple organ systems including the kidney, or primarily the kidney, as presented in Table 3–3.

TABLE 3–3. Classification of Glomerulonephritis by Serum C3

C3	Systemic Disease	Renal Disease
Normal	Henoch Schönlein purpura	IgA nephropathy
	Hemolytic uremic syndrome	Hereditary nephritis
	Goodpasture syndrome	MPGN
Low	SLE	MPGN
	Endocarditis/shunt infection	Postinfectious nephritis
		Complement deficiencies

Other tests are guided by the presumed diagnosis based on the above schema. The most common acute nephritis is post-infectious nephritis, which occurs 1–2 w following a streptococcal pharyngitis or 3–6 w following impetigo. The antistreptolysin O titre is increased in 60–80% of patients with postinfectious nephritis in the absence of early antibiotic treatment (Normal = < 166 Todd units). Other antistreptococcal antibody titers may be increased such as antistreptokinase and antiDNAase B, and, following impetigo, antihyaluronidase. C3 values are initially low and usually return to normal within 4–6 w. Prolonged depression of C3 is more suggestive of MPGN, complement deficiency, or SLE.

The diagnosis of hemolytic uremic syndrome is based on the finding of a microangiopathic hemolytic anemia, thrombocytopenia, and acute renal failure with hematuria and proteinuria. Liver transferases and serum amylase may be increased, along with the usual biochemical abnormalities of acute renal failure. Therapy is supportive with early institution of dialysis. The typical presentation of IgA nephropathy is recurrent episodes of gross hematuria immediately following an upper respiratory tract infection, with baseline microscopic hematuria with or without proteinuria. The diagnosis is based on renal biopsy findings of mesangial deposition of IgA. The serum IgA values may be normal, but if increased are suggestive of the diagnosis in the absence of a biopsy. Normal values are:

age 0–1 y:	0.0–0.8 g/L (0–80 mg/dL)
age 1–3 y:	0.2–1.0 g/L (20–100 mg/dL)
age 4–6 y:	0.3–2.0 g/L (30–200 mg/dL)
age 7–9 y:	0.3–3.1 g/L (30–310 mg/dL)
age 10–13 y:	0.5–3.6 g/L (50–360 mg/dL)
age 14–19 y:	0.5–3.5 g/L (50–350 mg/dL)

Alport's syndrome or hereditary nephritis is associated with high-frequency nerve deafness and ocular abnormalities and usually has an X-linked mode of inheritance. Diagnosis is based on multilaminar splitting of the glomerular capillary basement membrane and absence of the Goodpasture antigen on the basement membrane. HSP is a clinical diagnosis based on the presence of a purpuric skin rash, usually of the lower extremities, arthralgias, abdominal pain, and renal involvement, which may range from microscopic hematuria to a mixed nephritic and nephrotic syndrome. Goodpasture syndrome, which is rare in children, presents with pulmonary hemorrhage and renal disease. The diagnosis is confirmed by finding a circulating antiglomerular basement membrane antibody or by renal biopsy. Complement disorders may be associated with recurrent infections and various forms of renal disease.

Antineutrophil Cytoplasmic Antibody (ANCA) Associated Renal Disease

ANCA were first described in 1982 in patients with pauci-immune necrotizing glomerulonephritis and systemic vasculitis. They are specific for constituents of neutrophil azurophilic granules and monocyte lysosomes. Whether they are merely markers for disease or play a direct role in pathogenesis remains to be determined. They are useful in the classification of rapidly progressive glomerulonephritis and small vessel vasculitis, and in some diseases can be used to monitor response to therapy. Two patterns have been identified: C-ANCA, which produce cytoplasmic staining of neutrophils and are specific for proteinase 3, and P-ANCA, which artifactually redistribute around the cell nucleus when fixed in alcohol and are specific for myeloperoxidase. C-ANCA is a sensitive but not specific marker for Wegener's granulomatosis. Patients with disease limited to the kidneys have a higher frequency of P-ANCA, while those with pulmonary and sinus involvement have a higher incidence of C-ANCA.[39, 40] ANCA may also be found in patients with other diseases such as ulcerative colitis.

Hypercalciuria

Idiopathic hypercalciuria without hypercalcemia is a common cause of isolated microscopic hematuria and is associated with an increased risk of future urolithiasis. It is defined in children as a urinary calcium excretion of > 0.1 mmol/kg/day (> 4 mg/kg/day) or a calcium/creatinine ratio > 0.6 for mmol/L or > 0.2 for mg/dL. However, values are higher in infants and decrease over time. In a study of 215 patients ranging from infants to adults, the values for random urinary calcium/creatinine ratio shown in Table 3–4 were obtained.[41]

Other reports cite considerably lower normal values on first morning urines, than those quoted above for random urines.[42] This may be explained by the observation that first morning urines have significantly lower ratios when compared to 24-h urine collections.[43]

ACUTE RENAL FAILURE

Acute renal failure is defined as a sudden decrease in renal function, accompanied by the accumulation of nitrogenous wastes within the body. It may be accompanied by anuria, oliguria, or polyuria. Six major clinical syndromes are associated with an acute decline in glomerular filtration.

TABLE 3–4. Random Urinary Calcium/Creatinine Ratios

Age	n	mean Ca/Cr μmol/μmol (mg/mg)	95th Percentile μmol/μmol (mg/mg)
< 7 mo	103	0.67 (0.24)	2.42 (0.86)
7–18 mo	40	0.56 (0.20)	1.69 (0.60)
19 mo – 3 yr	41	0.30 (0.11)	1.18 (0.42)
adult	31	0.27 (0.10)	0.61 (0.22)

Source: Sargent JD, Stukel TA, Kresel J, Klein RZ. Normal values for random urinary calcium to creatinine ratios in infancy. J Pediatr 1993;123:393-7.

Prerenal Azotemia

Prerenal azotemia is caused by hypotension, hypovolemia, or inadequate renal perfusion such as may occur with hemorrhage or congestive heart failure. Physiological responses result in a reduction in GFR and increased tubular reabsorption of salt and water. Restoration of adequate circulating volume reverses the acute renal failure.

Acute Tubular Necrosis (ATN)

ATN occurs as a result of hypoperfusion, a nephrotoxic injury, or a combination of the two. Removal of the insult does not result in immediate improvement in renal function.

Acute Interstitial Nephritis

Acute interstitial nephritis causes a decrease in GFR because of interstitial inflammation. It is frequently non-oliguric renal failure, is often related to drugs or toxins, and is more common in adults.

Acute Glomerulonephritis

Acute glomerulonephritis results in a diminished GFR on the basis of vascular inflammation. The most common lesions in children are acute post-streptococcal nephritis and hemolytic uremic syndrome. Recovery of renal function depends on the underlying disease process.

Acute Renovascular Disease

In order for renovascular disease to cause acute renal failure, it must be a bilateral process or occur in a solitary kidney. A common cause in infants is renal vein thrombosis.

Post-renal Azotemia (Obstructive Uropathy)

Post-renal azotemia results from obstruction in the collecting system and may be due to intratubular obstruction (e.g., methotrexate, uric acid) or to extrinsic compression (e.g., tumor). Relief of the obstruction restores a normal GFR.

Examination of the urine sediment is crucial in evaluating the patient with acute renal failure. A sediment with renal tubular epithelial cells, granular casts, hematuria, and proteinuria supports a diagnosis of ATN. RBC casts are found in glomerulonephritis. Leucocyturia, especially with eosinophiluria, supports a diagnosis of interstitial nephritis. Detection of eosinophils in the urine sediment following Wright's staining is considered a useful indicator of acute interstitial nephritis. The use of Hansel's stain greatly enhances the recognition of urinary eosinophils.[44] Dipstick hematuria without cellular elements on microscopy is suggestive of hemoglobinuria or myoglobinuria. In acute renal failure, urinary sodium concentration differentiates between prerenal causes (Na < 10 mmol/L [mEq/L]) and intrinsic renal disease (Na > 20 mmol/L). Urine sodium concentration may also be used to assess the adequacy of fluid replacement in the volume contracted patient. Once the ECF space is replete, the urinary sodium will begin to rise. With intrinsic renal dis-

TABLE 3–5. Acute Rental Failure

Test	Prerenal	Renal	Postrenal
Urine osmolality (mOsm/kg H_2O)	> 500	250–400	300–400
Urine SG	> 1.020	< 1.010	–
U/P Osm	> 1.3:1	< 1.1:1	–
Urine Na (mmol/L)	< 20	> 40	> 40
FeNA (%)	< 1	> 1	> 3
Renal failure index	< 1	> 1	> 1
U/P Creatinine	> 40	< 20	< 20

SG = specific gravity
U/P Osm = urine to plasma osmolality
FeNa (%) = fractional excretion of sodium = [(U/P) Na ÷ (U/P) creatinine] x 100
Renal Failure Index = U Na ÷ [U/P] creatinine
U/P creatinine = urine to plasma creatinine

ease, the urinary sodium is a guide to the appropriate sodium concentration of replacement fluid.

Various ancillary tests may be necessary for diagnosis. They include urine myoglobin, therapeutic drug monitoring, toxicology screening, creatine kinase, and viral titers.

Management of the patient with acute renal failure involves close monitoring of acid-base and electrolyte status, urea, creatinine, calcium, phosphorus, albumin, magnesium, uric acid, and hematologic and coagulation parameters. Dialysis may be necessary to control the metabolic and fluid disturbances.[45,46] The laboratory tests useful in assessing patients with acute renal failure are listed in Table 3–5.

CHRONIC RENAL FAILURE

Numerous biochemical abnormalities occur in chronic renal failure (CRF), affecting multiple organ systems. A detailed review is beyond the scope of this chapter, and only salient features are discussed.

Anemia

CRF is characterized by a relative deficiency of erythropoietin, resulting in a progressive normochromic, normocytic anemia. With the advent of recombinant human erythropoietin (EPO), patients can now maintain satisfactory hemoglobin/hematocrit (Hb/Hct) values without transfusion. The National Kidney Foundation's Dialysis Outcome Quality Initiative (NFK-DOQI) has recently released clinical practice guidelines for the treatment of anemia of CRF.[47] An anemia workup should be initiated once a patients Hb/Hct falls below:

110 g/L/0.33 (11 g/dL/33%) for premenopausal females and pre-pubertal patients
120 g/L/0.37 (12 g/dL/37%) for postmenopausal females and adult males.

Evaluation of anemia should include determination of Hb, Hct, reticulocyte count, and iron indices (serum iron, total iron binding capacity [TIBC], percentage transferrin saturation [TSAT], and serum ferritin). Adequate stores of iron must be available before initiating EPO therapy. Iron supplementation, either orally or intravenously, is necessary in most patients on EPO. Normal values for iron indices are:

Serum Iron:		
newborn:	20–48 μmol/L	(112–268 μg/dL)
4 mo-1yr:	5–13 μmol/L	(28–73 μg/dL)
> 1 yr:	9–27 μmol/L	(50–151 μg/dL)
Iron Binding Capacity (TIBC):		
newborn:	11–31 μmol/L	(61–173 μg/dL)
> 1 yr:	45–72 μmol/L)	(251–402 μg/dL)
Serum Ferritin:		
1–12 mos:	14–400 μg/L	(14–400 ng/mL)
> 1 yr:	22–400 μg/L	(22–400 ng/mL)
Transferrin:		
0–5 days:	16–50 μmol/L	
1–9 yrs:	23–41 μmol/L	
10–19 yrs:	24–48 μmol/L	

Measurement of TIBC has been replaced, where available, by direct measurement of transferrin. TSAT is calculated by:

$$\text{TSAT} = \text{serum iron} \times 100 \div \text{TIBC}$$

$$\text{TSAT} = \text{serum iron} \times 100 \div (2 \times \text{transferrin})$$

The NFK-DOQI recommended target Hb/Hct for EPO treated patients is 110–120 g/L/ 0.33–0.36 (11–12 g/dL/33–36%). TSAT should be maintained ≥ 20% and ferritin ≥ 100 μg/L (≥ 100 ng/mL).

Failure to respond to EPO despite adequate EPO dose and iron stores should prompt a look for associated conditions such as hypothyroidism, hyperparathyroidism, aluminum toxicity, and folate deficiency.

Renal Osteodystrophy

CRF is characterized by a decrease in phosphorus excretion, consequent hypocalcemia, and a relative or absolute deficiency of 1,25-Dihydroxy Vitamin D. This results in secondary hyperparathyroidism and bone disease. Associated factors affecting bone integrity include aluminum toxicity and systemic acidosis. Monitoring of the patient with CRF includes measurement of calcium, phosphorus, alkaline phosphatase, parathyroid hormone level, and occasionally Vitamin D levels. Reference values for phosphate and alkaline phosphatase vary with age.[1] Parathyroid hormone concentrations vary with the laboratory and whether the N-terminal or C-terminal is assayed.

Drug Monitoring

As many drugs or their metabolites are excreted via the kidney, the potential for toxicity, both systemic and renal, exists if drug doses are not adjusted for diminished GFR. The use of therapeutic drug monitoring for patients with CRF taking such drugs as aminoglycosides and vancomycin is essential. Appropriate drug dosing monographs for CRF are available.[48]

Adequacy of Dialysis

Currently, much attention is being focused on ensuring the delivery of adequate dialysis and nutrition to patients with CRF. For both hemodialysis (HD) and peritoneal dialysis (PD) patients, this involves quantitation of residual renal function by measuring urinary urea, creatinine and volume on a timed collection, along with plasma urea and creatinine. In end-stage renal disease (ESRD), calculation of Ccr overestimates GFR as proportionately more creatinine is secreted rather than filtered; conversely, urea clearance (Cur) underestimates GFR. Thus, the average of Ccr and Cur is suggested as the best estimate of GFR in ESRD patients. Cur is calculated as per the formula on page 48 for Ccr, substituting urea for creatinine. Thus:

$$\text{Corrected GFR} = (\text{Ccr} + \text{Cur}) \div 2$$

expressed as L/wk and normalized to 1.73 m^2 BSA.

For PD, dose of delivered dialysis is calculated in two ways: peritoneal Ccr (PCcr) and Kt/V. Calculation of PCcr involves measuring creatinine concentration and volume from a 24-h collection of peritoneal dialysate, along with a plasma creatinine. PCcr is also expressed as L/wk/1.73m^2. With some methods, the high glucose concentration in PD fluid interferes with the measurement of creatinine. Each laboratory should test for this by measuring the creatinine and glucose concentration of fresh dialysate.[49] The correction factor is calculated by dividing creatinine (μmol/L) by glucose (μmol/L). Corrected dialysate creatinine concentration is:

$$\text{measured creatinine } (\mu\text{mol/L}) - [\text{glucose } (\mu\text{mol/L}) \times \text{correction factor}]$$

Kt/V urea is Cur(K) multiplied by time (t) and normalized by total body water (V), which is the volume of distribution of urea. It is calculated for both the delivered dialysis and the endogenous renal contribution. The peritoneal and residual renal components are calculated using plasma urea concentrations as well as the urea concentration from the timed urine and peritoneal dialysate collections.

Total Ccr and Kt/V for a given patient is the sum of residual renal and peritoneal values for each measure. A discussion of target values is beyond the scope of this text, but can be found in the NFK-DOQI guidelines, along with suggestions for the frequency of measurement.[50]

For HD, dialysis delivered dose is calculated either as Kt/V urea or as a urea reduction ratio (URR) per treatment. Calculation of Kt/V urea requires measurement of a pre- and post-dialysis urea for the given treatment, plus a pre-dialysis urea for the subsequent treatment. Additional information required is the pre- and post-dialysis patient weight, the actual time of treatment, and the effective clearance of the dialyzer. With these parameters, computer modeling is required to calculate the delivered Kt/V urea. Calculation of a URR is considerably easier, and requires only a pre-and post-dialysis urea measurement.

$$\text{URR} = 100\,(1 - [\text{post-dialysis urea} \div \text{pre-dialysis urea}])$$

The minimally acceptable URR for each HD session is 65%. Interested readers are referred to theNFK-DOQI guidelines.[51]

Total protein should also be measured on 24-h urine and dialysate collections to allow calculation of normalized protein catabolic rates as an indicator of nutrition. Alternatively, a 24-h urine urea permits calculation of the urea nitrogen appearance as a measure of dietary protein intake.

Renal Transplantation

The ultimate goal for infants and children with CRF is renal transplantation. As transplantation is still only a treatment and not a cure, children with renal transplants require long-term monitoring and medications. Immediately post-transplantation, electrolyte imbalances are common, including hypocalcemia, hypophosphatemia, and hypomagnesemia. Massive fluid replacement may result in changes in serum osmolality, which should be monitored. Current immunosuppression protocols use a combination of antilymphocyte globulin, OKT3, cyclosporine, FK506 (tacrolimus), azathioprine, MMF (mycophenolate mofetil), and prednisone. Measurement of cyclosporine values is necessary to achieve concentrations within what is currently regarded as the therapeutic range. Our center aims for concentrations measured by high-pressure liquid chromatography on whole blood of 200–250 μg/L during the first 3 months, 150–175 μg/L from 3–6 months, and 100–125 μg/L after 6 months. FK506 is measured by non-specific immunoassay in whole blood. Target levels are 10–15 ng/ml for the first 3 months post-transplantation, then 5–10 ng/ml thereafter.

RENIN ANGIOTENSIN SYSTEM

Renin is a proteolytic enzyme (molecular weight 31,000–40,000) predominantly formed and stored in the juxtaglomerular apparatus of the kidney and released into the renal vein and lymph. When released into the circulation, renin acts on its substrate angiotensinogen, an α2-globulin made mainly in the liver, to give a relatively inactive decapeptide, angiotensin I. Passage through the pulmonary circulation cleaves angiotensin I by a converting enzyme yielding the octapeptide, angiotensin II. A potent vasoconstrictor, angiotensin II also stimulates thirst and secretion of aldosterone, ADH, and catecholamines.

A number of factors control renin release, including renal tubular sodium concentration, renal perfusion pressure, and β-adrenergic vascular tone.

TABLE 3–6. Factors Influencing Renin Release

Increase in Renin Release	Decrease in Renin Release
DRUGS	DRUGS
Vasodilators	β-Adrenergic blockers
Diuretics	Mineralocorticoids
β-Adrenergic stimulators	α-Adrenergic stimulators
EDTA (via calcium efflux)	Lanthanum
HORMONES	HORMONES
Glucagon	Mineralocorticoids
Prostaglandins	Vasopressin
Norepinephrine and other catecholamines	Angiotensin
	Atrial natriuretic factor (ANF)
DIET	DIET
Sodium deprivation or loss	Salt load

From: Ingelfinger JR. Hypertension. Philadelphia: WB Saunders, 1982:48.

When renal nerves are stimulated, renin release increases. Sympathectomy will decrease baseline renin activity and also decrease renin secretion in response to sodium depletion. Central nervous system stimulation modulates renin release and the renal nerves must be intact for this to occur.

Various factors influencing renin release are listed in Table 3–6.

Hypertension

Normal blood pressure (BP) is defined as systolic and diastolic BPs less than the 90th percentile for age and sex. High-normal BP is defined as average systolic and/or diastolic BP between the 90th and 95th percentiles for age and sex. High BP is defined as average systolic and/or diastolic BP equal to or greater than the 95th percentile for age and sex on at least 3 occasions.[52]

The causes of hypertension are distinctly different for children as compared to adults. Most infants and children with hypertension have a secondary cause. Hypertension in the neonatal period is not rare. It may be secondary to a renal artery thrombosis from an improperly placed umbilical artery catheter. In a number of hypertensive infants, the cause is unknown; however, they may outgrow the problem by age 1 y (transient neonatal hypertension). The older adolescent is more like the adult in that the most common cause is essential or primary hypertension. A child who is age 10 or less and definitely has hypertension will most likely have a secondary cause. Renal disorders are by far the most common cause; however, a number of other causes must be excluded (see Table 3–7).

Investigation

The initial assessment is a thorough physical examination, looking for signs associated with the causal disease, such as upper-limb hypertension in coarctation of the aorta, abdominal bruit in renal artery stenosis, a café au lait skin lesion in neurofi-

TABLE 3–7. Causes of Hypertension in Children

RENAL:	Parenchymal causes: Chronic Pyelonephritis Acute or chronic glomerulonephritis Congenital defects: Polycystic kidney disease Segmental hypoplasia Ask-Upmark kidney Hemolytic uremic syndrome Renal transplant Renovascular: Intrinsic renal artery disease Fibromuscular lesions: intimal, medial, perimedial Neurofibromatosis Arteritis Extrinsic renal artery diseases Para-aortic tumors Para-aortic lymph nodes Para-aortic neurofibromata
ENDOCRINE:	Pheochromocytoma Congenital adrenal hyperplasia Hyperthyroidism Primary aldosteronism
VASCULAR SYSTEM:	Coarctation of the aorta Takayasu's arteritis
DRUG-RELATED:	Corticosteroids Amphetamine overdose Licorice Oral contraceptives
MISCELLANEOUS:	Essential hypertension Wilms tumor Neuroblastoma Burns

bromatosis, or a cushingoid appearance in cases of adrenal corticosteroid excess. The urinalysis and renal function tests are important. Plasma electrolytes and acid base measurements demonstrating a hypokalemic metabolic alkalosis suggest activation of the renin angiotensin system. Pheochromocytoma should be excluded in all patients by obtaining a 24 h urine for vanillylmandelic acid (VMA) and catecholamines. If the screen is positive, a CT scan, or more recently, magnetic resonance imaging (MRI) of the abdomen should be requested. ^{131}I metaiodobenzylguanidine (MIBG) scintigraphy can be useful for elusive or multiple tumors.

Most of the secondary causes of hypertension are easily excluded, with the exception of renal artery stenosis, the definitive test for which is a renal arteriogram. However, noninvasive evaluation should be done first. The renin system can be assessed by obtaining a peripheral vein renin and a 24 h urine for sodium excretion. Laragh et al.[53] have developed a nomogram for adults. The early response to the administration of the oral angiotensin converting enzyme inhibitor, captopril, has been shown to be useful in a number of adult studies. However, only preliminary results are available for children.

The captopril provocative test is performed with the patient at rest. A baseline renin is obtained, then captopril (0.35–0.7 mg/kg, maximum 25 mg) is given orally and 60 or 90 minutes later a repeat renin is obtained. A positive test is a plasma renin activity value of ≥ 3.3 ng/L/s (12 ng/mL/h) with an increase of ≥ 2.8 ng/L/s (10 ng/mL/h), or a relative increase of 150%, provided the initial renin value is ≥ 0.8 ng/L/s (3 ng/mL/h). A radionuclide renal scan may be useful as a screening test for renal artery stenosis and as an adjunct to the study, a single dose of captopril, as above, is given 1 h prior to the scan. Captopril will decrease the GFR of the affected kidney, which will manifest as decreased isotopic uptake by the kidney.

Antihypertensive Therapy

The monitoring of the effectiveness of antihypertensive drug therapy is by measuring the patient's blood pressure and looking for side effects. Laboratory tests are not necessary.

Diuretics

Hydrochlorothiazide is the most frequently used diuretic. It is necessary to monitor the patient for hypokalemia. The potassium sparing diuretics such as amiloride can cause hyperkalemia, especially if there is renal failure. Potent loop diuretics such as furosemide can cause serious electrolyte disturbances.

β-Adrenergic Blocking Agents

These drugs are the most commonly used antihypertensives. It is possible to measure blood concentrations of drugs such as propranolol; however, the usual clinical approach is to gradually increase the drug dose to a reasonable concentration while monitoring the heart rate and blood pressure.

Angiotensin Converting Enzyme (ACE) Inhibitors

Captopril was the initial drug in this class. However, there are now numerous ACE inhibitors with longer durations of action. There is a danger of hyperkalemia, especially if combined with a potassium-sparing diuretic. Renal failure is a well-recognized complication of ACE inhibitors when used to treat hypertension secondary to renal artery stenosis in a patient with a solitary kidney or with bilateral renal artery stenosis.

Angiotensin II Receptor Antagonist

Losartan is the first non-peptide selective blocker of the binding of angiotensin II to type 1 (AT1) angiotensin receptors, thereby preventing the action of angiotensin II.[54] This class of drugs has the same antihypertensive efficacy as ACE inhibitors. However, since there is no increase in bradykinin, patients do not experience the side effect of cough, as do 10% of patients treated with ACE inhibitors. Blockade of the action of angiotensin II leads to elevations in plasma levels of renin, angiotensin I, and angiotensin II.[55] How it fits into the armamentarium of antihypertensive therapies remains to be seen.

Sodium Nitroprusside

This is the preferred antihypertensive for the management of hypertensive crises. Prolonged use of this drug can cause cyanide poisoning. Thiocyanate blood concentrations should be monitored in cases of prolonged or high-dose therapy or in patients with renal failure.

Normotensive Hyper-reninemic Conditions

Diseases associated with salt and water loss, such as vomiting and diarrhea, lead to an increased plasma renin concentration. There are pediatric conditions in which the plasma renin can be very high (50–100 fold increase) and can even be diagnostic. Bartter syndrome is a form of renal sodium and potassium wasting. Such infants and children present with a hypokalemic metabolic alkalosis; in some, hyponatremia and hypomagnesemia are observed. The plasma renin activity is very high, but the blood pressure is normal. The urine has excessive sodium, potassium, and chloride, in spite of normal or low plasma values. Infants with cystic fibrosis, a common genetic disease, can present with identical plasma electrolyte and renin values; however, the urine has very low sodium and chloride values. The salt wasting in these infants is through loss from sweat. Finally, infants provided with a formula that is low in chloride can mimic Bartter syndrome; however, their urine will be nearly free of sodium and chloride.

DISTURBANCES OF ELECTROLYTES AND WATER

Pathophysiology

A large fraction of the body mass is water. The total body water is divided into two main compartments, intracellular fluid (ICF) and extracellular fluid (ECF). The ECF space has two major subdivisions, plasma and interstitial fluid. Using the volume of distribution of various markers, it is possible to measure total body water (e.g., using heavy water) and the ECF space (e.g., using bromide) and by subtracting the two, derive the ICF volume. These measurements are not routinely used in clinical medicine. The electrolyte composition of the ECF compared to ICF is quite different. Sodium is the major ECF cation and potassium is the major ICF cation. In the plasma, by subtracting anions from cations, an undetermined anion fraction or anion gap is obtained. It can be grossly calculated by the formula: $Na - (Cl + HCO_3)$ and is normally 10–15 mmol/L (mEq/L). An increased anion gap can be observed in lactic or ketoacidosis. The electrolyte concentration in the ICF is similar to plasma, but differs slightly because of the absence of negatively charged proteins in the ICF (e.g., Gibbs-Donnan equilibrium).

Because in children the body is composed of an even larger proportion of water, the incidence of acute disturbances of salt and water is commonplace. Dehydration or ECF volume contraction can be the result of a reduced intake of salt and water, or increased losses such as from the gastrointestinal tract in diarrhea, in the urine from an osmotic diuresis or adrenal insufficiency, from skin, or from the respiratory tract. Types of dehydration can be classified according to the plasma sodium concentration: isotonic dehydration (sodium 130–150 mmol/L [mEq/L]), hypertonic dehydration (sodium > 150 mmol/L [mEq/L]), and hypotonic dehydration (sodium < 130 mmol/L [mEq/L]).

Frequently, dehydrated patients will also have an acid base and potassium disturbance. In addition, there may be a component of renal failure. Urinalysis for protein, hemoglobin, sediment, specific gravity or osmolality, and sodium concentration will help separate prerenal versus renal failure.

Clinical Management

Acute ECF Volume Contraction

The management of such patients is based on physiological principles. The clinician must determine the following:

1. Type of dehydration (plasma sodium)
2. Magnitude of the dehydration (acute weight loss)
3. Presence of deficit of body potassium (plasma potassium)
4. Nature of the acid-base disturbance (measure blood acid-base status and anion gap)

The patient's electrolyte and water deficits are calculated and then added to the maintenance electrolyte and water requirements. In moderately and severely dehydrated patients, the early phase of management (first 2 h) is directed towards the restoration of circulatory integrity. The remainder of the first day is aimed at partial restoration of ECF sodium and water deficits and partial correction of acid-base disturbances. The final phase (days 1–4) is devoted to replacing potassium deficits, plus any remaining ECF volume and acid-base disturbances. Comprehensive reviews of this topic are available.[56, 57]

Renal Tubular Disorders

Bartter Syndrome

Bartter syndrome was originally described in children with growth failure associated with a hypokalemic metabolic alkalosis, hyper-reninemia, hyperplasia of the juxtaglomerular apparatus, and normal blood pressure.[58] It has since been described in all age groups. A mutation in the Na-K-2 Cl cotransporter, NKCC2, has been linked to Bartter syndrome.[59] Younger patients can have renal sodium wasting and more severe electrolyte and acid-base disturbances. Hypomagnesemia is present in some patients. Bartter syndrome is believed to be a heterogeneous disorder. The most common variant is Gitelman syndrome, which has a similar but milder presentation to Bartter syndrome. These patients are older, and may have tetany. They have hypomagnesemia, hypokalemia, and hypocalciuria. The genetic defect is due to a mutation in the thiazide-sensitive Na-Cl cotransporter in the distal convoluted tubule.[60]

The main focus of therapy is potassium chloride supplementation. Drugs such as indomethacin, ibuprofen, and amiloride have been used to reduce urinary potassium and water loss. Monitoring the progress of these patients requires serial measurement of plasma electrolytes and acid-base values.

A similar electrolyte disturbance is observed in cystic fibrosis, with a low chloride diet, in surreptitious vomiting (as in bulimia) and with diuretic or laxative abuse.

Cystinosis

Renal Fanconi syndrome is characterized by a number of proximal renal tubular defects involving excessive urinary losses of amino acids, glucose, uric acid, and phosphate. It is frequently associated with urinary sodium and potassium wasting, proximal renal tubular acidosis, tubular proteinuria, and hyposthenuria. There are numerous causes of Fanconi syndrome, but in children, cystinosis is the most common.

Cystinosis, an autosomal recessive disorder, typically presents in infancy as failure to thrive, polyuria, muscle weakness, photophobia, and rickets.[61] The diagnosis is suggested by the clinical picture, combined with Fanconi syndrome and a hypokalemic metabolic acidosis. The presence of cystine crystals in the cornea is diagnostic. The diagnosis is confirmed by measuring the leucocyte cystine content. The patients are managed by alkali and potassium supplementation and vitamin D if rickets is present. With time, cystine damages the thyroid gland and thyroxine supplementation is required. Eventually, renal failure develops and renal transplantation is necessary. There is growing experience using cysteamine or phosphocysteamine to slow the progression of the renal failure, and results are encouraging.[62]

Nephrogenic Diabetes Insipidus (NDI)

NDI is an inherited X-linked recessive disorder characterized by renal tubular unresponsiveness to antidiuretic hormone.[63] Affected boys present in infancy with hypernatremia associated with polyuria, polydypsia, unexplained fever, and growth failure. The mother who carries the gene may have a mild urinary concentrating defect. The genetic mutations for X-linked NDI[64] and the rarer autosomal recessive NDI[65] have been found.

There are many causes of acquired nephrogenic diabetes insipidus which must be excluded, such as medullary cystic disease, hypokalemia, drugs such as lithium, sickle cell disease, and excessive water intake. There may be a positive family history, and with the demonstration of hypernatremia and dilute urine the diagnosis is straightforward. Central diabetes insipidus is excluded by demonstrating unresponsiveness to vasopressin or deamino-8-D-arginine vasopressin (dDAVP). Management of such infants is focused on providing adequate water intake to maintain normonatremia. A low-solute diet is provided and hydrochlorothiazide will decrease free water clearance. Non-steroidal anti-inflammatory drugs such as indomethacin will reduce the polyuria. During the first two years of life, the child is at risk for dehydration with consequent brain injury, and therefore night-time nasogastric tube feeding may be required.

Chemical Analysis of the Urine

Urine dipsticks are currently available to test for protein (primarily albumin), blood (or heme pigment), specific gravity, pH, glucose, ketones, leukocyte esterase, nitrites, and bilirubin. Protein, blood, glucose, leukocyte esterase and nitrites have been covered in previous sections. The remaining tests are reviewed below.[66]

pH

Reagent strips for pH utilize a methyl red and bromthymol blue double indicator system. Urine pH monitoring is vital in the diagnosis of RTA (see page 53). Alkaline urine may be seen with infection with urea-splitting organisms, or with alkalemia. Monitoring of urine pH is also important in the treatment of urinary calculi.

Specific Gravity (SG)

Reagent strips for SG measure ionic concentration, based on a pKa change of pretreated polyelectrolytes. In healthy kidneys, SG is a measure of a patient's state of hydration, and can range from 1.001 to 1.035. In ARF, SG is useful in determining pre-renal states from intrinsic renal disease (see page 66). Very low SG may be seen with renal concentrating defects.

Ketones

Reagent strips for ketones are based on a color reaction with sodium nitroprusside, and are most sensitive for acetoacetic acid. Ketones are present in the urine during starvation and in diabetes mellitus. The latter is associated with concomitant glucosuria.

Bilirubin

Reagent strips for bilirubin are based on a diazo reaction. Bilirubin is not normally detected in the urine, but is detected with liver disease characterized by jaundice, and during hemolysis.

Antenatal Assessment of Fetal Renal Function

With the growing use of antenatal ultrasound, major and minor abnormalities of the fetal urinary tract are more frequently being diagnosed. The most common abnormality is hydronephrosis, either unilateral or bilateral. In utero intervention to decompress the dilated fetal urinary tract may be indicated in some patients. Assessment of fetal renal function is crucial to allow intervention only to those who will benefit from it.

Analysis of urine from normal fetuses demonstrates decreasing urinary sodium and phosphate values and increasing creatinine concentration with advancing gestational age.[67] In fetuses with renal dysplasia, high urinary sodium and calcium, and increasing urinary osmolality correlate with poor fetal renal outcome.[67–69] Favorable renal prognosis has been associated with urine Na < 43 mmol/L (100 mg/dL), chloride < 25 mmol/L (90 mg/dL), osmolality < 200, and Ca < 2 mmol/L (8 mg/dL). Elevated urinary β-2 microglobulin levels also correlate with poor renal outcome in numerous studies.[70, 71]

Fetuses with documented abnormalities of the urinary tract should also undergo karyotyping because of a significant association with chromosomal abnormalities.

SUMMARY

Excluding urinary tract infections, urinary tract and kidney disorders are not especially common in children. The many different disorders that do occur have been described in this chapter. An understanding of the physiology and etiology of these disorders is important in deciding the most appropriate laboratory tests to order.

REFERENCES

1. Barakat AY, Ichikawa I. Laboratory Data. In: Ichikawa I, ed. Pediatric textbook of fluid and electrolytes. Baltimore: Williams and Wilkins, 1990:478–500.
2. Katz M. Hyperglycemia-induced hyponatremia: calculation of expected serum sodium depression (letter). NEJM 1973;289:843.
3. Peterson LN, Levi M. Disorders of potassium metabolism. In: Schrier RW, ed. Renal and electrolyte disorders, 5th ed. Philadelphia: Lippincott-Raven, 1997:192–240.
4. Schwartz GJ, Brion LP, Spitzer A. The use of plasma creatinine concentration for estimating glomerular filtration rate in infants, children and adolescents. Ped Clin No Amer 1987;34:571–90.
5. Schwartz GJ. Does kL/Pcr estimate GFR or does GFR determine k? Ped Nephrol 1992; 6:512–5.
6. Hall JE, Guyton AC, Farr BM. A single-injection method for measuring glomerular filtration rate. Am J Physiology 1977;232:F72–F76.
7. Halperin ML, Goldstein MB. Fluid, electrolyte, and acid-base physiology: a problem based approach, 2nd ed. Philadelphia: WB Saunders, 1994.
8. Morris RCJ, Ives HE. Inherited disorders of the renal tubule. In: Brenner B, Rector FCJ, ed. The kidney, 4th ed. Philadelphia: W.B. Saunders, 1991:1596–1656.
9. Walton RJ, Bijvoet OLM. Nomogram for derivation of renal threshold phosphate concentration. Lancet 1975;2:309–10.
10. Alon U, Hellerstein S. Assessment and interpretation of the tubular threshold for phosphate in infants and children. Ped Nephrol 1994;8:250–1.
11. Kamel KS, Briceno LF, Sanchez MI, et al. A new classification for renal defects in net acid excretion. Am J Kid Dis 1997;29:136–46.

12. Rodriguez-Soriano J, Vallo A. Renal tubular acidosis. Ped Nephrol 1990;4:268–75.
13. Sheldon CA, Gonzalez R. Differentiation of upper and lower urinary tract infections: how and when? Med Clin No Amer 1984;68:321–33.
14. Pappas PG. Laboratory in the diagnosis of urinary tract infections. Med Clin No Amer 1991;75:313–25.
15. Benador D, Benador N, Slosman DO, et al. Cortical scintigraphy in the evaluation of renal parenchymal changes in children with pyelonephritis. J Pediatr 1994;124:17–20.
16. Uehling DT. Susceptibility factors in ascending urinary tract infection. In: Holliday MA, Barratt TM, Avner EA, eds. Pediatric nephrology, 3d ed. Baltimore: Williams and Wilkins, 1994:986–93.
17. Jodal U, Hansson S. Urinary tract infection: clinical. In: Holliday MA, Barratt TM, Avner EA, eds. Pediatric nephrology, 3d ed. Baltimore: Williams and Wilkins 1994:950–2.
18. Hellerstein S. Evolving concepts in the evaluation of the child with a urinary tract infection. J Pediatr 1994;124:589–92.
19. Hoberman A, Wald ER, Reynolds EA, Penchansky L, Charron M. Pyuria and bacteriuria in urine specimens obtained by catheter from young children with fever. J Pediatr 1994; 124:513–9.
20. Lohr JA, Portilla MG, Geuder TG, Dunn ML, Dudley SM. Making a presumptive diagnosis of urinary tract infection by using a urinalysis performed in an on-site laboratory. J Pediatr 1993;122:22–5.
21. Jakobsson B, Nolstedt L, Svensson L, et al. 99mTechnetium-dimercaptosuccinic acid scan in the diagnosis of acute pyelonephritis in children: relation to clinical and radiological findings. Ped Nephrol 1992;6:328–34.
22. Rosenberg AR, Rossleigh MA, Brydon MP, et al. Evaluation of acute urinary tract infection in children by dimercaptosuccinic acid scintigraphy: a prospective study. J Urology 1992;148:1746–9.
23. Conway JJ, Cohn RA. Evolving role of nuclear medicine for the diagnosis and management of urinary tract infection. J Pediatr 1994;124:87–90.
24. Stokland E, Hellstrom M, Jacobsson B, et al. Renal damage one year after first urinary tract infection: Role of dimercaptosuccinic acid scintigraphy. J Pediatr 1996;129:815–20.
25. Sochett E, Daneman D. Screening tests to detect microalbuminuria in children with diabetes. J Pediatr 1988;112:744–8.
26. Diabetes Control and Complications Trial Research Group. Effect of intensive diabetes treatment on the development and progression of long-term complications in adolescents with insulin-dependent diabetes mellitus: Diabetes Control and Complications Trial. J Pediatr 1994;125:177–88.
27. Mohammad KS, Bdesha AS, Snell ME, et al. Phase contrast microscopic examination of urinary erythrocytes to localise source of bleeding: an overlooked technique? J Clin Pathol 1993;46:642–5.
28. Crompton CH, Ward PB, Hewitt IK. The use of urinary red cell morphology to determine the source of hematuria in children. Clinical Nephrology 1993;39:44–9.
29. Tomita M, Kitamoto Y, Nakayama M, Sato T. A new morphological classification of urinary erythrocytes for differential diagnosis of glomerular hematuria. Clin Nephrol 1992;37:84–9.
30. Kitamoto Y, Tomita M, Akamine M, et al. Differentiation of hematuria using a uniquely shaped red cell. Nephron 1993;64:32–6.
31. Lettgen B, Wohlmuth A. Validity of G1-cells in the differentiation between glomerular and non-glomerular haematuria in children. Pediatr Nephrol 1995;9:435–7.
32. Naicker S, Poovalingam V, Mlisana K, et al. Comparative assessment of phase contrast microcopy and Coulter counter measurements in localizing the site of hematuria. S African Med J 1992;82:183–5.
33. Lettgen B, Hestermann C, Rascher W. Differentiation of glomerular and non-glomerular hematuria in children by measurement of mean corpuscular volume of urinary red cells using a semi-automated cell counter. Acta Paediatr 1994;83:946–9.
34. Fukuzaki A, Kaneto H, Ikeda S, Orikasa S. Determining the origin of hematuria by immunocytochemical staining for erythrocytes in urine for Tamm-Horsfall protein. J Urology 1996;155:248–51.

35. Guder WG, Hofmann W, Differentiation of proteinuria and haematuria by single protein analysis in urine. Clin Biochem 1993;26:277–82.
36. Bazzi C, Petrini C, Rizza V, et al. Characterization of proteinuria in primary glomerulonephritides. SDS-PAGE patterns: clinical significance and prognostic value of low molecular weight ("tubular") proteins. Am J Kidney Dis 1997;29:27–35.
37. Fitzwater DS, Wyatt RJ. Hematuria. Pediatrics in Review 1994;15:102–9.
38. Hebert LA, Cosio FG, Neff JC. Diagnostic significance of hypocomplementemia. Kidney International 1991;39:811–21.
39. Falk RJ. ANCA-associated renal disease. Kidney International 1990;38:998–1010.
40. Jennette JC, Falk RJ. Pathogenic potential of anti-neutrophil cytoplasmic autoantibodies. Laboratory Investigation 1994;70:135–7.
41. Sargent JD, Stukel TA, Kresel J, Klein RZ. Normal values for random urinary calcium to creatinine ratios in infancy. J Pediatr 1993;123:393–7.
42. Reusz GS, Dobos M, Byrd D, et al. Urinary calcium and oxalate excretion in children. Pediatr Nephrol 1995;9:39–44.
43. Alconcher LF, Castro C, Quintana D, et al. Urinary calcium excretion in healthy school children. Pediatr Nephrol 1997;11:186–8.
44. Nolan C, Anger MS, Kelleher SP. Eosinophiluria: a new method of detection and definition of the clinical spectrum. NEJM 1986;315:1516.
45. Brezis M, Rosen S, Epstein FH. Acute renal failure. In: Brenner BM, Rector FCJ, eds. The kidney, 4th ed. Philadelphia: W.B. Saunders, 1991:993-1061.
46. Thadhani R, Pascual M, Bonventre J. Acute renal failure. NEJM 1996;334:1448–60.
47. National Kidney Foundation–Dialysis Outcomes Quality Initiative. NFK-DOQI clinical practice guidelines for the treatment of anemia of chronic renal failure. Am J Kid Dis 1997;30(4 Suppl 3):S190–S240.
48. Bennett WM, Aronoff GR, Golper TA, et al. Drug prescribing in renal failure: dosing guidelines for adults, 3rd ed. Philadelphia: American College of Physicians, 1994.
49. Twardowski ZJ, Nolph KD, Khanna R, et al. Peritoneal equilibration test. Perit Dial Bulletin 1987;7:138–47.
50. National Kidney Foundation–Dialysis Outcomes Quality Initiative. NFK-DOQI clinical practice guidelines for peritoneal dialysis adequacy. Am J Kid Dis 1997;30(3 Suppl 2):S67–S136.
51. National Kidney Foundation–Dialysis Outcomes Quality Initiative. NFK-DOQI clinical practice guidelines for hemodialysis adequacy. Am J Kid Dis 1997;30(3 Suppl 2):S15–S66.
52. Second Task Force on Blood Pressure Control in Children. Report of the Second Task Force on Blood Pressure Control in Children, 1987. Pediatrics 1987;79:1–25.
53. Laragh JH, Baer L, Brunner HR, et al. Renin, angiotensin and aldosterone system in pathogenesis and management of hypertensive vascular disease. Amer J Medicine 1972;52:633–52.
54. Goodfriend TL, Elliott ME, Catt KJ. Angiotensin receptors and their antagonists. NEJM 1996;334:1649–54.
55. Goldberg MR, Bradstreet TE, McWilliams EJ, et al. Biochemical effects of losartan, a nonpeptide angiotensin II receptor antagonist, on the renin-angiotensin-aldosterone system in hypertensive patients. Hypertension 1995;25:37–46.
56. Winters RW, ed. The body fluids in pediatrics. Boston: Little, Brown and Co., 1973.
57. Ichikawa I, ed. Pediatric textbook of fluid and electrolytes. Baltimore: Williams and Wilkins, 1990.
58. Stein JH. The pathogenetic spectrum of Bartter's syndrome. Kidney International 1985; 28:85–93.
59. Simon DB, Karet FE, Hamden JM, et al. Bartter's syndrome, hypokalemic alkalosis with hypercalciuria, is caused by mutations in the Na-K-2Cl cotransporter NKCC2. Nature Genetics1996;13:183–8.
60. Simon DB, Nelson-Williams C, Bia MJ, et al. Gitelman's variant of Bartter's syndrome, inherited hypokalemic alkalosis, is caused by mutations in the thiazide-sensitive Na-Cl cotransporter. Nature Genetics 1996;12:24–30.
61. Schneider JA, Schulman JD. Cystinosis. In: Stanbury JB, Wyngaarden JB, Frederickson

DS, Goldstein JL, Brown MS, eds. The metabolic basis of inherited disease, 5th ed. New York: McGraw-Hill, 1983:1844–66.
62. Markello TC, Bernardini IM, Gahl WA. Improved renal function in children with cystinosis treated with cysteamine. NEJM 1993;328:1157–62.
63. Niadet P, Dechaux M, Trivin C, et al. Nephrogenic diabetes insipidus: clinical and pathological aspects. Adv Nephrol 1984;13:247–60.
64. Rosenthal W, Seilbold A, Antaramian A, et al. Molecular identification of the gene responsible for congenital nephrogenic diabetes insipidus. Nature 1992;359:233–5.
65. Deen PMT, Verdijk MAJ, Knoers NVAM, et al. Requirement of human renal water channel Aquaporin-2 for vasopressin-dependent concentration of urine. Science 1994;264:92–4.
66. Ringsrud KM, Linne JJ. Chemical examination of urine. In: Urinalysis and body fluids: a colortext and atlas. St Louis: Mosby-Year Book, 1995:42–79.
67. Nicolini U, Fisk NM, Rodeck CH, Beacham J. Fetal urine biochemistry: an index of renal maturation and dysfunction. Br J Obstet & Gynecol 1992;99:46–50.
68. Nicolaides KH, Cheng HH, Snijders RMJ, Moniz CF. Fetal urine biochemistry in the assessment of obstructive uropathy. Am J Obstet Gynecol 1992;166:932–7.
69. Johnson MP, Corsi P, Bradfield W, et al. Sequential urinalysis improves evaluation of fetal renalfunction in obstructive uropathy. Am J Obstet Gynecol 1995;173:59–65.
70. Lipitz S, Ryan G, Samuell C, et al. Fetal urine analysis for the assessment of renal function in obstructive uropathy. Am J Obstet Gynecol 1993;168:174–9.
71. Muller F, Dommergues M, Mandelbrot L, et al. Fetal urinary biochemistry predicts postnatal renal function in children with bilateral obstructive uropathies. Obstet & Gynecol 1993; 82:813–20.

CHAPTER 4

Biochemical Tests of Hepatic and Intestinal Disorders

J. Calvin, Ph.D., M.C.B., F.R.C.Path.
G.A. Maguire, Ph.D., M.C.B., F.R.C.Path.

INTRODUCTION

This chapter is divided into two sections in which we cover the clinical biochemistry of the liver and intestine, respectively.

THE LIVER

The liver is central to the homeostasis of the body in general and blood in particular. Its major metabolic functions are illustrated in Figure 4–1. The majority of blood proteins, apart from immunoglobulins, as well as the majority of blood lipids and glucose in the fasted state are manufactured in the liver. In addition, most of the low-molecular-weight constituents of blood are metabolized in the liver. These processes take place in the hepatocytes, which comprise 80% by weight and 60% by number of the total cells in the liver. Hepatocytes are "polar" cells having both a basolateral membrane facing the blood compartment and an apical membrane facing the bile compartment (the canaliculi). As illustrated in Figure 4–2, they are organized in sheets with "tight junctions" between each cell which keep the blood and bile compartments separate.

Histologically, the basic architecture of the liver (Figure 4–3) is simple but highly organized. Within a "portal triad" runs a branch of the portal vein, a branch of the hepatic artery, and a bile ductule. Portal triads are located on alternate corners of a hexagonal array of hepatocytes surrounding a central vein. Oxygenated

FIGURE 4–1. Major Metabolic Functions of the Liver

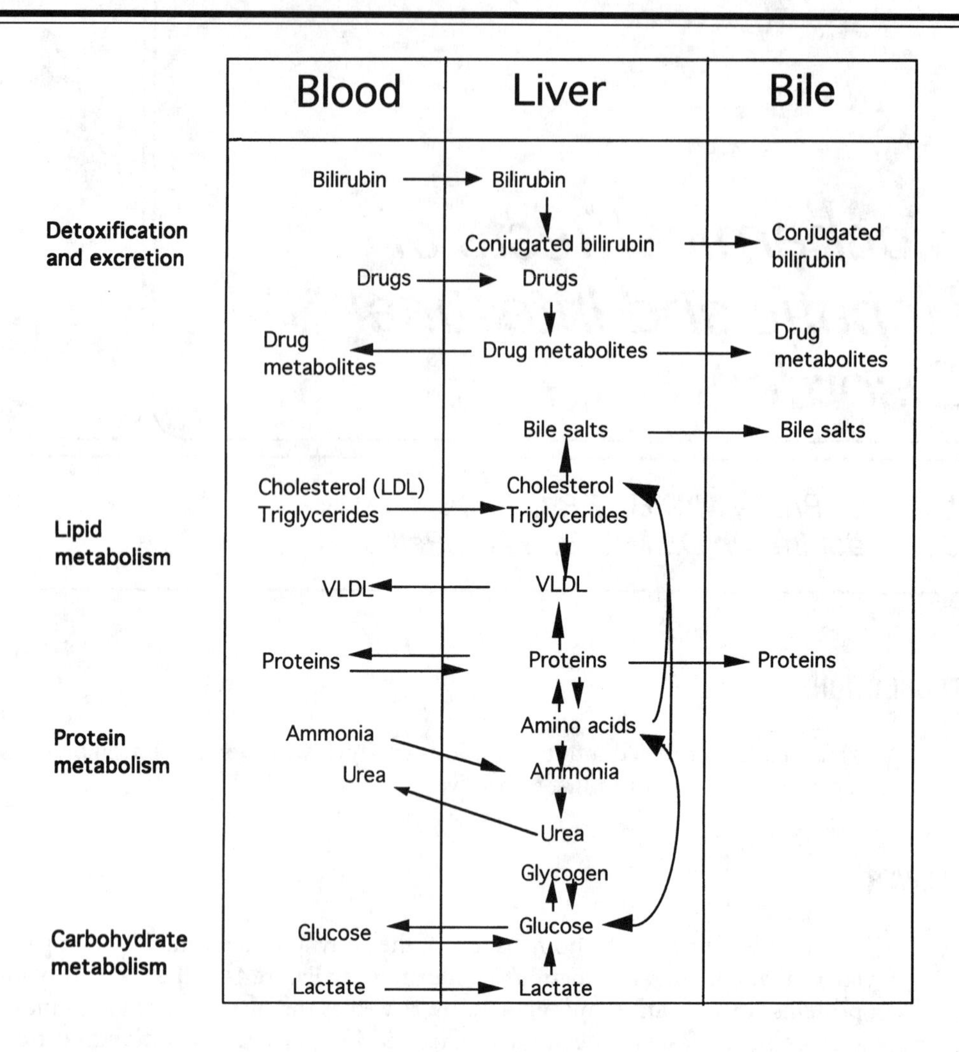

blood from the hepatic arteriole and substrate loaded blood from the portal venule mix and flow within the blood sinusoids over hepatocytes before draining via the hepatic venule.

There has been much debate on the definition of the functional unit of the liver, largely over the precise path mixed blood takes en route to the hepatic venule. Irrespective of this, it is clear that periportal hepatocytes—those hepatocytes closer to the portal triad—are exposed to relatively oxygen- and substrate-rich blood, and that perivenous hepatocytes—those closer to the central vein—are exposed to relatively oxygen- and substrate-poor blood. Hepatocytes located within each of these zones and in the intermediate zone exhibit differences in their enzyme composition and metabolic activity. For instance, periportal hepatocytes are relatively rich in

FIGURE 4–2. Schematic Diagram Illustrating the Association of Hepatocytes to Form Bile Canaliculi

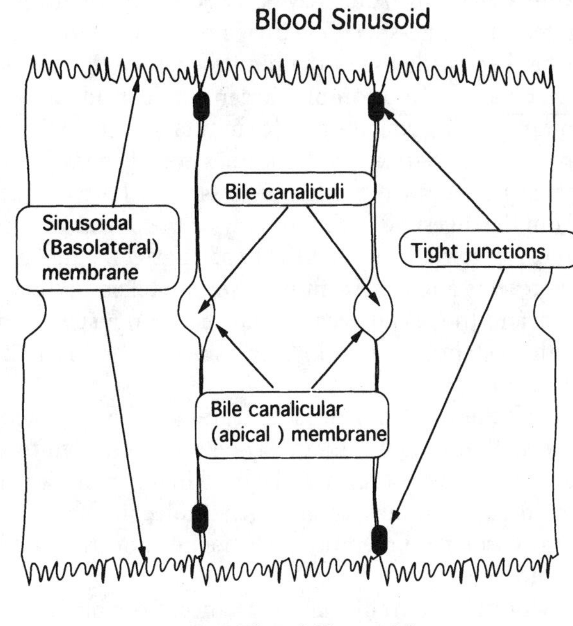

FIGURE 4–3. Schematic Representation of Liver Architecture

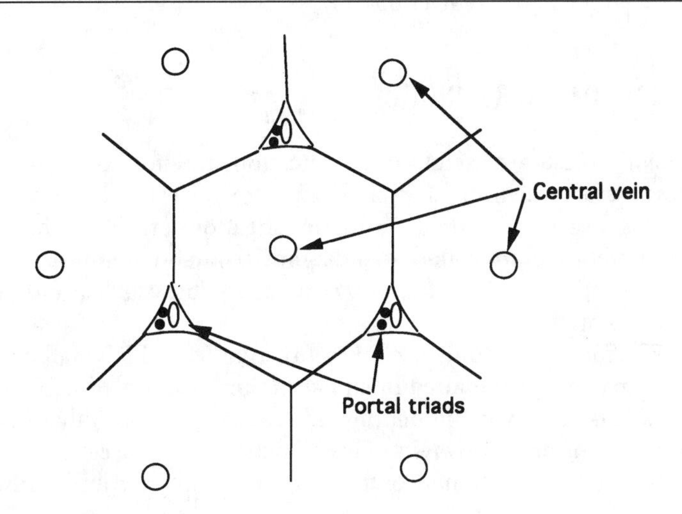

gluconeogenic and ureogenic activity, while those in the perivenous region are rich in glycolytic and ammoniagenic activities.[1] It is conceivable that alteration in the balance of the zones may be important pathologically. For instance, it is possible that overexpression of one zone may be associated with disease susceptibility. It has been suggested that zone-specific damage may release zone-specific markers,[2] but as yet there has been little use of these differences in the investigation of disease.

The liver is a large and complex organ with considerable reserve capacity. Several different processing routes operate simultaneously in the liver (see Figure 4–1). Low- and high-molecular-weight molecules are taken up from blood into the liver, where they may be degraded, further processed, and recycled or rerouted. They may originate from the digestive system by way of the portal vein or from other organs, including the liver itself, by way of the hepatic artery. Large molecules such as low-density lipoproteins and senescent proteins are taken up by specific receptors: the LDL receptor and the asialoglycoprotein receptor, respectively. These macromolecules are either catabolized within liver lysosomes or rerouted (possibly modified) back to blood or on to bile.

Small molecules such as glucose and amino acids are taken up by specific transport systems. Within the liver, they may be interconverted to some extent, or fully metabolized to generate energy or to be used in the manufacture of large molecules such as proteins, lipoproteins, or glycogen. Molecules processed for export may be released at the basolateral membrane of the hepatocyte into blood or at the apical membrane into bile.

Transcytotic transport of some substances from blood to bile takes place. Polymeric IgA is transported intact to bile, while substances such as bilirubin or some "xenobiotics," i.e., drugs and potentially toxic ingested materials, are processed before excretion in a chemically altered form directly into bile. Other processed xenobiotics are released into blood and ultimately excreted in urine. Owing to the large spare capacity of the liver, derangements in blood proteins, carbohydrates, and lipids are very insensitive indicators of liver dysfunction. These often become abnormal only in severe liver disease.

BIOCHEMICAL TESTS OF LIVER FUNCTION

Biochemical tests are useful for the detection and monitoring of liver diseases, but are less useful in their differential diagnosis. Similar biochemical test results can be present in a variety of liver diseases. Investigations other than biochemical tests are much more useful for differential diagnosis, notably noninvasive procedures such as ultrasound and CT scans and invasive procedures such as radionucleotide scans and liver biopsy.

The most commonly used liver function tests (LFTs) fall naturally into three groups: markers of impaired biliary secretion, markers of hepatocellular damage, and markers of enzyme induction and release. Of these, only markers of impaired biliary secretion are strictly tests of liver function; however, clotting studies can be used to assess synthetic functioning of the liver, but are not described further in this chapter.

Markers of Impaired Biliary Secretion

When biliary secretion is impaired, substances that are usually secreted into bile may be found in blood. These substances include bilirubin and bile acids. Of these, only bilirubin is routinely measured. Until recently, measurement of bile acids has been technically difficult. However, new methods employing tandem mass spectrometry now provide a means for automated measurement of bile acids in whole blood. Although not generally used as tests of liver function, these new methods have potential in screening for neonatal liver disease and are of value in the diagnosis of peroxisomal disorders.

Bilirubin Metabolism

It is important to understand the mechanism of bilirubin formation and excretion (Figure 4–4) to be able to interpret the changes in bilirubin that occur in health and disease. Within the reticulo-endothelial system, heme, which principally arises from the breakdown of hemoglobin, is metabolized to bilirubin. Bilirubin is extremely nonpolar and lipophilic and is only sparingly soluble in aqueous solutions. Within the blood it is extremely tightly bound to albumin (Kd $\approx 10^{-8}$ mol/L) and very little is free in solution.

Bilirubin (bound to albumin) circulates in the blood and is taken up by the liver. It dissociates from albumin prior to crossing the hepatocyte plasma membrane. This is unlike the metabolism of some other protein-bound blood components such as iron bound to transferrin, in which the whole transport protein is taken up into the liver by receptor-mediated endocytosis. Bilirubin is conjugated within the hepatic endoplasmic reticulum by a uridine diphosphate (UDP) glucuronyl transferase. Bilirubin has two potential sites of conjugation. In adults, the majority (70–90%) of conjugated bilirubin is conjugated at both sites to produce the diglucuronide, but a little monoglucuronide is produced.[3] In children, proportionately more monoglucuronide is formed.

Conjugated bilirubin is transported across the apical (bile canalicular) membrane into the bile canaliculus. Thus, in its passage across the liver it has to cross four separate membranes: the basolateral membrane, the endoplasmic reticulum membrane (twice), and the apical membrane. The transport processes involved are now well understood. No evidence exists to support a vesicular mechanism of transport,[4] and it is widely accepted that specific transport systems must be involved.[5]

Conjugated bilirubin thus enters the small intestine by way of bile. Bilirubin is further metabolized within the large intestine to urobilinogen by bacteria present in the gut. Some of this urobilinogen is absorbed from the intestine and enters the blood, much is in turn taken up by the liver from the portal vein, and a small proportion enters the general circulation, is filtered at the glomerulus, and enters urine. The normal form of bilirubin found in serum is therefore unconjugated bilirubin. Very little conjugated bilirubin is found in the blood of healthy individuals; it can only get there if something has gone wrong with the normal processing of bilirubin. Two possible mechanisms could be involved: either abnormal secretion of conjugated bilirubin across the basolateral membrane or regurgitation of bile into blood by gaps in tight junctions.

FIGURE 4–4. Metabolism and Excretion of Bilirubin in Health and Disease

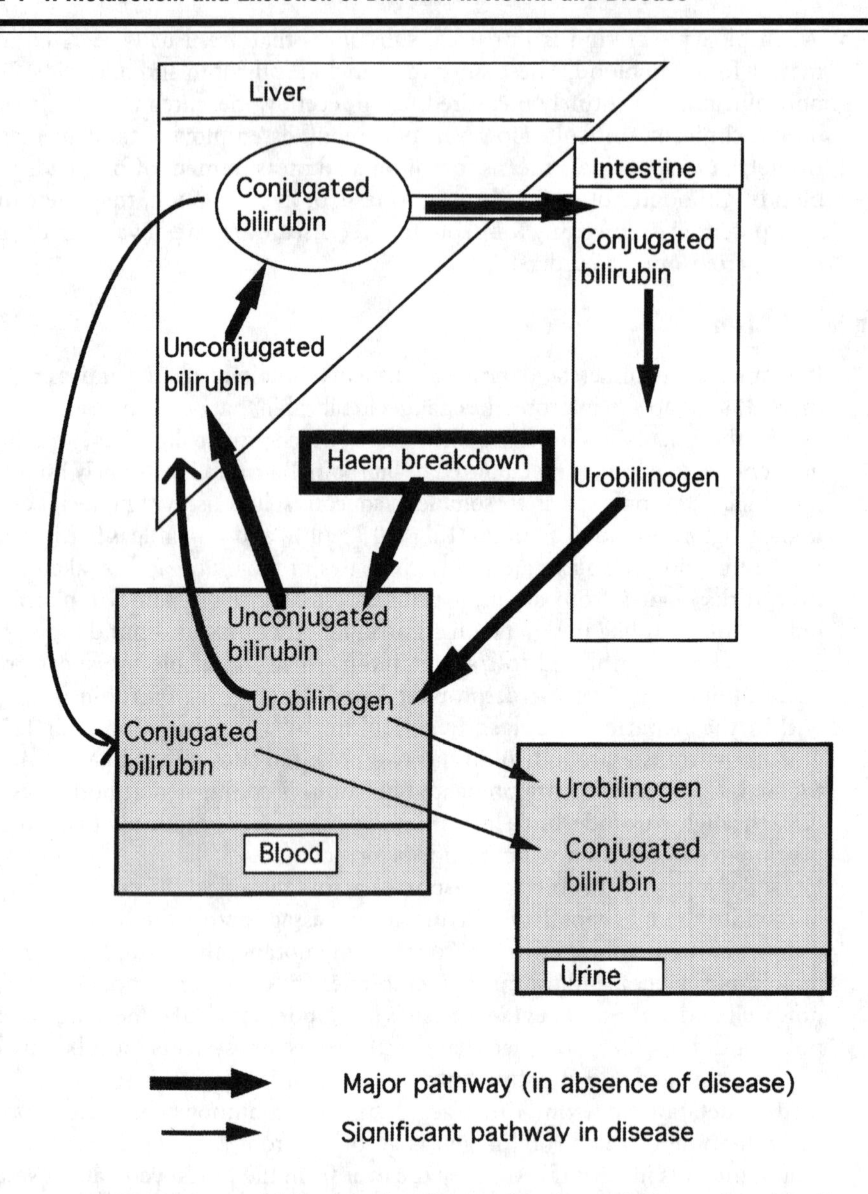

Unconjugated bilirubin, by virtue of its insolubility and its binding to albumin, is not filtered at the glomerulus and therefore does not enter urine. Conjugated bilirubin is more soluble in aqueous solutions and is less avidly bound to albumin; it is filtered at the glomerulus and can enter urine.

In addition to conjugated and unconjugated bilirubin, two more forms of bilirubin may be present in blood. "Delta" bilirubin is conjugated bilirubin that has become covalently bound to albumin. It is present in the blood of individuals who have had longstanding conjugated hyperbilirubinemia. "Free" bilirubin is unconjugated bilirubin that is not bound to albumin. Free bilirubin represents a tiny proportion of the total and is only of significance in severe unconjugated hyperbilirubinemia.

Measuring Bilirubin

A full description of analytical methods for measuring bilirubin is outside the scope of this chapter; for further information see Westwood.[6] However, an understanding of the basis of the methods used is needed to be able to interpret bilirubin results. Ideally, what is required is a method that quickly and reliably measures all four species of bilirubin in blood. Unfortunately, no such method exists. Total bilirubin—the sum of all the bilirubin species—is routinely measured quickly and accurately. The only method that reliably quantitates the four species of bilirubin is high-performance liquid chromatography (HPLC), but this method is too time-consuming for routine use. The methods in common use to measure the concentrations of the different bilirubin species produce results that are, at best, rough estimates.

Bilirubin can be measured on the basis of its intrinsic absorbance, usually measured at around its absorbance peak of 450 nm. These spectrophotometric methods measure the sum of all the bilirubin species present. However, since the molar absorptivity of each species is different (especially that of delta bilirubin), the results are an approximation. Bilirubinometers are based on the spectrophotometric technique and are widely used for the measurement of *total* bilirubin in neonates. Since delta bilirubin is not present in neonates to any great extent, these methods are sufficiently accurate. Bilirubin can be measured in neonates with an optical device that measures bilirubin transcutaneously. However, it cannot be used in patients who are undergoing phototherapy. In contrast, bilirubinometers can be used in this circumstance since the photodegradation products of bilirubin do not interfere in its measurement.

Laboratory methods for measuring bilirubin are usually based on the method of Jendrassik and Grof, in which bilirubin chemically reacts with a diazotizing reagent to produce a colored product. Depending on the exact conditions used—concentration of reagents, presence of "accelerators," pH, etc.—more or less of the different species of bilirubin present in the blood will be measured. Methods for the measurement of total bilirubin include an "accelerator" (e.g., caffeine) which ensures that all bilirubin species react.

Some methods, which do not include an accelerator and use a low pH, are described as "direct" methods. In general, direct bilirubin can be equated with conjugated bilirubin, but this is an oversimplification.

Those species of bilirubin which are more soluble, such as conjugated bilirubin and delta bilirubin, react more readily in direct methods and are predominantly measured. However, unconjugated bilirubin can react to a small extent. These methods are particularly inaccurate when the total bilirubin is normal or only mildly increased, in which case there is a tendency to overestimate the conjugated species.

For these reasons, it is not worthwhile to attempt to differentiate the type of hyperbilirubinemia by measuring direct bilirubin when the total bilirubin is not significantly elevated. "Indirect" reacting bilirubin can be calculated from the difference between the total and direct reacting bilirubin. No methods in common use specifically measure indirect bilirubin. The only routine method available to measure delta bilirubin is that using the Johnson and Johnson dry chemistry system. The usefulness of measuring delta bilirubin remains to be established.

Methods for the measurement of free bilirubin have been published.[7] Exactly what these methods measure is not apparent, and their practical usefulness has not been established.

Changes in Bilirubin in Diseased States

Hemolysis

The consequences for the observed changes in bilirubin metabolites in the various body compartments following hemolysis are readily predicted (Figure 4–4). Hemolysis (the lysis of red blood cells) releases large amounts of hemoglobin, the further processing of which leads to an increase in unconjugated bilirubin. This is taken up by its normal route into the liver and is conjugated and excreted into bile. Thus, there is increased delivery of bilirubin into the intestine, with consequent increased production of urobilinogen. There is therefore an increase in urobilinogen uptake into blood and thence to urine. There is no increase in urine bilirubin since there is no increase in conjugated bilirubin. Thus, the consequences of pure hemolysis are an increase in total bilirubin in blood; an increase in urobilinogen in urine; no increase in conjugated bilirubin in blood (indicated by little if any increase in "direct" bilirubin); and no increase in bilirubin in urine (see Table 4–1). Intravascular hemolysis is accompanied by a drop in the serum concentration of the hemoglobin-binding protein haptoglobin. However, the investigation of possible intravascular hemolysis is best pursued with hematological investigations.

TABLE 4–1. Typical Changes in Bilirubin and Its Metabolites in Hyperbilirubinemia of Different Causes

	Serum		Urine	
	Total Bilirubin	Conjugated Bilirubin	Bilirubin	Urobilinogen
Hemolysis	↑	N	N	↑
Physiological	↑	N	N	N
Liver Disease	↑	↑	↑	N/↓
Gilbert's Syndrome	↑	N	N	N/↓
Crigler-Najjar	↑	N	N	N/↓

↑= Increased N = Normal ↓ = Decreased

Physiological Jaundice

The causes of jaundice (discussed further on page 94) are multifactorial, including immaturity in the development of the bilirubin conjugating enzyme UDP glucuronyl transferase. There is no defect in the excretion of conjugated bilirubin into bile, and an *unconjugated* hyperbilirubinemia results. There is therefore no increase in urine bilirubin; nor is there an increase in urine urobilinogen, since the amount of bilirubin reaching the intestine has not increased.

Liver Disease

In most forms of liver disease, the ability to secrete conjugated bilirubin into bile is impaired and therefore a conjugated hyperbilirubinemia results. The ability of the liver to take up and conjugate bilirubin may also be impaired; thus, there may be an accompanying unconjugated hyperbilirubinemia. Since conjugated bilirubin is filtered at the glomerulus, there is an increase in urine bilirubin. Since the amount of bilirubin reaching the gut has decreased, the production of urobilinogen decreases and therefore urine urobilinogen is low.

Inherited Disorders of Bilirubin Metabolism

Apart from Gilbert's syndrome, all of these disorders are rare or very rare.

Gilbert's syndrome is a mild unconjugated hyperbilirubinemia which is associated with a decrease in hepatic conjugating activity. The condition is benign and usually presents between the ages of 10 and 30 y. Bilirubin concentrations rarely exceed about 100 µmol/L (6 mg/dL) and are usually less than 50 µmol/L (3 mg/dL). The bilirubin concentration is increased by fasting and reduced by phenobarbitone administration, which induces the hepatic conjugating enzyme. Although these observations can be used as the basis of confirmatory tests for the syndrome, usually diagnosis is by exclusion. Once all hematological and hepatic causes of hyperbilirubinemia have been eliminated, Gilbert's syndrome remains the only diagnosis left. Recently a genetic basis for this disease has been described[8] as the insertion of an additional TA in the regulatory TATA box upstream of the promoter for the UDP glucuronosyl transferase gene. The clinical usefulness of this as a test for Gilbert's syndrome remains to be established. The incidence of the syndrome has been estimated at 3–7%, with a male-to-female ratio between 2 to 1 and 7 to 1.

Crigler-Najjar syndrome is an inherited deficiency of the hepatic conjugating enzyme. In the rare Type 1, whose mode of inheritance is autosomal recessive, the enzyme is completely absent. This leads to a severe unconjugated hyperbilirubinemia (bilirubin > 340 µmol/L [20 mg/dL]), which is recognized within a few days of birth. Without intensive treatment, death from the neurological sequelae of kernicterus invariably occurs by age 18 m. However, with continuous phototherapy with or without plasmapheresis, patients can survive much longer. The only hope of cure is liver transplantation.

In Type 2 Crigler-Najjar syndrome, a partial deficiency of the enzyme leads to a less severe unconjugated hyperbilirubinemia (bilirubin 100–340 µmol/L [6–20 mg/dL]), which is usually recognized within the first year of life. It is probably inherited in an autosomal-dominant fashion, but with incomplete penetrance. It does not usually lead to clinical problems, but treatment with phenobarbitone will induce the conjugating enzyme and reduce the serum bilirubin concentration and thus the jaundice. Intermittent phototherapy for the first few months of life will further reduce the possibility of any clinically relevant hyperbilirubinemia.

Dubin-Johnson syndrome is predominantly a conjugated hyperbilirubinemia with about 60% of the total bilirubin being "direct" reacting. Jaundice is recognized by puberty in half of the cases and by age 20 y in two thirds. Bilirubin is usually less than 90 μmol/L (5 mg/dL) but can be up to 400 μmol/L (23 mg/dL). It is generally a benign disorder which is inherited in an autosomal-recessive fashion. Bilirubin is taken up and conjugated normally by the liver, but conjugated bilirubin fails to be excreted into bile. Thus, bilirubin is retained in the liver and regurgitated into blood. A characteristic bromosulfophthalein (BSP) test (discussed on page 93), in which BSP disappears normally from blood by 45 min but reappears at about 90 min, is pathognomonic for the syndrome. It is associated with a highly pigmented liver, presumably due to the accumulation of bilirubin metabolites. It is also associated with an abnormality of coproporphyrin excretion. Although the total urine coproporphyrin excretion is normal, 80–90% of it is in the form of coproporphyrin 1, whereas the usual proportion is 25%.

Rotor's syndrome is similar to the Dubin-Johnson syndrome in being a benign conjugated hyperbilirubinemia and has many similar features, including mode of inheritance, age at recognition, and degree of hyperbilirubinemia. However, the liver is not pigmented and the BSP test, in common with other hepatobiliary disorders, shows a reduction in clearance and no regurgitation. Urinary excretion of coproporphyrin is increased, with 60% being coproporphyrin I, which is similar to that of other hepatobiliary disorders and presumably reflects increased urinary excretion as a result of impaired hepatic excretion.

Tests of Hepatocellular Damage

Hepatocyte damage can occur in a variety of ways. Irrespective of the cause, when any individual cell is irreversibly damaged, its plasma membrane loses its integrity, allowing its soluble cytoplasmic contents to leak out and enter blood. The more complete the destruction, the more complete the release, and severe damage is associated with the leaking of the contents of intracellular organelles such as mitochondria. Thus, in theory, any of a number of the soluble components of the hepatocyte cytoplasm could be used as a marker of hepatocyte damage. A number of factors need to be considered when selecting a marker. An ideal marker would be easy and quick to measure, would be specific to the liver, and would have serum activity that reflects the severity of the damage. Markers with different plasma half-lives would be useful. One with a very short half-life would be useful for detecting recent and continuing liver disease, while one with a longer half-life would be useful in excluding liver disease.

The Transferases

The transferases are the most commonly used markers of hepatocellular damage and are quick and easy to measure. Hepatocytes contain both aspartate aminotransferase (AST) and alanine aminotransferase (ALT). ALT is not present to any great extent in tissues other than liver, so it is a more specific marker of liver disease. Within the liver it exhibits a periportal to perivenous gradient, and within the cell it is located exclusively in the cytoplasm. It has a plasma half-life of about 47 ± 10 h.

AST is present in liver, cardiac muscle, and skeletal muscle. There are both cytoplasmic and mitochondrial forms of the enzyme. The cytoplasmic form of the enzyme exhibits a periportal to perivenous gradient, but the mitochondrial enzyme is uniformly distributed. It has a plasma half–life of 17 ± 5 h.

In view of its specificity, ALT is the preferred marker of hepatocellular damage. However, in circumstances in which the origin of the enzyme is not in doubt, the shorter half-life of AST may be advantageous. For instance, it may be that AST is superior in the detection of new liver disease in the presence of existing liver disease, although formal studies to demonstrate this have not been performed.

Alpha-Glutathione S-Transferase

This is a cytoplasmic enzyme which is also largely liver specific. It is the most sensitive indicator of hepatocellular damage.[9] However, it is slow and expensive to measure, and therefore the test is not readily available. It has a very short half-life (less than 1 h) and is therefore excellent for detecting new liver disease.

Other Enzymes

Attempts have been made to detect zone-specific liver damage with zone-specific liver enzymes. Fructose 1,6-bisphosphatase and glutamate dehydrogenase have been used for this purpose. However, they are as yet untested, particularly in the pediatric setting.

Lactate dehydrogenase is not generally used as a marker of liver damage. However, it is present in the liver cytoplasm and will be increased in all circumstances in which ALT is increased. The liver contains the LD5 isoenzyme and is not measured in the specific LD1 assays used for the detection of myocardial infarction.

Serum Markers of Enzyme Induction and Release

These markers, such as alkaline phosphatase (ALP), gamma-glutamyl transpeptidase (GGT), and 5′-nucleotidase (5NT), are membrane-bound enzymes in the hepatocyte. They are not soluble and do not leak out of the cell when the plasma membrane is damaged; therefore, they are not good markers of hepatocellular damage. Increases in serum of the activity of soluble forms of these enzymes often accompany cholestasis. The exact mechanism of release of these enzymes is not known, but it is associated with hepatic induction of the enzyme (i.e., the total activity within the liver increases). 5NT is a relatively liver-specific enzyme, but its measurement in serum is not routinely performed, having been superseded by GGT. Although GGT is found in tissues other than the liver, including the kidney,[10] in practice the liver is usually the source of significant increases in serum GGT. An elevated serum GGT is a sensitive indicator of liver disease where induction (by anticonvulsants and alcohol) can be excluded.

Since ALP is found in tissues other than liver, an increase in its serum activity is not specific for liver disorder. Increases occur most notably in bone disease. However, in bone disease the increase is of a different isoenzyme from that which increases in liver disease. The different isoenzymes of ALP can be distinguished, if necessary, by a variety of techniques including electrophoresis. Alternatively, the bone isoenzyme can be measured specifically using an immunological assay.[11]

The interpretation of ALP results is complicated by the fact that there are two methods for its analysis commonly in use, one which uses diethanolamine (DEA) as its buffer and another which uses amino methyl propanol (AMP) as its buffer, and that the results of the former are approximately double those of the latter. Interpretation is further complicated by the changes in reference ranges with age.[12–14] ALP levels in neonates, particularly in premature neonates, are up to five times the upper limit of the normal reference range for adults (ULN). Older infants (from age 6 m) and prepubertal children have ALPs two- to threefold the ULN. The growth spurt occurring at puberty (any time from age 10 y onwards) increases the reference range to fivefold the ULN. These changes are due to increases in the serum activity of the bone isoenzyme. In the absence of disease, the serum activity of the liver isoenzyme remains fairly constant.

Induction and release of enzymes is not always pathological, and this can complicate interpretation. In particular, long-term administration of anticonvulsant drugs induces GGT. This does not usually affect ALP.

Other Biochemical Tests

Albumin

Serum albumin measurement has traditionally been considered to be a useful biochemical test of liver disease. However, it has poor sensitivity and specificity. The large reserve synthetic capacity of the liver means that severe liver disease is required to reduce albumin synthesis. This, coupled with the relatively long half-life (20 d) means that reduction in serum albumin is rare in acute liver disease. In chronic liver disease, the causes of the reduction in serum albumin which is observed are multifactorial. The poor specificity of a low serum albumin for liver disease is a result of its being non-specifically low in a number of disorders. It behaves as a negative acute phase reactant. Thus, its synthesis is reduced while those of positive acute phase reactants such as α_1-antitrypsin are increased. It can also be reduced as a result of increased loss in the urine or gut or hypervolemia. Despite these limitations, it can be of some use. For instance, a normal serum albumin makes the diagnosis of cirrhosis unlikely.[15]

Other Proteins

Immunoglobulins can be increased in chronic liver disease with a predominate increase in IgG in autoimmune liver disease. IgM is raised in viral hepatitis. Specific liver disorders associated with low ceruloplasmin or α_1-antitrypsin are described below. An elevated α-fetoprotein is found in primary hepatoma and during the first 12 m of life.[16]

Other Markers

In extremely severe liver disease, urea and glucose may be low and ammonia may be high, but these are poor tests of liver function. It is seldom worthwhile to measure ammonia in liver disease. The degree of elevation does not correlate with the degree of encephalopathy, and any child who is encephalopathic due to liver disease will have elevated ammonia. Ammonia is of course worth measuring in the investigation of Reye's syndrome (discussed on page 103) and in the investigation of suspected inborn errors of metabolism.

Dynamic Tests of Liver Function

A number of dynamic function tests have been described. In these, a bolus of a substance which is metabolized by the liver is given (usually intravenously) and samples of blood or breath are taken at timed intervals afterwards. The disappearance of the substance or the appearance of its metabolite is measured. The first such test described was that of bromosulfophthalein (BSP) clearance. This is rarely performed except in the investigation of the Dubin-Johnson syndrome. BSP is given as a bolus intravenous injection and its blood concentration is measured at intervals thereafter. It is taken up, conjugated, and excreted exactly as is bilirubin; therefore, it is cleared from the blood in a predictably time-dependent manner. In liver disease, its clearance is decreased.

Indocyanine green is an organic ion which can be used in the same way as BSP. Other such tests include the ^{14}C-aminopyrine breath test, in which $^{14}CO_2$ is monitored in breath following IV injection and the monoethylglycinexylidide (MEGX) test. MEGX is a metabolite of lidocaine given as an intravenous bolus. None of these tests is routinely performed.

BIOCHEMICAL CHANGES IN LIVER DISEASE

Typical changes in liver function tests in hemolysis, hepatitis, and obstructive liver disease are shown in Table 4–2. As mentioned previously, these changes are rarely diagnostic, and in many disorders a mixed pattern is demonstrated.

TABLE 4–2. Typical Changes in Liver Function Tests in Different Disease States

	Bilirubin	Alkaline Phosphatase	Alanine Aminotransferase
Hemolysis	↑	N	N
Obstructive Liver Disease	↑	↑	N
Hepatocellular Liver Disease	↑	N/↑	↑

↑= Increased N = Normal

Investigations of liver disease in childhood are usually divided into neonates and older infants/children. In all age groups, jaundice is an important sign of liver disease, but it is not always present. This term is used to describe a yellowing of the eyes and skin caused by the accumulation of bilirubin. There is some discrepancy in the literature as to the serum concentration of bilirubin at which jaundice becomes apparent. In children and adults, concentrations of 34–50 μmol/L (2–3 mg/dL) are cited; in neonates, higher concentrations of 85–150 μmol/L (5–8.8 mg/dL) are given.

NEONATAL JAUNDICE

In full-term infants, jaundice appearing before 2 d or persisting/appearing after 10 d requires further investigation. Estimation of total bilirubin and "direct" bilirubin is useful in this age group, despite technical problems with the measurement of the latter fraction. Presence of bilirubin in urine on dipstick testing is a sensitive indicator of elevated conjugated bilirubin; the urine will be dark and stools pale. Kelly[17] quotes 25% conjugated bilirubinemia as suspicious of liver disease. Mowat[18] considers an elevated total bilirubin, with more than 15% "direct reacting," to be significant, but points out that results should be interpreted in conjunction with urinalysis and conventional LFTs.

High concentrations of unconjugated, lipid-soluble bilirubin are toxic to the brain, causing kernicterus. Treatment involves phototherapy and/or exchange transfusion, depending on the severity and rate of increase. Phototherapy produces stereoisomers of bilirubin which are excreted in the bile without conjugation.

Causes of neonatal hyperbilirubinemia are listed in Table 4–3.

TABLE 4–3. Causes of Neonatal Hyperbilirubinemia

Unconjugated	Conjugated
Physiological (transient, appears day 1–2, resolves day 7–10 in term babies)	Cholestasis/liver disease
Severe bruising	Infection
Breast milk jaundice	Inherited disorders (see Table 4–4)
Hemolysis	Rare endocrine disorders
Inherited disorders of bilirubin conjugation	Total parental nutrition
Hypothyroidism	Drugs

Unconjugated Hyperbilirubinemia

Physiological Jaundice

Physiological jaundice occurs in up to 50% of normal babies. The jaundice becomes apparent after age 1–2 d and usually fades by age 7–10 d. These babies are otherwise well and thriving. In bottle-fed babies, serum bilirubin values are usually less than 200 µmol/L (11.7 mg/dL); in breast-fed babies, values are slightly higher. Even higher values may occur in premature infants; values peak later and may persist for up to 14 d. Several factors have been implicated, such as liver immaturity, increased bilirubin load from a reduced red cell survival, and reabsorption of bilirubin from the gut. Physiological jaundice may be exacerbated by additional problems, such as bruising at birth, dehydration, and infection.

Hemolysis

The appearance of jaundice within the first 48 h of life is likely to be due to a hemolytic cause. In developed countries, blood-group incompatibilities between the mother and child are now rare due to the use of anti-D immunoglobulin to prevent sensitization to the D antigen of the rhesus blood group system. ABO and other rare blood group incompatibilities can also produce hemolytic disease. A number of inherited abnormalities of the red cell may also present in this way, including spherocytosis, glucose-6-phosphate dehydrogenase deficiency, pyruvate kinase deficiency, and red cell membrane defects.

Breast Milk Jaundice Syndrome

A small proportion (approximately 2.5%) of breast-fed babies develop a prolonged unconjugated hyperbilirubinemia known as breast milk jaundice syndrome. Bilirubin values may be as high as 300 µmol/L (17.5 mg/dL). The jaundice resolves if breast milk is discontinued for a few days, and it is usually possible to restart breastfeeding without recurrence of jaundice or with only mild hyperbilirubinemia developing. It was thought that breast milk from mothers of affected babies contained high concentrations of an inhibitor(s) of glucuronyl transferase. The steroid 3α-30β-pregnanediol, free fatty acids, and milk lipase activity have been implicated, but there is poor correlation between milk concentrations and the degree of jaundice. More recent reports focus on β-glucuronidase activity in milk and increased reabsorption of hydrolyzed bilirubin glucuronide from the gut.

Hypothyroidism

Hypothyroidism is usually associated with prolonged unconjugated jaundice. This will be identified in neonatal screening programs or can easily be investigated by measurement of serum free thyroxine and thyroid stimulating hormone (TSH). Typically, the TSH is grossly increased, with values greater than 100 mU/L.

More detail on age-related values for thyroid function tests is given in Chapter 8, "Disorders of the Thyroid Gland."

Inherited Disorders

Inherited disorders of bilirubin metabolism causing unconjugated hyperbilirubinemia are discussed on page 89.

Conjugated Hyperbilirubinemia

Conjugated bilirubin in the neonate is always pathological and arises from a variety of causes.

Obstructive Jaundice

The main causes of extra hepatic biliary obstruction in the neonate are biliary atresia and choledochal cyst. Biochemical tests show a predominantly conjugated hyperbilirubinemia with raised liver enzymes. Biochemical tests are used to confirm liver disease and assess the severity. Diagnosis relies on ultrasound, technetium scan, biopsy, and ultimately laparotomy.

Infection

Many viral and bacterial infections cause hepatitis in the neonate. Investigation requires bacterial culture of blood and urine and viral serology. Serum IgM is raised in neonatal infection, whereas healthy infants have very low amounts of this immunoglobulin. The reference range up to the age of 2 w is 0.05–0.2 g/L.

Inherited Disorders

Several inherited metabolic disorders may present with a conjugated hyperbilirubinemia and raised liver enzymes in the neonate. Examples are given in Table 4–4. The table and the discussion that follows do not include presumed inherited conditions for which the biochemical basis is unknown, such as Byler disease and Alagille's syndrome. These disorders are discussed by Riely.[19]

α_1-Antitrypsin deficiency is a common inherited condition which may account for up to 40% of cases of neonatal hepatitis. α_1-antitrypsin (AAT) is a plasma glycoprotein synthesized by the liver. It has a low molecular weight of 52 KDa, permitting entry into tissue spaces. It is a member of the SERPIN family (serine protease inhibitors),[20] and its main function is the inhibition of neutrophil elastase. Elastase breaks down a number of proteins but has highest affinity for elastin, which is found

TABLE 4–4. Examples of Inherited Disorders which May Present with Neonatal Jaundice

Galactosemia	Tyrosinemia Type 1
Hereditary fructose intolerance	Zellweger's Syndrome
Cystic fibrosis	α_1-antitrypsin deficiency
Niemann-Pick Type C	Defects in bile acid synthesis

in the lungs. AAT contains an exposed site which mimics the enzyme's ideal substrate and prevents lung damage by binding elastase. Once bound, the entire complex is removed from the circulation and metabolized.[21]

AAT is encoded by a single gene on chromosome 14q32:1. The alleles are inherited co-dominantly. There are many genetic variants, originally assigned letters according to their mobility on starch gel electrophoresis. More than 75 variants are now known,[22] which necessitates addition of subscripts to the letters. The most common phenotype is protease inhibitor M (PI M). The majority of phenotypes give rise to functional AAT and normal serum concentrations. The clinically relevant phenotypes result in low or absent serum values or, very rarely, in functional change. AAT deficiency is associated with emphysema as a result of increased proteolytic damage to the lungs. In some phenotypes (PI Z, M_{MALTON}, M_{DUARTE}), AAT accumulates in the hepatocyte.

The ZZ genotype has been extensively studied and is known to be associated with liver disease. This genotype is relatively common with an incidence of between 1 in 1660 and 1 in 7000 in Caucasian populations of North European descent. The Z protein differs from the M protein by one amino acid and also differs in the composition of carbohydrate sidechains. It is synthesized at the normal rate, but only a small proportion is secreted by the hepatocyte. Plasma concentrations are approximately 15% of normal. Some of the newly synthesized Z protein is degraded and the remainder accumulates in the endoplasmic reticulum, predominantly in the periportal regions of the liver.

Approximately 15% of individuals with the Z phenotype present with neonatal hepatitis, or more rarely hemorrhagic disease. Biochemical abnormalities include increased bilirubin, aminotransferases, and alkaline phosphatase. Clinically and biochemically, the presentation may be indistinguishable from biliary atresia. Other patients with the Z phenotype may present later in childhood or adulthood with chronic liver disease and no reliable history of neonatal illness. Of the infants with neonatal hepatitis, about 30% progress to cirrhosis and death by age 20 y, approximately 5% of these in the first year. By age 10 y, approximately 45% have clinical and/or biochemical evidence of liver disease. Liver disease resolves in the remainder.

Quantitation of AAT is simple using immunochemical methods, but interpretation must take account of other factors that can increase AAT values. AAT is increased up to fourfold in the acute phase response to tissue injury, and, although not relevant to children, is increased by estrogens arising from pregnancy or oral contraceptives. In adults, the M phenotype gives a reference range of approximately 1–2 g/L. In young children, values are slightly lower.

AAT values may be low in hepatic necrosis and in protein-losing states. Absence of an AAT band is obvious on routine serum electrophoresis, but phenotyping should be undertaken using isoelectric focusing,[23] often in conjunction with immunofixation. Family studies are required to confirm the ZZ genotype. PCR methods are available and can be used for prenatal diagnosis.

Although all ZZ individuals accumulate AAT in hepatocytes, only a minority (20–40%) develop clinically significant liver disease. Hence, other factors have been implicated, such as increased hepatic damage from proteases originating from the gut, viruses, or bacteria.

The majority of hypotheses on the etiology of liver disease have concentrated on the intracellular accumulation of AAT. It appears that deficient phenotypes in which accumulation does not occur are not associated with liver disease. Susceptible individuals may have an additional genetic predisposition, such as altered autoimmunity, which acts together with environmental factors.

Perlmutter et al.[24] have found that the synthesis of "heat-shock" or stress proteins is increased in monocytes and hepatocytes (i.e., AAT-synthesizing cells) from PI ZZ individuals with liver disease. "Heat-shock" proteins are involved in the transport of proteins within the cell and the processing of incorrectly folded proteins within the endoplasmic reticulum. It is possible that abnormalities in this system may affect the accumulation of abnormal proteins in the cell, but it is not clear whether the observed differences in ZZ individuals with and without liver disease are cause or effect. Lomas et al.[25] have shown that the Z protein (*in vitro*) polymerizes at normal body temperature. Polymerization is accelerated at higher temperatures and with increased concentrations of protein. Z protein polymerized *in vitro* has an identical structure to AAT isolated from ZZ hepatocytes. On these grounds, it has been suggested that measures to reduce inflammation and fever in ZZ neonates would be wise precautions.

Currently, liver transplantation is the only treatment for chronic liver disease secondary to AAT deficiency. Successful transplantation converts the circulating AAT to the phenotype of the donor. Agents to increase the synthesis of AAT (e.g., tamoxifen, danazol) may worsen intracellular accumulation and are not used. Genetically engineered AAT is available but it is not known whether administration from an early age would affect the outcome of liver disease. Repeat infusions of AAT may improve or hasten liver damage depending on the mechanism(s) involved. Serpin-enzyme complex receptors have been identified on human hepatoma cells and monocytes. These bind AAT-elastase complexes and enhance the synthesis of AAT by feedback mechanisms.[26] Increased concentrations of AAT-elastase complexes from repeat infusion could, in theory, exacerbate accumulation of abnormal protein. Peptides which inhibit the polymerization of AAT may prove useful in the future.[25]

In *tyrosinemia Type 1* there is a deficiency of the enzyme fumarylacetoacetase which converts fumarylacetoacetate to fumarate and acetoacetate. The accumulating fumarylacetoacetate is converted to succinylacetoacetate and thence to succinylacetone. Tyrosine and methionine are increased and the infant may have a "cabbage-like" odor. Diagnosis requires the demonstration of succinylacetone excretion in the urine together with fumarylacetoacetase deficiency in fibroblasts or lymphocytes. The mechanism of liver and renal dysfunction is thought to involve enzyme inhibition by maleylacetoacetate, the precursor of fumarylacetoacetate.

Galactosemia is caused by a deficiency of galactose-1-phosphate uridyl transferase. This enzyme is required for the conversion of galactose (derived from lactose in milk) to glucose. Galactose-1-phosphate accumulates, trapping phosphate. High concentrations of galactose result in the production of potentially toxic compounds such as galactitol (thought to affect the lens of the eye and to be involved in the formation of cataracts) and galactonate, although the mechanism of liver damage is unclear. Urine-reducing substances and sugar chromatography should be undertaken but may give misleading results. In the absence of recent galactose ingestion, results will be negative. Conversely, galactosuria may be present in other forms of liver disease. Nevertheless, the finding of galactose in the urine should prompt withdrawal of lactose from the diet and subsequent assessment of the response of liver markers. Liver and renal dysfunction give rise to a generalized aminoaciduria. Diagnosis is based on the measurement of galactose-1-phosphate uridyl transferase activity in red cells.

Hereditary fructose intolerance is rare in neonates, as this condition does not present until fructose (or sucrose) is introduced into the diet. There is a deficiency in fructaldolase B which converts fructose-1-phosphate to dihydroxyacetone phosphate and D-glyceraldehyde, which can be fed into the glycolytic pathway or gluconeogenesis. This enzyme also reversibly splits fructose-1,6-bisphosphate in glycolysis/gluconeogenesis. Deficiency affects conversion of gluconeogenic precursors such as lactate to glucose. Fructose-1-phosphate accumulates, trapping phosphate. Serum phosphate and glucose may be decreased and plasma lactate increased. Fructose challenge tests are not recommended in infants. The clinical picture and a dietary history provide clues to the diagnosis. Fructosuria may be present if fructose has recently been ingested. Diagnosis requires measurement of fructaldolase B on liver tissue.

Zellweger's syndrome is the classical example of a peroxisomal disorder. Typically, affected babies present with dysmorphic features, hypotonia, and abnormal LFTs. Diagnosis involves the measurement of compounds metabolized or synthesized in peroxisomes, such as plasma very-long-chain fatty acids.

Niemann-Pick Type C is a lysosomal storage disease in which unesterified cholesterol is retained in the lysosomes. Bone marrow and rectal biopsy tissue show characteristic storage cells. Cultured fibroblasts show defective cholesterol esterification.

Cystic fibrosis may rarely present with neonatal hepatitis. This inherited disorder is discussed in more detail on page 121.

Other inherited disorders may present with hepatomegaly with or without raised aminotransferases (e.g., glycogen storage disease Type 1) and evidence of liver damage may be evident in disorders with predominantly a neurological presentation (e.g., urea cycle defects).

Investigation of a possible inherited metabolic disease will include the measurement of plasma lactate and ammonia, urine organic acids, and urine/blood amino acids. Urine orotic acid should be measured in an infant who has hyperammonemia and is suspected of having a urea cycle defect.

Inherited disorders of bilirubin metabolism causing conjugated hyperbilirubinemia are discussed on page 89.

For more information on the clinical presentation and the diagnosis of inborn errors of metabolism in the neonate, the reader is referred to Green and Morgan.[27]

Parenteral Nutrition

Prolonged parenteral nutrition has been associated with cholestatic liver disease in some neonates. This complication is more common in sick, premature infants than in full-term infants.

Endocrine Disorders

A number of rare endocrine abnormalities, including hypopituitarism, diabetes insipidus, hypoadrenalism, and hypoparathyroidism, may also present with jaundice in the neonatal period.

LIVER DISEASE IN OLDER CHILDREN

Infection

Both acute and chronic hepatitis in childhood are most commonly caused by viral infections. Acute infections include the hepatotrophic viruses (hepatitis A, B, C, D [hep-B dependent], and E) and many others, such as cytomegalovirus and Epstein-Barr virus (infectious mononucleosis). There may be hepatic involvement in numerous childhood viral illnesses, such as measles and adenoviruses. The patient may have no symptoms of liver involvement, and this is only detected by raised aminotransferases on liver function testing. Hepatitis B, C, and D can progress to chronic infection.

Results of conventional LFTs will vary depending on the time the specimen is obtained, the chronicity of the infection, and the degree of liver involvement. In acute hepatitis A, the aminotransferases typically are increased up to 4 d prior to the development of jaundice, although bilirubin is detectable in the urine at this stage. The aminotransferases usually peak below 1000 U/L and there is only a slight increase in ALP. Bilirubin is usually less than 350 μmol/L (20.5 mg/dL) and is predominantly conjugated. Increased aminotransferases may persist for several months.

Autoimmune Chronic Active Hepatitis

The presentation of autoimmune chronic active hepatitis varies from acute hepatitis to cirrhosis. Conventional LFTs usually show raised aminotransferases, hyperbilirubinemia, and often a low albumin. IgG is usually above 16 g/L and IgM may be increased. Non-organ-specific autoantibodies are present in most cases.

Inborn Errors of Metabolism

A wide range of inborn errors of metabolism are associated with liver damage. Conditions include urea cycle disorders, defects in fatty acid oxidation and mitochondrial oxidative phosphorylation, amino acid disorders, and glycogen storage diseases. Many of the disorders that present acutely in neonates occur as late-onset forms. The reader is referred to Chapters 16 and 17 for information on the investigation of defects in intermediary metabolism.

Lysosomal Storage Disorders

Lysosomal storage disorders may cause hepatomegaly and/or splenomegaly, together with a range of other features such as coarse facies, skeletal changes, and eye problems. Central nervous system involvement usually predominates. Investigation of lysosomal storage diseases relies heavily on clinical suspicion, as the diagnosis may require examination of bone marrow for storage cells and measurement of specific white cell enzymes.

Cystic Fibrosis

Liver complications are common in cystic fibrosis. Fatty infiltration of the liver is usual on liver biopsy and some 5–10% of adolescents have cirrhosis. Cystic fibrosis is discussed on page 121 in the section on intestinal disease.

α_1-Antitrypsin Deficiency

α_1-Antitrypsin deficiency (ZZ genotype) may present with liver disease in the older child. This condition is discussed on page 96 in the section on neonatal jaundice.

Wilson's Disease

Wilson's disease is an inherited disorder of copper metabolism. Inheritance is autosomal recessive with an incidence of 1 in 30,000. The gene has been mapped to chromosome 13q14:3 and encodes for a copper-transporting ATPase, similar to the protein affected in Menkes' disease.[28] In Wilson's disease, excretion of copper into the bile is defective and usually serum concentrations of the copper-containing protein ceruloplasmin are reduced. Copper accumulates in the liver and, once the hepatic storage capacity is overwhelmed, affects other tissues including the brain and kidneys. Early diagnosis is important, since without treatment the condition is fatal. Clinical presentation of Wilson's disease is variable. Although rare, it should be suspected in any child over the age of 5 y with unexplained liver disease and/or hemolytic anemia, and in older children with undiagnosed neurological abnormalities.

Any form of liver disease, acute or chronic hepatitis, cirrhosis, or fulminant liver failure may be the presenting feature in children with Wilson's disease. Diagnosis still relies on biochemical tests and careful examination of the eyes for evidence of copper deposition (Kayser-Fleischer rings). Kayser-Fleischer rings are virtually pathognomonic for Wilson's disease but may not be present in young children, so negative findings do not rule out the diagnosis. They are occasionally seen in severe cholestatic disease. Ceruloplasmin is below the reference range (0.2–0.6 g/L) in approximately 80% of patients. This protein may also be low in protein-losing states and fulminant hepatic failure from other causes. Conversely, ceruloplasmin is an acute phase protein and a low value associated with Wilson's disease may be increased into the normal range by increased synthesis during inflammation. Estrogens (from pregnancy and oral contraceptives) also increase the serum concentrations. Values in neonates are low (0.08–0.23 g/L in infants under 4 m), hampering diagnosis in siblings of affected children. Up to 20% of heterozygotes have low serum ceruloplasmin concentrations.

Baseline urine copper excretion is increased in the majority of cases, but false negatives and false positives do occur. Urine copper excretion is generally in excess of 64 μg/24 h (1.0 μmol/24 h) in Wilson's disease. Liver copper values are increased, with concentrations in excess of 250 μg/g dry weight (the normal range is 15–50 μg/g). Heterozygotes have intermediate values. However, there is overlap with other liver diseases, and the patient's clinical state and deranged clotting may exclude biopsy. In a study of 75 children with liver disease, da Costa et al.[29] found the penicillamine challenge test to be more specific than ceruloplasmin, liver copper, or baseline urine copper excretion in the diagnosis of Wilson's disease. Urine copper excretion pre- and post-penicillamine is assessed. In Wilson's disease urine copper excretion is greater than 1.6 mg/24 h (25 μmol/24 h) after 1 g of penicillamine (500 mg given before the start of the collection and a second dose 12 h later).

DNA methods that use flanking microsatellite markers are available and can be used in family studies.[30] Direct mutation analysis is difficult as there are a large number of mutations and most patients are compound heterozygotes. Two mutations account for approximately 38% of mutations in European patients.[31]

Treatment with the copper-chelating agent D-penicillamine is effective. Side effects may be a problem and alternative therapy includes the chelator trientine (triethylene tetramine dihydrochloride) and the use of zinc to reduce copper absorption. Patients should avoid foods containing high concentrations of copper (e.g., chocolate, broccoli, nuts). Discontinuation of therapy can have disastrous results, with irreversible liver damage occurring in a relatively short period.

Inherited Disorders

Inherited disorders of bilirubin metabolism are discussed on page 89.

Drugs

The liver receives a large volume of blood from the gut and is the main site for detoxification of ingested compounds. As such, it is especially vulnerable to damage from drugs and toxins. More than 500 drugs that cause liver damage have been reported in the literature. Some examples are given in Table 4–5. Drugs causing hepatocyte damage are divided into those producing predictable (often dose-dependent) reactions and those producing non-predictable reactions. Hepatic drug toxicity may take the form of any type of liver disease (including cancer), and conventional LFTs may show a cholestatic, hepatitic, or mixed pattern. Clinically, hepatic drug toxicity may resemble viral hepatitis. Drugs may affect a range of hepatic functions, such as bile production and transport within the cell or across cell membranes. Free radicals may be produced which inactivate enzymes and damage cell membranes, which in turn may trigger immunological responses. Some drugs are metabolized to reactive species; the extent of the damage will depend on the dose and the rate of metabolism. Toxicity may be influenced by the nutritional status of the individual and by enzyme induction. Idiosyncratic drug reactions occur in a very small number of patients given a particular drug. The mechanism is unclear but may result from an immunological response in affected individuals or alterations in metabolism.

TABLE 4–5. Drugs that May Cause Abnormal Liver Function

Drug	Example(s)
Steroid drugs	Oral contraceptives
Antibiotics	Sulfonamides, penicillin, tetracycline
Anticonvulsants	Carbamazepine, phenytoin
Anesthetics	Halothane
Analgesics	Salicylate, acetaminophen
Cytotoxics	Cyclophosphamide, 6-mercaptopurine
Antituberculous drugs	Rifampicin, isoniazid

Drugs producing predictable hepatotoxicity include cytotoxics, salicylate, acetaminophen (paracetamol), and ferrous sulfate. Metabolism of acetaminophen produces reactive compounds which damage the hepatocyte. The perivenular regions of the liver are rich in drug-metabolizing enzymes and are relatively anoxic. In less severe poisoning the damage tends to be perivenular, but with higher doses generalized hepatic necrosis occurs. In severe cases, renal failure develops. Liver damage is detectable 2–3 d after ingestion by increases in aminotransferases and bilirubin. Acetaminophen and iron overdose and treatment are discussed in Chapter 21, "Therapeutic Drug Monitoring and Clinical Toxicology in a Pediatric Hospital."

A small number of patients (approximately 1%) given sodium valproate develop symptomatic hyperammonemia yet have normal conventional LFTs. It has been proposed that drug metabolites inhibit carbamyl phosphate transferase and hence the urea cycle. Patients who develop hyperammonemia when given sodium valproate should be investigated for a possible underlying defect in this cycle.[32]

Many solvents are associated with liver damage, including those inhaled by "glue-sniffing" (e.g., toluene, trichloroethylene). Drugs of abuse such as cocaine and heroine may produce increased serum aminotransferases. Others may also be hepatotoxic or may be "cut" with toxic compounds. Hepatotoxic effects of alcohol should not be forgotten in the pediatric context.

Reye's Syndrome

Reye's syndrome is an acute non-inflammatory encephalopathy with liver dysfunction. It can occur at any age but most often in childhood. It is a rare but serious disorder with a high mortality, and a large percentage of survivors suffer permanent brain damage. Typically, vomiting and altered consciousness develop in a child who appears to be recovering from a common viral illness such as influenza or chicken pox. The patient is not usually jaundiced and there are no clinical signs of liver disease. Approximately 30% of children have convulsions. There may be spontaneous recovery or progression to coma and brain death. Death in Reye's syndrome is a result of marked cerebral edema. There is fatty infiltration of the liver and other organs including muscle. The liver has a characteristic appearance on biopsy. Electron microscopy shows abnormalities in mitochondrial structure and many of the

TABLE 4–6. Changes in the Serum Concentrations of Intermediary Metabolites in Reye's Syndrome

Glucose	low
Lactate	raised
Triglycerides	raised
Free fatty acids	raised
Ammonia	raised
Ketones	raised

biochemical changes are consistent with generalized mitochondrial dysfunction. Liver aminotransferases are high—at least three times the upper limit of normal—with increased serum ammonia and, in severe cases, hypoglycemia. Prothrombin time is prolonged. Creatine kinase is increased and in severely affected children may be greater than ten times the upper limit. In survivors, the mitochondria recover and liver function tests return to normal in up to 6 d. There is derangement of many intermediary metabolites, consistent with reduced energy production by the mitochondria (see Table 4–6). Uncontrolled lipolysis and reduced β-oxidation result in high concentrations of free fatty acids, which in turn are converted to dicarboxylic acids and excreted in the urine. The encephalopathy is thought to be caused by compounds normally detoxified by the liver, including ammonia, mercaptans, fatty acids, and neurotransmitter substances.

The diagnosis of classical Reye's syndrome is reserved for cases in which there is no obvious cause for the cerebral edema and liver dysfunction. Other causes of coma with abnormalities of liver function tests, such as severe infections and prolonged hypoxia, should be ruled out.

It is now known that several inborn errors of metabolism may present with a Reye's syndrome-like illness that presents a similar clinical, biochemical, and histological picture (Table 4–7). Medium-chain acyl-CoA dehydrogenase deficiency is the most commonly identified. In this condition, ketones are inappropriately low relative to the free fatty acid concentration. Organic acid disorders, urea cycle de-

TABLE 4–7. Inborn Errors of Metabolism Presenting with a Reye's Syndrome-like Illness

Ornithine transcarbamylase deficiency	Glutaric aciduria type 2
Carbamyl phosphate synthetase deficiency	Biotinidase deficiency
Late-onset citrullinemia	Isovaleric acidemia
Medium-chain acyl-CoA dehydrogenase deficiency	Ethylmalonic adipic aciduria
Primary carnitine deficiency	Fructose-1,6-diphosphatase deficiency
Long-chain acyl-CoA dehydrogenase deficiency	Propionic acidemia
Carnitine palmitoyl transferase deficiency	α_1-antitrypsin deficiency
3-hydroxy, 3-methylglutaryl-CoA lyase deficiency	Pyruvate dehydrogenase deficiency
Methylmalonic aciduria	

fects, and a host of others have been reported as presenting in this way. Clues that an inborn error is present include positive family history, consanguinity, or a history of similar episodes, but all children with a Reye's syndrome-like illness need expert investigation for an underlying metabolic disorder. It is important to make the diagnosis so that appropriate treatment is given and counseling is made available to the parents on the likelihood of subsequent pregnancies being affected. If death is likely, blood specimens and urine should be collected and arrangements made for the collection of tissue samples into appropriate medium.[33]

Drugs and toxins have also been implicated in the development of Reye's syndrome-like illnesses. Much attention has focused on salicylate, and the general use of aspirin for children under age 12 y has been limited as a safeguard.

Benign Transient Hyperphosphatasemia (Idiopathic Hyperphosphatasemia of Infancy)

Transient marked increases in serum ALP are not uncommon in children.[34] These increases are apparently benign, with no clinical or biochemical evidence of liver or bone disease, and typically occur in children under age 5 y. Stein et al.[35] reported an increase in ALP ranging from 3- to 56-fold (median 15-fold) in a series of 21 cases. Crofton[34] found a seasonal variation in the incidence in a series of 35 children. Electrophoresis shows a diffuse band corresponding to the bone isoenzyme and a second band intermediate in mobility to the main liver band and "biliary" ALP. Results of inhibitor, heat, neuraminidase, sialidase, and lectin treatment are consistent with the second band being a liver isoenzyme with increased sialylation. The increased sialic acid content of the liver isoenzyme may slow the hepatic clearance. The etiology is uncertain and induction by viral infection has been proposed. The enzyme activity usually falls to normal within 4 m.

Acute Liver Failure

Acute liver failure may occur at any age from a variety of causes such as viral infection, drugs, inborn errors of metabolism, and autoimmune disease.

LIVER TRANSPLANTATION

Orthotopic liver transplantation is now a therapeutic option for acute and chronic liver disease and certain inborn errors of metabolism.[36] In children, biliary atresia is the most common indication, followed by cirrhosis associated with AAT deficiency. The inborn errors of metabolism include conditions with direct liver involvement, some with high potential of malignant change (e.g., tyrosinemia Type 1), or diseases in which the liver is not affected directly but transplantation prevents toxic damage to other organs; such diseases include primary hyperoxaluria Type 1, homozygous familial hypercholesterolemia, and Crigler-Najjar Type 1. Other inherited disorders in which liver transplantation has been undertaken include Byler disease (familial cholestasis), Wilson's disease, cystic fibrosis, defects of fatty acid oxidation, urea cycle defects, and glycogen storage diseases 1, 3 and 4.

Timing of transplantation is important. Outcome is poorer in patients who are critically ill at transplantation. However, because the risks of liver transplantation are considerable, there is a reluctance to transplant a relatively well child. Children should be referred to specialist centers early so that their clinical progress can be carefully monitored and the option of transplantation considered before liver decompensation or malignancy occurs. Prior to transplantation, conventional LFTs (bilirubin, ALT, AST, albumin) may be completely normal or grossly abnormal, depending on the underlying disease for which transplantation is indicated. For detailed discussion of indications, contra-indications, and timing of the operation, the reader is referred to Mowat.[37] Donors are matched for blood group, size, and, whenever possible, cytomegalovirus status. The donor's LFTs should be normal. The use of "reduced livers"—liver segments from larger donors—has increased the number of transplants in children. In some centers, liver lobes from living, related donors, usually a parent, have been used.

During the operation there is frequent monitoring of acid/base status, electrolytes, glucose, and ionized calcium, often using instruments in the operating room. After surgery, the child will be ventilated for a variable length of time and nursed in an intensive care unit. In the early stages, conventional LFTs, acid/base status, and glucose are closely monitored. In the immediate post-operative period, liver aminotransferases are usually markedly increased (approximately 1000 IU/L, higher if a reduced liver has been transplanted), but in the absence of complications, enzymes fall to normal within a week or two.

There are many potentially life-threatening complications that may occur after transplantation. Early complications include primary graft nonfunction, acute rejection, thrombosis, and infection. Later, chronic, irreversible ductopenic rejection may be a problem. Complications may necessitate regrafting. Approximately 15% of recipients do not survive the first year; in subsequent years, the annual death rate is much lower at 1–2%. The majority of recipients usually have normal growth and development.

Life-long immunosuppression is required to prevent graft rejection. Cyclosporine is the main treatment, usually in combination with corticosteroids and, in some centers, azathioprine. Antilymphocytic antibody preparations, such as the monoclonal anti-T cell antibody OKT3, are used to treat steroid-resistant rejection. Cyclosporine is a lipophilic cyclic peptide isolated from the fungus *Tolypocladium inflatumgams*. It reduces T cell mediated attack by inhibiting cytokine production at an early point in T cell activation. Unfortunately, cyclosporine has a number of important side effects, including hepatic, renal, and neurotoxicity. Blood concentrations after oral administration are highly variable, especially in liver transplant recipients, in whom both absorption and clearance of the drug will be affected by changes in liver function. Monitoring is required to maintain therapeutic concentrations while minimizing side effects.

Tacrolimus (FK-506) is a newer immunosuppressive drug that is isolated from the soil fungus *Streptomyces tsukubaensis*. It differs in structure from cyclosporine and is more potent, but appears to act in a similar way. Methods are available for measuring plasma and whole-blood concentrations. Studies comparing tacrolimus and cyclosporine as the primary immunosuppressive therapy in *de novo* liver transplant recipients have shown that tacrolimus reduces the incidence of acute, steroid-resistant, and chronic rejection at the expense of a higher incidence of toxic side effects.[38] Therapeutic drug monitoring of cyclosporine and tacrolimus is discussed in Chapter 21.

Numerous tests, including conventional LFTs, are used to monitor allograft function. As in any other clinical situation, these tests are not specific for a particular type of liver damage (e.g., rejection), and interpretation may be difficult. Many other investigations—ultrasound, cholangiography, angiography, liver biopsy, viral and microbiological studies—may be required to identify the cause of disordered LFTs. α-Glutathione-S-transferase (GST) may prove to be a useful marker of liver cell damage in this situation. GST concentrations fall more rapidly than aminotransferases following uncomplicated transplantation as well as in successful treatment of acute rejection.[9] Figure 4–5 shows the time course of GST and conventional LFTs in a child after liver transplantation.

THE INTESTINAL TRACT

Normal Absorption

The digestion and absorption of food requires the concerted interaction of all parts of the gastrointestinal (GI) tract (Figure 4–6). The macromolecules of fat, carbohy-

FIGURE 4–5. Post-operative Changes in Liver Function Tests in a Pediatric Liver Transplant Recipient

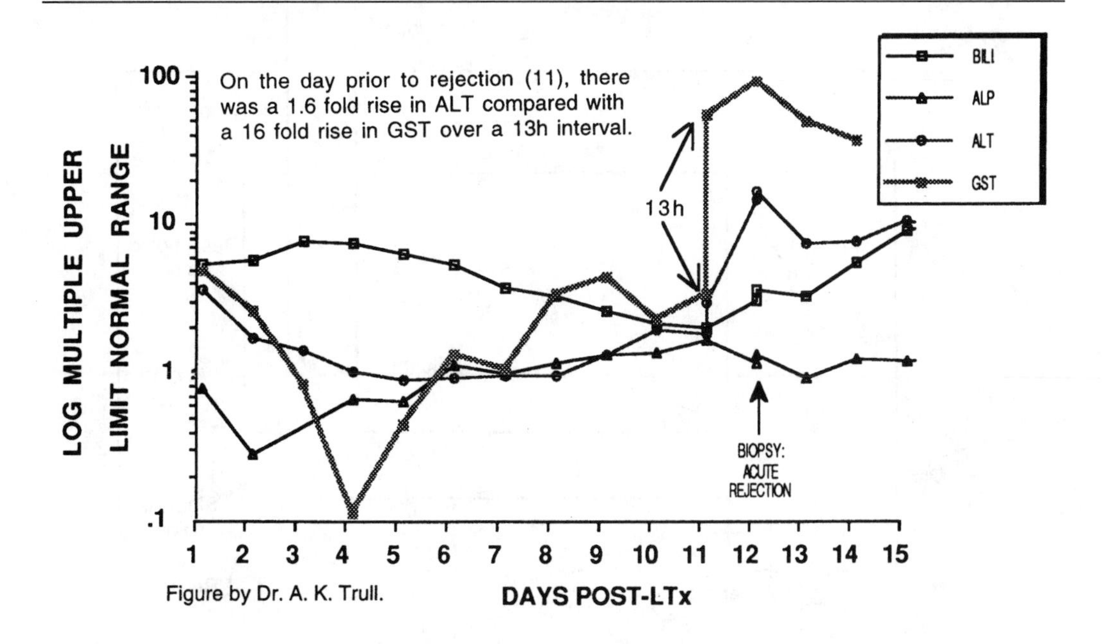

Figure by Dr. A. K. Trull.

FIGURE 4–6. Schematic Representation of the Gastrointestinal System

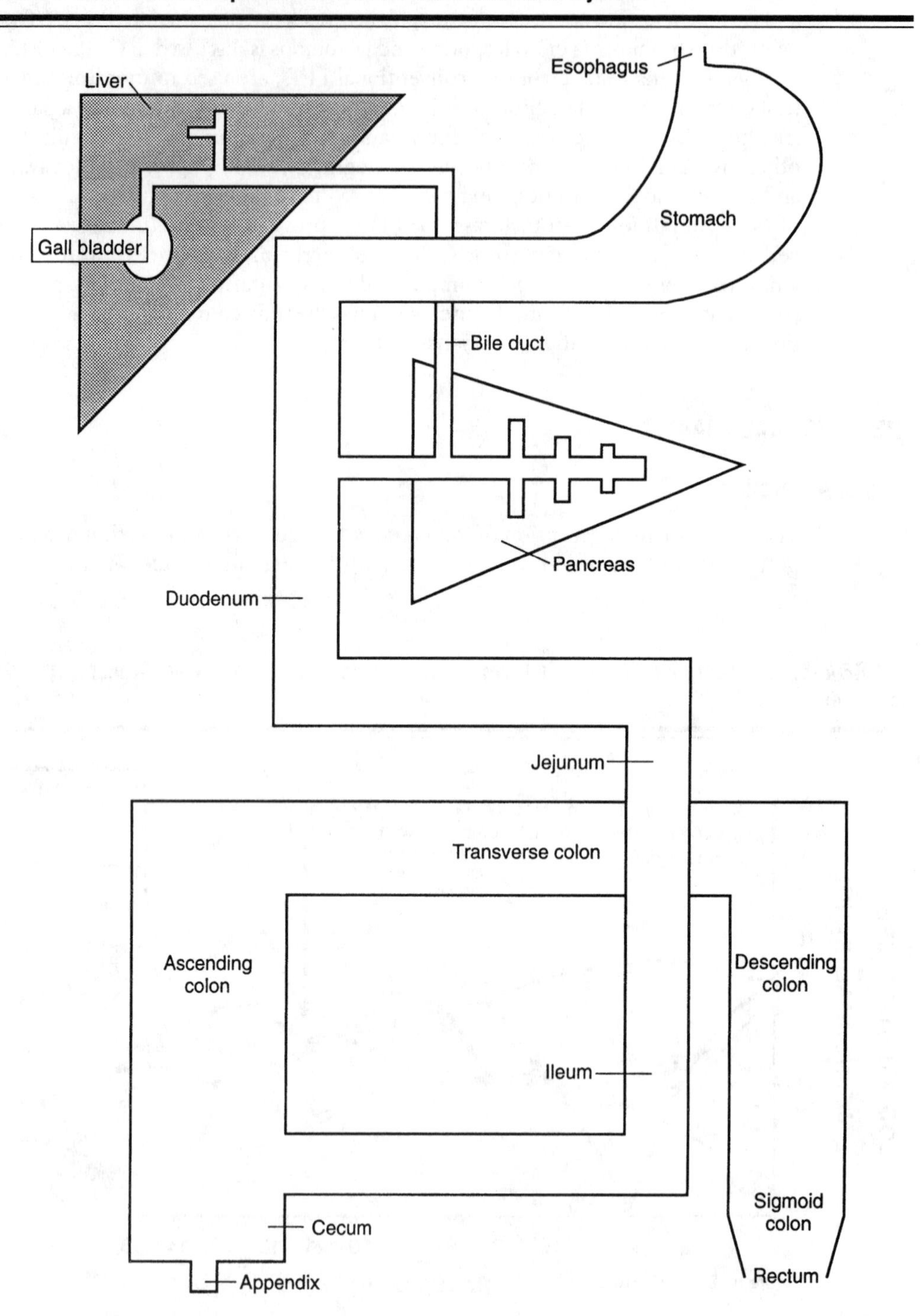

TABLE 4–8. Digestion of Carbohydrates, Proteins, and Lipids

Substrate	Enzyme (Proenzyme)	Activator	Source of Enzyme	Catalytic Function or Products
		CARBOHYDRATE		
Starch	Salivary α-amylase	$C1^-$	Salivary glands	Hydrolyzes 1,4α linkages, producing α-limit dextrin maltotriose, and maltose
Starch	Pancreatic α-amylase	$C1^-$	Exocrine pancreas	Same as salivary α-amylase
Maltose, maltriose	Maltase	—	Intestinal mucosa	Glucose
Lactose	Lactase	—	Intestinal mucosa	Galactose and glucose
Sucrose	Sucrase*	—	Intestinal mucosa	Fructose and glucose
Limit dextrins	Isomaltase*	—	Intestinal mucosa	Glucose
		PROTEINS		
Proteins and polypeptides	Pepsins (pepsinogens)	HCl	Stomach	Cleave peptide bonds adjacent to aromatic amino acids
Proteins and polypeptides	Trypsin (trypsinogen)	Entero-peptidase	Exocrine pancreas	Cleaves peptide bonds adjacent to arginine or lysine
Proteins and polypeptides	Chymotrypsins (chymotrypsinogens)	Trypsin	Exocrine pancreas	Cleave peptide bonds adjacent to aromatic amino acids
Elastin, some other proteins	Elastase (proelastase)	Trypsin	Exocrine pancreas	Cleaves bonds adjacent to alphatic amino acids
Proteins and polypeptides	Carboxypeptidase A (procarboxypeptidase A)	Trypsin	Exocrine pancreas	Cleaves carboxy terminal amino acids that have aromatic or branched aliphatic side chains
Proteins and polypeptides	Carboxypeptidase B (procarboxypeptidase B)	Trypsin	Exocrine pancreas	Cleaves carboxy terminal amino acids that have basic side chains
Polypeptides	Aminopeptidases	—	Exocrine pancreas	Cleave N-terminal amino acid from peptide
Dipeptides	Aminopeptidases	—	Exocrine pancreas	Two amino acids
Di-, tri-, and tetrapeptides	Various peptidases	—	Cytoplasm of mucosal cells	Amino acids
		LIPIDS		
Triglycerides	Pancreatic lipase Pancreatic colipase	—	Exocrine pancreas	Monoglycerides and fatty acids
Cholesteryl esters	Pancreatic esterase	—	Exocrine pancreas	Cholesterol
Lecithin	Phospholipase A (prophospholipase A)	Trypsin	Exocrine pancreas	Lysolecithin

*Sucrase and isomaltase are separate polypeptide chains that are parts of a single hybrid molecule.

drate and protein must first be digested (broken down to small molecules) by gastrointestinal enzymes prior to absorption in the small intestine. The normal absorption of macromolecules requires digestive enzymes, a functioning intestine, and a functioning liver. Table 4–8 lists the processes involved in the digestion of carbohydrates, proteins, and lipids. Table 4–9 lists the principal absorption sites.

For the normal absorption of water and small molecules such as salts and water-soluble vitamins, only a functioning intestine is required. As with the liver, the GI tract has a large reserve capacity and normal absorption can occur despite reduced functioning capacity. In an adult, the GI tract is about 8 meters long; the duodenum is about 20 cm, the jejunum and ileum are together about 6 meters (40% jejunum, 60% ileum), and the colon is about 1.1 meters. Over 50% of the small intestine can be removed before generalized malabsorption becomes likely.[39]

Lipids

The major lipids in the human diet are triglycerides and cholesterol esters. They are digested and absorbed mainly in the small intestine. Lipids are first emulsified into droplets by bile salts acting in conjunction with phospholipids and monoglycerides. This process (with the help of pancreatic colipase, which displaces the emulsifying agents, binds to the fat droplet, and anchors pancreatic lipase) allows the access of pancreatic lipase and pancreatic esterase, which act upon the lipids to release monoglycerides, fatty acids, and cholesterol. These combine with phospholipids and bile salts to form micelles which transport the lipids to the mucosal cell surface, where they diffuse out of the micelle and cross the enterocyte plasma membrane. The bile salts are released for further micelle formation, ultimately being absorbed, principally in the terminal ileum.

TABLE 4–9. Principal Absorption Sites for Nutrients

	Location of Absorptive Capacity			
	Small Intestine			
Substance	Duodenum and Jejunum	Proximal Ileum	Distal Ileum	Colon
Sugars (glucose, galactose, etc.)	+	+++	+	0
Neutral amino acids	+	+++	+	0
Basic amino acids	+	+	+	?
Water-soluble vitamins	+++	+	0	0
Fatty acid absorption and conversion to triglyceride	+++	++	+	0
Bile salts	0	+	+++	0
Vitamin B_{12}	0	+	+++	0
Fe^{2+}	+++	+	+	?
Sodium and water	+++	+	+++	+++

Within the enterocyte, lipids are resynthesized into triglycerides and cholesterol esters. These are packaged into chylomicrons and secreted into the lymphatic system by a process of exocytosis. Chylomicrons are lipoproteins containing apo B48 as their major apolipoprotein. Thus, normal absorption of lipid requires an adequate bile flow, adequate pancreatic secretions, and sufficient functioning small intestine.

Carbohydrates

Starches and sugars are the principal sources of digestible carbohydrate in the human diet. Non-digestible complex carbohydrates can be metabolized by the microbiological flora of the large intestine, and the low-molecular-weight products thereof absorbed. They are therefore of some nutritional benefit. Starch is digested to some extent by salivary amylase, but principally within the small intestine by pancreatic amylase. The products are oligosaccharides, maltose (a disaccharide of glucose), small glucose polymers and "limit dextrins." The enzymes for further digestion are located on the intestinal luminal cell membrane. Disaccharides are split by the disaccharidases. Maltase acts on maltose and small glucose polymers to produce glucose. Lactase splits lactose from milk into glucose and galactose. Sucrase splits sucrose from the diet into glucose and fructose. Limit dextrins are cleaved by α-limit dextrinase, also known as isomaltase. The monosaccharides so formed are transported into small intestinal mucosal cells principally by the Na^+/glucose cotransporter. Thus, normal absorption of carbohydrate requires pancreatic secretions and a normally functioning small intestine with a full complement of disaccharidases.

Proteins

Approximately half of the protein digested in the gastrointestinal tract comes from gastrointestinal secretions and desquamated cells.[40] Digestion starts in the stomach where pepsins (formed by the action of HCl on pepsinogens) cleave peptide bonds next to aromatic amino acid residues. Digestion continues in the small intestine where pancreatic endo- and carboxypeptidases (released as inactive proenzymes) and mucosal cell surface amino- and dipeptidases release amino acids. Amino acids are absorbed in the small intestine by Na^+/amino acid cotransporters. A transport system for di- and tripeptides is also present. Thus, normal absorption of protein requires pancreatic secretions and a functioning small intestine.

Vitamins

Fat-soluble vitamins are absorbed with lipids. Vitamin B_{12} binds to intrinsic factor secreted by parietal cells of the stomach and the complex is absorbed (as are bile salts) in the terminal ileum. Other water-soluble vitamins are absorbed in the upper small intestine.

Abnormal Absorption

Generalized malabsorption of fat, protein, and carbohydrate can be due to an insufficient or abnormally functioning intestine or to insufficient pancreatic secretions. Common intestinal causes of malabsorption are villous atrophy (coeliac disease, tropical sprue) and surgical resection or inflammation (e.g., Crohn's disease). Pancreatic insufficiency can be due to cystic fibrosis or chronic pancreatitis.

Steatorrhoea (fatty stools) may be the presenting feature of generalized malabsorption. Other presenting features may be weight loss or failure to thrive. The consequences of vitamin deficiencies may lead to the suspicion of malabsorption and prompt its investigation. In fat malabsorption, the absorption of fat soluble vitamins is reduced. This may lead to vitamin D deficiency and rickets. This would be suspected by the observation of a low serum calcium and a raised serum alkaline phosphatase. Anemia, both microcytic and megaloblastic, may be due to the failure to absorb iron, folate, or vitamin B_{12}.

Malabsorption of specific substances in isolation can occur. Lack of bile salts leads to isolated fat malabsorption. Lack of bile salts can be due to biliary obstruction, but this cause will be obvious. The patient will be clinically jaundiced and will have abnormal liver function tests. Lack of bile salts may also be due to small bowel bacterial overgrowth, known as "stagnant loop" or "blind loop" syndrome. Unlike the large intestine, the small intestine is normally sterile; if it does become contaminated, bacteria can degrade bile salts, leading to a functional bile salt deficiency.

"Stagnant loop" syndrome may also lead to vitamin B_{12} deficiency, the bacteria-consuming intrinsic factor. Malabsorption of vitamin B_{12} may also be the result of diseases of the terminal ileum such as Crohn's disease.It may be due to acquired or congenital intrinsic factor deficiency, but this is rare in children. Malabsorption may be suspected as a result of the consequences of this vitamin deficiency (i.e., megaloblastic anemia).

Malabsorption of disaccharides is due to deficiency of a particular enzyme. The disaccharide, being undigested in the small intestine, enters the large intestine, where it causes an osmotic diarrhea.

In protein-losing enteropathy absorption may be normal, but the gut is abnormally permeable to plasma proteins, resulting in increased loss in the feces.

INVESTIGATION OF INTESTINAL DISEASE

Biochemical tests often take second place in the investigation of intestinal disease. In many instances, microbiological tests, imaging techniques, and endoscopy/biopsy provide more useful diagnostic information. The best diagnostic test is histological examination of an intestinal biopsy specimen; flattened villi suggest gluten sensitive enteropathy (coeliac disease) or tropical sprue. The histological appearance may suggest Crohn's disease or infiltration. Radiological investigations may be useful in detecting infiltration.

Infections are a common cause of diarrhea and vomiting in children. The stools may contain blood and mucus, and tests for fecal reducing substances may be positive as a result of rapid transit and impaired absorption. Illness may be prolonged by secondary lactose intolerance following damage to the mucosa. The following discussion of biochemical tests in intestinal disease assumes that infectious causes of gut dysfunction have been excluded.

Severe gut conditions requiring surgery (e.g., necrotizing enterocolitis in the neonate) are not covered in this chapter. Biochemical tests are of no value in diagnosis, although routine biochemical support will be required.

Malabsorption

Malabsorption is the common result of a variety of diseases. The biochemical tests used in the investigation of malabsorption are discussed here. Specific GI diseases and individual tests used in their investigation are discussed in later sections.

Fecal Fat

Fecal fat estimation is currently the best indicator of fat malabsorption, but fecal fat only becomes abnormal when more than 90% of pancreatic function is lost. The patient should be on a high-fat diet for 1–2 d prior to and during the test (in adults more than 70 g/d). Specimen collection constitutes a major problem in children, as collection must span a period of at least 3 d and preferably 5 d. Timing can be improved by adding markers to the diet. The fat content is usually measured using Van de Kamer's titration method.[41] In children aged 1 y to puberty, fecal fat loss is approximately 2 g/24 h (7 mmol/24 h), with values greater than 3.5 g/24 h (12 mmol/24 h) considered abnormal.[42] In older children, loss is less than 7% of the fat intake; in infants, loss can be up to 15% ("physiological steatorrhea").

The steatocrit is a simple screening test for fat malabsorption. Random stool specimens are homogenized and centrifuged and the non-fat solid and upper fat layers are estimated. The fat layer is expressed as a percentage of the non-fat solid layer. Normal values are up to 2%, with higher values in young infants. Even with the modifications described by Lloyd et al.,[43] waxy stools with a high fibrous content may cause analytical problems, and technically the method performs better with stools from infants.

Other tests of fat malabsorption such as measurement of serum triglycerides after a fatty meal or measurement of breath $^{14}CO_2$ following ^{14}C-triolein ingestion, although aesthetically more acceptable, have not proved as clinically useful as fecal fat estimation.

Tests of Pancreatic Function

Serum Enzymes

Chronic pancreatitis, in which there is a defect in pancreatic exocrine function leading to malabsorption, is not associated with leakage of pancreatic enzymes into blood. However, in acute pancreatitis, leakage of pancreatic enzymes does occur. Repeated bouts of acute pancreatitis will lead to development of chronic pancreatitis. Two enzymes—amylase and lipase—have been found to be of use in the diagnosis of acute pancreatitis; there is no significant difference between them in their diagnostic usefulness.[44] Amylase is easier to measure and is therefore preferred.

However, amylase is present in the salivary gland and increased serum concentrations can be found in diseases of this gland, such as mumps. Specific pancreatic amylase assays are available, but their routine use is of questionable value since the origin of serum amylase is usually not in doubt.

Pancreatic stimulation tests are technically difficult and are rarely performed. A tube is positioned in the duodenum and fluid collected following IV injection of secretin with or without cholecystokinin/pancreozymin. Noninvasive tests are more practical.

Pancreolauryl Test

This test for normal pancreatic enzyme secretions is designed for use in adults but can be used in children.[45] Fluorescein dilaurate is ingested and, in the absence of pancreatic disease, is digested by pancreatic lipase to release fluorescein, which is absorbed into the bloodstream and ultimately excreted into urine. Thus, low excretion of fluorescein may be the result of abnormal digestion, abnormal absorption, or abnormal renal function. To compensate for the latter two, fluorescein alone is taken on another day. The urinary excretion of fluorescein after taking fluorescein dilaurate is compared to that after taking fluorescein. A normal result is greater than 30%. The BT-PABA (N-benzoyl-1-tyrosyl-para-amino-benzoic acid) test is similar. In this test, PABA is released by the action of chymotrypsin and is measured in urine. To compensate for renal function, the test is repeated with unconjugated PABA.

Fecal Enzymes

Measurement of pancreatic enzymes such as chymotrypsin and trypsin in feces can be used to screen for pancreatic insufficiency. Fecal pancreatic enzymes are reduced in severe pancreatic insufficiency, but these tests are insensitive in mild cases. Fecal chymotrypsin is considered more reliable than trypsin, as it is more resistant to degradation in the gut. Simple photometric assays are available using synthetic substrates such as succinyl-ala-ala-pro-phe-4-nitroanilide.[46] The enzyme is first solubilized using detergent and high salt concentrations. Results are affected by transit time as enzymes are inactivated in the colon. Antibiotic treatment may inhibit bacterial breakdown, leading to falsely normal results. Pancreatic supplements should be stopped 5 d prior to the test.[47] A new test for detecting pancreatic dysfunction has become available which involves the measurement of fecal pancreatic elastase.[48] This enzyme is measured immunologically which overcomes the problem of interference of bovine pancreatic extracts in the chymotrypsin assay.[49]

Tests of Intestinal Function

In these tests, substances that cross the intestinal membrane intact are ingested and their subsequent urinary excretion measured.[50] For a normal result to be obtained, both intestinal and renal function must be normal. The substances used are often non-metabolized sugars such as monosaccharides. Although they are of no nutritional benefit, these monosaccharides are absorbed. In intestinal disease, their absorption is diminished as the area of functioning gut is diminished.

Xylose Absorption Test

The xylose absorption test is the most widely known test but is nonetheless rarely used. A test dose of 5 g is ingested and urine collected for 5 h. Greater than 25% of the dose should be excreted. This test relies on normal renal function; when this is in doubt, the 1 h blood concentration (corrected for surface area) is more reliable and should be > 0.7 mmol/L.

Permeability Tests

Disaccharides (e.g., lactulose) and large molecules (e.g., Cr-EDTA) are generally absorbed minimally. In intestinal disease, however, the gut becomes more permeable to them, probably via a paracellular mechanism, and their absorption increases. This fact has been utilized in some newer intestinal permeability tests, such as the ratios of lactulose/mannitol or ^{51}Cr EDTA/^{14}C mannitol absorption (Table 4–10). The use of a ratio not only increases the discrimination of the test, since the changes in the urinary excretion of the two test compounds are in opposite directions, but also avoids the problem of abnormal renal function affecting the interpretation.

Fecal Electrolytes and Osmolality

Diarrhea can be divided into secretory and osmotic types. In osmotic diarrhea, malabsorbed nutrients or poorly absorbed compounds (e.g., laxatives such as lactulose) enter the colon, where the action of bacteria produces osmotically active compounds which retain water in the colon. In secretory diarrhea, the normal handling of electrolytes by the gut is disrupted. Determination of the fecal osmotic gap may help in the investigation of diarrhea, but is not diagnostically useful, at least in adults,[51] presumably because diarrhea is often caused by several mechanisms working together. In secretory diarrhea, the measured osmolality of the stool water is similar to the calculated osmolarity (i.e., 2([Na] + [K]) mmol/L). In osmotic diarrhea, the measured osmolality is usually considerably higher than the calculated osmolarity (e.g., an osmotic gap of 100 mmol/Kg). For measurement of fecal osmolality, the stool specimen needs to be sufficiently liquid to allow centrifugation and

TABLE 4–10. Intestinal Permeability Tests

Test Substance(s)	Absorption and excretion in active small bowel Crohn's or villous atrophy
Xylose	decreased
^{51}Cr EDTA	increased
Lactulose	increased
Mannitol	decreased
Lactulose/mannitol ratio	increased
^{51}Cr EDTA / ^{14}C mannitol	increased

separation of a water supernatant. Specimens should be fresh, as continued degradation of stool constituents by bacteria may increase the measured osmolality.

Tests for Small Bowel Bacterial Overgrowth (Blind Loop Syndrome)

The best tests for this disorder are breath tests, and various options are available. Some tests depend upon the fact that normally by the time the gut contents come into contact with bacteria in the large intestine, most of the absorption of the test substances has already occurred, and thus they are not available to be acted upon by gut bacteria. Other tests use a non-absorbable, non-digestible substance and depend on the production of bacteria-specific substances such as hydrogen (H_2) when the substance comes into contact with bacteria. This will occur earlier when the small intestine is contaminated with bacteria. Interpretation of these tests can be difficult, particularly in circumstances in which the gut contents reach the large intestine more quickly than is normal. In these circumstances, there may not be time for complete absorption in the small intestine, and the unabsorbed substances will be available to the bacteria of the large intestine.

In the lactulose H_2 breath test, the non-digestible sugar lactulose is ingested. H_2 is a product of bacterial metabolism which is absorbed into the bloodstream and ultimately lost via the exhaled breath. It can be easily measured using small desktop instruments. Usually little H_2 is detectable for about 2 h following the ingestion of lactulose. This represents the time taken for the lactulose to reach the large intestine. If H_2 is detected earlier, this could be due to bacterial contamination of the small intestine or intestinal hurry. Figure 4–7 shows the results of a lactulose H_2 breath test in a normal patient and one with Blind Loop syndrome.

FIGURE 4–7. Typical Response of Breath H_2 to the Ingestion of Lactulose in a Normal Patient Compared to One with Blind Loop Syndrome

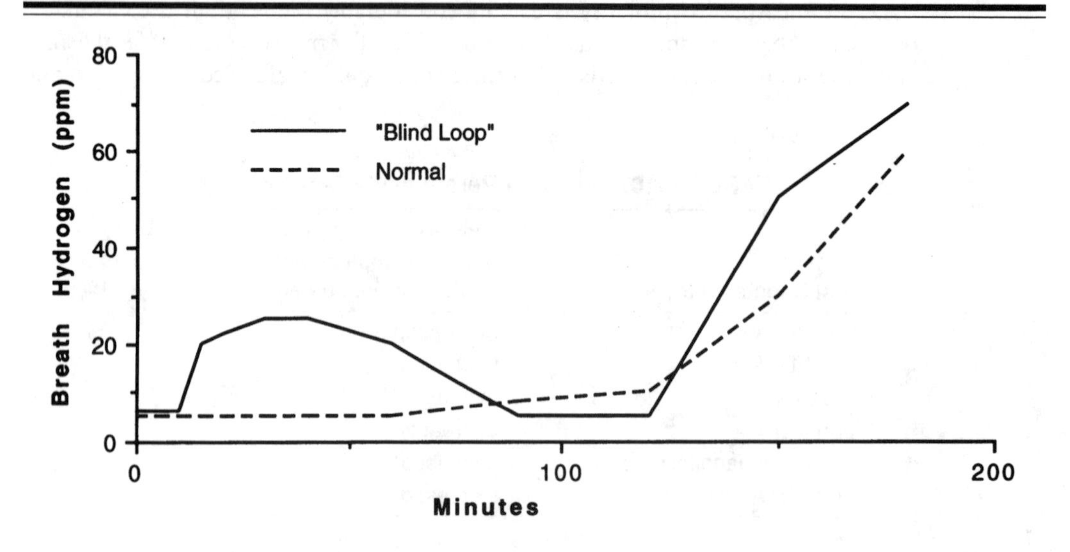

FIGURE 4–8. Typical Response of Breath H_2 to the Ingestion of Glucose in a Normal Patient Compared to One with Blind Loop Syndrome

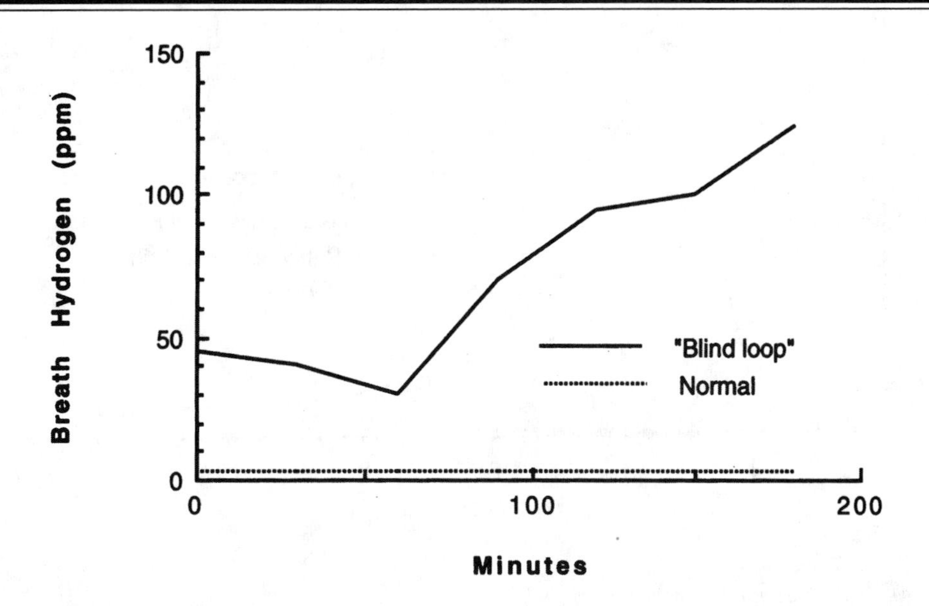

In the glucose H_2 breath test, glucose is ingested. Normally, little H_2 appears as it is all absorbed before it comes into contact with bacteria. However, H_2 will appear in the breath if there is bacterial contamination of the small intestine or intestinal hurry. Figure 4–8 shows the results of a glucose H_2 breath test in a normal patient and one with Blind Loop syndrome.

In the ^{14}C glycocholate breath test, radioactively labelled bile salt is ingested. Figure 4–9 illustrates the typical response. Normally all of the bile salt is absorbed before it reaches the large intestine, and very little of its metabolite ($^{14}CO_2$) is produced over the next few hours. Appearance of $^{14}CO_2$ in breath means that the ^{14}C glycocholate has been degraded by bacteria, either as a result of its reaching the large intestine, as in diseases of the terminal ileum leading to decreased bile salt absorption, or as a result of the presence of bacteria in the small intestine. Breath radioactivity is easily measured by trapping the expired $^{14}CO_2$ in alkali and then measuring its radioactivity in a scintillation counter.

Testing for urinary indican (indoxyl sulfate) is obsolete. Indoxan is a product of bacterial metabolism of tryptophan. Normally all tryptophan will be absorbed in the small intestine and will not come into contact with bacteria unless the small intestine is contaminated.

Tests for Disaccharidase Deficiency

The definitive test for disaccharidase deficiency is the assay of the suspected missing enzyme in a biopsy specimen. Biochemical tests are simpler but less discriminatory.

FIGURE 4–9. Typical Responses of Breath $^{14}CO_2$ to the Ingestion of ^{14}C Glycocholate

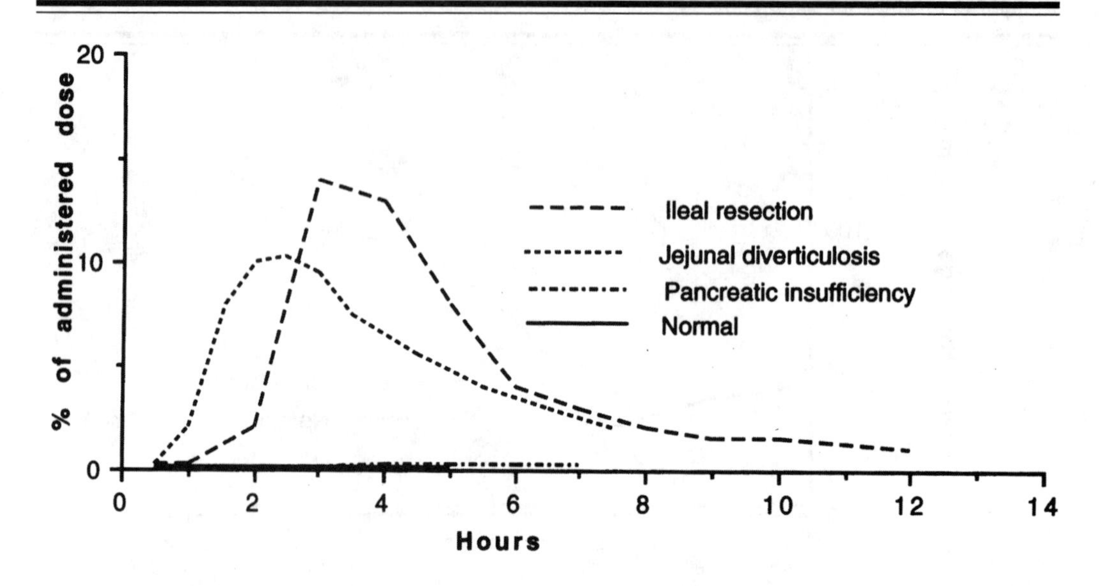

Lactose Tolerance Test

The test protocol for the lactose tolerance test is the same as that for the glucose tolerance test except that lactose is given. With a normal gut lactase, the rate of increase of blood glucose should be similar to that in the glucose tolerance test.

Lactose Breath Test

In the lactose H_2 breath test, lactose is ingested and the appearance of H_2 in the breath is followed. In the presence of a normal lactase activity, H_2 should not appear in the breath since it should all be absorbed in the small intestine. In lactase deficiency, H_2 is detected in breath.

Fecal pH and Sugars

There is wide variation in normal fecal pH depending on the diet. pH values of < 5 suggest fermentation of unabsorbed sugars to organic acids and gases in the colon. In malabsorption of specific sugars, the stools are usually watery, frothy, and irritant. Clinitest tablets (Ames) are most often used to check fresh feces for reducing substances and will detect sugars such as glucose, lactose, and maltose. Sucrose does not react but can be converted to a reducing sugar by briefly boiling the sample with dilute hydrochloric acid. Identification of any sugars present can be undertaken using thin-layer chromatography and Clinistix (Ames) which will detect glucose only. Normal stool may contain small amounts of reducing substances (up to 0.25%). Values greater than 0.5% are abnormal and values of 0.25–0.5% are suspicious.[52] False negatives arise if the offending sugar is completely broken down in the colon.

Tests for Vitamin B_{12} Absorption

In the Schilling test, both ^{58}Co-cyanocobalamin and ^{57}Co-cyanocobalamin intrinsic factor complex are taken orally followed by cyanocobalamin given intramuscularly. The intramuscular injection of cyanocobalamin is to saturate the body stores to allow the absorbed vitamin B_{12} to be excreted. The excretion of radioactivity is measured in a 24 h urine collection. Intrinsic factor deficiency leads to malabsorption of vitamin B_{12} (and hence subnormal excretion of ^{58}Co-cyanocobalamin) but not to malabsorption of B_{12} intrinsic factor complex (and hence the excretion of ^{57}Co-cyanocobalamin is normal). Diseases of the terminal ileum will lead to malabsorption of B_{12} intrinsic factor complex (and hence the excretion of both ^{57}Co-cyanocobalamin and ^{58}Co-cyanocobalamin will be subnormal).

Tests for Laxative Abuse

Urine can be screened for common laxatives such as phenolphthalein and Rheon (the active ingredient of senna and cascara), and fecal magnesium can be estimated to screen for abuse of magnesium salts.[53]

Tests of Protein-losing Enteropathy and Intestinal Bleeding

Fecal Occult Blood

Although fecal occult blood testing is undertaken infrequently in children, the test can detect or confirm intestinal bleeding in a variety of conditions and, as in adults, is sometimes used in the investigation of unexplained anemia. Blood loss may be intermittent, so testing is usually conducted on three random stool specimens. The commonly used Haemoccult slides (Smith Kline Beecham Corp., USA) detect the peroxidase activity of heme by the oxidation of guaiac resin to give a blue coloration to the test strips. Fecal samples are collected on filter paper impregnated with resin and allowed to dry for 24 h before the developing solution of hydrogen peroxide is applied. Ingestion of high doses of vitamin C can produce false-negative results, and it is recommended that the patient avoid vitamin C preparations for 3 d prior to and during the test. Depending on the sensitivity of the test method, it may be necessary to avoid a high intake of foods that can give false-positive results, such as red meat.

Fecal α_1-Antitrypsin (fecal AAT)

Small amounts of relatively low-molecular-weight proteins are normally lost in the stools each day. Increased permeability occurs when there is inflammation of the gut wall, mucosal damage, and/or edema. Abnormalities in or damage to lymphatic drainage may also increase protein loss. In severe cases of "protein-losing enteropathy" serum albumin and other serum proteins such as transferrin are reduced. Increased urinary loss of protein should first be excluded.

The protease inhibitor AAT is relatively resistant to degradation by enzymes in the gut and can be estimated in the feces as a measure of protein loss.[54] Fecal AAT is quantitated by radial-immunodiffusion or nephelometric/turbidimetric techniques on aqueous extracts of random stool samples. The reference range is < 0.2 mg/g wet weight, providing serum concentrations of AAT are normal.[55] Fresh samples should be analyzed or stored frozen to reduce AAT degradation. Concentrations are increased in gastrointestinal bleeding as well as in protein-losing enteropathy.[55] A negative result does not exclude protein-losing enteropathy; for example, false negatives occur in patients with low serum AAT concentrations.

Fecal AAT measurement is considerably simpler but less accurate than isotope methods of detecting protein-losing enteropathy. The latter are difficult to conduct in children and involve the administration of radioactive substances. ^{51}Chromium-labelled albumin is given intravenously and fecal loss (without urine contamination) is measured over 2–3 d.

Food-Sensitive Enteropathies

Transient food-sensitive enteropathies may occur in infancy but usually resolve by age 2 y. Coeliac disease is a more severe, permanent intolerance of gluten. Presentation is variable. Typically, young children present with diarrhea, vomiting, abdominal distension, malnutrition, weight loss, and growth failure. The disease may be more insidious in older children, who may present with short stature, anemia, delayed puberty, or a variety of non-gastrointestinal complaints. Biochemical tests are of no help in the diagnosis other than to document malabsorption. α-Gliadin antibodies are found in 80–90% of children with untreated coeliac disease and provide a useful screening test.[56] This test is not specific as these antibodies are found in other intestinal disorders. Serum titres of antibodies to reticulum and endomysium are also increased in untreated disease.[57] The antibody titre falls on gluten withdrawal and may be normal by 6 months. A rise in titre thereafter is a good indicator of non-compliance. Recently transglutaminase has been shown to be the target antigen for anti-endomysial antibodies and an ELISA test for anti-transglutaminase antibodies has been developed. This assay is potentially more specific and sensitive than the anti-gliadin assay.[58] Intestinal biopsy shows a typical flattened appearance of the mucosa which reverts to normal on a gluten-free diet.[59]

Inflammatory Bowel Disease

Inflammatory bowel disease is defined as chronic inflammation of the intestinal tract in the absence of a detectable pathogen. Specific examples are ulcerative colitis and Crohn's disease. Inflammatory bowel disease is much rarer in children than adults, although the symptoms are similar. In children, there are the added problems of poor growth and delayed puberty. An infectious cause should be excluded, followed by radiological investigations, endoscopy, and biopsy. Assessment of the acute phase response may help distinguish Crohn's disease from ulcerative colitis. The response is poor or absent in ulcerative colitis, with acute phase protein concentrations lower than expected for the degree of inflammation. Crohn's disease produces a more marked acute phase response. C-reactive protein and α_1-antichymotrypsin provide a useful screen for inflammation in adults and may be used to monitor progress.[60] There is no acute phase response in irritable bowel syndrome.

Pancreatic Disease

Both acute and chronic pancreatitis occur in children, albeit rarely. Causes of acute pancreatitis differ from those seen in adults and include trauma, infection, and drugs or toxins. Chronic pancreatitis in childhood is often secondary to anatomical abnormalities or may be inherited as an autosomal-dominant condition. As in adults, amylase and lipase are increased in acute pancreatitis but are of little help in the diagnosis of chronic pancreatitis. Pancreatic enzymes are also increased in a variety of conditions associated with abdominal pain. Conversely, values may not be markedly increased in severe necrotizing pancreatitis.

Cystic fibrosis and the Shwachman-Bodian syndrome are inherited disorders associated with pancreatic insufficiency. Cystic fibrosis (discussed below) is the most common cause of pancreatic insufficiency in childhood. The Shwachman-Bodian syndrome is very rare and is associated with neutropenia as well as pancreatic insufficiency.

Inherited Disorders

Cystic Fibrosis

Cystic fibrosis is a common inherited disorder with an incidence of 1 in 2,000 in Caucasian populations. Inheritance is autosomal recessive. The gene has been mapped to chromosome 7q31 and encodes a protein named the cystic fibrosis transmembrane conductance regulator (CFTR). Over 200 mutations associated with the disease have been described.[61] In Northern Europe, approximately 70% of cystic fibrosis patients have a mutation which results in the loss of phenylalanine at amino acid position 508 (ΔF508). The incidence of this mutation varies in different ethnic groups. The CFTR protein acts as a chloride channel in the apical membrane of epithelial cells and may have other functions. Different mutations affect synthesis of the protein, the localization of the protein in the appropriate membrane, the regulation of the chloride channel, or the chloride channel activity. In the common mutation ΔF508, the protein has chloride channel activity but does not localize appropriately.[62]

In cystic fibrosis there is a reduction in chloride ion transport and associated water, leading to increased sweat electrolytes and viscous mucus secretions. The main clinical problems are chronic lung disease and pancreatic insufficiency. Liver disease is common in older children but may be asymptomatic. Viscous secretions impair ciliary action in the lungs, and affected individuals suffer from repeated chest infections leading to lung damage. Pancreatic and liver damage is thought to arise from blockage of ductules with hyperproteinemic secretions.

Up to 15% of affected neonates present with intestinal obstruction resulting from abnormally sticky meconium which fails to pass ("meconium ileus"). Others may present with failure to thrive and malabsorption and/or recurrent chest infections. Approximately 85% of affected children suffer from malabsorption. This is treated with enzyme supplements. A subgroup of patients have less severe disease with adequate pancreatic function and milder lung disease. It is thought that these milder forms are associated with mutations in which the epithelial cells have some residual chloride channel activity.

The sweat test, wherein sweat is collected by pilocarpine iontophoresis, is the most useful test in the diagnosis of cystic fibrosis. A small electric current forces pilocarpine into the skin and this stimulates sweating. The sweat is collected onto a preweighed gauze or filter paper or by capillary action into a Macroduct collecting device. Sweat electrolytes or osmolality are then measured. Analysis of sodium plus chloride is considered better than sodium alone, particularly in equivocal cases.[63] In children with cystic fibrosis, sweat sodium and chloride are each greater than 60 mmol/L. The osmolality is greater than 220 mOsm/Kg. Interpretation of sweat test results should take account of clinical findings and tests of pancreatic function. Equivocal sweat tests should be repeated or DNA studies may be undertaken in patients for whom doubt still remains. DNA tests may be used to screen for cystic fibrosis carriers in some populations.

Measurement of immunoreactive trypsin in dried blood spots can be used to screen neonates for cystic fibrosis.[64] In healthy individuals, a small amount of trypsinogen enters the bloodstream from the pancreas. Any free trypsin generated is rapidly bound to α_1-antitrypsin and α_2-macroglobulin. Trypsinogen and a large proportion of the trypsin bound to α_1-antitrypsin can be measured by immunoassay (immunoreactive trypsin, or IRT). Two forms of trypsinogen are produced by the pancreas. The more cationic form is measured in most assays. This is also the more stable of the two forms and is present in greater amount. Since pure preparations of trypsinogen are difficult to prepare and the immunoreactivity of trypsin and trypsinogen are essentially the same, inhibited trypsin is used as the immunogen and for calibration.

In neonates with cystic fibrosis, blood IRT concentrations are increased. However, some normal neonates show a transient increase in IRT, so a second blood test is necessary to confirm that the hypertrypsinemia is prolonged. Infants with a repeat positive screening test should then have a sweat test performed. Some screening protocols incorporate IRT measurement followed by analysis of the most common Δ508 mutation.[65]

Other Inherited Disorders

A number of inherited disorders affect the normal processes of digestion and absorption in the gut. Table 4–11 lists examples.

Adult hypolactasia is the most common inherited deficiency. Most mammals naturally lose lactase after weaning, since milk is not a normal dietary component thereafter. Some races do not retain lactase, and activity falls to 10% or less of the activity in infants. The age of onset of this decline varies in different ethnic groups. Persistence of lactase activity is inherited as an autosomal-dominant trait. Worldwide, this deficiency affects between a third and half of the human race. Symptoms are often minor—abdominal pain, diarrhea, flatulence—and may only occur with loading tests. The congenital form of lactase deficiency is extremely rare and presents with severe diarrhea soon after birth. A transient secondary deficiency of lactase is common following damage to gut mucosa, such as occurs after diarrheal infection. Investigation of suspected disaccharidase deficiency is discussed in an earlier section of this chapter.

TABLE 4–11. Inherited Disorders Affecting Gut Function

Defect	Nutrient(s) Affected	Symptoms/Signs	Inheritance	Investigations
Absence or marked reduction of brush border sucrase-isomaltase activity	Maldigestion of sucrose and dextrins	Diarrhea with or without vomiting when sucrose/dextrins introduced into diet	Autosomal recessive	Acid feces containing sucrose Reduced sucrase activity on intestinal biopsy
Marked reduction of brush border lactase activity	Maldigestion of lactose	Neonatal form (rare): diarrhea, vomiting, malnutrition Late-onset form (common): flatulence, abdominal pain, diarrhea	Autosomal recessive Persistence of lactase activity into adulthood inherited as autosomal dominant	Acid feces containing lactose Reduced lactase activity on intestinal biopsy.
Reduced activity of brush border trehalase activity	Maldigestion of trehalose (disaccharide found in edible mushrooms)	Abdominal pain, diarrhea following consumption of large amount of trehalose	Autosomal dominant	Acid feces containing trehalose Reduced trehalase activity on intestinal biopsy
Defect in Na^+/glucose cotransporter	Malabsorption of glucose and galactose	Severe diarrhea, dehydration Failure to thrive	Autosomal recessive	Acid feces containing glucose and galactose. Normal activity of brush border disaccharidases. Flat glucose tolerance test, normal xylose tolerance test.
Congenital enteropeptidase deficiency (decreased activation of trypsin and hence other pancreatic proteases)	Maldigestion of proteins	Diarrhea, vomiting, failure to thrive. Adaptation occurs; normal diet tolerated later in life	Autosomal recessive	Analysis of duodenal fluid for protease activity ± enteropeptidase in reaction mixture. Enteropeptidase activity on intestinal biopsy.
Lysinuric protein intolerance. Defective transport of lysine, arginine, ornithine. "Functional" deficiency of ornithine in urea cycle.	Decreased absorption of lysine, arginine, ornithine. Increased loss in urine	Diarrhea, vomiting, failure to thrive. Hepatomegaly	Autosomal recessive	Raised urine and low plasma lysine, arginine, and ornithine. Raised blood ammonia and increased orotic acid excretion following a protein load.
Abetalipoproteinemia (defective apo B48 and B100)	Malabsorption of lipids	Steatorrhea, acanthocytosis, ataxia, retinitis pigmentosa	Autosomal recessive	Low serum cholesterol and triglycerides. Absent chylomicrons, LDL, VLDL, and apo B.
Pancreatic lipase deficiency	Maldigestion of lipids	Gross steatorrhea	Autosomal recessive	Fecal fat Lipase activity in duodenal fluid
Familial chloride diarrhea	Defective reabsorption of chloride from ileum and colon	Severe diarrhea, dehydration	Autosomal recessive	High fecal chloride loss.
Acrodermatitis enteropathica	Defective zinc absorption	Diarrhea, failure to thrive, skin lesions	Autosomal recessive	Serum zinc usually low. Low serum alkaline phosphatase (Zn dependent). Monitor clinical response to oral zinc.

For further information see Scriver CR, Beaudet AI, Sly WS, Valle D, eds. The metabolic basis of inherited disease, 7th ed. New York: McGraw-Hill, 1994 and McKusick VA. Mendelian inheritance in man, 10th ed. Baltimore: The Johns Hopkins University Press, 1992.

REFERENCES

1. Jungermann K, ed. Zonal liver cell heterogeneity. Enzyme 1992;46:1–168.
2. Kress S, Katz N. Discrimination between periportal and pericentral necrosis of rat liver by determination of glutamine synthetase and other enzyme activities in serum. Eur J Clin Chem Clin Biochem 1993;31:733–8.
3. Gourley GR. Bilirubin metabolism and neonatal jaundice. In Suchy FJ. Liver disease in children. St. Louis, MO: Mosby, 1994:108.
4. Maquire GA, Mullock BM, Branch WJ, Luzio JP. The intracellular location of bilirubin. Biochem Soc Trans 1987;15:448.
5. Moseley RM. Hepatology elsewhere: A molecular basis for jaundice in intrahepatic and extrahepatic cholestasis. Hepatology 1997;26:1682–84.
6. Westwood A. The analysis of bilirubin in serum. Ann Clin Biochem 1991;28:119–30.
7. Goldfinch ME, Maguire GA. Investigation of the use of bilirubin oxidase to measure the apparent unbound bilirubin concentration in human plasma. Ann Clin Biochem 1988;25:73–7.
8. Clarke DJ, Moghrabi N, Monaghan G, et al. Genetic defects of the UDP-glucuronosyl transferase-1 (UGT1) gene that causes familial non-haemolytic unconjugated hyperbilirubinaemias. Clin Chim Act 1997;266:63–74.
9. Trull AK, Facey SP, Rees GW, et al. Serum α-glutathione S-transferase: a sensitive marker of hepatocellular damage. Transplantation 1994;58:1345–51.
10. Nemesanszky E, Lott JA, Gamma-glutamyltransferase and its isoenzymes: progress and problems. Clin Chem 1985;31:797–803.
11. Price CP, Milligan TP, Darte C. Direct comparison of performance characteristics of two immunoassays for bone isoform of alkaline phosphatase in serum. Clin Chem 1997;43:2052–7.
12. Crofton PM. Wheat-germ lectin affinity electrophoresis for alkaline phosphatase isoforms in children: age-dependent reference ranges and changes in liver and bone disease. Clin Chem 1992;38:663–70.
13. Mayne PD, Kovar IZ. Calcium and phosphorus metabolism in the premature infant. Ann Clin Biochem 1991;28:131–42.
14. Price CP. Multiple forms for human serum alkaline phosphatase: detection and quantitation. Ann Clin Biochem 1993;30:355–72.
15. Whicher J, Spence C. When is serum albumin worth measuring? Ann Clin Biochem 1987;24:572–80.
16. Soldin SJ, Hicks, JM, Godwin, et al. Pediatric reference ranges for alpha-fetoprotein. Clin Chem 1992;38:959–60.
17. Kelly DA. Jaundice in the neonate. Med Int 1994;22:461–4.
18. Mowat AP. Liver disorders in childhood, 3rd ed. London: Butterworth, 1994:28–9.
19. Riely CA. Familial intrahepatic cholestasis syndrome. In: Suchy FJ. Liver disease in children. St. Louis, MO: Mosby 1994:443–59.
20. Carrell RW, Evans DL, Stein PE. Mobile reactive centre of serpins and the control of thrombosis. Nature 1991;353:576–8.
21. Carrell RW. α1-antitrypsin: molecular pathology, leukocytes and tissue damage. J Clin Invest 1986;78:1427–31.
22. Brantly M, Nukiwa T, Crystal RG. Molecular basis of alpha-1-antitrypsin deficiency. Amer J Med 1988;84(Suppl. 6A)13–31.
23. Jeppson J-O. Franzen B. Typing of genetic variants of α1-antitrypsin by electrofocusing. Clin Chem 1982;28:219–25.
24. Perlmutter DH, Schlesinger MJ, Pierce JA, Punsal PI, Schwartz AL. Synthesis of stress proteins is increased in individuals with homozygous Pi ZZ α1-antitrypsin and liver disease. J Clin Invest 1989;84:1555–61.
25. Lomas DA, Evans DL, Finch JT. The mechanism of Z α1-antitrypsin accumulation in the liver. Nature 1992;357:605–7.
26. Perlmutter DH, Glover GI, Riventa M, Schasteen CS, Fallon RJ. Identification of a serpin-

enzyme complex receptor on human hepatoma cells and human monocytes. Proc Natl Acad Sci USA 1990;87:3753–7.
27. Green A, Morgan I. Neonatology and clinical biochemistry. ACB Venture publications, 1993:94–121.
28. Tanzi RE, Petrukhin K, Chernov I, et al. The Wilson disease gene is a copper transporting ATPase with homology to the Menkes disease gene. Nature Genet 1993;5:344–50.
29. da Costa CL, Baldwin D, Portmann B, Lolin Y, Mowat AP, Mieli-Vergani G. Value of urinary copper excretion after penicillamine challenge in the diagnosis of Wilson's disease. Hepatology 1992; 15:609–15.
30. Liang TJ, ed. Hepatology elsewhere (Wilson's disease). Hepatology 1994;20:529–35.
31. Thomas GR, Forbes JR, Roberts EA, et al. The Wilson disease gene: spectrum of mutations and their consequences. Nature Genetics 1995;9:210–17.
32. Green A. When and how should we measure plasma ammonia? Ann Clin Biochem 1988;25:199–209.
33. Green A, Hall SM. Investigation of metabolic disorders resembling Reye's syndrome. Arch Dis Child 1992;67:1313–7.
34. Crofton PM. What is the cause of benign transient hyperphosphatasaemia: a study of 35 cases. Clin Chem 1988;34:335–40.
35. Stein P, Rosalki SB, Foo AY, Hjelm M. Transient hyperphosphatasaemia of infancy of early childhood: clinical biochemical features of 21 cases and literature review. Clin Chem 1987;33:313–8.
36. Mowat AP. Orthotopic liver transplantation in liver-based metabolic disorders. Eur J Pediatr 1992;151(Suppl. 1):S32–S38.
37. Mowat AP. Liver disorders in childhood, 3rd ed. London: Butterworth, 1994:433–52.
38. Calne RY. Immunosuppression in liver transplantation. NE J Med 1994;331:1154–5.
39. Kelly KA, Wolff BG. Crohn's disease. In: Sabiston DC, ed. Textbook of surgery, 14th ed. Philadelphia: PA. WB Saunders Co., 1991:843–51.
40. Ganong WF. Review of medical physiology, 16th ed. E. Norwalk CT: Appleton and Lange, 1993:431.
41. Gowenlock AH, ed. Varley's practical clinical chemistry, 6th ed. London: Heinemann Medical Books, 1990:701.
42. Navarro J, Schmitz J., eds. Paediatric gastroenterology. Oxford: Oxford University Press, 1992:463, 472.
43. Lloyd D. Rawashden MO, Booth IW, Brown GA. The steatocrit: an improved procedure. Ann Clin Biochem 1992;29:535–40.
44. Wong ECC, Butch AW, Rosenblum JL, Ladenson JH, Scott M. The clinical chemistry laboratory and acute pancreatitis. (Washington University case conference). Clin Chem 1993;39:234–43.
45. Dalzell AM, Heat DP. Fluorescein dilaurate test of exocrine pancreatic function in cystic fibrosis. Arch Dis Child 1990;65:788–9.
46. Kaspar P, Moller G, Wahlefeld AW. New photometric assay for chymotrypsin in stool. Clin Chem 1984;30:1753–7.
47. Lawson N, Chesner I. Tests of exocrine pancreatic function. Ann Clin Biochem 1994;31: 305–14.
48. Wallis C, Leung T, Cubitt D, Reynolds A. Stool elastase as a diagnostic test for pancreatic function in children with cystic fibrosis. Lancet 1997;350:1001.
49. Stein J, Jung M, Sziegoleit A, et al. Immunoreactive elastase 1: clinical evaluation of a new non-invasive test of pancreatic function. Clin Chem 1996;42:222–6.
50. Laker MF, Bartlett K. Tubeless tests of small intestinal function. Rec Adv Biochem 1985;3: 195–219.
51. Ladefoged K, Schaffalitzky de Muckadell OB, Jarnum S. Faecal osmolality and electrolyte concentrations in chronic diarrhoea: do they provide diagnostic clues? Scan J. Gastroenterol 1987;22:813–20.
52. Hicks JM, Boeckx RL, Pediatric clinical chemistry. Philadelphia PA: WB Saunders Co., 1984:9.

53. Duncan A, Cameron A, Stewart MJ, Russell RI. Diagnosis of the abuse of magnesium and stimulant laxatives. Ann Clin Biochem 1991;28:568–73.
54. Dinari G, Rosenbach Y, Zahavi I, Sivan Y, Nitzan M. Random fecal α1-antitrypsin excretion in children with intestinal disorders. Amer J. Dis Child 1984;138:971–3.
55. Morrow RJ, Lawson N, Ussaini SH, Asquith P. The usefulness of faecal haemoglobin, albumin and α1-antitrypsin in the detection of gastrointestinal bleeding. Ann Clin Biochem 1990; 27:208–12.
56. Miles J, Charles P, Riches P. A review of methods available for the identification of both organ-specific and non-organ-specific autoantibodies. Ann Clin Biochem 1998;35:19–47.
57. Challacombe D. When is a coeliac? The Lancet 1994;343:188.
58. Dieterich W, Ehnis T, Bauer M, et al. Identification of tissue transglutaminase as the autoantigen of celiac disease. Nature Medicine 1997;3:797–80.
59. Patchett SE, Alstead EM, Kumar PJ, Case 30–1994: antiendomysial antibodies and celiac disease. (Letter). N Eng J Med 1994;331:1776.
60. Calvin J. Neale G. Fotheby KJ, Price CP. The relative merits of acute phase proteins in the recognition of inflammatory conditions. Ann Clin Biochem 1988;25:60–6.
61. Nelson M, Margetts BM, Black AE, Recent advances in cystic fibrosis research. J Pediatr 1993;122:985–8.
62. Welsh MJ. The path of discovery in understanding in the biology of cystic fibrosis and approaches to therapy. Amer J Gastro 1994;89(Suppl. 8)S97–S105.
63. Green A, Dodds P, Pennock C. A study of sweat sodium and chloride: criteria for the diagnosis of cystic fibrosis. Ann Clin Biochem 1985;22:171–4.
64. Heeley AF, Bangard SK. The neonatal detection of cystic fibrosis by measurement of immunoreactive trypsin in blood. Ann Clin Biochem 1992;29:361–76
65. Gregg RG, Simantel A, Farrell PM, et al. Newborn screening for cystic fibrosis in Wisconsin: comparison of biochemical and molecular methods. Pediatr 1997;99:819–24

FURTHER READINGS

Millward-Sadler GH, Wright R, Arthur MJP, eds. Wright's liver and Biliary disease, 3rd ed. London: WB Saunders, 1992.
Scriver CR, Beaudet AL, Sly WS, Valle D, eds. The metabolic basis of inherited disease, 7th ed. New York: McGraw-Hill, 1994.
Holton JB, ed. The inherited metabolic disease, 2nd ed. Edinburgh: Churchill Livingstone, 1994.

CHAPTER 5

Cardiovascular Disorders

Ronald V. Lacro, M.D.

INTRODUCTION

Cardiovascular disorders in the pediatric population include both congenital and acquired conditions. This chapter explores the biologic and pathogenetic mechanisms that underlie the principal congenital malformations of the cardiovascular system, as well as the major forms of acquired heart disease affecting infants, children, and adolescents.

CONGENITAL CARDIOVASCULAR MALFORMATIONS

Diagnosis and management of *structural* congenital heart defects account for most of the caseload of the typical pediatric cardiologist. Congenital malformations of the cardiovascular system, which have an overall incidence of about 0.4% among live-born infants, constitute an etiologically heterogeneous group of birth defects having a variety of known and unknown causes.[1] For most structural malformations, the biochemical basis for the developmental error is largely unknown. However, vigorous research efforts are currently directed at elucidating the biochemical, cellular, and genetic mechanisms involved in normal and abnormal cardiovascular development. A pathogenetic classification of cardiovascular malformations has been useful in designing and conducting such research.

Pathogenetic Classification of Congenital Cardiovascular Malformations

The traditional nomenclature for classifying structural heart defects is based on presumed embryologic events or on anatomic characteristics and location. Earlier classification systems, although helpful in naming complex cardiac defects, may have obscured important pathogenetic relationships. More recently, congenital heart defects have been classified according to disordered mechanisms. This newer classification scheme, which is undergoing continuous reassessment and modification, is based on the assumption that there is a limited repertoire of developmental mechanisms and a relatively wide spectrum of phenotypic expression.[2]

Clark has identified six major pathogenetic mechanisms which are likely to be involved in the majority of cardiovascular malformations (Table 5–1).[3] Figure 5–1 illustrates a straightforward relationship wherein one etiology (I) acts through a single pathogenic mechanism (A) to produce a single anatomic malformation (1). However, for many congenital cardiovascular malformations, multiple etiologies (I, II, III) act through a single mechanism (A) to produce a spectrum of anatomic abnormalities (1, 2, 3). For example, deletions involving the long arm of chromosome 22 and prenatal exposure to retinoic acid (multiple etiologies) may act through a single mechanism (disruption of neural crest cell migration) to cause a spectrum of conotruncal malformations, including truncus arteriosus, interrupted aortic arch type B, and tetralogy of Fallot. Although the specific defects within each group are heterogeneous, they share the disordered mechanism.

Evaluation of cases of congenital heart disease according to mechanistic groups can help to clarify relationships among malformations, suggest underlying genetic and biochemical mechanisms, and elucidate familial patterns and recurrence risks for relatives.[4] Genetic and biochemical investigations will lead invariably to a better understanding of the biologic basis of structural development.

Ectomesenchymal Tissue Migration Abnormalities (Neural Crest Migration Abnormalities) (Table 5–2)

The tissue that ultimately forms and septates the outflow tract of the heart originates in the neural crest and branchial arch mesenchyme. Kirby and associates used the quail-chick chimera to show that specific regions of neural crest are major con-

TABLE 5–1. Classification of Defects by Pathogenetic Mechanisms

Ectomesenchymal tissue migration abnormalities
Defects associated with abnormalities of intracardiac blood flow
Cell death abnormalities
Extracellular matrix abnormalities
Abnormal targeted growth
Situs and looping defects

FIGURE 5–1. Relationship of Etiology, Pathogenic Mechanism, and Anatomic Abnormality

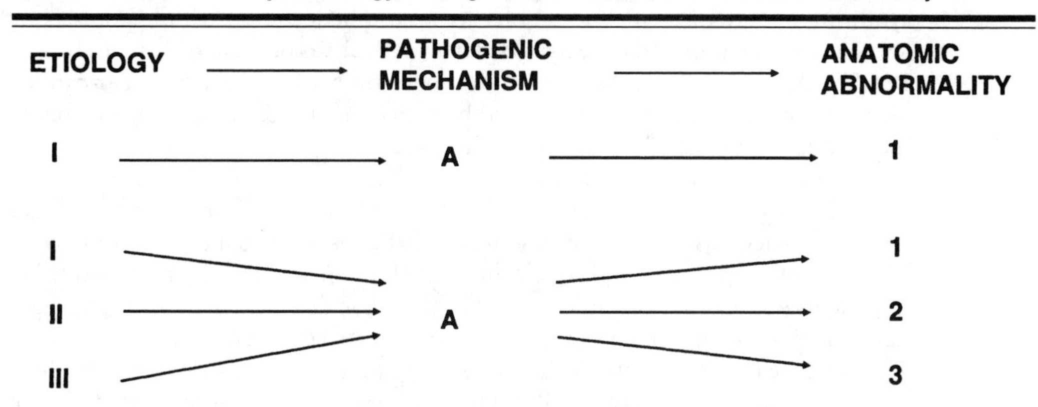

Source: Clark EB. Growth, morphogenesis, and function: the dynamics of cardiovascular development. In: Moller JM, Neal WA, eds. Fetal, neonatal, and infant heart disease. New York: Appleton-Century-Crofts, 1989:1–22.

stituents of the conotruncal septation process.[5–7] Ectomesenchymal cells from neural crest are essential for expression of tissue derivatives of each branchial arch and pouch. In addition, neural crest cells course through arches 4, 6, and probably 3 to participate in septation of the conotruncus and aortic sac. Mechanical ablation of small amounts of preotic neural crest produces a spectrum of conotruncal malformations, including truncus arteriosus and subarterial ventricular septal defect.[6] Conotruncal malformations, particularly type B interruption of the aortic arch, trun-

TABLE 5–2. Ectomesenchymal Tissue Migration Abnormalities

Conotruncal septation defects
Increased mitral-aortic separation (a clinically silent *forme fruste*)
Subarterial or malalignment ventricular septal defect
Double outlet right ventricle
Tetralogy of Fallot with or without pulmonary atresia
Aorticopulmonary window
Truncus arteriosus communis
Branchial arch defects
Interrupted aortic arch, type B
Double aortic arch
Right aortic arch with mirror image branching
Aberrant subclavian artery
Abnormal conotruncal cushion position
D-transposition of the great arteries

cus arteriosus, and tetralogy of Fallot, are overrepresented in patients with DiGeorge syndrome, where these malformations are seen in association with hypoplasia or aplasia of the thymus and parathyroid gland (derivatives of branchial arches III and IV). Tetralogy of Fallot is also one of the common cardiac defects in velo-cardio-facial syndrome, which is characterized by congenital heart defects, palatal abnormalities, learning disability, and a characteristic facies.

Previous studies have shown deletions and microdeletions of chromosome 22, within region 22q11, in the majority of patients with DiGeorge syndrome and velo-cardio-facial syndrome, and in some familial cases of congenital heart disease.[8–12] More recently, microdeletions of chromosomal region 22q11 have been identified in patients with non-syndromic conotruncal cardiac defects,[13] demonstrating a genetic contribution to the development of some isolated conotruncal malformations. The presence of a microdeletion in the 22q11 region can be easily detected by fluorescent *in situ* hybridization (FISH). Ongoing research is attempting to delineate the gene or genes on the long arm of chromosome 22 involved in neural crest, branchial arch, and conotruncal development.

Other human neural crest/branchial arch syndromes which have an overrepresentation of conotruncal malformations and which are associated with abnormalities of branchial arch derivatives include the facio-auriculo-vertebral spectrum (oculo-auriculo-vertebral dysplasia, hemifacial microsomia, Goldenhar syndrome), CHARGE association, thalidomide embryopathy, and retinoic acid embryopathy. While abnormalities of ectomesenchymal migration probably account for many conotruncal septal defects and branchial arch defects, the pathogenesis of D-transposition of the great vessels is thought to involve failure of the conotruncal cushions to spiral.[14]

Defects Associated with Abnormalities of Intracardiac Blood Flow (Table 5–3)

Change in volume distribution of intracardiac blood flow may be a mechanism in the pathogenesis of right and left heart defects. Experimental manipulation of the intracardiac blood flow affects cardiac morphogenesis. For example, reduction in fetal mitral valve inflow produces a spectrum of left ventricular volume ranging from mild left ventricular hypoplasia to severe hypoplastic left heart syndrome with aortic and mitral atresia.[15] Any event that results in decreased aortic blood flow and increased pulmonary artery and ductal blood flow may lead to one of the defects in the spectrum of left-sided flow defects.[16]

During fetal life, left heart blood flow crosses the atrial septum through the foramen ovale. The ratio of the area of the foramen ovale to the area of the atrial septum is an index of transatrial blood flow.[17] There is an inverse correlation between this ratio and the size of the left heart. In normal hearts, the ratio is about 0.20. The ratio is increased significantly in hearts with an obligatory *in utero* right-to-left shunt (increased left heart flow). The ratio is decreased in obstructive left heart defects (decreased left heart flow). The ratio is increased in the presence of secundum atrial septal defect, suggesting that secundum atrial septal defects may be

TABLE 5–3. Defects Associated with Abnormalities of Intracardiac Blood Flow

Left heart defects
Bicuspid aortic valve
Aortic valve stenosis
Coarctation of the aorta
Interrupted aortic arch, type A
Hypoplastic left heart, aortic atresia, and mitral atresia
Right heart defects
Secundum atrial septal defect
Bicuspid pulmonary valve
Pulmonary valve stenosis
Pulmonary valve atresia and intact ventricular septum
Perimembranous ventricular septal defect

a consequence of increased transatrial blood flow. In perimembranous ventricular septal defect, the foramen ovale/atrial septum area ratio is greater than normal, suggesting that the ventricular septum may remain patent because of an *in utero* left-to-right shunt.[18] In the human fetus with a ventricular septal defect, transventricular blood flow is often left-to-right.[19]

Extracellular Matrix Abnormalities (Table 5–4)

The endocardial cushions (atrioventricular and conotruncal) consist primarily of glycosaminoglycans separating the endocardium and the myocardium, and constitute the largest proportion of extracellular matrix in the embryo. Fusion of opposing cushions results in the formation of the tricuspid and mitral orifices at the atrioventricular level, and the pulmonary and aortic orifices in the outflow tract. Cushion adhesion begins with the transformation of endocardial cells overlying the cushions into mesenchymal cells (Figure 5–2). This epithelial-mesenchymal transformation is initiated by ES1 antigens which are secreted by myocardial cells and are associated with fibronectin within the myocardial basement membrane (myocardial "adherons").[20–22] During activation, the endothelium exhibits many morphological and molecular characteristics, including cellular hypertrophy, Ca^{2+} influx, loss of cell-cell contacts via a down-regulation of the neural cell adhesion molecule

TABLE 5–4. Extracellular Matrix Abnormalities

Endocardial cushion defects
Ostium primum atrial septal defect
Atrioventricular canal type ventricular septal defect (inflow)
Complete atrioventricular canal defect
Dysplastic pulmonary or aortic valve

FIGURE 5–2. Molecular Summary of the Mechanism for the Segmental Formation of Cushion Mesenchyme

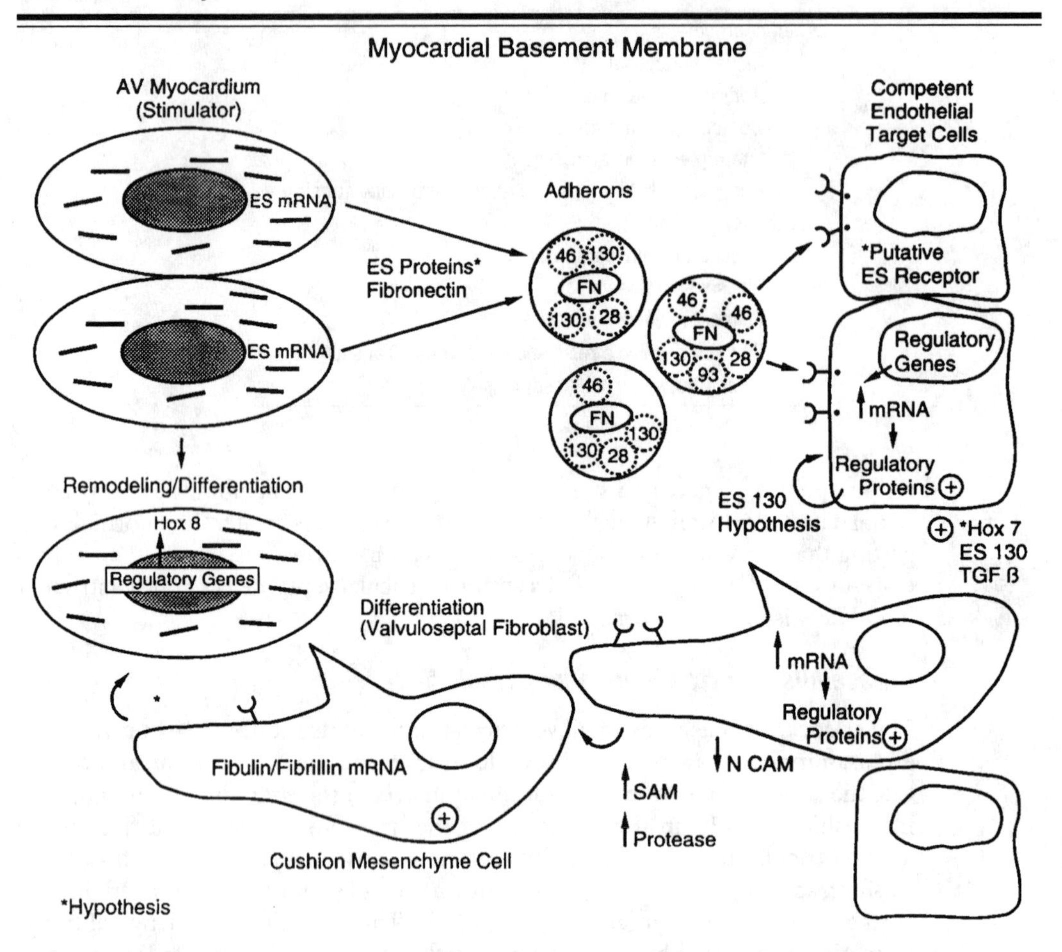

Source: Markwald RR.: Cellular and molecular studies of normal and abnormal heart segmental development. Proc Greenwood Genet Center 1994;13:51–54.

(N-CAM), Golgi polarization, and expression of HOX-7, the ES protein ES130, TGF-β, substrate adhesion molecules (SAM), and urokinase-type plasminogen activator. (Further discussion is available elsewhere.[20–22]) The "activated" endothelial cells acquire a fibroblastic morphology and invade the adjacent extracellular matrix to form cardiac cushion tissue, which contributes to valvar and septal tissues of the mature heart. The high frequency of atrioventricular canal defects in Down (Trisomy 21) syndrome may be a clue to the genetic mechanism of the process.[23–24]

TABLE 5–5. Cell Death Abnormalities

Ebstein malformation of the tricuspid valve
Muscular ventricular septal defect

Cell Death Abnormalities (Table 5–5)

Controlled cell death is an important molding process in the embryonic heart.[25] The tricuspid valve cusps are almost exclusively derived from the interior of the embryonic right ventricular myocardium by a process of undermining the right ventricular wall.[26] Abnormalities of this process of reabsorption of ventricular myocardium may lead to the Ebstein malformation with displacement of the functional tricuspid valve annulus into the right ventricle (Figure 5–3). The muscular ventricular septum forms early in development as trabeculations at the apex of the heart coalesce and the margins of the cardiac tube grow toward the endocardial cushions and atrioventricular orifice.[27] Muscular ventricular septal defects may arise either from abnormal trabecular organization or secondarily from foci of cellular death that occur during active cardiac remodeling.[2]

FIGURE 5–3. Pathogenesis of Ebstein Malformation

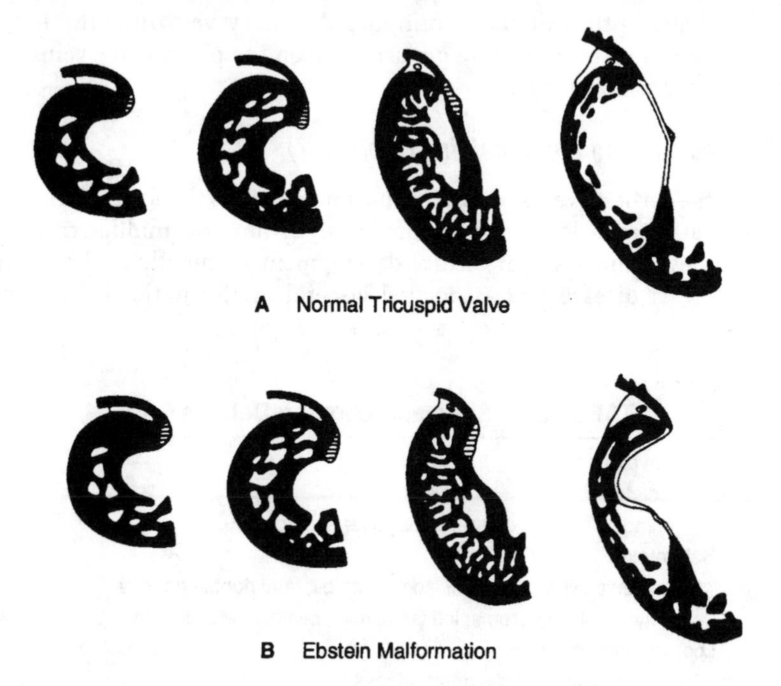

Adapted from: Van Mierop LHS, Gessner IH. Pathogenetic mechanisms in congenital cardiovascular malformations. Prog Cardiovasc Dis 1972;15:67–85.

TABLE 5–6. Abnormal Targeted Growth

Anomalous pulmonary venous connection
Partially anomalous pulmonary venous connection
Totally anomalous pulmonary venous connection
Cor triatriatum

Abnormal Targeted Growth (Table 5–6)

The pulmonary veins form as an outpouching of endothelial-lined mesenchymal tissue from the lung buds and coalesce into the common pulmonary vein that bridges across the splanchnic space and fuses with the posterior wall of the primitive left atrium at 5 weeks gestation.[28] By further remodeling, the common pulmonary vein is gradually absorbed into the posterior wall of the left atrium such that the four pulmonary veins enter the heart individually by 8 weeks gestation. The mechanism is undefined but likely involves an attraction between the pulmonary veins and the left atrium. In the chick embryo, following experimental excision and reimplantation of the lung bud in an inverted orientation, venous connection from lung bud to the left atrium was established in 80% of cases.[29] If connection of the common pulmonary vein to the left atrium does not occur, venous drainage to systemic veins persists (totally anomalous pulmonary venous connection). If absorption of the common pulmonary vein into the left atrium is incomplete, a membrane may persist between the pulmonary veins and the left atrium (cor triatriatum).

Situs and Looping Abnormalities (Table 5–7)

One of the earliest events in cardiac morphogenesis is the formation of the normal D (dextral)-cardiac loop from the previously symmetric, midline cardiac tube. Abnormalities at this stage of cardiac development frequently lead to complex congenital heart disease and associated visceral malformations. In humans, situs

TABLE 5–7. Situs and Looping Defects

Situs inversus totalis
Isolated
Immotile cilia syndrome, Kartagener syndrome
Heterotaxy
Asplenia syndrome; right isomerism; bilateral rightsidedness
Polysplenia syndrome; left isomerism; bilateral leftsidedness
Looping abnormalities
L-transposition of the great arteries
Ventricular inversion

abnormalities (heterotaxy syndrome) have been observed in pedigrees consistent with autosomal dominant, autosomal recessive, and X-linked recessive inheritance, suggesting that multiple genes regulate cardiac looping and determine cardiac and visceral situs. A gene for familial situs abnormalities has recently been mapped to human chromosome Xq24-27.1.[30]

Experiments in the *iv/iv* mouse are consistent with a control gene, the presence of which defines the normal relationship of situs solitus. In the absence of the control gene (recessive mutation), there is a random chance of situs inversus or situs solitus.[31] Cardiac abnormalities are found in 40% of developing *iv/iv* embryos, and the spectrum of abnormalities is strikingly similar to that seen in humans with heterotaxy syndrome.[32] The *iv* locus has been mapped to the sub-telomeric region of mouse chromosome 12, which is syntenic (homologous) with distal human chromosome 14.[33]

Situs inversus totalis can occur without associated cardiac or visceral anomalies. Immotile cilia syndrome (Kartagener syndrome, primary ciliary dyskinesia) is an autosomal-recessive disorder associated with defects in the ultrastructure of the central core of cilia and sperm tails. Although situs inversus totalis can be seen in immotile cilia syndrome, this condition is generally considered separate from the heterotaxy syndromes. However, the coexistence of ciliary abnormalities and polysplenia has been reported.[34, 35] The role of ciliary abnormalities in situs determination has not been clarified.

Genetic Counseling

When possible, identification of a specific diagnosis or etiology improves accuracy in the prediction of prognosis and the estimation of recurrence risk.[36] The requirements for optimal genetic counseling for cardiovascular malformations include:

1. a thorough understanding of the anatomy, management, and outcome of the particular defect;
2. identification of other affected family members and careful pedigree analysis for prediction of familial risks;
3. identification of associated malformations or syndromes;
4. options for prenatal diagnosis.

Ideally, genetic counseling should be provided by both a dysmorphologist knowledgeable about cardiac defects and outcome and by a pediatric cardiologist with a keen awareness and interest in genetic issues.[37]

Up to 25% of individuals with a congenital heart defect have an associated extracardiac malformation, often as part of a multiple malformation syndrome.[38] Such syndromes are caused by chromosomal aberrations, teratogens, genetic abnormalities, and unknown causes. For multiple malformation syndromes, the prognosis and recurrence risk for congenital heart disease depend largely on the underlying syndrome.

ACQUIRED PEDIATRIC HEART DISEASE

The major forms of acquired heart disease in the pediatric population include Kawasaki syndrome, rheumatic fever, infective endocarditis, cardiomyopathies, myocardial ischemia/infarction, arrhythmias, lipid disorders, and systemic arterial hypertension.

Kawasaki Syndrome

Kawasaki syndrome, a leading cause of acquired heart disease in children, is a disease of unknown etiology marked by acute vasculitis. The syndrome occurs predominantly in infancy and early childhood and is characterized by fever, bilateral nonexudative conjunctivitis, erythema of the lips and oral mucosa, changes in the extremities, rash, and cervical lymphadenopathy. Coronary artery aneurysms or ectasia develop in approximately 15–25% of children with the disease and may lead to myocardial infarction, sudden death, or chronic coronary artery insufficiency.[39]

The cause of Kawasaki syndrome is unknown. Antecedent viral infections of the upper respiratory tract and exposure to freshly cleaned carpets have been associated with the disease.[40, 41] Immunoregulatory abnormalities may contribute to the pathogenesis of Kawasaki syndrome. During the acute phase, there is a marked deficiency of suppressor T-cells, helper T-cells become activated, and there are increased numbers of B-cells spontaneously secreting IgG and IgM antibodies.[42] Recent investigations have explored the possibility that this high level of immune activation could be associated with endothelial damage. IgM antibodies in the sera of children with acute Kawasaki syndrome cause complement-mediated killing of gamma interferon-treated, cultured, human vascular endothelial cells.[43] In addition, IgG and IgM antibodies in sera from patients with acute disease have been reported to cause lysis of cultured human vascular endothelial cells stimulated with interleukin-1 or tumor necrosis factor.[44] These observations suggest that mediator secretion by activated T-cells and macrophages could promote vascular injury in Kawasaki syndrome.

By definition of the Centers for Disease Control,[45] the child with Kawasaki syndrome must have fever lasting 5 or more days without other reasonable explanation and satisfy at least four of the following five criteria:

1. bilateral conjunctival injection (associated with anterior uveitis);
2. at least one of the following mucous membrane changes: injected or fissured lips, injected pharynx, or "strawberry tongue";
3. at least one of the following extremity changes: erythema of the palms and soles, edema of the hands or feet, or periungual desquamation;
4. polymorphous exanthem that is rarely vesicular or bullous and is often accentuated in the perineum, where it may be associated with local desquamation;
5. acute nonsuppurative cervical lymphadenopathy (at least one node 1.5 cm or larger in diameter).

In addition to these principal signs, many other significant symptoms and signs frequently are present in children with Kawasaki syndrome,[39] including arthralgia and arthritis, urethritis associated with sterile pyuria (mononuclear white cells rather than polymorphonuclear), aseptic meningitis associated with a mild mononuclear cerebrospinal fluid pleocytosis with normal glucose and protein, hydrops of the gallbladder with or without obstructive jaundice, diarrhea, vomiting, and abdominal pain. Cardiovascular manifestations during the acute phase include tachycardia, gallop rhythm, pericardial effusion, and congestive heart failure due to a myopericarditis. Transient mitral and aortic regurgitation also can be seen. During the subacute phase, congestive heart failure may result from myocardial dysfunction secondary to ischemia or infarction, with or without valvular regurgitation. Clinical symptoms and signs of Kawasaki syndrome may be particularly subtle or absent in infants less than 6 months of age—the subgroup at highest risk for coronary lesions.[46]

Coronary artery ectasia or aneurysms occur in 15–25% of children with Kawasaki syndrome.[47–49] During the first week of the illness children who will develop aneurysms cannot be clearly distinguished from those who will remain unaffected. The duration of fever, presumably reflecting the severity of ongoing vasculitis, has been confirmed as a powerful predictor of coronary artery aneurysms.[50–52] Other reported risk factors for formation of coronary artery abnormalities include male gender, age under 1 year, hemoglobin less than 10 g/dL, a white cell count greater than 30,000/mm^3, an erythrocyte sedimentation rate greater than 101 mm/h (Westergren), increased C-reactive protein, and persistence of elevation of C-reactive protein or sedimentation rate for more than 30 days.[39] Echocardiography may reveal dilatation of the coronary arteries, beginning 7 days after the first appearance of fever. The coronary artery dilatation usually peaks 3–4 weeks after onset of the illness. The arterial lesions of Kawasaki syndrome gradually transform over time, sometimes with apparent partial or total regression of aneurysms and sometimes with the development of stenosis or occlusions.[53] The likelihood of resolution of the aneurysm appears to be determined largely by its initial size. Smaller aneurysms have a greater likelihood of regression. Vessels that do not undergo resolution may show persistence of aneurysmal morphology, or development of stenosis, occlusion, or abnormal tortuosity.

Children with so-called giant aneurysms (aneurysms with a maximum diameter greater than 8 mm) have the worst prognosis. Few of these aneurysms regress and most progress to stenosis or obstruction, usually within 1–3 years.[54–56] Patients with giant aneurysms are at highest risk for myocardial infarction, and nearly all late deaths from Kawasaki syndrome occur in this subgroup.

High doses of gamma-globulin administered intravenously have been demonstrated to be safe and effective in reducing the incidence of coronary artery abnormalities when given early in the course of Kawasaki syndrome.[57–60] Furthermore, abnormalities of left ventricular systolic function and contractility improve more rapidly in children treated in the acute phase with high doses of intravenous gamma-globulin.[61] Finally, high doses of intravenous gamma-globulin reduce fever and laboratory indicators of the acute-phase response.[60] Some data suggest that gamma-globulin works, in part, by blocking immune activation,[62] but the mechanism by which gamma-globulin ameliorates the vasculitis of Kawasaki syndrome is not completely understood. Other therapeutic agents useful in the management of Kawasaki syndrome include salicylates, antithrombotic therapy, and thrombolytic therapy.

Laboratory findings in the acute stage of Kawasaki syndrome[39] include increases in acute phase reactants and erythrocyte sedimentation rate; a high leukocyte count with a left shift; a normocytic, normochromic anemia; and increased platelet turnover, together with marked hypercoagulability in the acute phase. Thrombocytosis typically peaks 3–4 weeks after onset of the fever. Increases of liver transferases, usually two- to threefold, are common in the acute phase, usually with a cholestatic profile of increased bilirubin and alkaline phosphatase. The increase of erythrocyte sedimentation rate typically persists after resolution of the fever—a feature that may help to distinguish Kawasaki syndrome from common viral illnesses.

Rheumatic Fever

Acute rheumatic fever[63] is a poorly understood autoimmune reaction that follows a group A, beta-hemolytic streptococcal pharyngitis. It is a self-limited disease that involves joints, skin, brain, and serous surfaces. Nevertheless, the chronic cardiac valve damage causes significant morbidity and mortality well beyond the period of acute illness.

Rheumatic fever is found mainly in poverty-stricken populations. The disease was a common cause of morbidity and mortality in the United States early in this century, but currently is much less prevalent. However, rheumatic fever has recently reappeared in parts of the United States in sufficient numbers to warrant concern.[64] There are mounting numbers of reports from all parts of the United States including Ohio, the Rocky Mountain states, Pennsylvania, Hawaii, and Florida.[65–70]

The pathogenesis of rheumatic fever is not clearly delineated. The current hypothesis, which reconciles the disparate clinical features, may be stated as follows:[63] In a genetically susceptible individual, repeated, untreated streptococcal infections in early life sensitize the child to the possibility of rheumatic fever. Sometime after age 2 y, a beta-hemolytic, group A, streptococcal pharyngitis sets off an unusually high antibody response. After recovery from the pharyngitis there is a 10-day latent period of relative well-being, after which an autoimmune response involving the excess streptococcal antibodies begins which lasts many weeks and gradually damages the left heart valves. Later, a recurrent streptococcal infection may reactivate the disease. There is continuing valve damage after clinical evidence of rheumatic activity has subsided.

Clinical manifestations of acute rheumatic fever include:

- *fever*;
- *migratory polyarthritis*, most often involving the knees, hips, ankles, elbows, wrists, and shoulders;
- *erythema marginatum*, a distinctive rash present in only a small percentage of patients with acute rheumatic fever but virtually pathognomonic when present;

- firm *subcutaneous nodules* over hard bony surfaces such as the elbows, wrists, shins, knees, ankles, vertebral column, and occiput;
- *Sydenham's chorea* (St. Vitus' dance).

Carditis is mainly manifested by the appearance of murmurs and/or a friction rub. Symptoms of congestive heart failure are relatively uncommon.

The major pathologic findings are inflammatory lesions found in the heart, blood vessels, brain, and serous surfaces of the joints and pleura. The pathologic picture is characterized by a distinctive and pathognomonic granuloma, the *Aschoff body*, consisting of perivascular infiltration of cells and fibrinoid protoplasm. Aschoff bodies are found in all patients with acute clinical rheumatic activity, and in many patients with chronic rheumatic valvular disease as well,[71] suggesting that many patients with this disorder have subclinical, active, rheumatic fever over periods of many years.

Extensive studies of group A, beta-hemolytic streptococcus have focused largely on the layer of the capsule that contains the M proteins, used to identify streptococcal types, and to a lesser extent on the carbohydrate layer, used to group the streptococci. The M protein is structurally similar to the heart muscle protein, tropomyosin.[72] There is cross-reactivity of heart muscle antigens derived from the myocardial sarcolemma with streptococcal antigens.[73–76] The sera of patients with rheumatic fever react with heart tissues, but not when the antibodies have been absorbed by streptococcal antigens.[77] Furthermore, streptococcal antibodies can be identified in the caudate nucleus of patients who have had chorea.[78]

The revised Jones Criteria provide guidance for the diagnosis of rheumatic fever (see Table 5–8).[79] Laboratory data support but do not confirm the diagnosis of

TABLE 5–8. Jones Criteria (Revised) for Guidance in the Diagnosis of Rheumatic Fever

Major Manifestations	Minor Manifestations
Carditis	*Clinical:*
Polyarthritis	Previous rheumatic fever or rheumatic heart disease
Chorea	Arthralgia
Erythema marginatum	Fever
Subcutaneous nodules	*Laboratory:*
	Acute phase reactions
	ESR, C-reactive protein, leukocytosis
	Prolonged P-R interval on ECG

Plus: Supporting evidence of preceding streptococcal infections (increased ASO or other streptococcal antibodies; positive throat culture for group A streptococcus; recent scarlet fever)
The presence of two major criteria, or of one major and two minor criteria, indicates a high probability of the presence of rheumatic fever if supported by evidence of a preceding streptococcal infection. The absence of the latter should make the diagnosis doubtful, except in situations in which rheumatic fever is first discovered after a long latent period from the antecedent infection (e.g., Sydenham's chorea or low-grade carditis).[79]

rheumatic fever. A throat culture from an untreated patient often grows hemolytic streptococci. The antistreptolysin-O titer is increased and may continue to rise, sometimes to remarkably high levels. Other streptococcal antibodies may be increased. The erythrocyte sedimentation rate and C-reactive protein are almost invariably increased. The sedimentation rate may be normal in an affected child with severe liver congestion, but this is rarely seen in practice. The sedimentation rate must be corrected for anemia, because anemia is common in these patients.

Therapy includes penicillin treatment and prophylaxis, non-steroidal anti-inflammatory drugs, steroids, and phenothiazines for children with chorea.[80,81]

Infective Endocarditis

Recent advances in the diagnosis and treatment of infectious endocarditis have decreased the mortality rate of this illness from virtually 100% in the pre-antibiotics era to approximately 10% in recent years.[82] Infectious endocarditis occurs almost exclusively in individuals with preexisting anatomic anomalies of the cardiovascular system. The incidence varies with the specific lesion; individuals at highest risk include those with cyanotic heart disease (e.g., tetralogy of Fallot), those with ventricular septal defect with aortic regurgitation or stenosis, those with prosthetic valves, and those who have undergone recent cardiac surgery. Significant additional risk factors include dental diseases, antecedent dental procedures and other surgical procedures followed by bacteremia, extracardiac infections which may be the source of bacteremia, or intravenous injection of drugs by addicts.[83]

Diagnosis of infective endocarditis requires one of the following three criteria:

1. pathologic evidence of endocarditis (e.g., at cardiac surgery);
2. at least two sets of blood cultures obtained by separate venipunctures positive for the same organism with no source of bacteremia other than the heart;
3. a clinical course compatible with infective endocarditis.

The clinical course of infective endocarditis is variable and depends on the virulence of the infecting organism. Prompt diagnosis requires that the clinician have a high index of suspicion, particularly when evaluating any child with structural heart disease who has fever of unknown origin or other nonspecific manifestations of infection. Symptoms may include fever, anorexia, weight loss, pallor, night sweats, malaise, arthralgias, and myalgias. Changing murmurs and development of congestive heart failure result from infection and consequent destruction of intracardiac structures. Physical signs attributable to embolic or immunologic phenomena include splinter hemorrhages, retinal hemorrhages, Janeway lesions, Osler nodes, splenomegaly, clubbing, arthritis, glomerulonephritis, and aseptic meningitis. There may be neurologic complications including emboli, hemorrhage, meningitis, toxic encephalopathy, and headache. Arterial embolization may affect the lungs, kidneys, spleen, brain, and large vessels.

In the pathogenesis of infective endocarditis,[84] local turbulence is believed to promote the formation of a network of fibrin and platelets on the endocardial surface, which is colonized later by microorganisms entering the bloodstream from a distant site. The microthrombus protects the infecting microorganisms from normal host defense mechanisms and antibiotic penetration, necessitating the use of high-dose parenteral antimicrobial agents for long periods of time. The considerable morbidity and mortality associated with infectious endocarditis make its prompt diagnosis, treatment, and prevention matters of great importance.

Streptococcus viridans is the most common causative organism of infective endocarditis in children and adults.[85–87] Staphylococcal endocarditis has become increasingly common, now accounting for approximately one-fifth of cases. Among patients without preexisting heart disease, *Staphylococcus aureus* is the most common causative organism.[85,86] *Staphylococcus aureus* is also the most common causative organism in endocarditis associated with intravenous injection of drugs in addicts, which typically involves the right side of the heart more often than the left. A variety of other organisms may be found. Gram-negative and fungal endocarditis occur most often following cardiac surgery or in debilitated patients. Blood cultures are negative in approximately 10–15% of cases of infective endocarditis.[86,87]

In addition to positive blood cultures, laboratory abnormalities in infective endocarditis often include anemia, leukocytosis, increased erythrocyte sedimentation rate, hematuria, diminished complement component 3, and mildly increased bilirubin. Echocardiography may demonstrate vegetations and myocardial abscesses.

Cardiomyopathy

The term *cardiomyopathy* includes all entities in which myocardial pathology is the dominant feature and there is no gross structural basis for the cardiac dysfunction.[88] The revised World Health Organization classification system defines cardiomyopathy based on physiologic or hemodynamic features: dilated, hypertrophic, and restrictive.[89] The etiology may be known or unknown, and any one individual may show characteristics of more than one physiologic category over time.

Dilated cardiomyopathies are characterized by impaired ventricular systolic function. Affected individuals typically present with congestive heart failure. In rare instances, arrhythmias or conduction disturbances may be the presenting signs.

Hypertrophic cardiomyopathies rarely produce congestive heart failure as a first symptom, although occasionally this occurs much later in the course of the disease. Initial symptoms may include dyspnea, angina, palpitations, syncope, and even unexpected sudden death. Ventricular systolic function is not impaired; indeed, function may be hyperkinetic. Obstructive and nonobstructive forms exist. Left ventricular compliance is decreased (stiff left ventricle), leading to progressive diastolic dysfunction. Often there is mitral regurgitation.

Restrictive cardiomyopathies are rare in the pediatric population. Restrictive myopathies are characterized by impaired diastolic function (poor compliance) similar to that seen in constrictive pericarditis but usually limited to the left ventricle. Systolic function is preserved. The cavity of the left ventricle is small and the left atrium is dilated. Clinically, there is dyspnea and right-sided heart failure.

TABLE 5–9. Non-genetic Causes of Cardiomyopathy

Cardiovascular conditions	Toxin or drug
Atherosclerotic coronary artery disease	Anthracyclines (andriamycin)
Kawasaki syndrome	Steroids/ACTH
Hypertension	Catecholamines
Dysrhythmia	Iron overload
Congenital heart defect	Immunologic disease
Chronic alteration of circulatory volume	Granulomatous disease
Cardiac transplantation	Connective tissue disease
Recent major cardiac surgery or invasive cardiothoracic procedure	Lupus erythematosus
Obesity	Endocrine disease
Pulmonary parenchymal or vascular disease	Hypo- and hyperthyroidism
Pregnancy or 3 months postpartum period	Hypoparathyroidism
Infection or Postinfection	Pheochromocytoma
Viral	Infant of a diabetic mother
Septicemia	Hypoglycemia
Postmyocarditis	Tyrosinemia
Acquired immune deficiency syndrome	Nutritional deficiency
Rheumatic fever	Thiamine deficiency
Radiation	Kwashiorkor
Malignancy	Pellagra
	Selenium deficiency

Source: Adapted from Schwartz ML et al.[90]

The differential diagnosis of cardiomyopathy includes many genetic and non-genetic causes. Those conditions that are not primarily genetic are listed in Table 5–9. Genetic conditions associated with cardiomyopathy can be classified into four etiologic categories which are not mutually exclusive:[90]

1. inborn errors of metabolism,
2. multiple malformation syndromes,
3. neuromuscular diseases,
4. familial isolated cardiomyopathy disorders (cardiomyopathy without other features).

Inborn errors of metabolism (Table 5–10) are further subdivided into three subgroups based on pathogenesis: storage or infiltrative disease, diminished energy production, suspected cardiotoxic intermediary metabolites. (Inborn errors of metabolism are discussed further in Chapter 17.)

Individuals with *storage diseases* typically develop coarse or dysmorphic facial features, organomegaly, skeletal deformities, short stature, or chronic encephalopathy associated with a neurodegenerative course. In contrast, affected individuals with *diminished energy production* or *accumulation of toxic metabolites* may present

TABLE 5–10. Inborn Errors of Metabolism Associated with Cardiomyopathy*

Infiltrative (Storage)

- Disorders of glycogen metabolism
  - Glycogen storage disease type II (Pompe disease; acid maltase deficiency) (H)
  - Glycogen storage disease type III (Cori disease; debranching enzyme deficiency) (H) +
  - Glycogen storage disease type IV (Andersen disease; branching enzyme deficiency) (D) +
  - Glycogen storage disease type IX (cardiac phosphorylase kinase deficiency) (H) +
  - Glycogen storage disease with normal acid maltase (H)
- Disorders of mucopolysaccharide degradation
  - Mucopolysaccharidosis type I (Hurler syndrome) (H, D)
  - Mucopolysaccharidosis type II (Hunter syndrome) (H)
  - Mucopolysaccharidosis type III (Sanfilippo syndrome) (H)
  - Mucopolysaccharidosis type IV (Morquio syndrome) (H)
  - Mucopolysaccharidosis type VI (Maroteaux-Lamy syndrome) (D)
  - Mucopolysaccharidosis type VII (Sly syndrome) (H)
- Disorder of glycosphingolipid degradation
  - Fabry disease (H)[1]
- Disorder of glycosylceramide degradation
  - Gaucher disease (H)[1]
- Disorder of phytanic acid oxidation
  - Refsum disease (D, H)
- Disorders of combined ganglioside/mucopolysaccharide and oligosaccharide degradation
  - GM_1 gangliosidosis (H, D)
  - GM_2 gangliosidosis (Sandhoff disease) (H, D)
- Disorder of glycoprotein metabolism
  - Carbohydrate-deficient glycoprotein syndrome (neonatal olivopontocerebellar syndrome)
- Disorder of oxalic acid metabolism (oxalosis)[1]

Diminished Energy Production

- Disorders of pyruvate metabolism
  - Pyruvate dehydrogenase complex deficiency (Leigh disease) (H)
- Disorders of oxidative phosphorylation
  - Complex I deficiency (D)
  - Complex II deficiency
  - Complex III deficiency (hystiocytoid cardiomyopathy) (H)
  - Complex IV deficiency (muscle and Leigh disease forms) (H)
  - Complex V deficiency (H)
  - Combined respiratory chain deficiencies
    - Mitochondrial transfer RNA mutations
      - MELAS syndrome (H)
      - MERRF syndrome (H, D)
    - Mitochondrial DNA deletions and duplications
      - Kearns-Sayre syndrome (H)
    - Barth syndrome (3-methyl-glutaconic aciduria Type II) (H, D)
    - Sengers syndrome (H)
- Disorders of fatty acid metabolism (pathogenesis also includes toxic metabolites)
  - Primary or systemic carnitine deficiency (carnitine uptake deficiency) (H, D)
  - Muscle carnitine deficiency (H, D)
  - Carnitine palmitoyl transferase type I deficiency
  - Carnitine acylcarnitine translocase deficiency
  - VLCAD: Very-long-chain acyl-CoA dehydrogenase deficiency (H)
  - LCAD: Long-chain acyl-CoA dehydrogenase deficiency (H)
  - LCHAD: Long-chain 3-hydroxyacyl-CoA dehydrogenase deficiency (D, H)
  - SCAD: Short-chain 3-hydroxyacyl-CoA dehydrogenase deficiency
  - Multiple acyl-CoA dehydrogenase deficiency (glutaric acidemia type II) (H)

Toxic Intermediary Metabolites

- Disorders of amino acid or organic acid metabolism
  - Propionic acidemia (D)
  - Methylmalonic acidemia
  - Malonic acidemia
  - Beta-ketothiolase deficiency (D)
  - Mevalonic acidemia
  - Tyrosinemia (H)

Source: Adapted from Schwartz ML et al.[90]

*For references, see source. Echocardiographic or pathological patterns are indicated for characterized diagnoses: H = hypertrophic CM; D = dilated CM; + = pathogenesis also includes toxic metabolites. MELAS = mitochondrial encephalopathy, lactic acidosis, and strokelike episodes; MERFF = myoclonic epilepsy, ragged red fibers; CoA = Coenzyme A

[1]Reported only in adults.

with symptoms and signs indicative of multiple vital organ dysfunction, acute or chronic encephalopathy, muscle weakness, hypotonia, growth retardation, failure to thrive, recurrent vomiting, and lethargy. Finally, patients with *diminished energy production* may present in biochemical crisis with marked hypoglycemia, metabolic acidosis, or hyperammonemia.

Malformation syndromes (Table 5–11) are nonrandomly occurring, recognizable patterns of major and minor anomalies that can often be attributed to a specific etiology. Cardiomyopathy, although uncommon in malformation syndromes, can be found with consistency in some syndromes. In particular, hypertrophic cardiomyopathy is common in Noonan syndrome (10–20%). All individuals with cardiomyopathy warrant a careful examination for minor and major malformations. Chromosomal analysis and further genetic evaluation may be indicated.

Neuromuscular diseases (Table 5–12), generally characterized by muscle weakness, affect the lower motor unit at the level of either the peripheral nerve or skeletal muscle. These include muscular dystrophies, congenital myopathies, metabolic myopathies, and ataxias. Some of these disorders, particularly Duchenne and Becker muscular dystrophy, can be diagnosed by specific molecular genetic testing (i.e., abnormalities in dystrophin).

TABLE 5–11. Malformation Syndromes Associated with Cardiomyopathy*

Autosomal dominant inheritance
Noonan syndrome (H)
Cardio-facio-cutaneous syndrome (H)
LEOPARD syndrome/lentiginosis/multiple lentigines syndrome (H)
Neurofibromatosis type I (H)
Beckwith-Wiedemann syndrome (H)
Telecanthus, multiple congenital anomalies (H)
Deaf-mutism (H)
Costello syndrome (H)
Autosomal recessive inheritance
Hypogonadism, multiple congenital anomalies, mental retardation (D)
Microcephaly, mental retardation (D)
Palmoplantar keratosis (H)
Total lipodystrophy, insulin resistance, leprechaunism (H)
X-linked recessive inheritance
Cutis laxa, skeletal abnormalities (H)
Microphthalmia, linear skin defects (H, D)
Simpson-Golabi-Behmel-Rosen syndrome

Source: Adapted from Schwartz ML et al.[90]
*For references and additional syndromes, see source. Echocardiographic or pathological patterns are indicated for characterized diagnoses: H = hypertrophic cardiomyopathy; D = dilated cardiomyopathy.

TABLE 5–12. Neuromuscular Disorders Associated with Cardiomyopathy*

Muscular dystrophies
- Duchenne muscular dystrophy (D)
- Becker muscular dystrophy (D)
- Autosomal recessive muscular dystrophy (D)
- Myotonic dystrophy (H, D)
- Emery-Dreifuss muscular dystrophy (D)
- Limb-girdle muscular dystrophy (D)
- Congenital muscular dystrophy

Congenital myopathies
- Centronuclear (myotubular) myopathy (D)
- Nemaline rod myopathy (D, H)
- Minicore-multicore myopathy (D, H, R)

Metabolic myopathies (See Table 5–10)

Ataxias
- Friedreich ataxia (H)
- Refsum disease (D, H)

Source: Schwartz ML et al.[90]
*For references, see source. Echocardiography or pathological patterns are indicated for characterized diagnoses: H = hypertrophic cardiomyopathy; D = dilated cardiomyopathy; R = restrictive cardiomyopathy.

TABLE 5–13. Familial Isolated Cardiomyopathy*

Autosomal dominant inheritance
- Familial hypertrophic cardiomyopathy
  - Defect in cardiac beta-myosin heavy chain (linkage to chromosome 14q11-q12)
  - Defect in cardiac troponin T (linkage to chromosome 1q3)
  - Defect in alpha-tropomyosin (linkage to chromosome 15q2)
  - Defect in cardiac myosin binding protein-C (linkage to chromosome 11p11.2)
  - Linkage to chromosome 7q3 with Wolff-Parkinson-White syndrome
- Familial cardiomyopathy with multiple mitochondrial DNA deletions (D)
- Familial dilated cardiomyopathy with linkage to chromosome 1p
- Familial restrictive cardiomyopathy
- Parchment right ventricle and arrhythmogenic right ventricle
- Noncompaction of the left ventricle

X-linked inheritance
- Dilated cardiomyopathy (defect in dystrophin)

Autosomal recessive inheritance
- Cardiac phosphorylase kinase deficiency (H)
- Familial dilated cardiomyopathy
- Familial hypertrophic cardiomyopathy

Maternal (mitochondrial) inheritance
- C3303T tRNA Leu
- T9997C tRNA Gly

Source: Adapted from Schwartz et al.[90]
*For references, see source. Echocardiographic or pathological patterns are indicated for characterized diagnoses: H = hypertrophic cardiomyopathy; D = dilated cardiomyopathy

Familial isolated cardiomyopathy disorders (familial cardiomyopathy without other features) (Table 5–13) include hypertrophic, dilated, and restrictive types, and can be associated with a variety of inheritance patterns. Abnormalities of myocardial cytoskeletal and contractile proteins (e.g., dystrophin, cardiac beta-myosin heavy chain, alpha-tropomyosin, and cardiac troponin T) have been identified in some cases of isolated familial cardiomyopathy.[91–95] In the case of familial hypertrophic cardiomyopathy due to mutations of the cardiac beta-myosin heavy chain, genotyping is helpful in predicting prognosis.[96]

The diagnostic evaluation for an individual presenting with cardiomyopathy should include careful consideration of all genetic and non-genetic etiologies of cardiomyopathy. The workup must be tailored to the individual's presenting features, risk factors, family history, and severity of involvement. Effective diagnosis and management require a multidisciplinary approach involving specialists in cardiology, genetics, metabolism, and pathology.[90]

Myocardial Ischemia and Infarction

Although myocardial ischemia and infarction are relatively rare in children, there are a number of important congenital and acquired causes. The most common congenital cause is anomalous origin of the left coronary artery from the pulmonary artery. Early studies suggested that this lesion alone may account for 25% of all cases of myocardial infarction in childhood.[97] Kawasaki syndrome, a vasculitis of unknown etiology, has its most profound effects when it involves the coronary arteries. It is the most common acquired cause of myocardial ischemia and infarction in children. Aneurysmal dilation of the coronary arteries occurs in 15–25% of cases; however, the incidence has been significantly reduced since the initiation of intravenous gamma-globulin therapy in the early stages of the disease. Myocardial infarction occurs in a small proportion of cases of Kawasaki syndrome, particularly those with giant aneurysms.

Increases in circulating concentrations of cardiac enzymes have been used as markers of myocardial damage from ischemia.[98] Serum aspartate aminotransferase (AST), lactate dehydrogenase (LDH), and creatine kinase (CK) are the principal enzymes in clinical use. The enzymes are released after irreversible tissue injury. Because these enzymes are present in many tissues, the specificity is reduced; however, the sensitivity is excellent.

Measurement of isoenzymes of LDH and CK has improved the specificity.[98] The isoenzymes of LDH are composed of four subunits which are different combinations of a heart (H) or muscle (M) type and show different electrophoretic mobilities. LDH_1 is present in heart muscle and is the component released after myocardial infarction. Similarly, CK isoenzymes are dimers of either muscle (M) or brain (B) subunits. CK-MB is found almost exclusively in heart muscle, and increased concentrations are very specific for myocardial injury.

In adults, the first enzyme released after acute myocardial infarction is CK, which is increased by 4–6 hours, peaks (two- to tenfold) by 24 hours, and declines over 3–4 days. AST activity is increased by 6–12 hours, peaks at 18–36 hours, and declines over 3–4 days. LDH has the slowest rise, with initial increase being present by 24–48 hours, peaks occurring within 3–6 days, and values returning to normal by 14 days. Increases in the LDH_1 fraction precede increases in the total LDH and may be present by 8–24 hours. There is some evidence that the enzyme changes in children with myocardial infarction are qualitatively similar to adults, but the peak concentrations, especially of CK, may be reduced.[99] In pediatric practice, CK isoenzymes are most frequently used.

Cardiac troponin I and troponin T are polypeptide subunits of the myofibrillar regulatory troponin complex. Both are unique myocardial antigens expressed as tissue-specific isoforms[100, 101] and show a high sensitivity and specificity for myocardial injury.[102–108] They are not found in skeletal muscle during neonatal development or during adulthood, even after acute or chronic injury of skeletal muscle. As such, increases do not occur in plasma, even in patients with acute or chronic skeletal muscle disease, unless acute myocardial injury is present.[102] The sensitivity of cardiac troponin I and troponin T is similar to that of CK-MB for the diagnosis of acute myocardial infarction.[102–108] Furthermore, increases in cardiac troponin I and troponin T persist for up to 5–7 days in plasma, permitting flexibility in the timing of blood sampling. Measurement of cardiac troponin I and/or cardiac troponin T levels is a sensitive and specific method for the diagnosis of perioperative myocardial infarction, avoiding the high incidence of false diagnoses associated with the use of CK-MB as a diagnostic marker.[109] Clinical availability of cardiac troponin measurement is limited at the present time, but is likely to increase in the near future. A recent study found that increased donor serum cardiac troponin T concentrations measured just prior to organ retrieval were associated with significant increases in the inotropic requirements immediately following cardiac transplantation, suggesting that some degree of myocardial injury had occurred before organ donation.[110] Increased donor cardiac troponin T values may be a useful predictor of early allograft dysfunction and may influence the decision to use the heart for transplantation.

Cardiac Arrhythmias

The ability to generate action potentials is the distinguishing feature of excitable membranes. The cardiac action potential (AP) is caused by the transmembrane movement of ions and is divided into "phases" which show qualitative and quantitative differences in various cardiac tissues, as illustrated in Figure 5–4:[111]

Phase 0: Rapid influx of sodium ions which depolarizes the membrane.

Phase 1: Early repolarization, which is carried by potassium ions and makes the membrane potential less positive.

Phase 2: Plateau phase, which is characterized by the slow inward calcium current. The degree of plateau current varies in different tissues.

Phase 3: Repolarization phase, which is carried by potassium ions and returns the membrane potential toward the negative resting value.

Phase 4: Membrane potential has returned to its resting value.

FIGURE 5–4. Action Potentials

A. Fast-Response or Sodium-Channel Action Potential

Diagrammatic action potential of a "fast response" cardiac cell. Depolarization during phase 0 is caused by rapid sodium influx.

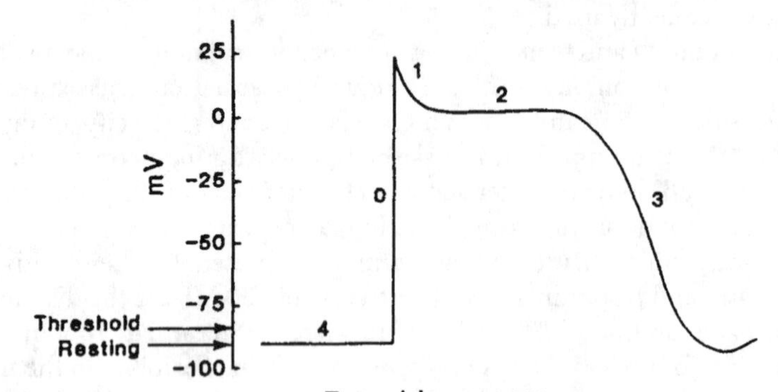

Found in: Atrial Myocytes
HIS–Purkinje Cells
Ventricular Myocytes
Accessory Pathways

B. Slow-Response or Calcium-Channel Action Potential

Diagrammatic action potential of a "slow response" cardiac cell. Depolarization during phase 0 is due to calcium and sodium influx. Note gradual spontaneous depolarization during phase 4, which imparts the property of automaticity to such cells.

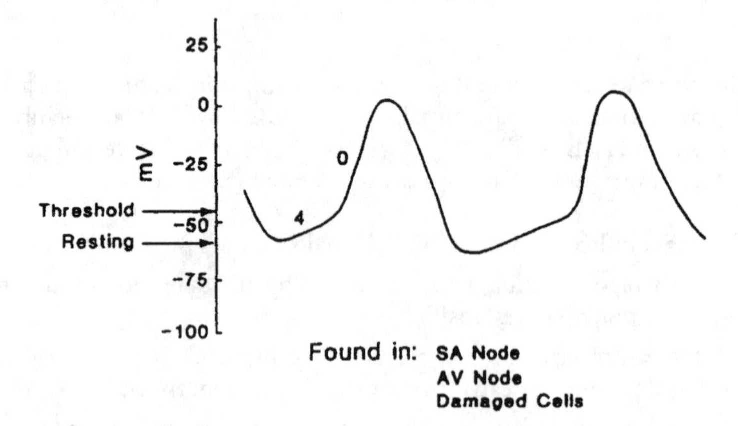

Found in: SA Node
AV Node
Damaged Cells

Source: Walsh EP. Electrocardiography and introduction to electrophysiology techniques. In: Fyler DC, ed. Nadas' pediatric cardiology. Philadelphia: Hanley & Belfus, 1992;117–158.

Two distinct types of cardiac action potentials have been observed.[111] The most common, known as the "fast-response" or "sodium channel" type (Figure 5–4A), occurs in cells of atrial muscle, ventricular muscle, His-Purkinje cells, and probably in accessory atrioventricular conduction tissue (such as the Kent bundle in Wolff-Parkinson-White syndrome). These cells generally register a resting potential at around –90 mV and rely upon sodium ions as the positive charge carrier for their initial rapid phase 0 depolarization.

The second variety of action potential, which occurs predominantly in cells of the sinus node and the AV node, is referred to as the "slow response" or "calcium channel" type (Figure 5–4B). It is distinguished by a blunt contour for the initial phase 0 upstroke, and utilizes calcium (along with some sodium) to provide the inward ionic current for depolarization. An important feature of many slow-response cells is the property of automaticity. Upward drift of the diastolic potential during phase 4 enables the cell to reach threshold of its own accord and thereby act as a natural pacemaker for the heart. Some fast-response cells may be capable of spontaneous automaticity, but at much slower rates.

Arrhythmias result from disorders of impulse generation (too fast or too slow), disorders of impulse conduction (block or reentry), or any combination thereof.[112] The sinus node, by virtue of its rapid spontaneous depolarization, is normally the pacemaker of the heart. Premature beats and tachyarrhythmias may preempt sinoatrial node activity secondary to disorders of automaticity or reentry. Abnormally slow heart rates (bradycardia and block) result from depression of depolarization in pacemaker cells and/or block of electrical activation. A detailed discussion of clinical patterns of arrhythmias and their underlying pathogenetic mechanisms is beyond the scope of this chapter.

Antiarrhythmic drugs are commonly classified according to their effects on cardiac action potentials. Initially proposed in 1970 by Vaughan Williams, the drugs are divided into four major groups:[113]

Class I: Local anesthetic agents that reduce upstroke velocity of phase 0 in atrial, ventricular, and Purkinje cells (sodium channel blockers: quinidine, procainamide, disopyramide, lidocaine, phenytoin, mexiletine, tocainide, flecainide, propafenone).

Class II: Drugs that inhibit sympathetic activity (beta blockers).

Class III: Drugs that prolong duration of the action potential without changing phase 0 (amiodarone, bretylium, sotalol).

Class IV: Drugs that block the slow inward current (calcium channel blockers: verapamil).

The capability to measure the plasma concentration of the most commonly used antiarrhythmic drugs is widely available (see Chapter 21). However, there must be a clear relationship between the plasma drug concentration and the pharmacodynamic or toxic effects in order to provide maximal benefit. Multiple age-related changes in body composition, drug metabolism, and renal elimination may combine to make precise drug dosing complicated. Procainamide is a class I antiarrhythmic agent which is acetylated in the liver to *N*-acetylprocainamide (NAPA). NAPA exhibits class III antiarrhythmic properties. The capacity of rapid acetylation is a Mendelian-dominant trait. Approximately 50% of North Americans are "slow acetylators" who have higher concentrations and slower clearance of procainamide. Therapeutic monitoring of procainamide serum concentrations should include determinations of procainamide and NAPA.

Abnormalities in serum electrolytes can precipitate or exacerbate arrhythmias, particularly abnormalities in serum potassium, calcium, and magnesium concentrations.[98] Digitalis toxicity is enhanced by hypokalemia, and infusions of potassium can be effective in suppressing the abnormal ectopic activity seen with increased digoxin concentrations. Magnesium deficiency appears to exacerbate the pro-arrhythmic nature of other electrolyte abnormalities. In particular, ventricular extrasystoles in hypokalemic patients may not resolve until both potassium and magnesium are corrected. The arrhythmias associated with digoxin toxicity may be worse in the presence of hypomagnesemia.

Lipid Disorders and Systemic Arterial Hypertension

For information on these forms of acquired heart disease in the pediatric population, refer to Chapter 18, "Disorders of Lipid and Lipoprotein Metabolism in Children and Adolescents," and Chapter 3, "Kidney and Urinary Tract Disorders."

REFERENCES

1. Ferencz C, Rubin JD, McCarter RJ, et al. Congenital heart disease prevalence at live birth: the Baltimore-Washington Infant Study. Am J Epidemiol 1985;121:31–36.
2. Clark EB. Growth, morphogenesis, and function: the dynamics of cardiovascular development. In: Moller JM, Neal WA, eds. Fetal, neonatal, and infant heart disease. New York: Appleton-Century-Crofts, 1989:1–22.
3. Rose V, Clark E. Etiology of congenital heart disease. In: Freedom RM, Benson LN, Smallhorn JF, eds. Neonatal heart disease. London: Springer-Verlag, 1992:3–17.
4. Boughman JA, Berg KA, Astemborski JA, et al. Familial risks of congenital heart defect assessed in a population-based epidemiologic study. Am J Med Genet 1987;26:839–47.
5. Kirby ML, Gale TF, Stewart DE. Neural crest cells contribute to normal aorticopulmonary septation. Science 1983;220:1059–61.
6. Kirby ML, Turnage KL, Hays BM. Characterization of conotruncal malformations following ablation of "cardiac" neural crest. Anat Rec 1985;213:87–93.
7. Kirby ML, Bockman DR. Neural crest and normal development: a new perspective. Anat Rec 1984;209:1–6.
8. Driscoll DA, Budarf ML, Emanuel BS. A genetic etiology for DiGeorge syndrome: consistent deletions and microdeletions of 22q11. Am J Hum Genet 1992;50:924–33.
9. Driscoll DA, Spinner NB, Budarf ML, et al. Deletions and microdeletions of 22q11.2 in velo-cardio-facial syndrome. Am J Med Genet 1992;44:261–68.
10. Scambler PJ, Carey AH, Wyse RKH, et al. Microdeletions within 22q11 associated with sporadic and familial DiGeorge syndrome. Genomics 1991;10:201–6.
11. Scambler PJ, Kelly D, Lindsay E, et al. Velo-cardio-facial syndrome associated with chromosome 22 deletions encompassing the DiGeorge locus. Lancet 1992;339:1138–39.

12. Wilson DI, Goodship JA, Burn J, et al. Deletions within chromosome 22q11 in familial congenital heart disease. Lancet 1992;340:573–75.
13. Goldmuntz E, Driscoll D, Budarf ML, et al. Microdeletions of chromosomal region 22q11 in patients with congenital conotruncal cardiac defects. J Med Genet 1993;30:807–12.
14. Van Mierop LHS, Alley RD, Kausel HW, Stranahan A. Pathogenesis of transposition complexes. I. Embryology of the ventricles and great arteries. Am J Cardiol 1963;12:216–25.
15. Harh JY, Paul MH, Gallen WJ et al. Experimental production of hypoplastic left heart syndrome in the chick embryo. Am J Cardiol 1986;10:127–32.
16. Lacro RV, Jones KL, Benirschke K. Pathogenesis of coarctation of the aorta in the Turner syndrome: a pathologic study of fetuses with nuchal cystic hygromas, hydrops fetalis, and female genitalia. Pediatrics 1988;81:445–51.
17. Atkins DL, Clark EB, Marvin WJ. Foramen ovale/atrial septum area ratio: a marker of transatrial blood flow. Circulation 1982;66:281–83.
18. Hawkins JA, Clark EB, Marvin WJ, et al. Foramen ovale/atrial septal ratio: evidence for different pathogenic mechanisms in congenital heart defects. Pediatr Res (Suppl) 1985;19:326A.
19. Hornberger LK, Sahn DJ, Reed K, et al. Flow across ventricular septal defects in the human fetus (abstract). Circulation 1989;80 (suppl 4):176.
20. Markwald RR. Cellular and molecular studies of normal and abnormal heart segmental development. Proc Greenwood Genet Center 1994;13:51–54.
21. Markwald RR, Mjaatvedt CH, Krug EL, Sinning AR. Inductive interactions in heart development: role of cardiac adherons in cushion tissue formation. Ann N Y Acad Sci 1990;588:13–25.
22. Rezaee M, Isokawa K, Halligan N, Markwald RR, Krug EL. Identification of an extracellular 130-kDa protein involved in early cardiac morphogenesis. J Biol Chem 1993;268:14404–11.
23. Kurnit DM, Aldridge JF, Matsuoka R, Matthysse S. Increased adhesiveness of trisomy 21 cells and atrioventricular canal malformations in Down syndrome: a stochastic model. Am J Med Genet 1985;20:385–99.
24. Kurnit DM, Layton WM, Matthysse S. Genetics, chance, and morphogenesis. Am J Hum Genet 1987;41:979–95.
25. Pexieder T. Cell death in the morphogenesis and teratogenesis of the heart. Adv Anat Embryol Cell Biol 1975;51:1–100.
26. Van Mierop LHS, Gessner IH. Pathogenetic mechanisms in congenital cardiovascular malformations. Prog Cardiovasc Dis 1972;15:67–85.
27. Ben-Shachar G, Arcilla R, Lucas RV et al. Ventricular trabeculations in the chick embryo and their contribution to the ventricular and muscular septal development. Circ Res 1985;57:759–66.
28. Neill CA. Development of the pulmonary veins with reference to embryology of anomalies of pulmonary venous return. Pediatrics 1956;18:880–87.
29. Clark EB, Martini DR, Rosenquist GC. Spectrum of pulmonary venous connections following lung bud inversion in the chick embryo. In: Pexieder T, ed. Perspectives in cardiovascular research: mechanisms of cardiac morphogenesis and teratogenesis, Vol. 5. New York: Raven Press, 1981:419–30.
30. Casey B, Devoto M, Jones KL, Ballabio A. Mapping a gene for familial situs abnormalities to human chromosome Xq24-q27.1. Nature Genetics 1993;5:403–7.
31. Brueckner M, McGrath J, D'Eustachio P, et al. Establishment of left-right asymmetry in vertebrates: genetically distinct steps are involved in biological asymmetry and handedness. CIBA Found Symp 1991;162:202–18.
32. Icardo JM, de Vega S. Spectrum of heart malformations in mice with situs solitus, situs inversus, and associated visceral heterotaxy. Circulation 1991;84:2547–58.
33. Brueckner M, D'Eustachio P, Horwich AL. Linkage mapping of a mouse gene, iv, that controls left-right asymmetry of the heart and viscera. Proc Natl Acad Sci USA 1989;86:5035–38.
34. Teichberg S, Markowitz J, Silverberg M, et al. Abnormal cilia in a child with the polysplenia syndrome and extrahepatic biliary atresia. J Pediatr 1982;100:399–401.
35. Schidlow DV, Moriber Katz S, Turtz MG, et al. Polysplenia and Kartagener syndromes in a sibship: association with abnormal respiratory cilia. J Pediatr 1982;100: 401–2.

36. Lacro RV. Dysmorphology. In: Fyler DC, ed. Nadas' pediatric cardiology. Philadelphia: Hanley & Belfus, 1991:37–55.
37. Lin AE, Garver KL. Genetic counseling for congenital heart defects. J Pediatr 1988;113: 1105–9.
38. Greenwood RD, Rosenthal A, Parisi L, et al. Extracardiac abnormalities in infants with congenital heart disease. Pediatrics 1975;55:485–92.
39. Newburger JW. Kawasaki syndrome. In: Fyler DC, ed. Nadas' pediatric cardiology. Philadelphia: Hanley & Belfus, 1992;319–27.
40. Rauch AM. Kawasaki syndrome: critical review of U.S. epidemiology. Prog Clin Biol Res 1987;250:33–44.
41. Rauch AM. Kawasaki syndrome: review of new epidemiologic and laboratory developments. Pediatr Infect Dis J 1987;6:1016–21.
42. Leung DY. Immunologic abnormalities in Kawasaki syndrome. Prog Clin Biol Res 1987;250:159–65.
43. Leung DY, Collins T, Lapierre LA. Immunoglobulin M antibodies present in the acute phase of Kawasaki syndrome lyse cultured vascular endothelial cells stimulated by gamma interferon. J Clin Invest 1986;77:1428–35.
44. Leung DY, Geha RS, Newburger JW, et al. Two monokines, interleukin 1 and tumor necrosis factor, render cultured vascular endothelial cells susceptible to lysis by antibodies circulating during Kawasaki syndrome. J Exp Med 1986;164:1958–72.
45. Morens DM, Anderson LJ, Hurwitz ES. National surveillance of Kawasaki disease. Pediatrics 1980;65:21–25.
46. Burns JC, Wiggins JW Jr, Toews WH, et al. Clinical spectrum of Kawasaki disease in infants younger than 6 months of age. J Pediatr 1986;109:381–84.
47. Kato H, Ichinose E, Inoue O, et al. Myocardial infarction in Kawasaki disease: clinical analyses in 195 cases. J Pediatr 1986;108:923–27.
48. Kato H, Ichinose E, Yoshioka F, et al. Fate of coronary aneurysm in Kawasaki disease: serial coronary angiography and long-term follow-up study. Am J Cardiol 1982;49:1758–66.
49. Suzuki A, Kamiya T, Kuwahara N, et al. Coronary arterial lesion of Kawasaki disease: cardiac catheterization findings of 1100 cases. Pediatr Cardiol 1986;7:3–9.
50. Daniels SR, Sprecker B, Capannari TE, et al. Correlates of coronary artery aneurysm formation in patients with Kawasaki disease. Am J Dis Child 1987;141:205–7.
51. Ichida F, Fatica NS, Engle MA, et al. Coronary artery involvement in Kawasaki syndrome in Manhattan, New York: risk factors and role of aspirin. Pediatrics 1987;80:828–35.
52. Koren G, MacLeod SM. Difficulty in achieving therapeutic serum concentrations of salicylate in Kawasaki disease. J Pediatr 1984;105:991–95.
53. Butler DF, Hough DR, Friedman SJ, et al. Adult Kawasaki syndrome. Arch Dermatol 1987;123:1356–61.
54. Nakano H, Ueda K, Saito A, et al. Repeated quantitative angiograms in coronary arterial aneurysm in Kawasaki disease. Am J Cardiol 1985;56:846–51.
55. Tatara K, Kusakawa S. Long-term prognosis of giant coronary aneurysms in Kawasaki disease. Prog Clin Biol Res 1987;250:579.
56. Tatara K, Kusakawa S. Long-term prognosis of giant coronary aneurysm in Kawasaki disease: an angiographic study. J Pediatr 1987;111:705–10.
57. Furusho K, Kamiya T, Nakano H, et al. High-dose intravenous gammaglobulin for Kawasaki disease. Lancet 1984;2:1055–58.
58. Furusho K, Kamiya T, Nakano H, et al. Japanese gammaglobulin trials for Kawasaki disease. Prog Clin Biol Res 1987;250:425–32.
59. Nagashima M, Matsushima M, Matsuoka H, et al. High-dose gammaglobulin therapy for Kawasaki disease. J Pediatr 1987;110:710–12.
60. Newburger JW, Takahashi M, Burns JC, et al. The treatment of Kawasaki syndrome with intravenous gamma globulin. N Engl J Med 1986;315:341–47.
61. Newburger JW, Sanders SP, Burns JC, et al. Left ventricular contractility and function in Kawasaki syndrome: effect of intravenous gamma globulin. Circulation 1989;79:1237–46.

62. Leung DY, Burns JC, Newburger JW. Reversal of lymphocyte activation in vivo in the Kawasaki syndrome by intravenous gammaglobulin. J Clin Invest 1987;79:468–72.
63. Fyler DC. Rheumatic fever. In: Fyler DC, ed. Nadas' pediatric cardiology. Philadelphia: Hanley & Belfus, 1992;305–18.
64. Kaplan EL, Hill HR. Return of rheumatic fever: consequences, implications, and needs. J Pediatr 1987;111:244–46.
65. Hosier DM, Craenen JM, Teske DW, et al. Resurgence of acute rheumatic fever. Am J Dis Child 1987;141:730–33.
66. Congeni B, Rizzo C, Congeni J, et al. Outbreak of acute rheumatic fever in northeast Ohio. J Pediatr 1987;111:176–79.
67. Veasy LG, Wiedmeier SE, Orsmond BS, et al. Resurgence of acute rheumatic fever in the intermountain area of the United States. N Engl J Med 1987;316:421–27.
68. Wald ER, Dashefsky B, Feidt C, et al. Acute rheumatic fever in western Pennsylvania and the tristate area. Pediatrics 1987;80:371–74.
69. Chun LT, Reddy V, Yamamoto LG. Rheumatic fever in children and adolescents in Hawaii. Pediatrics 1987;79:549–52.
70. Tolaymat A, Goudarzi T, Soler GP, et al. Acute rheumatic fever in north Florida. South Med J 1984;77:819–23.
71. Thomas WA, Averill JH, Castleman B, et al. The significance of Aschoff bodies in the left atrial appendage: a comparison of 40 biopsies removed during mitral commissurotomy with autopsy material from 40 patients dying from rheumatic fever. N Engl J Med 1983;249:761–65.
72. Mische SM, Manjula BN, Fischetti VA. Relation of streptococcal M protein with human and rabbit tropomyosin: the complete amino acid sequence of human cardiac alpha tropomyosin, a highly conserved contractile protein. Biochem Biophys Res Commun 1987;142:813–18.
73. Kaplan MH, Craig JM. Immunologic studies of heart tissue. VI. Cardiac lesions in rabbits associated with autoantibodies to heart induced by immunization with heterologous heart. J Immunol 1963;90:725–33.
74. Kaplan MH, Suchy ML. Immunologic relation of streptococcal and tissue antigens. II. Cross-reaction of antisera to mammalian heart tissue with a cell wall constituent of certain strains of group A streptococci. J Exp Med 1964;119:643–50.
75. Kaplan MH, Svec KH. Immunologic relation of streptococcal and tissue antigens. III. Presence in human sera of streptococcal antibody cross-reactive with heart tissue. Association with streptococcal infection, rheumatic fever, and glomerulonephritis. J Exp Med 1964;119:651–66.
76. Kaplan MH, Meyeserian M, Kushner I. Immunologic studies of heart tissue. IV. Serologic reactions with human heart tissue as revealed by immunofluorescent methods: isoimmune, Wassermann, and autoimmune reactions. J Exp Med 1961;113:17–36.
77. Zabriskie JB. Rheumatic fever: the interplay between host, genetics, and microbe. Circulation 1985;71:1077–86.
78. Husby G, van de Rijn I, Zabriskie JB, et al. Antibodies reacting with cytoplasm of subthalamic and caudate nuclei neurons in chorea and acute rheumatic fever. J Exp Med 1976;144:1094–110.
79. Stollerman GH, Markowitz M, Taranta A, et al. Jones criteria (revised) for guidance in diagnosis of rheumatic fever. Circulation 1965;32:664–68.
80. Markowitz M, Gordis L. Rheumatic fever, 2nd ed. Philadelphia: W.B. Saunders, 1972.
81. Dajani AS, Bisno AL, Chung KJ, et al. Prevention of rheumatic fever: a statement for health professionals by the committee on rheumatic fever, endocarditis, and Kawasaki disease of The Council on Cardiovascular Disease in the Young, the American Heart Association. Circulation 1988;78:1082–86.
82. Sande MA, Kaye D, Root RK. Endocarditis. Contemporary issues in infectious diseases, Vol. 2. New York, Churchill Livingstone, 1984.
83. Newburger JW. Infective endocarditis. In: Fyler DC, ed. Nadas' pediatric cardiology. Philadelphia: Hanley & Belfus, 1992;369–75.

84. Levison ME. Pathogenesis of infective endocarditis. In Kaye D, ed. Infective endocarditis. Baltimore: University Park Press, 1975.
85. Bayliss R, Clarke C, Oakley CM, et al. The microbiology and pathogenesis of infective endocarditis. Br Heart J 1983;50:513–19.
86. Committee on Rheumatic Fever and Infective Endocarditis. Prevention of bacterial endocarditis. JAMA 1990;264:2919–22.
87. Johnson DH, Rosenthal A, Nadas AS. A forty-year review of bacterial endocarditis in infancy and childhood. Circulation 1975;51:581–88.
88. Colan SD, Spevak PJ, Parness IA, et al. cardiomyopathies. In: Fyler DC, ed. Nadas' pediatric cardiology. Philadelphia: Hanley & Belfus, 1992;329–61.
89. World Health Organization. Report of the WHO/IFSC task force on the definition and classification of cardiac myopathies. Br Heart J 1980;44:672–73.
90. Schwartz ML, Cox G, Lin AE, et al. A clinical approach to genetic cardiomyopathy in children. Circulation 1996;94:2021–38.
91. Hengstenberg C, Schwartz K. Molecular genetics of familial hypertrophic cardiomyopathy. J Mol Cell Cardiol 1994;26:3–10.
92. Kelly DP, Strauss AW. Inherited cardiomyopathies. N Engl J Med 1994;330:913–19.
93. Geisterfer-Lowrance AAT, Kass S, Tanigawa G, et al. A molecular basis for familial hypertrophic cardiomyopathy: a beta cardiac myosin heavy chain gene missense mutation. Cell 1990;62:999–1006.
94. Tanigawa G, Jarcho JA, Kass S, et al. A molecular basis for familial hypertrophic cardiomyopathy: a cardiac alpha/beta myosin heavy chain hybrid gene. Cell 1990;62:991–98.
95. Thierfelder L, Watkins H, MacRae C, et al. Alpha-tropomyosin and cardiac troponin T mutations cause familial hypertrophic cardiomyopathy: a disease of the sarcomere. Cell 1994;77: 701–12.
96. Watkins H, Rosenzweig A, Hwang D-S, et al. Characteristic and prognostic implications of myosin missense mutations in familial hypertrophic cardiomyopathy. N Engl J Med 1992;326:1108–14.
97. Franciosi RA, Blanc WA. Myocardial infarcts in infants and children. 1. A necropsy study in congenital heart disease. J Pediatr 1968;73:309–19.
98. Gow RM, Dyck J, Rebeyka IM, Rose V, Freedom RM. Cardiovascular disorders. In: Soldin SJ, Rifai N, Hicks JMB, eds. Biochemical basis of pediatric disease. Washington: AACC Press, 1992;113–39.
99. Towbin JA. Myocardial infarction in childhood. In: Garson A Jr, Bricker JT, McNamara DG, eds. The science and practice of pediatric cardiology. New York: Lea & Febiger, 1990;1684–722.
100. Toyota N, Shimada Y. Differentiation of troponin in cardiac and skeletal muscles in chicken embryos as studied by immunofluorescence microscopy. J Cell Biol 1981;91:497–504.
101. Martin AF, Orlowski J. Molecular cloning and developmental expression of the rat cardiac-specific isoform of troponin I. J Mol Cell Cardiol 1991;23:583–88.
102. Adams JE III, Bodor GS, Davila-Roman VG, et al. Cardiac troponin I: a marker with high specificity for cardiac injury. Circulation 1993;88:101–6.
103. Cummins B, Auckland ML, Cummins P. Cardiac-specific troponin I radioimmunoassay in the diagnosis of acute myocardial infarction. Am Heart J 1987;113:1333–44.
104. Larue C, Calzolari C, Bertinchant JP, et al. Cardiac-specific immunoenzymometric assay of troponin I in the early phase of acute myocardial infarction. Clin Chem 1993;39:972–79.
105. Bodor GS, Porter S, Landt Y, et al. Development of monoclonal antibodies for an assay of cardiac troponin-I and preliminary results in suspected cases of myocardial infarction. Clin Chem 1992;38:2203–14.
106. Katus HA, Looser S, Hallermayer K, et al. Development and in vitro characterization of a new immunoassay of cardiac troponin T. Clin Chem 1992;38:386.
107. Burlina A, Zaninotto M, Secchiero S, et al. Troponin T as a marker of ischemic myocardial injury. Clin Biochem 1994;27:113–21.
108. Wu AHB, Valdes R Jr, Apple FS, et al. Cardiac troponin-T immunoassay for diagnosis of acute myocardial infarction. Clin Chem 1994;40:900–7.

109. Adams JE III, Sicard GA, Allen BT, et al. Diagnosis of perioperative myocardial infarction with measurement of cardiac troponin I. N Engl J Med 1994;330:670–74.
110. Anderson JR, Hossein-Nia M, Brown P, et al. Donor cardiac troponin-T predicts subsequent inotrope requirements following cardiac transplantation. Transplantation 1994;58:1056–57.
111. Walsh EP. Electrocardiography and introduction to electrophysiologic techniques. In: Fyler DC, ed. Nadas' pediatric cardiology. Philadelphia: Hanley & Belfus, 1992;117–58.
112. Walsh EP. Cardiac arrhythmias. In: Fyler DC, ed. Nadas' pediatric cardiology. Philadelphia: Hanley & Belfus, 1992;377–433.
113. Vaughan Williams EM. Classification of antiarrhythmic drugs. In: Sandoe E, Flensted-Janse E, Olsen KH, eds. Symposium on cardiac arrhythmias. Sodertalje, Sweden: AB Astra, 1970;449–72.

CHAPTER 6

Growth Disorders

Raphaël Rappaport, M.D.
Jean-Claude Souberbielle, Ph.D.

INTRODUCTION

Growth from birth to adolescence is closely related to health, so any deviation from the normal growth rate may be the presenting symptom or the complication of an intercurrent disease, or lead to the diagnosis of a defect in skeletal development or its endocrine control. A number of biochemical tools contribute to the diagnosis. Their use is initially guided by the clinical analysis. The majority of problems related to growth that occur in the childhood period are due to growth retardation rather than to increases in growth.

PHYSIOLOGY OF GROWTH

Growth from birth until adulthood is determined by genetic and environmental factors. Among these is nutrition, which is essential to allow the optimal effect of hormones and growth factors. Therefore, a long-lasting, chronic disease can impair growth by interfering with nutrient intake and utilization, as well as by impairing specific organ functions and imposing a condition of chronic stress.

The endocrine control of skeletal growth is primarily dependent on growth hormone (GH) secretion and bioactivity as is demonstrated by pituitary dwarfism. It has been shown that GH does not stimulate bone growth or cartilage activity *in vitro* by direct action, but needs the presence of a growth factor initially called somatomedin and now known as insulin-like growth factor I, or IGF I. This somatomedin hypothesis has been verified by the finding that IGF I is produced by the liver and most cells of the body and that it stimulates target cells, in particular cartilage growth plates, thereby controlling endochondral ossification. More recently, this classical view has been challenged by the evidence of direct effects of GH on cartilage. It is now appreciated that locally produced IGF I, stimulated by GH, acts by an autocrine/paracrine mechanism. The cell-to-cell interaction is superimposed on the endocrine circulating IGF effect. GH and IGF I are necessary for other hormones, such as thyroid hormones and sex steroids, to fully express a complete and appropriate stimulation of skeletal growth.

Growth Hormone and Growth Factors

The GH/IGF I axis is presently viewed as central to the control of growth (see Figure 6–1). Schematically, the growth response depends on (1) the availability of both GH and IGF I, which are assessed by measurement of their circulating concentrations; and (2) on their biological activity, which may depend on circulating forms of GH, on various proteins binding IGF I, on their receptors, and on as yet poorly defined cartilage and bone factors involved in the tissue responsiveness to endocrine control.

FIGURE 6–1. The Endocrine and Paracrine Control of Skeletal Growth

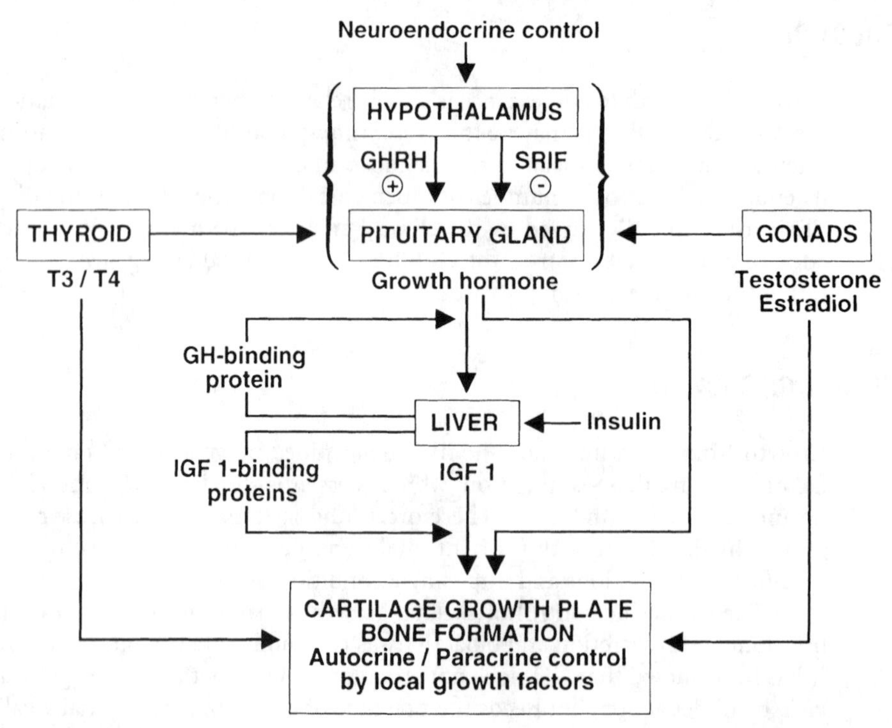

From: Rappaport R. A touch of growth. Horm Res 1991:36;166–73. Reprinted with permission.

Growth Hormone

Human GH (hGH) is a protein secreted by the pituitary gland, with a molecular weight of 22 kD consisting of a single peptide chain of 191 amino acid residues. The hGH genes reside within a cluster of five loci: normal GH, or GH 1; two human chorionic somatomammotropin, or hCS A and B; one hCS pseudogene; and a variant GH, or GH 2, only expressed in the placenta. Expression of the GH gene GH1 utilizes two different splicing sequences. This alternative splicing forms the basis of the 20 kD variant of hGH. The two 22 kD and 20 kD forms are co-secreted and circulate in the plasma in percentages of 80 and 20, respectively, independently of age and sex.[1]

Neuro-endocrine Control

The pituitary receives information from the central nervous system through the hypothalamus, which receives and modulates a large number of neurotransmitters as well as hormonal and metabolic signals.[2] The final common pathway for integration of these signals involves two hypothalamic neuropeptides which are hypophysiotropic hormones: somatostatin (somatotropin release inhibiting factor, or SRIF), which has an inhibitory influence, and growth hormone releasing hormone, or GHRH, which exerts a stimulatory effect. Many of the data on neuro-endocrine control come from rodent studies, such as those designed to selectively exclude the effect of one of the hormones using specific antibodies.[3] Although there are definite species differences, it is likely that in the human most of the other hypothalamic neuropeptides or monoamines also act via the SRIF/GHRH pathway.

The GHRH neurones are mainly located in the arcuate nucleus. GHRH (secreted as GHRH 1-44) selectively stimulates *in vitro* and *in vivo* growth hormone secretion. Analogs have been synthesized such as the GHRH 1-29, which has an activity identical to that of the natural peptide. A partial loss of responsiveness, also considered as partial GHRH receptor desensitization with depletion of GH stores, has been observed in normal human subjects receiving several boluses of GHRH. This effect is much less striking than the severe desensitization observed in the effect of gonadotropin releasing hormone analogs and seems to have no clinical relevance. In contrast, the GH response to a supramaximal dose of GHRH was preserved during 14 days' continuous GHRH infusion with increased serum IGF I concentrations. This observation established the therapeutic potential of GHRH in hypopituitary children.

Other signals play a role in the control of GHRH secretion. For instance, the *in vitro* secretion of GHRH is inhibited by IGF I. This control may involve hypothalamic GHRH production at a post-transcriptional level.[4]

Somatostatin, or SRIF, is found in the hypothalamus but also in the pancreas. It is a family of peptides including somatostatin-14 and somatostatin-28, which is the most potent. Newly synthesized molecules have a longer half-life. SRIF exerts its activity through specific pituitary membrane receptors, inhibiting both GH and thyroid stimulating hormone (TSH) secretion. SRIF inhibits or modulates GH secretion by blocking the stimulatory effect of GHRH. It also mediates the GH and IGF I negative-feedback effect on growth hormone secretion which stimulates SRIF release. SRIF does not interfere with GRF binding to pituitary somatotrophs.[5]

GH Secretion Patterns

The patterns of GH secretion vary among species. Generally, bursts or pulses of secretion occur at variable intervals, separated by periods during which GH sometimes fails to reach detectable concentrations. In the human, GH is episodically secreted in intermittent bursts, the majority of which occur during the night. During the day, GH secretion may be related to exercise, stress, and nutrient intake. A new method for calculating the secretory rate, deconvolution analysis, provides information of clinical relevance.[6]

Rat experiments indicate that SRIF is important for maintaining low basal concentrations, whereas pulsatile GH secretion is dependent on GHRH activity. In addition, variations in SRIF secretion contribute to the pattern of pulsatile secretion. Hence, the control of GH secretion depends on asynchronous periodic release of GHRH and SRIF; pulses of GH secretion would be expected to occur at times of maximal GHRH and minimal SRIF activity. It has been stated that the variability in the response of GH to a supramaximal dose of GHRH in normal subjects reflects varying hypothalamic SRIF secretion at time of GHRH stimulation.

Resting concentrations of GH in plasma taken at random vary with age. At birth, the mean concentration is 33 ng/mL. It declines within a few months to the prepubertal concentration of 3–5 ng/mL until the pubertal rise. These changes go along with parallel changes in secretion rates as estimated from spontaneous profiles. GH secretion rises during abrupt hypoglycemia and is suppressed by acute hyperglycemia. A high-protein meal or intravenous infusion of amino acids induces release of GH, probably by hypothalamic control. Growth hormone secretion is stimulated during fasting in normal persons and is also observed in protein-deprived, malnourished children. This effect is possibly due to the suppression of the normal feedback control of plasma IGF I. It is of interest that obesity induces a blunted GH response to pharmacological stimulation and decreases spontaneous secretion,[7] whereas stress is a potent stimulus of GH release. A characteristic feature is the sleep-associated rise of GH; this nocturnal rise is mainly related to sleep onset and is correlated with EEG changes of slow-wave sleep, although the phenomena are not directly interdependent.

GH Binding Protein and GH Receptor

Fifty percent of the circulating GH is estimated to be in a complexed form in association with a soluble specific high-affinity and low-capacity binding protein. This protein has more affinity for the 22 kD than the 20 kD form of GH. It represents the extracellular portion of the monomeric GH receptor, which belongs to the cytokine superfamily receptors.[8] Dimerization of the GH receptor is necessary for GH activity. At present there is no evidence that the binding protein may have an effect on the *in vivo* kinetics of GH and its biological activity. The regulatory mechanism of production of the binding protein by proteolytic cleavage in the human remains unknown.

Insulin-like Growth Factors

Growth hormone exerts its growth-promoting effect on somatic tissues by inducing peptide growth factors, termed insulin-like growth factors (formerly somatomedins). Specific peptides of this kind are IGF I and IGF II. These factors were isolated on the basis of their insulinomimetic effects on fat and muscle, their GH-dependent effect on cartilage, and their mitogenic effect on cultured fibroblasts. They regulate functional cell differentiation. Their biological role is determined primarily by the receptors expressed in the target cells and the tissue expression of their genes.[9, 10]

Both IGF I and IGF II structures are very similar to proinsulin, and it is thought that both IGFs and insulin have evolved from a common ancestor. The gene structures of the IGFs have been well investigated. The IGF I gene is localized on the long arm of chromosome 12; the IGF II gene is on chromosome 11 downstream from the insulin gene. The expression of IGFs' genes varies between organs and during development in the fetus. It is generally considered that IGF II is dominant in embryonic fetal life. In contrast, IGF I is present in the fetal circulation at low concentrations and increases from birth to adulthood. As the expression of IGF I in liver appears to parallel its serum concentration, it is likely that in the postnatal life the liver is the major source of IGF I in circulation.

GH has a key role in regulating IGF production, and the production of IGF I (more than IGF II) is dependent on the presence of mature growth hormone receptors. IGF I increases gradually in serum until puberty. At puberty, its dramatic increase is essentially GH-mediated under the control of sex steroids.[11, 12] IGF I production is also dependent on other hormones. Thyroid hormones may modulate the GH effect on liver production of IGF I. Insulin may participate in the control of IGF I release, as has been shown in experimental animals. The role of glucocorticoids is not elucidated, although high doses may suppress circulating IGF I concentrations and GH secretion. They also have a direct negative effect on cartilage growth.

There are two specific IGF receptors. The Type 1 IGF receptor has a structure similar to that of the insulin receptor. It binds IGF I and IGF II (with higher affinity for IGF I) and cross-reacts weakly with insulin. The Type 2 receptor essentially binds IGF II. Its structure is very different from that of the Type 1 receptor and its function is unknown. Growth effect would therefore depend mostly on signaling related to the IGF Type 1 receptor.

IGF Binding Proteins

Six binding proteins known as IGFBP-1 to IGFBP-6 have been isolated and some are produced by recombinant technique.[13, 14] More than 90% of the IGFs circulate in bound forms with specific binding proteins localized in two main fractions in serum: a ternary 150 kD complex containing IGFBP-3 and preferentially binding IGF I, and the 40 kD complex containing other binding proteins as well as IGFBP-3 and having a higher affinity for IGF II. The physiology of IGFBP-1 and IGFBP-3 has been extensively studied.[15] The major circulating binding protein is IGFBP-3, which has a long half-life. IGFBP-3 is glycosylated and consists of two components of 41.5 kD and 38.5 kD, respectively, when analyzed by Western blot. As for IGF I, IGFBP-3's circulating concentration shows little change over 24 h. There is a steady age-dependent increase with a peak during puberty and a further decline. It is positively correlated with GH secretion. In contrast, the 40 kD complex shows an inverse relationship with growth hormone. It contains two other IGF binding proteins, IGFBP-1 and IGFBP-2, along with IGFBP-3. IGFBP-1 is negatively influenced by nutrition and insulin secretion. Its function may be minimal in respect to postnatal growth.[16]

The binding proteins lengthen the half-life of the IGF peptides and change their clearance. They also control biological activity by modulating their transfer and binding to cell surface receptors. Some have been shown to have both inhibitory and stimulatory effects. This is a critical issue currently under investigation.

Endocrine and Paracrine Control of Growth

The concept of IGF I as principal GH-dependent agent of postnatal growth is consistent with the extreme situation of Laron dwarfism, wherein serum IGF I is barely detectable but concentrations of GH are normal to high. Recombinant human IGF I stimulates growth of hypophysectomized mice and of Snell dwarf mice and is able to mimic the effects of GH on epiphyseal plate width and trabecular bone formation. It stimulates growth of children with Laron dwarfism. Interestingly, it was recently reported that intrauterine growth retardation with postnatal growth failure were associated with IGF I gene deletion.[17]

It is now recognized that GH, in addition to controlling IGF I production, has a direct effect on growth of tissues. According to the Green hypothesis, GH would induce differentiation of precursors of prechondrocytes with clone formation, whereby these cells acquire the capacity to produce IGF I and to respond to it.[18] It was suggested that this activation of the IGF I gene is independent of the effect of GH on the liver and results from a direct interaction between GH and cartilage. Furthermore, pulsatile treatment with physiological doses of GH induces a three- to fivefold increase in concentrations of IGF I mRNA in rat growth plates, whereas continuous infusion is less effective. Thus, the local paracrine and autocrine action plays a major role in skeletal growth: IGFs act primarily as local regulators of cell growth and differentiation. However, it is still difficult to determine the respective role of systemic and locally produced IGF I. This dual mechanism may explain the poor correlation between circulating IGF I concentrations and growth rates. The highest growth rates observed in infancy, accompanied by the lowest blood IGF I concentrations, may reflect a predominant paracrine/autocrine control at that age.

Isaksson et al. have proposed a sequence of events leading to bone growth as a dual effector theory for GH action: the effect of GH is limited to a precursor cell population which differentiates and thereby produces local IGF I and IGF binding proteins leading to chondrocyte proliferation and differentiation.[19]

Thyroid Hormones

Thyroid hormones play a central role in skeletal maturation. They stimulate GH secretion and control the effect of GH on IGF I production. In addition, thyroid hormones require the presence of GH to exert a full effect, since GH accelerates the conversion of thyroxine into its active metabolite, triiodothyronine. However, it is likely that thyroid hormones also have a direct effect on the skeleton, as thyroid treatment accelerates bone maturation in pituitary dwarfs not treated with hGH.

Sex Steroids and Pubertal Growth

Growth at puberty is dependent on the interaction of GH, IGF I, and sex steroids. Height increase accelerates and skeletal maturation results in fusion of the epiphyseal cartilages when the final height is reached. Secretion of GH is increased by sex steroids through augmented amplitude of GH secretion episodes, although frequency of pulses is not affected. The threshold level of GH secretion required to obtain a pubertal growth is not known. There is some evidence that it may be low.

Estrogen, in low doses, stimulates growth without an increase in IGF I concentrations, and similar findings have been reported in boys receiving oxandrolone, an anabolic steroid. These findings correspond to *in vitro* evidence that chondrocytes respond to estradiol and dihydrotestosterone with an increased synthesis of proteoglycans. In addition, the presence of estrogen receptors has been demonstrated in these cells, with a higher affinity for estrogen at puberty than before puberty. These findings provide a rationale for the therapeutic use of low doses of sex steroids at initiation of puberty in hypogonadotropic patients in order to promote growth.

Glucocorticoids

There is no evidence that cortisol at physiological concentrations regulates growth. However, glucocorticoids at pharmacological doses do inhibit cartilage activity and decrease GH secretion.

Growth and Nutrition

Growth retardation occurs during chronic malnutrition or voluntary reduction of caloric intake as in anorexia nervosa. The characteristic sequence of events includes increased GH secretion and low IGF I concentrations reflecting a state of cellular resistance to GH. Fasting induces a decrease in membrane GH-binding capacity, whereas a post-receptor defect is observed during protein restriction. Both conditions contrast with normal or elevated GH secretion, resulting in decreased ability to generate IGF I. Low IGF I circulating concentrations therefore appear to be a sensitive index of nutritional status.[16, 20] Insulin is essentially acting indirectly by allowing normal fuel utilization, as neither cartilage nor bone tissue in culture show a response to that peptide.

Catch-up Growth

Catch-up growth with a return to the child's own growth channel occurs after any temporary growth disturbance such as malnutrition, corticotherapy, renal acidosis, or chronic dehydration. Catch-up growth may be incomplete if the disease is not fully cured or if it has caused permanent cellular lesions. Its mechanism is not well understood; factors such as nutrition and GH secretion may play a role, in addition to a cellular control that is still unknown.

DIAGNOSTIC BASIS FOR BIOCHEMICAL INVESTIGATION

Short Stature

Failure to grow and/or short stature may be the presenting symptom of endocrine disorders or chronic diseases.[21] The key sign is a low-for-age growth rate. It should be distinguished from the frequent nonpathological condition of normal short stature with normal growth rate. This is only possible if a reliable growth curve is available. A number of causes must therefore be ruled out before the diagnosis of genetic or constitutional short stature is considered. Most of these causes are presented in Table 6–1. This is the framework for radiological and biochemical investigation. The most frequently encountered chronic diseases are malnutrition, chronic disorders of digestive absorption, chronic renal failure, emotional deprivation, and primary skeletal disorders. Endocrine causes include late-onset hypothyroidism, growth hormone deficiency, and delayed puberty.

TABLE 6–1. Causes of Growth Failure and Short Stature

Clinical Diagnosis	Biochemical Findings
Genetic short stature	Normal
Constitutional delay in growth	Normal
Constitutional delay in puberty	Transient GH deficiency; Delayed sex steroid secretion
Intra-uterine growth retardation	Possible GH deficiency
Psychosocial dwarfism	Low or normal GH, low IGF I
Malnutrition, protein-calorie deficiency or chronic disease	Normal or high GH, low IGF I
Genetic bone disease	Normal
Turner syndrome in girls	46,XO karyotype
Hormonal abnormalities	
GH deficiency	
Isolated deficiency	Low GH, low IGFI
Multiple pituitary deficiency	+ low T4, low cortisol and absence of puberty
Genetic hypopituitarism	Low GH, low IGF I
Genetic GH insensitivity	Lack of GH binding; low IGFI; Normal or high GH
Other hormones	
Hypothyroidism (primary)	Low T4, high TSH
Cortisol excess	High urinary cortisol
Diabetes mellitus (not controlled)	High HbA1C
Diabetes insipidus (not controlled)	Chronic dehydration

TABLE 6–2. Etiology of Growth Retardation According to Age

Infancy	Intrauterine growth retardation Calorie deficiency (malnutrition, coeliac disease) Metabolic diseases, renal failure Hypothyroidism Hypopituitarism
Childhood	Genetic short stature Calorie deficiency (psychosocial dwarfism, coeliac disease) GH deficiency Hypothyroidism Genetic bone disease Turner syndrome (girls) Cushing syndrome
Puberty	Constitutional delay Turner syndrome (girls) Hypopituitarism Anorexia nervosa Chronic diseases

At first, a critical analysis of the child's growth should be performed, focusing on his or her perinatal history, growth curve, weight-to-height ratio, and growth rate for chronological age and for bone age using appropriate reference data. Causes of growth retardation vary with age (Table 6–2). Specific problems arise with abnormal timing of puberty (Table 6–3). In most cases, the clinical features generally provide a valuable guideline for the choice of biochemical and hormonal evaluation (Table 6–4).

TABLE 6–3.Typical Investigation for Growth Disturbance in Relation to Abnormal Puberty

Clinical Presentation	Estradiol* Testosterone	LH/FSH	Diagnosis
Delayed Puberty (retarded growth and bone maturation)	low	low	delayed puberty hypogonadotropinism
	low	high	primary gonadal failure
Precocious puberty (acclerated growth and bone maturation)	high	pubertal level	central precocious puberty
	high	low	primary gonadal hyperfunction
	DHEAS high	normal	premature pubarche
	17 OHP high	normal	congenital virilizing adrenal hyperplasia

*indication of concentration by comparison with normal for chronological age
DHEAS = Dehydroepiandrosterone Sulfate
17 OHP = 17-hydroxyprogesterone
LH = Luteinizing Hormone
FHS = Follicle Stimulating Hormone

TABLE 6–4. Growth Retardation: Guidelines for Clinical Biochemical Evaluation

Cause	Clinical Signs	Plasma Biochemical/ Hormonal Signs	Possible Diagnosis
Familial and neonatal history	Parental short stature and/or pubertal delay	Normal	Genetic/constitutional growth retardation
	Poor economic status	Normal GH, low IGF I	Calorie/protein deficiency
	Disturbed family, child abuse	Normal GH, low IGF I	Psychosocial dwarfism
	Small for date and/or	Normal	Intrauterine growth retardation
	dysmorphic features	Normal	Chromosomal, skeletal disorders
Endocrine causes	GH deficiency features, hypoglycemia or growth retardation associated with midline defects or perinatal asphyxia secondary to cranial irradiation or brain tumor	Low GH, low IFG I	Isolated GH deficiency or multiple pituitary deficiencies
	isolated (sporadic or familial)	Low GH, low IGFI	Isolated GH deficiency (GRF deficiency); GH gene deletion
		High GH, low IFGI	GH receptor mutation: GH insensitivity
	Hypothyroidism	Low T4/T3, high TSH	Primary hypothroidism
	Obesity, osteoporosis	High plasma/urinary cortisol	Cushing syndrome
	Corticoid therapy	Low DHEA sulfate	Iatrogenic
	Delayed puberty	Lack of sex steroid secretion	Delayed puberty (transient or organic)
	Polyuria, polydipsia	Failure to concentrate urines	Diabetes insipidus with vasopressin deficiency
	Diabetes mellitus	Normal GH, low IGF I	Poor control
Non-endocrine causes	Anemia, rickets	Low 25OHD3, anemia, low iron	Vitamin D deficiency and iron deficiency
	Turner features (girl)	46, XO karyotype	Turner syndrome
	Low weight for height	Normal GH, low IGF I	Malnutrition, anorexia nervosa
	Chronic diarrhea	Antigliadin antibodies, low folate	Coeliac disease
	Abdominal pain, fever	Accelerated sedimentation rate	Crohn's ileitis
	Anemia, edema	Increased creatinine, urea	Chronic renal failure
	Polyuria, polydipsia	Failure to respond to vasopressin	Diabetes insipidus with vasopressin resistance

TABLE 6–5. Elements of Routine Evaluation of a Child with Short Stature and/or Decreased Growth Rate

History and physical examination
Skull X-ray, bone age on left hand
CBC, folate, carotene, antigliadin antibodies, ESR
Plasma electrolytes, creatinine, BUN
Karyotype in females
Thyroid function: T4, TSH
Growth hormone response to pharamacological stimulation and/or spontaneous profiles on nightime or 24 hr.
IGF I and IGF BP 3

One should focus on treatable causes of short stature. Therefore, it may be advisable to perform a laboratory screening for diseases such as renal failure and coeliac disease and to consider the possibility of thyroid or GH deficiency. The latter is a crucial issue (Table 6–5). Another approach relates to known chronic diseases, during which growth failure may be severe and long lasting.

It may be relevant to consider the various mechanisms of growth retardation in such affected children before deciding therapy. These mechanisms may be quite variable, such as primary metabolic disturbances, treatment-related iatrogenic negative effects on growth, secondary skeletal lesions and/or resistance to endogenous GH, caloric and protein deprivation, or psychosocial disturbance. The laboratory investigation will contribute to assessing some of these hypotheses in a given case. In growth retardation, it may be useful to consider the information provided by the combined evaluation of GH and IGF I secretion, as described in Table 6–6.

The Diagnosis of Growth Hormone Deficiency

Schematically, children with GH deficiency have retarded bone age and decreased growth rate (below 4.5 cm/yr before puberty), documented at least during a year follow-up. Classically, GH deficiency is diagnosed when two consecutive stimulation tests show concordant low peak GH values with low circulating IGF I values. However, since there is no gold standard for GH deficiency definition, it remains necessary to compare test results with the clinical data, especially when a child is referred for non-familial short stature with borderline growth velocity for age.

As shown in view (a) of Figure 6–2, the diagnostic procedure usually begins with a GH stimulation test eventually conducted after sex steroid priming. If the GH responses are discrepant, it is necessary to further investigate the patient by measuring plasma IGF I. Alternatively, it may be less costly, more pleasant for the patient, and more appropriate to first measure plasma IGF I and IGFBP-3 concentrations. Low values, with few exceptions, are strong indicators of GH deficiency and should be confirmed by a GH stimulation test, shown in view (b) of Figure 6–2.[22] Overnight spontaneous GH profiles may be helpful, although less practical and more costly.

TABLE 6–6. Growth Retardation due to Abnormalities of the Growth Hormone/IGF I Axis Classified According to Plasma Concentrations

LOW GH, LOW IGF I	
Primary GH Deficiency	
Genetic:	Autosomal dominant or recessive, X-linked recessive
	GH gene mutation, GRF receptor gene mutation
Idiopathic:	Isolated GH deficiency (probably GHRH deficiency)
Primary Multiple Pituitary Hormone deficiency	
Genetic:	Autosomal or X-linked, recessive
Developmental:	Midline defects (cleft lip and palate)
	Pituitary aplasia
	Optic-septo dysplasia
Organic:	Cranial irradiation
	Hypothalamic-pituitary tumors
	Trauma
Idiopathic:	Perinatal trauma and asphyxia
	Pituitary stalk interruption (on MRI)
Secondary GH Deficiency	
Chronic malnutrition	
Hemochromatosis, psychosocial dwarfism, thalassemia	
HIGH GH, LOW IGF I	
Primary GH Insensitivity	
Laron-type dwarfism (GH receptor gene mutation and absent plasma GH binding protein)	
Genetic dwarfism with low GH receptor activity (pygmy)	
Secondary GH Insensitivity	
Acute fasting	
Chronic malnutrition, protein-calorie deficiency	
Bioinacive but Immunoreactive GH	
HIGH GH, NORMAL TO HIGH IGF I	
Chronic renal failure with excess in IGF BP-3 (supposed resistance to GH/IGF I)	
Primary IGF I receptor defect (not demonstrated)	

If GH deficiency is documented, magnetic resonance imaging (MRI) should be performed to diagnose a craniopharyngioma or a less frequent tumor, or to document pituitary anatomy. Pituitary stalk-interruption with an ectopic neuropost-hypophyseal bright spot and anterior pituitary hypoplasia indicates that GH deficiency, generally part of idiopathic multiple pituitary deficiencies, will be permanent and requires long-term GH therapy.[23] A recent finding was the great frequency of transient GH deficiency, mostly in boys with pubertal delay. Most authors would consider that GH treatment is rarely required in these children.

FIGURE 6–2. Flowchart for the Diagnosis of Growth Hormone Deficiency. View (a): starting with GH stimulation test. View (b): starting with IGF I measurement.

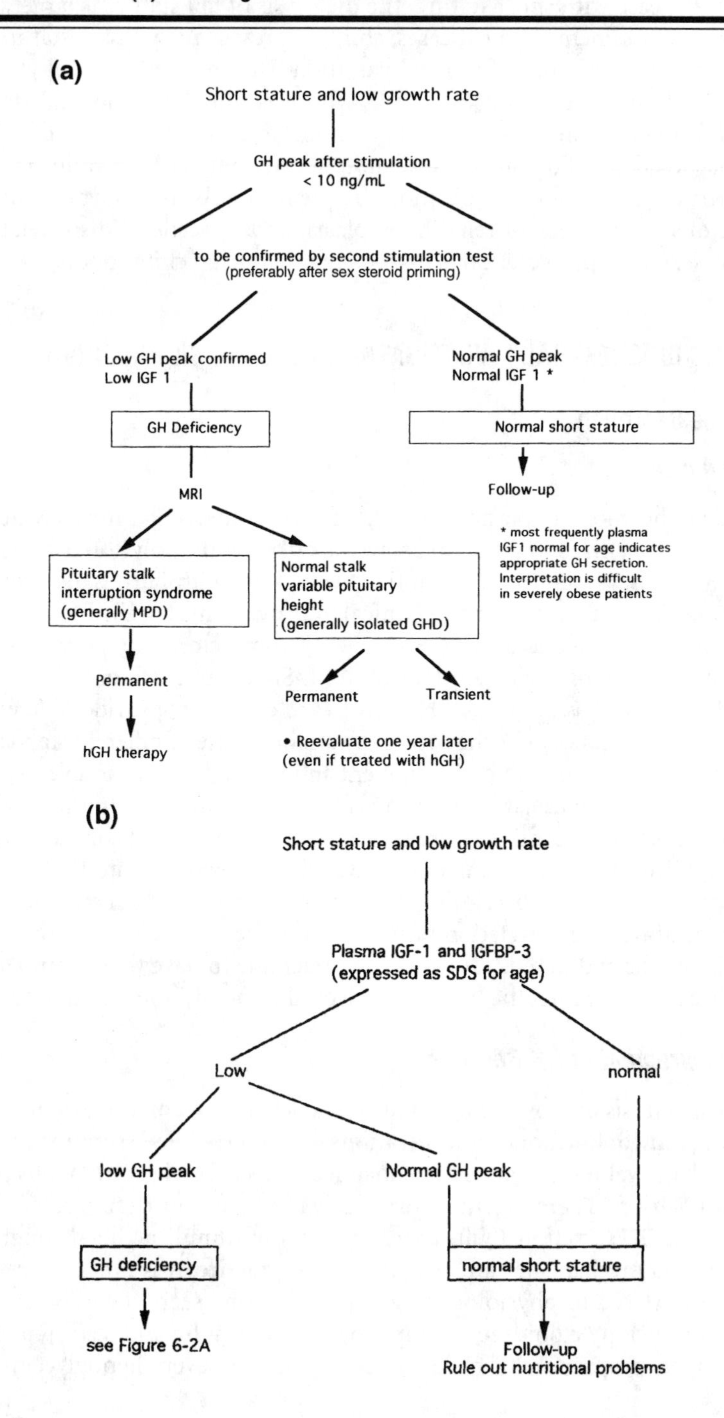

Tall Stature

As is the case with short stature, the diagnosis of tall stature is largely based on the clinical assessment. In most cases, children presenting with tall stature have no disease but are extremes of normal variation. However, accelerated growth with advanced bone maturation in a child who was initially of normal stature suggests primary endocrine disorders and hormonal evaluation is required with various approaches, depending on age, sex, and pubertal status of the child. The main causes are true precocious puberty (more frequent in girls than boys), virilization due to late onset congenital adrenal hyperplasia, and hyperthyroidism related to Grave's disease. GH hypersecretion is extremely rare during childhood.

HORMONAL AND BIOCHEMICAL INVESTIGATION: CLINICAL SIGNIFICANCE

Growth Hormone Secretion

GH Assays

Growth hormone in plasma consists of various molecular forms which may not be equally recognized in different assays.[1] Until recently, polyclonal competitive radioimmunoassays were used in routine evaluation, with fairly satisfactory agreement between most assay systems. Technical improvements have led to new assays such as immunoradiometric assay (IRMA) with monoclonal or polyclonal antibodies, immunoenzymometric assay (IEMA or ELISA), immunofluorometric assay (IFMA), and oligoclonal assay (OCA). However, each assay may provide different results, as a number of factors can be the source of variability: use of different standards, heterogeneity of epitope recognition by different antibodies,[24–26] and variable matrix effects.[27]

For clinical use, it is important to have full information on the characteristics of the assay to determine reference values in physiological conditions and to have a comparison with other current assays when growth hormone deficiency is to be diagnosed. Distinct discriminant values may be needed for various assays. A high degree of relative correlation has been found between assays, but absolute potency estimates have differed.[24] It would be preferable to have them compared to a reference assay, for which the best choice would be a polyclonal antibody.

Measurement of GH Secretion

The diagnosis of growth hormone deficiency is based on the evidence of low circulating growth hormone concentrations and inferred low secretion. The use of random basal values has failed to be diagnostic because of spontaneous pulsatility and short half-life. Therefore, the most widely used procedure is pharmacological stimulation of GH secretion. Quite a large number of stimuli, acting through as yet poorly identified mechanisms, are used in clinical practice. It is not known which is most closely related to physiological growth hormone secretion. The commonly used stimuli include clonidine, L-Dopa, ornithine, insulin-induced hypoglycemia, and glucagon-propranolol. The last two may induce severe hypoglycemia and require close follow-up by experienced personnel. The arginine stimulation test is less potent and has more false-negative results. By convention, failure to achieve a maximum stimulated GH concentration of 7 or 10 ng/mL using conventional RIAs defines classical GH deficiency. This cut-off value should be lower when using some of the monoclonal assays.

Because of the variability of the peak GH response, use of two different stimuli is recommended. It is generally accepted that concordant decreased responses to two consecutive tests are sufficient for a diagnosis of GH deficiency. This is most frequently observed in patients with severe GH deficiency, decreased growth rate, and typical features of hypopituitarism, or in children with organic pituitary deficiency. Difficulties in the assessment of GH secretion arise when children with isolated short stature are investigated in view of hGH therapy. A great many studies have been performed to determine the best diagnostic procedure. The pharmacological stimulation tests often provide discrepant results when two consecutive tests are performed.[28] Furthermore, the level of response may vary according to the stimulus used for testing.

Therefore, assessment of maximum spontaneous GH secretion by sampling at frequent intervals or by continuous withdrawal during 12–24 h periods has been proposed, with results expressed as spontaneous peak values or integrated concentrations of GH (IC-GH). The measurement of spontaneous secretion levels was found to be highly reproducible when continuous withdrawal was used.[28] It is generally accepted that some children with low stimulated GH concentrations have spontaneous GH profiles and IC-GH in the normal range,[29] but the contrary can also occur.

To interpret the individual data, one must also take into account the large range of IC-GH values obtained in normal children.[29, 30] The occurrence of such a discrepancy has led to the concept of neurosecretory dysfunction. This is an ill-defined condition which relies on limited information in the child with normal stature and may only reflect inevitable discrepancies between various methods for which diagnostic cut-off values remain arbitrary. Therefore, important additional information is provided by plasma IGF I concentrations (see discussion below).

Whatever the technique used, thyroid function should be normal or adequately replaced at time of testing. In boys with delayed puberty, transient low GH secretion may be corrected by administration of testosterone as a depot preparation 50 mg i.m. once or 100 mg/M^2 every 2 weeks for 2 months. Alternatively in both sexes, and especially in patients with pubertal delay, sex steroid priming at first stimulation test may be performed by giving ethinyl-estradiol 40 μg/m2 divided in 3 doses for 2 days preceding the GH stimulation test. According to a recent study, the peak GH values are then increased to the pubertal range, improving the diagnostic value of the stimulation test.[31] In addition, a negative correlation exists between GH concentration and adiposity expressed as body mass index (BMI) or percentage of body fat.[7]

Urinary GH

GH is excreted in the urine as natural 22 kD GH. A very small fraction of injected GH is recovered in the urine. The GH excretion in hypopituitary children is significantly diminished; however, in idiopathic growth failure, as assessed by current plasma GH measurements, some children have values in the range of classical GH deficiency.[32] Urinary GH measurement has some pitfalls and difficulties: quality, duration of urine collection, and poor reproducibility over several days. At present, urinary GH assays have not proved to be more reliable than the conventional diagnostic approach. They remain to be validated as screening procedures in the future. Reference values have been recently published.[33]

Markers of GH Action and Skeletal Growth

As described above, the circulating concentrations of IGF I and eventually IGFBP-3 reflect the secretion of growth hormone and at present should be considered the best markers of GH activity in relation to growth. The only important limitation is their close dependence on nutritional status, especially for IGF I. Other markers more specifically related to skeletal growth have been studied. The serum concentrations of protein constituents of the connective tissues have been shown to be correlated with growth rate and to increase after GH administration. Therefore, radioimmunoassays have been performed for the measurement of serum Type I procollagen[34] and Type III procollagen extension peptides[35] or osteocalcin, also called bone gla protein.[36] The latter is specifically secreted by the osteoblasts. However, none of these marker measurements may contribute to defining the etiology of short stature.

GH Binding Protein

At present, the high-affinity protein can be measured in plasma as the plasma GH binding activity, using various separation techniques.[37, 38] Simpler radioimmunoassay techniques should allow a more thorough evaluation of its physiological and clinical significance. Its concentration is very low at birth, rises during childhood, and reaches adult values by age 20–30 years. However, there is no definite evidence that it reflects the number of GH receptors. Its measurement provides useful clinical information for rare but genetic conditions of GH insensitivity; it is undetectable in most patients with Laron dwarfism because of mutations in extracellular binding domains of the GH receptor.[39–40] In certain short populations, such as the African pygmies and New Guinea people, a decreased concentration of GH binding protein was found, possibly indicating a partial end organ resistance.[41]

Insulin-like Growth Factors

IGF Assays

Until recently, the initial radioimmunoassay was the most widely used direct measurement of IGF I (Somatomedin-C) in serum and plasma samples. It was suggested that a preincubation with antiserum before adding the tracer—a so-called nonequilibrium technique—avoided the interference from binding proteins. It was also stressed that such a technique was affected by many variables, such as the sample type—serum, heparin or EDTA plasma—and handling conditions—acidification, freezing/thawing, or age of sample.[42] This easy and inexpensive technique is feasible, since the affinity of the anti-IGF I antibodies most widely used, such as that provided by the National Institutes of Health, have a higher affinity than binding proteins for IGF I. In this assay, normal male adult plasma is used as a standard to which an arbitrary concentration of 1 unit/mL is attributed. However, it is now most frequently required that the binding proteins be removed in order to measure the total amount of circulating IGF I.

Acid gel filtration represents the reference technique, but it is difficult to apply to routine measurements. Alternative techniques to remove binding proteins are currently used: microcolumns C18 or acid ethanol extraction.[9] The latter technique has been improved by a cryoprecipitation step which reduces residual IGFBPs to a level that does not interfere with the immunoassay.[43] In a recent assay, excess of IGF II is used to displace the IGFBP's bound IGF I, avoiding the necessity of an extraction step.[44] A new generation of immunoradiometric assays using simple extraction techniques allows an accurate determination of plasma IGF I in most clinical conditions. In any case, high-affinity antisera are needed for the radioimmunoassay. Use of recombinant IGF I as a reference standard now allows expression of concentrations in ng/mL and comparison among laboratories. Whatever the extraction technique used, the possibility of significant interferences of IGF I binding proteins needs to be considered in patients with chronic renal failure.

For IGF II measurement, variable antibodies have been used: polyclonal antibody with minimal cross-reactivity with IGF I, specific antibody prepared against a synthetic peptide derived from the C domain of IGF II, or a competitive protein binding assay.[9] IGF II does not play a significant role in postnatal growth; therefore, it is not routinely measured.

IGF I Significance

The concentrations of IGF I in serum have been studied from birth until adolescence, and quite a number of reference values are available. They show differences in absolute values but a substantial agreement in age-related changes, with a progressive increase in concentration during childhood and a marked increase at puberty. Because of their age dependence, the data should preferably be expressed as age- and sex-related *Z* score values, taking into account age and pubertal status, for better interpretation of individual data and group comparison.[45] Such a procedure requires appropriate normative data. IGF I secretion is essentially growth hormone dependent, provided there is no malnutrition or chronic disease, since the latter may be accompanied by low plasma IGF I values. Because IGF I concentrations show little diurnal variation, GH secretion and plasma IGF I are now measured in combination for the diagnosis of GH deficiencies.

Several studies investigated the diagnostic value of IGF I measurement. It was found that most but not all children with a low GH response to provocative stimulation had plasma IGF I values below the normal range for age. Although GH-sufficient children with short stature may have lower IGF I concentrations, the conclusion of a recent study indicated that IGF I values may have clinical use in predicting GH response to stimulation.[46] Unfortunately, whatever technique is used, there is an overlap between normal short and GH-deficient children which is even more likely to occur in children below age 6 years when physiological values are in the low range. Because of a negative correlation between body mass index (BMI) and GH secretion, a normal IGF I value may help to rule out GH deficiency in a short stature child with increased adiposity.[6]

Because of the strong influence of nutrition, plasma IGF I concentration may also be used to monitor therapy for malnutrition. Recovery from deprivation correlates with increasing plasma IGF I concentrations. This is a more sensitive measure of recovery than assays for plasma prealbumin, retinol binding protein, or transferrin.

IGFBP-3 and Other IGF Binding Proteins

IGFBP-3 secretion is greatly GH dependent, with low levels in patients with GH deficiency or genetic insensitivity. Its plasma concentrations measured by RIA[47] increase soon after birth and remain constant thereafter until puberty. Interestingly, there is no circadian variation. Most of the IGFBP-3 is bound to the large 150 kD complex and does not cross the capillary barrier. Although large variability in IGFBP-3 levels was found in hypopituitary patients, the recent development of new RIAs has rapidly contributed to its evaluation. IGFBP-3 appears to be a reliable marker of GH activity in early childhood because of its high plasma concentration at that age. A characteristic feature of chronic renal failure is an increase in IGFBP-3. It is decreased in chronic malnutrition and during prolonged fasting.[14] At present, measurement of the other binding proteins is not part of routine evaluation except for IGFBP-1; its circulating levels decline from birth to puberty, with considerable diurnal variations and a nocturnal peak. It is found in amniotic fluid and maternal serum during gestation. It is increased during fasting, chronic malnutrition, and noncontrolled diabetes. In GH-deficient children, there is an inverse correlation between IGFBP-1 and GH levels. It was shown that IGFBP-1 concentrations were inversely correlated to plasma insulin, and low IGFBP-1 values were also reported in states of insulin resistance.[41] Only preliminary results were reported on IGF binding proteins in the urine.[41]

Reference Values

Because of difficulty in investigating children with normal stature, only a few studies provide reference data for GH response to pharmacological stimulation, GH secretion as calculated from spontaneous profiles, and IGF I concentration in plasma. Furthermore, these reference data depend on the type of assay used by the authors, as noted in the accompanying figure and tables. The following data were selected:

1. Plasma IGF I and IGF II concentrations (Table 6–7)
2. Peak GH responses to pharmacological stimulation (Table 6–8)
3. Serum IGFBP-3 concentrations (Table 6–9).
4. Spontaneous GH during nighttime (Figure 6–3)

TABLE 6–7. Plasma IGF I and IGF II Concentrations by Age and Sex (values obtained by RIA after acid gel filtration)

Age (yr)	NORMAL			NORMAL SHORT STATURE			GH DEFICIENCY		
	n	IGF-I	IGF-II	*n*	IGF-I	IGF-II	*n*	IGF-I	IGF-II
Boys									
<3	10	77 ± 33	480 ± 85	3	38 ± 39	477 ± 640	0		
3–5	9	157 ± 103	573 ± 259	5	80 ± 75	244 ± 100*	9	28 ± 17*	288 ± 227*
6–8	15	211 ± 112	607 ± 185	9	99 ± 41*	339 ± 139*	9	38 ± 20*	271 ± 137*
9–11	10	301 ± 173	505 ± 189	8	148 ± 109	580 ± 380	11	101 ± 94*	409 ± 380
12–14	38	466 ± 188	500 ± 114	5	207 ± 94	490 ± 171	5	92 ± 76*	352 ± 164
>15	14	516 ± 139	531 ± 107	1	252	384	4	73 ± 75*	603 ± 201
Girls									
<3	10	134 ± 53	419 ± 145	0			0		
3–5	15	247 ± 175	526 ± 201	3	103 ± 52	300 ± 129	7	31 ± 35*	273 ± 145*
6–8	20	298 ± 151	601 ± 228	4	198 ± 42	704 ± 119	8	47 ± 67*	452 ± 444
9–11	16	366 ± 109	522 ± 135	4	196 ± 126*	412 ± 220	7	60 ± 59*	286 ± 138*
12–14	26	521 ± 164	498 ± 116	1	90	231	7	54 ± 23*	509 ± 361
>15	14	464 ± 141	466 ± 145	1	122	824	1	25*	669

Values expressed as mean ± SD nanograms per milliliter. Means were compared by repeated analysis of variance for each age group.

*Significantly different from normal patients ($P < 0.05$). IGF-I and IGF-II concentrations in normal short and GH-deficient children were not significantly different form each other in any other group.

From: Rosenfeld RG, Wilson DM, Lee DK. Insulin-like growth factors I and II in evaluaiton of growth retardation. J Pediatr 1986; 109:428–433. Reprinted by permission.

TABLE 6–8. Peak GH Responses to Treadmill Exercise and Arginine-Insulin Stimulation in Normal Boys and Girls

	Peak GH (ng/ml)	
Pubertal Stage	**mean ± SD**	**0.5% confidence limit**
Stage 1 Placebo	6.9 ± 4.2	1.9 - 20.3
E.E.*	18.7 ± 9.2	7.2 - 40.5
Stage 2	9.0 ± 4.6	3.0 - 21.3
Stage 3	17.0 ± 7.9	4.4 - 49.3
Stage 4	22.0 ± 11.3	6.6 - 56.7
Stage 5	28.5 ± 14.3	9.3 - 69.0

*Ethinyl-estradiol priming in both sexes. Plasma GH was measured by polyclonal RIA. The highest response to the three tests (exercise, arginine, and insulin) was recorded. There was no difference according to sex. Adapted from Marin G, Domené HM, Barnes KM, et al. J Clin Endocrinol Metab 1994;79:537–41.

TABLE 6–9. Serum Levels of IGFBP-3 in Healthy Children at Various Ages (mg/L)

Age Group (Male/Female Combined)	Percentile		
	5th	**50th**	**95th**
0–1 week	0.42	0.77	1.39
1–4 weeks	0.77	1.29	2.09
1–3 months	0.87	1.48	2.54
3–6 months	0.98	1.61	2.64
6–12 months	1.07	1.72	2.76
1–3 years	1.41	2.05	2.97
3–5 years	1.52	2.25	3.32
5–7 years	1.66	2.44	3.59
7–9 years	1.82	2.63	3.80
9–11 years	2.12	3.01	4.26
11–13 years	2.22	3.30	4.89
13–15 years	2.31	3.48	5.24
15–17 years	2.33	3.39	4.95
20–30 years	2.20	3.29	4.93

Adapted from: Blum WF, Ranke MB, Kietzmann K. Gauggel E, Zeisl HJ, Bierich JR. A specific radioimmunoassay for the growth hormone (GH)-dependent somatomedin-binding protein: its use for diagnosis of GH deficiency. J Clin Endocrinol Metab 1990;70:1292–8.

FIGURE 6–3. The Mean Nighttime GH Concentration in Normal Children According to Bone Age (top panel) and Pubertal Stage (bottom panel). Individual values (points) and 95% confidence limits are presented. GH assay: polyclonal antibody at Hazeltone Biotechnologies.

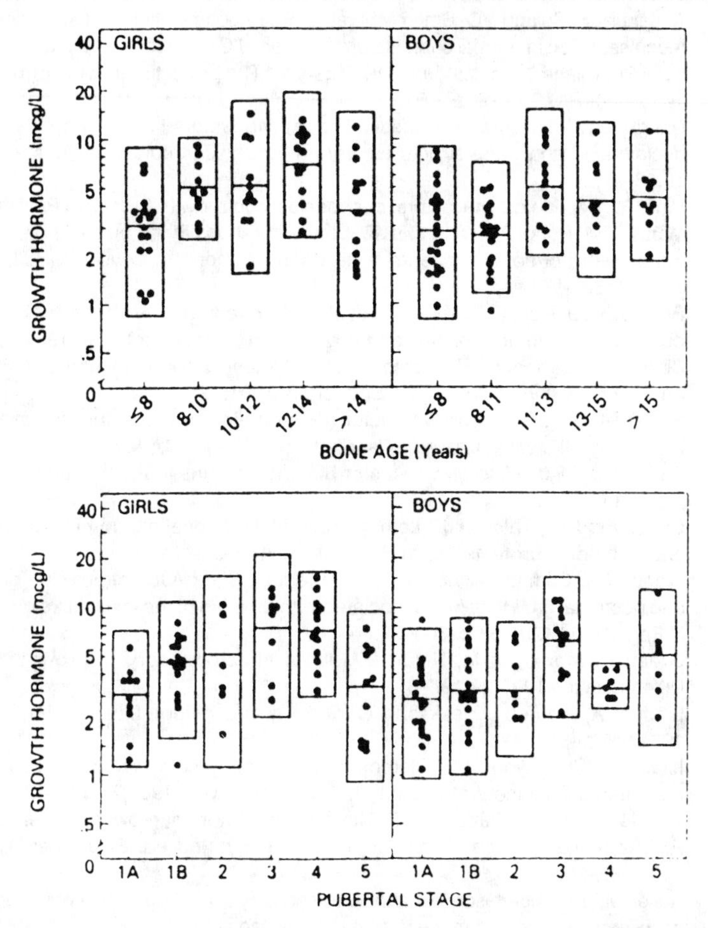

Source: Rose SR, Municchi G, Barnes KM, et al. Spontaneous growth hormone secretion increased during puberty in normal girls and boys. J Clin Endocrinol Metab 1991:73;428–35. Reprinted with permission.

REFERENCES

1. Baumann G. Growth hormone binding proteins and various forms of growth hormone: Implications for measurements. Acta Paediatr Scand 1990;370:72–80.
2. Martin JB. Neural regulation of growth hormone secretion. N Engl J Med 1973;288:1384–93.
3. Tannenbaum GS, Painson JC, Lapointe M, et al. Pituitary hypothalamic somatostatin. Interplay of somatostatin and growth hormone-releasing hormone in genesis of episodic growth hormone secretion. Metabolism 1990;39:35–9.
4. Thorner MO, Vance ML, Evans WS, et al. Physiological and clinical studies of GRF and GH. Recent Prog Horm Res 1986;42:589–640.

5. Frohman LA, Downs TR, Kelijman M, et al. Somatostatin secretion and action in the regulation of growth hormone secretion. Metabolism 1990;39:43–5.
6. Veldhuis JD, Carlson ML, Johnson ML. The pituitary gland secretes in bursts: appraising the nature of glandular secretory impulses by simultaneous multiple-parameter deconvolution of plasma hormone concentrations. Proc Natl Acad Sci USA 1987;84:7686–90.
7. Abdenur JE, Soland VC, Smith MM, et al. Body composition and spontaneous growth hormone secretion in normal short stature children. J Clin Endocrinol Metab 1994;78:277–82.
8. Kelly PA, Djiane J, Postel-Vinay MC, Edery M. The prolactin/growth hormone receptor family. Endocr Rev 991;12:235–51.
9. Daughaday WH, Rotwein P. Insulin-like growth factors I and II. Peptide, messenger ribonucleic acid and gene structures, serum, and tissue concentrations. Endocr Rev 1989; 10:68–91.
10. Hintz RL. Peptide growth factors, oncogenies, and growth. Curr Opin Pediatr 1990;2:786–93.
11. Martha PM, Rogol AD, Veldhuis JD, et al. Alterations in the pulsatile properties of circulating growth hormone concentrations during puberty in boys. J Clin Endocrinol Metab 1989;69:563–70.
12. Rose SE, Municchi G, Barnes KM, et al. Spontaneous growth hormone secretion increases during puberty in normal girls and boys. J Clin Endocrinol Metab 1991;73:428–35.
13. Binoux M, Roghani M, Hossenlop P, et al. Molecular forms of human IGF binding protein: physiological implications. Acta Endocrinol 1991;124:41–7.
14. Baxter RC. Insulin-like growth factor (IGF) binding proteins: the role of serum IGFBPs in regulating IGF availability. Acta Paediatr Scand 1991;372:107–14.
15. Baxter RC. Insulin-like growth factor binding proteins in the human circulation: a review. Horm Res 1994;42:140–44.
16. Underwood LE, Thissen JP, Lemozy S, et al. Hormonal and nutritional regulation of IGF-I and its binding proteins. Horm Res 1994;42:145–51.
17. Woods KA, Camacho-Hübner C, Savage MO, Clark AJL. Intrauterine growth retardation and postnatal growth failure associated with deletion of the insulin-like growth factor I gene. N Engl J Med 1996;335:1363–67.
18. Green H, Morikawa M, Nixon L. A dual effector theory of growth hormone action. Differenciation 1985;29:195–8.
19. Lindhal A, Isgaard J, Isaksson O. Growth and differentiation. Clin Endocrinol Metab 1991;5:671–87.
20. Isley WL, Underwood LE, Clemmons DR. Dietary components that regulate serum somatomedin-C concentrations in humans. J Clin Invest 1983;71:175–82.
21. Van den Brande L, Rappaport R. Normal and abnormal growth. In: Bertrand J, Rappaport R, Sizonenko PC, eds. Pediatric endocrinology, 2nd ed. Baltimore: Williams & Wilkins 1993:185–207.
22. Rosenfeld RG, Albertsson-Wikland K, Cassorla F, et al. Diagnostic controversy: the diagnosis of childhood growth hormone deficiency revisited. J Clin Endocrinol Metab 1995;80:1532–40.
23. Adan L, Souberbielle JC, Brauner R. Diagnostic markers of permanent idiopathic growth hormone deficiency. J Clin Endocrinol Metab 1994;78:353–8.
24. Reiter EO, Morris AH, McGillivray MH, Weber D. Variable estimates of serum growth hormone concentrations by different radioassay systems. J Clin Endocrinol Metab 1988;66:68–71.
25. Celniker AC, Chen AB, Wert RM, Sherman B. Variability in the quantitation of circulating growth hormone using commercial immunoassays. J Clin Endocrinol Metab 1989;68:469–76.
26. Bowsher RR, Apathy JM, Ferguson AL, et al. Cross reactivity of monomeric and dimeric biosynthetic human growth hormone in commercial immunoassays. Clin Chem 1990;63:362–66.
27. Felder RA, Hall RW, Martha P, et al. Influence of matrix on concentrations of somatotropin measured in serum with commercial immunoradiometric assays. Clin Chem 1989;35/7:1423–26.
28. Zadik Z, Chalew SA, Gilula Z, Kowarski AA. Reproducibility of growth hormone testing procedures: a comparison between 24-hour integrated concentration and pharmacological stimulation. J Clin Endocrinol Metab 1990;71:1127–30.

29. Rose SR, Ross JL, Uriarte M, et al. The advantage of measuring stimulated as compared with spontaneous growth hormone levels in the diagnosis of growth hormone deficiency. N Engl J Med 1988;319:201–7.
30. Rose SR, Municchi G, Barnes KM, et al. Spontaneous growth hormone secretion increases during puberty in normal girls and boys. J Clin Endocrinol Metab 1991;73:428–35.
31. Marin G, Domene HM, Barnes KM, et al. The effects of estrogen priming and puberty on the growth hormone response to standardized treadmill exercise and arginine-insulin in normal girls and boys. J Clin Endocrinol Metab 1994;79:537–41.
32. Albini CH, Sotos J, Sherman B, et al. Diagnostic significance of urinary growth hormone measurements in children with growth failure: correlation between serum and urine growth hormone. Pediatr Res 1991;29:619–22.
33. Main KM, Jarden M, Angelo L, et al. The impact of gender and puberty on reference values for urinary growth hormone excretion: a study of 3 morning urine samples in 517 healthy children and adults.J Clin Endocrinol Metab 1994;79:865–71.
34. Carey DE, Goldberg B, Ratzan SK, et al. Radioimmunoassay for type I procollagen in growth hormone-deficient children before and during treatment with growth hormone. Pediatr Res 1984;19:8–11.
35. Danne T, Grüters A, Schuppan D, et al. Relationship of procollagen type III propeptide-related antigens in serum to somatic growth in healthy children and patients with growth disorders. J Pediatr 1989;114:257–60.
36. Johansen JS, Jensen SB, Ris BJ, et al. Serum bone Gla protein: a potential marker of growth hormone (GH) deficiency and the response to GH therapy. J Clin Endocrinol Metab 1990;71:122–26.
37. Baumann G. Growth hormone binding proteins: biochemical characterization and assays. Acta Endocrinol 1991;124:21–6.
38. Fontoura M, Hocquette JF, Clot JP, et al. Regulation of the growth hormone binding proteins in human plasma. Acta Endocrinol 1991;124:10–3.
39. Amselem S, Duquesnoy BS, Attree O, et al. Laron dwarfism and mutations of the growth hormone-receptor gene. N Eng J Med 1989;321:989–95.
40. Rosenbloom AL, Guevara-Aguirre J, Rosenfeld RG, Fielder PJ. The little women of Loja: growth hormone-receptor deficiency in an inbred population of southern Ecuador. N Engl J Med 1990;323:1367–74.
41. Cohen P, Fielder PJ, Hasegawa Y, et al. Clinical aspects of insulin-like growth factor binding proteins. Acta Endocrinol 1991;124:74–85.
42. Furlanetto RW. Pitfalls in the somatomedin C radioimmunoassays. J Clin Endocrinol Metab 1982;54:1084–6.
43. Breier BH, Gallagher BW, Gluckman PD. Radioimmunoassay for insulin-like growth factor I: Solutions to some potential problems and pitfalls. J Endocrinol 1991;128:347–57.
44. Blum WF, Ranke MB, Kietzmann K, et al. A specific radioimmunoassay for the growth hormone (GH)-dependent somatomedin-binding protein: its use for diagnosis of GH deficiency. J Clin Endocrinol Metab 1990;70:1292–8.
45. Rosenfeld RG, Wilson DM, Lee PDK. Insulin-like growth factors I and II in evaluation of growth retardation. J Pediatr 1986;109:428–33.
46. Lee PDK, Wilson DM, Rountree L, et al. Efficacy of insulin-like growth factor I levels in predicting the response to provocative growth hormone testing. Pediatr Res 1990;27:45–51.
47. Rutanen EM, Pekonen F. Assays for IGF binding proteins. Acta Endocrinol 1991;124:70–3.

CHAPTER 7

The Diagnosis of Pediatric Reproductive Disorders

Claude J. Migeon, M.D., Gary D. Berkovitz, M.D., Patricia Y. Fechner, M.D.

INTRODUCTION

Human reproduction is necessary for the conservation of the species and is based on well established patterns of sexual dimorphism that are determined at sex differentiation. Reproductive function covers nearly the whole life span of human subjects. The first major stage is *sex differentiation*, which takes place during fetal life and includes the fertilization of the egg by a sperm, followed by establishment of chromosomal sex and the development of the fetus along male or female lines. Infancy and childhood are not considered as important periods for reproduction, although there is a process of learning and rehearsal of future sex life during that time. The next major stage is *puberty*, during which the gonads and sex organs mature. This is followed by the stage of *male-female bonding, pregnancy*, and *child rearing*. Post-menopausal age in women and old age in men are considered to have little relevance to the life cycle of reproduction, although grandparents may play an important role in inculcating the societal values of the family to the youth.

This chapter focuses specifically on *reproductive disorders* as related to *sexual differentiation* and *pubertal development*.

SEXUAL DIFFERENTIATION

Biochemistry and Physiology

The sexual differentiation of the human fetus is a complicated process which involves various types of cell differentiation and cell multiplication. In a simplified manner, one can describe four major steps (for details, see Migeon et al.[1]):

1. Fertilization and determination of genetic sex
2. Formation of organs common to both sexes
3. Gonadal differentiation
4. Differentiation of the internal ducts and external genitalia

Fertilization

Without doubt, the first step in sex differentiation takes place at fertilization. An egg with a complement of 23 chromosomes, including an X chromosome, will be conjugated with a sperm that includes either a 23,X chromosome complement or a 23,Y complement. Hence, at conception the first diploid cell has either a 46,XX or 46,XY complement, which establishes the *genetic sex*.

Formation of Organs Common to Both Sexes

Following the rapid cell multiplication of the fertilized egg, there is cell differentiation with formation of various sex organs similar in both sexes, specifically the *gonadal ridges*, the *internal ducts*, and the *external genitalia*.[2] The genital ridges can be easily recognized by 5 w of gestation. At that time, they already have been invaded by the germ cells that have migrated from the wall of the yolk sac and have entered the fetus by way of its caudal part. The eventual differentiation of the germ cells into ova or spermatogonia will occur later and will be based on whether the gonad has become an ovary or a testis.

By 6 w of fetal life, fetuses of both sexes have two sets of internal ducts, the *Müllerian ducts* and the *Wolffian ducts*. At 6 w gestation the external genitalia appear female and include a genital tubercule, the genital folds, urethral folds, and a urogenital sinus.

Gonadal Differentiation

This important event is the commitment of the gonadal ridge to become either an ovary or a testis. In males, the commitment to testicular determination is triggered by the product of a gene located on the Y chromosome. This product has been termed "testis determining factor" (TDF). Figure 7–1 shows a map of the short arm of the Y chromosome indicating the location of the pseudoautosomal region, the region of X-Y pairing during meiosis. The figure also shows the TDF locus, which was determined by genetic analysis of subjects with abnormal sex differentiation.[3] A gene from the TDF locus was isolated and named "sex determining region Y chromosome" (SRY). It is now well established that the product of the SRY gene is necessary for testis determination[3] and that SRY is identical with TDF. However, it is also clear that a number of other genes located on autosomes and possibly on the X chromosome are necessary for the formation of normal male gonads. At this time, it is not clear whether SRY triggers all these other genes simultaneously, or whether there is an orderly cascade in which SRY triggers a second gene, the product of which triggers a third, and so on. SRY is a DNA binding protein that interacts with specific sequences. It has also been shown to bend DNA upon binding, and this may play an important role in influencing transcription of target genes.[4]

FIGURE 7–1. Map of the Short Arm of the Y Chromosome (Yp)

The upper part of the figure shows the loci of SRY and ZFY genes in relation to the pseudoautosomal region of the Y chromosome. The lower part of the figure shows the locus of the testis-determining factor (TDF) and the map of the various probes used for mapping studies, including pY53.3, a 2.1kb fragment of genomic DNA which contains the sex determining region of the Y (SRY).

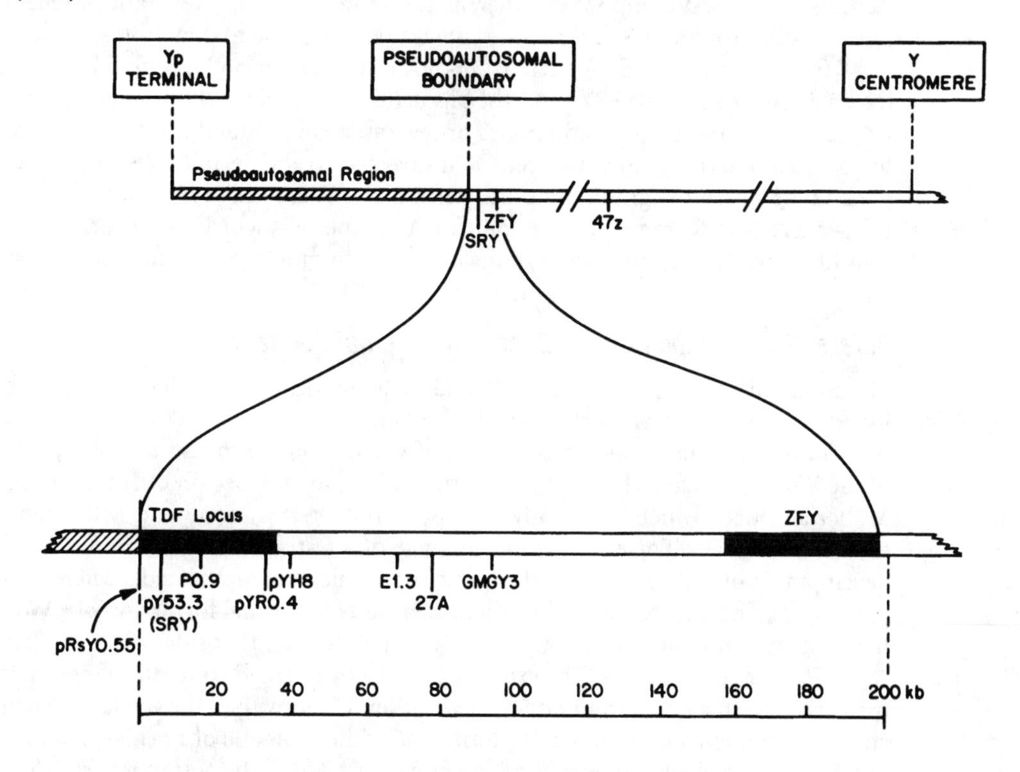

From: Migeon CJ, Berkovitz GD. Congenital defects of the external genitalia in the newborn and prepubertal child. In Carpenter SE, Rock J, eds. Pediatric and adolescent gynecology. New York: Raven Press, 1992:79.

Histologically speaking, the first sign of testicular determination is the appearance of *Sertoli cells*, which rapidly agglutinate to each other to form the seminiferous tubules.[5] In this process, the Sertoli cells surround the germ cells and isolate them from the rest of the testis. About 2 w after the appearance of the Sertoli cells, *Leydig cells* can be detected in the interstitial spaces and steroid secretion starts shortly thereafter.

It is important to note that the Sertoli cells will secrete the Müllerian inhibiting substance (MIS) shortly after their differentiation. Although the granulosa cells also secrete MIS, its production occurs much later in relation to the start of its production by the Sertoli cells.

Shortly after their appearance, the Leydig cells begin producing the male hormone, testosterone.[6] Testosterone arises from the transformation of cholesterol by a series of biosynthetic steps, as shown in Figure 7–2. Most of these steps involve a hydroxylation requiring electron transfer and a specific cytochrome P450 for each step. Cytochrome P450scc is needed for hydroxylation of carbons 20 and 22, as well as for the removal of the cholesterol side chain.

As to cytochrome P450c17, it permits 17α-hydroxylation as well as removal of the two carbon side chain, resulting in formation of C19 steroids or *androgens*. The enzyme 3β-hydroxysteroid dehydrogenase (3β-HSD) transforms the inactive Δ^5-steroids to active Δ^4-compounds, whereas 17-ketoreductase converts androstenedione to testosterone and 5-α reductase converts testosterone to dihydrotestosterone.

In the absence of SRY, such as in 46,XX subjects or 46,XY individuals who have a deleted or mutant SRY gene, the bipotential gonadal ridge becomes an ovary. At present, it is not clear whether one (or several) gene product(s) is (are) required for ovarian determination. The cells that give rise to the Sertoli cells in the male gonad differentiate as granulosa cells in the ovary. These cells eventually surround the germ cells to form primordial follicles. As to the cells which give rise to Leydig cells in the testis, they also occur in the ovary but in much smaller number and are located near the hilus and form the hilar cells.

Differentiation of the Internal Ducts and External Genitalia

The mechanisms by which the ducts and genitalia differentiate have been established by the pioneering work of Jost and Josso.[7]

In the male, the testicular secretion of testosterone permits the development of the Wolffian ducts, whereas the secretion of MIS by the Sertoli cells inhibits the Müllerian ducts, which eventually disappear. Both testosterone and MIS express their effects locally. For example, the absence of a testis on one side results in the development of a female duct with absence of a male duct on that side, whereas the presence of a normal testis on the other side results in normal formation of a Wolffian duct and normal inhibition of the Müllerian duct on that side.

The masculinization of the external genitalia by the high concentrations of testosterone in the male starts around 8 w of gestation. The growth of the genital tubercule and of the urethral folds results in the formation of the penis and of a penile urethra. As to the labio-scrotal folds, they enlarge and fuse, starting from the posterior part to form the scrotum. The full masculinization of the external genitalia of the male requires the local metabolism of testosterone to dihydrotestosterone, a more potent androgen.[8]

FIGURE 7–2. Biosynthetic Pathway of Testosterone from Cholesterol

It requires two cytochromes P450 (P450scc and P450c17) as well as a 3β-ol-dehydrogenase (3β-SDH) and a 17-ketosteroid reductase. The figure also shows the pathway from cholesterol to the adrenal steroids, cortisol and aldosterone.

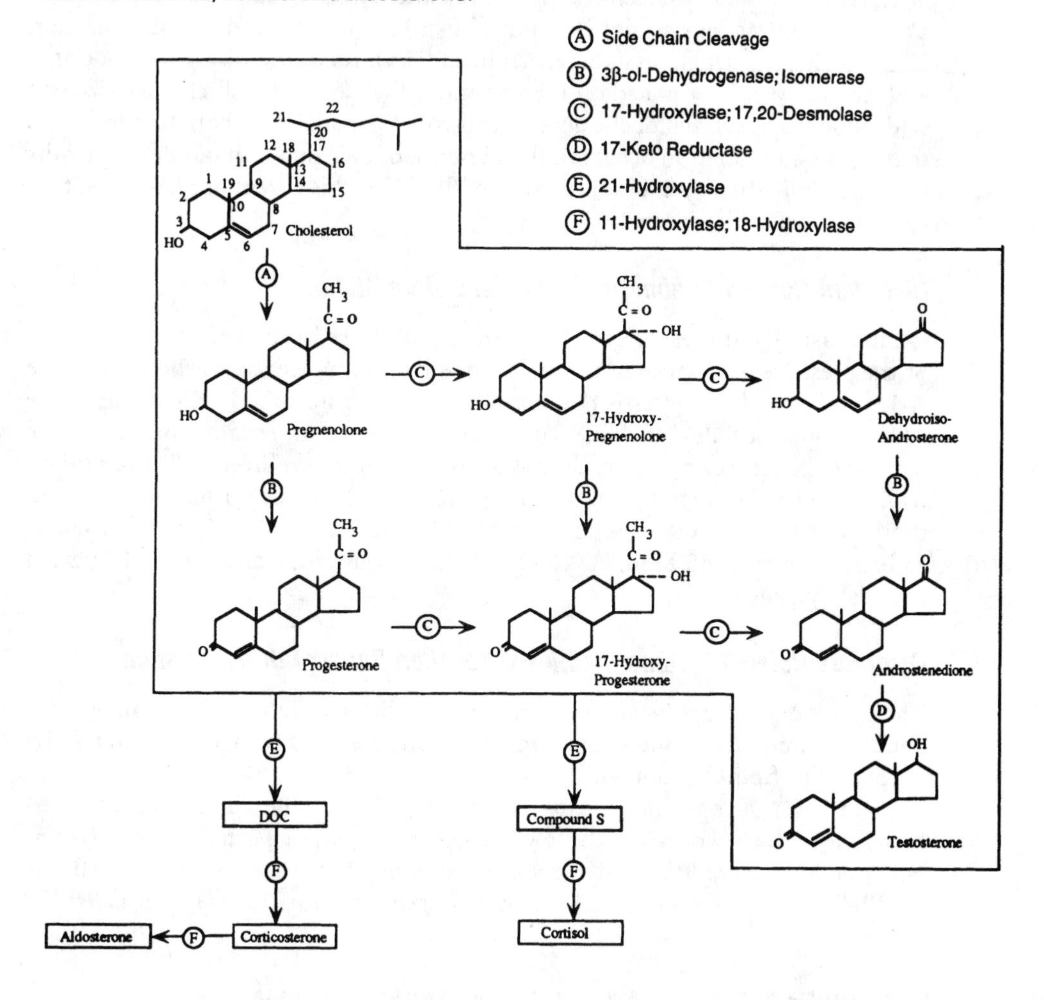

It must be added that the process of masculinization of the male fetus requires the presence of a normal androgen receptor, a protein which is coded by a gene located on chromosome Xq12.[9]

In the female, the absence of ovarian secretion of testosterone results in the disappearance of the male ducts whereas the lack of secretion of MIS at the appropriate time results in development of the female ducts. In addition, the absence of androgen results in growth arrest of the genital tubercule forming the clitoris, while the folds become the labia majora and minora.

Abnormal Sexual Differentiation

In view of the complexity of normal sexual differentiation described above, it is not surprising that abnormalities of sexual differentiation can have many causes.[1] The disorders that can occur after the gonads have been committed to becoming ovaries or testes are now well understood. They are either an abnormal masculinization of a female fetus (female pseudohermaphroditism) or an insufficient masculinization of the male fetus (male pseudohermaphroditism). As to the disorders associated with the early part of gonadal differentiation, they are not well characterized or understood. The model for the genetic control of gonadal differentiation indicates that testis determination occurs in the presence of SRY or a mutation that permits testis determination even in the absence of SRY. If SRY is absent or SRY action fails to occur, ovarian determination takes place.

Disorders Related to Abnormal Gonadal Differentiation

On the basis of our present knowledge, one could make a classification on the basis of the presence or absence of normal testis-determining genes. As shown in Table 7–1, *conditions lacking testis determination* include normal 46,XX females, the "47,XXX superfemales," the 45,X Turner syndrome and its variants, and the 46,XY females (complete or pure gonadal dysgenesis or Swyer's syndrome). *The conditions with normal or partial testis determination* (Table 7–2) include normal 46,XY males, the 47,XXY Klinefelter syndrome, "45,X males," "46,XX males," 46,XX true hermaphrodites, the mosaic 45,X/46,XY, 46XY true hermaphrodites, and the 46,XY partial gonadal dysgenesis.[10]

Disorders Related to Abnormalities Other than Gonadal Differentiation

The causes of *female pseudohermaphroditism* are listed in Table 7–3. As can be seen, abnormal amounts of androgens can arise from the fetus (congenital adrenal hyperplasia) or from the mother.[11]

In 46,XY *male pseudohermaphroditism* (Figure 7–3), the concentrations of testosterone in the newborn may be low (*steroid enzyme defect, partial gonadal dysgenesis, true hermaphroditism*). If the concentrations of testosterone are normal, the possibilities are *5α-reductase deficiency, androgen insensitivity*, or *"timing defect."*[12]

CLINICAL AND LABORATORY EVALUATION OF AMBIGUOUS GENITALIA IN THE NEWBORN PERIOD

It is of interest that the diagnosis of sex at birth is made rather superficially by visual evaluation of the appearance of the external genitalia. Clearly, this is sufficient in the large majority of cases. However, the fact the genitalia appear appropriately formed does not rule out the possibility of abnormalities. For example, a normal-appearing female may have an abnormal karyotype such as 47,XXX super female, 45,X (Turner syndrome) or, rarely, 46,XY pure gonadal dysgenesis. Similarly, a nor-

TABLE 7–1. Conditions with Absent SRY Gene Product

	Normal Female 46,XX	"Super-Female" 47,XXX	Turner 45,X 45,X/46,XX (Variants)	"46,XY Female" 46,XY [-]
External Genitalia	F	F	F	F
Internal Ducts	F	F	F	F
Gonads				
In utero	Ovaries	Ovaries	Ovaries	Ovaries
Adults	Ovaries	Ovaries	Streaks (ovaries rarely)	Streaks
Fertility	Yes	Yes (limited)	No (yes rarely)	No

[-] Deleted or Mutant SRY. Mutation of another gene needed for SRY action.

TABLE 7–2. Conditions with Normal or Partial Testis-Determining Function

	46,XY Normal	47,XXY Klinefelter	45,X Male	46,XX Male	46,XX True H	45,X/ 46,XY	46,XY True H	46,XY Partial Gonadal Dysgenesis
External Genitalia	M	M	M	M	Amb	M/Amb/F	Amb	Amb
Internal Ducts	M	M	M	M	Variable	Variable	Variable	Variable
Gonads								
In utero	Testes	Testes	Testes	Testes	Ovo-testes	Variable	Ovo-testes	Ovo-testes (?)
Adults	Testes	Testes* (no sperm)	Testes (no sperm)	Testes* (no sperm)	Ovo-testes	Variable	Ovo-testes	Dysgenetic gonads
Fertility	Yes	No	No	No	Variable	Variable	Variable	No

*Hyalinized Tubules

TABLE 7–3. Classification of Female Pseudo-Hermaphroditism in Subjects with 46,XX Karyotype

Excess fetal androgen
- 21-Hydroxylase deficiency
  - Partial (simple virilizing form)
  - More Complete (salt-losing form)
- 11-Hydroxylase deficiency (hypertensive form)
- 3β-Hydroxysteroid dehydrogenase deficiency

Excess maternal androgen
- Iatrogenic
- Virilizing tumor of ovary or adrenal

Congenital abnormalities
- Structural or teratogenic factors

FIGURE 7–3. Diagram of the Causes of Ambiguous Genitalia in 46,XY Infants

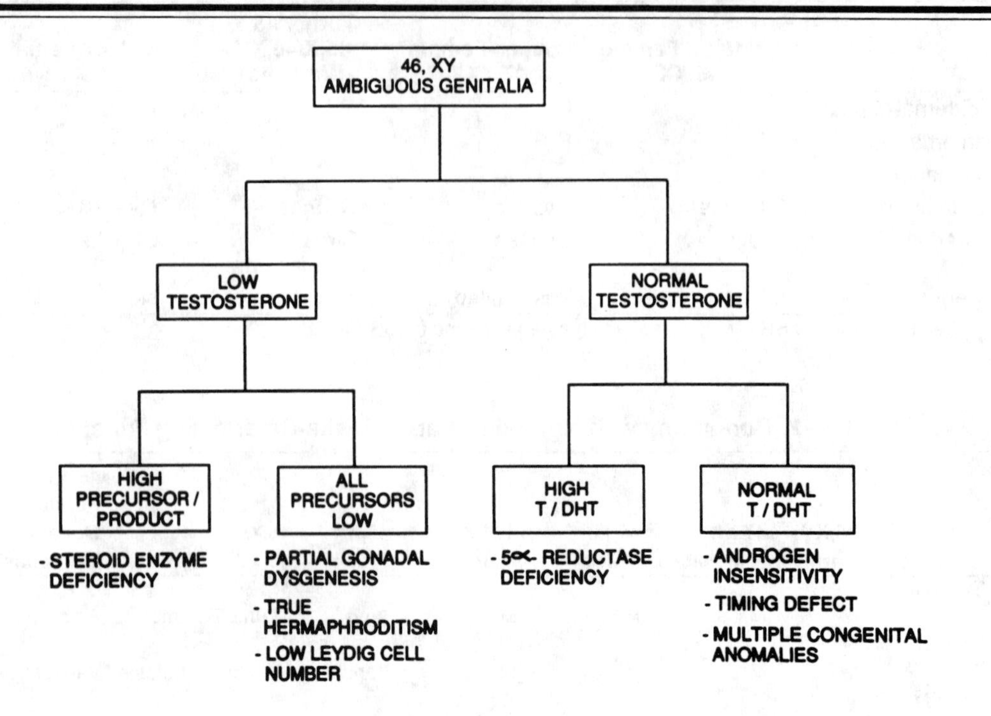

From: Migeon CJ, Berkovitz GD. Congenital defects of the external genitalia in the newborn and prepubertal child. In Carpenter SE, Rock J, eds. Pediatric and adolescent gynecology. New York: Raven Press, 1922:84.

mal-appearing male may have an abnormal karyotype such as 47,XXY (Klinefelter syndrome) or, rarely, 46,XX (46,XX male). Complete deficiency of one of the enzymes needed for cortisol biosynthesis can result in full masculinization of the genitalia of a female fetus. However, in such cases, no gonads are palpated in the scrotum.

Ambiguous external genitalia in newborns usually are related to partial rather than complete forms of the various disorders described above. This complicates further the diagnosis of the etiology of the problem. The evaluation of the infant must be carried out as an emergency, first because life-threatening symptoms such as salt loss can develop, and second because a decision must be made as rapidly as possible about whether the infant will be reared as male or female.

The work-up needed for this situation has been discussed previously.[13] The measurement of the various precursors of androgens as well as testosterone and dihydrotestosterone should be done. A karyotype should also be obtained, and the genital structures should be evaluated by sonogram and genitogram. Following is a recommended schedule for tests which takes in consideration the physiology of steroid secretion in the newborn and the turnover times of some of the tests.

Day 1 or 2: Karyotype, including study of fluorescent Y chromosome and of possible mosaicism. Concentrations of testosterone and dihydrotestosterone in single blood sample in order to compare the values of these two steroids.

Day 3 or 4: Concentrations of 17α-hydroxyprogesterone, 17α-hydroxypregnenolone, and androstenedione, also in a single blood sample.

Day 5 or 6: Sonogram of the gonads and internal ducts followed by genitogram (retrograde injection of contrast substance through the urogenital sinus).

Day 10 to 12: Repeat concentrations of 17α-hydroxyprogesterone, 17α-hydroxypregnenolone, androstenedione, testosterone, and dihydrotestosterone.

In addition, throughout the period of evaluation it is important to check concentrations of serum electrolytes and blood glucose at least once a day. This is necessary in order to detect the possibility of the development of an adrenal crisis with salt loss and hypoglycemia.

Although sex chromosomes do not always reflect the genetic endowment of a subject, the karyotype remains capital in the diagnosis of the cause of ambiguous genitalia. As shown in Figure 7–4, a 46,XX karyotype will orient toward the possibility of female pseudohermaphroditism and true hermaphroditism. With a 46,XY

FIGURE 7–4. Diagram of the Causes of Ambiguous Genitalia in Infants, Depending upon the Sex Chromosome Complement (46,XY, 46,XX, or Other Karyotypes)

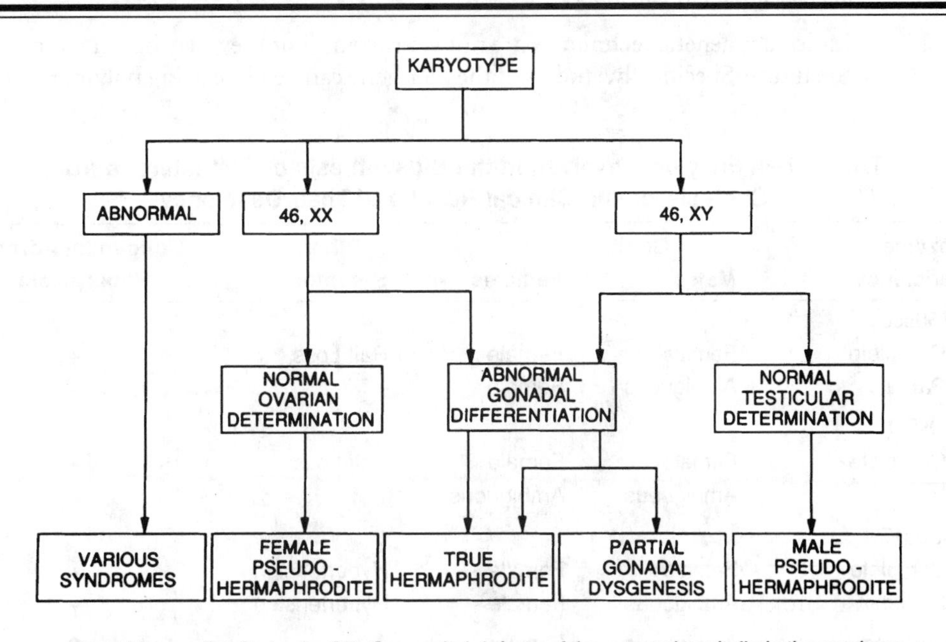

From: Migeon CJ, Berkovitz GD. Congenital defects of the external genitalia in the newborn and prepubertal child. In Carpenter SE, Rock J, eds. Pediatric and adolescent gynecology. New York: Raven Press, 1922:83.

karyotype, the possibility of male pseudo-hermaphroditism, true hermaphroditism, and partial gonadal dysgenesis will be considered.

The study of the concentrations of androgens and their precursors will be helpful in further delineating the causes of the ambiguous genitalia. In 46,XY subjects with low testosterone concentrations, increased androgen precursor values will permit determination of the enzyme deficiency involved (Table 7–4), whereas low precursor values will suggest partial gonadal dysgenesis or true hermaphroditism. In 46,XY subjects with normal male concentrations of testosterone a high testosterone/dihydrotestosterone (T/DHT) ratio (> 12 in newborns) will make the diagnosis of 5α-reductase deficiency, whereas a normal T/DHT ratio will suggest either androgen insensitivity (i.e., androgen receptor abnormality) or a "timing defect."

Reference Ranges

Cytogenetic Laboratory

We have already emphasized the importance of careful karyotype studies. It must be emphasized that a search for mosaicism should be carried out, as the presence of a Y chromosome in a small number of cells can result in gonadal differentiation along male lines. For this reason, a search for fluorescent Y can be helpful, even though the fluorescence arises from the long arm of the chromosome whereas the short arm bears the SRY gene, near the junction with the pseudoautosomal region.

Molecular Biology Laboratory

Molecular genetic techniques are not yet routine, but they may become more so in the future. Specifically, studies of the SRY gene can be done using polymerase chain

TABLE 7–4. Enzymes Involved in the Biosynthesis of Testosterone from Cholesterol and Clinical Results of Their Deficiency

Enzyme Deficiency	Genitalia in Males	Genitalia in Females	Other Symptoms	Congenital Adrenal Hyperplasia
P450scc				
Complete	Female	Female	Salt Loss	+
Partial	Ambiguous	Female	–	+
3β-HSD				
Complete	Female	Female	Salt Loss	+
Partial	Ambiguous	Ambiguous	–	+
P450c17				
Complete	Female	Female	Hypertension	+
Partial	Ambiguous	Female	Hypertension	+
17-ketoreductase	Ambiguous	Female	–	0
5α-reductase	Ambiguous	Female	–	0

reaction (PCR) amplification and sequencing of this gene. This permits the detection of the presence of this gene, as in 46,XX males, or of its deletion or mutation, as in 46,XY females.[14]

Another application of this technique is being investigated for the study of the androgen receptor gene. PCR amplification of each of the 8 exons of this gene along with methods that permit detection of point mutations can be used to rule out androgen insensitivity.[15]

Hormonal Assays

Study of the concentrations of androgens and their precursors are particularly important. In a normal male infant, the concentrations of testosterone are about half of the values of adult males at age 1–3 d; then they tend to decrease somewhat until age 6–7 d, when they go back to 5.2–10.4 nmol/L (150–300 ng/dL) for the next 8–12 w of life. This is followed by a drop to very low concentrations for the rest of infancy and childhood until puberty.[16]

By comparing the ratio of androstenedione to testosterone (in a normal male at 1–2 w of age, usually < 1) and of testosterone to dihydrotestosterone (range = 2.5–7.5), it is possible to determine whether there is a deficiency of 17-ketoreductase and 5α-reductase, respectively.

Normal concentrations of plasma testosterone and androstenedione are shown in Figure 7–5. It must be noted that testosterone should be purified in some way, such as LH-20 column chromatography, before testosterone assay. Direct assay of samples in the first 6 m of life may result in spurious levels.[17]

The placenta secretes large amounts of progesterone and 17α-hydroxyprogesterone; these steroids cross to the fetus, and their concentrations at birth in cord blood and in the infant are extremely high. However, their half-life is quite short, and by the third day of life values are representative of the infant's secretion of these steroids. (A similar comment applies to androstenedione.) If the results of the progesterone and 17α-hydroxyprogesterone concentrations obtained at 3 d are inconclusive, it might be necessary to repeat these assays at 6–7 d of life.

The concentrations of plasma 17α-hydroxyprogesterone are particularly important to the diagnosis of congenital adrenal hyperplasia due to 21-hydroxylase deficiency. However, there can be a major cause of error if this steroid is measured directly on plasma by routine RIA. Normal newborns have huge concentrations of Δ^5-steroids conjugated as sulfates, which have a markedly prolonged half-life and which interfere with the assay of 17α-hydroxyprogesterone. The concentrations of Δ^5-steroid-sulfates decrease slowly with age, so that their interference becomes minimal by 2–4 m of age. For this reason, most laboratories use a purification procedure for the determination of this steroid in infants up to 4–6 m of age. In our laboratory, we use a Sephadex-LH20 column chromatography of the plasma extract; it has the advantage of purifying and separating progesterone and 17α-hydroxyprogesterone.

Normal concentrations of plasma 17α-hydroxyprogesterone are shown in Figure 7–6.

FIGURE 7–5. Concentrations of Plasma Testosterone and Androstenedione in Normal Male and Female Infants, Children, and Adults. (To convert testosterone and androstenedione to SI units [nmol/L], multiply by 0.0347 and 0.0349.)

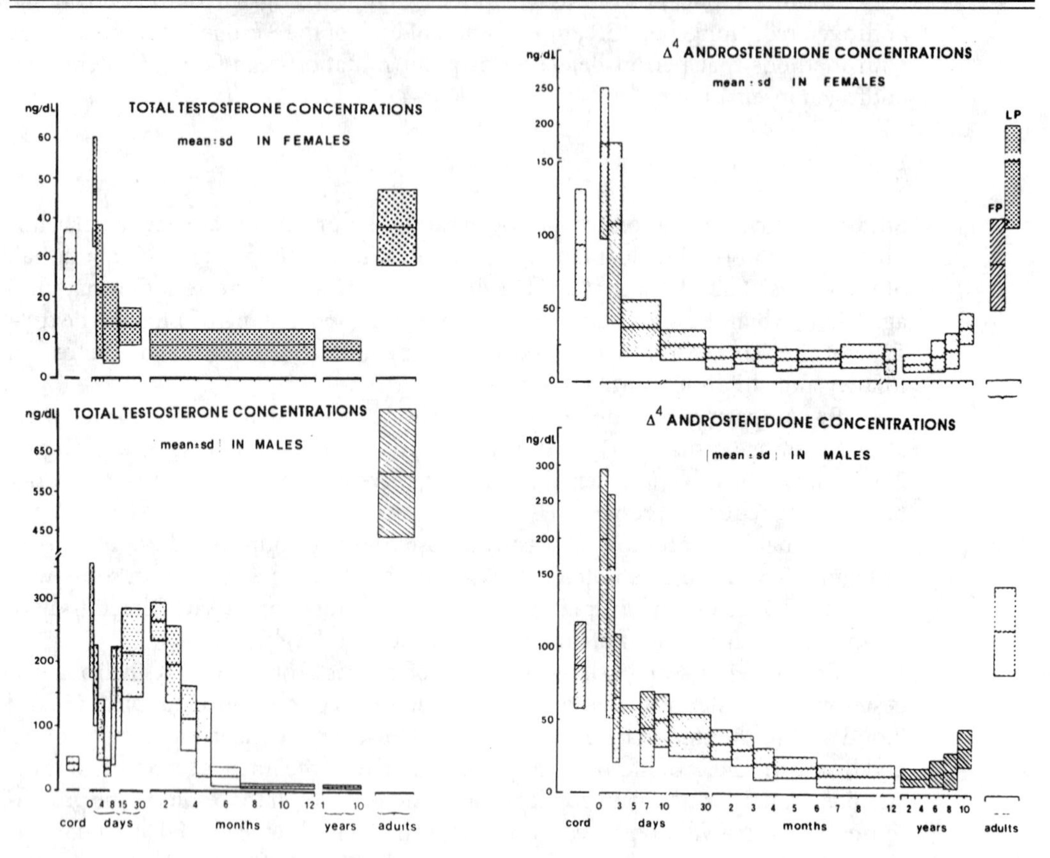

From: Migeon CJ, Forest MG. Androgens in biological fluids. In: Rothfeld B, ed.. Nuclear medicine in vitro, 2d ed. Philadelphia: J.B. Lippincott, 1983:156-57.

ABNORMALITIES OF PUBERTY

Puberty is the series of events that permit a child to become a young adult. These events occur in an orderly fashion, resulting in adult secretion of gonadal hormones and in attainment of reproductive capacity. Puberty involves the maturation of the gonads or *gonadarche* and the secretion of adrenal androgens or *adrenarche.*

Biochemistry and Physiology

During childhood, hypothalamic gonadotropin releasing hormone (GnRH) is suppressed, leading to low concentrations of pituitary gonadotropins, luteinizing hormone (LH), and follicle stimulating hormone (FSH). The first indication of puberty

FIGURE 7–6. Concentrations of Plasma 17α-hydroxyprogesterone in Normal Male and Female Infants

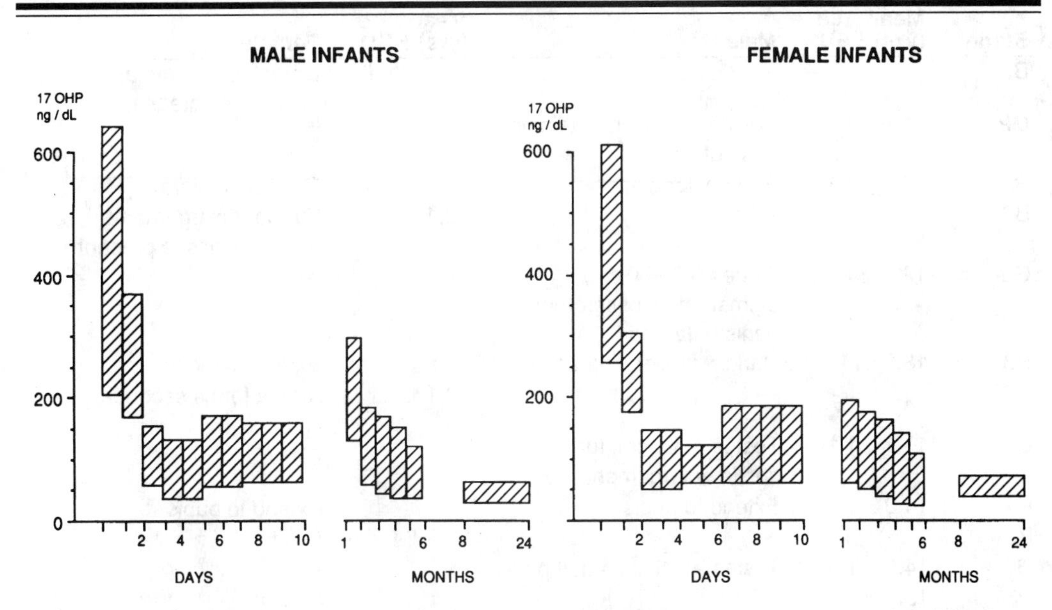

Adapted from: Forest MG, Cathiard AM. Ontogenic study of plasma 17α-hydroxyprogesterone in the human. Pediatric Research 1979;12:6-11.

is the release of the inhibition of the GnRH secretion. The pulsatile secretion of GnRH every 60–90 min leads to a pulsatile pattern of LH and FSH. This occurs initially during sleep. As puberty progresses, the pulsatile pattern also occurs during the day, until there is no longer a diurnal pattern of secretion.

A gradual rise in the adrenal androgens—dehydroepiandrosterone (DHEA), dehydroepiandrosterone sulfate (DHEA-S), and androstenedione—starts 1–2 y prior to the physical changes of puberty (age 6–7 y in girls and 7–8 y in boys). The cause of the increase in androgen production has been postulated to be the secretion of a pituitary peptide hormone, probably related to but different from ACTH. This presumed hormone is called Adrenal Androgen Stimulation Hormone (AASH).

Females

The normal age of onset of puberty in females is 8–13 y. The first signs of puberty are usually the growth spurt and the development of breast buds. However, in 15% of girls, the first sign of puberty is the development of pubic hair. Tanner and Marshall have devised a scale for staging breast and pubic hair development in females (Table 7–5), where stage I is prepubertal and stage V is adult.[18] Pubertal development is usually completed in 2–6 y, and menarche usually occurs at Tanner stage IV, i.e., 2.3 ± 1.0 y after the onset of breast bud development. In girls, the pubertal growth spurt begins with breast budding but is maximal in mid-puberty. The current average age of menarche is 12.8 y (range 10–16 y). In many girls, the early menstrual cycles are anovulatory until the mechanism for LH surge has matured.

TABLE 7–5. Stages of Adolescent Sexual Development

Stage*	Mean Age (yrs) ± SD	Male	Mean Age (yrs) ± SD	Female
B2		—	11.1 ± 1.1	Breast "bud" areolar diameter increases
G2	11.6 ± 1.1	Testes 2.5–3.2 cm; thinning of scrotum		—
P2	13.4 ± 1.1	Sparse, long		On labia majora
B3		—	12.1 ± 1.1	Further enlargement; glandular tissue present
G3	12.8 ± 1.1	Testes 3.3–4.0 cm; pigmentation of scrotum; penis enlarged		—
P3	13.9 ± 1.5	Darker, curlier, coarser		Extend to mons
B4		—	13.1 ± 1.1	Areola forms secondary mound
G4	13.7 ± 1.1	Testes ≥ 4.1 cm; further penile enlargement		—
P4	14.3 ± 1.1	Extend to pubis		Extend to pubis
B5		—	15.3 ± 1.7	Adult
G5	14.9 ± 1.6	Testes ≥ 4.5 cm; adult penis		—
P5	15.1 ± 1.1	Adult		Adult

*B = breast stage, G = gonadal stage, P = pubic hair stage

Males

Tanner developmental stages of external genitalia and pubic hair are also used to describe the progression through puberty (Table 7–5), with Tanner stage I being prepubertal and Tanner stage V being adult.[19]

The average age for the onset of puberty in boys is 9–14 y. Most boys complete puberty in 3–4.5 y. In contrast to girls, the pubertal growth spurt in boys occurs later in pubertal development (Tanner stages III-IV for genitalia). This growth spurt results from increased testosterone and growth hormone production. IGF-I concentrations rise through puberty and peak at Tanner stage IV. The onset of spermatogenesis occurs at about Tanner stage IV for genitalia.

The earliest sign of puberty in a boy is the enlargement of testes. Testes greater than 2.5 cm in length (or 3 cc in volume) are consistent with the onset of puberty. The increase in testicular size is predominantly secondary to an increase in seminiferous tubule size. But there is also an increase in the Leydig cell size. The further increase in genitalia and pubic hair development are primarily due to increasing testosterone production through puberty.

Precocious Puberty

Precocious puberty is the onset of puberty in girls prior to age 8 y or in boys prior to age 9 y.[20] These children present with tall stature for their age and secondary sex characteristics. *Central precocious puberty* is a premature activation of the hypotha-

TABLE 7–6. Etiologies of Central Precocious Puberty

1. Idiopathic
2. Central Nervous System Involvement
   a) Tumor: Hamartoma, Astrocytoma, Glioma
   b) Neurofibromatosis
   c) Injuries: Hydrocephalus, Meningitis, Encephalitis, Head Trauma
3. Severe Primary Hypothyroidism

lamic GnRH pulse generator, whereas *peripheral precocious puberty* is independent of GnRH function.[21] In addition, one distinguishes *contrasexual precocity*, in which there is excessive production of estrogens in males or excessive production of androgens in females.

The incidence of precocious puberty is much greater in girls than in boys.

Central Precocious Puberty

In this type of precocity, there is early activation of the hypothalamic GnRH pulse generator, resulting in pubertal LH/FSH pulse patterns. The etiologies of central precocious puberty are listed in Table 7–6. The idiopathic forms are much more frequent in girls than in boys, accounting for the markedly greater incidence of all types of sexual precocity in girls. The incidence of precocious puberty due to an identifiable CNS lesion is approximately the same in both sexes.[22]

Peripheral Precocious Puberty

Children with peripheral precocious puberty do not have a mature hypothalamic-pituitary-gonadal axis. Rather, the stimulus for the sex steroid production is independent of the GnRH pulse generator. In girls the sexual precocity is due to estrogen exposure, whereas in boys the sexual precocity is due to androgen exposure. The etiologies of peripheral precocious puberty are summarized in Table 7–7.

Both gonadal and adrenal tumors are extremely rare in both sexes. McCune-Albright syndrome is thought to be due to an abnormality of a G-protein subunit associated with the LH receptor that results in the secretion of gonadal steroids

TABLE 7–7. Etiologies of Peripheral Precocious Puberty

GIRLS	BOYS
McCune-Albright Syndrome (café au lait spots, precocious puberty and fibrous dysplasia)	McCune-Albright Syndrome
Ovarian Tumors (Cysts)	Testicular Tumors
Feminizing Adrenal Tumors	Masculinizing Tumors
Ectopic hCG Tumors	Congenital Adrenal Hyperplasia
	Ectopic hCG Tumors
	Premature Leydig Cell Maturation

despite the absence of LH stimulation. Recently some cases of premature Leydig cell maturation or familial male precocious puberty have been found to be due to mutations in the LH receptor.[23]

Contra-sexual Precocious Puberty

Gynecomastia appearing before the onset of puberty in a male is extremely rare and may be caused by an estrogen secreting adrenal tumor. Virilization and hirsutism in prepubertal girls are also rare and may be due to congenital adrenal hyperplasia or an androgen secreting adrenal or ovarian tumor.

Incomplete Precocious Puberty

Premature thelarche is the isolated development of breasts in girls before age 8 y. It usually occurs in the first 4 y of life, and often it regresses completely. A transient increase in LH/FSH and estradiol concentrations can be observed on occasion. However, gonadotropin and steroid concentrations are usually low and there is no activation of the GnRH pulse generator. In addition, there is no estrogenization of the vaginal mucosa and no significant advancement in bone age. In some of the patients, one small ovarian cyst can be found by pelvic sonogram. In such cases, the cyst is the source of estrogens. Rupture and disappearance of the cyst result in breast regression.

Premature adrenarche occurs between age 4–8 y. There is predominantly pubic hair development, often only on the labia in girls. In addition, there may be apocrine odor and axillary hair. There may be mild to moderate acceleration of growth velocity with a slight advancement of bone age. Estrogen and testosterone concentrations are prepubertal, but there is an increased concentration of adrenal androgens, particularly DHEA and DHEA-S, which may rise to pubertal values. Gonadotropin levels remain prepubertal. Puberty occurs at a normal time in these individuals.

Evaluation of Precocious Puberty

The evaluation of children with precocious puberty should begin with a complete history with particular attention to:

- the age at onset of pubertal signs
- the rapidity of progression of symptoms
- history of CNS insult
- family history of puberty
- medications (contraceptive pills, androgens, etc.) accessible to the child
- the growth curve, to assess an acceleration of growth velocity.

On physical examination, a careful neurologic work-up should be obtained and pubertal staging should be made. In males, the testes should be palpated for the presence of a mass. Virilization with no testicular enlargement in boys implies an extra-testicular source of androgens. The skin should also be examined for café au lait spots, which could indicate McCune-Albright syndrome, or for lesions of neurofibromatosis; both conditions are associated with precocious puberty.

Initial laboratory evaluation to determine whether the precocious puberty is of central or peripheral origin should include the determination of the concentration of *gonadotropins* (LH/FSH), *gonadal steroids* (testosterone, estradiol) and *adrenal steroids* (17-hydroxyprogesterone [17-OHP], androstenedione [Δ], DHEA and DHEA-sulfate). In addition, a *bone age* and a set of *thyroid function tests* (T_4 RIA, T_3 resin uptake, T_{index}, and TSH) should be obtained. In order to minimize the effect of episodic LH/FSH secretion, it is recommended that 4 serial blood samples be obtained at 20 min intervals. Assays can be obtained using a blood pool of the 4 samples, or preferably on each sample. Depending on the results of basal values, work-up will be performed as shown in Figure 7–7.

If pubertal values of gonadotropins and gonadal hormones are found, then *central precocious puberty* must be considered and a differential diagnosis of its various causes must be done as shown in Table 7–6. A brain MRI is important in order to study the possibility of tumors.

FIGURE 7–7. Diagram of the Work-up of Children with Signs of Precocious Puberty

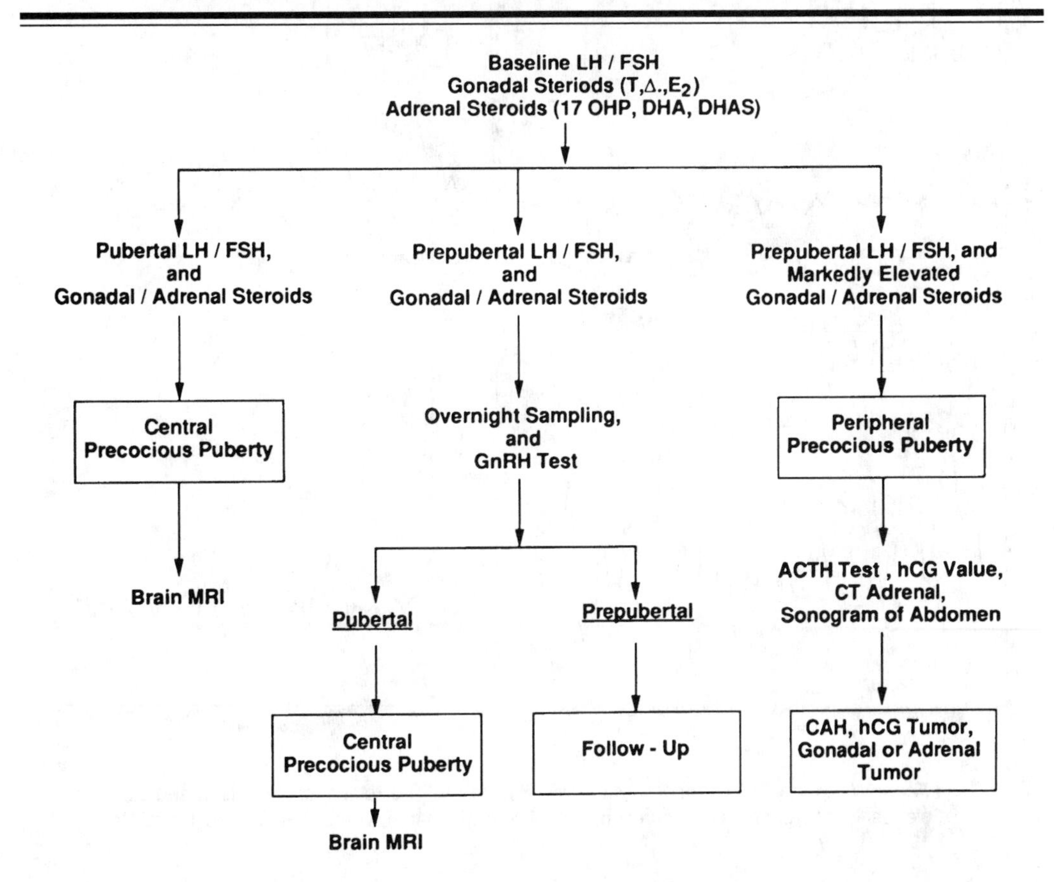

If prepubertal values of LH/FSH and steroids are reported, it will be necessary to perform an overnight blood sampling (every 20 min from 2 AM to 6 AM for LH/FSH, and every hour for gonadal steroids) and a GnRH test (at 8 AM, an IV slow push of 100 micrograms of GnRH is given, followed by blood sampling every 20 min for 2 h). Because LH/FSH are secreted only at night in the early stages of puberty (Figure 7–8), a daytime sampling may give misleading information. As to the GnRH test, it will result in LH/FSH concentrations in the adult range if the subject is in early puberty (stage II). When the results of the overnight sampling and GnRH tests are indicative of a prepubertal status, close follow-up is in order.

The presence of markedly increased gonadal and/or adrenal steroids along with prepubertal LH/FSH will suggest a peripheral cause for the sexual precocity

FIGURE 7–8. Pattern of LH Concentrations in Pre-puberty, Early-to-Mid Puberty, Mid-to-late Puberty, and Adulthood. The pattern of sleep stages is also shown for each pubertal stage.

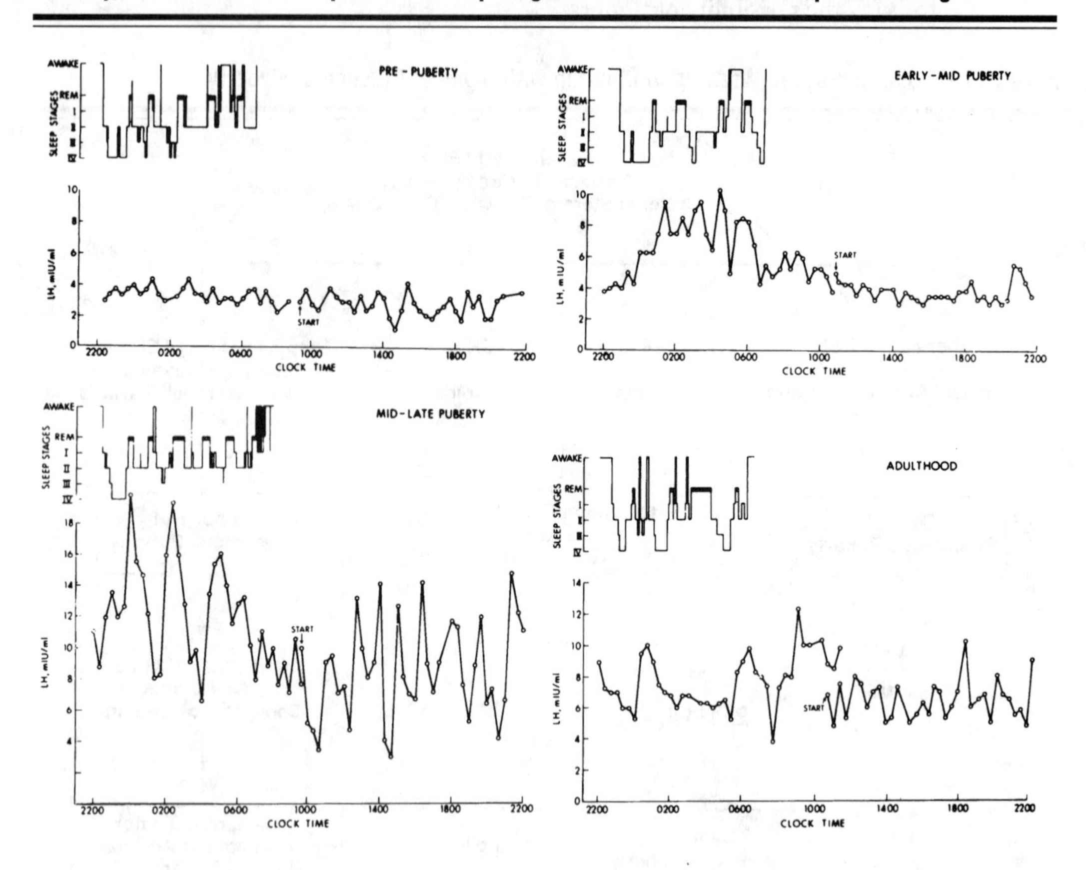

From: Weitzman ED, Boyar RM, Kapen S, Hellman L. The relationship of sleep and sleep stages to neuroendocrine secretion and biological rhythm in man. Rec Prog Horm Res 1975;31:399.

(see Table 7–7). An ACTH test (0.25 milligrams of 1–24 ACTH, IV slow push, is given followed by blood sampling at 0, 30, and 60 min for 17-hydroxyprogesterone and progesterone) will help determine whether congenital adrenal hyperplasia is the cause of precocity. An increased hCG concentration will suggest an hCG producing tumor. CT of adrenal glands and sonogram of abdomen/pelvis may also be indicated.

Patients with McCune-Albright syndrome present the triad precocious puberty, fibrous dysplasia, and café au lait spots, although they may have only two signs of the triad. A bone scan is necessary to look for the changes of fibrous dysplasia.

Delayed Puberty

Definition and Classification

We usually consider that puberty is delayed in a male in whom there is no noticeable testicular enlargement by the age of 14 y and in females if there is no breast development by the age of 13 y. In girls, the definition of primary amenorrhea is the lack of menstrual period by age 16 y or by the failure to menstruate within about 3 y of the onset of breast development.[24]

In many cases the delayed puberty will eventually resolve and result in normal maturation. However, in other cases the delayed puberty will be associated with a hypogonadism that will remain for a lifetime.

The classification of the causes of delayed puberty is based on whether the problem is central, i.e., related to the hypothalamus-pituitary, or is due to primary gonadal deficiency (Table 7–8). This permits us to distinguish *hypogonadotropic hypogonadism* from *hypergonadotropic hypogonadism*. In the first condition there is an inability to produce LH/FSH, whereas in the second condition a defect in gonadal function results in a compensatory increase of the secretion of GnRH by the hypothalamus and LH/FSH by the pituitary. A GnRH test showing little or no increase of gonadotropin concentration is typical of the prepubertal state due to central disorders, whereas the GnRH test will show an accentuated response of LH and FSH in primary gonadal disorders.

TABLE 7–8. Classification of the Causes of Delayed Puberty

	Site of Defect	Gonadotropin	LH/FSH Response to GnRH	Gonadal Steroids
Constitutional delay, Reversible hypogonadotropism	Delayed maturation of hypothalamus	Low	Prepubertal	Low
Permanent hypogonadotropism	Hypothalamus or pituitary	Low	Prepubertal or absent	Low
Hypogonadotropism related to increased androgens	Adrenal or gonadal androgens	Low	Prepubertal	Elevated
Hypergonadotropic hypogonadism	Gonads	Elevated	Accentuated	Low

Constitutional Delay and Reversible Hypogonadotropism

The term *constitutional delay* applies to subjects whose pubertal maturation occurs after the normal average age but is eventually established and is normal from there on. This is the most common cause of pubertal delay, particularly in boys.

Certain conditions result in a *delayed secretion of gonadotropins* that is reversible following the correction of the original condition. Such conditions include malnutrition, as in starvation or anorexia nervosa, the latter problem arising more often in girls than in boys. Another delaying factor is strenuous exercise. It has been observed in children involved in competitive sports such as gymnastics, swimming, running. A number of systemic diseases (severe cardiovascular or respiratory disorders, inflammatory bowel disease, renal tubular acidosis, poorly controlled diabetes mellitus) can also result in delay of gonadotropin secretion. There have also been cases of delayed puberty reported to be related to psychopathological problems. As already mentioned, an improvement in all those conditions will eventually result in the development of puberty.

Permanent Hypogonadotropic Hypogonadism

As seen in Table 7–9, tumors as well as other destructive disorders of the pituitary hypothalamic area can result in an inability to secrete GnRH and/or LH/FSH. Similarly, various congenital anomalies of the central nervous system can result in hypogonadotropism. Some of them are associated with various syndromes such as septo-optic dysplasia, Kallmann's syndrome, and some cases of Prader-Willi syndrome. In some patients, the anatomical anomaly cannot be determined and the etiology is termed "idiopathic hypopituitarism."

Hypogonadotropism Related to Increased Androgen Secretion

In some cases, the androgens arise from the adrenals (virilizing adrenal tumor or congenital adrenal hyperplasia due to 21-hydroxylase deficiency or to 11-hydroxylase deficiency). In other cases, the androgens are gonadal in origin. In girls, it can

TABLE 7–9. Permanent Hypogonadotropic Hypogonadism as Cause of Delayed Puberty

1. Tumors of Pituitary, Hypothalamus, Optic Chiasma, Third Ventricle
   Adenoma, Craniopharyngioma
   Glioma, Dysgerminoma
2. Destructive Disorders
   Histiocytosis, Sarcoidosis, Lupus
3. Head Trauma
   Hemorrhage
4. Congenital Anomalies
   Pituitary Aplasia
   Deficient LH/FSH or GnRH secretion related to various syndromes
   Idiopathic Hypopituitarism

be related to polycystic ovaries or ovarian tumors (adrenal rest tumor, hilar cell tumor, arrhenoblastoma). In boys, this might be related to a Leydig cell tumor.

The clinical picture in such cases is that of androgen effects including virilism without estrogenic effect in girls and without testicular development in boys. Clearly, the treatment of such conditions is to remove or suppress the origin of androgen hypersecretion. This will permit the establishment of puberty.

Hypergonadotropic Hypogonadism

In these patients it is necessary to correlate the appearance of the external genitalia with the karyotype. When the karyotype is requested, instructions should be given to look for mosaicism and search for fluorescent Y chromosome. In most instances it will also be important to obtain a sonogram of the abdomen in order to obtain information about the ovaries and Müllerian ducts in girls and of the testes in males whose gonads are not palpable in the scrotum. A careful physical examination as well as a complete recording of the medical history will also be important in establishing the cause of the hypergonadotropic hypogonadism.

Hypergonadotropic Hypogonadism with Normal-Appearing Female External Genitalia (Table 7–10)

If a normal 46,XX karyotype is obtained, one must consider a number of conditions. The *46,XX gonadal dysgenesis* might be recognized on the basis of the abdominal sonogram, which would show the presence of streak gonads. The *steroid*

TABLE 7–10. Hypergonadotropic Hypogonadism with Normal Female External Genitalia

1. Karyotype 46,XX
   - a) 46,XX Gonadal Dysgenesis
   - b) Steroid Enzyme Deficiency
     P450c17, 3βD-HSD, P450scc
   - c) Resistant Ovaries
   - d) Other Ovarian Disorders
     Oophoritis (auto-immune)
     Radiation, Chemotherapy
     Bilateral Torsion or Tumor
2. Karyotype 46,XY
   - a) 46,XY "Pure Gonadal Dysgenesis"
   - b) Steroid Enzyme Deficiency
     P450c17, 3β-HSD, P450scc
   - c) Androgen Insensitivity Syndrome
3. Karyotype 45,X and Variants
   Turner Syndrome
4. Karyotype 47,XXX

enzyme deficiencies are characterized by an inability to synthesize androgens and estrogens. In 17α-hydroxylase deficiency there is a concomitant hypertension, whereas the deficiency of either 3β-hydroxysteroid dehydrogenase (3β-HSD) or side-chain cleavage enzyme (P450scc) is usually associated with a salt-losing syndrome. As to the other ovarian disorders, they will have a history of *autoimmune abnormality*, *chemotherapy* and/or *radiation*, or of *surgical operation* for bilateral ovarian torsion or tumor. The syndrome of *resistant ovaries* is usually diagnosed by exclusion of all other possible abnormalities.

If a 46,XY karyotype is reported, then one should consider the *46,XY pure gonadal dysgenesis*. In this condition, the gonadal tissue disappears fairly early in fetal life, resulting in completely normal female phenotype and streak gonads which can be detected by sonogram. As to the *steroid enzyme deficiencies* in subjects with 46,XY karyotype, they must be complete in order to result in a female phenotype, this being rather rare. Finally, there is the possibility of *androgen insensitivity syndrome* characterized by the presence of testes in the abdomen or the labial folds with normal male testosterone secretion. In these subjects, the lack of androgen receptor function results in an inability to express androgen effects. Although there is a short vagina, there are no Müllerian structures and little or no Wolffian structures. The LH concentrations are always elevated, but much less than in other conditions of hypergonadotropic hypogonadism. At puberty, the subjects develop breasts, but usually no pubic or axillary hair, and of course no menstruation. The locus of the androgen receptor gene is on the X chromosome, and androgen insensitivity is an X-linked disorder.

If the karyotype is 45,X (or one of its variants), one is dealing with *Turner syndrome*. This condition is characterized by streak gonads and short stature, as well as many other congenital malformations. The patients have an increased incidence of cardiovascular malformations, particularly coarctation of the aorta. There is also an increased incidence of thyroid antibodies and of hypothyroidism, and frequently congenital kidney malformations. The latter might be observed at the time of the abdominal sonogram.

Finally, the karyotype can on occasion be 47,XXX, sometimes termed "super female." Some of these patients tend to have a delayed puberty, and many of them have premature menopause.

Hypergonadotropic Hypogonadism with Normal Male External Genitalia (Table 7–11)

If the karyotype is 46,XY, the diagnosis of "*vanishing testes*" will be made if gonads cannot be localized. This syndrome is thought to be due to a destruction of the testes taking place after gonadal differentiation, since the normal male external genitalia is evidence of previous androgenic masculinization. In *Noonan's syndrome* or "*male Turner syndrome*," one can observe a number of the congenital malformations found in 45,X Turner syndrome, including the short stature. However, the testicular function may be fairly normal as far as Leydig cell function is concerned, but most of patients are azoospermic. One could also be dealing with *partial testicular dysgenesis*, a poorly understood syndrome characterized by partial but variable malformation of the testes usually with a variably decreased Leydig cell function.

TABLE 7–11. Hypergonadotropic-Hypogonadism with Normal Male External Genitalia

1. Karyotype 46,XY
   a) Anorchia ("Vanishing Testes")
   b) Noonan's Syndrome (Male Turner)
   c) Partial Testicular Dysgenesis
   d) Other Testicular Disorders
      Inflammation (auto-immune)
      Bilateral Trauma or Tumor
      Radiation-Chemotherapy
2. Karyotype 46,XX
   "46,XX Males"
3. Other Karyotypes
   a) 47,XXY (Klinefelter) and Variants
   b) Some 47,XYY
   c) Some 45,X/46,XY

One must also consider the possibility of an *autoimmune disorder* involving the testes. As to a *trauma* or *tumor* of the gonads, it must be bilateral in order to result in hypogonadism. In other cases, there is a previous history of *radiation* or *chemotherapy*, as in the treatment of a leukemic disorder in childhood.

In "46,XX males" it is thought that a part of the Y chromosome has been translocated to one of the two X's. For all purposes, such a patient is somewhat similar to a subject with 47,XXY Klinefelter syndrome. Some of these patients, as well as some with a 47,XYY complement and those with a mosaicism 45,X/46,XY, present with delayed puberty.

Evaluation of Delayed Puberty

Based on the classification described above, the first step is to determine the gonadotropin function by measuring LH/FSH concentration in serum as well as the response to the administration of GnRH. The methods used are similar to those described for sexual precocity.

If there is *hypogonadotropism*, it is usually easy to determine whether the etiology is a hypersecretion of androgens. The androgens to be measured include the adrenal androgens (DHEA, its sulfate, and androstenedione) as well as testosterone. If *21-hydroxylase deficiency* is considered, then plasma 17-hydroxyprogesterone concentration should also be determined, whereas if *11-hydroxylase deficiency* is possible, plasma 11-deoxycortisol concentration must be measured. In some patients it might be necessary to use a dexamethasone suppression test: Complete androgen suppression will be obtained in congenital adrenal hyperplasia, but no such suppression will be observed in cases of *virilizing adrenal or ovarian tumors*.

As to the *reversible forms* of hypogonadotropism, they can usually be suspected by appropriate history. However, this might not always be possible, in which case the work-up of suspected *permanent hypogonadotropism* must be carried out. This usually includes an MRI of the head as well as the full work-up of the other pituitary hormones, specifically growth hormone, TSH, and ACTH. The brain MRI will usually detect tumors as well as other destructive processes. It will also detect *pituitary aplasia* as well as *septo-optic dysplasia*. However, in some cases no abnormality of the pituitary hypothalamic area will be found, in which case one can entertain the diagnosis of *idiopathic hypopituitarism*.

If *hypergonadotropism* has been demonstrated, then a karyotype must be obtained. If there is an abnormality of sex chromosomes (such as 45,X or 47,XXY), or if the sex chromosome complement of the karyotype is normal but incongruous with the phenotype of the external genitalia of the patient (46,XX male, 46,XY female), then the diagnosis can readily be made. On the other hand, if the karyotype is that expected for the phenotype of the external genitalia, then the diagnosis may be slightly more complicated. In those patients, a sonogram of the abdomen can be helpful in determining the status of the gonads. In some male patients with scrotal testes, gonadal biopsy may be necessary to determine the type of lesion present.

REFERENCES

1. Migeon CJ, Berkovitz GD, Brown TR. Sexual differentiation and ambiguity. In: Kappy MS, Blizzard RM, Migeon CJ, eds. Wilkins' the diagnosis and treatment of endocrine disorders in childhood and adolescence, 4th ed. Springfield IL: Charles C Thomas, 1994:573–715.
2. Langman J. Medical embryology, 2nd ed. Baltimore: Williams and Wilkins, 1969.
3. Koopman P, Gubbay J, Vivian N, et al. Male development of chromosomally female mice transgenic for Sry. Nature 1991;351:117–21.
4. Ferrari S, Harley VR, Pontiggia A, et al. SRY, like HMG1, recognizes sharp angles in DNA. EMBO Journal 1992;11:4497–506.
5. Magre S, Jost A. The initial phases of testicular organogenesis in the rat: an electron microscopy study. Arch Anat Microsc Morphol Exp 1980;69:297–318.
6. Ewing L, Brown BL. Testicular steroidogenesis. In: Johnson AD, Gomes WR, eds. The testis, Vol. 4. New York: Academic Press, 1977:239–87.
7. Josso N, Picard JY. Antimüllerian hormone. Physiol Rev 1986;66:1038–90.
8. Siiteri PK, Wilson JD. Testosterone formation and metabolism during male sexual differentiation in the human embryo. J Clin Endocrinol Metab 1974;38:113–25.
9. Migeon BR, Brown TR, Axelman J, Migeon CJ. Studies of the locus for androgen receptor: localization on the human X chromosome and evidence for homology with Tfm locus in the mouse. Proc Natl Acad Sci USA 1981;78:6339–43.
10. Grumbach MM, Conte FA. Disorders of sexual differentiation. In: Wilson JD, Foster DW, eds. Williams textbook of endocrinology, 8th ed. Philadelphia: WB Saunders, 1992:853–951.
11. Donohoue PA, Berkovitz GD. Female pseudohermaphroditism In: Rock JA, ed. Seminars in reproductive endocrinology, Vol. 5, No. 3. New York: Thieme-Stratton Medical Publishers, 1987:233–41.
12. Migeon CJ. Male pseudohermaphroditism. Annales d'Endocrinologie (Paris) 1980;41:311–43.
13. Migeon CJ, Berkovitz GD. Congenital defects of the external genitalia in the newborn and prepubertal child. In: Carpenter SE, Rock J, eds. Pediatric and adolescent gynecology. New York: Raven Press, 1992:77–94.
14. Berkovitz GD, Fechner PY, Marcantonio SM, et al. The role of the sex-determining region of the Y chromosome (SRY) in the etiology of 46,XX true hermaphroditism. Hum Genet 1992;88:411–16.

15. Brown TR, Lubahn DB, Wilson EM, et al. Naturally occurring mutant androgen receptors from subjects with complete androgen insensitivity are defective in transcriptional activation. Molecular Endocr 1990;4:1759–72.
16. Forest MG, Sizonenko PC, Cathiard AM, Bertrand J. Hypophyso-gonadal function in humans during the first year of life. I. Evidence for testicular activity in early infancy. J Clin Invest 1974;53:818–28.
17. Fugua JS, Sher ES, Migeon CJ, Berkovitz GD. Assay of plasma testosterone during the first six months of life: importance of chromatographic purification of steroid. Clin Chem, in press.
18. Marshal WA, Tanner JM. Variations in pattern of pubertal changes in girls. Arch Dis Child 1969;44:291–303.
19. Marshal WA, Tanner JM. Variations in pattern of pubertal changes in boys. Arch Dis Child 1970;45:13–23.
20. Grumbach MM, Styne DM. Puberty: ontogeny, neuroendocrinology, physiology, and disorders. In: Wilson JD, Foster DW, eds. Williams textbook of endocrinology, 8th ed. Philadelphia: WB Saunders, 1992:1139–221.
21. Kaplan SL, Grumbach MM. Pathogenesis of sexual precocity. In: Grumbach MM, Sizonenko PC, Aubert ML, eds. Control of the onset of puberty. Baltimore: Williams and Wilkins, 1990:620–68.
22. Rogol A, Blizzard R. Variations and disorders of pubertal development. In: Kappy MS, Blizzard RM, Migeon CJ, eds. Wilkins' the diagnosis and treatment of endocrine disorders in childhood and adolescence, 4th ed. Springfield, IL: Charles C Thomas, 1994:858–917.
23. Shenker A, Lane L, Kosugi S, et al. A constitutively activating mutation of the luteinizing hormone receptor in familial male precocious puberty. Nature 1993:365:652–654.
24. Job J-C, Chaussain J-L, Toublanc J-E. Delayed puberty. In: Grumbach MM, Sizonenko PC, Aubert ML, eds. Control of the onset of puberty. Baltimore: Williams and Wilkins, 1990:588–619.

CHAPTER 8

Disorders of the Thyroid Gland

Wellington Hung, M.D., Ph.D., F.A.A.P., F.A.C.E., F.A.C.P.

INTRODUCTION

Thyroid hormones are essential for the general growth and development of the infant and child, particularly in the differentiation and function of the central nervous system. They are necessary elements in the maturational events involved in the transition of the newborn to the adult.

The thyroid gland is bi-lobed and the lobes are connected by an isthmus. The isthmus usually overlies the region of the second to fourth tracheal cartilages. In normal children, the right lobe is often the larger of the two lobes. The thyroid gland produces the thyroid hormones 3,5,3′,5′-thyroxine (T_4), and 3,5,3′-triiodothyronine (T_3).

Thyroid hormone homeostasis is controlled by the hypothalamus and anterior pituitary gland. Thyrotropin-releasing hormone (TRH) is produced by several hypothalamic nuclei and is secreted into the hypophyseal portal system and carried to the anterior pituitary to bind to cell membrane receptors on thyrotrophic cells. The structure of TRH has been shown to be pyroglutamyl-histyl-prolinamide, and this tripeptide has been synthesized. TRH stimulates the thyroid cells to increase the synthesis and release of T_4 and T_3. These hormones, in turn, feed back on the pituitary thyrotroph to suppress synthesis of TSH.

In the human fetus, pituitary TSH is detectable at 8–10 w of gestation.[1] Pituitary TSH concentrations are low until 16 w of gestation and are increased significantly at 28 w. Serum TSH is detectable at 10 w of gestation.[2]

The secretion of TSH is pulsatile, the pulse frequency being about 8–12 pulses per 24 h and the pulse amplitude about 0.5 mU/L. In infants, children, and adolescents, serum TSH concentrations exhibit a circadian rhythm.[3–4] The development of the circadian rhythm begins after the first month of life. The circadian pattern of serum TSH is characterized by declining values throughout the morning, nadir values in the afternoon, and an approximate doubling, or surge, at night, with peak values in the early morning. Regulatory factors involved in the modulation of the endogenous rhythm of TSH secretion include sleep, dopamine, and glucocorticoid secretion.

Feedback control of TSH secretion occurs at both the pituitary and hypothalamic levels. At the pituitary, low concentrations of circulating thyroid hormones result in increased TSH secretion, while increased concentrations of thyroid hormones suppress TSH secretion. Feedback inhibition by thyroid hormones on the thyroid gland itself has been described.

THYROID HORMONE SYNTHESIS

Iodine and amino acids are essential substrates for the formation of T_4 and T_3. After iodide is absorbed from the gastrointestinal tract, it enters the iodine pool of the body. From the pool, iodide is removed by trapping in the follicular cells of the thyroid gland or is excreted in the urine.

Immediately after entrance of iodide into the thyroid, iodination of organic compounds occurs and is dependent upon oxidation of iodide to iodine. Thyroid hormones are first synthesized as a prohormone, thyroglobulin (Tg). Thyroglobulin is a glycoprotein consisting of amino acids connected in peptide linkage. Tg is a normal secretory product of the thyroid gland and can be measured by radioimmunoassay (RIA) in the serum. Interlaboratory variations for serum values exist because an international standard has not been established.

T_4 and T_3 are secreted by the thyroid gland in a T_4:T_3 ratio of 10:1. Twenty percent of T_3 is directly secreted by the thyroid, while 80% is converted from T_4 by peripheral deiodination, catalyzed by T_4-5′-deiodinase.

In pathologic states, a greater proportion of T_3 comes from direct thyroidal secretion. T_3 is three to four times more potent than T_4.

Although T_4 and T_3 secretion is primarily regulated by TSH, it may also be regulated by iodide and various growth factors. Extrathyroidal T_3 production is also regulated; it is decreased by starvation and virtually all illnesses, increased by overfeeding, decreased in hypothyroidism, and increased in hyperthyroidism.

Most, if not all, thyroid hormone actions are mediated by regulation of gene expression, through binding of T_3 receptor complexes to specific response elements of different genes.[5] The T_3 nuclear receptors are structurally similar to many steroid hormone receptors. The affinity of the receptor for T_3 is approximately tenfold higher than the affinity for T_4.

3,3′5′-triiodothyronine, or reverse T_3 (RT_3), is formed primarily from peripheral monodeiodination of T_4. The inner ring deiodination of T_4 by 5′-deiodinase forms RT_3. The distinction between formation of T_3 and RT_3 does not appear to be a random event and may be one of the host defense mechanisms against protein deficiency. The metabolic activity of RT_3 is almost nil.

TRANSPORT OF THYROID HORMONES

Transport of T_4 and T_3 in plasma involves binding to protein carriers. Approximately 75% of serum T_4 is bound to an inter-alpha globulin (T_4-binding globulin or TBG); 20% is bound to albumin and 5% to a prealbumin, thyroxine-binding prealbumin (TBPA). T_4 binds with approximately 10 times the affinity of T_3 to these protein carriers, and this accounts for the much greater concentration of T_4 and T_3 found in normal plasma. A small amount of T_4 is loosely attached to erythrocytes. It is estimated that although free and bound T_4 are in equilibrium, at any given time only 0.016% to 0.064% of the total circulating T_4 is not bound. This minute fraction is referred to as free thyroxine (FT_4). Although quantitatively insignificant, the free hormone concentrations indicate more accurately the metabolic status of an individual, since only in this form can it traverse the cellular membranes and exert its function.

PHYSIOLOGIC CHANGES OF THYROID FUNCTION TESTS DURING THE PEDIATRIC AGE

The proper interpretation of serum TSH, T_4, T_3, RT_3, resin T_3 uptake (RT_3U) or thyroid hormone binding ratio (THBR), and Tg concentrations in pediatric patients requires a knowledge of the age-dependency of these hormones. Importantly, pre-term and small-for-gestational-age (SGA) newborns have serum thyroid hormone values different from those of full-term newborns.

THYROID-STIMULATING HORMONE

Serum TSH can be measured by RIA, and conventional RIA can easily detect patients with primary hypothyroidism; however, because of assay insensitivity, RIA cannot differentiate low-normal from abnormally low values. In the early 1980s, immunometric assays (IMA) for serum TSH became available that are referred to as "sensitive" TSH (sTSH) or second-generation TSH assays. The sTSH-IMA are approximately 10 to 100 times as sensitive as TSH-RIA and are capable of discriminating very low TSH values found in hyperthyroidism from those found in healthy euthyroid patients.[6] These assays have a sensitivity of 0.1 mU/L. These second-generation sTSH assays are currently used in clinical practice. Efforts to develop still more sensitive assays have led to a third generation of assays utilizing immunochemiluminescence assay. The third-generation assay has an approximately tenfold greater sensitivity of 0.01 mU/L. This assay allows differentiation of patients with non-thyroidal illnesses and low serum TSH values from hyperthyroidism. This assay also allows more precise adjustment of exogenous thyroxine dosage prescribed to hypothyroid patients. Suppression of the serum TSH concentration measured by sensitive assays has been shown to be highly predictive of a suppressed response to TRH stimulation, thus obviating the need in most situations for performing a TRH test (see discussion below).

In the newborn infant, there is a great increase in serum TSH concentrations at the time of birth. An acute increase in values occurs within the first few minutes of life, and peak values are observed approximately 30 min following delivery.[1] Values decrease rapidly thereafter, falling to 50% of the peak values by 2 h of life. Serum TSH concentrations decrease further, so that by 48 h of age they are only slightly higher than cord blood values. The complete explanation for this striking increase in TSH concentrations is not known. There is evidence that the increase may be due, at least in part, to the drop in body temperature experienced by the newborn after delivery. Serum TSH values from birth to age 20 y are presented in Table 8–1.

THYROTROPIN-RELEASING HORMONE (TRH) STIMULATION TEST

Synthetic TRH causes release of TSH from the anterior pituitary glands of normal infants, children, and adolescents.[7] Serum TSH values increase in normal children and adolescents within 10 min after intravenous administration of TRH, peak at 20–45 min, and then decline to baseline values by 2 h. The TRH test allows us to (1) distinguish hypothalamic TRH deficiency from pituitary TSH deficiency as the cause of hypothyroidism; (2) evaluate pituitary TSH reserve; and (3) offer a confirmatory test for hyperthyroidism. As previously mentioned, the availability of sTSH assays obviates the need to perform TRH testing in most instances.

TABLE 8–1. Serum TSH values (mU/L) by Age Determined by sTSH by Immunoradiometric Assay (IRMA)

Age	Serum TSH
Premature Infants (gestational age in weeks)[1]	
25–27	0.2–30.3
28–30	0.2–30.6
31–33	0.7–27.9
34–36	1.1–21.6
Infants, Children, and Adults[2]	
1–4 d	1.0–39.0
2–20 w	1.7–9.1
5–24 m	0.8–8.1
2–7 y	0.7–5.7
8–20 y	0.7–5.7
21–45 y	0.4–4.2

[1]Serum obtain during first week of life. *Source:* Adams LM, Emery JR, Clark SJ et al. Reference ranges for newer thyroid function tests in premature infants. J Pediatr 1994;126:122–7.

[2]*Source:* Nelson JC, Clark SJ, Borut DL et al. Age-related changes in serum free thyroxine during childhood and adolescence. J Pediatr 1993;123:899–905.

THYROXINE-BINDING GLOBULIN

The TBG concentration is high in cord blood and decreases to adult values by 20 years of age (see discussion below). Serum TBG values at term are higher in healthy, full-term newborns than in SGA newborns. A positive correlation is present between serum TBG and thyroid hormone concentrations.

Serum concentrations of TBPA are higher in the full-term newborn than in the SGA newborn; however, the serum concentration of TBPA is *lower* in the SGA newborn than in the premature newborn. Serum TBG values from birth to age 19 y are presented in Table 8–2.

The serum concentrations and binding of the thyroxine-binding proteins vary with physiologic and pathologic states (Table 8–3) and affect serum T_4 and T_3 concentrations.[8] Alterations in TBG concentration or binding usually do not affect the FT_4, and it is therefore useful to measure this if one suspects an abnormality in the serum values of T_4-binding proteins.

FAMILIAL DYSALBUMINEMIA

This is an autosomal disorder in which affected patients synthesize albumin with increased affinity and/or capacity to bind T_4 but not T_3. These patients have increased serum T_4 and free T_4 (FT_4-I) indices, but their serum T_3 and TSH values are normal and they are clinically euthyroid. The FT_4I values are high because the abnormal binding involves only T_4 and is not recognized by the RT_3U study (see discussion below). A similar abnormality in TBPA has been reported.

THYROXINE

Peak serum concentrations of T_4 in the newborn are reached 24 h after birth (see Table 8–4) and then slowly decrease over the first weeks of life.[9] Healthy premature and SGA newborns have qualitatively similar but quantitatively decreased changes in T_4 when compared to full-term newborns. During the first 7 weeks of life, serum

TABLE 8–2. Thyroxine-Binding Globulin by RIA [values expressed in mg/L (mg/dL)]

Age	Males	Females
1–5 d	22–42 (2.2–4.2)	22–42 (2.2–4.2)
1–11 m	16–36 (1.6–3.6)	17–37 (1.7–3.7)
1–9 y	12–28 (1.2–2.8)	15–27 (1.5–2.7)
10–19 y	14–26 (1.4–2.6)	14–30 (1.4–3.0)

From: Nichols Institute Reference Laboratories, San Juan Capistrano, CA. Reproduced with permission.

TABLE 8–3. Causes of Abnormal Serum Concentration and/or Binding of Thyroxine-Binding Proteins

	TBG	TBPA
Hypothyroidism	inc	
Genetic	inc or dec	N
Estrogens	inc	dec
Pregnancy	inc	dec
Hepatic Disease	inc or dec or N	dec
Androgens	dec	dec
Anabolic Steroids	dec	
Nephrosis	dec	
Severe Hypoproteinemia	dec	
Phenytoin (Dilantin)	dec	
Glucocorticoids (High Dosage)	dec	dec
Salicylate (Aspirin)	N	dec
Heroin	inc	
Methadone	inc	
Acute Stress		dec
Chronic Illness		dec
Thyrotoxicosis		dec

inc = increased; dec = decreased; N = normal

TABLE 8–4. Age-Related Values for Serum T_4 and T_3

Age	T_4 nmol/L (μg/dL)	T_3 nmol/L (ng/dL)
Cord		
30 w	73.5–201.2 (5.7–15.6)	0.08–2.17 (5–141)
25 w	78.7–216.7 (6.1–16.8)	
40 w	85.1–233.5 (6.6–18.1)	
45 w	91.6–250.3 (7.1–19.4)	
1–5 d	180.2–365.5 (14–28.4)	1.54–11.4 (100–740)
1–11 m	92.7–202.1 (7.2–15.7)	1.62–3.77 (105–245)
1–4 y		1.62–4.14 (105–269)
5–9 y		1.45–3.71 (94–241)
1–9 y	77.2–182.8 (6–14.2)	
10–14 y		1.26–3.28 (82–213)
15–19 y		1.23–3.23 (80–210)
10–20 y	60.5–159.6 (4.7–12.4)	

From: Fisher DA. The thyroid gland. In: Brook CGD, ed. Clinical paediatric endocrinology, 2d ed. Oxford: Blackwell Scientific Publications 1989:313 and Nichols Institute Reference Laboratories, San Juan Capistrano, CA. Reproduced with permission.

T_4 values are significantly lower in SGA than in full-term infants, and even lower values are present in premature infants. After approximately 50 days of age, comparable serum T_4 concentrations are present in all three maturity groups of infants. Between 1 and 15 years of age, there is a gradual decrease in concentration of T_4 with increasing age. Causes of hyperthyroxinemia are listed in Table 8–5, some of which have been presented in Table 8–3. It is important to remember that hyperthyroxinemia does not equal hyperthyroidism.

Causes of decreased serum thyroid hormone binding or hypothyroxinemia are listed in Table 8–6. Inherited TBG disorders are X-linked and may be complete or partial. Salicylates and furosemide in high doses may cause decreased T_4 and T_3 binding because they are competitive physicochemical inhibitors of T_4 and T_3 binding to TBG. Patients with severe non-thyroidal illnesses may have low albumin and TBPA values, and therefore T_4 and T_3 binding are decreased.

FREE THYROXINE (FT_4)

A number of *in vitro* methods have been developed to estimate serum FT_4 levels.[10] The results vary from one method to another depending on the assay used and the presence of accompanying non-thyroidal disorders. Most FT_4 methods are inappropriate in the presence of significant alterations of T_4 binding to serum carrier proteins.

In vitro FT_4 methods include:

1. FT_4 index methods that correct total T_4 values using an assessment of T_4 binding proteins;
2. Equilibrium dialysis or ultrafiltration methods that separate FT_4 from bound hormone using a semipermeable membrane; and

TABLE 8–5. Causes of Hyperthyroxinemia in Pediatrics

I. Hyperthyroidism
II. Increased Serum Binding of Thyroid Hormones
  A. TBG
  B. Thyroxine-binding albumin
    1. Familial dysalbuminemic hyperthyroxinemia
  C. TBPA
    1. Inherited abnormal TBPA
  D. Anti-T_4 antibodies
III. Non-Thyroidal Illnesses
  A. Medical illnesses
  B. Psychiatric illnesses
IV. Drug-Induced Hyperthyroxinemia
V. Generalized thyroid hormone resistance

TABLE 8–6. Causes of Decreased Serum Thyroid Binding or Hypothyroxinemia in Pediatrics

I. Hypothyroidism
II. Decreased Thyroxine-Binding Proteins
    A. Thyroxine-binding globulin
        1. Androgens
        2. Anabolic steriod hormones
        3. Inherited complete or partial TBG deficiency
        4. Non-thyroidal illnesses
        5. Glucocorticoids
    B. Thyroxine-binding pre-albumin
        1. Non-thyroidal illnesses
        2. Glucocorticoids
    C. Thyroxine-binding albumin
        1. Non-thyroidal illnesses
III. Drug-Related Inhibition of Binding
    A. Salicylates in high doses
    B. Furosemide in high doses
IV. Illness-Related Inhibition of Binding
    A. Protein inhibitors
    B. Fatty acid inhibitor

3. Immunoextraction or RIA methods that estimate FT_4 by either a T_4 analogue or two-step-back titration with a solid-phase T_4 antibody and do not use semi-permeable membranes to separate free from bound hormone.

The concentration of cord FT_4 is higher than the mean maternal value, but the difference is not statistically significant. Serum FT_4 concentrations peak at 24 h of life and then decrease slowly over the first weeks of life. Similar to T_4, serum FT_4 concentrations correlate positively with increasing gestational age and birth weight. FT_4 concentrations decrease progressively with age during childhood. Age-related values of free T_4 are presented in Table 8–7.

The free T_4 index (FT_4–I) is an estimate for FT_4. It is calculated from two test results: total T_4 and thyroid hormone binding ratio (THBR) or resin T_3 uptake (RT_3U). THBR is another term for RT_3U which emphasizes its distinction from T_3-RIA. The THBR is an indirect estimate of the FT_3 fraction which is obtained by adding labeled T_3 to serum and measuring how much of it remains free for binding to a matrix such as an ion-exchange resin. Thus, THBR provides an indirect estimate of TBG binding activity in the serum. TBG levels are influenced by a variety of factors, as discussed earlier. Fluctuations in TBG concentrations lead to changes in T_4 and T_3 levels which may give a false diagnosis of thyroid dysfunction in euthyroid patients. THBR normal values for age vary with the test procedure and the individual laboratory. THBR varies shortly after birth, but does not change significantly between 1 year of age and adulthood (see Table 8–8).

TABLE 8–7. Age-Related Values of Free T_4 by Direct Equilibrium Dialysis [values expressed in pmol/L (ng/dL)]

Age	Free T_4	
Premature Infants (gestational age in weeks)[1]		
25–27	7.7–28.3	0.6–2.2
28–30	7.7–32.8	0.6–3.4
31–33	12.9–38.9	1.0–3.8
34–36	15.4–56.6	1.2–4.4
Infants, Children and Adults[2]		
1–4 d	28.3–68.2	2.2–5.3
2–30 w	11.6–29.6	0.9–2.3
5-24 m	10.3-23.2	0.8-1.8
2–7 y	12.9–27.0	1.0–2.0
8–20 y	10.3–24.5	0.8–1.9
21–45 y	11.6–32.2	0.9–2.5

[1]Serum obtain during first week of life. *Source:* Adams LM, Emery JR, Clark SJ et al. Reference ranges for newer thyroid function tests in premature infants. J Pediatr 1994;126:122–7.

[2]*Source:* Nelson JC, Clark SJ, Borut DL et al. Age-related changes in serum free thyroxine during childhood and adolescence. J Pediatr 1993;123:899–905.

TABLE 8–8. Thyroid Hormone Binding Ratio (THBR) or Resin T_3 Uptake (RT_3U) by Age

Age	THBR
Cord	0.70–1.11
1–3 d	0.83–1.17
1 w	0.70–1.05
1–12 m	0.70–1.05
1–3 y	0.78–1.14
3–10 y	0.75–1.18
Pubertal children and adults	0.85–1.15

From: Pediatric Endocrine Syllabus, Endocrine Sciences, Calabasas, CA. Reproduced with permission.

TABLE 8–9. Free T_4 Index (ug/dL) Calculated from T_4 and THBR

Age	FT_4-I
Cord	6.0–13.2
1-3 d	9.9–17.5
1 w	7.5–15.1
1-12 m	5.0–13.0
1-3 y	5.4–12.5
3-10 y	5.7–12.8
Pubertal Children & Adults	4.2–13.0

From: Pediatric Endocrine Syllabus, Endocrine Sciences, Calabasas, CA. Reproduced with permission.

FT_4-I values at various ages calculated from total T_4 and THBR are presented in Table 8–9.

REVERSE T_3

T_4 is the major secretory product of the thyroid gland and is metabolized in peripheral tissues to either T_3 or 3,3′,5′-triiodothyronine (rT_3). rT_3 is metabolically *inactive.* A variety of disorders and drugs can inhibit the conversion of T_4 to T_3, resulting in low serum T_3 levels. These include uncontrolled diabetes mellitus, chronic liver disease, renal failure, malnutrition, trauma, burns, propanolol and glucocorticoids. Collectively, these disorders are referred to as nonthyroidal illness (NTI; see below). In many patients with NTI, serum rT_3 levels are increased while T_3 levels are decreased. Measurement of rT_3 may be useful in the diagnosis of NTI. Values for rT_3 are given in Table 8–10.

THYROGLOBULIN

Under physiological conditions, Tg can be found in low concentrations in the blood and values in cord blood are higher than the maternal values. Age-related values are presented in Table 8–11.

TABLE 8–10. Reverse T_3 (rT_3)

Age	rT_3 nmol/L (ng/dL)
1 m – 20 y	0.15–0.54 (10–35)

From: Nichols Institute Reference Laboratories, San Juan Capistrano, CA. Reproduced with permission.

TABLE 8–11. Thyroglobulin (ng/mL or µg/L)

Age	Thyroglobulin
Cord (term)	15–101
Birth–35 m	11–92
3–11 y	5.6–42
12–17 y	2.7-22

From: Nichols Institute Reference Laboratories, San Juan Capistrano, CA. Reproduced with permission.

MISCELLANEOUS THYROID TESTS

Antibodies to T_4 and T_3

On very rare occasions, patients, particularly those with Graves' disease, CLT, and non-thyroidal illnesses, may have serum antibodies to T_4 or T_3.[11] Depending on the method used, the value for T_4 may be spuriously high or low. RIA methods based on double antibody techniques will give higher values than methods using talc or charcoal to separate bound and free hormones.

Circulating antithyroid hormone autoantibodies can cause artifactual effects on RIAs for total and FT_4 and T_3 and give the clinician confusing information about a patient's thyroid status; i.e., discrepancies between physical findings and laboratory thyroid hormone tests results.[12] In this situation, the presence of autoantibodies to T_4 or T_3 should be considered. Radiobinding assays for detection of anti-T_3 and anti-T_4 autoantibodies are available from commercial laboratories.

Thyroid Antibodies

Patients with thyroid autoimmune disease develop antibodies to three major classes of antigen: thyroglobulin; thyroid microsomal antigen, specifically thyroid peroxidase; and the thyroid cell TSH receptor protein.[13] Most patients with thyroid autoimmune disease have circulating antibodies to Tg (ATG) as well as antiperoxidase antibody (anti-TPO). Both ATG and anti-TPO are useful markers of thyroid autoimmune diseases, including chronic lymphocytic thyroiditis, Graves' disease, and variants of these disorders.

Other antibodies of clinical importance are directed against the TSH receptor. There are a number of methods for measuring TSH receptor antibodies (TRAb). Assays for TSH receptor stimulating immunoglobulins (TSIs) have been developed, and TSIs are now believed to produce the hyperthyroid state in Graves' disease.[13]

In patients with Graves' disease who are to be treated with antithyroid drugs, the finding of very high serum concentrations of TSI prior to starting therapy indicates the high probability of failure of therapy. The assay is also useful in predicting those patients who will relapse at the end of the drug treatment period.

Radioactive Thyroidal Uptake, Scintiscanning, and Ultrasonography

Normal values for 24 h thyroidal ^{123}I uptake vary geographically because of regional variations in dietary iodine content and therefore must be determined locally for each part of the country. This test is being used less frequently in pediatric patients because of several factors:

1. The increased intake of stable iodides through food preservatives, antiseptics, and drugs has lowered the normal range of uptake, so it may not discriminate between normal subjects and patients with hypothyroidism.
2. Although ^{123}I reduces the dose of radiation to the thyroid gland as compared with ^{125}I or ^{131}I, some tissue radiation is still present.
3. The test is time-consuming and moderately expensive.

Thyroid scintiscanning may be useful in determining the etiology of congenital hypothyroidism—i.e., ectopia or aplasia of the thyroid gland—and in the evaluation of nodules of the thyroid gland and goiters.

Ultrasonography is useful for determining thyroid size in pediatric patients and in determining the cause of diffuse goiters.[14] Data on thyroid volume in normal controls have been published. There is no significant difference in thyroid volume between boys and girls, and there is a gradual increase in volume with age.

APPLICATION OF THYROID FUNCTION TESTS TO THE MORE COMMON THYROID PROBLEMS IN PEDIATRIC PATIENTS

Hyperthyroidism

In over 90% of pediatric patients, hyperthyroidism is due to Graves' disease. Graves' disease is an autoimmune disease in which TSI antibodies bind to TSH receptors on thyrocytes and stimulate thyroid hormone synthesis, resulting in the clinical manifestations of thyrotoxicosis. Given a patient in whom there is clinical reason to suspect hyperthyroidism, the initial tests should include serum total T_4, total T_3, and sTSH. In almost all pediatric patients with Graves' disease, both serum T_4 and T_3 are increased and sTSH is abnormally suppressed. However, a few patients will have hyperthyroidism due to isolated increases in serum T_3 (T_3-toxicosis), and the serum T_4 is normal or even low. Measurement of T_4 and FT_3 can be used in place of total T_4 and T_3 if the clinician suspects that increased serum concentrations of thyroid hormones may be abnormally affected by the patient's serum thyroxine-binding proteins. An extremely rare cause of hyperthyroidism in pediatric patients is excessive secretion of TSH from a pituitary tumor (see causes of hyperthyroxinemia listed in Table 8–5). Radioactive iodine uptake studies and TRH testing are rarely necessary to establish a diagnosis of hyperthyroidism. TSI assay is not indicated for diagnostic purposes.

Comparison of serum test results in hyperthyroxinemic and hypothyroxinemic states is shown in Table 8–12. Hyperthyroxinemia is not synonymous with hyperthyroidism.

Very rarely, an euthyroid pediatric patient may have increased serum T_4 and/or a normal FT_4-I but normal values of sTSH. Possible causes of this combination of

TABLE 8–12. Comparison of Serum Thyroid Function Tests in Hyperthyroxinemic and Hypothyroxinemic States

	T_4	Free T_4 Index	Free T_4	T_3	sTSH
HYPERTHYROXINEMIC STATES					
Euthyroid					
Hyperthyroxinemia					
Non-thyroidal illnesses (Euthyroid sick syndrome)	inc	inc	inc	N, dec	N
Drug-induced	inc	inc	inc	N, dec	N, inc
High TBG states	inc	N	N	inc	N
Dysalbuminemia	inc	inc	N	N	N
Generalized thyroid hormone resistance	inc	inc	inc	inc	N, inc
Hyperthyroidism	inc	inc	inc	inc	dec
HYPOTHYROXINEMIC STATES					
Non-thyroidal illnesses (Euthyroid sick syndrome)	dec	dec	N	dec	inc, N, dec
Low TBG states	dec	dec	N	N, dec	N
Primary hypothyroidism	dec	dec	dec	dec	inc
Secondary hypothyroidism	dec	dec	dec	dec	dec

inc = increased, dec = decreased, N = normal

findings include familial dysalbuminemic hyperthyroxinemia or the presence of anti-T_4 and/or anti-T_3 antibodies. If thyrotoxicosis factita is suspected, it can be ruled out by determination of serum hTg. Since hTg is produced by the thyroid gland, its serum concentration will be decreased in thyrotoxicosis factita.

Hypothyroidism

In pediatric patients with suspected hypothyroidism, the most specific and sensitive screening test is the serum total T_4 concentration. Specificity is increased by determining the serum FT_4 or FT_4-I, thereby eliminating those patients with low serum TBG. Accuracy is improved by measuring serum sTSH. Patients with mild hypothyroidism due to *primary* hypothyroidism have increased sTSH even when the serum T_4 and FT_4 concentrations are only borderline low. However, in the presence of hypothalamic or pituitary disease causing hypothyroidism, the sTSH concentrations are low or in the normal range.

TRH testing might allow distinguishing patients with hypothalamic hypothyroidism from those with pituitary hypothyroidism. The classic response to TRH in patients with hypothalamic hypothyroidism is a delayed increase in serum TSH following TRH administration. In pituitary hypothyroidism, TSH should not increase after TRH administration. However, there have been exceptions in both categories.

Neonatal Screening for Hypothyroidism

The incidence of congenital hypothyroidism in non-endemic areas of the world is approximately 1 in 4,000 live births.[15] Congenital hypothyroidism is the most common endocrine cause of infant mental retardation that is preventable with early therapy. Recent experience indicates that large-scale, routine screening of newborns for congenital hypothyroidism is practical and cost-effective.[15] Filter-paper disc blood spots are collected in the neonatal period and eluates utilized for measurement of TSH and T_4. In most screening programs in the United States, the primary screening test is the T_4, and in those samples with T_4 values in the lower 10%, a follow-up measurement of TSH in the same sample is performed. All neonates with suspected hypothyroidism by screening tests require follow-up measurement of serum TSH and T_4 before a definitive diagnosis of hypothyroidism is made.

False-positive and false-negative results occur with filter-paper thyroid screening and must be followed with serum testing if indicated.[16]

NON-THYROIDAL ILLNESSES

A variety of non-thyroidal illnesses (NTI) produce alterations in thyroid function in non-hospitalized, but more frequently in hospitalized, pediatric patients in whom no intrinsic thyroid disease exists.[17] The pathologic states producing these alterations include any acute or chronic medical illness, trauma, major surgery, caloric restriction and fasting, and acute psychiatric disorders. The precise mechanism(s) responsible for the changes in thyroid hormone indices with NTI has not been elucidated.

The most common thyroid hormone abnormality in NTI is a depression in serum total T_3 and FT_3 concentrations producing the "low T_3 state." In this condition, the serum FT_4 and sTSH concentrations are normal.

A subgroup of patients with the low T_3 state may also have a low serum T_4 concentration producing the "low T_3–low T_4 state." The serum sTSH is low in this situation.

EVALUATION OF THYROID STATUS IN PATIENTS RECEIVING LEVO-THYROXINE THERAPY

Treatment of Hypothyroidism

In the patient treated for primary hypothyroidism, the correct dose of levo-thyroxine is that dose that normalizes the clinical symptoms and the serum T_4 and sTSH concentrations. Monitoring the serum sTSH concentration to be sure that it remains in the normal range will prevent over-treatment with levo-thyroxine, which is especially important in pediatric patients. In patients with hypothyroidism due to hypothalamic or pituitary failure, restoration of serum T_4 to the normal range is the only laboratory blood test available for determining the appropriate replacement dose of levo-thyroxine. If a patient has a normal T_4 or FT_4 but increased sTSH, the most likely explanation is poor compliance. The patient probably ingested enough levo-thyroxine just prior to the office visit to raise the T_4 and FT_4, whereas sTSH concentrations reflect more the long-term average hormonal status.

Unsubstantiated Hypothyroidism

Pediatricians are occasionally presented with patients receiving thyroid hormone therapy for unsubstantiated hypothyroidism, in which case the question of whether the correct diagnosis was made needs to be answered. If the original diagnosis is in question, the answer can be obtained by discontinuing the hormone abruptly and measuring serum T_4 or FT_4 and sTSH 6 weeks later. Nearly all patients with primary hypothyroidism will have a low serum T_4 and increased sTSH at that time, whereas euthyroid patients will have a normal serum T_4 after a transient drop below normal. Failure to find an increased sTSH value combined with a low T_4 raises the possibility of pituitary hypothyroidism which can be investigated by a TRH test.

A variation of the above thyroid hormone withdrawal test has been devised in situations where there is a reluctance to discontinue thyroid hormone therapy completely. In this test, the patient is given Liothyronine (L-triiodothyronine sodium salt) in replacement doses for 28 days. Serum T_4 is measured at the end of this time, while the patient is still receiving Liothyronine. In patients with primary or secondary hypothyroidism, serum T_4 concentrations are below 12.9 nmol/L (1.0 μg/dL). Euthyroid patients have serum T_4 concentrations above 15.5 nmol/L (1.2 μg/dL).

GOITERS

The incidence of goiters in school-age children and adolescents is approximately 4–6%. The most common cause is autoimmune chronic lymphocytic thyroiditis (CLT), or Hashimoto's thyroiditis. CLT is the single most frequent thyroid disease seen in pediatrics and is the most common cause of acquired hypothyroidism. Colloid or simple goiter is the second most common cause of euthyroid goiters in pediatric patients. The patient with CLT is usually clinically euthyroid and the goiter is completely asymptomatic.

The presence of ATG and particularly anti-TPO autoantibodies is consistent with the diagnosis of CLT. However, antithyroid antibodies may not be detected even in histologically proven cases. Serum values of T_4 and T_3 may be normal, low, or even high. Serum TSH concentrations are usually normal, but may be increased despite normal serum T_4 concentrations. Thyroid scintiscanning may show thyromegaly with asymmetrical or patchy areas of radioisotope uptake. A definite diagnosis of CLT may require fine-needle biopsy.

Almost all pediatric patients with colloid goiters are asymptomatic and euthyroid. These patients have normal thyroid function studies and no detectable serum antithyroid antibodies.

THYROID CANCER

Carcinoma of the thyroid gland is rare in pediatrics. Almost all patients are clinically euthyroid. Serum T_4, T_3, and TSH determinations are helpful in determining the functional status of the thyroid gland but are not useful in establishing a diagnosis. Serum Tg lacks specificity as a marker of thyroid cancer when used preoperatively, but is useful in detecting postoperative recurrence of differentiated thyroid carcinoma. The measurement of serum calcitonin is essential if one suspects medullary thyroid carcinoma. Patients with this tumor may have normal or elevated basal values of serum calcitonin that increase after intravenous infusion of calcium or pentagastrin.

Thyroid scintiscanning is not particularly helpful in distinguishing between benign and malignant thyroid lesions. A definitive diagnosis of malignancy can be made only by histopathologic examination.

EFFECTS OF DRUGS ON THYROID HORMONE MEASUREMENTS

Pediatricians are occasionally required to determine whether patients may have hypothyroidism or hyperthyroidism at a time when they are taking medications that alter thyroid function tests.[17] The effects of commonly prescribed drugs on thyroid function are presented in Tables 8–3 and 8–6.

Phenytoin (Dilantin) therapy in euthyroid pediatric patients results in a decrease in serum T_4 and FT_4 values to subnormal values and either normal or slightly decreased values of serum T_3 and FT_3. Serum TSH is in the normal range. Treatment of patients with carbamazepine (Tegretol) and rifampin results in subnormal concentrations of FT_4.

Some drugs act predominantly by decreasing the rate of peripheral conversions of T_4 and T_3. These drugs include glucocorticoids in "stress" doses and propranolol hydrochloride in high doses. This results in decreased concentrations of serum T_3 and FT_3, normal or increased concentrations of serum T_4 and FT_4, and usually normal serum TSH concentrations. Large doses of glucocorticoids, however, may cause serum sTSH values to be suppressed and may also depress TBG and TBPA values, resulting in decreased serum concentrations of T_4 and sTSH.

Dopamine and glucocorticoid infusions in the large doses used in intensive-care units can cause decreased serum concentration of sTSH.

CLINICAL SYNDROMES OF THYROID HORMONE RESISTANCE

The syndromes of resistance to thyroid hormones are a group of clinically heterogeneous disorders characterized by reduced responses of target tissues to elevated serum levels of thyroid hormones.[18] Generalized resistance of thyroid hormones (GRTH), in which most or all of the tissues of the body are variably resistant to thyroid hormones, have been described. In addition, selective pituitary resistance to thyroid hormones (PRTH), in which predominantly the pituitary gland is resistant, has been described. GRTH is much more common than PRTH.

GRTH is most commonly inherited as an autosomal dominant disorder characterized by partial resistance of both the pituitary gland and peripheral tissues to the effects of thyroid hormone. As a result of this generalized resistance, pituitary and peripheral tissue requirements are not met by normal amounts of thyroid hormones. TSH secretion consequently increases and stimulates excessive thyroid hormone production to a level sufficient to satisfy pituitary requirements for feedback inhibition of TSH. Serum concentrations of T_4, FT_4, and T_3 are elevated, but TSH levels, rather than being suppressed, are normal or increased. However, these patients are euthyroid or mildly hypothyroid.

PRTH is characterized by thyroid hormone resistance in the pituitary gland, while peripheral tissues retain normal responsiveness. Since the pituitary is resistant, normal amounts of thyroid hormone do not inhibit pituitary TSH secretion. As a result, TSH secretion is excessive, causing overproduction of thyroid hormones in amounts sufficient to satisfy pituitary requirements. The increased T_4 and T_3 concentrations are excessive for peripheral tissues and the patients are clinically hyperthyroid. In these patients, the presence of a TSH-secreting pituitary adenoma should be ruled out. The serum alpha-subunit of TSH is almost always increased in the presence of a thyrotroph adenoma.

Thyroid hormone resistant syndromes must be excluded in patients with increased serum T_4 and T_3 concentrations in order that inappropriate therapeutic measures not be initiated in an attempt to decrease serum thyroid hormone concentrations.[19]

REFERENCES

1. Burrow GN, Fisher DA, Larsen PR. Maternal and fetal thyroid function. New Engl J Med 1994;331:1072–8.
2. Thorpe-Beeston JG, Nicolaides KH, Felton CV et al. Maturation of the secretion of thyroid hormone and thyroid-stimulating hormone in the fetus. New Engl J Med 1991;324:532–6.
3. Rose SR, Nisula BC. Circadian variation of thyrotropin in childhood. J Clin Endocrinol Metab 1989;68:1086–90.
4. Mantagos S, Koulouris A, Makri M, Vagenakis G. Development of thyrotropin circadian rhythm in infancy. J Clin Endocrinol Metab 1992;74:71–4.
5. Brent GA. The molecular basis of thyroid hormone action. New Engl J Med 1994;331:847–53.
6. Klee GG, Hay ID. Role of thyrotropin measurements in the diagnosis and management of thyroid disease. Clinics Lab Med 1993;13:673–82.
7. Rapaport R, Sills I, Patel U, et al. Thyrotropin-releasing hormone stimulation tests in infants. J Clin Endocrinol Metab 1993;77:889–94.
8. Bartalena L, Robbins J. Variations in thyroid hormone transport proteins and their clinical implications. Thyroid 1992;2:237–45.
9. Fisher DA. The thyroid gland. In: Brook CGD, ed., Clinical paediatric endocrinology, 2nd ed. Oxford: Blackwell Scientific Publications 1989:313.
10. Elkins R. Analytic measurements of free thyroxine. Clinics Lab Med 1993:13:599–630.
11. Sakata S, Nakamura S, Miura K. Autoantibodies against thyroid hormones or iodothyronines. Ann Int Med 1985;103:579–89.
12. Pryds O, Hadberg A, Kastrup KW. Circulating autoantibodies to thyroid hormones: a diagnostic pitfall. Acta Pediatr Scand 1987;76:685–7.

13. Mooij P, Drexhage HA. Autoimmune thyroid disease. Clinics Lab Med 1993;13:683–97.
14. Chanoine JP, Toppet V, Lagasse R, Spehl M, et al. Determination of thyroid volume from the neonatal period to late adolescence. Eur J Pediatr 1991;150:395–9.
15. Dussault JH. Neonatal screening for congenital hypothyroidism. Clinics Lab Med 1993;13: 645–52.
16. Willi SM, Moshang Jr T. Diagnostic dilemmas: results of screening tests for congenital hypothyroidism. Pediatr Clinics N Am 1991;38:555–66.
17. Chopra IJ. Nonthyroidal illness syndrome or euthyroid sick syndrome? Endocr Pract 1996;2:45–52.
18. Kopp P, Kitajima K, Jameson JL. Syndrome of resistance to thyroid hormone: insights into thyroid hormone action. Proc Soc Exp Biol Med 1996;211:49–61.
19. Usala SJ. New developments in clinical and genetic aspects of thyroid hormone resistance syndromes. The Endocrinologist 1995;5:68–76.

CHAPTER 9

Disorders of the Adrenal Gland

G. Michael Addison, M.A., M.B., B.Chir., M.Sc., Ph.D.

ADRENAL CORTEX

Steroid Structure and Nomenclature

The naturally occurring steroids are based on a four ring structure, the cyclopentanoperhydrophenanthrene nucleus (Figure 9–1). The nucleus is modified by the introduction of hydroxyl and carbonyl groups, aliphatic side chains, and the production of unsaturated double bonds to produce the steroid hormones. Orientation of the substituted groups is either toward the reader, α, or away, β, with the plane of the steroid nucleus in the plane of the page. A systematic nomenclature has been described for steroids by the International Union of Pure and Applied Chemistry (IUPAC),[1] but in order to facilitate usage the important steroids and metabolites have been given shorter common names (Table 9–1). It is the author's opinion that the older nomenclature wherein steroid hormones were identified by single letters should be abandoned.

Biosynthesis of Adrenal Steroids

The adrenal cortex synthesizes three classes of steroid hormones; glucocorticoids, mineralocorticoids, and androgens. Classical pathways for the synthesis of these steroids (Figure 9–2) have been established for many years, but with the advent of the newer techniques of molecular biology there has been considerable increase in our knowledge of the enzymes involved in steroidogenesis. A brief outline is given below. Further details are available elsewhere.[2,3]

FIGURE 9–1. Steroid Structure

The identification of the four carbon rings and the numbering of the individual carbons is shown for the basic steroid nucleus and cholestane, the nucleus of cholesterol.

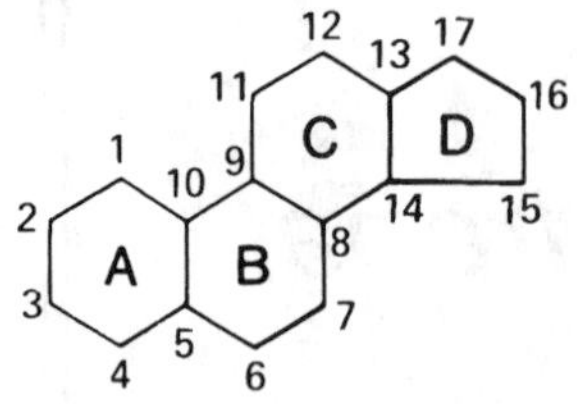

Cyclopentanoperhydrophenanthrene

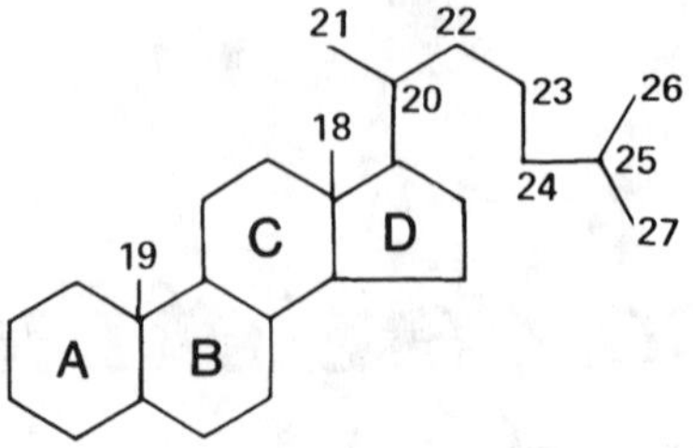

Cholestane

Adrenal steroids are derived from cholesterol, which either enters the cell in the form of LDL or is possibly synthesized *in situ* from acetate. Cholesterol is converted to the C21 steroid pregnenolone with the loss of a 6-carbon side chain. This is believed to involve three steps: 20α-hydroxylation, 22-hydroxylation, and the oxidative cleavage of the C20–C22 bond. Alternative routes for the metabolism of pregnenolone exist. In the synthesis of glucocorticoids, the first step is the 17-hydroxylation to 17α-hydroxypregnenolone, which is then converted by oxidation at C3 and isomerization to 17α-hydroxyprogesterone (17OHP). This is termed the Δ^5 pathway. 17OHP is further metabolized to cortisol by hydroxylations at C21 and C11.

Adrenal androgens are also derived from 17α-pregnenolone, but there is loss of the 2-carbon side chain to yield the C19 steroid dehydroepiandrosterone (DHA) before oxidation at C3 and isomerization to androstenedione. Testosterone is prob-

TABLE 9–1. Adrenal Steroid Nomenclature

Common Name	IUPAC Nomenclature
Cholesterol	cholest-5-en-3β-ol
Pregnenolone	3β-hydroxypregn-5-en-20-one
Progesterone	pregn-4-ene-3, 20-dione
17α-hydroxypregnenolone	3β, 17α-dihydroxypregn-5-en-20-one
17α-progesterone	17α-hydroxypregn-4-ene-3, 20-dione
11-deoxycortisol	17α, 21-dihydroxypregn-4-ene-3, 20-dione
11-deoxycorticosterone	21-hydroxypregn-4-ene-3, 20-dione
Cortisol	11β, 17, 21-trihydroxypregn-4-ene-3, 20-dione
Corticosterone	11β, 21-dihydroxypregn-4-ene-3, 20-dione
18-hydroxycorticosterone	11β, 18, 21-trihydroxypregn-4-ene-3, 20-dione
Aldosterone	11β,21-dihydroxy-18-al-pregn-4-ene-3,20-dione
Dehydroepiandrosterone	3β-hydroxyandrost-5-en-17-one
Androstenedione	androst-4-ene-3,17-dione

FIGURE 9–2. Pathways of Adrenal Steroid Biosynthesis

The enzymes catalyzing each step are:

1. P450scc (20,22-desmolase)
2. 3β-hydroxysteroid dehydrogenase
3. P450c17 (17α-hydroxylase)
4. P450c21 (21-hydroxylase)
5. P450c11β (11-hydroxylase)
6. P450c18 (corticosterone methyltransferase I and II)
7. P450c17 (17,20 desmolase)
8. Steroid sulphotransferase

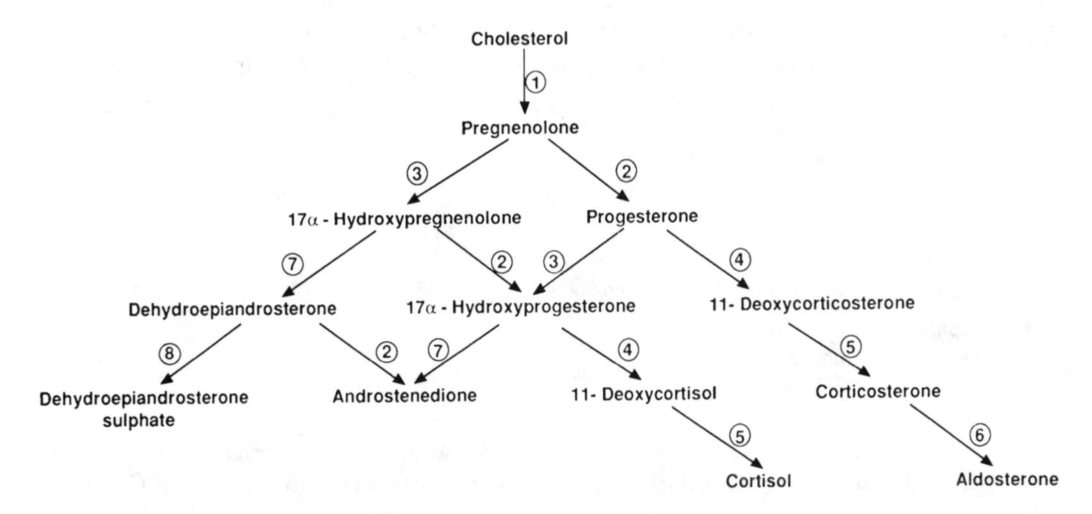

ably not produced in the normal adrenal gland, but adrenal androgens can be converted to testosterone by peripheral metabolism.

The mineralocorticoids do not have a hydroxyl group at C17, and synthesis proceeds via the Δ^4 pathway from pregnenolone to progesterone. Hydroxylations at C21 and C11 produce corticosterone, which is converted to aldosterone in a two-step procedure involving hydroxylation at C18 and subsequent dehydrogenation. An alternative pathway involving a second C18 hydroxylation followed by loss of a water molecule has been proposed.

Recent advances in molecular genetics and biochemistry have increased our understanding of adrenal steroid biosynthesis, but at the same time revealed unexpected complexity. Of the seven enzymes involved (Table 9–2), five are members of the cytochrome P450 superfamily and four of these are multifunctional and catalyze more than one reaction in the pathways. Cytochrome P450scc, the 20,22 desmolase enzyme, catalyzes three sequential hydroxylations and subsequent C-C cleavage. Cytochrome P450c17 catalyzes both the hydroxylation at C17 and a C-C cleavage (17,20 desmolase). These two activities occur at separate catalytic sites.

The situation is even more complex with cytochromes P450c11 and P450c18, which are the products of two closely related genes, CYP11B1 and CYP11B2, on chromosome 8. P450c11 11β-hydroxylates deoxycortisol and deoxycorticosterone to corti-

TABLE 9–2. Adrenal Steroid Biosynthetic Enzymes

Enzyme	Previous Name	Cellular Localization	Chromosome	Gene	EC Number
P450scc	20,22-desmolase	Mitochondria	15q23–q24	CYP11A1	1.14.15.6
3β-hydroxy-steroid dehydrogenase, Δ5,4-oxo-steroid isomerase	unchanged	Microsome and Mitochondria	1p13	HSDB3	1.1.1.51 5.3.3.1
P450c17	17-hydroxylase	Microsome	10q24q25	CYP17	1.14.99.9
"	17,20-desmolase	Microsome	10q24q25	CYP17	—
P450c11	11β-hydroxylase	Microsome	8q21–22	CYP11B1	1.14.15.4
P450c18	18-hydroxylase (corticosterone methyl oxidase I)	Mitochondria	8q21–22	CYP11B2	1.14.15.5
P450c18	18-dehydroxylase (corticosterone methyl oxidase II)	Mitochondria	8q21–22	CYP11B2	—
P450c21	21-hydroxylase	Microsome	6P21.3	CYP21	1.14.99.10
Steroid sulpho-transferase	unchanged	—	—	—	2.8.2.15

sol and corticosterone respectively. P450c18 also has 11β-hydroxylase activity, but in addition catalyzes the oxidative conversion of corticosterone to aldosterone. Other tissues which produce steroid hormones, including the ovary and testis, lack P450c11 and P450c21 activity and cannot produce glucocorticoids or mineralocorticoids.

3βHSD is a member of the aldo-keto reductase superfamily. The enzyme is widely distributed in many tissues, and two genes, Type I and II, have been identified, although there is some evidence that further genes may be found. Some of the isoforms of 3βHSD could result from post-transcriptional or post-translational modification. The sixth enzyme is steroid sulphotransferase, which converts DHA to DHA sulphate (DHAS), which is the major adrenal androgen.

The adrenal cortex is divided into three zones, a subcapsular zona glomerulosa; the zona reticularis, next to the adrenal medulla; and separating these two, the zona fasciculata.

Functionally, the glomerulosa acts as a separate gland. The absence of P450c17 results in the sole production of mineralocorticoids and in particular aldosterone. Cells of the glomerulosa are the only site for P450c18 activity; thus, aldosterone is not produced elsewhere in the adrenal. In the human, the function of the fasciculata and reticularis is to produce glucocorticoids and adrenal androgens, respectively, although the separation of this function is not absolute.

Recent developments in our knowledge of the molecular genetics of steroidogenesis, and in particular the multifunctional nature of the cytochrome P450 enzymes, have complicated rather than simplified the understanding of steroid hormone biosynthesis.[4] It is easy to understand that the gene expression for the various enzymes can be tissue or cell specific. However, in the case of P450c17, for example, there is a need for explanations as to why some patients can present with a clinical picture suggestive of 17α-hydroxylase deficiency, while others have symptoms of 17,20 desmolase deficiency and yet others present with a mixture. Another problem is the presentation of patients with congenital adrenal lipoid hyperplasia (P450scc deficiency), in whom the gene appears to be normal. Other factors must be involved in the control of steroid biosynthesis, defects of which could cause disease phenotypically indistinguishable from deficiencies of the specific enzymes.

These questions and others have caused some scientists to question the classical pathways of steroidogenesis[5,6] and to propose that many of the properties of the steroid biosynthetic pathways are a consequence of the physical organization of the enzymes as multifunctional units.

Control of Adrenal Steroid Biosynthesis[4,7]

The chief regulator of adrenal glucocorticoid and androgen biosynthesis is the pituitary polypeptide ACTH. The available evidence does not support the hypothesis of an alternative androgen-stimulating hormone. ACTH has both acute and chronic effects which are the consequence of the binding of ACTH to a specific receptor on the cell surface and the resultant stimulation of the production of cyclic adenosine monophosphate (AMP). The primary acute effect is to increase binding of cholesterol to P450scc; other effects include the stimulation of the hydrolysis of cholesterol esters and enhanced transport of cholesterol into the mitochondria, probably involving the steroid carrier protein 2. The result of these effects is a rapid increase in hormone production.

The chronic effect of ACTH is to increase the synthesis of not only the steroidogenic cytochrome P450s but also associated proteins and enzymes involved in electron transfer—adrenodoxin, adrenodoxin reductase, and NADPH-cytochrome P450 reductase.

ACTH is also involved in the maintenance of adrenal cortical mass. Stimulation of the adrenal with ACTH leads to hypertrophy of cells. This action appears to be mediated by other factors, e.g., insulin-like growth factor 2 (IGF2) through a paracrine effect. Other mitogenic factors are involved with ACTH to cause hyperplasia.

ACTH release from the anterior pituitary is in turn controlled by another peptide hormone corticotrophin releasing factor (CRF). A circadian rhythm of ACTH secretion with a peak in the morning and a nadir in the late evening is paralleled by changes in plasma cortisol concentration. Superimposed on this basic rhythm, CRF and hence ACTH release can be stimulated by a large number of "stress" factors. The release of ACTH is also controlled through a negative feedback loop by plasma cortisol (glucocorticoid) concentration. Reduction of cortisol concentration for whatever reason will result in an increased release of ACTH, producing in turn the acute and chronic effects of ACTH on the adrenal and resulting in restoration of appropriate plasma cortisol concentration. If the adrenal cortex is unable to synthesize cortisol as a result of an inherited disorder of steroid biosynthesis, then the negative feedback loop will be interrupted. Prolonged effects of ACTH result in the increase of adrenocortical mass and overproduction of steroid precursors, which is termed congenital adrenal hyperplasia (CAH). If the cortex is damaged by a disease process, it may be unable to respond to increased plasma ACTH concentrations.

Aldosterone biosynthesis is controlled directly by the extracellular concentrations of sodium and potassium and also by the renin-angiotensin system. There is a feedback control loop between aldosterone and renin synthesis mediated by extracellular sodium. A decrease in ECF sodium stimulates renin release and production of angiotensin II, which in turn stimulates aldosterone synthesis and sodium retention by the renal tubules. ACTH does not appear to have a major effect on mineralocorticoid biosynthesis, at least in normals, but may be important in patients in salt-losing states.[8]

There is histological evidence that the adrenal cell is pluripotential[9] and it is possible that the life of a single adrenal cell involves migration as it ages through the glomerulosa via the fasciculata to the reticularis, where it eventually dies. In turn, it will synthesize mineralocorticoid, glucocorticoid, and adrenal androgens. It has been suggested that the vascular system of the adrenal gland can support a metabolic gradient of steroids between the various zones which can influence the cell to produce different steroid hormone, depending on its position in the cortex.

There is a complex interplay between the immune system and the biosynthesis and action of the steroid hormones.[10] Some cytokines can stimulate ACTH release while in turn glucocorticoids are immunosuppressive agents. The effect of these relationships has not been well investigated.

Catabolism and Excretion of Steroids[11]

Steroids are excreted principally in the urine after undergoing one or more enzymic modifications to render them more water soluble. These may include reduction, oxidation, hydroxylation, side chain cleavage, and conjugation, usually as glucuronides or sulphates. The liver is the main organ of steroid catabolism, but other tissues, including the adrenal itself, are also involved. Analysis of the products of steroid catabolism may sometimes cause diagnostic difficulties if it is not appreciated that the liver can convert Δ^5 to Δ^4 steroids, i.e., pregnenolone derivatives to progesterone derivatives.

Urine contains large numbers of steroid metabolites which used to be determined mainly based on the chemical reactions of substituted groups, e.g., 17-hydroxysteroids, oxosteroids, and oxogenic steroids, but these have largely been displaced by specific plasma assays (usually radioimmunoassays) or gas chromatographic techniques for specific metabolites. The major urinary metabolites of cortisol are given in Table 9–3.

Investigation of Adrenal Function

Tests of adrenal function are of two types. In the first, basal secretion of the steroids is measured using a single plasma or urine sample. Dynamic tests, on the other hand, require two or more samples and are used to test the integrity of the control mechanisms of the hypothalamic-pituitary-adrenal (HPA) axis. The use of computer-assisted

TABLE 9–3. Urinary Steroid Metabolites of Cortisol

Metabolite	Mean Excretion (%)
Free C21 Steroids	
Cortisol	1.7
Cortisone	1.7
Conjugated C21 Steroids	
Tetrahydrocortisol	17.8
Allotetrahydrocortisol	9.5
Tetrahydrocortisone	24.1
20α-cortol	1.9
20β-cortol	4.5
20α-cortolone	11.4
20β-cortolone	8.2
Conjugated C19 Steroids	
11-oxoetiocholanolone	3.1
11β-hydroxyetiocholanolone	3.9
11β-hydroxyandrosterone	1.0
Other Neutral Steroids	11.4

imaging technology has enhanced the investigation of adrenal disorders considerably and allows a more selective use of biochemical tests in individual patients.

Several adrenal steroids, including cortisol, 17OHP, androstenedione, testosterone, and aldosterone, can be assayed in saliva. The salivary concentration of unconjugated steroids closely correlates with the plasma free steroid concentration. Saliva has been used as an alternative test in clinical situations such as the diagnosis of Cushing syndrome or adrenal hypofunction or in monitoring therapy of 21-hydroxylase deficiency CAH.[12,13] Steroid concentration in saliva is 1–5% of plasma concentration and separate pediatric reference ranges should be established.

Basal Tests

Glucocorticoids

It should be noted that reference ranges quoted below for plasma cortisol determinations both in basal and dynamic tests usually have been derived from the now abandoned fluorometric methods. Modern radioimmunoassay methods are much more specific and give values 85–90% of those given by fluorimetry.

Plasma Cortisol. A random cortisol estimation is difficult to interpret due to the variability of cortisol excretion during the day and should be avoided if possible. Age-related quantitative data for plasma cortisol concentration in the first few weeks of life is contradictory, but there is a much wider range of cortisol concentration, particularly in neonates, and a nadir at 7 days. Diurnal rhythm and adult values are achieved by 3 months.

Urine Free Cortisol. This is a useful screening test for excess cortisol production (Cushing syndrome). An excretion of < 200 nmol/24 h in urine is found in normal children.

Mineralocorticoids

In order to test the adrenal end of the renin-aldosterone feedback loop, it is necessary to measure both aldosterone and renin. It is essential to know the plasma and urinary electrolytes and hence the patient's sodium balance in order to interpret the results. Thus, there is no simple test of mineralocorticoid production. It is, however, useful to measure renin alone in the control of the therapy of 21-hydroxylase deficiency CAH to monitor mineralocorticoid replacement.

Because renin measurements are highly method dependent, it is inappropriate to publish reference ranges which should be established in each laboratory. Both plasma renin and aldosterone fall throughout childhood, but there is insignificant correlation between them when population-based reference ranges are established.[14] Reference ranges are best constructed by measuring both hormones in the same blood sample and plotting the results on a graph. Results from patients can be assessed by plotting on the graph of normal results and assessing any disturbance of the relationship between renin and aldosterone.

Adrenal Androgens

Age-related reference ranges for the adrenal androgens androstenedione DHA and DHAS are given in Table 9–4. Unlike the glucocorticoids, concentrations of adrenal DHA and DHAS are relatively stable in blood and timing of samples is less critical. Androstenedione, on the other hand, shows considerable circadian variation.

Steroid Hormone Precursors

In certain adrenal disorders, especially steroid biosynthetic defects and adrenal tumors, large quantities of steroid precursors may be secreted by the gland. These may be detected in blood or urine. In the latter case, analysis by gas-liquid chromatography,[15,16] with or without mass spectroscopy, is required, and this is the province of specialized and experienced laboratories.

17α-hydroxyprogesterone (17OHP)

As with cortisol, 17OHP has a marked circadian rhythm. Timing of samples is important in infants and children but not crucial in neonates if specimens are being used for the diagnosis of 21-hydroxylase deficiency CAH, since circadian rhythm is not yet established. Age-related reference ranges are given in Table 9–4.

11-Deoxycortisol

The immediate precursor of cortisol, 11-deoxycortisol is increased in 11-hydroxylase deficiency CAH. This metabolite has not been studied in depth to provide an age-related reference range. Normal concentrations in childhood are < 60 nmol/L.

TABLE 9–4. Reference Ranges for Adrenal Steroids in Infancy, Childhood, and Puberty*

Age	17α-Hydroxyprogesterone ng/100ml (nmol/L)	Dehydroepiandrosterone ng/100ml (nmol/L)		Dehydroepiandrosterone Sulphate μg/100ml (μmol/L)	Androstenedione ng/100ml (nmol/L)		Aldosterone ng/100ml (nmol/L)
	M + F	M	F	M + F	M	F	M + F
0–1 d	170–2500 (5–75)	320–1100 (11–39)	460–1200 (16–42)	15–370 (0.4–10)	15–145 (0.5–5.0)	15–175 (0.5–6.0)	
1–7 d	30–350 (1–10)	90–870 (3.0–30)	120–930 (4–32)	4–110 (0.1–3.0)	20–110 (0.7–3.8)	25–95 (0.9–3.3)	
7–28 d	0–250 (0–8.0)	45–580 (1.5–20)	90–580 (3–20)	4–33 (0.1–1.2)	25–160 (0.9–5.5)	9–90 (0.3–3.0)	
1–12 m	0–170 (0–5.0)	9.0–290 (0.3–10)	17–170 (0.6–6.0)	0.4–11 (0.01–0.3)	6–90 (0.2–3.0)	6–145 (0.2–5.0)	5.8–110 (0.16–3.0)
1–4 y	0–100 (0–3.0)	12–90 (0.4–3.0)	20–45 (0.7–1.6)	7.0–75 (0.2–2.0)	6–35 (0.2–1.2)	6–45 (0.2–1.5)	2.5–36 (0.07–1.0)
4–10 y (P1)	0–100 (0–3.0)	25–300 (0.9–10)	12–200 (0.4–7.0)	4–180 (0.1–4.8)	25–190 (0.8–3.0)	3–60 (0.1–2.0)	1–22 (0.03–0.6)
P2	0–130 (0–4.0)	50–580 (1.8–20)	60–1700 (2.0–60)	40–260 (1.0–7.0)	15–120 (0.5–4.0)	30–145 (1.0–5.0)	1.5–2.2 (0.04–0.06)
P3	30–200 (1.0–6.0)	130–640 (4.5–22)	125–1900 (4.4–65)	75–280 (2.0–7.5)	18–145 (0.6–5.0)	30–200 (1.0–7.0)	1.5–2.2 (0.04–0.06)
P4	30–230 (1.0–7.0)	190–730 (6.5–25)	170–1700 (6.0–60)	90–330 (2.5–9.0)	15–220 (0.5–7.5)	18–260 (0.6–9.0)	1.5–2.2 (0.04–0.06)
P5	30–250 (1.0–8.0)	230–730 (8.0–25)	220–810 (7.5–28)	110–440 (3.0–12.0)	40–260 (1.3–9.0)	18–260 (0.6–9.0)	1.5–2.2 (0.04–0.06)

**Note:* These reference ranges are for guidance only. They have been derived from published and unpublished sources using different methodologies and varying numbers of subjects. In addition, parametric statistics frequently have been used when the data clearly are not normally distributed. Readers are advised to consult the local laboratory for more relevant reference ranges or to develop their own.

Dynamic Tests

Hypothalamic-Pituitary-Adrenal (HPA) Axis

Circadian Rhythm

ACTH and cortisol secretion has a pronounced diurnal rhythm, with a peak between 0800 and 1000 h and a nadir between 1800 and 0200 h. The circadian rhythm can be assessed by means of paired blood specimens taken at the appropriate times. This test is not reliable immediately after hospitalization, when stress temporarily abolishes the rhythm. Its main use is in screening patients for Cushing syndrome, in which the circadian rhythm is lost. The relationship between the two hormones can be assessed by measuring ACTH in the same samples.

Dexamethasone Suppression Tests

Overnight Single Dose. This is a screening test for hypercortisolism and is performed by giving a dose of l mg dexamethasone at 2400 h and taking a blood specimen for the determination of plasma cortisol at 0800 h. In the normal child, the morning plasma cortisol is markedly suppressed.

Low-Dose Dexamethasone. Following a basal 24-h urine collection for urine free cortisol determination, the patient is given 5 μg/kg dexamethasone every 6 h for 48 h. A second 24-h urine collection is then made. Diurnal plasma cortisol determinations also can be made on days 1 and 4. Failure to suppress either the urine free cortisol or the plasma cortisol establishes the diagnosis but not the etiology of Cushing syndrome.

High-Dose Dexamethasone. This test, which is rarely required in pediatric practice, is similar to the low-dose test, the difference being that the dose of dexamethasone is increased to 2 mg every 6 h. The test is used to help distinguish pituitary Cushing disease from hypercortisolism due to adrenal tumors. This distinction is more easily made by imaging.

Metyrapone Test

Metyrapone (2-methyl-1,2-bis-(3′-pyridyl)-propan-1-one) inhibits steroid 11β-hydroxylase, resulting in a decrease in the synthesis of cortisol. If the HPA axis is normal, the consequence is a reduction in the negative feedback control on ACTH synthesis and release. As a result of the increased plasma ACTH, the adrenal cortex is stimulated and there is increased secretion of the cortisol precursor 11-deoxycortisol (compound S), which can be measured in the plasma.

Standard Metyrapone Test. Oral metyrapone, 3.0 mg/m^2, is given every 4 h for 6 doses. Blood is collected 4 h after the last dose for the estimation of cortisol, 11-deoxycortisol, and ACTH. Alternatively, three 24-h urine collections for the determination of 17-oxogenic steroids should be made to include a basal day, the treatment day, and post-treatment day. A failure to respond to metyrapone could be due to a failure of pituitary reserve or adrenal response. The urinary 17-oxogenic steroid measurements will not distinguish these two, while the plasma determinations will.

Short Metyrapone Test. 30 mg/kg metyrapone is given at 2400 h and a blood specimen taken for measurement of cortisol, 11-deoxycortisol, and ACTH at 0800 h.

Insulin Hypoglycemia (Stress) Test

Hypoglycemia produced as a response to intravenous insulin is a potent stress stimulus for the release of ACTH. It is often used to test the secretion of growth hormone simultaneously. The normal dose of soluble insulin, 0.1–0.15 U/kg, should be reduced to 0.05 U/kg if ACTH deficiency is strongly suspected. *This test should only be performed in a specialized pediatric unit and precautions must be taken to ensure that immediate medical treatment is available should a severe response to insulin occur.* For HPA axis assessment, samples are taken at 0 (fasting), 15, 30, 60, and 120 min for glucose and cortisol. ACTH can also be measured at these times. For an adequate test, the blood glucose should fall to < 2.2 mmol/L. Plasma cortisol should rise at least 250 nmol/L and a peak should exceed 550 nmol/L in a normal response.

ACTH Stimulation Tests

These tests are used to examine the ability of the adrenal cortex to respond to stimuli, or occasionally to help differentiate steroid biosynthetic defects by increasing the total or exaggerating the relative production of steroid precursors.

Short ACTH Test. A basal blood specimen is followed by administration of 250 $\mu g/m^2$ Synacthen® (1-24 ACTH), either intramuscularly or intravenously. Further blood specimens are taken at 30 and 60 min for the measurement of cortisol. A rise of plasma cortisol by at least 250 nmol/L and a peak value of > 550 nmol/L indicates a normal response. An insufficient response may be due to either primary adrenal disease or prolonged absence of endogenous ACTH stimulation of the gland.

17OHP can be measured using this test in the evaluation of 21-hydroxylase deficiency. This is especially useful if the patient has been started on therapy as a consequence of a clinical diagnosis or in the evaluation of heterozygotes or patients with late-onset CAH.

Long ACTH Test. Following a baseline cortisol estimation, an oral dose of 1 mg Synacthen® is given daily for 3 days. A second blood specimen is taken 6 h after the third dose. In normals and patients with secondary adrenal deficiency, there will be a rise of at least three times the basal value to a peak of > 800 nmol/L. In primary adrenal disease, the response to the prolonged administration of Synacthen® is suppressed.

Low-Dose ACTH Stimulation Test. Recently an ACTH stimulation test using 1 µg 1–24 ACTH has been described.[17] This test is thought to be more physiological and to detect more subtle changes in adrenal function. Experience with this test is limited in children, but it could prove to be of great value in pediatrics.

Mineralocorticoids

As mentioned above, the close interrelationship between aldosterone and renin requires that both be measured simultaneously in the investigation of disorders of mineralocorticoid production. In addition, testing requires knowledge and manipulation of the electrolyte status of the patient.

Salt (Sodium) Restriction

DAY 1: Measure baseline plasma electrolytes, aldosterone, and renin. Collect 24-h urine for electrolytes and creatinine.
DAYS 2-6: Administer a low-sodium diet, 10–20 mmol/d; collect 24-h urines on days 5 and 6 for electrolytes and creatinine.
DAY 6: Collect plasma for electrolytes, aldosterone, and renin after the patient has been erect for 1 h.

In normal subjects, the urine sodium excretion will fall to < 20 mmol/L and the plasma renin and aldosterone will rise by a factor of three.

Diseases of the Adrenal Cortex

Classification of adrenocortical disorders is complex. In Tables 9–5 and 9–6, an initial separation into primary and secondary disorders has been made, with subsequent divisions based on whether the disease produces under- or over-function of the gland. The steroid hormones can be looked at individually under each of the headings, but it should be emphasized that, particularly with inborn errors of steroid biosynthesis, deficiency of one steroid hormone is not infrequently associated with deficiency or excess of another.

Many of the conditions listed in Tables 9–5 and 9–6 are extremely rare. The most common primary disorders are 21-hydroxylase deficiency CAH and adrenal tumors, while the most common secondary disorders are adrenal hypofunction resulting from steroid therapy and hypopituitarism. Adrenocortical disease should be suspected in any child with unexplained disturbances of electrolyte metabolism and in abnormalities of sexual maturation.

21-Hydroxylase Deficiency CAH

CAH due to a deficiency of 21-hydroxylase is the most common inborn error of adrenal steroid biosynthesis. It manifests itself in four clinical forms: salt loss, prenatal virilization of females, precocious sexual development in late infancy and childhood, and a late-onset or non-classical form. The first three are usually diagnosed in infancy or childhood, but rare cases are found among adults. Approximately two-thirds are salt wasting. Non-classical CAH usually presents in females in adolescence or adulthood with signs of androgen excess. The prevalence of the infantile forms is approximately 1:7000 to 1:12,000 births. Rarely, a very high prevalence occurs in closed ethnic groups, e.g., 1:500 found in Yupik Inuits in Alaska. On the other hand, the prevalence of non-classical CAH is much higher, at 1:100 in Caucasian populations and 1:30 in Ashkenazi Jews.

All types of 21-hydroxylase deficiency are due to defects of the CYP21 gene (previously called CYP21B) on chromosome 6. This is one of a pair of reduplicated genes. The second, CYP21P (previously known as CYP21A), is a highly homologous but nonfunctional pseudogene. The two genes are situated in the class III region of the HLA complex, and each is closely linked to two complement genes, C4A

TABLE 9–5. Classification of Pediatric Primary Adrenocortical Disorders

Adrenocortical Hyperfunction	Adrenocortical Hypofunction
Glucocorticoid excess	Glucocorticoid deficiency
Adrenal adenoma	Steroid biosynthetic defects:
Adrenal carcinoma	21-hydroxylase deficiency
Mineralocorticoid excess	17α-hydroxylase deficiency
Adrenal glomerulosa adenoma (Conn syndrome)	11β-hydroxylase deficiency
Adrenocortical nodular hyperplasia	Congenital unreponsiveness to ACTH
Steroid biosynthetic defects:	Mineralocorticoid deficiency
17α-hydroxylase deficiency	Steroid biosynthetic defects
11β-hydroxylase deficiency	Corticosterone methyl oxidase deficiency (CMOD) type I and II
Adrenal tumors secreting deoxycorticosterone or corticosterone	Adrenal androgen deficiency
Dexamethasone suppressible hyperaldosteronism	Steroid biosynthetic defect
Adrenal androgen excess	17, 20-desmolase deficiency
Adrenal adenoma	Delayed adrenarche
Adrenal carcinoma	Mixed adrenal steroid deficiency
Steroid biosynthetic defects	Steroid biosynthetic defects
21-hydroxylase deficiency	20, 22 desmolase deficiency
11β-hydroxylase deficiency	3β-hydroxysteroid dehydrogenase deficiency
Mixed adrenal hormone excess	21-hydroxylase deficiency
Adrenal tumors	Combined 17α-hydroxylase and 17, 20-desmolase deficiency
	Congenital adrenal hypoplasia
	Adrenoleukodystrophy
	Wolman disease
	Adrenal crisis of acute infection (Waterhouse-Friderichsen syndrome)
	Autoimmune adrenal disease

TABLE 9–6. Classification of Pediatric Secondary Adrenocortical Disorders

Adrenocortical Hypofunction	Adrenocortical Hyperfunction
Hypopituitarism	Pituitary tumors
Isolated ACTH deficiency	Ectopic ACTH secreting tumors
Hypothalamic defect	Hyperaldosteronism secondary to renal disease
Intracranial tumors, craniopharyngioma	Pseudohyperaldosteronism
Adrenal suppression as a consequence of glucocorticoid therapy	
Following removal of unilateral adrenal tumor	
Steroid therapy in mothers during pregnancy	

FIGURE 9–3. Map of Human Chromosome 6

The 21-hydroxylase gene is shown within the class III HLA cluster. The active gene 21 and pseudogene 21P are shown in relationship to the two reduplicated complement genes, C4B and C4A.

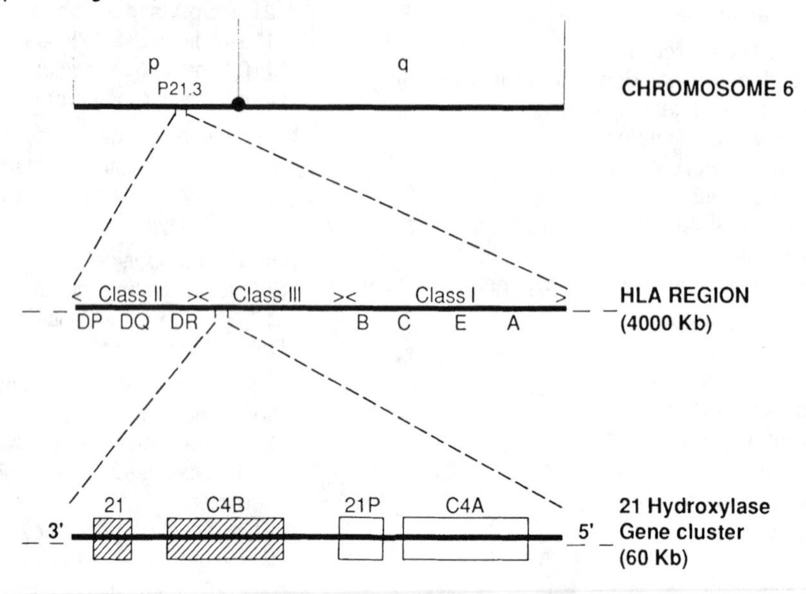

and C4B respectively (Figure 9–3). The reduplication facilitates unequal crossover at meiosis, with the possibility of total loss of the functional CYP21 gene or its conversion by a combination of variable quantities of DNA from CYP21 and CYP21P to a gene which is not capable of producing native enzyme. Point mutations can also occur.

The complex molecular pathology of 21-hydroxylase deficiency[18] has helped in part to explain the different clinical manifestations of the disease. Patients who are homozygous for CYP21 gene deletions or large-scale gene conversions or compound heterozygotes for both major gene defects usually are found to have salt wasting. On the other hand, point mutations on one chromosome associated with mild or severe alleles on the other chromosome also have been associated with classical salt wasting CAH. Simple virilizing 21-hydroxylase deficient patients with both CYP21 alleles severely affected has not been described so far, and the mutations associated with this variety of 21-hydroxylase deficiency have not been identified. Non-classical CAH has been associated with a G to T (val to leu) mutation.

While it is interesting to try to link the different clinical presentations of 21-hydroxylase deficiency to specific genetic abnormalities, it should be noted that families with affected siblings, presumably with the same genetic defects, can have different clinical phenotypes. It is therefore probable that the phenotypic variability of 21-hydroxylase deficiency is due in part to other factors. There is some evidence that 21-hydroxylase (P450c21) exists in heterogeneous forms with different substrate specificities, at least in the bovine adrenal.[19] This heterogeneity may result from post-transitional modification, e.g., differential gene splicing or alteration in sialic acid content or phosphorylation. Thus, the question of relating genotype to phenotype in 21-hydroxylase deficient CAH remains to be resolved.

Of great interest is the observation of aldosterone production in patients homozygous for CYP21 deletion or with one allele being deleted and the other coding for a nonfunctional protein. Although extra adrenal 21-hydroxylation cannot be ruled out entirely, evidence points to another enzyme in the adrenal gland with 21-hydroxylase activity, possibly induced by high levels of precursors.[20]

Diagnosis

21-hydroxylase deficiency should be suspected in patients with any of the clinical presentations described above. In salt-losing states or in patients with ambiguous genitalia, diagnosis is urgent. The use of urinary pregnanetriol estimation has been abandoned in favor of the measurement of plasma 17OHP concentrations by immunoassay. In infantile forms, the concentration of 17OHP is normally greatly increased, but patients with non-classical CAH may have basal plasma 17OHP within the normal range. Heterozygotes for severe forms of 21-hydroxylase deficiency may have elevated basal 17OHP concentrations. Differentiation of these groups can be aided by using a short ACTH stimulation test, with measurement of 17OHP, cortisol, and 11-deoxycortisol. Non-classical CAH patients will have an increase of 17OHP > 40 nmol/L (normals < 15 nmol/L) at 30 min. Differentiation of heterozygotes is accomplished by the use of 17OHP: deoxycortisol ratios which are increased above the normal value of < 12 at 30 min.

The finding of an increased 17OHP concentration is not confined to patients with 21-hydroxylase deficiency. They are frequently found in sick full-term or healthy premature infants who may also be hyponatremic, and therefore give rise to diagnostic confusion.[21,22] It may be necessary to do several 17OHP estimations and also a short ACTH test to help diagnosis. Patients with 21-hydroxylase deficiency may have basal plasma cortisol within the normal range and some increase on ACTH stimulation. In addition, increased 17OHP has been reported in other steroid biosynthetic defects, e.g., 11β-hydroxylase and 3β-hydroxysteroid dehydrogenase defects. The findings have led to the reports of combined 11β- and 21-hydroxylase deficiencies. However, the most likely explanation is the peripheral metabolism of steroid precursors, e.g., 17-hydroxypregnenolone to 17OHP ($\Delta^5 \rightarrow \Delta^4$). GLC of urine steroid metabolites may help resolve these problems.

Screening[23]

Following the development of 17OHP assays from dried blood spots,[24] neonatal screening programs for the early detection of 21-hydroxylase deficiency have been established successfully in North America, Europe, and Japan. Since salt-wasting infants usually present with life-threatening salt-losing crises in the second week of life, the timing of screening is critical and must be early enough to allow detection before onset of symptoms. There are problems with cross-reacting steroids in neonatal blood which may give a false-positive test, and also increased concentrations of 17OHP are found in premature and low-birth-weight infants. Screening for 21-hydroxylase deficiency, although practical, remains an area of controversy and has not been universally adopted.[25, 26]

Prenatal Diagnosis and Treatment

Since the masculinization of female fetuses occurs in the latter part of the first trimester of intrauterine life, early identification of fetuses in families at risk and treatment with dexamethasone has been attempted in order to prevent these changes.[27,28] Infants are identified as female by chromosome analysis and as affected by the use of a combination of amniotic fluid 17OHP concentrations and HLA typing of amniotic cells, or by DNA analysis using chorionic villus sampling.

The results of this approach in infants at risk have been the absence of virilization in a third, minor or partial virilization in a further third, and severe virilization in the remaining third. It has been suggested that the results could be improved by starting treatment as early as possible in pregnancy, even pre-conception, and stopping treatment if the fetus is found to be male or unaffected. The effectiveness of dexamethasone in suppressing the fetal adrenal can be assessed by measuring maternal urinary estriol, which is derived from fetal dehydroepiandrosterone by placental metabolism.

11β-Hydroxylase Deficiency

11β-hydroxylase deficiency is the second most common inborn error of steroid biosynthesis but accounts for only 5–15% of cases.[29] Presentation is similar to 21-hydroxylase deficiency, but hypertension is also present in the majority of cases. Patients may have hypoglycemia and alkalosis. Biochemical diagnosis is established by finding an increased plasma deoxycortisol concentration or a raised urinary excretion of tetrahydro-deoxycortisol.

Clinical variants of 11β-hydroxylase deficiency have been described.[30] In the severe form, it appears that 11β-hydroxylation of both 17-hydroxy and 17-deoxysteroids is affected, while in milder forms only 11β-hydroxylation of 17-hydroxysteroids is reduced.

The cause of the hypertension in these patients is unclear. The suggestion that it is caused by the increased plasma concentration of deoxycorticosterone does not fit clinical findings of normotensive patients with high concentrations or severe hypertension in patients with only mild increases of plasma deoxycorticosterone. An alternative suggestion is that the steroid causing hypertension could be 18-hydroxy,11-deoxycorticosterone because of the multiple activities of cytochrome P45011β.

3β-Hydroxysteroid Dehydrogenase, $\Delta^{5\text{-}4}$ Oxosteroid Isomerase Deficiency

3β-hydroxysteroid dehydrogenase, $\Delta^{5\text{-}4}$ oxosteroid isomerase (3βHSD) is found also in ovary, testis, liver, and brain. Deficiencies of all groups of steroids are found in patients with 3βHSD deficiency, but because the enzyme is present in the gonads and is required for androgen biosynthesis, ambiguous genitalia can be found in both males and females.

The classical form of 3βHSD deficiency is associated with salt loss which is usually severe, but mild and non-salt-losers have been described. The condition does not always present with the same severity in families. A non-classical form of 3βHSD has been described which presents in females with premature adrenarche, oligomenorrhea, and/or hirsutism; it is reported to be present in 15% of hirsute women.

Diagnosis is made by measuring the Δ^5 steroids 17α-hydroxypregnenolone and pregnenolone in plasma, or by estimating the Δ^5: Δ^4 ratio of steroid metabolites in urine.

Inborn Errors of Aldosterone Biosynthesis

Two types of aldosterone biosynthetic defect have been described, corticosterone methyloxidase deficiency types I and II (CMOD I and II). Almost all patients described have had CMOD II. Presentation is usually with failure to thrive, dehydration, hyponatremia, and hypokalemia. Older children may have failure to grow and/or postural hypotension, and affected siblings have been described without symptoms.

Diagnosis depends on elimination of other causes of hyponatremia associated with salt wasting. Biochemical diagnosis requires the measurement of plasma aldosterone and renin; aldosterone is normal or low in the presence of a high renin concentration. Measurement of urinary aldosterone, metabolites of aldosterone and its precursors, deoxycorticosterone and corticosterone, and their 18-hydroxyl derivatives help differentiate the condition from pseudohypoaldosteronism.[31]

The Role of Molecular Genetics in the Diagnosis of Adrenal Biosynthetic Defects

Following the identification and structural analysis of the various genes involved in steroid biosynthesis, a large number of studies reporting genetic analysis have been published. Not unexpectedly, each inherited disorder has been associated with several gene defects. This decreases the usefulness of genetic analysis in establishing the primary diagnosis. However, where the genetic defect has been identified in a known patient, the information is of use in family studies, genetic counseling, and prenatal diagnosis.

Steroid-Producing Adrenal Tumors

Adrenal tumors producing steroids are very rare. Approximately 5% of all pediatric adrenal tumors arise in the cortex, and the incidence is between 0.1 and $0.4/10^6$/year. There is an increased incidence in early childhood, and female-to-male ratios between 2:1 and 5:1 have been reported. Adrenocortical carcinomas are said to be more common than adenoma,[32] but this has been disputed.[33]

The clinical presentation of adrenal tumors in children is predominantly one of precocious puberty and/or virilization. This may be associated with signs of hypercortisolism (Cushing syndrome), or even occasionally feminization. Aldosterone secreting tumors and asymptomatic (non-hormone producing) tumors are very rare but form a higher proportion of adrenal tumors in adults.

The role of the biochemistry laboratory in establishing the diagnosis of adrenal tumor has been modified considerably by modern computerized imaging techniques. However, there remains the problem of differentiating benign adenoma from malignant carcinomas, which is sometimes difficult even with histology. Measurement of plasma and urinary steroids and responses to trophic hormones and suppression tests have all been used. Because of the rarity of the tumors, large series take many years to collect, during which testing procedures and methodologies change; hence, it becomes difficult to evaluate the most useful biochemical markers. In addition, certain techniques such as GLC involve hydrolysis of conjugates before analysis, complicating comparisons with RIA techniques which measure conjugates such as dehydroepiandrosterone sulphate (DHAS).

Serum hormone measurements are claimed to have advantages over urine, but the difficulties of obtaining suitable urine collections from children are overemphasized and it is a non-invasive technique. In addition, GLC of urinary steroid metabolites allows the detection of unusual steroids which may be useful markers both in diagnosis and in monitoring treatment.

Two major patterns of steroid secretion have been observed in pediatric virilizing adrenal tumors.[34] In the first of these, urinary ketosteroid excretion is high (> 50 μmol/24 h), serum testosterone is markedly raised for age, and the principal steroid produced is dehydroepiandrosterone (DHA). In the second major pattern, urinary ketosteroid excretion is lower (< 20 μmol/24 h), serum testosterone is moderately raised, and the major steroid produced is 11β-hydroxyandrosterone. Both patterns can be associated with either adenoma or carcinoma, although carcinoma is more frequent and the prognosis worse in the group producing DHA. However, the overall prognosis of adrenal tumors in children is relatively good following surgery.

Tumors detected in early infancy are sometimes associated with increased excretion of 16-oxygenated-3β-hydroxyl-5-ene steroids, which are produced normally in the neonatal period. These tumors lack 3βHSD activity.

Cushing Syndrome in Children

Accurate figures on the incidence of Cushing syndrome in children are not available, but it is of the same order as that for adrenal tumors. It should be noted that many patients diagnosed as having Cushing syndrome in adult life have symptoms that began in childhood. The differential diagnosis of Cushing syndrome from simple obesity and iatrogenic Cushing syndrome from the therapeutic use of exogenous steroids are common pediatric problems.

Cushing syndrome may result from overproduction of ACTH as a consequence of hypothalamic-pituitary disease (Cushing disease) or from ectopic ACTH secretion from non-adrenal tumors. As a consequence of the increased circulating ACTH, the patients have bilateral adrenal hyperplasia. Approximately 50% of all pediatric cases of Cushing syndrome are ACTH dependent, the majority of these being in the older age group. The remaining cases are ACTH independent and are caused by adrenal adenomas or carcinomas. Rare syndromes causing ACTH independent disease are primary adrenal micronodular dysplasia (PAND) and McCune-Albright syndrome.

The biochemical diagnosis of Cushing syndrome is relatively simple. The most useful initial screening tests are the 24-h urine free cortisol excretion[35] or the overnight dexamethasone test. Urine free cortisol can be raised in the very obese. If these tests give borderline or increased values, a low-dose dexamethasone test will separate patients whose cortisol is raised for reasons of stress, in whom the plasma or urinary cortisol will be normalized.

The differential diagnosis of the various etiologies of Cushing syndrome requires the measurement of plasma ACTH concentration, performance of the high-dose dexamethasone suppression test, and the results of imaging procedures of the pituitary and adrenal areas. Unmeasurable plasma ACTH is diagnostic of primary adrenal disease, usually a tumor. ACTH within the "normal range" may be found in Cushing disease or ectopic ACTH, but this is very rare in children. It should be remembered that ACTH is normally suppressed by increased cortisol production; therefore, even though the ACTH concentration falls within the normal range, it is, in fact, inappropriately increased. Imaging may resolve the problem, but selective venous sampling and the establishment of the presence of an ACTH gradient may be required. High plasma ACTH concentration is usually associated with ectopic ACTH. The high-dose dexamethasone suppression test can give both positive and negative results in either pituitary or adrenal Cushing syndrome.

The other tests previously used in the diagnosis of Cushing syndrome—diurnal rhythm of plasma cortisol, insulin tolerance test, and metyrapone test—are almost certainly no longer of value.

Adrenocortical Hypofunction

Decreased production of one or more of the adrenal steroid hormones may be caused by one of a large heterogeneous group of conditions.[36] (See Tables 9–5 and 9–6.) These may be primary diseases of the adrenal glands or may be secondary resulting from either decreased stimulation by ACTH or renin as a consequence of hypothalamic-pituitary disease or renal disease, respectively.

The predominant etiologies of the adrenal hypofunction vary according to age. In the neonate and in early infancy, steroid biosynthetic defects, sporadic or familial congenital adrenal hypoplasia, panhypopituitarism, and maternal steroid therapy are the major causes. In later infancy and childhood, iatrogenic adrenal suppression as a result of glucocorticoid therapy is by far the major cause, with inborn errors of steroid biosynthesis, autoimmune adrenal disease, adrenoleukodystrophy (peroxisomal disease), and hypopituitarism also contributing to cases of adrenal hypofunction. Acute destruction of the adrenal gland in fulminating infection (Waterhouse-Friderichsen syndrome) is found at any age.

The biochemical diagnosis of adrenocortical hypofunction is established by use of tests of basal steroid hormone excretion, of the intactness of the HPA axis, and by the response of the adrenal to the stimulus of exogenous ACTH. The measurement of plasma ACTH is extremely helpful in distinguishing primary from secondary adrenal failure. Diurnal rhythm of ACTH and cortisol secretion is often maintained in primary or secondary disease and is not a useful test. The insulin stress test should be used with great caution in the diagnosis of adrenal failure if there is a danger of severe hypoglycemia, and in most cases of severe hypoadrenalism the short ACTH test can be adequately substituted.[37]

One of the most common but difficult biochemical problems associated with the assessment of adrenal hypofunction is the testing of the status of the HPA axis prior to or after withdrawal of glucocorticoid therapy. The question being asked is whether or not the HPA axis can respond to natural stress conditions—e.g., infection or trauma—to produce appropriate quantities of cortisol. A normal response to pharmacological tests such as insulin hypoglycemia or ACTH stimulation tests may not accurately reflect the true status of the HPA axis and the ability of the patient to respond to stress with an adequate secretion of cortisol. The metyrapone test may be more useful in these circumstances, but 11-deoxycortisol assays are not readily available. The low-dose ACTH test is claimed to be useful in assessing responsiveness in patients currently taking steroids.[17] It may be that the use of adrenal responses to different amounts of ACTH will be the most suitable test of adrenal hypofunction, but this has not yet been validated in children.

ADRENAL MEDULLA

The adrenal medulla has a different embryological derivation from the adrenal cortex and is normally considered as separate in terms of biochemistry, physiology, and pathology. However, there exist strong interrelationships between the adrenal cortex and medulla.[38] This is most obvious when considering response to stress: both cortisol and epinephrine (adrenaline) are released in response to stressful stimuli, and there is well recognized modulation of tissue sensitivity to epinephrine by cortisol. There is also some evidence for reciprocal cooperation between steroid and catecholamine synthesis.

The pathology of the adrenal medulla consists essentially of two disorders, both tumors: neuroblastoma and pheochromocytoma. The diagnosis of these conditions depends heavily on the measurement of catecholamines and their metabolites.

Catecholamine Biosynthesis

The adrenal medulla produces two principal catecholamines, norepinephrine (noradrenaline) and its methylated derivative, epinephrine, in the ratio 1:9. These are produced from the amino acid tyrosine by a series of enzymatic steps (Figure 9–4). Tyrosine hydroxylase converts tyrosine to dihydroxyphenylalanine (DOPA), which is then metabolized to the physiologically active metabolite dopamine through the action of DOPA-decarboxylase. Norepinephrine and epinephrine are produced from dopamine by the sequential action of dopamine β-hydroxylase and phenylalanine N-methyl transferase (PNMT), respectively.

The formation of DOPA takes place in the mitochondria, where activity of the rate-limiting enzyme tyrosine hydroxylase is regulated by ACTH and by feedback inhibition from epinephrine and norepinephrine. Synthesis of dopamine and epi-

FIGURE 9–4. Biosynthesis of Catecholamines

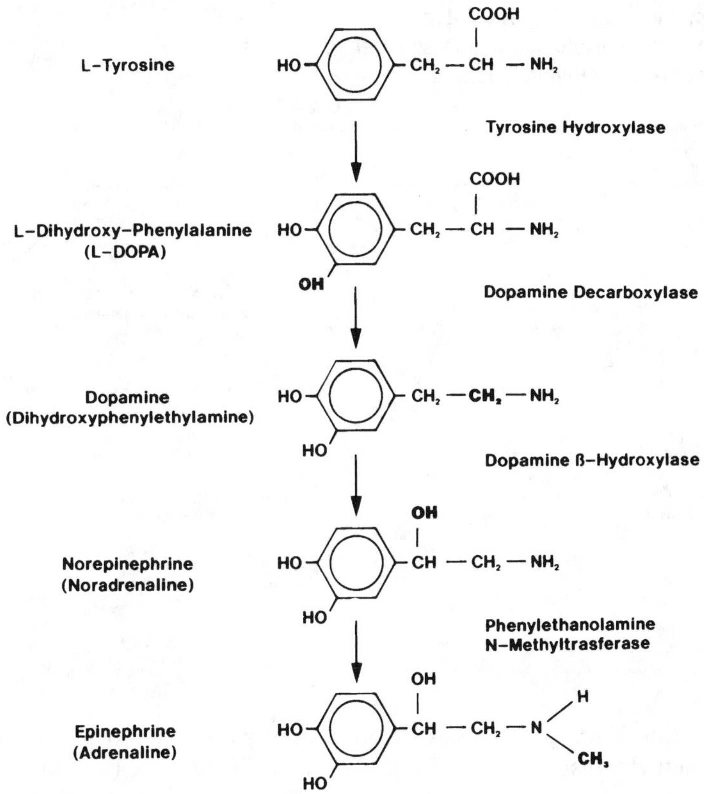

L-Tyrosine — HO–C₆H₄–CH_2 — CH(COOH) — NH_2

Tyrosine Hydroxylase

L-Dihydroxy-Phenylalanine (L-DOPA) — HO–(OH)C₆H₃–CH_2 — CH(COOH) — NH_2

Dopamine Decarboxylase

Dopamine (Dihydroxyphenylethylamine) — HO–(HO)C₆H₃–CH_2 — CH_2 — NH_2

Dopamine ß-Hydroxylase

Norepinephrine (Noradrenaline) — HO–(HO)C₆H₃–CH(OH) — CH_2 — NH_2

Phenylethanolamine N-Methyltrasferase

Epinephrine (Adrenaline) — HO–(HO)C₆H₃–CH(OH) — CH_2 — N(H)(CH_3)

nephrine occurs in the cytoplasm, but dopamine β-hydroxylase activity is found in chromaffin storage granules. Conversion of norepinephrine to epinephrine is sensitive to local corticosteroid concentrations. Catecholamine synthesis also occurs in the autonomic nervous system and in the brain, although the balance of the different bioactive catecholamines synthesized differs in these tissues.

Catecholamine Metabolism

In catecholamine catabolism (Figure 9–5), a considerable number of closely related metabolites are produced from DOPA, dopamine, norepinephrine, and epinephrine.[39] The important ones from the clinical laboratory diagnostic point of view are the metanephrines, normetanephrine and metanephrine, produced from norepinephrine and epinephrine respectively and usually measured as total metanephrines; homovanillic acid (HVA, 4-hydroxy-3-methoxy-phenylacetic acid), produced from dopamine; and 4-hydroxy-3-methoxy-mandelic acid (HMMA), also known as vanillylmandelic acid (VMA), produced from dopamine, norepinephrine, and epi-

FIGURE 9–5. Catabolism of Catecholamines

The enzymes catalyzing each step are:
1. Monoamine oxidase and aldehyde dehydrogenase
2. Catechol-O-methyl transferase

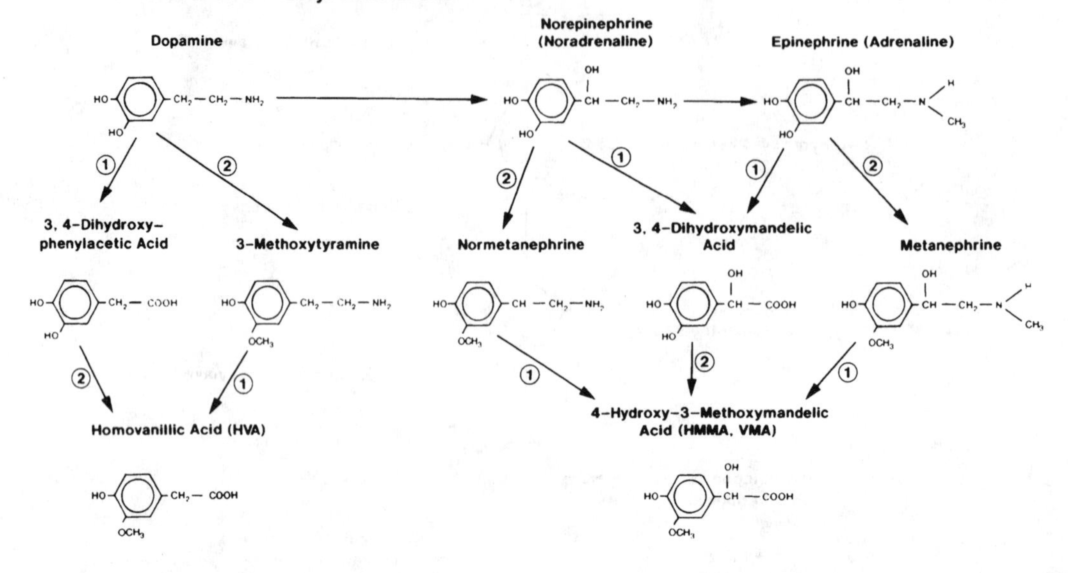

nephrine. These metabolites are produced by the action of two enzymes, catechol-O-methyl transferase (COMT) and monoamine oxidase (MAO). Both enzymes are widely distributed, with high concentrations in liver, brain, and sympathetic nervous tissue. Catecholamines and their O-methylated derivatives are excreted in the urine, partly as sulphate and glucuronide conjugates.

Investigation of Adrenal Medullary Function

Urine

Total catecholamines, free catecholamines (norepinephrine, epinephrine, and dopamine), metadrenalines, and HVA and HMMA excretion in urine have all been used to diagnose neuroblastoma and pheochromocytoma. With the development of HPLC and electrochemical detectors, the group assays (total catecholamines and metadrenalines) are of reduced usefulness in pediatric practice; with very rare exceptions, HVA, HMMA, dopamine, and norepinephrine determinations are sufficient. Total metadrenaline excretion remains useful as a preliminary screening test for pheochromocytoma. HPLC methods, as well as allowing more specific differentiation of the individual catecholamines, overcome almost all the problems of interferences from drugs and dietary substances which caused serious problems with the older chemical methods.

For a long time, diagnosis has rested on the use of 24-h urine collections, with results expressed either as absolute quantity excreted per day or as a ratio to the amount of creatinine excreted. Because of the real but overemphasized problems of collecting 24-h urine specimens, particularly from very young children, a number of groups have used random urine collections[40] and expressed results as creatinine ratios. Available information on sensitivity and specificity of random urine collections is sparse. However, there is some indication that this technique could miss smaller tumors unless several specimens are analyzed.[41] Both adrenal catecholamine secretion and renal creatinine excretion have circadian rhythms, and to be more useful there is a need to standardize the time of the random urine collection.

Because of the instability of some of the catecholamines and metabolites at neutral pH, urines must be acidified to pH 1 immediately after voiding. HVA and VMA appear to be stable in unacidified urine when collected onto filter paper for population screening (see discussion below). Additional precautions to be taken before urine collection include the avoidance of stressful procedures such as surgery, which will give rise to a physiological increase in catecholamine excretion.

The urine excretion of catecholamines and metabolites is age related even when corrected for creatinine, and reference ranges quoted in the literature for the same or different methods vary widely. It is therefore important, as for the adrenal steroids, for each laboratory to establish and use its own reference range relevant to the techniques used. Selection of the control group should be done with care; healthy children may not be the most appropriate, and the use of hospitalized or ill patients should be considered.[42] Seasonal variation in catecholamine excretion has been reported, but this has not proven to be a practical problem.

Reference ranges derived in our laboratory using HPLC and electrochemical detection from 24-h collections from hospitalized patients are given in Table 9–7.

The measurement of total HVA—i.e., free plus conjugated HVA—has been proposed as a useful alternative investigation when the free urinary HVA is borderline.[43] However, the alternative measurement of dopamine and/or noradrenaline was not considered in these patients.

TABLE 9–7. Reference Ranges for Catecholamines and Their Metabolites*

	UPPER LIMIT** OF NORMAL EXCRETION mmol/mol creatinine (μg/mg creatinine)			
AGE	Norepinephrine	Dopamine	HMMA (VMA)	HVA
<1 year	0.25 (0.37)	1.8 (2.4)	15.0 (26.3)	22.0 (35.5)
1–2 years	0.20 (0.30)	1.5 (2.0)	12.0 (21.1)	17.0 (27.4)
3–4 years	0.15 (0.22)	0.9 (1.22)	8.0 (14.0)	15.0 (24.2)
5–9 years	0.14 (0.21)	0.8 (1.08)	7.0 (12.3)	10.0 (16.1)
10–15 years	0.11 (0.16)	0.7 (0.95)	7.0 (12.3)	7.0 (11.3)

**NOTE:* These reference ranges were derived from urines collected over 18–24 hours into sufficient acid to reduce pH to below 3.0. The reference population consisted of patients in whom an adrenal medullary tumor was suspected, but whose final diagnosis excluded neuroblastoma or pheochromocytoma. Analysis was by HPLC with electrochemical detection.

**The upper limit of normal is defined as the 0.95 fractile, determined using non-parametric methods.

Plasma

As an alternative to urine collections, the measurement of epinephrine, norepinephrine, dopamine, and metabolites, both free and conjugated, has been used. The advantages are that there is no requirement for 24-h collections; that interferences from drugs are reduced; that the measurements are suitable for monitoring catecholamine secretion in response to stimuli, i.e., in dynamic tests; and that plasma can be used in anuric patients. Against these, however, are several major disadvantages: lack of stability of catecholamines in plasma, requiring special handling procedures; lower concentrations, requiring more sensitive assays; and single-point estimations of fluctuating concentrations are obtained, rather than the integrated values obtained using timed urines. In addition, plasma catecholamine concentration is affected by a number of physiological variables, including age, circadian rhythms, exercise, posture, temperature, feeding, stress, and electrolyte balance, as well as pathological conditions such as heart disease, diabetes, hypertension, etc.[44] This means that plasma catecholamine determinations should be performed under carefully controlled and standardized conditions.

Information on age-related pediatric reference ranges for plasma catecholamines is very limited, and only very small numbers of subjects have been studied.[45] What information is available suggests that plasma free epinephrine and norepinephrine are raised in infants under 2 years of age. In studies using mass fragmentography of much larger numbers of subjects, an exponential decline of plasma HMMA and HVA concentrations was shown throughout childhood, with changes in concentration of 40X and 5X for HVA and HMMA respectively between the first day of life and the late teens.[46]

Pheochromocytoma

Pheochromocytomas are very rare catecholamine-secreting tumors arising from the adrenal medulla or less commonly from extra-adrenal chromaffin tissue. Patients frequently present with headache, and on examination are found to be hypertensive; alternative presenting symptoms include profuse sweating and diarrhea. Some patients are asymptomatic but are found to be hypertensive on routine health examinations. Approximately 1% of children with hypertension have pheochromocytoma,[47] although it is probable, as with adrenocortical tumors, that a number of patients who present with pheochromocytoma in adulthood have had symptoms beginning in childhood.

Tumors are found more frequently in boys (M:F ratio 1.8:1), and 35–40% are single tumors of the adrenal medulla. Twenty percent of children have bilateral adrenal tumors, while the remainder have single extra-adrenal tumors or multiple tumors. Early studies reported low prevalence (10%) of malignancy, similar to that in adults, but more recent studies have given prevalence rates for malignancy as high as 60%.

Familial pheochromocytomas are well recognized either as a separate entity or in association with disorders such as multiple endocrine neoplasia, neurofibromatosis, and von Hippel-Lindau syndrome.

The biochemical diagnosis of pheochromocytoma has been the subject of much study and controversy. These arguments concern not only whether plasma or urine is the optimum specimen, but also which analyte or combination of analytes gives the best sensitivity and specificity. These arguments relate more to the needs of adult patients, in whom the differentiation from benign essential hypertension is a major logistical problem. In the pediatric population, the measurement of 24-h urinary total metadrenalines and free catecholamine excretion will detect almost all cases. Occasional false positives due to stress or exogenous catecholamine administration may be found. If the index of suspicion is high and urine results persistently normal when the patient is hypertensive, then plasma catecholamine determinations may help, but these have not proved necessary in our series.

Neuroblastoma

Neuroblastoma accounts for 7–10% of all pediatric malignancies, with an annual incidence of 1:100,000 children. However, the overall incidence figure disguises the fact that neuroblastoma is predominantly a disease of infancy, being the most common non-hemopoietic tumor in the first two years of life.

The role of the laboratory in the diagnosis, prognostic evaluation, and monitoring of treatment of children with neuroblastoma has been studied extensively. Interpretation of the data is confusing and is complicated by the fact that there is still considerable debate as to exactly which tumors should be included under the heading of neuroblastoma. A number of other neuroectodermal tumors have been classified as neuroblastomas,[48] and these tumors are found more frequently in older patients and in atypical sites.

Neuroblastomas are tumors derived from cells of neuroectodermal origin. They are classified clinically into types I to IV and IVs, depending on the primary site and degree of spread. This classification has prognostic significance, and a considerable amount of effort has gone into attempts to biochemically differentiate between the different stages.

Diagnosis of neuroblastomas has relied essentially on the measurement of HVA and HMMA in 24-h urine collections. Increase in the excretion of one or more catecholamine metabolites can be found in neuroblastoma. This method reportedly fails to diagnose 5–10% of patients, who are then referred to as "non-secretors." A wider selection of catecholamine metabolites will enable the diagnosis of additional cases of neuroblastoma. In our experience of 104 sequential cases investigated by HPLC of 24-h urines, 100 were detected by HVA alone and an additional 2 cases by the combination of HVA and dopamine. HMMA did not increase the diagnostic sensitivity. Both non-secretors in our series had atypical extra-abdominal tumors.

The pattern of urinary metabolite excretion has not proved to be a useful marker in disease staging, although it has been reported that high HMMA excretion is associated with disseminated tumors (stages III, IV, and IVs). In our series, there was no significant difference in the pattern of secretion of HVA, HMMA, and dopamine in patients under 1 year of age and in those over age 1, the former group including a higher proportion of stage I and II tumors.

Plasma HVA and HMMA measurements have not proved to be more useful than urinary determinations. Normal values are found in 12% of all neuroblastoma patients, and the prevalence of normal values increases to 50% in patients with stages I and II.[49]

A large number of biochemical markers have been used in attempts to provide prognostic indicators for neuroblastoma patients. These include the absolute quantity and pattern of urinary catecholamine metabolite excretion, and plasma concentrations of catecholamines (epinephrine, norepinephrine, and DOPA), dopamine β-hydroxylase, L-amino acid decarboxylase, LDH, ferritin, and neurone-specific enolase. Non-biochemical prognostic indicators include age, stage, chromosomal number (ploidy), N-myc oncogene amplification, and expression and reaction with various monoclonal antibodies. Of all the prognostic markers, age, sex, N-myc, and ploidy have been the most successful and the biochemical markers less so.

Screening for Neuroblastoma

Treatment of neuroblastoma remains problematical, and the overall prognosis is relatively poor. Because of this, it has been thought worthwhile to develop population screening programs for the preclinical detection of tumors, as there is a significantly better prognosis for patients with stage I or stage II disease. These programs were first introduced and widely applied in Japan after the development of assays for HMMA and HVA on filter paper collections of urine. Infants were screened at about 6 months of age. Initially, chemical methods were used for HMMA with large numbers of false positives and false negatives, but the use of HPLC overcame these problems. Reports of the Japanese screening programs were highly promising, with early detection and treatment appearing to produce a remarkable improvement in prognosis.

However, screening for neuroblastoma has not received universal acceptance.[50] Neuroblastoma is a tumor which appears to have a high incidence of spontaneous regression, especially tumors appearing in early infancy. This, taken with the fact that following screening there appeared to be a doubling of the incidence of neuroblastoma in Japan, raised the possibility that some of the tumors detected on screening at age 6 months would have spontaneously regressed, and hence that patients were subjected to unnecessary treatment. The only way to resolve the controversy is a large-scale controlled trial. Such a trial is presently underway in North America.

REFERENCES

1. Briggs MH, Brotherton J. Steroid biochemistry and pharmacology. London: Academic Press, 1971:1–22.
2. Gower DB. Biosynthesis of the corticosteroids. In: Makin HLJ, ed. Biochemistry of steroid hormones, 2nd ed. Oxford: Blackwell Scientific Publications, 1984:117–69.
3. Gower DB. Biosynthesis of the androgens and other C19 steroids. In: Makin HLJ, ed. Biochemistry of steroid hormones, 2nd ed. Oxford: Blackwell Scientific Publications, 1984:170–206.
4. Miller WL. Molecular biology of steroid hormone synthesis. Endocrinol Rev 1988;9:295–318.

5. Lieberman S, Greenfield NJ, Wolfson A. A heuristic proposal for understanding steroidogenic processes. Endocrinol Rev 1984;4:128–48.
6. Lieberman S, Prasad VVK. Heterodox notions on pathways of steroidogenesis. Endocrinol Rev; 1990;11:469–93
7. Waterman MR, Simpson ER. Regulation of steroid hydroxylase gene expression is multifactorial in nature. Rec Prog in Horm Res 1989;45:533–63.
8. Biglieri EG, Wajchenberg BL, Malerbi DA, et al. The zonal origins of the mineralocorticoid hormones in the 21-hydroxylation deficiency congenital adrenal hyperplasia. J Clin Endocrinol Metab 1981;53:964–69.
9. Hornsby PJ. The regulation of adrenocortical function by control of growth and structure. In: Anderson DC, Winter J, ed. The adrenal cortex. London: Butterworths, 1985:1–31.
10. Bateman A, Singh A, Kral T, Solomon S. The immune-hypothalamic-pituitary-adrenal axis. Endocrinol Rev 1989;10:92–112.
11. Peterson RE. Metabolism of adrenal cortical steroids. In: Christy NP, ed. The human adrenal cortex. New York: Harper and Row, 1971:87–187.
12. Addison GM, Chard C, Price DA. Steroid hormone metabolism. In: Hicks JM, Boeckx RL, eds. Pediatric clinical chemistry. Philadelphia: Saunders, 1984:240–94.
13. Riad-Fahmy D, Read GF, Walker RF, Griffith K. Steroids in saliva for assessing endocrine function. Endocrinol Rev 1982;3:367–95.
14. Dillon MJ, Ryness JM. Plasma renin activity and aldosterone concentration in children. Brit Med J 1975;4:316–19.
15. Shackleton CHL, Honour JW. Simultaneous estimation of urinary steroids by semi-automated gas chromatography: investigation of neonates and children with abnormal steroid synthesis. Clin Chim Acta 1976;69:267–83.
16. Shackleton CHL, Taylor NF, Honour J. An atlas of gas chromatographic profiles of neutral urinary steroids in health and disease. Delft: Packard-Becker BV, 1980.
17. Dickstien G, Shechechner C, Nicholson W, et al. Adrenocorticotrophin stimulation test: effect of basal cortisol level, time of day and suggested new sensitive low dose test. J Clin Endocrinol Metab 1991;72:773–78.
18. Strachan T. Molecular pathology of congenital adrenal hyperplasia. Clin Endocrinol 1990;32:373–93.
19. Narasimhulu S. Heterogeneity of the bovine adrenal steroid 21-hydroxylase. Endocrinol Res 1989;15:67–84.
20. Speiser PW, Agder L, Ueshiba H, et al.. Aldosterone synthesis in salt wasting congenital adrenal hyperplasia with complete absence of adrenal 21-hydroxylase. N Engl J Med 1991:145–49.
21. Murphy JF, Joyce BG, Dyas J, Hughes IA. Plasma 17-hydroxyprogesterone concentration in ill newborn infants. Arch Dis Child 1983;58:532–34.
22. Knudtzen J, Aakvaag A, Bergsjo P, Markestad Y. Elevated 17-hydroxyprogesterone levels in premature infants. Acta Paediatr Scand 1991;80:96–97.
23. Pang SY, Wallace AM, Hofman L, et al. Worldwide experience in newborn screening for classical adrenal hyperplasia due to 21-hydroxylase deficiency. Pediatrics 1988;81:866–74.
24. Pang S, Hotchkiss J, Drash AL, et al. Microfilter paper method for 17-alpha-hydroxyprogesterone radioimmunoassay: its application for rapid screening for congenital adrenal hyperplasia. J Clin Endocrinol Metab 1977;45:1003–8.
25. Addison GM. Workshop on screening for congenital adrenal hyperplasia (steroid 21-hydroxylase deficiency). J Inher Metab Dis 1986;9 Suppl 1:111–14.
26. Virdi NK, Rayner PH, Rudd BT, Green A. Should we screen for congenital adrenal hyperplasia? A review of 117 cases. Arch Dis Child 1987;62:659–62.
27. Forest MG, Betuel H, David M. Prenatal treatment in congenital adrenal hyperplasia due to 21-hydroxylase deficiency: update 88 of the French multicentric study. Endocrinol Res 1989;15:277–301.
28. Speiser PW, Laforgia N, Kato K, et al. First trimester prenatal treatment and molecular genetic diagnosis of congenital adrenal hyperplasia. J Clin Endocrinol Metab 1990;70:838–48.

29. Porter B, Finzi M, Leiberman E, Moses S. The syndrome of congenital adrenal hyperplasia in Israel. Paediatrician 1977;6:100–5.
30. Zadik Z, Kahana L, Kaufman, M, et al. Salt loss in hypertensive form of congenital adrenal hyperplasia (11β-hydroxylase deficiency). J Clin Endocrinol Metab 1984;58:384–88.
31. Honour JW, Dillon MJ, Shackleton CHL. Analysis of steroids in urine for differentiation of pseudohypoaldosteronism and aldosterone biosynthetic defects. J Clin Endocrinol Metab 1982;54:384–88.
32. Daneman A. Adrenal neoplasms in children. Sem Roentgen 1988;23:205–15.
33. Grant DB. Virilizing adrenal tumours. In: Forest MG, ed. Androgens in childhood. Paediatric and adolescent endocrinolgy. Basel; Karger 1989;19:236–46.
34. Honour JW, Price DA, Taylor, NF, et al. Steroid biochemistry of virilising adrenal tumours in childhood. Eur J Paediatr 1984;142:165–69.
35. Jones KL. The Cushing syndromes. Pediatr Clin North Am 1990;37:1313–32.
36. Forest MG. Adrenal steroid deficiency states. In: Brook CDG, ed. Clinical paediatric endocrinology. Oxford; Blackwell Scientific Publications, 1981:396–428.
37. Clayton RN. Diagnosis of adrenal insufficiency (editorial). Brit Med J 1989;298:271–72.
38. Weinkove C, Anderson DC. Interactions between the adrenal cortex and medulla. In: Anderson DC, Winter JSD, eds. Adrenal cortex. London: Butterworths, 1985:208–34.
39. Gjessing LR. Biochemistry of functional neural crest tumours. Adv Clin Chem 1968;11:81–131.
40. Tuchman M, Morris CL, Ramnaraine ML, et al. Value of random urinary homovanillic acid and vanillylmandelic acid levels in the diagnosis and management of patients with neuroblastoma: comparison with 24-hour urine collections. Pediatrics 1985;75:324–28.
41. Nishi M, Miyake H, Takeda T, et al. Can a patient with neuroblastoma be diagnosed by a single urine sample collected randomly? Oncology 1991;48:31–33.
42. Worthington DJ, Hammond EM, Eldeeb BB, et al. Neuroblastoma: when are urinary catecholamines and their metabolites "normal"? Ann Clin Biochem 1988;25:620–26.
43. Tuchman M, Stoeckeler JS. Conjugated versus "free" acidic catecholamines in random urine samples: significance for the diagnosis of neuroblastoma. Pediatr Res 1988;23:576–79.
44. Barrand MA, Callingham BA. The catecholamines: adrenaline, noradrenaline and dopamine. In: Gray CH, James VHT, eds. Hormones in blood, 3rd ed., Vol 5. London: Academic Press, 1983:55–124.
45. Eichler I, Eichler HG, Rotter M, et al. Plasma concentrations of free and sulfoconjugated dopamine, epinephrine and norepinephrine in healthy infants and children. Klinische Wochenschrift 1989;67:672–75.
46. Hunneman DH, Jonas W, Gabriel, M. Gahr M. Effect of age on homovanillic acid and 4-hydroxy-3-methoxymandelic acid levels in plasma. Eur J Pediatr 1986;145:555–57.
47. Deal JE, Sever PS, Barrat TM, Dillon MJ. Pheochromocytoma: investigation and management of 10 cases. Arch of Dis Child 1990:65;269–74.
48. Triche TJ. Neuroblastoma and other childhood neural tumours. Pediatr Pathol 1990;7:175–93.
49. Gahr M, Hunneman DH. The value of determination of homovanillic and vanillylmandelic acids in plasma for the diagnosis and follow up in neuroblastoma in children. Eur J Pediatr 1987;146:489–93.
50. Murphy SB, Cohn SL, Craft AW, et al. Do children benefit from mass screening for neuroblastoma? Consensus statement from the American Cancer Society Workshop on Neuroblastoma Screening. Lancet 1991;377:344–46.

CHAPTER 10

Disorders of Calcium and Phosphorus Metabolism in Infants and Children

Ran Namgung, M.D., Ronald Bainbridge, M.D., Maria Lourdes A. Cruz, M.D., Reginald C. Tsang, M.D.

INTRODUCTION

Calcium (Ca), phosphorus (P), magnesium (Mg), vitamin D, calcitonin (CT), and parathyroid hormone (PTH) form part of an intricate network of systems that maintain the stability of the skeleton and regulate several Ca and P related metabolic activities. The increased need for Ca and P during infancy and childhood requires optimal functioning of the systems of absorption, transport, and assimilation of these minerals. Disorders in any of several steps in these systems may result in prolonged and severe consequences in the affected child. Early recognition of the physical and biochemical signs associated with these disorders, and subsequent treatment, may allow possible diminution of the consequences.

BIOCHEMISTRY AND PHYSIOLOGY

Less than 1% of the total body Ca is in the extracellular compartment, while approximately 98% is in bone. Serum Ca is approximately 50% ionized, 40% protein bound (90% to albumin), and 10% chelated to citrate, phosphate, and other anions. Serum total and ionized calcium (iCa) concentrations are usually tightly regulated within narrow ranges. Ionized Ca concentration is the physiologically active form of Ca and is more tightly regulated than total serum Ca concentrations. Neonatal serum ionized Ca increases with gestational age and cord blood concentrations are higher than paired maternal levels.[1] In term infants serum iCa declines progressively to reach a nadir at 24 hours.[2] A circadian pattern has been described for serum iCa concentration, with a variation of 0.08 mmol/L (0.32 mg/dL), the reference range being 1.2–1.3 mmol/L (4.8–5.2 mg/dL) in adults and 1.1–1.4 mmol/L (4.4–5.6 mg/dL) in term infants.[2,3] Season, diet, and race also appear to affect serum Ca concentrations.[4] Binding of Ca to albumin is pH dependent, increasing at higher pH and decreasing at lower pH, thereby effecting changes in serum iCa concentration.[5]

The distribution of total body P is approximately 80% in bone, 9% in skeletal muscle, and 11% in extracellular fluid and other tissues. Less than 1% of body phosphorus is found in serum. Serum P is approximately 55% dissociated, 35% complexed to the cations, sodium, Ca^{2+} and Mg^{2+}, and 10% protein bound. Serum P concentration is not as tightly regulated as serum Ca concentration and varies with nutritional status, age, race, and season.[4] Measurements of serum P include both inorganic and organic phosphates and probably partly explain the wide variation observed in serum P measurements. Serum concentrations of Ca and P are regulated by PTH, vitamin D, CT, and Mg (see Figure 10–1).

Parathyroid Hormone

Parathyroid hormone is an 84 amino-acid polypeptide secreted by the parathyroid glands. The hormonal activity resides in the amino terminal 1-34 fragment. In normal adults, only 5–30% of the circulating immunoreactive hormone is intact PTH; the rest consists of inactive C-terminal fragments.[6] Parathyroid hormone secretion is acutely increased in response to decreases in serum Ca concentration and decreased by increased Ca concentration. Acute changes in serum Mg concentration affect PTH secretion in a manner similar to Ca. However, chronic Mg deficiency inhibits PTH secretion.[7]

Parathyroid hormone regulates both serum Ca and P concentrations through its action on bone, gut, and kidneys (Figure 10–1). PTH acts synergistically with vitamin D initially on bone to release Ca and P. The mechanism of acute PTH action involves stimulation of osteoclastic activity while inhibiting osteoblastic activity. The intracellular mechanisms involved include activation of a cyclic adenosine monophosphate (cAMP) dependent system.

The long-term effect of PTH on bone is to stimulate both osteoclast and osteoblast activity, resulting in the characteristic histologic lytic bone changes observed in hyperparathyroidism.[8] Since PTH facilitates the conversion of 25-hydroxy vitamin D (25-OHD) to 1,25-dihydroxy vitamin D [$1,25(OH)_2D$], it is indirectly involved in active intestinal absorption of Ca. The action of PTH on the kidney increases distal tubular Ca reabsorption, and inhibits proximal tubular reabsorption of P, resulting in phosphaturia. Renal tubular reabsorption of amino acids, sodium, and bicarbonate is also inhibited by PTH. Parathyroid hormone binds to receptors on the basolateral membrane of renal tubular cells, which in turn activates a stimulatory G protein, a subunit of which activates adenylate cyclase to form cAMP. Cyclic AMP triggers a cascade of other intracellular events to effect the changes in tubular reabsorption described above.[9] The net result is a lowering of serum P and increase in serum Ca concentrations (Figure 10–1).

FIGURE 10–1. Effects of Various Calciotropic Hormones on Different Organ Systems and Their Overall Effects on Serum Calcium (Ca) and Phosphorus (P) Concentrations

Parathyroid hormone (PTH) increases bone release of Ca and P and increases renal Ca reabsorption and P excretion, resulting in an overall increase in serum Ca but a decrease in P concentrations. Vitamin D (Vit.D), as 1,25$(OH)_2$D, stimulates intestinal Ca and P absorption, bone Ca and P resorption, and renal Ca and P reabsorption, resulting in an overall increase in serum Ca and P concentrations. Calcitonin (CT) acts mainly to decrease bone resorption and renal reabsorption of Ca and P, resulting in an overall decrease in serum Ca and P concentrations.

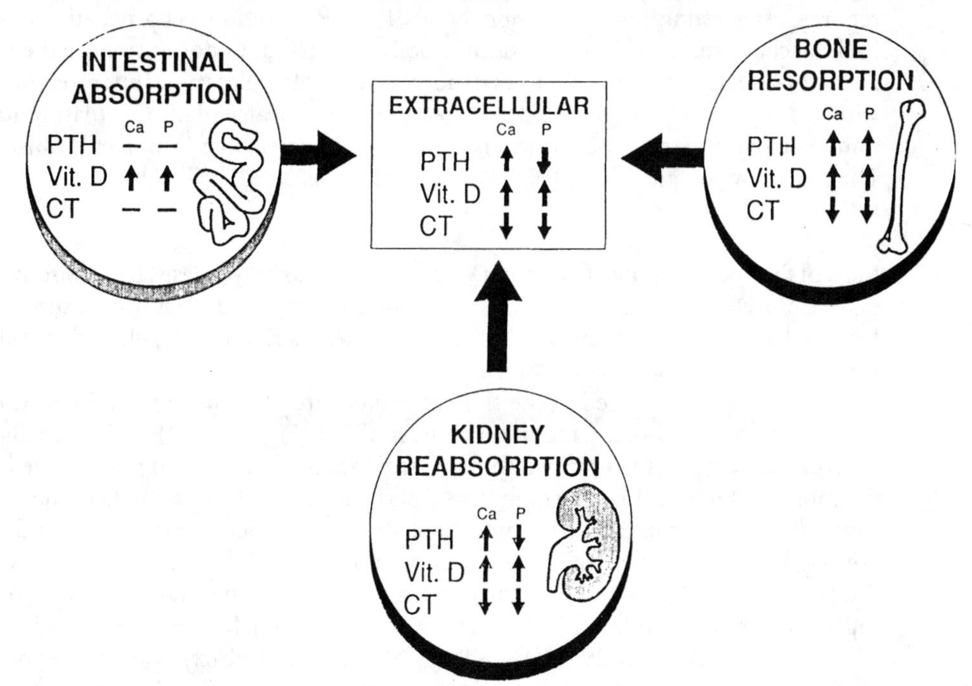

Parathyroid-hormone-related peptides (PTHrPs) are a novel class of peptide hormones.[10] PTH and PTHrP genes appear to be members of the same gene family. PTHrP shares marked homology with PTH (8 of the first 13 amino acids are identical) and binds to a common PTH-PTHrP receptor.[11] PTHrP undergoes extensive tissue-specific processing; three major secretory forms of the peptide—an amino-terminal, a mid-region, and a carboxyl-terminal species—appear to exert different biological actions.[12] The PTH-like action of the PTHrP molecule, bioactivities involved in Ca regulation, are confined to the amino terminal region. In addition to the endocrine effects of PTHrP, a growing body of evidence suggests non-PTH-like actions of PTHrP, such as a local role for PTHrP in epithelial growth and differentiation.[13] PTHrP also stimulates placental Ca transport (an effect confined to the central sequences of the molecule) by stimulating a placental Ca pump that is responsible for maintaining relative hypercalcemia in the fetus,[14] and has osteoclast inhibitory actions in the rat (confined to the carboxyl-terminal domain).[15] The physiological actions of PTHrP are thought to be mainly autocrine or paracrine. The significance of the non-PTH-like actions of PTHrP in normal physiology is not clear.

PTHrP biologic activity and immunoreactivity exist in many tissues (endocrine and nonendocrine), including the human fetus by as early as 7 weeks of gestation and the placenta.[16] Plasma amino terminal PTHrP (1-86) is detectable at low concentrations in fetuses and newborns between 19 and 41 weeks of fetal life, similar to that of their mothers and normal controls.[17] Increased serum immunoreactive PTHrP (1-34) in chronic profound hypocalcemia (idiopathic hypoparathyroidism) has been reported, suggesting increased endogenous PTHrP secretion via a negative feedback mechanism: the elevated immunoreactive PTHrP does not normalize the decreased serum Ca levels, but declines to normal (undetectable) values after treatment with 1-alpha-OHD_3, following the correction of hypocalcemia.[18] Circulating immunoreactive PTHrP concentrations are low or undetectable in normal subjects. The exact physiologic role of PTHrP remains to be defined.[19, 20]

Vitamin D

Most of the body's supply of vitamin D is derived from skin synthesis. Dietary sources of vitamin D assume importance only in children deprived of sun exposure. An intact biliary, pancreatic, and small intestinal system is required for the normal absorption of this fat-soluble vitamin.

Vitamin D_3 is formed in the skin after exposure of its precursor, 7-dehydrocholesterol, to ultraviolet irradiation from sunlight (Figure 10–2). 7-dehydrocholesterol is first converted to provitamin D_3, which is further thermally isomerized to vitamin D. Vitamin D binding globulin (DBG) transports the vitamin D to the liver for further transformation. After intestinal absorption, dietary vitamin D_3 and D_2 are also transported on DBG to the liver. Vitamin D is 25 hydroxylated to 25-hydroxy vitamin D (25-OHD) in the liver. This process is not tightly regulated, allowing for accumulation of 25-OHD, the concentration of which is regarded as an index of body vitamin D status. 25-OHD undergoes further 1α-hydroxylation in the proximal renal tubular cell. The enzyme involved in this conversion, 25-OHD 1α-hydroxylase, is tightly regulated, and its activity is stimulated by hypocalcemia, hypophosphatemia, and increased PTH concentration, and inhibited by increases in serum Ca, P, and $1,25(OH)_2D$.

1,25-dihydroxy vitamin D is the most physiologically active form of vitamin D. It acts by binding to cytoplasmic vitamin D receptors which later migrate to the nucleus to mediate its actions.[21] Its primary sites of action are the gut, bone, and kidney, similar to PTH (Figure 10–1). $1,25(OH)_2D$ stimulates active intestinal Ca absorption. $1,25(OH)_2D$ acts to enhance intestinal P absorption by stimulating sodium-dependant transepithelial P absorptive mechanisms (co-transport of sodium and P at the brush border).[22, 23] In bone, both osteoblast and osteoclast activity are stimulated, with the net result being bone remodelling and increased mineralization. 1,25-dihydroxy vitamin D enhances renal tubular reabsorption of Ca in concert with PTH. Vitamin D status also appears to be affected by season, diet, gender, and race.[4]

FIGURE 10–2. Normal Vitamin D Metabolism

Vitamin D_2 from diet, and Vitamin D_3 from diet and skin photoconversion, are hydroxylated in the liver to 25-OHD. 25-OHD undergoes further hydroxylation in the kidney to form $1,25(OH)_2D$ which is stimulated by parathyroid hormone (PTH). $1,25(OH)_2D$ is responsible for increasing bone resorption and intestinal calcium and phosphorus absorption. PTH acts synergistically with $1,25(OH)_2D$ to increase bone resorption.

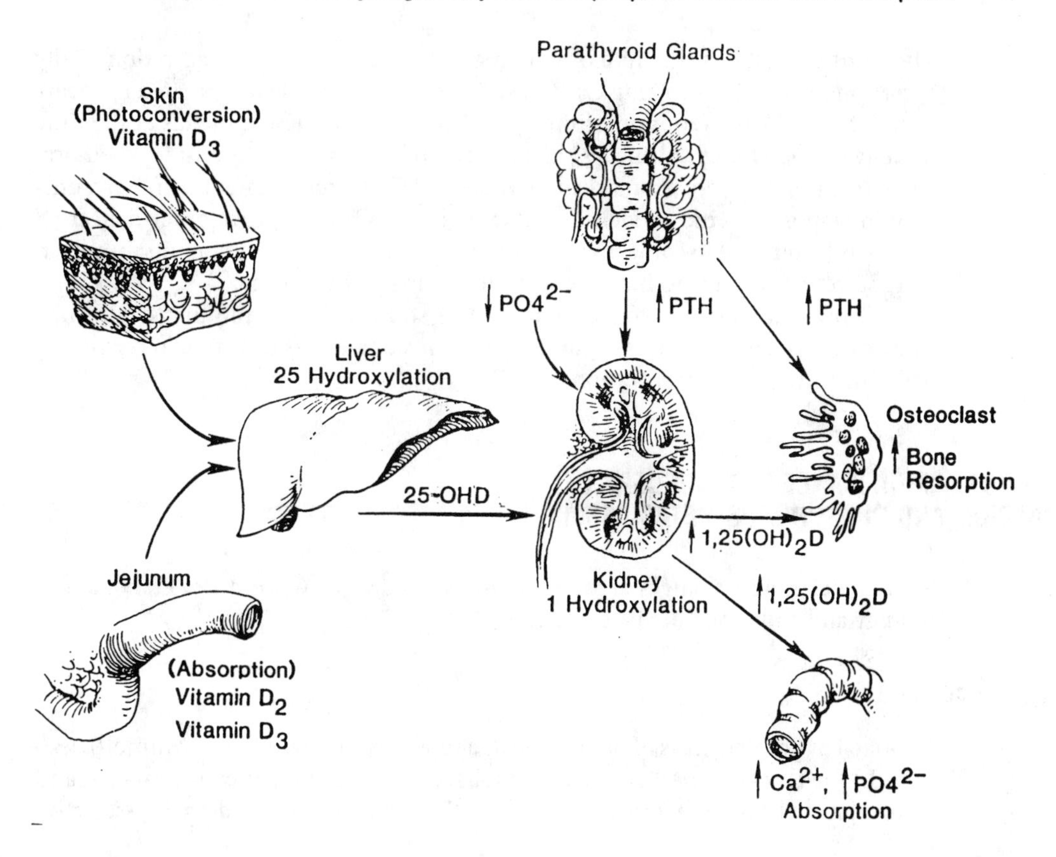

Calcitonin

Calcitonin (CT), a 32-amino acid peptide, is produced by the C-cells of the thyroid gland. Its secretion is stimulated by hypercalcemia, hypermagnesemia, gastrin, pancreozymin, and glucagon.[24] Hypocalcemia has the opposite effect.[24]

Calcitonin lowers serum Ca concentration by direct inhibition of osteoclast-mediated bone resorption (decreasing the amount of Ca and P released from bone) and secondarily by increasing renal Ca and P excretion (at high doses).[25] (Figure 10–1). However, in the absence of CT, serum Ca remains fairly well regulated, raising questions as to its importance in normal regulation of serum Ca concentration.

Serum CT concentrations are increased in the newborn infant and may remain so well into infancy. In both normal term infants and infants of diabetic mothers, serum CT concentrations increase postnatally regardless of serum Ca concentration.[26] The exact physiologic significance of this increase is unclear.

NEWBORN

The third trimester is the time of maximal intrauterine Ca and P accretion. Daily accretion rates of 117–150 mg Ca/kg and 74 mg P/kg have been estimated for near-term fetuses.[27, 28] Interruption of the placental supply of these minerals at the time of delivery therefore predisposes the neonate to hypocalcemia at a time when oral feeds are limited. There is a marked increase in PTH secretion after birth,[29] presumably in response to the sudden decrease in serum Ca concentration at delivery.[30] This may be blunted in some preterm infants as compared to term infants; however, PTH secretion appears to increase with increasing postnatal age.

Serum $1,25(OH)_2D$ concentrations rise steadily during the first day of life. The exact mechanism of this occurrence remains unclear, as is its role in regulating neonatal serum Ca concentrations.

CLINICAL SIGNIFICANCE OF DISORDERS OF CALCIUM AND PHOSPHORUS METABOLISM

Some biochemical changes associated with disorders of Ca and P metabolism in infancy and childhood are listed in Table 10–1.

Hypocalcemia

Neonatal hypocalcemia is often defined as a total serum calcium of < 2 mmol/L (8.0 mg/dL) for term infants,[2] or < 1.75 mmol/L (7.0 mg/dL) for preterm infants, and serum ionized Ca < 1.1 mmol/L (4.4 mg/dL),[2, 26] using the modern ion-selective electrode.

Traditionally, neonatal hypocalcemia has been classified as either early or late. "Early" neonatal hypocalcemia occurs during the first 48 hours of life, while "late" neonatal hypocalcemia occurs toward the end of the first week of life. In some cases, the distinction between the two conditions may not be clear-cut.

Early neonatal hypocalcemia occurs as a result of the inability of the neonate to adequately compensate for the sudden cessation of placental Ca supply after birth. The usual protective changes observed in calciotropic hormone secretion may be blunted. Preterm infants may or may not exhibit the surge in PTH secretion observed in term infants at birth,[31] and their restricted oral Ca intake may aggravate the problem. Birth asphyxia may result in an increase in serum CT concentration and may delay enteral feeding, both of which may theoretically aggravate neonatal

TABLE 10–1. Some Biochemical Changes in Disorders of Calcium and Phosphorus Metabolism in Infancy and Childhood*

Disorder	Serum Phosphorus Concentration	Parathyroid Hormone Concentration	Serum $1,25(OH)_2D$ Concentration	Serum 25-OHD Concentration	Urinary Calcium Excretion	Urinary Phosophorus Excretion
HYPOCALCEMIA						
Parathyroid disorders						
Hypoparathyroidism						
Congenital	↑	↓	↓	N	↓	↓
Transient or functional	↑	↓	↓	N	↓	↓
Pseudohypoparathyroidism	↑	↑	↓	N	↓	↓
Vitamin D disorders						
Vitamin D deficiency	↓	↑	N; ↑	↓	↓; Var	↓
Hepatic disease	↓	↑	N; ↓	↓	↓; Var	↓
Renal disease	↑	↑	↓	N	↓; Var	↓
Vitamin D dependent rickets, type I	↓	↑	↓	N; ↑	↑; Var	↓
Vitamin D dependent rickets, type II	↓	↑	Very ↑	N; ↑	↓; Var	↓
Mineral disorders						
Hypomagnesemia	N	N; ↓	N; ↓	N	↓	N
High phosphate load	↑	↑	↓	N	↓	↑
HYPERCALCEMIA						
Iatrogenic	N	↓	↓	N	↑	N
Low P intake	↓	↓	↑	N	↑	↓
Hyperparathyroidism	↓	↑	↑	N	↑	↑
Vitamin D intoxication	N; ↑	↓	N; ↑	↑	↑	↑
Subcutaneous fat necrosis	N	↓	N; ↓	N	↑	N
Idiopathic hypercalcemia of infancy	N	↓	N; ↓	N	↑	N
Benign familial hypocalciuric hypercalcemia	N	N; ↑	N	N	↑	N
Immobilization	N	↓	N; ↓	N	↑	N
HYPOPHOSPHATEMIA						
Inadequate P intake	N; ↑	↓	↑	N	↑	↓
Hyperparathyroidism	↑	↓	↑	N	↑	↑
Hypophosphatemic rickets	N	N	N; ↓	N	N	↑
HYPERPHOSPHATEMIA						
Parathyroid disorders						
Hypoparathyroidism	↓	↓	↓	N	↓	↓
Pseudohypoparathyroidism	↓	↑	↓	N	↓	↓
Thyrotoxicosis	N; ↑	N; ↑	N; ↓	N	N; ↑	N; ↑
High phosphate intake	↓	↑	↓	N	↓	↑
Renal failure	↓	↑	↓	N	↓	↓

*N = normal, Var = variable, ↑ = increased, ↓ = decreased

hypocalcemia.[32] Early neonatal hypocalcemia in infants of diabetic mothers may be related to Mg insufficiency and consequently to impaired PTH secretory activity.[33] In most cases, early neonatal hypocalcemia resolves within the first week of life. Prolonged hypocalcemia should prompt the physician to investigate other, more permanent causes.

Late neonatal hypocalcemia may be a manifestation of a congenital defect, a result of disorders of vitamin D metabolism, or a result of Mg and P mineral disturbance. Congenital hypoparathyroidism is the most significant cause of late-onset hypocalcemia which has to be treated early in life, and is discussed below. Vitamin D problems include insufficient dietary vitamin D intake or production due to liver or renal disease (resulting in decreased intestinal Ca absorption and renal Ca reabsorption), congenital deficiency of renal 1-hydroxylase (Vitamin D dependent rickets, type I), and $1,25(OH)_2D$ resistance (Vitamin D dependent rickets, type II). Of the mineral problems, it is important to detect the presence of hypomagnesemia, whether transient or due to hereditary intestinal Mg malabsorption or renal Mg losses, since hypocalcemia generally cannot be corrected until hypomagnesemia is alleviated. As mentioned earlier, the relationship between hypocalcemia and hypomagnesemia may be related to the important role of Mg in PTH secretion. High phosphate loads, usually dietary (see discussion below), lead to hyperphosphatemia and secondary hypocalcemia.

Treatment consists of Ca supplementation at doses of 30–75 mg elemental Ca/kg/d, titrated to the response of the patient. When tolerated by the patient, we recommend the use of the intravenous form of 10% Ca gluconate (9.4 mg elemental Ca/mL), given *orally* in 4–6 divided doses.[34] Otherwise, Ca gluconate given intravenously must be administered carefully, since it may cause cardiac arrhythmia and skin necrosis. Since most causes of hypocalcemia in the neonate are transient, the duration of supplemental Ca therapy varies with the cause of hypocalcemia; commonly as little as 2–3 days for early neonatal hypocalcemia is needed. Ca supplementation is usually required for long periods in the case of hypocalcemia caused by malabsorption or hypoparathyroidism.

Hypercalcemia

Hypercalcemia is defined as total serum Ca concentration of > 2.7 mmol/L (10.8 mg/dL), or serum ionized Ca concentration > 1.4 mmol/L (5.6 mg/dL).[2,4] In pathologic hypercalcemia, elevation of serum Ca^{2+} usually occurs simultaneously with elevation of total Ca; however, elevated total Ca may occur without elevation of Ca^{2+}. Hypercalcemia in the neonate is usually iatrogenic and due to: administration of Ca salts for treatment of hypocalcemia or for prophylaxis during exchange transfusions; the use of thiazide diuretics which depress urinary Ca excretion; and hyperalimentation errors, either excess Ca or insufficient P. Human milk feeding of preterm infants may lead to hypophosphatemia because of the low P content of human milk relative to preterm needs, and this in turn may cause secondary hypercalcemia.

Other rarer causes of hypercalcemia in the newborn which may have a metabolic or familial basis include: hyperparathyroidism (primary or secondary to maternal hypoparathyroidism; vitamin D intoxication (parents who are food faddists may give large doses of vitamins to their infants); hypercalcemia associated with subcutaneous fat necrosis (usually in asphyxiated, large-for-gestational-age infants: increased prostaglandin-E activity, increased release of Ca from fat and tissues, and unregulated production of $1,25(OH)_2D$ from macrophages infiltrating fat necrotic lesions have been postulated to be responsible for the hypercalcemia.)[35] Idiopathic infantile hypercalcemia, associated with Williams syndrome (elfin facies, developmental delay, failure to thrive, heart disease) is associated with mutations in the elastin gene on the long arm of chromosome 7;[36] there may be a vitamin D hyperresponsive state, and a blunted calcitonin response to Ca loading may contribute. In benign familial hypocalciuric hypercalcemia (FHH), the infant may have signs of severe hyperparathyroidism; the condition is inherited as an autosomal-dominant trait with high penetrance.[37, 38] In older children, immobilization hypercalcemia may occur.

Treatment consists of correction of the underlying cause and removal of iatrogenic or external causes, for example, Ca supplementation of human milk given to preterm infants, stopping of excessive vitamin D intake, and surgical removal of hyperparathyroid glands. Treatment of severe hypercalcemia associated with subcutaneous fat necrosis and idiopathic infantile hypercalcemia consists of removal of dietary Ca and vitamin D as well as avoidance of sunlight exposure. In severe cases, hydration, diuresis, and steroids may be required. Minimal information is available on the use of hormonal and other drug therapy for neonatal hypercalcemia. Short-term treatment with salmon calcitonin (4–8 IU/kg every 12 h, subcutaneously or intramuscularly), prednisone (1–2 mg/kg/day), or a combination may be useful.[39] Recombinant human calcitonin, bisphosphonates, and amylin may be useful.[40] The onset of action of these therapies is slow, and the hypocalcemic effect of calcitonin may not be evident. In familial cases in which patients are asymptomatic, supportive treatment may suffice. Exercise may prevent the occurrence of immobilization hypercalcemia.

Hypophosphatemia

Hypophosphatemia is usually defined as serum P concentrations < 1.55 mmol/L (4.8 mg/dL) in formula-fed infants under 18 months of age.[4] Transient causes include hypophosphatemia induced by respiratory (mechanical ventilation) alkalosis and low dietary P intake. The latter may occur in a preterm infant fed human milk, since the P content of human milk is low relative to the preterm infant's needs.[41] Vitamin D deficiency results in hypophosphatemia. Dietary P deficiency is unusual in children because of their proclivity for dairy products. However, in the critically or chronically ill child, inadequate P in total parenteral nutrition, frequent dosing of P-binding antacids (aluminum binds P in the gut), or excessive stool losses can cause hypophosphatemia.[42]

Metabolic causes of hypophosphatemia include hyperparathyroidism (decreased renal P reabsorption due to PTH action); renal losses associated with Lowe's syndrome (renal tubular acidosis with proximal tubule P losses, mental retardation, failure to thrive, cataracts, and rickets); and X-linked or other familial hypophosphatemia. Management consists of treatment of the underlying causes for transient hypophosphatemia; surgical removal of the parathyroid glands in hyperparathyroidism; and P, Vitamin D, and alkali supplementation in Lowe's syndrome. Serum P concentrations < 0.65 mmol/L (2 mg/dL) must be treated to avoid symptoms. The child can be treated with 2–6 mg elemental P/kg in oral phosphate supplements divided three to four times daily. P supplements should be administered at times when they will not antagonize other medications.[42]

Hyperphosphatemia

Hyperphosphatemia in infants up to 18 months of age is defined as serum P concentrations > 2.7 mmol/L (8.4 mg/dL).[4] In older children and adolescents, serum P concentrations > 2 mmol/L (6.0 mg/dL) are considered to be in the hyperphosphatemic range. Hyperphosphatemia may be caused by a decrease in urinary P excretion or by sudden release of intracellular P into the extracellular space.

Causes of hyperphosphatemia in infants and children are usually limited to parathyroid disorders (hypoparathyroidism and pseudohypoparathyroidism, both of which demonstrate decreased renal P excretion); renal failure (decreased P excretion); increased dietary P load from cow's-milk-based formula and cereals; and tumor lysis syndrome (in severe hemolytic syndromes and chemotherapy of lymphomas or leukemias, sudden lysis of a large volume of cells may result in a burden of extracellular P that exceeds maximal urinary excretion).[43] Treatment consists of treatment of the underlying cause and reduction of exogenous sources of P. The use of intestinal P binders in renal failure may also be needed. Extreme P elevations as a result of cell lysis can be treated with saline bolus and intravenous mannitol to increase urinary excretion if renal function is normal. However, extreme elevations of P (> 10–12 mg/dL) and continued cell lysis make it prudent to prepare for dialysis because renal function may deteriorate. The treatment of severe hyperphosphatemia in acute renal failure is hemodialysis. Hemodialysis followed by continuous hemofiltration can be successful.[44, 45]

Neonatal Hypoparathyroidism

Neonatal hypoparathyroidism may be transient or permanent.[46] Transient neonatal hypoparathyroidism may occur in preterm infants, as well as in infants of insulin-dependent diabetic mothers (IDMs), in whom there may be a blunted PTH response to low serum Ca concentrations. This phenomenon has been termed "functional hypoparathyroidism."[31] About 30% of preterm infants and 50% of IDMs present with hypocalcemia in the first few days of life, and may have signs such as jitteriness, tetany, seizures, or cardiac arrhythmias. Treatment consists of continued provision of adequate Ca supply, either enterally or parenterally, at a dose of about 75 mg elemental Ca/kg/d until Ca homeostatic mechanisms of the infants become functional. This disease entity usually lasts for a few days, after which Ca supplementation may be weaned and eventually discontinued.

Transient neonatal hypoparathyroidism may also occur in infants of untreated hyperparathyroid mothers. Maternal hypercalcemia secondary to excess PTH activity leads to fetal hypercalcemia, which inhibits fetal parathyroid gland hormone production. The management is similar to management of the hypocalcemic preterm infant or infant of a diabetic mother. The disorder may last for several weeks.

Several case reports have identified patients who recovered from transient neonatal hypoparathyroidism, but who redeveloped hypocalcemia when followed to childhood and adolescence.[47–49] It has been suggested that patients who are thought to have transient hypoparathyroidism should undergo a carefully conducted sodium-EDTA test later in life, after a period of stable eucalcemia, to identify those who would be at increased risk for subsequent development of permanent hypoparathyroidism.[47] Patients with minimally functioning parathyroid glands would theoretically not be able to mount the expected increase in PTH secretion during hypocalcemia induced by the EDTA test. These patients should be followed closely thereafter so that when hypocalcemia recurs, therapy can be reinstituted speedily. Transient neonatal hypoparathyroidism has recently been linked to a deletion within chromosome 22q 11. This deletion has been identified in patients with DiGeorge and velocardiofacial (Shprintzen) syndromes.[49, 50]

Congenital hypoparathyroidism is a permanent condition accompanied by hypocalcemia. It is associated with agenesis, dysgenesis, or hypoplasia of the parathyroid glands. The disorder may be transmitted as an X-linked or autosomal-dominant gene, but may also occur as a sporadic mutation (so-called "idiopathic"). There are no characteristic physical features in congenital hypoparathyroidism, unless it is associated with a genetic disorder such as ring chromosomes. These infants present with unremitting hypocalcemia and very low or undetectable serum PTH concentrations ("hormone deficient hypoparathyroidism") and increased serum P concentrations. The average age of onset of symptoms, however, is during the adolescent years.

It is important to detect and treat the resultant hypocalcemia, especially in infancy, since prolonged and/or severe hypocalcemia may be associated with cardiac arrhythmias, tetany, seizures, and mental retardation. Candida infection of the nails and mouth may occur in one-sixth of patients. A feature of untreated early hypoparathyroidism in later infancy and childhood is dental hypoplasia. Management consists of lifelong vitamin D treatment, usually in the form of $1{,}25(OH)_2D$ at a dose of 0.03–0.08 μg/kg/d, preferably given in twice-daily doses. Older children may not require as much vitamin D. This form of vitamin D is used since there is inadequate PTH stimulus for renal conversion of 25-OHD to the active form $1{,}25(OH)_2D$. Further, the short half-life of the drug allows for ease of management. Ca supplements may also be additionally required. Adequacy of treatment is assessed by normalcy of serum Ca concentrations and return of serum P concentrations to normal.

Pseudohypoparathyroidism is another variant of parathyroid gland dysfunction. In contrast to idiopathic hypoparathyroidism, parathyroid glands in individuals affected by this disorder are hyperplastic and actively secreting increased amounts of PTH. In this disorder, the problem is deficient end-organ responsiveness to PTH ("hormone resistant hypoparathyroidism"). Also in contrast to idiopathic hypoparathyroid individuals, who have no dysmorphic features, individuals with pseudohypoparathyroidism are characteristically short and thickset, with round facies, short necks, and short fingers and toes at birth. Hypocalcemia, subcutaneous soft tissue calcific nodules, dental hypoplasia, and various degrees of developmental delay and mental retardation may develop later in infancy and childhood.

Diagnosis is based on persistent hypocalcemia in the face of markedly increased (rather than low) serum PTH concentrations, in association with hyperphosphatemia and the above-mentioned physical stigmata. Confirmation of the diagnosis requires an intravenous PTH infusion test in which skeletal and/or renal cell response to PTH is assessed: in normal individuals, urinary cAMP (an index of PTH effect on plasma membrane adenyl cyclase activity) and/or urinary phosphate excretion are increased in response to the PTH challenge.[46] This response is diminished or nearly absent in pseudohypoparathyroid individuals.

As in idiopathic hypoparathyroidism, treatment consists of lifelong treatment with 1,25$(OH)_2$D and Ca.

Neonatal Hyperparathyroidism

Neonatal hyperparathyroidism occurs less often than neonatal hypoparathyroidism and may be primary or secondary.[46] Primary neonatal hyperparathyroidism is usually caused by an autosomal recessive gene, although it may also be familial or occur as part of multiple endocrine adenomatosis. The condition is associated with failure to thrive (poor weight gain and growth), increased serum PTH concentrations, hypercalcemia, hyperphosphaturia leading to hypophosphatemia, and hypercalciuria sometimes leading to nephrocalcinosis. Skeletal demineralization may occur in untreated cases, as Ca is continually "leached" out from bone by excessive amounts of circulating PTH. Surgical removal of the parathyroid glands is crucial; otherwise, the prognosis is poor. Both neonatal severe hyperparathyroidism (NSHPT) and familial hypocalciuric hypercalcemia (FHH) appear to occur secondary to mutations in the human Ca^{2+} sensing receptor gene on chromosome 3.[51, 52] Patients with NSHPT are homozygous and FHH heterozygous for the defective gene.

Secondary hyperparathyroidism may occur in infants of mothers with untreated hypoparathyroidism and in the presence of maternal and neonatal renal tubular acidosis.[53, 54] Hypocalcemia in the mother leads to compensatory fetal parathyroid gland hyperplasia, with subsequent increased PTH secretion. The biochemical findings can be similar to those found in primary hyperparathyroidism, except that infants commonly present with lytic bone lesions with little effect on serum Ca concentrations. The diagnosis is confirmed by identification of hypoparathyroidism in the mother. In most cases, the condition is transient and only requires supportive treatment during the rare hypercalcemic period. Rarely, steroids, furosemide, and calcitonin may be required.

Hyperparathyroidism in Older Children

Hyperparathyroidism in older children is more commonly secondary.[46] Children suffering from liver failure may have reduced conversion of dietary vitamin D_3 to 25-OHD. The resultant poor absorption of Ca leads to hypocalcemia, which in turn stimulates parathyroid gland hyperactivity. In children with chronic renal disease, inadequate or absent renal conversion of 25-OHD to its active form, $1,25(OH)_2D$, leads to hypocalcemia and subsequent secondary hyperparathyroidism.

In these children, skeletal deformities due to rickets (so-called hepatic or renal rickets) may occur. Hyperchloremic acidosis due to excess PTH and increased alkaline phosphatase due to increased bone turnover may be detected. Aminoaciduria and urinary cAMP excretion may also be increased. Detection of increased PTH concentrations is best done with the use of the intact PTH molecule assay.[55] Treatment for secondary hyperparathyroidism is treatment of the primary disorder.

In the occasional instances of primary hyperparathyroidism in childhood, adenomas are the usual etiology. Surgery is the treatment of choice.

Nutritional Causes of Ca and P Disorders

In preterm infants, Ca and P requirements are high. The high requirements are related to mineral deprivation due to early delivery, poor intestinal absorption of cow's-milk-based formula, and use of calciuretic medication, especially in sick preterm infants. Inadequate provision of these minerals can increase the risk of hypocalcemia, hypophosphatemia, hypercalciuria, and rickets in these infants.

The high Ca and P requirements can be partially met by parenteral solutions and adequately met by most milk formulae specially formulated for preterm infants. Additionally, the use of human milk fortified with Ca, P, and protein in preterm infants has been advocated to ensure adequate supply and optimize growth.[41] In parenteral solutions, the amounts of Ca and P will determine the stability of the minerals; a Ca:P ratio of 1.3–1.7:1 (by weight) is also important to ensure proper Ca homeostasis.[56]

In term infants, the relatively high P content of standard commercial formulae (due to the naturally high P content of cow milk from which these formulae are derived) may result in hyperphosphatemia and secondary hypocalcemia. Evaporated milks, in particular, have high P content and readily cause hypocalcemia. Some of these hypocalcemic infants will develop neonatal tetany and seizures. Commercial milk has been reformulated to improve the Ca:P ratio, and hypocalcemic tetany is less frequent, though still seen.

The high P and fiber load of many cereals given to infants as first foods could also conceivably cause problems in term infants. Phosphorus increases Ca-P complexing and may compete with Ca absorption, while phytate and fibers bind Ca within the intestinal lumen. The resultant inadequate Ca absorption may lead to hypocalcemia. Recently, higher serum PTH concentrations have been found in infants fed cereal at age 4 months versus those who were started on cereal at age 6 months, but there was no apparent effect on bone mineral content.[57]

Maternal preferences, beliefs, and habits play a direct and important role in the nutrition of infants, whether the mothers choose to provide human or commercial milk to their babies. Breast-fed infants of mothers who are on macrobiotic diets (food sources limited to grains, cereals, fruits, nuts, and vegetables, with prohibition of foods from animal sources, including dairy products) and who are not supplemented with vitamin D have been documented to have low serum 25-OHD, Ca, and P concentrations and suffer from an increased risk of rickets, especially in temperate climates.[58–60] Infants of vegetarian mothers who provide dairy products to their infants do not appear to suffer from this problem. Milk from these mothers also appears to be adequate in Ca and P.

Mothers with inadequate sun exposure due to dress customs may also be vitamin D deficient, especially if they are vegetarian; their infants will be susceptible to vitamin D deficiency, particularly if they are likewise shielded from sun exposure. The numerous reports of rickets in countries like Saudi Arabia attest to this phenomenon.[60, 61] Conversely, infants of mothers who believe in taking large amounts of vitamin supplements which contain vitamins A and D are at risk for developing hypercalcemia. Both of these vitamins increase bone resorption with subsequent increase in serum Ca concentrations.

Rickets

Rickets is a disease of growing bone and is a mineralization defect of bone and cartilage. It is therefore seen only in childhood. Bone formation is multifaceted, involving several organ systems and nutritional components. Defective functioning of any of several steps in this complex process can cause rickets. Disturbances in vitamin D, PTH, Ca, P and alkaline phosphatase homeostasis can contribute to poor bone mineralization.

Vitamin D deficiency may occur in the presence of severely restricted sunlight exposure or increased skin pigmentation in temperate climates, the skin being the major organ of vitamin D production.[60, 61] Deficiency may also occur with decreased dietary vitamin D intake and vitamin D malabsorption. This is of particular concern in children of strict vegetarians, as diets already deficient in vitamin D may be made worse by the binding of vitamin D with dietary fiber, inhibiting its absorption.[4, 58, 59]

Deficiency or absence of the hepatic microsomal enzyme 25-hydroxylase may occur with hepatocellular failure (hepatic rickets), while renal 25(OH) vitamin D, 1α-hydroxylase deficiency may occur as an autosomal-recessive disorder (vitamin D dependency rickets type I) or in the presence of renal failure (renal rickets). In vitamin D dependent rickets type II, $1,25(OH)_2D$ is normally produced but is unable to act due to an absence or defective functioning of the vitamin D receptor. This disorder is inherited in an autosomal-recessive manner and is secondary to a point mutation in the vitamin D receptor gene.[62] Rickets has also been described in infants and children on chronic anticonvulsant therapy, especially dilantin and phenobarbitone. Both drugs alter hepatic vitamin D metabolism and inhibit gastrointestinal transport mechanisms.[63, 64] The metabolism and excretion of vitamin D is increased, with subsequent decrease in serum 25(OH)D. Vitamin D stimulated intestinal uptake of Ca may be reduced.

Hypophosphatemic rickets is an X-linked dominant disorder characterized by decreased proximal renal tubular P reabsorption.[65] Rickets occurs at a few months of age and is usually associated with normal or elevated PTH, normal or low $1{,}25(OH)_2D$, and normal or low serum Ca. This is the most common form of childhood rickets in America. Rickets associated with hypophosphatemia is commonly encountered in preterm infants who are fed human milk exclusively, and in those on parenteral nutrition.[66]

Rickets is also observed in alkaline phosphatase deficiency which may present as the infantile (autosomal recessive) or childhood (unknown inheritance) form.[67] Decreased bone alkaline phosphatase activity with normal serum Ca and P is observed in these children.

While the clinical presentation of rickets varies somewhat depending on the etiology, several features occur consistently. The typical metaphyseal widening and fraying with disruption of the epiphyseal plate is most prominent in weight-bearing joints. Proximal muscle hypotonia and weakness is prominent, while aminoaciduria is commonly found in those cases related to vitamin D deficiency with associated elevations of PTH.[68]

Management of childhood rickets depends on the underlying diagnosis. Various combinations of vitamin D or its analogs plus Ca and P supplementation are administered. Frequent monitoring of serum Ca, P, alkaline phosphatase, PTH, urine for hypercalciuria, and skeletal radiographs for healing are essential for good medical care of affected children.

REFERENCE RANGES

Reference values of Ca, iCa, P, PTH, CT, $1{,}25(OH)_2D$, 25-OHD, UCa excretion, and TRP are given in Table 10–2. Conversion factors are:

Ca mg/dL × 0.25 = mmol/L

P mg/dL × 0. 323 = mmol/L

Ca mmol/L × 2 = mEq/L

P mmol/L × 2 = mEq/L

25-OHD ng/mL × 2.5 = nmol/L

$1{,}25(OH)_2D$ pg/mL × 2.4 = pmol/L

Acknowledgments: The authors wish to thank Ms. Nilda Barbieri for her assistance in the preparation of this chapter.

TABLE 10–2. Normal Values (Mean ± 1 SD unless otherwise indicated)

	Ca mmol/L (mg/dL)	iCa mmol/L (mg/dL)	P mmol/L (mg/dL)	PTH ng/L pg/mL	CT ng/L pg/mL	$1,25(OH)_2D$ pmol/L (pg/mL)	25-OHD nmol/L (ng/mL)	UCa excretion* mg/kg/d	TRP** mmol/L (mg/dL)
Cord Blood	255 ± .15	1.45 ± .07	1.56 ± .2	3.4 ± .91[2]	58 ± 19[3]	81.4 ± 23	33 ± 8	—	—
	(10.2 ± .60)[1]	(5.83 ± 30)[1]	(4.8 ± .6)[2]			(33.9 ± 9.8)[2]	(13 ± 3)[4]	—	—
0–18 months[5]									
Black	2.43 ± .15	1.31 ± .04	2.08 ± .22	11.5 ± .4	65 ± 35	168 ± 62	133 ± 45		
	(9.73 ± .60)	(5.24 ± .18)	(6.47 ± .69)			(70 ± 26)	(53 ± 18)		
White	2.41 ± .15	1.30 ± .06	2.19 ± .29	12.3 ± .5	61 ± 34	137 ± 15	128 ± 43		
	(9.67 ± .59)	(522 ± .25)	(6.78 ± .92)			(57 ± 25)	(51 ± 17)		
Summer	2.36 ± .14	1.30 ± .04	2.20 ± .26	12.5 ± .3	75 ± 35	146 ± 41	133 ± 40		
	(9.46 ± .56)	(5.21 ± .17)	(6.83 ± .81)			(61 ± 17)	(53 ± 16)		
Winter	2.47 ± .11	1.30 ± .04	2.08 ± .26	11.0 ± .5	46 ± 30	173 ± 62	113 ± 45		
	(9.91 ± .44)	(5.23 ± .18)	(6.44 ± .80)			(72 ± 26)	(45 ± 18)		
Children	2.35 ± .17	1.14 ± .13	1.13 ± .22	11.0 ± 35[8]	32 ± 22[9]	120 ± 13	88 ± 23	2.4[12]	1.15–2.44
	(9.40 ± .70)[6]	(4.59 ± .52)[7]	(3.50 ± .70)[6]			(50 ± 5.5)[10]	(35.2 ± 9.2)[11]		(3.56–7.55)[8]
					Summer	73 ± 5	66 ± 6		
						(30.4 ± 2.3)[13]	(26.5 ± 2.4)[13]		
					Winter	56 ± 5	49 ± 5		
						(23.4 ± 2.3)[13]	(19.4 ± 2.1)[13]		

*Urinary calcium excretion

**Tubular reabsorption of phosphate per liter glomerular filtrate.

Source:

[1]American Journal of Diseases of Children 1988;142:516–18

[2]Journal of Pediatric Gastroenterology Nutrition 1994;19:220–7

[3]Journal of American College of Nutrition 1990;9:358–62

[4]Journal of Clinical Endocrinology and Metabolism 1987;65:588–91

[5]Journal of Pediatrics 1986;77:891–96

[6]American Journal of Clinical Pathology 1978;69:24–31

[7]Pediatric Research 1973;7:485–93

[8]Archives of Diseases in Childhood 1991;65:1208–11

[9]Pediatric Research 1977;11:112–16

[10]Kidney International 1990;38:528–35

[11]Journal of Pediatrics 1977;91(6):904–8

[12]Archives of Diseases in Childhood 1974;49:97–101

[13]Pediatric Research 1991;30:654A

REFERENCES

1. Pitkin R, Cruikshank D, Schauberger C, et al. Fetal calciotropic hormones and neonatal calcium homeostasis. Pediatrics 1980;66:77–82.
2. Loughead JL, Mimouni F, Tsang R. Serum ionized calcium concentration in normal neonates. Am J Dis Child 1988;142:516–18.
3. Markowitz M, Rotkin L, Rosen, JR. Circadian rhythm of blood minerals in humans. Science 1981;213:672–74.
4. Specker BL, Lichtenstein P, Mimouni F, Tsang R. Calcium-regulating hormone and minerals from birth to 18 months of age: a cross-sectional study. II. Effects of sex, race, age, season, and diet in serum minerals, parathyroid hormone, and calcitonin. Pediatr 1986;77:891–96.
5. Root AW, Harrison H. Recent advances in calcium metabolism. J Pediatr 1976;88:1-18, 177–99.
6. Segre GV, Habener JF, Powell D, et al. Parathyroid hormone in human plasma: immunochemical characterization and biological implications. J Clin Invest 1972;51:3163–72.
7. Chase LR, Slatopolsky E. Secretion and metabolic efficacy of parathyroid hormone in patients with severe hypomagnesemia. J Clin Endocrinol Metab 1974;38:363–71.
8. Mundy GR, Roodman G. Osteoclast ontogeny and function. In: Peck W, ed. Bone and mineral research, Vol. 5. Amsterdam: Elsevier, 1987.
9. Chase LR, Aurbach G. Parathyroid functions and the renal excretion of 3´,5´-adenylic acid. Proceedings of the National Academy of Sciences 1967;58:418–525.
10. Suva LJ, Winslow GA, Wettenhall RE, et al. A parathyroid hormone-related protein implicated in malignant hypercalcemia: cloning and expression. Science 1987;237:893–6.
11. Kong XF, Schipani E, Lanske B, et al. The rat, mouse and human genes encoding the receptor for parathyroid hormone-related peptide are highly homologous. Biochem Biophys Res Commun 1994;201:1058
12. Yang KH, dePapp AE, Soifer NE, et al. Parathyroid hormone-related protein: evidence for isoform- and tissue-specific posttranslational processing. Biochemistry 1994;33;7460–9.
13. Moniz C, Bruton PB, Malik AN, et al. Parathyroid hormone-related peptide in normal human fetal development. J Mol Endocrinol 1990;5:259–66.
14. Care A, Abbas S, Pickard D, et al. Stimulation of ovine placental transport of calcium and magnesium by mid-molecule fragments of human parathyroid hormone-related protein. J Exp Physiol 1990;75:605–8.
15. Fenton A, Kemp B, Kent G, et al. A carboxyl-terminal peptide from the parathyroid hormone-related protein inhibits bone resorption by osteoclasts. Endocrinology 1991;129:1762–8.
16. Moseley JM, Hayman JA, Danks JA, et al. Immunohistochemical detection of parathyroid hormone-related protein in human fetal epithelia. J Clin Endocrinol Metab 1991;73:478–84.
17. Papantoniou NE, Papapetrou PD, Antsaklis AJ, et al. Circulating levels of immunoreactive parathyroid hormone-related protein in human fetuses and newborns. Eur J Endocrinol 1996;134:437–42.
18. Mune T, Katakami H, Morita M, et al. Increased serum immunoreactive parathyroid hormone-related protein levels in chronic hypercalcemia. J Clin Endocrinol Met 1994;78:575–80.
19. Roskams T, Desmet V. Parathyroid-hormone-related peptides. A new class of multifunctional proteins. Am J Pathol 1997;150;779–85.
20. Bilezikian JP. Parathyroid hormone-related peptide in sickness and health. N Engl J Med 1990;322:1151–3.
21. Pike J, Haussler M. Association of 1,25-dihydroxyvitamin D_3 with cultured 3T6 mouse fibroblasts: cellular uptake and receptor mediated migration to the nucleus. J Biol Chem 1983;259:854–60.
22. Peterlik M, Wasserman RH. Effect of vitamin D on transepithelial phosphate transport in chick intestine. Am J Physiol 1978;234:E379–88.
23. Hildman B, Storelli C, Danisi G, Murer H. Regulation of Na+-Pi cotransport by 1,25-dihydroxyvitamin D3 in rabbit duodenal brush border membrane. Am J Physiol 1982;242:G533–9.

24. David L, Salle BL, Putet G, Grafmeyer DC. Serum immunoreactive calcitonin in low birthweight infants: Description of early changes; effects of intravenous calcium infusion; relationships with early changes in serum calcium, phosphorus, magnesium, parathyroid hormone, and gastric levels. Pediatr Res 1981;15:803–8.
25. Holtrop ME, Raisz LG, Simmons HA. The effects of parathyroid hormone, colchicin, and calcitonin on the ultrastructure and the activity of osteoclasts in organ culture. J Cell Biol 1974;60:346–55.
26. Mimouni F, Loughead J, Tsang R, Khoury J. Postnatal surge in serum calcitonin concentrations: no contribution to neonatal hypocalcemia in infants of diabetic mothers. Pediatr Res 1990;28:493–95.
27. Shaw J. Parenteral nutrition in the management of sick low birthweight infants. Pediatr Clin North Am 1973;20:333–58.
28. Zeigler E, O'Donnel A, Nelson S, Fomon S. Body composition of the reference fetus. Growth 1976;40:329–41.
29. Saggese G, Baroncelli GI, Bertelloni S, Cipolloni C. Intact parathyroid hormone levels during pregnancy, in healthy term neonates and in hypocalcemic preterm infants. Acta Paediatr Scand 1991;80:36–41.
30. Schedewie HK, Odell WD, Fisher DA, et al. Parahormone and perinatal calcium homeostasis. Pediatr Res 1979;13:1–6.
31. Venkataraman PS, Tsang RC, Chen IW. Pathogenesis of early neonatal hypocalcemia: Studies of serum calcitonin, gastrin, and plasma glucagon. J Pediatr 1987;110:599–603.
32. Tsang RC, Chen I, Hayes W, et al. Neonatal hypocalcemia in infants with birth asphyxia. J Pediatr 1974;84:428–33.
33. Tsang RC, Kleinman LI, Sutherland JM, Light IJ. Hypocalcemia in infants of diabetic mothers. J Pediatr 1972;80:384–95.
34. Cruz ML, Tsang R. Disorders of calcium and magnesium homeostasis. In: Yeh T, ed. Neonatal therapeutics. St. Louis: Mosby Year Book, 1991.
35. Finne PH, Sanderud J, Aksnes L, et al. Hypercalcemia with increased and unregulated 1,25-dihydroxyvitamin D production in a neonate with subcutaneous fat necrosis. J Pediatr 1988;112:792–4.
36. Ewart AK, Morris CA, Atkinson D, et al. Hemizygosity at the elastin locus in a developmental disorder, Williams Syndrome. Nat Genetics 1993,5:11–16.
37. Firek AF, Kao PC, Heath H III. Plasma intact parathyroid hormone (PTH) and PTH-related peptide in familial benign hypercalcemia: greater responsiveness to endogenous PTH than in primary hyperparathyroidism. J Clin Endocrinol Metab 1991;72:541–6.
38. Sopwith AM, Burns C, Grant DB, et al. Familial hypocalciuric hypercalcemia: association with neonatal primary hyperparathyroidism and possible linkage with HLA haplotype. Clin Endocrinol 1984;21:57–64.
39. Wisneski LA. Salmon calcitonin in the acute management of hypercalcemia. Calcif Tissue Int 1990; 46(Suppl):26.
40. Wimalawansa SJ, Gunasekera RD, Datta HK. Hypocalcemic actions of amylin amide in humans. J Bone Miner Res 1992;7:1113–6.
41. Steichen JJ, Krug-Wispé SK, Tsang R. Breastfeeding the low birth weight infant. Clini Perinatol 1987;14(1):131–71.
42. Fouser L. Disorders of calcium, phosphorus, and magnesium. Pediatr Annals 1995;24:38–46.
43. Sakarcan A, Quigley R. Hyperphosphatemia in tumor lysis syndrome: the role of hemodialysis and continuous veno-venous hemofiltration. Pediatr Nephrol 1994;8:351–3.
44. Monballyu J, Zachee P, Verberckmoes R, Boogaerts MA. Transient acute renal failure due to tumor-lysis-induced severe phosphate load in a patient with Burkitt's lymphoma. Clin Nephrol 1984;22:47–50.
45. Shinaberger JH, Mille JH, Von Albertini B, et al. Phosphate removal by conventional dialysis (CHD), high efficiency dialysis (HEHD) and high flux hemofiltration (HFHDF). (Abstract). Kidney Int 1987;31:245.
46. Tsang RC, Noguchi A, Steichen J. Pediatric parathyroid disorders. Pediatr Clin North Am 1979;26(1):223–49.

47. Cruz ML, Mimouni F, Tsang R. Transient hypoparathyroidism. J Pediatr 1992;120:332.
48. Kooh SW, Binet A. Partial hypoparathyroidism: a variant of transient congenital hypoparathyroidism. Am J Dis Child 1991;145:877–80.
49. Paul E, Fleischman A, Greig F, Saenger P. Transient congenital hypoparathyroidism: resolution and recurrence. Pediatr Res 1994;35:206A.
50. Driscoll D, Salvin J, Sellinger B, et al. Prevalence of 22q11 microdeletions in DiGeorge and velocardiofacial syndromes: implications for genetic counselling and prenatal diagnosis. J Med Genet 1993;30:813–17.
51. Pollak M, Brown E, Chou Y, et al. Mutations in the human Ca^{2+} sensing receptor gene cause familial hypercalciuric hypercalcemia and neonatal severe hyperparathyroidism. Cell 1993;75:1297–1303.
52. Pollak MR, Chou Y-H, Marx SJ, et al. Familial hypocalciuric hypercalcemia and neonatal severe hyperparathyroidism: effects of mutant gene dosage on phenotype. J Clin Invest 1994; 93:1108–12
53. Savani R, Mimouni F, Tsang R. Maternal and neonatal hyperparathyroidism as a consequence of maternal renal tubular acidosis. Pediatrics 1993;91:661–63.
54. Igarashi T, Sekine Y, Kawato H, et al. Transient neonatal distal renal tubular acidosis with secondary hyperparathyroidism. Ped Nephrol 1992;6:267–69.
55. Bergenfelz A, Norden NE, Ahren B. Intact parathyroid hormone assay is superior to mid region assay in the EDTA-infusion test in hyperparathyroidism. Clin Chim Acta 1991;197:229–36.
56. Koo WWK, Tsang R. Mineral requirements of low-birth weight infants. J Am Coll Nutrition 1991;10(5):474–86.
57. Bainbridge R, Mimouni F, Landi T, et al. Effect of rice cereal feedings on bone mineralization and calcium homeostatis in low milk formula fed infants. J Am Coll Nutr 1996;15:383–8.
58. Dagnelie PC, Vergote F, van Staveren WA, et al. High prevalence of rickets in infants on macrobiotic diets. Amer J Clin Nutri 1990;51:202–8.
59. Dwyer J, Dietz W, Andrews E, et al. Nutritional status of vegetarian children. Am J Clin Nutr 1982;35:204–16.
60. Clemens T, Adams SJ, Henderson S, et al. Increased skin pigment reduces the capacity of skin to synthesize vitamin D_3. Lancet 1982;1:74–76.
61. Belton NR, Elidrissy ATH, Gaafer TH. Maternal vitamin D deficiency as a factor in the pathogenesis of rickets in Saudi Arabia. In: Norman AW, Herrath DV, Grigoleit HG, ed. Vitamin D. chemical, biochemical, and clinical endocrinology of calcium metabolism. Berlin: de Gruyter, 1982.
62. Sone T, Marx S, Liberman U, Pike J. A unique point mutation in the human vitamin D receptor chromosomal gene confers hereditary resistance to 1,25 dihydroxy vitamin D_3. Molec Endocr 1990;4:623–31.
63. Uy C. Anticonvulsant drugs and rickets. Pediatr Rev 1983;4:315.
64. Koch H, Kraft D, Von Herrath D. Influence of diphenylhydantoin and phenobarbital on intestinal calcium transport in the rat. Epilepsia 1972;13:829–34.
65. Chan J, Alon U, Hirschman G. Renal hypophosphatemic rickets. J Pediatr 1985;106:533–44.
66. Koo WWK, Antony G, Stevens L. Continuous nasogastric phosphorus infusion in hypophosphatemic rickets of prematurity. Am J Dis Child 1984;138:172–75.
67. Fallon M, Teitelbaum S, Weinstein R, et al. Hypophosphatasia: clinicopathologic comparison of the infantile, childhood and adult forms. Medicine 1984;63:12–24.
68. Scriver C. Rickets and the pathogenesis of impaired tubular transport of phosphate and other solutes. Am J Med 1974;57:43–49.

CHAPTER 11

Disorders of Carbohydrate Metabolism in Infants and Children

Denis Daneman, M.B., B.Ch., F.R.C.P.(C)

INTRODUCTION

Abnormalities of carbohydrate metabolism, specifically diabetes mellitus and hypoglycemic disorders, are encountered fairly frequently in the pediatric population. Diabetes mellitus is more common in older children and adolescents, while hypoglycemia occurs more often in the neonate. These disorders are dealt with in this chapter in two sections. The first section discusses diabetes mellitus: its classification, etiology, epidemiology, presentation, and management. The second section covers the hypoglycemic syndromes: their classification, diagnosis, and management.

DIABETES MELLITUS

Diabetes mellitus in children may be classified as Type 1 (formerly insulin-dependent diabetes); Type 2 (formerly non-insulin-dependent diabetes), referred to as maturity-onset diabetes in the young (MODY) when it occurs as an autosomal-dominant condition; and other types of diabetes.[1] In children, the latter includes diabetes associated with cystic fibrosis; iron-overload diabetes due to transfusion therapy for thalassemia major or other anemia; and diabetes resulting from drug administration, such as corticosteroids alone or in combination with agents such as L-asparaginase.[2] Disturbances of glucose homeostasis associated with endocrine excess syndromes, such as Cushing's syndrome, pheochromocytoma, and growth hormone excess, are quite uncommon in childhood. Occasionally seen are patients with impaired glucose tolerance in the childhood age group.[3] This may represent the very earliest phase of Type 1 diabetes or occasionally a hyperglycemic response to the stress of an intercurrent illness. Impaired glucose tolerance of varying severity may also be found in association with a number of syndromes, including Refsum's syndrome, Friedreich's ataxia, Alström's syndrome, Prader-Willi syndrome, Lawrence-Moon-Biedl syndrome, Werner's syndrome, and Turner's syndrome.

Type 1 Diabetes

Etiology and Pathogenesis

Presently, evidence strongly suggests that Type 1 diabetes stems from an autoimmune attack on the β-cells of the islets of Langerhans.[4] The major thrusts of research in this area have focused on attempts to determine which components of the immune system mediate the attack, which factor(s) trigger(s) the reaction, and what allows it to persist until all β-cells have been destroyed. Current wisdom suggests that at least two factors are required for the expression of Type 1 diabetes: genetic susceptibility and external (environmental) agents. These combine in an as yet undetermined manner to precipitate the immune changes leading to the development of Type 1 diabetes. Evidence for an environmental trigger in the pathogenesis of Type 1 diabetes includes the fact that most genetically predisposed individuals never develop diabetes; that there are geographical and ethnic variations in diabetes incidence not explained by genetic factors alone; that there is discordance in identical twins (only 30–50% are concordant); that there are known β-cell toxins that can induce diabetes (e.g., streptozotocin, alloxan, and the rodenticide Vacor); and that certain viral (e.g., Coxsackie B4 and rubella) and food constituents (possibly cow's milk albumin) may be related to the development of the disorder.[4]

MacLaren and others have postulated a series of events, starting with exposure to a foreign antigen and ending with β-cell destruction, to explain the pathogenesis of Type 1 diabetes.[5,6] This schema is presented below, but it must be pointed out that, although feasible, it remains unproven.

Most likely, the process leading to Type 1 diabetes starts as a vigorous immune response either to a foreign, and as yet unidentified, antigen which closely resembles (immune mimicry) a normal component on the β-cell (e.g., coxsackie virus protein, cow's milk protein, glutamic acid decarboxylase), or to an environmental insult (e.g., β-cell tropic virus or β-cell superantigen expression) which may generate cytokines and other inflammatory mediators that induce expression of adhesion molecules in the vascular endothelium of the pancreatic islets.[5] These antigens are ingested by macrophages somewhere in the body and present the mimic antigen or autoantigen (in close association with a class II major histocompatibility complex [MHC] molecule) to helper T cells, which in turn are able to secrete interleukins that activate other helper cells, as well as antibody-producing B cells and cytotoxic T cells. In the pancreas, the sensitized cytotoxic T cells may, for example, recognize the natural "twin" of the foreign antigen, i.e., the autoantigen on the β-cell wherever it is bound by the ubiquitous class I MHC molecules. Antibodies bind the β-cells as well, impairing them either directly or indirectly by eliciting help from other parts of the immune system, for example, by binding complement. Involvement of macrophages and further stimulation of helper T cells may amplify and sustain the destruction.

As the attack proceeds, the β-cells become progressively damaged, overproducing class I molecules and amplifying the cytotoxic T cell response. The damaged cells also display class II molecules, which should induce the immune system to suppress autoimmunity. However, in Type 1 diabetes, the opposite occurs: more helper T cells are stimulated. Thus, genetic susceptibility to Type 1 diabetes demands an inherent defect in the establishment of tolerance to β-cell autoantigens allowing amplification of the autoimmune process.[5] Damage to the β-cells may release sequestered antigens, which even further stimulate the immune system, allowing acceleration of β-cell damage.

In the schema presented above, the immune markers, such as islet cell antibodies (ICA), insulin autoantibodies (IAA), and antibodies to glutamic acid decarboxylase (anti-GAD) which are present in the majority of subjects either before or at the time of diagnosis of Type 1 diabetes, are considered indicators of the immune attack on the β-cells rather than participants in the battle itself.[7–10] The exception to this may be the antibodies directed against the GAD on the surface of the β-cell (see discussion below).[11]

Immune Markers

A number of antibodies have been identified, either before or at the time of diagnosis of Type 1 diabetes.[12] These include the islet cell antibodies, insulin autoantibodies, antibodies to GAD65 and 67, to carboxypeptidase H, to the surface protein ICA69, and to certain gangliosides.[12] Their presence supports the immune pathogenesis of Type 1 diabetes and may be helpful in predicting those individuals likely to develop diabetes in the future. The most studied of these antibodies is the islet cell antibody (ICA), which develops against an islet cell cytoplasmic glycoprotein.[13] This antibody is not specific to the β-cell and is directed at all islet cells. It is detectable at diagnosis in the majority of individuals with Type 1 diabetes and its presence in non-diabetic first-degree relatives of Type 1 diabetes probands is highly predictive of future diabetes. For example, Bottazzo and colleagues have demonstrated that 100% of ICA-positive individuals with titers > 100 JDF units will develop diabetes over a 10-year period of observation.[14] The predictive value of ICA positivity in the general population—i.e., those, not at high risk for diabetes—is much less certain.

The ICA assay is subject to methodological problems, and international workshops have set up strict assay standards.[15] Newer assays have been developed which more accurately detect the ICA antibody, i.e., assays for ICA 512 or IA2.[16] These assays are likely to be the most appropriate for large-scale screening of first-degree relatives of those with Type 1 diabetes, or even the population at large. At present, no interventions exist which will predictably prevent the ongoing destruction of the β-cells in the islets, and so population screening with ICA or other antibody assays remains within the realm of research.[13]

Antibodies to the insulin molecule—insulin autoantibodies (IAA)—have been noted prior to the initiation of insulin therapy in at least one-third to one-half of children with new-onset Type 1 diabetes.[9, 10, 17, 18] These antibodies most likely develop in response to the release of insulin or insulin-degradation products from the β-cell damaged by the immune attack.

Also present in patients with Type 1 diabetes are antibodies directed at the enzyme, glutamic acid decarboxylase (GAD). In contrast to the ICA, this is a β-cell specific antigen.[11, 19–22] The importance of GAD remains to be demonstrated, although it may prove to be a pivotal antigen in the pathogenesis of Type 1 diabetes.

Genetic Susceptibility

There is no doubt that susceptibility to Type 1 diabetes is inherited in a polygenic manner. Susceptibility seems to be most closely related to class II or the D group of histocompatibility locus antigens (HLA).[23, 24] The contribution of the HLA region to disease has recently been referred to as IDDM1 (closest perhaps to the gene for tissue necrosis factor alpha (TNFα).[25] Over 95% of patients with Type 1 diabetes have HL DR-3 and/or -4 present. The presence of HLA DR-2 appears to confer protection against the development of Type 1 diabetes. More recently, attention has focused on the DQ region of the D-locus, and specifically on the amino acid at position 57 on the β-chain.[23] The presence at this position of an aspartic acid (ASP) residue appears to protect against the development of diabetes, while a non-ASP residue confers susceptibility. This may be a critical region of the class II molecule responsible for binding the "autoantigen" involved in the pathogenesis of Type 1 diabetes. Tighter binding in the presence of the non-ASP residue may increase the likelihood of recognition by T-cells which mediate the immune attack.[5, 22, 23]

A number of other Type 1 diabetes genes have been identified, for example, IDDM2 on chromosome 11p15, associated with the insulin and IGF-2 genes; IDDM3 on chromosome 15q26; IDDM4 on chromosome 11q13, associated with the fibroblast growth factor (FGF) gene; and IDDM5 on chromosome 6q25, located near the estrogen receptor (ERS) and superoxide dismutase loci. The relevance of these other genes to Type 1 diabetes susceptibility remains to be elucidated.[25, 26]

Metabolic Factors

Prior to the clinical expression of Type 1 diabetes, glucose homeostasis is normal. However, decreased first-phase insulin secretion in response to an intravenous glucose tolerance test has been demonstrated in individuals later presenting with classical Type 1 diabetes.[27] Furthermore, there are some individuals who have transient hyperglycemia associated with intercurrent illness or glucocorticoid use, months or even years before clinical presentation of Type 1 diabetes.[3]

Epidemiology

Type 1 diabetes is considered one of the most common chronic diseases of childhood, affecting 1 in 300 to 600 individuals by the age of 20 years.[28] The incidence varies with geographical location, with the lowest incidence being noted in countries closest to the equator and increasing with distance from the equator.[29] This suggests a climatic effect on incidence. Incidence figures of less than 1 new case per 100,000 population per year in Japan, to 10–20 or more per 100,000 in North America, to the highest levels of about 40 per 100,000 in Finland have been reported.

Diabetes affects both sexes equally and may occur at all ages. However, there is a low incidence in infants and toddlers, a peak in early school-age children, and a second, larger peak in early adolescence, occurring earlier in girls than in boys.[30] Some data also suggest a seasonal effect on presentation: a larger number of cases present in the winter months (November to March in the Northern Hemisphere) than during the summer. Mini-epidemics have been reported, suggesting the possible role of infectious agents in the final triggering process.[31]

The presence of Type 1 diabetes in a family member increases the risk in other first-degree relatives of developing the disease.[32] Table 11–1 summarizes this risk. Furthermore, HLA-typing can also help predict risk of diabetes: if a sibling of a proband with diabetes is HLA-identical, his or her relative risk is increased 90–100-fold; if only haplo-identical, the increase is 35–40-fold; if HLA-nonidentical, the relative risk is not increased above the background population.

Presentation and Diagnosis

Although a few children are identified as having diabetes on routine health visits, most present with a history of a few days to a few weeks of typical symptoms of hyperglycemia: polyuria (nocturia, enuresis); polydypsia; polyphagia; weight loss (often with increased appetite); lethargy; and proceeding to frank ketoacidosis (vomiting, dehydration, abdominal pain, etc.). In our experience, about one-quarter of children present in diabetic ketoacidosis (DKA), defined by a venous pH < 7.30 and serum bicarbonate concentration < 15 mmol/L.[33] Most of the remainder present with ketonuria, but without full-blown acidosis. A small minority present before ketosis develops, and in these the differential diagnosis of MODY or other type of

TABLE 11–1. Risk of Developing Type 1 Diabetes in First-Degree Relatives

Individual with Type 1 Diabetes	Risk to Offspring/Sibling
Father	6%
Mother	2%
Sibling	5%
HLA-identical	15%
Haplo-identical	5%
No HLA identity	1%
Offspring	6%
Both parents	5%
Identical twins	30–50%
Nonidentical twins	5%

diabetes will depend on observation of the natural history of the disease. Most will progress to obvious insulin dependence.

In the vast majority of children, the diagnosis of diabetes is made by the presence of the classical symptoms in association with glycosuria, hyperglycemia, and ketonuria. Measurement of acid-base and electrolyte status is only necessary to confirm the clinical picture of ketoacidosis. In the absence of ketonuria or if hyperglycemia is an incidental finding, observation of the course of the disorder plus determination of ICA status may be helpful. Glucose tolerance testing is never required to make the diagnosis of Type 1 diabetes.

Approach to the Management of Type 1 Diabetes

Management of the child with newly diagnosed diabetes requires initial correction of the DKA and stabilization of the hyperglycemia, as well as ongoing education and support for the child and his or her family to enable them to carry out effective self-management at home.[34] Long-term care involves helping the child achieve "optimal" metabolic control, preventing the short-term complications of hypoglycemia and ketoacidosis, and early detection and intervention for the long-term micro- and macrovascular complications. Since diabetes requires the acquisition of numerous self-management skills, psychosocial issues must receive substantial attention, both anticipatory guidance and intervention in the event stress arises, either in the form of an intercurrent illness or psychological stress.

Treatment of Diabetic Ketoacidosis

Table 11–2 summarizes briefly the key components of ketoacidosis management. Central to the pathogenesis of DKA is insulin deficiency; increased concentrations of the counter-regulatory hormones (glucagon, epinephrine, cortisol and growth hormone) may exacerbate the hyperglycemia and ketosis, but cannot initiate DKA on their own.[35] Insulinopenia leads to intracellular starvation in the presence of hyperglycemia.

The hyperglycemia causes the osmotic diuresis and accompanying loss of electrolytes (sodium, potassium, phosphate) in the urine. This diuresis will lead ultimately to dehydration. Insulinopenia also leads to lipolysis (and eventually to ketogenesis) and proteolysis. Ketogenesis will produce the metabolic acidosis.

Serum potassium concentrations initially rise, due both to failure to enter the cells and to leeching from the cells in exchange for hydrogen ions. This is followed by decreasing serum concentrations as more potassium is lost in the urine. Because of the osmotic effect of glucose in the intravascular space, blood pressure will be maintained until very late in the process. Similarly, serum sodium concentrations will appear spuriously low, as will the hematocrit. A high serum sodium concentration suggests extreme free-water loss and severe dehydration.

In treating DKA, care must be taken not to overhydrate the child, since this may predispose to the development of cerebral edema, an often fatal complication of DKA.[36]

TABLE 11–2. Treatment of Diabetic Ketoacidosis

1. FLUID REPLETION	Initial fluids to contain normal saline, infused at 10 mL/kg body weight/h for the first hour, and then at 5 mL/kg/hr depending on the degree of dehydration. When plasma glucose concentration falls < 15 mmol/L or falls at a rate of > 5–10 mmol/h, change to 5% dextrose in 0.9% saline. Chart intake and output very carefully to document ongoing repletion. *Beware of either too rapid or too slow rehydration, and of too much free water provision.*
2. INSULIN REPLACEMENT	As soon as the diagnosis of DKA is made, an IV infusion of regular human insulin is begun at the rate of 0.1 unit/kg/h, switching to 0.02–0.05 units/kg/h when the plasma glucose concentration falls < 15 mmol/L. The objective is to maintain glucose concentration in the 6–15 mmol/L range to avoid either hypo- or hyperglycemia. Insulin may also be administered by the intramuscular or subcutaneous route if intravenous infusion is not possible.
3. ALKALI THERAPY	Administration of bicarbonate is indicated only in more severe DKA: pH < 7.20 and serum bicarbonate < 12 mmol/L. The amount of bicarbonate is calculated to increase serum concentration to 12 mmol/L: half the repletion amount may be given over the first 20–30 min, the rest administered over the following 2–4 h.
4. POTASSIUM REPLACEMENT	After the child has voided, KCl should be added to the IV fluid: e.g., 20–30 mmol/L if the concentration is above 4.5 mmol/L, and 30–40 mmol/L if below this level.
5. MONITORING	Careful monitoring of the clinical status (level of consciousness, blood pressure, pulse, etc.) as well as assessment of fluid balance is essential with regular measurement of plasma glucose (every hour for the first 4–6 h and every 2 h thereafter), acid-base and electrolyte status (every 4 h until correction has occurred).
6. OTHER FACTORS	All children should be given nothing by mouth at least during the early stages of therapy. The use of nasogastric tubes and urinary catheters can be avoided unless the child is comatose. Precipitating factors (such as intercurrent illness) should be dealt with if present.

Stabilization of the Hyperglycemia and Family Education

Once the ketoacidosis has been corrected, the child is usually started on three daily insulin injections: an intermediate-acting insulin and short-acting insulin before breakfast, a short-acting before supper, and an intermediate acting at bedtime.[34] We prefer to begin all children on human insulin. The intermediate-acting insulin may be either NPH (isophane) or Lente, and the short-acting preparation is regular (soluble/crystalline) insulin. Recently, an insulin analog (Lispro, Humalog®, Lilly) has been introduced which is quicker in onset, reaches a higher peak, and has a shorter duration of action than regular insulin preparations.[37] It has been shown to decrease postprandial glucose concentrations and decrease the risk of nocturnal hypoglycemia when compared with regular insulin.[37, 38] Approximately two-thirds to three-quarters of the daily dose is given in the morning, although the dose must be carefully tailored to individual needs. We increase the dosage slowly to achieve plasma glucose concentrations in the 4–10 mmol/L (~72–180 mg/dL) range before the main meals. Tighter blood glucose targets (e.g., 4–7 mmol/L [~72–126 mg/dL]) can then be established on an individual basis.

An essential part of the diabetes treatment regimen is a nutritional plan that is balanced in terms of total energy content, types of nutrients (50–55% carbohydrate with an emphasis on complex carbohydrates, 30–35% fat with decreased saturated fat intake, and 15–20% protein), and timing of meals and snacks. The meal plan must also be tailored to individual needs, since noncompliance is virtually assured in any child provided with an inadequate diet. Nutritional counseling requires assurance that the family understands not only the basic meal plan, but also how to adjust the food intake during nonbasal conditions, such as with exercise or during intercurrent illness.

Regular blood glucose and urine glucose and ketone testing is begun, and again is tailored to individual needs.[39] For all children with diabetes, we advise blood glucose testing two to four times daily: before breakfast and dinner, with testing before lunch, at bedtime, and in the early morning hours as indicated. During initial stabilization, the children and their parents are taught how to perform self-monitoring of blood glucose (SMBG) and results are checked by simultaneous capillary specimens sent to the chemistry laboratory. Quality control of the accuracy of SMBG is essential, whether performed by patients or hospital personnel, and whether by visually-read strips or reflectance meters.[40]

During initial stabilization, which may occur either during an initial hospitalization or as an out-patient, depending on the center, the family must be educated in all aspects of diabetes care.[41] Experience demonstrates that hospitalization is only required for those with DKA. Ambulatory management has been accomplished in many centers without a risk of hospital readmission for either metabolic deterioration or hypoglycemia.[42] This education process is family-centered and is best carried out in a center that has extensive experience in the care of children with diabetes. It is also best carried out by a multidisciplinary diabetes health care team which includes, in addition to the responsible physician, a diabetes nurse, dietician, behavioral specialist (social worker or psychologist), public health nurses, and laboratory facilities for performance of measurements such as hemoglobin A1c (HbA1c), serum lipids, and thyroid function tests (thyroxine and TSH concentrations).

For most families, the education program will include information about the pathophysiology of diabetes (hyperglycemia and ketoacidosis); administration of insulin and adjustment of insulin dose requirements; performance of SMBG; meal planning; the causes, recognition, and treatment of hypoglycemia; the effect of intercurrent illness on diabetes control and management; and the long-term complications of diabetes. An integral part of the education program is support for the child and family in dealing with the psychosocial impact of the diagnosis.[41] In those families whose educational level is low or whose anxiety about the initial diagnosis is severe, a less intensive educational approach ("survival skills only") at the time of diagnosis is indicated. For all families, however, diabetes education only begins at diagnosis and must continue throughout the lifetime of the individual.

Early Clinical Course

The initial clinical and biochemical abnormalities of Type 1 diabetes respond dramatically to treatment, usually with correction within 24–36 h of diagnosis. Within a few days to a few weeks of starting insulin therapy, most children enter into the "honeymoon" or partial remission period, during which time stable metabolic control is achieved relatively easily and insulin dose requirements fall.[33] Complete remission (i.e., cessation of the need for insulin therapy) is much less common and leads inevitably to the reinstitution of insulin therapy after a period of weeks to months. The remission period has been presumed to be due to β-cell recovery after correction of the initial severe hyperglycemia. However, changing peripheral insulin sensitivity, food intake (initially high to correct for weight loss) and restored physical activity may all play a role in the expression of this early phase of diabetes in these children.[43]

Attempts have been made to alter the early course of Type 1 diabetes by the use of immune modulation therapies (e.g., cyclosporine, prednisone, interferon, azathioprine)[5, 44] None of these approaches has proved either effective or entirely safe. Since more than 90% of β-cells are presumed to have been destroyed by the time of disease presentation, it is unlikely that this type of therapy will ever be able to completely ameliorate the disease. However, preservation of even a small amount of residual β-cell mass may render the diabetes less severe and thus more easily controlled with current therapy.

Objectives of Diabetes Therapy

The overall objective of therapy should be to achieve normal glucose homeostasis, thereby preventing both the short- and long-term complications of the disorder. Recently incontrovertible evidence has been presented that shows a linear relationship between metabolic control and the relative risk for the development and progression of diabetes-related microvascular complications in adolescents and young adults with Type 1 diabetes.[45, 46] However, there are a few caveats associated with these data:

1. Normoglycemia, or near normoglycemia, is extremely difficult to achieve using either conventional (two or three daily injections) or intensive (continuous insulin infusion pumps or multiple daily injections) insulin therapy. In children's diabetes centers, less than 5% of the children with diabetes have HbA1c values within the nondiabetic range after the honeymoon period.[47]
2. Attempts to achieve normoglycemia are associated with a significant (2–3-fold) increase in episodes of severe hypoglycemia.[48]
3. Studies have not yet demonstrated the safety, efficacy, or necessity of intensive diabetes management in prepubertal children. In fact, data (discussed below) suggest that the years before puberty contribute less to the development of microvascular complications than do the pubertal and postpubertal years.

Despite these reservations, the following objectives should be pursued in the treatment of children with Type 1 diabetes:

1. Control the signs and symptoms of hyperglycemia (polyuria, polydipsia, etc.).
2. Prevent DKA.
3. Avoid all but mild, occasional hypoglycemia that can be easily recognized and treated.
4. Maintain normal growth and physical development.
5. Maintain normal lipid profiles and prevent, wherever possible, the development of obesity.
6. Set realistic goals of therapy for each child.
7. Ensure optimum understanding of diabetes by each child and his or her family.
8. Provide psychosocial support for the child and family.
9. Ensure smooth transition from pediatric to adult diabetes care.
10. Provide surveillance for diabetes-related complications.

Therapeutic goals should guide the family and health care team toward optimal physical and emotional well-being and should be individualized to the specific needs and abilities of each child. For example, less strict blood glucose targets are necessary in infants and younger children with diabetes to prevent hypoglycemia, whereas in highly motivated adolescents and young adults, near normoglycemia occasionally may be feasible and should be encouraged. Problems arise when either (a) unrealistic expectations are placed on the child and family, or (b) responsibility for self-management is shifted to the child at too early an age.[49]

Routine Follow-up

All children with diabetes should be seen by their health care team at regular intervals (three to four times a year) in order to evaluate their progress. Attention should focus specifically on diabetes-related issues such as insulin dose requirements, dietary compliance and satisfaction, results of blood glucose measurements performed at home, symptoms and frequency of hypo- and hyperglycemia, intercurrent illnesses and their impact on diabetes control, adequacy of growth and sexual development, and psychosocial adjustment to the diabetes, including school attendance and performance. Physical examination should include height and weight measurement with plotting on appropriate growth curves, blood pressure measurement, fundus examination, palpation of the thyroid gland and liver, and inspection of injection sites.

These routine follow-up visits provide the opportunity to improve understanding of diabetes, make appropriate adjustments in the treatment regimen, and intervene in the event any medical or psychosocial problems are detected. They also allow techniques of insulin injection, SMBG, and meal planning to be assessed. Furthermore, regular measurement of HbA1c and annual measurement of thyroid function can be accomplished at these visits. Urine testing for microalbuminuria (e.g., by means of an albumin excretion rate in a timed overnight urine collection) and ophthalmologic examination should be performed annually in children over 12–15 years of age with diabetes of more than 5 years duration.[50]

The specific components of the diabetes treatment regimen include the following:

- insulin therapeutics
- nutritional planning
- exercise and its impact on metabolic control
- monitoring techniques
- hypoglycemia recognition and treatment
- psychosocial issues.

INSULIN. For the child with Type 1 diabetes, insulin administered by injection is essential for life. Most children are treated with human insulin products given as twice- or three-times-daily injections of mixtures of intermediate- and short-acting preparations (e.g., NPH plus regular or lispro insulin). More intensive therapy, using three or four daily injections has begun to receive more attention, although insulin infusion pumps have not received good acceptance by children.[51] Insulin dose must be tailored to the individual needs of each child: there are no easy prescriptions. Insulin requirements change on a dynamic basis in relation to changes in food intake, exercise patterns, etc. In younger children and those following a more conventional therapeutic approach, we recommend changes in the basic insulin dose based on patterns of blood glucose concentrations observed over 3–5 day periods. Most children use algorithms ("sliding scales") to adjust the amount of the short-acting insulin at each dose based on ambient blood sugar and planned exercise.

DIET. Meal planning is an essential component of diabetes management.[52] The plan for each child must include sufficient caloric intake to meet the needs for normal growth and development. Attention must also be paid to the types of foods and timing of meals and snacks. For very young children (< 4–5 y), a strict meal plan (exchange type diet) will likely be impossible to institute. Rather, these children require a balanced approach to diet, stressing timing of meals, mix of foods and avoidance of hypoglycemia. In older children, a more structured meal plan is an integral part of the diabetes regimen. In many older children and adolescents, carbohydrate counting has proven a valuable approach to nutritional planning.

EXERCISE. Children with diabetes are at risk from exercise-related hypoglycemia because of the increased glucose utilization by muscle during exercise, combined with their inability to switch off absorption of the subcutaneously administered insulin (and, in fact, the increased absorption due to increased blood flow to the exercising limbs).[53] Care must be taken, therefore, to provide sufficient calories on a daily basis to avoid hypoglycemia during usual amounts of physical activity, with extra calories provided when an extraordinary amount of exercise is planned. Late post-exercise hypoglycemia (i.e., hypoglycemia occurring many hours after completion of the period of exercise) occurs in some individuals. Its presence can be detected and prevented by more frequent glucose monitoring when physical activity changes.

Physical fitness has been shown to have certain salutary effects on those with diabetes. It improves efficiency of glucose utilization, insulin sensitivity, and perhaps also overall morbidity and mortality from diabetes.

MONITORING METABOLIC CONTROL. Monitoring of metabolic control can be divided into two aspects: self-monitoring of blood and urine glucose concentrations at home, and objective monitoring using specifically HbA1c measurement.[54, 55] All children and their families should be taught to perform self-monitoring of both blood glucose and urine glucose and ketones at home. Emphasis should be placed on accuracy of testing and a plan agreed upon for frequency of each type of testing. For daily monitoring, we prefer blood glucose testing before meals with target concentrations of blood glucose as follows: 6–10 mmol/L (~110–180 mg/dL) for infants and toddlers; 4–10 mmol/L (~72–180 mg/dL) for children; 4–8 mmol/L (~72–140 mg/dL) for older children and adolescents; and 4–7 mmol/L (~72–130 mg/dL) for those receiving intensive management. Additional testing should be performed as indicated, including more frequent testing following changes in the treatment regimen, during intercurrent illness, to monitor the effects of exercise on the diabetes control, etc. Urine testing for glucose needs only be used to complement the blood testing. Urine ketone testing, however, is essential during intercurrent illness and when blood glucose concentrations are well above the target range (e.g., > 15 mmol/L [> 270 mg/dL]).

Debate continues over the best techniques for blood and urine testing. Accuracy, ease of use, affordability, durability, and portability are some of the factors to be considered when choosing self-monitoring techniques. Most people prefer the glucose meters, which have become increasingly user-friendly.

HbA1c has become the gold standard measure of long-term metabolic control.[55] The observation that hemoglobin is glycated in proportion to the average blood glucose concentration over the life span of the red cell (90–120 days) provided the long-sought-after objective assessor of diabetes control. Measurement of

HbA1c is subject to a number of potential problems, mostly methodological, including failure to remove the labile fraction (pre-HbA1c) prior to measurement, difficulties in comparing measurement by different methods, and lack of availability of appropriate standards.[56] Nevertheless, when measured appropriately, HbA1c allows tracking of metabolic control in individual patients over time. HbA1c measurement does not replace the need for daily self-monitoring, nor, if high, does it indicate which specific changes need to be made in the diabetes regimen.

HbA1c measurement in large clinic populations has shown that very few children or adults with diabetes achieve nondiabetic concentrations.[46, 47] Mean HbA1c concentrations in children's diabetes clinics are, on average, 1.5 to 2 times the mean of the nondiabetic population. A useful formula is that the mean blood glucose concentration in the nondiabetic population is about 5 mmol/L (90 mg/dL) and mean HbA1c approximately 5%. For every 1% increase in HbA1c there is an approximately 1.5–2 mmol/L (~25–35 mg/dL) rise in mean blood glucose concentration.[5] Thus, an HbA1c of 8% reflects a mean glucose of about 9.5–11 mmol/L (~170–200 mg/dL), far from normoglycemia.

In addition to monitoring blood glucose at home and regular measurement of HbA1c levels, it is important that all children with diabetes have their serum lipids and thyroid function tests checked on a regular basis. Lipid abnormalities are associated with poor metabolic control, but are also widespread in the population at large. Hypercholesterolemia and hypertriglyceridemia are additional risk factors for the development of macrovascular complications of diabetes. We have suggested lipid screening within 6 months of diagnosis and again during adolescence in those in whom the initial concentrations are normal. More frequent measurements and family studies will be necessary for those children and adolescents with high serum lipids despite adequate metabolic control. Annual TSH measurement is indicated to detect early evidence of thyroid dysfunction.

HYPOGLYCEMIA. Hypoglycemia is a serious and constant risk in all individuals treated with insulin. It is clear that insulin delivery in Type 1 diabetes is not physiological; any small change in the diabetes treatment regimen may precipitate hypoglycemia.[48, 57, 58] Identifiable causes of hypoglycemia include: excess (intentional or unintentional) insulin administration; missed, delayed, or decreased size of a meal or snack; and insufficient extra caloric ingestion during periods of increased physical activity. Sometimes, the cause of the hypoglycemia may not be identifiable. Symptoms of hypoglycemia include those due to adrenergic responses ("early warning symptoms," including shakiness, anxiety, pallor, hunger, etc.) and those due to neuroglycopenia (abnormal behavior, confusion, convulsion, coma).

Prevention of hypoglycemia depends on the ability to predict changes in the treatment program that may predispose to these episodes. This requires regular blood glucose monitoring and insulin dose decreases when glucose concentrations are below or in the lower part of the target range. Treatment of hypoglycemia involves ingestion of concentrated simple carbohydrate at the first symptoms of a hypoglycemic reaction. For those with significant neuroglycopenia, injection of glucagon or intravenous glucose will rapidly correct the hypoglycemia.

Mild, occasional hypoglycemia is likely to occur in most insulin-treated individuals and probably has no long-term consequences. Severe hypoglycemia, on the other hand, may occasionally have serious neurological consequences and will invariably increase anxiety about the diabetes treatment. These episodes should be avoided as far as possible. Nevertheless, a number of studies demonstrate that about one-third of children with Type 1 diabetes will have one or more episodes of severe hypoglycemia during their lifetimes.

PSYCHOSOCIAL ISSUES. The development of a chronic disorder such as diabetes places significant stress on both child and family.[59–62] In many families, this does not cause any serious consequences; in some, however, the additional burden of dealing with the diabetes routines may lead to psychosocial distress. It is essential that the health care team involved in the care of these children and their families be aware of the role that psychosocial factors play in the achievement of stable diabetes control, and, also the impact of this disorder on normal child and adolescent development. The availability of social workers and psychologists as members of the multidisciplinary diabetes health care team is essential in dealing with these problems, both in terms of anticipatory guidance and crisis intervention.

Intensive Diabetes Management[45, 46]

The Diabetes Control and Complications Trial (DCCT) and other intervention studies have demonstrated unequivocally the relationship between metabolic control and the onset and progression of diabetes-related complications. These data provide strong motivation for attempts to improve the level of metabolic control for everyone with diabetes. In many, this can be achieved with more careful attention to different aspects of conventional treatment. However, for the majority, intensive diabetes management will be required. This treatment approach requires a multifaceted plan that includes all of the following:

1. More intensive patient education and motivation.
2. Frequent contact between the patient and the multidisciplinary health care team.
3. Frequent (4 or more times per day) blood glucose self-monitoring.
4. Careful balance of food intake, activity, and insulin dosage.
5. A multicomponent insulin regimen (e.g., regular or lispro insulin before meals and NPH at bedtime or a continuous subcutaneous insulin infusion pump).
6. Self-adjustment of insulin dosage according to preset algorithms to meet blood glucose targets.

This treatment approach provides opportunity for the achievement of tighter levels of metabolic control than can be achieved with conventional (two doses per day of insulin) treatment. However, the major downside of this approach is a two- to three-fold increase in the risk of severe hypoglycemia.[48] Furthermore, the studies reported to date have involved only adolescents and adults with Type 1 diabetes. Safety and efficacy in younger children, both in terms of achieving lower HbA1c levels and in diminishing the impact of complications, remains to be proved.

Surveillance for Long-Term Complications

The years before puberty are thought to contribute little, if anything, to the long-term complications of Type 1 diabetes. This suggests that the clock starts ticking on these complications at about the time when adolescent development begins.[63] This indicates a possible role for sex hormones and/or growth factors in the pathogenesis of the complications. Thus, surveillance for complications need only begin after puberty has begun and a significant duration of diabetes has elapsed. The American Diabetes Association, for example, has suggested that after age 15 years and 5 years duration of diabetes, all individuals with diabetes should undergo routine annual ophthalmologic examinations. This includes dilatation of the pupil and careful examination of the fundus, with or without the addition of stereofundus photography or fluorescein angiography. In this way, early background retinopathy can be detected and followed if it progresses towards pre- or frank proliferative retinopathy.

Similarly, all those with Type 1 diabetes should be screened regularly for the presence of diabetic nephropathy.[64,65] Traditionally, this has involved blood pressure measurement and use of a dipstick to detect proteinuria. It is evident that blood pressure screening is a vital part of diabetes management: detection and adequate treatment of hypertension has been demonstrated to slow progression of nephropathy. Detection of microalbuminuria, before the onset of frank proteinuria (i.e., stage of incipient nephropathy), has been shown to be a predictor of later development of progressive nephropathy.[66] Whether intervention at this stage in the normotensive adolescent will prevent progression of renal disease remains to be proved.

Macrovascular disease surveillance implies regular measurement of serum lipid concentrations and intervention strategies to maintain these within the normal range if increased. Routine physical examination should also include neurological assessment and foot inspection in teens with long-duration diabetes.

Summary

Type 1 diabetes is a common and complex metabolic disorder with significant implications for both short- and long-term health. It is clear that a multidisciplinary health care approach is required to assist children and their families in dealing with the medical and psychosocial impact of the disease. This requires a considerable effort both on the part of the health care team and other health professionals involved in providing the services (e.g., laboratory measurements, eye examinations) essential for optimum care. Advances in recent years have served to increase the complexity of the treatment approach. Hopefully, ongoing research efforts will yield new evidence that will allow prevention in high-risk individuals and simplify treatment of patients with established disease.

Type 2 Diabetes in the Young

Type 2 diabetes, although rare before age 30 years, can occur in young people.[67] Two types of presentation have been reported: (1) sporadic cases of Type 2 diabetes, and (2) MODY, which implies Type 2 diabetes with autosomal dominant inheritance.[67] The frequency of these conditions has been reported to vary from as low as 0.15%

of all diabetic patients in Germany, to 4.8% of those with diabetes < 25 years of age in India, to as high as 10% of all cases of youth-onset diabetes among Black Americans in the United States. The frequency with which this condition is misdiagnosed as Type 1 diabetes is unknown, but is likely relatively low, particularly where there is a strong family history of MODY/Type 2 diabetes or when the diabetes is asymptomatic at presentation.

Since MODY is an autosomal-dominant condition, large multigenerational pedigrees exist, which has facilitated genetic studies. To date, three MODY susceptibility loci have been detected:[68, 69, 70]

1. *MODY 1, on chromosome 20q encoding the gene for hepatocyte nuclear factor-4α.* Affected subjects in this pedigree show disorders of carbohydrate metabolism ranging from very mild to severe. Approximately 30% require insulin treatment, and vascular complications do occur.
2. *MODY 2, on chromosome 7p encoding the glucokinase gene:* Many different mutations have been noted in the glucokinase gene, almost invariably presenting with a milder form of diabetes. Among these subjects, < 2% require insulin, and vascular complications are rare.
3. *MODY3, on chromosome 12q encoding the gene for hepatic nuclear factor-1α:* In this condition, hyperglycemia is associated with abnormal patterns of glucose-stimulated insulin secretion.

Diagnosis of MODY or sporadic Type 2 diabetes in youngsters depends on the presence of abnormal glucose concentrations, usually in the absence of ketosis. Oral glucose tolerance testing is not required if fasting plasma glucose concentrations are above 7.0 mmol/L (126 mg/dL) or a random level above 11.1 mmol/L (200 mg/dL) is noted.[1] In the asymptomatic individual, diagnosis requires confirmation of abnormal glucose levels.

Treatment of MODY or sporadic Type 2 diabetes in young people consists primarily of dietary management, with addition of oral hypoglycemic agents where necessary. Insulin administration should be reserved for those patients who are unable to achieve glycemic targets on diet and oral agents.[69]

HYPOGLYCEMIC DISORDERS

In comparison with older children and adults, glucose homeostasis in newborn infants and young children is in a more precarious state, balanced between obligatory glucose requirements on the one hand and the ability to maintain an adequate supply of glucose during fasting on the other. This is thought to be the result largely of the relatively higher proportion of brain mass to body size in these youngsters.[71] Postabsorptive glucose flux rates in children (35 ± 2 μmol/kg/min) are almost three times as high as in adults (12.8 ± 0.5 μmol/kg/min). Similarly, glucose flux during fasting is also significantly higher (23 ± 3 and 9.8 ± 0.5 μmol/kg/min in children and adults respectively).[72] Despite this increased requirement for glucose, hepatic glycogen content in normal children is enough to meet the demand for up to 18 h.

Thereafter, gluconeogenesis becomes the primary source of endogenous glucose production. The relatively smaller muscle mass in newborns and infants relative to body size may also compromise their ability to mobilize sufficient gluconeogenic substrate to maintain their higher glucose requirements.[71]

Fatty acid availability is also of great importance in the maintenance of glucose homeostasis in infants and children.[73] The relatively faster decrease in glucose concentration and increase in ketone body concentrations during fasting in children indicate an acceleration in the normal adaptation to fasting observed in adults.

The higher glucose flux rates, limited gluconeogenic capacity, and rapid rate of fatty acid metabolism in young infants suggest that any abnormalities in the mobilization, interconversion, and utilization of a variety of substrates will place these children at much greater risk for the development of hypoglycemia than is the case in older children and adults.[74]

Definition of Hypoglycemia

The earlier definitions of hypoglycemia in the newborn period were derived from neonates fasted for up to 72 h.[71] Despite ongoing debate as to the exact concentration of plasma glucose that reflects hypoglycemia, and despite inadequate long-term neurodevelopmental studies, the older definitions are no longer considered tenable. For practical purposes, any neonate with a plasma glucose concentration below 2.2 mmol/L (40 mg/dL), and any child whose glucose is below 2.5 mmol/L (45 mg/dL), should be evaluated for hypoglycemia. Those in whom concentrations are between 2.2–2.5 and 2.8 mmol/L (40–50 mg/dL) should be carefully observed.[74]

Signs and Symptoms of Hypoglycemia

In the neonate and infant, the signs and symptoms of hypoglycemia are likely to be fairly non-specific (e.g., irritability and/or lethargy, hypotonia, feeding problems, cyanosis, apnea or tachypnea, hypothermia, pallor) and easily confused with those of other common conditions, including any central nervous system abnormality, cardiac failure, congenital heart disease, sepsis, respiratory distress syndrome, or other metabolic disturbance such as hypocalcemia. Careful monitoring of plasma glucose concentrations in all newborns has become mandatory over the first hours of life to prevent the development of hypoglycemia.

In older infants and children, the clinical presentation of hypoglycemia may be divided into signs and symptoms arising from catecholamine responses (sweating, weakness, shakiness, tachycardia, anxiety, hunger, pallor) and those from neuroglycopenia (headache, confusion or abnormal behavior, convulsions or coma). Repeated or prolonged episodes of severe hypoglycemia may result in permanent brain damage; the effects of asymptomatic hypoglycemia on brain development remain uncertain.[75, 76]

Causes of Hypoglycemia in Infants and Children

Table 11–3 presents the disorders associated with hypoglycemia in infants and children based on the etiology of these conditions. In the immediate neonatal period,

TABLE 11–3. Hypoglycemic Disorders of Infants and Children

ABNORMAL HORMONE SECRETION
- Hyperinsulinism*
  - Transient Neonatal:
    - Infant of diabetic mother
    - Erythroblastosis fetalis
    - Beckwith-Wiedemann syndrome
  - Persistent/Sustained:
    - Mutation in SUR/Kir6.2 gene
    - Hyperinsulinism/hyperammonemia syndrome
    - Insulinoma
- Drug-induced:
  - Insulin, oral hypoglycemic agents
  - Growth hormone deficiency**
  - ACTH or cortisol deficiency**
  - ? Glucagon deficiency*
  - ? Somatostatin deficiency
  - ? Thyroid hormone deficiency

ABNORMAL SUBSTRATE AVAILABILITY
- Ketotic hypoglycemia**
- Hypoglycemia associated with surgery

ABNORMAL FUEL METABOLISM
- Inborn errors of metabolism***
  - Carbohydrate:
    - Glycogen storage disease
    - Defective hepatic gluconeogenesis
  - Amino acids:
    - Maple syrup urine disease
  - Fatty acids:*
    - Systemic carnitine deficiency
  - Transient or acquired defects
    - Small-for-gestational-age infants
    - Other causes:
      - Reye's syndrome
      - Alcohol ingestion
      - Salicylates
      - Cyanotic congenital heart disease

*Hypoketotic syndromes: suppressed or defective ketogenesis
**Hyperketotic syndromes: "exaggerated" ketogenesis
***Organic acidosis: lactic acidosis, hepatomegaly, associated features

most episodes of hypoglycemia are transient and associated with either small-for-gestational-age or preterm infants, other stress situations, or infants of diabetic mothers. Persistent neonatal or infantile hypoglycemia is far less common, but usually due to (in descending order of frequency) hyperinsulinism, other hormonal deficiency, or an inborn error of metabolism. After 1 year of age, ketotic hypoglycemia, a condition seen with declining frequency, is the most common diagnosis.

Abnormal Hormone Secretion

Hyperinsulinism

Hyperinsulinism results in an increase in peripheral glucose utilization (particularly by fat and muscle cells) and a decrease in hepatic glucose production, the latter likely the more important determinant of the hypoglycemia.[74] High insulin concentrations also suppress mobilization of other endogenous substrates, leading to suppression of ketogenesis and proteolysis.

TRANSIENT NEONATAL HYPERINSULINISM. Hypoglycemia in the infant of the diabetic mother (IDM) is the direct result of prolonged maternal hyperglycemia leading to fetal and neonatal hyperinsulinemia.[77] Other defects such as decreased glucagon secretion and delayed induction of gluconeogenic enzymes may exacerbate the hypoglycemia.[77–79] This condition can be prevented by the achievement of meticulous glucose homeostasis in the pregnant mother with diabetes, particularly in the late stages of gestation and during labor and delivery.[80]

Hypoglycemia in infants with erythroblastosis fetalis has been attributed to hyperinsulinism associated with β-cell hyperplasia.[81] The reason for this remains unknown. Similarly, in the Beckwith-Wiedemann syndrome, a rare syndrome characterized by omphalocele, macroglossia, visceromegaly, and abnormal ear creases, transient, and occasionally more persistent, hyperinsulinemic hypoglycemia has been noted.[82]

PERSISTENT HYPERINSULINEMIC HYPOGLYCEMIA OF INFANCY (PPHI). Most children with sustained hyperinsulinism present within the first year of life, either in the immediate newborn period, when they may appear similar to the IDM (i.e., macrosomia), or later in the first year.[83]

The pathologic findings in children with hyperinsulinism may vary greatly; in many, there is a generalized increase in β-cells, either in relation to the pancreatic ducts (nesidioblastosis), scattered singly or in small numbers throughout the pancreas, or an increase in the number and size of the islets of Langerhans.[84] In some, pancreatic histology may appear normal. The preferred term, islet cell dysplasia or dysmaturation, suggests a functional defect in insulin secretion rather than a specific pathologic entity.[84, 85]

A distinct insulinoma is extremely uncommon in young children. More common findings include either focal or diffuse increases in islet cells ("adenomatosis") not confined to β-cells.

The pathology of the pancreas in neonates and infants with hyperinsulinism cannot be predicted by either the clinical presentation or by results of dynamic testing (e.g., glucose responses to insulin secretogogues such as tolbutamide or leucine). The relative infrequency of insulinomas in children suggests that imaging techniques (ultrasound, CT scan, magnetic resonance) are unlikely to be helpful in localizing the pathology in more than a small minority of cases.[84, 85]

Recent data suggests that PHHI may be inherited as an autosomal-recessive condition. There is strong evidence for such a transmission in a number of multiplex families, and simplex cases may be similarly inherited.[86] Whether this is a homogeneous condition both from pathophysiologic as well as genetic standpoints remains to be settled. Recent genetic analysis has found that familial hyperinsulinism maps to chromosome 11p14–15.2, a short distance from the insulin gene.[87] In Saudi Arabian and Ashkenazi Jewish families, constituting the largest number of families studied so far, multiple mutations in the SUR/Kir6.2 gene have been found. There is also evidence of autosomal-dominant transmission in which the hyperinsulinism is associated with hyperammonemia. Detailed analyses suggest that this condition is due to a defect involving a site common to amino acid regulation of both pancreatic insulin secretion and hepatic urea synthesis.[88]

Initial therapy for PHHI consists of intravenous glucose infusion to prevent life-threatening hypoglycemia. Inability to control hypoglycemia with infusion rates of 12–15 mg/kg/min of glucose should lead to addition of other agents including glucagon (IV infusion), somatostatin (IV infusion of native somatostatin or SC injection of a long-acting analog) and diazoxide orally.[83–85] The use of glucagon and somatostatin is confined mainly to preoperative stabilization of these patients. In a few cases, long-acting analogs of these two hormones have been employed over prolonged periods in a effort to avoid surgery.[89, 90]

Diazoxide (10–20 mg/kg/day divided into three equal doses) may control the hyperinsulinism and has been used indefinitely in some cases.[83] In the newborn, diazoxide may cause sodium and water retention with resultant hypertension and cardiac failure; these side-effects may be controlled by the addition of a thiazide diuretic.[74, 83] Other side effects of diazoxide include hypertrichosis, hyperuricemia, and neutropenia. Careful monitoring of blood glucose concentrations will help prevent hyperglycemia-related problems.

In the infant in whom hypoglycemia persists despite intensive medical management, and/or in whom significant side effects of drug therapy are noted, subtotal (> 95%) pancreatectomy becomes the treatment of choice.[91, 92] Intraoperative ultrasonography may help in localizing areas of adenomatosis. Transient postoperative hyperglycemia, which may necessitate insulin therapy, suggests effective treatment. In a significant number of patients, however, subtotal pancreatectomy fails to control the hyperinsulinism; in these children, further medical or surgical management may be required. Total pancreatectomy will almost certainly result in insulin dependence and malabsorption.

In a proportion of these patients, spontaneous remission has been reported months to years after introduction of medical management.[83] Thus, in children controlled on diazoxide, repeat testing should be carried out at intervals to assess the need for ongoing treatment.

DRUG-RELATED HYPERINSULINISM. Accidental ingestion of oral hypoglycemic agents may cause hyperinsulinemic hypoglycemia in children. Factitious hypoglycemia due to malicious (i.e., intentional) insulin administration to infants or children has been reported.[93, 94] This should be regarded as a form of child abuse. Measurement of insulin and C-peptide concentrations will be useful in diagnosis: high insulin with undetectable C-peptide concentrations are diagnostic.[93]

Growth Hormone, ACTH, and Cortisol Deficiencies

Children with hypopituitarism (growth hormone deficiency with or without associated ACTH deficiency) have a propensity to develop hypoglycemia. This tends to occur in those hypopituitary children somewhat underweight for height rather than those with the more typical pudgy, relatively overweight appearance.[95] Findings in the neonatal period which may suggest hypopituitarism include the presence of a micropenis in males, hyperbilirubinemia, or midline facial defects such as cleft lip or palate.

The pathogenesis of hypoglycemia in these disorders is uncertain. At the time of hypoglycemia, these children are ketotic, have low insulin concentrations, and low concentrations of the gluconeogenic substrates alanine and glutamine. They also have a blunted glycemic response to administered glucagon. It is likely that growth hormone and ACTH increase hepatic glucose production and decrease peripheral utilization by facilitating fatty acid and amino acid mobilization and by opposing the hepatic effects of insulin.

Hypopituitarism as a cause of hypoglycemia is usually self-limited: children over 3–4 years of age do not require growth hormone to maintain euglycemia. Replacement therapy with growth hormone and hydrocortisone, increasing the latter three- to fivefold during periods of stress, should eliminate the risk of hypoglycemia.

Occasionally, children in whom hyperinsulinism and hypopituitarism coexist have been described.[83] The reason remains elusive; perhaps serious hyperinsulinemic hypoglycemia may lead to pituitary infarction.

Hypoglycemia may also complicate the presentation of Addison's disease or other causes of adrenal insufficiency in children. Hypoglycemia is a relatively uncommon feature in the presentation of congenital adrenal hyperplasia.

Other Hormone Deficiencies

Isolated glucagon or somatostatin deficiencies have been proposed as possible mechanisms for hypoglycemia due to hyperinsulinism, i.e., loss of paracrine control of insulin secretion.[96, 97] Proof of these entities remains unconvincing. The role of thyroid hormones in maintenance of glucose homeostasis in infants and children is probably minimal. There are, however, reports of hypoglycemia associated with hypothyroidism, which is reversible with appropriate replacement therapy.

Abnormal Substrate Availability

Ketotic Hypoglycemia

This is the most common cause of hypoglycemia in children presenting beyond the first year of life.[71, 74] Nevertheless, the incidence of this condition has decreased over the past 20 years. Generally, it presents between 12 months and 4 or 5 years of age and spontaneously remits by 6–8 years.

Normal children exhibit ketonemia, but not symptomatic hypoglycemia, 24–36 h after introduction of a hypocaloric, ketogenic diet (high in fat and low in carbohydrate). In children with ketotic hypoglycemia, within 8–16 h after introducing a similar diet, both ketonemia and symptomatic hypoglycemic usually develop.[98] Similar results are found in response to a monitored fast lasting 21–24 h. Ketotic hypoglycemia may be the extreme end of the spectrum of normal responses to fasting in children in this age group.

The pathophysiologic mechanism responsible for this condition is unknown. The importance of hypoalaninemia (alanine is an important gluconeogenic amino acid) and abnormal adrenomedullary responses remains uncertain.[99, 100]

Hypoglycemia usually manifests in these infants in association with an intercurrent illness or during periods of reduced caloric intake. Monitoring for ketonuria at such times may help prevent hypoglycemia. Treatment consists of regular meals high in carbohydrate and protein, particularly during these periods of catabolism.

Hypoglycemia Associated with Surgery

There are numerous reports of hypoglycemia complicating the post-operative period in children.[101, 102] The possible mechanisms include: prolonged preoperative fasting, intra- and post-operative stress with increased demands for energy, and the effects of a variety of medications on glucose production and utilization. Intravenous glucose infusions and glucose monitoring prevent this complication.

Abnormal Fuel Metabolism

Inborn Errors of Metabolism

Deficiencies of enzymes important in mobilization, interconversion and utilization of a variety of substrates may be associated with hypoglycemia.[74] These autosomal-recessive errors of carbohydrate, amino acid, or fatty acid metabolism are generally associated with failure to thrive, developmental delay, hepatomegaly, and metabolic (lactic or organic) acidosis.

CARBOHYDRATE. *Glycogen Storage Disease and Disorders of Hepatic Gluconeogenesis.*[103] Deficiency of one of the enzymes responsible for hepatic glycogen synthesis (glycogen synthetase deficiency) or release (deficiency of the debrancher enzyme and defective/deficient activation of hepatic phosphorylase) will cause hypoglycemia by decreasing availability of glucose in the post-absorptive state.

Glycogen storage disease, Type I, due to glucose-6-phosphatase deficiency, is the most common of these inborn errors. Hydrolysis of glucose-6-phosphate is essential for the release of hepatic glucose via either gluconeogenesis or glycogenolysis. Deficiency of the enzyme causes prolonged hypoglycemia early in infancy. The mobilization of glycogen and induction of gluconeogenesis result in the production of lactate rather than glucose leading to lactic acidosis. This metabolic error thus leads to accumulation of hepatic glycogen and fatty infiltration of the liver, the latter being responsible for the marked hepatomegaly. Other features include psychomotor and growth retardation, hyperlipidemia, and hyperuricemia. Diagnosis depends on demonstration of fasting hypoglycemia in association with hepatomegaly and metabolic (lactate) acidosis. A hallmark of Type I disease is an absent glycemic response to glucagon, a potent glycogenolytic hormone. Confirmation of diagnosis depends on direct enzyme determination in a liver biopsy specimen.

Treatment of these conditions is aimed at preventing hypoglycemia. This can be achieved by constant intravenous or intragastric infusion of glucose. This has been translated into frequent daytime feedings with constant nocturnal intragastric infusion or late-evening ingestion of a slow release form of glucose, namely raw cornstarch.[104]

Three other types of glycogen storage disease may also occur in infancy with findings similar to those described for Type I disease: amylo-1,6-glucosidase deficiency (Type 3), hepatic phosphorylase deficiency (Type 6) and phosphorylase kinase deficiency (Type 9).

Deficiency of hepatic fructose-1,6-diphosphatase also results in defective gluconeogenesis. Clinical features are similar to those in glycogen storage disease, Type I. Treatment consists of a diet high in carbohydrate (55–60%), and low in fat (30%). Intravenous glucose infusion may be required during periods of catabolism.

Other enzyme deficiencies associated with carbohydrate metabolism that may lead to hypoglycemia include pyruvate decarboxylase, phosphoenolpyruvate carboxykinase, galactose-1-phosphate uridyl transferase (galactosemia) and fructose-1-phosphate aldolase (hereditary fructose intolerance).

AMINO ACIDS. Hypoglycemia is noted in patients with branched-chain α-ketoacid dehydrogenase deficiency (Maple Syrup Urine Disease [MSUD]) during periods when concentrations of branched-chain amino acids and α-ketoacid are very high, e.g., during illness or other stress.[105] The etiology of the hypoglycemia is unknown. Other defects in amino acid metabolism that may be associated with hypoglycemia include methylmalonic aciduria, glutaric acidemia, and ethylmalonicadipic aciduria. The treatment of these disorders involves limiting intake of the offending amino acid, with caloric supplementation during times of stress.

FATTY ACIDS. Genetic disorders of mitochondrial fatty acid oxidation have emerged as important diagnostic considerations in infants and children with hypoglycemia, cardiomyopathy, or skeletal muscle weakness.[106] Some of these disorders are associated with hypoglycemia which occurs in association with hypoketonemia, but not hyperinsulinism. Medium-chain acyl-coenzyme A dehydrogenase (MCAD) deficiency is the most common of these, with a frequency as high as 1 in 10,000 births. Patients may present with profound hypoglycemia, floppiness, hepatomegaly, encephalopathy, and increased concentrations of free fatty acids, ammonia, and liver and muscle enzymes (creatine kinase and lactic dehydrogenase).[106–108] The disorders may be mistaken for either sudden infant death syndrome (SIDS) or Reye's syndrome. Sixteen different defects have been identified that involve almost all possible enzyme steps in the pathway of fatty acid oxidation.

Diagnosis depends on finding hypoglycemia in the absence of ketonuria. This suggests the need for measurement of concentrations of insulin, ketone bodies, free fatty acids, lactate, and free and total carnitine. Urine should also be analyzed for volatile and non-volatile organic acids.

The mechanism of hypoglycemia in these disorders is unknown but may relate either to accelerated rates of glucose utilization or to decreased glucose production. Treatment includes frequent feedings and oral carnitine replacement. During periods of catabolism, intravenous glucose infusion may become essential. The risk of attacks of illness declines with advancing age as body mass and fasting tolerance improves. As many as half of the affected children may never have an attack and thereby remain undetected. This reflects that in order to manifest with these conditions, affected individuals must have not only the enzyme defect, but also be exposed to the stress of fasting.

Miscellaneous

Small-for-Gestational-Age (SGA) Infants

Many SGA infants develop transient neonatal hypoglycemia. This may be due to a number of mechanisms, including decreased substrate stores, increased demand for substrate due to intercurrent stress, or a delay in induction of the enzyme systems required for gluconeogenesis.

Once identified, SGA infants should have their glucose concentrations monitored carefully over the first days of life to prevent hypoglycemia. Early feeding and/or intravenous infusions of glucose are warranted, particularly in those with significant neonatal illness.

Other Causes

Salicylate compounds may produce hypoglycemia and ketones by poorly defined means. A history of salicylate ingestion should be sought in all acutely hypoglycemic infants. Ethyl alcohol inhibits hepatic gluconeogenesis and may also produce hypoglycemia. Hypoglycemia in cyanotic congenital heart disease may be due to poor hepatic perfusion, resulting in a decreased rate of hepatic glucose production.

Reye's syndrome often follows a viral illness (influenza A or B, varicella) and may be compounded by the administration of aspirin. Hypoglycemia is prominent in younger children presenting with this condition and can be prevented by administration of glucose.

Investigation of Hypoglycemia[109, 110]

The diagnosis of hypoglycemia depends on the accurate laboratory measurement of plasma glucose concentration, and not merely by reagent strips with or without reflectance meters. Demonstration of a plasma glucose concentration below 2.2–2.5 mmol/L (40–45 mg/dL) should trigger further evaluation.

The history and physical examination give important clues to possible etiology. For example, age at presentation is clearly important. In newborns, large-for-gestational-age infants are more likely to be hyperinsulinemic, whereas SGA infants are more prone to substrate deficiency. The finding of a micropenis and hyperbilirubinemia should raise the suspicion of hypopituitarism. Children diagnosed beyond 1 year of age are most commonly suffering from ketotic hypoglycemia.

Although many diagnostic tests have been utilized in the diagnosis of hypoglycemia in infants and children, most often only a thorough history, physical examination, and limited testing are required. The oral glucose tolerance test contributes very little to the diagnosis and should not be used in evaluating hypoglycemia in the pediatric population. Of utmost importance is obtaining a so-called "critical blood sample," i.e., a blood specimen taken at the time of hypoglycemia in which not only plasma glucose but also hormones (growth hormone, cortisol, and insulin) and metabolites (ketone bodies, lactate, fatty acids, venous blood gas) are measured. This specimen may be obtained when the infant presents to the emergency room or after performance of a monitored fast in which glucose is measured at regular intervals. In young infants, omission of one or two feedings may be sufficient to produce the hypoglycemia; in older children a fast of up to 24–30 h may be required. In older children, the fast should begin after supper, so that hypoglycemia is likely to occur between 9:00 AM and 6:00 PM the following day. Table 11–4 outlines results of glucose, hormone, and metabolite testing at the time of hypoglycemia in the different diagnostic categories.

The presence of hypoglycemia in the absence of ketonuria/ketonemia is strongly suggestive of hyperinsulinism. In these infants, a glucagon stimulation test (0.03 mg/kg intravenously) performed at the time of hypoglycemia will result in a significant glycemic response (< 1.1–1.7 mmol/L or 20–30 mg/dL increment in the first 10 min).[111] The hyper-responsiveness to glucagon is due to the presence of excess hepatic glucose deposition resulting from the hyperinsulinism. Provocative tests of insulin secretion provide no diagnostic advantage.

TABLE 11–4. Investigation of Hypoglycemia in Childhood Critical Blood Sample

	Hyper-insulinism	Inborn Error	Ketotic Hypoglycemia	Hormone (GH/ Cortisol Deficiency
Glucose	↓	↓	↓	↓
Lactate	N	↑	N	N
B-hydroxybutyrate	↓	N	↑	↑
Free fatty acids	↓	N	↑	↑
Growth hormone	N/↑	↑	↑	N/↓
Cortisol	N/↑	↑	↑	N/↓
Insulin	↑*	↓	↓	↓
Associated features	LGA**	Hepatomegaly Developmental/ growth delay Metabolic acidosis Hyperlipidemic Hyperuricemic		Newborn: micropenis hyperbilirubinemia hypothyroidism Older: short stature

*may be within the "usual" physiologic range.
**large for gestational age

Hypoglycemia and hypoketonemia may also be seen in disorders of ketogenesis, i.e., fatty acid oxidation defects. In these children, plasma carnitine concentrations and a search for urinary organic acids may prove helpful.

Hypoglycemia without hepatomegaly but with ketonemia/uria starting after 1 year of age is often indicative of ketotic hypoglycemia. These children will have low plasma insulin concentrations at the time of hypoglycemia, as well as a blunted response to glucagon administration. Growth hormone and ACTH or cortisol deficiency may be confused with ketotic hypoglycemia. These conditions can be excluded by finding normal/increased concentrations at the time of hypoglycemia. If not found, dynamic testing for these hormones may be required.

The combination of hypoglycemia, hepatomegaly, and metabolic acidosis suggests an abnormality of hepatic gluconeogenesis or glycogenolysis. The presence of nonglucose-reducing sugars in the urine points to a diagnosis of galactosemia. The specific defects in gluconeogenesis are best determined by measuring specific enzyme activities in a liver biopsy specimen. Disorders of amino acid and fatty acid metabolism depend on accurate measurement of urinary metabolites and liver (or muscle) biopsy specimens.

To diagnose factitious hypoglycemia, simultaneous insulin and C-peptide measurement will reveal high insulin concentrations in the absence of detectable C-peptide.

SUMMARY

Hypoglycemia is a rare condition in young infants and children beyond the immediate newborn period. Its presence suggests a significant pathological disorder. A careful history, physical examination, and investigation should help define the different etiologies and allow specific treatment.

REFERENCES

1. The Expert Committee on the Diagnosis and Classification of Diabetes Mellitus. Report of the Expert Committee on the Diagnosis and Classification of Diabetes Mellitus. Diabetes Care 1997;20:1183–97.
2. Shuman CR. Diabetes mellitus: definition, classification and diagnosis. In Galloway J, Potvin J, Shuman C. Diabetes mellitus (9th ed.). Indianapolis: Lilly, 1988:1–14.
3. Schatz DA, Kowa H, Winter WE, Riley WJ. Natural history of incidental hyperglycemia and glycosuria of childhood. J Pediatr 1989;115:676–80.
4. Rossini AA, Greiner DL, Friedman HP, Mordes JP. Immunopathogenesis of diabetes mellitus. Diabetes Rev 1993:1;43–75.
5. Atkinson MA, MacLaren NK. The pathogenesis of insulin-dependent diabetes mellitus. New Eng J Med 1994:331;1428–36.
6. Eisenbarth GS. Type I diabetes: a chronic autoimmune disease. N Engl J Med 1986;314: 1360–68.
7. Bottazzo GF, Florin-Christensen A, Doniach D. Islet cell antibodies in diabetes mellitus with autoimmune polyendocrine deficiencies. Lancet 1974;ii:1279–83.

8. Palmer JP, Asplin CM, Clemens P, et al. Insulin antibodies in insulin-dependent diabetics before insulin treatment. Science 1983;222:1337–39.
9. Sochett E, Daneman D. Relationship of insulin autoantibodies to presentation and early course of IDDM in children. Diabetes Care 1989;12:517–23.
10. Maclaren NK. How, when, and why to predict IDDM. Diabetes 1988;37:1591–94.
11. Baekkeskov S, Nielsen J, Marner B, et al. Autoantibodies in newly diagnosed diabetic children immunoprecipitate human pancreatic islet cell proteins. Nature (Lond.) 1982;298:167.
12. Thai A-C, Eisenbarth GS. Natural history of IDDM. Diabetes Rev 1993;1:1–14.
13. Eisenbarth GS. Genes, generator of diversity, glycoconjugates, and autoimmune beta-cell insufficiency in type I diabetes. Diabetes 1987;36:355–64.
14. Tarn AC, Dean BM, Schwarz G, et al. Predicting insulin-dependent diabetes. Lancet 1980;i: 845–50.
15. Gleichmann H, Bottazzo GF. Progress toward standardization of cytoplasmic islet cell-antibody assay. Diabetes 1987;37:578–84.
16. Wherrett D, Daneman D. Can we predict and prevent insulin-dependent diabetes mellitus? Can J Diagnosis 1997;14:83–92.
17. Arslanian SA, Becker DJ, Rabin B, et al. Correlates of insulin antibodies in newly diagnosed children with insulin-dependent diabetes before insulin therapy. Diabetes 1985; 34:926–30.
18. Atkinson MA, Maclaren NK, Riley WJ, et al. Are insulin autoantibodies markers for insulin-dependent diabetes mellitus? Diabetes 1986;35:894–98.
19. Baekkeskov S, Landin M, Kristensen JK, et al. Antibodies to a 64000-Mr islet cell protein precede the clinical onset of insulin-dependent diabetes. J Clin Invest 1987;79:926–34.
20. Christie MR, Daneman D, Champagne P, Delovitch TL. Persistence of serum antibodies to a Mr-64000 islet cell protein after onset of Type I diabetes. Diabetes 1990;39:653–56.
21. Baekkeskov S, Warnock G, Christie M, et al. Revelation of the specificity of 64k autoantibodies in IDDM serums by high-resolution 2-D electrophoresis. Unambiguous identification of 64k target antigen. Diabetes 1989;38:1133–41.
22. Baekkeskov S, et al. Identification of the 64K autoantigen in insulin-dependent diabetes as the GABA-synthesizing enzyme glutamic acid decarboxylase. Nature 1990;347:151–52.
23. Todd JA, Bell JI, McDevitt HO. HLA-DQ β-gene contributes to susceptibility and resistance to insulin-dependent diabetes mellitus. Nature (Lond.) 1987;329:599–604.
24. Todd JA. Genetic control of autoimmunity in type I diabetes. Immunology Today 1990;11: 122–29.
25. Thomson G. Identifying complex disease genes: progress and paradigms. Nat Genet 1994; 8:108–10.
26. Field LL, Tobias R, Magnus T. A locus on chromosome 15q26 (IDDM3) produces susceptibility to insulin-dependent diabetes mellitus. Nat Genet 1994;8:189–94.
27. Srikanta S, Ricker AT, McCulloch DK, et al. Autoimmunity to insulin, β-cell dysfunction, and development of insulin-dependent diabetes mellitus. Diabetes 1986;35:139–42.
28. Drash AL. Diabetes mellitus in the child and adolescent. Curr Prob Pediatr 1986;16:417–542.
29. Green A, Gale EAM, Patterson CC. Incidence of childhood-onset insulin-dependent diabetes mellitus: the EURODIAB ACE study. Lancet 1992;339:905–9.
30. Fleegler FM, Rogers KD, Drash AL, et al. Age, sex, and season of onset of juvenile diabetes in different geographic areas. Pediatr 1979;63:374–79.
31. Rewers M, LaPorte RE, Walczak M, et al. Apparent epidemic of insulin-dependent diabetes mellitus in midwestern Poland. Diabetes 1987;36:106–13.
32. Poussier P, Schiffrin A, Ciampi A, et al. The risk of developing disease for siblings of patients with insulin-dependent diabetes mellitus. Clin Invest Med 1991;14:1–8.
33. Sochett EB, Daneman D, Clarson C, Ehrlich RM. Factors affecting and patterns of residual insulin secretion during the first year of type I (insulin-dependent) diabetes mellitus in children. Diabetologia 1987;30:453–59.
34. Sochett E, Daneman D. Staying on top of diabetes in children and adolescents. The Canadian Journal of Diagnosis 1993;10:52–63.

35. Foster D, McGarry J. The metabolic derangements and treatment of diabetic ketoacidosis. New Engl J Med 1983;309:159–69.
36. Harris GD, Fiordalisi I. Physiologic management of diabetic ketoacidemia. Arch Pediatr Adolesc Med 1994;148:1046–52.
37. Garg SK, Carmain JA, Braddy KC, et al. Premeal insulin analogue insulin lispro vs. Humulin® insulin treatment in young subjects with Type 1 diabetes. Diabetic Medicine 1996;13;47–52.
38. Pfutzner A, Kustner E, Frost T, et al. Intensive insulin therapy with insulin lispro in patients with type 1 diabetes reduces the frequency of hypoglycemic episodes. Exp Clin Endocrinol Diabetes 1996;104:25–30.
39. Daneman D, Siminerio L, Transue D, et al. The role of self-monitoring of blood glucose in the routine management of children with insulin-dependent diabetes mellitus. Diabetes Care 1985;8:1–4.
40. Clarson C, Daneman D, Frank M, et al. Self-monitoring of blood glucose: how accurate are children with diabetes at reading Chemstrip bG? Diabetes Care 1985;8:354–58.
41. Wexler P. The social worker and the child with juvenile diabetes mellitus. In Traisman HJS, ed. Management of juvenile diabetes mellitus. St.Louis: Mosby, 1980:272–79.
42. Chase HP, Crews KR, Garg S, et al. Outpatient management vs. in-hospital management of children with new-onset diabetes. Clin Pediatr (Phila) 1992;31:450–6.
43. Yki-Jarvinen H, Koivisto V. Natural course of insulin resistance in type I diabetes. N Engl J Med 1986;315:224–30.
44. Marks JB, Skyler JS. Immunotherapy of type I diabetes mellitus. J Clin Endocrinol Metab 1991;72:3–9.
45. The DCCT Trial Research Group. The effect of intensive treatment of diabetes on the development and progression of long-term complications in insulin-dependent diabetes mellitus. New Eng J Med 1993;329:977–86.
46. The DCCT Research Group. Effect of intensive diabetes treatment on the development and progression of long-term complications in adolescents with insulin-dependent diabetes mellitus: Diabetes Control and Complications Trial. J Pediatr 1994;125:177–88.
47. Mortensen HB, Hougaard P, for the Hvidøre Study Group on Childhood Diabetes. Comparison of metabolic control in a cross-sectional study of 2,873 children and adolescents with IDDM from 18 countries. Diabetes Care 1997;20:714–20.
48. The DCCT Research Group. Epidemiology of severe hypoglycemia in the Diabetes Control and Complications Trial. Am J Med 1991;90:450–59.
49. Daneman D. When should your child take charge? Diabetes Forecast May 1991:61–66.
50. Position statement of the American Diabetes Association. Eye care guidelines for patients with diabetes mellitus. Diabetes Care 1988;11:745–46.
51. Brink SJ, Stewart C. Insulin pump treatment in insulin-dependent diabetes mellitus: children, adolescents and young adults. JAMA 1986;255:617–21.
52. Delahanty LM, Halford BN. The role of diet behaviors in achieving improved glucose control in intensively treated patients in the Diabetes Control and Complications Trial. Diabetes Care 1993;16:1453–58.
53. Horton ES. Prescription for exercise. Diabetes Spectrum 1991;4:250–7.
54. Skyler JS. Patient self-monitoring of blood glucose. Clinical Diabetes 1983;1:12–17.
55. Daneman D. Glycated hemoglobin and the assessment of diabetes control. The Endocrinologist 1994;4:33–43.
56. Baynes JW, Bunn HF, Goldstein DE, et al. National diabetes data group: report of the expert committee on glycosylated hemoglobin. Diabetes Care 1984;7:602–6.
57. Daneman D, Frank M, Perlman K, et al. Severe hypoglycemia in children with insulin-dependent diabetes mellitus: frequency and predisposing features. J Pediatr 1989;115:681–85.
58. Gale E. The frequency of hypoglycemia in insulin-treated diabetic patients. In Serrano-Rios M, Lefebvre P, eds. Diabetes. Amsterdam: Elsevier, 1985:934–37.
59. Kovacs M, Feinberg TL, Paulauskas R, et al. Initial coping responses and psychosocial characteristics of children with insulin-dependent diabetes mellitus. J Pediatr 1985;106:827–34.
60. Koski M-L. The coping process in childhood diabetes mellitus: a critical review. Acta Paediatr Scand 1980;Suppl 198:1–56.

61. Hauenstein EJ, Marvin RS, Snyder AL, Clarke WL. Stress in parents of children with diabetes mellitus. Diabetes Care 1989;12:18–23.
62. Jacobson AM, Hauser ST, Wolfsdorf JI, et al. Psychologic predictors of compliance in children with recent onset of diabetes mellitus. J Pediatr 1987;110:805–11.
63. Kostraba J, Dorman J, Orchard T, et al. Contribution of diabetes duration before puberty to development of microvascular complications in IDDM subjects. Diabetes Care 1989;12: 686–93.
64. Mogensen CE, Christensen CK, Vittinghus E. The stages in diabetic renal disease. Diabetes 1983;32(Suppl 2):64–78.
65. Sochett E, Daneman D. Microalbuminuria in children with insulin-dependent diabetes mellitus. J Pediatr 1988;112:744–48.
66. Mogensen CE, Christensen CK. Predicting diabetic nephropathy in insulin-dependent patients. N Engl J Med 1984;311:1430–32.
67. Fajans SS. Scope and heterogeneous nature of MODY. Diabetes Care 1990;13:49–64.
68. Fajans SS, Bell GI, Bowden DW, et al. Maturity-onset diabetes of the young. Life Sciences 1994;55:412–22.
69. Froguel P, Velho G. Maturity-onset diabetes of the young. Curr Opin Pediatr 1994;6:482–85.
70. Kaisaki PJ, Menzel S, Lindner T, et al. Mutations in the hepatocyte nuclear factor-1 alpha gene in MODY and early onset NIDDM: evidence for a mutational hotspot. Diabetes 1997;46:528–35.
71. Cornblath M, Schwartz R. Disorders of carbohydrate metabolism in infancy, 2nd ed. Philadelphia: WB Saunders, 1976.
72. Haymond MW, Howard C, Ben-Galim E, et al. Effects of ketosis on glucose flux in children and adults. Am J Physiol 1983;245:E373–78.
73. Haymond MW, Karl E, Clarke WL, et al. Differences in circulating gluconeogenic substrates during short-term fasting in men, women and children. Metabolism 1982;31:33–4.
74. Haymond MW. Hypoglycemia in infants and children. Endocrinology Clinics of North America 1989;18:211–52.
75. Griffiths AD, Bryant GM. Assessment of effects of neonatal hypoglycemia: a study of 41 cases with matched controls. Arch Dis Child 1971;46:819–27.
76. Jacobs DG, Haka-Ikse K, Wesson DE, et al. Growth and development in patients operated on for islet cell dysplasia. J Pediatr Surg 1986;21:1184–89.
77. Pildes RS. Infants of diabetic mothers. N Engl J Med 1973;289:902–4.
78. Williams PR, Sperling MA, Racasa Z. Blunting of spontaneous and amino-acid stimulated glucagon secretion in infants of diabetic mothers (IDM). (Abstract). Diabetes 1975;24:411.
79. Susa JB, Cowett RM, Oh W, et al. Suppression of gluconeogenesis and endogenous glucose production by exogenous insulin administration in the newborn lamb. Pediatr Res 1979;13:594–98.
80. Rovers G, Gargiulo M, Nicolin V. Maximal tolerated insulin therapy in gestational diabetes. Diabetes Care 1980;34:89–94.
81. Barrett CT, Oliver TK. Hypoglycemia and hyperinsulinism in infants with erythroblastosis fetalis. N Engl J Med 1968;278:1260–63.
82. Cohen MD, Gorlin RJ, Feingold M, et al. The Beckwith-Wiedemann syndrome: seven new cases. Am J Dis Child 1971;122:515–19.
83. Stanley CA, Baker L. Hyperinsulinism in infants and children. Adv Pediatr 1976;122:515-55.
84. Jaffe R, Hashida Y, Yunis E. Pancreatic pathology in hyperinsulinemic hypoglycemia of infancy. Lab Invest 1980;42:356–65.
85. Aynsley-Green A, Polak J, Bloom S, et al. Nesidioblastosis of the pancreas: definition of the syndrome and the management of severe neonatal hyperinsulinemic hypoglycemia. Arch Dis Child 1981;56:496–508.
86. Thornton PS, Sumner AE, Ruchelli ED, et al. Familial and sporadic hyperinsulinism: histopathologic findings and segregation analysis support a single autosomal recessive disorder. J Pediatr 1991;119:721–24.
87. Glaser B, Chiu KC, Anker R, et al. Familial hyperinsulinism maps to chromosome 11p14–15.1, 30 cM centromeric to the insulin gene. Nat Genet 1994;7:185–88.

88. Weinzimer SA, Stanley CA, Berry GT, et al. A syndrome of congenital hyperinsulinism and hyperammonemia. J Pediatr 1997;130:661–4.
89. Thornton PS, Alter CA, Levitt Katz LE, et al. Short- and long-term use of octreotide in the treatment of congenital hyperinsulinism. J Pediatr 1993;123:637–43.
90. Glaser, Hirsch HJ, Landau H. Persistent hyperinsulinemic hypoglycemia of infancy: long-term octreotide treatment without pancreatectomy. J Pediatr 1993;123:644–50.
91. Schiller M, Krausz M, Meyer S, et al. Neonatal hyperinsulinism: surgical and pathologic considerations. J Pediatr Surg 1980;15:16–20.
92. Gough MH. The surgical treatment of hyperinsulinism in infancy and childhood. Br J Surg 1984;71:75–78.
93. Bauman WA, Yalow RS. Child abuse: parenteral insulin administration. J Pediatr 1981; 99:588–91.
94. Scarlett JA, Mako ME, Rubenstein AH, et al. Factitious hypoglycemia: diagnosis by measurement of serum C-peptide immunoreactivity and insulin binding antibodies. N Engl J Med 1977;297:1029–32.
95. Hopwood NJ, Forsman PJ, Kenny FM, Drash AL. Hypoglycemia in hypopituitary children. Am J Dis Child 1975;129:918–22.
96. Vidnes J, Oyasaeter S. Glucagon deficiency causing severe neonatal hypoglycemia in a patient with normal insulin secretion. Pediatr Res 1977;11:943–49.
97. Kollie LA, Monneus LA, Cejka V. Persistent neonatal hypoglycemia due to glucagon deficiency. Arch Dis Child 1978;53:422.
98. Colle E, Ulstrom RA. Ketotic hypoglycemia. J Pediatr 1964;64:632–51.
99. Senior B. Ketotic hypoglycemia. J Pediatr 1973;82:555–56.
100. Christensen NJ. Hypoadrenalinemia during insulin hypoglycemia in children with ketotic hypoglycemia. J Clin Endocrinol Metab 1974;38:107–12.
101. Kelnar CJH. Hypoglycemia in children undergoing adenotonsillectomy. Br Med J 1976;1: 751–52.
102. Shumake LB. Postoperative hypoglycemia in congenital hypertrophic pyloric stenosis. South Med J. 1975;68:223.
103. Hers H-G, Van Hoof F, De Barsy T. Glycogen storage diseases. In: Stanbury JB, Wyngaarden JG, Fredrickson DA, eds. The metabolic basis of inherited disease. New York: McGraw-Hill, 1989.
104. Chen YT, Cornblath, M., Sidbury, JB. Cornstarch therapy in type I glycogen storage disease. N Engl J Med 1984;310:171–75.
105. Haymond MW, Karl IE, Feigin RD, et al. Hypoglycemia and maple syrup urine disease: Defective gluconeogenesis. Pediatr Res 1973;7:500–8.
106. Glasgow AM, Engel AG, Bier D, et al. Hypoglycemia, hepatic dysfunction, muscle weakness, cardiomyopathy, free carnitine deficiency and long-chain acyl carnitine excess responsive to medium chain triglyceride diet. Pediatr Res 1968;17:319.
107. Engel AG, Banker BQ, Eiben RM. Carnitine deficiency: Clinical, morphological and biochemical observations in a fatal case. J Neurol Neurosurg Psychiat 1977;40:313.
108. Stanley CA, Hale DE, Coates PM, et al. Medium chain acyl-CoA dehydrogenase deficiency in children with nonketotic hypoglycemia and low carnitine levels. Pediatr Res 1983;17:877–84.
109. Grupposo PA, Schwartz R. Hypoglycemia in children. Pediatrics in Review 1989;11:117–24.
110. Phillip M, Bashan N, Smith CPA, Moses SW. An algorithmic approach to diagnosis of hypoglycemia. J Pediatr 1987;110:387–90.
111. Finegold DN, Stanley CA, Baker L. Glycemic response to glucagon during fasting hypoglycemia: an aid in the diagnosis of hyperinsulinism. J Pediatr 1980;96;257–59.

CHAPTER 12

Neurologic and Psychiatric Disorders

Roger J. Packer, M.D.
Stephen I. Deutsch, M.D., Ph.D.

INTRODUCTION

Discoveries in the neurosciences have ushered in a new era in the understanding and treatment of childhood neurologic and psychiatric disorders. Elucidations of the biochemical, cellular, and genetic mechanisms of childhood neurologic disease will, no doubt, result in alterations and refinements of treatment. Discussed in this chapter are the pathobiology and rationale for the treatment of some of the more common neurologic and psychiatric diseases of childhood.

EPILEPSY

Clinical Aspects

The epilepsies are recurrent convulsive and nonconvulsive seizures caused by temporary excessive and hypersynchronous discharges of cortical neurons. It has been estimated that one of every 11 people will have at least one seizure by the age of 80, and that 3% of the population have recurrent, unprovoked seizures.[1] The highest incidence of epilepsy occurs in children under 5 years of age, and 1–2 children out of every 1,000 will have recurrent convulsions.

A variety of different conditions, such as breathholding spells, vasovagal episodes, gastroesophageal reflux, and psychogenic disorders, may mimic epilepsy, so correct clinical diagnosis is the cornerstone of appropriate management. Clinical manifestations of epilepsy include generalized motor involvement (tonic, clonic, or tonic-clonic), staring episodes with or without automatisms, partial motor movements, or loss of postural tone. These manifestations often vary within an individual patient.

Although a variety of different classification systems exists, the most widely recognized is the schema developed by the International League Against Epilepsy (ILAE).[2] The ILAE classification utilizes two broad categories of seizures: those arising in one cerebral hemisphere, primarily accompanied by focal electroencephalographic abnormalities (partial or focal seizures); and those with clinical and electrocortical manifestations of involvement of both cerebral hemispheres from onset (generalized seizures). Distinction between seizure types is often blurred and arbitrary, as focal seizures with rapid secondary generalization may mimic generalized seizures. The clinical manifestation of seizures may also depend on the age of the patient. Appropriate classification requires inclusion of the age of onset and remission of the epileptic seizure, the interictal neurologic status of the patient, the etiology and trigger mechanism of the attacks, the interictal and ictal EEG, the response to antiepileptic medication, the remission rate, and the genetics of the seizure type.

Although diagnosis is clinical, electroencephalography remains the primary tool for evaluating patients and abetting classification. In general, focal epileptiform activity indicates a partial or localized epilepsy, in contradistinction to generalized epileptiform discharges, which suggest generalized epilepsy. Interictal electroencephalographic abnormalities are seen in probably no more than 50% of patients on the initial electroencephalogram.[1] Multiple recordings performed with various stimulation techniques, such as hyperventilation and sleep deprivation, or with more refined recording techniques may increase this yield to as high as 90%.

Neuroimaging studies are useful in the understanding of epilepsy, but in themselves are rarely diagnostic. Magnetic resonance imaging has proven more sensitive than CT in detecting small cerebral lesions related to epilepsy.[3] Neuroimaging is indicated in all children with partial seizures and possibly the majority of children with recurrent generalized seizures. Other neuroimaging studies, such as positron emission tomography and single photon emission computed tomography (SPECT), are presently primarily research techniques. However, since these techniques may show interictal metabolic abnormalities in patients with otherwise normal neuroimaging studies, they may become more clinically useful in the future.[3]

Pathophysiology

The major cellular events involved in the generation of epileptogenic foci are slowly unfolding.[4] During epileptiform discharges there are marked abnormalities in ion transport, with shifts in the ratio between extracellular and intracellular potassium, sodium, and calcium. A variety of neurotransmitters have been implicated in the epileptogenic process, including gamma-amino-butyric acid, glycine, glutamate, and catecholamines. Determination of which of these events are primary and which are secondary remains to be elucidated. These cellular events all result in the electrical synchronization necessary for the epileptic foci to spread and become clinically evident.

Treatment

The effective treatment of epilepsy is highly dependent on appropriate diagnosis of the type of epilepsy present and an understanding of the natural history of the disease. Some forms of childhood epilepsy, such as febrile seizures, have a relatively stereotypical presentation, a limited period of expression, and may not require treatment. Other forms of childhood epilepsy, including "benign rolandic epilepsy" and absence seizures, carry excellent prognoses, and excessive treatment may be more damaging than the epilepsy itself. Anticonvulsant medication remains the cornerstone of treatment for most childhood epilepsies. The mechanisms of action of anticonvulsant drugs are incompletely understood and consist of an interplay between their effects on neurotransmitter action, repetitive neuronal firing mechanisms, neuronal networks, and cellular ionic transport.[5,6] The combination of these effects and the pharmacokinetic properties of the drugs determine their spectrum of action and clinical efficacy.

The decision to treat a patient must be based on the likelihood of recurrent seizures, potential side effects of the drugs, the consequence of further seizures on the patient's life, and the probability that treatment will effectively reduce the risk of future seizures. Estimates of the rate of recurrence of seizures within the first year after a single unprovoked convulsion are hard to come by, and an incidence ranging between 16% and 62% has been suggested.[7] Recurrence seems more likely if the patient is neurologically abnormal or if there is a strong family history of recurrent unprovoked convulsions. A partial seizure or an abnormal interictal electroencephalogram also seems to increase the likelihood of epilepsy.

Role of Laboratory in Treatment

Assessment of drug concentrations has become an integral part of the management of children with epilepsy. However, there is an increasing tendency to rely too heavily on drug concentrations in patient care decisions. Monitoring of drug concentrations is an important adjunct to the management of epileptic patients. However, drug concentrations should be considered as an aid and a guide, not the prime determinant of patient management. Some patients experience excellent seizure control on relatively low concentrations of drugs, while others tolerate concentrations which are above the accepted therapeutic range and require such dosages for adequate seizure control (see Table 12–1). Drug concentrations are especially useful for patients on two or more drugs. Assays for the more commonly used drugs, including phenobarbital, phenytoin, carbamazepine, valproate, and possibly ethosuximide, should be available on an immediate basis, 24 h per day, at centers caring for many patients with epilepsy.

The optimal approach to determining the pharmacokinetic aspects of an anticonvulsant would be to obtain multiple serum specimens at different times after a drug is taken; however, this approach is rarely practical. More commonly, to avoid the problem of erratic initial absorption, trough drug concentrations are monitored to aid in determining appropriate drug dosages. In general, the metabolism of an anti-epileptic drug is faster in children than adults. However, in the neonatal

TABLE 12–1. Therapeutic Profile of Common Anticonvulsants

Drug	Serum Half-Life (h)	Therapeutic Drug Concentrations (ug/mL)
Phenobarbital		15–35
Neonates	63–98	
Infants	47 ± 8	
Children (< 15 years)	37–73	
Adults	64–141	
Phenytoin		10–20
Neonates	7–140*	
Infants and Children	11.6–31.5*	
Adults	7–42*	
Carbamazepine		8–12
Neonates	8–37	
Infants and Children	3–32	
Adults	11–22	
Valproic Acid		50–100(120?)
Neonates	10–67	
Infants and Children	4–10	
Adults	12–16	
Ethosuximide		40–100
Infants and Children	15–68	
Adults	50–60	

*At therapeutic drug concentrations. Lower at low doses.

period, metabolism may be relatively slower, requiring modification of dosage. Toxicity, especially sedation, may be related to either drug accumulation of anticonvulsants with long half-lives or peak concentrations of an individual drug. In these cases, measuring "peak" drug concentrations at a time when absorption should be maximum, or multiple drug concentrations to determine the elimination of a drug, may be useful.

Another important role of the laboratory is the monitoring of the effect of a given drug on other organs. Routine monitoring of hematologic and hepatic function for patients taking drugs such as carbamazepine and valproate is recommended, although their utility is poorly substantiated.

Partial and Secondarily Generalized Seizures

Phenytoin, carbamazepine, phenobarbital, and primidone are essentially equally as effective in control of partial and secondarily generalized seizures.[1,5] One drug may be effective when the other drug is not. Other agents, such as valproate and clonazepam, may also be effective. These drugs differ substantially in their side effects and pharmacokinetic properties; these differences are most useful in determining the best choice of drug for an individual patient.

Phenytoin

Phenytoin exerts its effects by varying mechanisms including alterations in ionic transport, changes in neurotransmitter action (including the enhancement of gamma-amino-butyric acid), decreases in neuronal repetitive firing, and the facilitation of neuronal network inhibitory mechanisms.[5] The drug may either be given by oral or intravenous routes. The oral absorption of phenytoin is slow and variable, with maximum blood concentrations occurring within 4 to 8 h.[5,7,8] Absorption in the neonatal/early infancy period is often incomplete and unreliable. Another problem with oral delivery of the drug in infants is the variable concentration of oral suspensions, as phenytoin may precipitate in the bottom of the bottle. The drug is 90% bound to plasma proteins in adults, but to a lesser extent in neonates. It is taken up in brain within minutes after intravenous administration.

Calculation of the appropriate daily dose of phenytoin in an individual patient can be difficult, as the metabolism of the drug changes with age and is dependent on serum concentrations.[5,7,8]

Phenytoin is primarily metabolized in the liver and elimination follows Michaelis-Menten pharmacokinetics, so that enzymes responsible for eliminating the drug become saturated at higher dosages. The half-life of the drug becomes longer as the plasma concentration increases. At higher plasma values, a small increase in dosage will result in progressively greater plasma concentrations. The steady-state half-life of phenytoin is quite long in the neonates (ranging up to 57 h) and progressively declines over the first few months of life. Initially, dosages in the range of 5–8 mg/kg/d are needed in children and adolescents; much higher oral dosages are usually required in the neonatal period. Therapeutic blood concentrations range between 10 and 20 ug/mL. However, there is a great degree of variability for a given patient, and some patients will tolerate and respond to much higher concentrations.

Since a large number of drugs have been reported to interact with phenytoin, monitoring of drug concentrations is needed for patients on multiple medications.

The most frequently encountered symptoms of phenytoin toxicity include nausea, sedation, tremor, and slow cognition.[7] Increased seizures have been reported in patients with increased phenytoin concentrations; however, some patients tolerate drug concentrations well above the accepted safe range with little or no toxicity and improved seizure control. In addition, diphenylhydantoin at drug concentrations in the normally accepted effective range may precipitate minor motor seizures and a pseudo-degenerative clinical picture. The actual effect of phenytoin on intellectual status of children is unsettled and demonstrable cognitive sequelae are mild and difficult to reproduce in studies. Long-term effects of phenytoin on the cerebellum have been suggested. In children, especially girls, troublesome side effects include hirsutism, coarsening of facial features, and gingival hyperplasia. These side effects usually relegate phenytoin to a secondary role in the management of females (and some males) with seizures. Phenytoin also has teratogenic side effects and use in pregnancy is to be avoided, when possible.

Fosphenytoin

Fosphenytoin is a phosphate-ester prodrug of phenytoin which, after absorption, is metabolized by phosphatase enzymes in a number of tissues to phenytoin.[9] The primary advantage of fosphenytoin over phenytoin is its free solubility in aqueous solutions. Its mechanism of action and spectrum of activity is identical to that of phenytoin. Fosphenytoin binds competitively to the same plasma protein sites as phenytoin and phenytoin plasma concentrations are higher than expected in the presence of fosphenytoin.[10] After administration and absorption, the half-life of fosphenytoin's conversion to phenytoin is rapid, occurring in between 15 and 18 minutes in most patients.[10]

Fosphenytoin's major clinical benefit, as compared to phenytoin, is that it has less local toxicity when given intramuscularly or intravenously if there is extravasation. Its major side effects are similar to that of phenytoin. Cardiac depression with fosphenytoin occurs; however, it seems to cause such depression at a higher rate of infusion (150 mg of phenytoin equivalence per minute compared to 50 mg per minute for phenytoin) and thus can be infused more rapidly.[9] This may be due to the elimination of propylene glycol derivatives. Thus, although the conversion of fosphenytoin to phenytoin potentially slows its effectiveness in treating status epilepticus, this is partially offset by the more rapid rate of infusion possible with fosphenytoin.

Carbamazepine

Carbamazepine is available only in an oral preparation. Gastrointestinal absorption is somewhat unpredictable, but seems relatively good at all ages, with maximum absorption occurring 4–8 h after intake.[5, 7, 11] Distribution of the agent is uniform and the half-life of the drug is initially long (greater than 24 h), but in children falls to a mean of 9 h after chronic use. As is the case with phenytoin, carbamazepine is metabolized primarily in the liver. Carbamazepine interacts with many drugs. The effects of drug interactions between carbamazepine and other drugs which are metabolized by the liver are somewhat less predictable than is the case for phenytoin.

Carbamazepine affects sodium and potassium membrane permeability at a cellular level.[5] It also affects the release of various neurotransmitters, although the specific mechanism of biochemical action (if there is one) is poorly characterized. It has varied effects on neuronal firing mechanisms.

Initial side effects of carbamazepine include ataxia, nausea, and lethargy.[5, 7] These side effects usually disappear after chronic administration. Inappropriate release of antidiuretic hormone may occur. Dose-related bone marrow depression and hepatic toxicity are the most common severe side effects of medication. Low white-cell counts occur relatively frequently with the drug, but a reduction in drug dose is necessary only when there is a progressive, severe fall in counts. Severe aplastic anemia and hepatotoxic reaction are idiosyncratic. Monitoring of liver functions and blood counts in patients taking the drug is recommended, although its utility is unproven.

Monitoring of drug concentrations is a useful adjunct to carbamazepine use, as best seizure control has been reported with drug concentrations ranging between

8 and 12 ug/mL.[5,7] Once again, there is a great deal of patient variability; some patients tolerate higher concentrations of the drug and others experience good seizure control at lower drug concentrations.

Carbamazepine has been used widely in pediatrics due to the lack of cosmetic side effects, lack of sedation, and little disturbance of cognitive functions. [5,7] It has become a drug of choice for most children (especially girls) with partial and secondarily generalized seizures. However, since it has to be given more frequently than phenytoin due to its relatively short half-life, compliance becomes a more pressing issue with this drug.

Phenobarbital

Phenobarbital is the anticonvulsant with the longest experience of use.[12] It can be used orally, intravenously, or, in rare cases, intramuscularly. Phenobarbital is readily and completely absorbed after oral administration and reaches peak concentrations after 1–3 h.[12] It is evenly distributed throughout tissues and has an extremely long elimination half-life. This is especially true in neonates, where the half-life may be greater than 96 h. However, in later infancy and childhood, the half-life usually falls significantly (usually in the 40–50 h range). After intravenous injection, the drug is delivered to brain, but at a somewhat slower rate than is phenytoin.

Phenobarbital has a direct effect on neuronal excitability and synaptic transmission.[5] It has a variety of pharmacologic effects which are primarily postsynaptic and include enhancement of gamma-amino-butyric acid, antagonism of the excitatory effects of glutamate, and direct effects on ion conductance.

The drug dosage needed to obtain adequate serum concentration varies widely with age. In neonates and young children, 4–5 mg/kg/d may be needed to maintain adequate drug concentrations, whereas dosages in the 1–3 mg/kg/d range are needed in older children and adults. The range of effective serum concentrations of the drug is quite wide (15–35 ug/dL). Similarly, the side effects of the drug may occur at varied serum concentrations.

The most common side effects of phenobarbital include somnolence and ataxia.[12] As many as 40% of infants and children may experience a paradoxical effect, with increased irritability, behavioral abnormalities, and hyperactivity. This effect may or may not be dose related. Chronic use of the drug seems to cause difficulty in cognition. Some researchers have postulated a permanent effect on cognitive abilities after chronic use of the drug, but this is far from conclusively proven.[13] The detrimental effects on cognition and behavior have resulted in a secondary role for phenobarbital in the management of most childhood epilepsies. However, it probably remains the safest proven effective therapy for febrile seizures.

One phenobarbital derivative, mephobarbital, has been utilized because of anecdotal reports of its lower incidence of associated hyperactivity.[12] Mephobarbital is rapidly metabolized to phenobarbital, and it seems most likely that the utility of mephobarbital is related to lower overall phenobarbital concentrations than an intrinsic effect of the drug.

Primidone

Primidone is administered orally. The drug is metabolized to phenobarbital and phenylethylmalonamide (Pema). The primidone and its two major metabolites all have independent anticonvulsive activity.[5] It is unclear which derivative (or derivatives) is effective in controlling seizures in an individual patient. More frequent doses of the drug result in higher primidone levels and possibly better control of associated generalized seizures. Dosage is usually increased slowly due to problems with oversedation. The appropriate switch-over dose between phenobarbital and primidone is variable, and to obtain phenobarbital equivalent concentrations, doses of primidone 3–9 times greater than phenobarbital are necessary.

Monitoring drug concentrations in patients on primidone can be difficult. Seizure control usually best correlates with the phenobarbital concentrations, but both the primidone and the Pema concentrations have been related to seizure control. Side effects are similar to those of phenobarbital.

Generalized Seizures

Although a variety of drugs, such as phenytoin, phenobarbital, and carbamazepine, are effective against generalized tonic-clonic seizures, valproate is probably the single most effective drug.[1] A variety of different benzodiazepine derivatives may also be effective, especially in myoclonic seizures. Ethosuximide is probably equally effective as valproate for the treatment of absence seizures.

Valproate

Valproate is presently available only in an oral preparation. Although the drug may be used in a short-acting preparation, it is most commonly used in a long-acting preparation which is well absorbed.[6, 14] The longer acting, slower release form of valproate has a half-life of somewhere between 15 and 20 h. The drug is bound to plasma proteins, is lipophilic, and has a wide volume of distribution. Valproate is more slowly eliminated in neonates, but reaches adult metabolism by approximately 3 months of age.[15]

Valproate's main mechanism of action seems to be the enhancement of neurotransmission at gamma-amino-butyric acid synapses.[6] It also decreases brain aspartic acid concentrations and increases the concentration of glycine.

Valproate is usually started in a relatively low dose of 10 mg/kg/d and is slowly increased to 30–50 mg/kg/d. Blood concentration measurements are somewhat useful, as concentrations of 50–100 mg/L are usually needed for seizure control. However, higher drug values can, at times, be tolerated and can be somewhat more efficacious. There are extensive interactions between valproate and other antiepileptic drugs. It tends to increase phenobarbital concentrations and decrease measured concentrations of phenytoin. However, since it competes with phenytoin for protein-binding sites, there may be a relative increase in free phenytoin. Ethosuximide concentrations tend to rise when valproate is added. Drug concentrations of valproate are usually lowered by the concomitant use of other anticonvulsants.

Some side effects of valproate are related, while others are not.[14] The drug may cause a decrease in appetite and gastrointestinal side effects, including cramping and diarrhea. However, it may also cause an increase in appetite and weight gain, especially in adolescent girls. The two major side effects of valproate are bone marrow suppression and hepatotoxicity. Thrombocytopenia is usually dose related, but an idiosyncratic aplastic anemia may also occur.

Mildly increased transaminase concentrations and mild increase of ammonia are common in patients taking valproate. These increases tend to be dose related. However, fatal idiosyncratic hepatotoxicity (irreversible upon cessation of the drug) may occur. This has been primarily reported in children under age 2 y, although occasionally older children have similar sequelae. Potential hepatic toxicity has limited the use of the drug in younger children, except in extreme circumstances. The use of carnitine has been proposed as a useful adjunct for patients with dose-related hepatic dysfunction or unexplained lethargy or somnolence. However, the efficacy of this drug remains unproven. Fatal pancreatitis with associated disseminated intravascular coagulopathy may also occur with valproate.

Because of these side effects, patients require serial monitoring of blood counts, including platelet counts, and liver function tests while on valproate. However, such monitoring probably is not helpful in cases of idiosyncratic toxicity. Since valproate has little detrimental effect on cognition, it has become the drug of choice for many older children with generalized epilepsy.

Ethosuximide

Ethosuximide is given orally.[14] It is a member of a family of drugs including phensuximide and methsuximide. Although these other suximide derivatives may have a slightly broader spectrum of activity, they are usually utilized as second-line drugs.

Ethosuximide is absorbed rapidly, with maximum plasma concentrations occurring at 3 h. It is primarily metabolized in the liver and tends to have a relatively long elimination half-life of 30–60 h. It can be given once daily; however, because of intestinal side effects, it is usually prescribed 2 times a day.

The mechanism of action of ethosuximide is poorly characterized.[6] It does seem to have effects on ionic transport, and concentrations of gamma-hydroxybutyric acid are decreased after chronic treatment with the drug.

The drug usually reaches a steady state 5–12 d after initiation of dose. Effective blood concentrations tend to range in the 40–100 ug/mL dose. Dose-related side effects include nausea, abdominal discomfort, and anorexia. A variety of idiosyncratic side effects may occur, but they tend to be relatively infrequent. The drug may cause deleterious effects on behavior and cognition. However, because of the relative infrequency of severe side effects, it probably remains the drug of choice for simple absence seizures of childhood.

Benzodiazepines

The benzodiazepines are a group of drugs including diazepam, clonazepam, clorazepate, and lorazepam.[5, 12] These drugs may be effective in many types of epilepsy. They all are rapidly absorbed from the gastrointestinal tract. They are widely distributed within body tissues and because of this distribution initially have a relatively short half-life. However, conversion to active metabolites such as N-dimethyldiazepam results in products with a long half-life (50–120 h). The half-life tends to increase with age.

The benzodiazepines induce a wide variety of antiepileptic changes.[5] Almost all neurotransmitters are altered in some way by benzodiazepine administration. There are also specific receptors in the nervous system for the benzodiazepines, and it is probable that at least some of the efficacy of these drugs is related to these receptors.

Acute use of benzodiazepines may cause respiratory depression and hypotension. Chronic use is associated with drowsiness, incoordination, irritability, and hypotonia. Cognitive impairment and behavioral disturbances may also occur.

Newer Anticonvulsants

Until 1992, no anti-epileptic agent had been approved by the FDA since the introduction of valproate in 1982.[16] In 1992, two new anticonvulsants, felbamate and gabapentin, were approved for use and two others, lomatrigine and vigabatrin, are pending approval. Although these anticonvulsants have not been widely tested or utilized in children and have been primarily evaluated in adults, they will likely be utilized for children with refractory epilepsy. Exactly where they will fit in the management schema of childhood epilepsy remains to be determined, and their pharmacokinetic properties, potential utility, and known side effects will be briefly reviewed.

Felbamate

Approved for use in 1992, felbamate is available only in oral preparation.[16] Its half-life is 19–20 h when given alone, but shortens significantly to 14–15 h in patients who are taking other anticonvulsants, such as phenytoin or carbamazepine. Felbamate levels seem to decrease with chronic administration, suggesting induction of metabolism. Felbamate is a competitive inhibitor of phenytoin metabolism and reduction in phenytoin dosage is usually necessary at initiation of felbamate therapy. Felbamate also decreases valproic clearance and valproate doses also must be decreased before the felbamate is added. Felbamate effects on carbamazepine are less clear-cut, as felbamate usually causes a decrease in carbamazepine levels but increases carbamazepine epoxide.

Felbamate has been primarily shown to be of benefit in patients with partial seizures but seems to have a relatively large spectrum of action. It is somewhat effective in children with Lennox-Gastaut and in patients with atypical absence.

The mechanism of action of felbamate is unknown, but it does inhibit both NMDA responses and potentiates GABA responses. There is not a clear-cut relationship between felbamate serum drug levels and efficacy. Although felbamate drug levels are available from multiple commercial drug laboratories, a true therapeutic range has not been determined, nor has a clear relationship been shown between felbamate drug levels and toxicity. The effects of felbamate on other drug levels have already been mentioned.

When felbamate was introduced, no serious toxicity was expected. Patients occasionally developed headaches, nausea, and anorexia. Insomnia was a significant problem, especially in older patients. However, after its introduction in 1992, an unexpected association with severe hepatic dysfunction, including deaths related to irreversible hepatic damage, and aplastic anemia was seen. For this reason, the use of felbamate has been significantly curtailed and only those patients who have had a significant response to the drug have been maintained on therapy.

Gabapentin

Gabapentin is an oral agent which is rapidly absorbed after oral administration.[16] Maximum elimination plasma levels occur 2–3 h after the ingestion of the drug. Gabapentin has linear kinetics with plasma concentrations directly related to the dose. Gabapentin's half-life in adults is between 5 and 7 h. It has not been extensively used in children. Unlike other anticonvulsants, gabapentin is neither protein bound nor metabolized, being excreted unchanged in the urine. Gabapentin does not induce liver enzymes and does not have a significant effect on other antiepileptic drugs. This allows the drug to be quickly titrated to a therapeutic dose.

Gabapentin's mechanism of action appears to be different from that of other anticonvulsants. It binds at selective receptor sites on neurons concentrated in the hippocampus and neocortex.

Gabapentin has been primarily tested in adults and seems to be most useful as adjunct therapy in patients with refractory partial seizures. Its efficacy in different types of seizure types is still being evaluated. Gabapentin has caused relatively infrequent toxicities, and side effects primarily include somnolence, dizziness, and ataxia. These effects are not clearly dose-related, nor have they been reliably related to serum blood levels. Drug level monitoring is usually not employed in patients taking gabapentin.

Lamotrigine

Lamotrigine is rapidly absorbed after oral administration and in adults peaks in the plasma in approximately 2–3 h.[16] In patients not on hepatic enzyme-inducing drugs, its half-life is approximately 24 h, but is shortened in patients taking other anticonvulsants. The drug is metabolized by the liver and approximately 90% of the drug is excreted as the 2-N-glucuronic acid conjugate. Valproate increases the half-life of Lamotrigine. Studies suggest that the drug is effective as an adjunct in patients with partial and generalized seizures. It has also been of some use in patients with Lennox-Gastaut seizures.

Lamotrigine's mechanism of action is similar to that of phenytoin, as it blocks voltage-sensitive sodium channels. It stabilizes neuronal membrane and inhibits glutamate.

It is unclear whether Lamotrigine drug levels will be useful in the evaluation of efficacy and potential toxicity, although drug levels are commercially available. Side effects reported with Lamotrigine include blurred vision, ataxia, diplopia, dizziness, and somnolence. The most common side effect, however, has been skin rash, occurring in up to 10% of patients. This has resulted in a Stevens-Johnson-like syndrome in some patients.

Topiramate

Topiramate is an oral agent with rapid absorption with peak absorption approximately 2 h after ingestion.[17] It is not significantly metabolized after absorption and is excreted mainly as unchanged drug in the urine. Topiramate has a relatively low binding to plasma proteins and it has a half-life of approximately 21 h after single or multiple dosing.

Topiramate is a structurally novel compound which reduces the duration of spontaneous epileptiform bursts of neuronal firing in experimental studies.[18] It also reduces the frequency of action potential solicited by a depolarizing electrical current, which may be due to the ability of the drug to reduce the frequency at which voltage-activated sodium channels are activated.[19] Topiramate also enhances GABA activity.[20]

Topiramate has been primarily tested in adults and has been shown to be effective in adults as adjunctive therapy and as monotherapy for refractory partial onset seizures.[17] It may also be effective in patients with primary generalized epilepsy with a variety of different seizure types. An open-label pilot study of 17 patients between 4 and 28 years of age with Lennox-Gastaut syndrome demonstrated that topiramate, as adjunctive therapy, resulted in a greater than 50% reduction of seizures in 75% of patients.[21]

Topiramate's primary side effects include nausea, lethargy, nystagmus, dizziness, dysarthria, and tremor.[17] It may result in excessive nervousness and difficulty with attention and concentration. Less frequently it will cause weight loss and renal stones. It rarely will cause hepatotoxicity or hematological difficulties.

Vigabatrin

Vigabatrin is also an oral agent that is rapidly absorbed, reaching peak levels within 1–2 h.[16] Its half-life is 6–8 h. It is not protein-bound and is excreted unchanged in the urine. Vigabatrin results in a decrease of phenytoin levels but does cause a significant increase in other anticonvulsant serum levels. Vigabatrin's mechanism of action is believed to be related to alterations in GABA.

Clinical trials have been primarily performed in adults, but vigabatrin has been extensively tested in children with refractory seizures. There seems to be clear efficacy to patients with complex partial seizures, and as an adjunct drug for patients with intractable partial seizures. Children with partial epilepsies seem to benefit the most from vigabatrin, although children with Lennox-Gastaut and infantile spasms also have benefited.

In children, vigabatrin's primary side effects are agitation and hyperactivity, which occurs in 4–26% of patients. Sedation was noted in a sizable minority of patients, as was occasional insomnia, nausea, vomiting, and ataxia. In animal studies, vigabatrin has been shown to cause intramyelinic vacuolation or edema in rodent and dog brains; to date, this toxicity has not been seen in humans, although an association between drug use and optic neuritis has been raised.[22] Drug levels may be useful in monitoring vigabatrin efficacy, but, as with the other newer anticonvulsants, relationships between vigabatrin efficacy and toxicity and serum drug levels have not been well delineated.

Status Epilepticus

The treatment of status epilepticus deserves separate mention.[23] A variety of drugs can be used to treat status epilepticus, and there is reason to believe that rapid control will result in fewer long-term sequelae. The benzodiazepines are the most rapidly effective drugs in the treatment of status epilepticus; however, their use can induce depression of respiration and hypotension. Diazepam has a relatively short half-life, as its effects usually are limited to approximately 30 min. Lorazepam has a longer half-life (4–8 h) and is probably equivalent to diazepam in efficacy. The acute monitoring of benzodiazepine drug concentrations is usually not useful in the management of status epilepticus.

Phenytoin has almost as rapid an onset of action as the benzodiazepine derivatives. It has a relatively long half-life and does not cause significant central nervous system depression. For these reasons it is the drug of choice when monitoring the level of consciousness is of major importance in patients with recurrent seizures. Doses of 18–20 mg/kg will result in drug concentrations of 18–26 ug/mL, levels which are often needed for the control of status epilepticus. Acute monitoring of drug concentrations post-infusion can be a useful adjunct to treatment of patients receiving phenytoin. Fosphenytoin is increasingly used, instead of phenytoin, for treatment of status epilepticus.[24] As stated previously, fosphenytoin has significant advantages over phenytoin in that it can be given intramuscularly and causes less toxicity when given intravenously if there is extravasation at the intravenous site. Also, its infusion at a higher rate equivalent than phenytoin (150 mg/min phenytoin equivalent) may partially overcome the need for conversion of phosphenytoin to phenytoin by body phosphatases and make it equally as efficacious as phenytoin in the treatment of status epilepticus.

Phenobarbital is also used frequently in patients with status epilepticus. However, it has a less rapid onset of action than the benzodiazepines or phenytoin. It also depresses consciousness and respiration, especially when used after a benzodiazepine. Usually doses of 10–30 mg/kg are needed for seizure control. Monitoring of drug concentrations also can be useful in the determination of optimum dose of the drug.

MIGRAINE HEADACHES

Headaches are extremely common in pediatric patients. The term "headache" covers a wide variety of symptoms and has many different causes.[25] Migraine is a specific form of headache that may occur in up to 5% of patients by age 15. Half of all individuals who develop migraine headaches have their first attack before age 20. In children, the classical migraine headache is uncommon, and a variety of different criteria have been proposed for diagnosing childhood migraine. In essence, a diagnosis is made in a child who has recurrent headaches, often associated with nausea or vomiting, that are throbbing and relieved primarily by rest.[26] There is usually a family history of migraine and auras may occur, but are less frequent than in adults. The episodes may be triggered by specific phenomena, such as anxiety, fatigue, stress, menses, and diet (chocolate, nitrites, and monosodium glutamate). By definition, patients will have no other reason for the headaches.

Despite the common nature of this disorder, the underlying pathophysiology of migraine headaches has never been fully elucidated.[27] Abnormalities of regional cerebral blood flow have been documented in patients with migraine. Initially, there is a period of cortical hypoperfusion which may be associated with an aura or other focal neurologic deficits; rebound hyperperfusion has not been documented.

The role of neurotransmitters as a cause or a sequelae of this vascular change remains unclear. Serotonin has been most commonly implicated as the major neurotransmitter involved in migraine attacks. This is because serotonin is known to cause vasoconstriction in certain vascular structures and vasodilation in others. However, a direct relationship with serotonin has never been proven, and other neurotransmitters, including the prostaglandins, prolactin, and gamma-amino-butyric acid, have also been implicated in migraine. Others have postulated that migraine is a state of central neuronal hyperexcitability and that a variety of different excitatory amino acids cause an activation of neuronal depolarization.

Recently, much of the new concepts concerning a pathogenesis for migraine headaches have centered on the trigeminovascular system.[28] This trigeminovascular system focuses on the double-ended trigeminal sensory axon as a major component of the migraine circuit, as its axon has one terminal on the pain-sensitive cranial vessels and the other terminal on the nucleus caudalis trigeminalis. Orthodromic conduction from the blood vessel wall through the trigeminal nucleus will transmit pain from the vessel to the brain by liberating transmitter substances. Antidromic conduction will cause dilatation and inflammation of the vessel, which has been termed neurogenic inflammation. In this way, the trigeminovascular system can function as a mechanism through which impulses from the higher centers of the brain can impact via the nucleus caudalis trigeminalis to send discharges down the trigeminal sensory axon, thus resulting in "inflamed vessels" and a vascular headache. Through such a mechanism, outside stimuli, such as stress and bright light, can access the pain mechanism and cause a vascular headache.

Receptors located at either end of the trigeminal axon vessel wall can be manipulated to potentially relieve or prevent vascular headaches.[29] This has intensified interest on serotonin receptors which are on the surface of the trigeminovascular system; however, other sites may also be important in migraine, including opioid, histamine, and neurokinin receptors. Neocortical spreading depression, an electrophysiological phenomena, may be one mechanism to initiate a migraine headache.[30] One biochemical mechanism may be decreased intracellular magnesium levels.[29, 30]

The continuum between migraine headaches and tension headaches remains controversial. It has been postulated that the pathophysiology of various types of headaches, which have been clinically separated, may be quite similar.

Treatment

As can be expected, given the uncertainty concerning the pathogenesis of migraine attacks, treatment has been primarily empiric.[31] In general, most patients with infrequent headaches do not require any specific treatment.[31] At times, avoidance of situations or foods that trigger migraine can decrease the frequency of attacks. Other forms of nonpharmacological treatment include psychotherapy and biofeedback.

Abortative Treatment

In adults, medications that acutely abort the attack, such as ergotamine and various combinations of ergotamine derivatives, are most commonly used. These drugs seem to be useful only early in the course of the migraine (best used during the aura), and since most children do not have well-defined auras or cannot determine when their headaches are beginning, the use of these drugs in pediatrics is quite limited. Ergotamines are well absorbed after oral dosage, but plasma concentrations after rectal administration are higher.[32] Peak plasma concentrations after oral administration are achieved after 2 h. For reasons which are unclear, administration of caffeine simultaneous with the ergotamines increases its rate of absorption and peak plasma concentrations. This has led to the use of combinations of caffeine and ergotamines in various treatment preparations. Ergotamine can also be given intramuscularly. The effective intramuscular dose is approximately 10% of the oral dose and absorption from the intramuscular site is lower.

Ergotamines are primarily metabolized by the liver and excreted in the bile. Drug level monitoring has not been useful in determining ergotamine efficacy. Elevated levels of ergotamine are toxic and chronic overuse may cause vascular abnormalities, including coldness and numbness of the feet and legs and muscle pain. Ergotamines may also cause headaches, nausea, vomiting, diarrhea, and dizziness.

Sumatriptan and Other 5-HTP Type 1 Receptor Agonists

Sumatriptan is an antimigraine medication that is a selective agonist for the 5-hydroxytryptophan type 1 receptor.[33, 34] It may be given by subcutaneous injection, oral administration, or intranasal spray. After subcutaneous injection, Sumatriptan reaches a peak serum concentration within minutes (12 minutes in adult trials) and has extremely high bioavailability.[33] Very little of the Sumatriptan is protein bound, and its half-life is approximately 2 h. When given subcutaneously, Sumatriptan reduces headaches in 63% of subjects beginning within 30 min after injection. Sumatriptan is also effective when given orally, but has a relatively slow onset of action; the majority of patients report relief 2–4 h after a dose.[33] The efficacy of oral Sumatriptan is limited by the penetration of the gut blood barrier and the drug is said to have a 14% bioavailability.[33, 35] Gastric stasis and vomiting also interfere with oral absorption. Intranasal injection overcomes the gut blood barrier and also overcomes the need for subcutaneous injection.[34] After intranasal administration, pain relief was achieved at 2 h in over 60% of patients. After initial efficacy, approximately one-third of patients will develop recurrent headaches and possibly require more medication.[33-36]

Although Sumatriptan has been primarily tested in adults, it has been utilized in older children with migraine. It is the first antimigraine abortive medication that seems to have efficacy after the migraine has been present for more than a few minutes.

Other similar drugs are or will soon be available. Zolmitriptan is a drug that is quite similar to Sumatriptan.[37, 38] It has better oral bioavailability than Sumatriptan and may have an extended duration of action. It also has a greater lipid solubility and ability to penetrate the blood brain barrier. Bioavailability studies suggest a 40% absorption rate and an efficacy rate equal to or superior to Sumatriptan. Recurrence rates after Zolmitriptan seem similar to those seen with Sumatriptan. Naratriptan has a longer half-life and a higher oral bioavailability than Sumatriptan.[39] For this reason, Naratriptan may also offer some clinical advantage over Sumatriptan.

With all of these derivatives, adverse side effects are similar. Nearly 40% of patients experience tingling, heat sensations, and burning sensations. Flushing, chest discomfort, and increased drug discomfort may also be noted. Weakness, pain, and stiffness have been found in adult trials. Ten percent of patients will develop some degree of dizziness. Given these drugs' relatively short half-life, measurement of serum or plasma drug levels is usually not an issue. It has been suggested that repeating the dose of Sumatriptan 30–45 min following initial dose may be more effective, but this has not been clearly shown. It should also be noted that these drugs have not been widely tested in pediatrics. Studies with Sumatriptan and Naratriptan have been completed and children over 12 years of age have shown similar toxicity profiles.

Prophylactic Treatment

If migraines are frequent enough to require treatment, most pediatric patients respond best to chronic prophylactic treatment. There is no such thing as a best medication for migraine. Results seem as dependent on the enthusiasm of the caregiver as on the drug itself.

Propranolol

Propranolol is probably the most widely used prophylactic agent for migraine.[31] Its effects include prevention of arterial dilatation through blocking beta receptors, blocking of catecholamine-induced platelet aggregation, decreased platelet adhesiveness, and prevention of epinephrine release. Patients are usually begun at 10–20 mg/d, and dosage is increased until the symptoms are relieved or bradycardia occurs.

Propranolol is given only as an oral drug for migraine. Although it is rapidly absorbed, after absorption it is rapidly cleared through the liver, which results in low overall bioavailability and marked interindividual differences of plasma concentrations after oral administration. Propranolol is bound to plasma proteins and is usually completely metabolized before urinary excretion. After chronic oral administration, the half-life of the drug is approximately 4 h, so its use often requires multiple dosages during the day. Side effects of propranolol include acute heart failure, precipitation of asthma in predisposed patients, and masking of the early symptoms of hypoglycemia. Nausea, vomiting, and mild diarrhea have been reported, as have been rare central nervous system effects including hallucinations, nightmares, and insomnia. Drug concentration monitoring usually is not useful, and the best measure of potential toxicity is probably pulse rate taken approximately 45 min after an oral dose.

Cyproheptadine

Cyproheptadine can also be used as prophylaxis.[31] It has both antihistamine and calcium channel-blocking properties. Cyproheptadine is well absorbed after oral use and has a relatively long half-life, allowing for twice-daily dosage. Its side effects include drowsiness and dry mouth. In children, it may also cause weight gain. Again, dosage is variable and is usually slowly increased until symptoms of sedation are seen. Patients usually begin on approximately 4 mg a day, in divided dosages, and the dose is increased as tolerated.

Calcium Channel Blockers

Recently calcium channel blockers have been used in patients with migraine.[31] In fact, some researchers report that these drugs are the treatment of choice in patients with migraine. The use of calcium channel blockers in pediatrics has been limited to date, and the overall safety of these drugs and how they should be used is poorly documented. The most common calcium channel blocker utilized in children with migraine is Verapamil. Verapamil is well absorbed following oral administration, but is rapidly metabolized by the liver[40]; only approximately 20% of the dose of Verapamil given reaches the systemic circulation. The half-life of Verapamil varies dependent on age; in older children the drug has a longer plasma half-life and a decreased clearance than in adults. Children can be dosed on a twice-daily basis. Side effects of Verapamil include cardiac toxicity, hypotension, nausea, vomiting, constipation, and hepatotoxicity.

Other Agents

Nonsteroidal anti-inflammatory drugs have been widely used in adults.[31] Their safety, especially in regard to long-term gastrointestinal side effects, is poorly documented in children. Amitriptyline has also been used in children with migraine, especially in those patients who seem to have a mixed-headache syndrome.

Amitriptyline is well absorbed after oral administration, but due to its long half-life and significant variability in drug metabolism, drug levels may vary. Monitoring of blood levels, however, has been found to be of some use. Measurement of blood concentrations may be helpful, but it is usually as effective to monitor dose-related side effects, including dizziness, dry mouth, visual blurring, and urinary retention.

Anti-epileptics, such as phenytoin and phenobarbital, also have been recommended for the prevention of migraine.[26] A relationship between drug concentrations and efficacy has not been shown. Methysergide is a drug with known antiserotonergic effects. Although it is an effective drug in treating migraine, its long-term use may cause retroperitoneal, pleural, and cardiac fibrosis. Use in pediatrics has been quite limited.

MOVEMENT DISORDERS (excluding Gilles-de-la-Tourette's Syndrome)

Movement disorders are not an uncommon accompaniment of many neurologic illnesses.[41] A variety of different movements may occur, including tremor, myoclonus, chorea, athetosis, and dystonia. Multiple types of abnormal movements may occur in the same patient. Appropriate treatment is dependent on correct clinical diagnosis. The neuronal pathways involved in the control of movement are extremely complex. The motor cortex, brainstem, cerebellum, and spinal cord all play a role in the coordination of movements.However, the basal ganglia or its direct connections are the areas most commonly implicated as the cause of movement disorders. The neuronal pathways that course through the basal ganglia and their interactions are extremely complex and involve a variety of neurotransmitters, including dopamine, serotonin, gamma-amino-butyric acid, glutamic acid, epinephrine, and acetylcholine. Treatment is usually aimed at modulating a believed imbalance between neurotransmitters. Although these neurotransmitters and their roles are increasingly being elucidated, most treatment remains empiric.

Dystonia/Choreoathetosis

In cases where localized treatment with drugs such as botulism toxin is not possible, symptomatic treatment for dystonia usually involves anticholinergic drugs.[42] Monitoring of drug concentrations is usually unnecessary in these conditions, as these anticholinergic drugs are slowly increased until there is evidence of undue toxicity, usually sedation. Some patients will benefit from additive treatment with benzodiazepine derivatives, levodopa, or bromocriptine. Other drugs which are at times effective include carbamazepine, tetrabenazine, clonazepam, and baclofen.

Choreoathetosis may also respond to pharmacological treatment. Therapy with different agents probably working by different mechanisms, such as haloperidol, diazepam, and valproate, has been reported to be beneficial. Drug concentration monitoring for patients on these medications usually is not particularly helpful. The use of phenothiazine derivatives and drugs such as haloperidol is limited by the potential long-term side effects of these drugs on movement, including the development of acute and tardive dyskinesias.

TOURETTE'S SYNDROME

Clinical Aspects

Tourette's syndrome (TS), first described in 1885, is characterized by tics, i.e., rapid, repetitive, and purposeless contractions of muscle groups. Typically, the tics first present in the facial region and often progress in a cephalocaudal fashion to involve other muscle groups. Phonic tics are included in the syndrome and consist of barks, grunts, sniffling, and other guttural noises. Vocal tics can also include words and phrases. Coprolalia (i.e., the explosive utterance of obscenities) is one of the more dramatic features of TS and occurs with a frequency of about 30%. Motor tics tend to precede vocal tics. The symptoms tend to wax and wane in severity throughout the course of the disorder. Recently, investigators have been impressed with the phenomenological experience of patients with TS, especially descriptions of the "inner tension" associated with efforts to suppress the "irresistible" urge to tic and the relief experienced following discharge of a tic.

A major survey of school children in Monroe County, New York, suggested that a low estimate of the prevalence of TS is 28.7 cases per 100,000 pupils.[43] The data also suggested that milder presentations of TS exist in the community; for example, only 18 of 41 identified children required pharmacotherapy. In this survey, among the biological relatives of 39 probands about whom family history could be obtained, 56.4% had tics or TS.

Obsessive-compulsive disorder (OCD) can coexist with TS or be another alternative phenotypic expression of the genotype for TS. The frequency of coexisting OCD in 27 probands with TS was 52%,[44] and it is likely that OCD is an alternative expression of TS. A genetic relationship between Attention Deficit/Hyperactivity Disorder (ADHD) and TS[44] has not been proven. Although 60% of 27 TS probands demonstrated coexisting ADHD, there was no enrichment of ADHD among biological relatives of TS probands who did not also manifest ADHD. In the absence of biological markers, the genetic relatedness of ADHD and TS is hard to study because attentional problems, hyperactivity, and impulsiveness may be the earliest manifestations of TS itself. Also, coexistence of the two disorders may be a function of the high prevalence rate of ADHD in the general population rather than a genetic relatedness.

Pathophysiology

There is enormous interest in the likelihood that, at least in some patients, the onset OCD and tic disorders in childhood results from autoimmune phenomena associated with group A beta-hemolytic streptococcal infections.[45] For example, symptom exacerbations in a subgroup of children with OCD and tic disorders are temporarily associated with this type of active infection. The acronym PANDAS, which stands for pediatric autoimmune neuropsychiatric disorders associated with streptococcal infections, is used to designate these disorders in children. In a recent study, a group of children with PANDAS were shown to have a significantly higher frequency of a specific DR+ surface antigen on their peripheral blood cells (designated D8/17), compared with a group of normal control children. Furthermore, the frequency of the D8/17 cell surface marker in the children with PANDAS was similar to that seen in a comparison group of children with Sydenham's chorea, an autoimmune disorder of the basal ganglia caused by beta-hemolytic streptococcal infections. Interestingly, 90–100% of patients with a history of rheumatic fever are D8/17 positive, compared with a basal rate of 5–15% in healthy volunteers, suggesting that it may be a trait marker of susceptibility to beta-hemolytic streptococcal infection. This observation of an increased frequency of the D8/17 cell surface marker in children with PANDAS suggests that its measurement could identify children at risk to develop PANDAS, and immunomodulatory therapies may have an important role in the treatment of some children with OCD and tic disorders, including Tourette's syndrome.[45]

The substantia nigra, basal ganglia, and their interconnections with the frontal cortex are probable sites of anatomic involvement in TS.[44] The pathophysiology of TS is not likely to be confined to an abnormality of a single retrotransmitter system. The possible effectiveness of clonidine, an alpha$_2$-adrenergic agonist, in the treatment of TS would implicate noradrenergic mechanisms.[46] The potential relatedness of OCD to TS and the salutary effects of selective serotonin-reuptake blockers in the treatment of OCD have stimulated interest in serotonergic abnormalities.[44] Dopaminergic mechanisms are implicated by the salutary therapeutic effects of D-2 dopamine receptor antagonists and the reported lowered CSF levels of homovanillic acid (HVA) at baseline and after probenecid loading in patients with TS.[44]

Diminished presynaptic dopaminergic activity may also result in postsynaptic dopamine receptor supersensitivity. This increased sensitivity of postsynaptic dopamine receptors would explain the therapeutic action of D-2 receptor antagonists and agents that dampen presynaptic dopaminergic activity. Moreover, hypersensitive dopamine receptors could explain the heightened sensitivity of some patients to exacerbation of their tics following psychostimulant administration.

In an innovative *in vivo* morphometric study, 10 pairs of monozygotic twins concordant for Tourette's syndrome (TS), but discordant for the severity of tics, were studied with quantitative magnetic resonance imaging (MRI) scans.[47] In general, the more severely affected twins had small (about 6%) but significant reductions of their right caudate volumes. Specifically, a reduction of the volume of the anterior portion of the right caudate was observed in nine of the more severely affected twins, compared with their less severely affected co-twins. Also, an association was found between a loss of the normal asymmetry of lateral ventricular volume and severity. Severity appeared to be associated with a reduction of left lateral ventricular volume and a reversal of the normally observed "left greater than right" asymmetry. Because of the genetic identity of the twin pairs, environmental insults that probably occurred prenatally are the likely causes of the structural changes associated with severity. Consistent with this speculation, greater tic severity has been reported in the monozygotic twin with the lower birthweight. Also, there was a correlation between the difference scores within monozygotic twin pairs for tic severity and birthweight. In any event, these data further implicate the caudate nucleus in the pathophysiology of TS.

Treatment

The mainstay of the pharmacotherapy of TS is a dopamine antagonist (especially haloperidol or pimozide) administered in low, individually titrated doses.[48, 49] Clinical trials with more selective D-2 dopamine receptor antagonists are especially promising. Neuroleptic medications do not totally remit tics, but are effective in reducing the severity of the symptomatology by as much as 80% in as many as 80% of affected patients.

Haloperidol has been the most widely used drug. Typically, maximal daily dosages of haloperidol are below 10 mg. Children are very sensitive to the extrapyramidal and sedative side effects of haloperidol; limitations to dosing may also result from subtle side effects such as cognitive blunting, depression, and school phobia. Haloperidol tends to have an erratic and unpredictable pattern of absorption. The drug is highly lipophilic, highly protein bound, and accumulates in brain. Haloperidol has a long elimination half-life and the biological effects of single doses persist for up to 24 h. Haloperidol is metabolized by N-dealkylation. The resultant breakdown products are conjugated with glucuronic acid and are inactive. Drug monitoring is usually not helpful. Concentrations greater than 6 ng/mL have been found to be associated with increased side effects in children.

Movement disorders are the most common severe side effect of haloperidol and include tardive dyskinesias, which are abnormal involuntary movements, particularly of the face or tongue. The reported rates of tardive dyskinesia in children have ranged between 29% and 63%. Other side effects are common and include sedation, dizziness, confusion, and seizures. Neuroleptic malignant syndrome, manifested by hyperthermia and extrapyramidal symptoms, is a rare but potentially fatal side effect. Another potential side effect in childhood is development of increased anxiety or depression. In young children, haloperidol is begun at 0.25 mg/d, and dosage adjustments, if necessary, are made about weekly.

Pimozide may be associated with fewer side effects than haloperidol.[48-50] Moreover, pimozide, a diphenylbutylpiperidine compound, possesses the additional property of blockade of voltage-sensitive calcium ion channels,[51] which may be very relevant to its therapeutic action in TS. Pimozide drug monitoring has not been found to be of utility in evaluating response to treatment.

Calcium channel antagonists (especially of the dihydropyridine class) have been reported to be therapeutically effective in a few cases when administered alone or in combination with a neuroleptic medication.[52, 53] Dampening of noradrenergic transmission by low doses of clonidine may be effective in about 50% of patients.[46] When effective, the onset of clonidine's therapeutic action may emerge slowly over the course of months. Moreover, clonidine may influence preferentially a different profile of symptoms than neuroleptic medications, especially the inner tension associated with the disorder.

Although psychostimulants may exacerbate tics, some authors advocate their adjunctive administration with neuroleptic medications.[49, 55] The rationale for psychostimulant administration is twofold: psychostimulants address the ADHD often associated with TS, and they antagonize the unpleasant side effects of sedation and depression associated with neuroleptic medication. The availability of selective serotonin-reuptake blockers, their salutary therapeutic effects in OCD, and the high frequency of coexisting OCD in patients with TS have stimulated interest in trials in patients with TS and OCD. There is also some provocative data showing that opiate antagonists may reduce the frequency of motor and phonic tics.[56]

Risperidone, an atypical antipsychotic medication with prominent D_2 and 5-HT_2 receptor-blocking properties, shows promise as an effective medication for treatment of the tics in TS.[57] Thirty eight children, adolescents, and adults with TS enrolled in a 4-week open-label trial of risperidone. The motor and vocal tics of the patients were not adequately treated by conventional neuroleptic medications and clonidine, either because of poor response or limiting side effects. The primary outcome measure of efficacy was the Yale Global Tic Severity Scale (YGTSS), which was administered at baseline and after 4 weeks of active medication. Fifteen patients had the commonly associated comorbidities of OCD ($n = 98$), attention deficit/hyperactivity disorder (ADHD; $n = 5$), or both comorbid conditions ($n = 1$). Nine patients with OCD were treated concurrently with serotonin reuptake blockers and four patients with ADHD received methylphenidate during the trial. At the end of the trial, the titrated dosages of risperidone ranged from 0.5 mg to 9 mg (mean = 2.7 mg).

Twenty-two of the 31 patients (58%) improved and 8 patients (21%) withdrew from the trial prematurely because of an inability to tolerate the side effects. Interestingly, side effects included akathisia ($n = 4$) and dystonic reactions ($n = 2$); in a similar dosage range , extrapyramidal side effects are reported to occur rarely in patients with schizophrenia. Also, in one patient who remained on risperidone after the conclusion of the trial because of significant improvement of self-abusive tics, galactorrhea occurred and prompted discontinuation of risperidone. There was no obvious statistical relation between response to treatment with risperidone and age, gender, severity, and types of tics, dose, or concomitant medications and diagnoses. In summary, risperidone may become a useful additional medication for the treatment of TS.

A variety of open-label observations suggest that nicotine can potentiate the therapeutic actions of neuroleptic medications in the treatment of motor and vocal tics in TS.[58] In these studies, the mode of nicotine delivery has been the chewing of Nicorrette® gum and the application of a transdermal nicotine patch (TNP). The experiences of 16 children with TS (14 males and 2 females) aged 9–15 years treated with TNP, titrated to deliver 7 mg of nicotine in 24 h, and concomitant neuroleptic medications were reported. The concomitant neuroleptic medications included haloperidol ($n = 11$), pimozide ($n = 4$), and perphenazine ($n = 1$). The primary outcome measure of efficacy in this trial was the Yale Global Tic Severity Scale (YGTSS). After thefirst application of TNP, mean tic severity on the YGTSS was reduced significantly by 36%. Moreover, 12 of the 16 patients improved, showing total score reductions ranging from 25% to 80%; total improvement was equal to or greater than 50% in 6 patients.

The responses to the first application of TNP were assessed at various times, ranging from 1 to 120 days after initial application. Clearly, this lack of uniformity in the time of assessment, together with the absence of a placebo control, confound any meaningful attempt at the quantitative assessment of the size of the therapeutic effect because peak effects could be missed and improvements could be epiphenomena of naturally occurring variability in the course and severity of symptoms.

Fourteen of the children received a second application of TNP, which corroborated the beneficial impressions associated with the first application. In fact, after the second application, some patients appeared to have become sensitized to its therapeutic effect. Side effects of TNP included itching at the site of application, nausea and vomiting. The authors were encouraged by a potential therapeutic indication for TNP in the treatment of patients with TS.

OBSESSIVE-COMPULSIVE DISORDER

Clinical Aspects

The phenomenology of obsessive-compulsive disorder (OCD) shows a marked continuity between the presentations in childhood and adulthood.[60] Children experience their rituals and/or preoccupations as unreasonable, causing substantial interference with their lives. Rituals occur more frequently than obsessions, although they often coexist, and "pure" ritualizers can be identified (i.e., patients whose rituals were executed without accompanying mental content). "Washing," "repeating" and "checking" rituals are most common; obsessions tend to focus on avoidance of dirt and contamination, danger to self and family, and religiosity.

The emergence of OCD in the presence of a "compulsive" personality disorder is relatively rare in children. In one series of patients, children had a higher than expected presentation of coexisting developmental disability.[60] Consistent with the literature on adults, other associated disorders include depression (probably secondary to OCD) and anxiety. Even in children, rituals are performed secretively, delaying their recognition by parents by about 4–6 m. Also, parents frequently participate in the rituals; they often prepare checklists and provide reassurance that everything is orderly.

OCD occurs in the first-degree biological relatives of about 25% of patients. The pattern of symptoms in affected family members differs from that in probands. A minimum estimate for the lifetime prevalence rate of 0.4% is postulated.[61]

In a series of 70 consecutive pediatric OCD cases, there was a 2 to 1 ratio of affected males to females; moreover, males had an earlier age of onset.[62] There is a higher likelihood of chronic motor tics in both patients with childhood-onset OCD and their first degree relatives, especially male relatives. In one series, at least 20% of the children with OCD had chronic motor tics. These data are consistent with a relationship between OCD and Tourette's syndrome and support a rationale for haloperidol potentiation of selective serotonin reuptake inhibitors in the treatment of refractory conditions.[63] There is also an increased statistical association between hyperactivity and learning disability in children with OCD. It is now realized that in many instances pediatric OCD is a chronic disorder that may require long-term maintenance pharmacotherapy with selective serotonin reuptake inhibitors.[63] In a 2- to 5-year followup of 54 children and adolescents treated for OCD, 13% remained severely impaired and 30% continued to have moderate disability. Social avoidance because of the patient's symptomatology is a "malignant" complication of pediatric OCD and a poor predictor of outcome.

Pathophysiology

A variety of converging evidence implicates a neurologic abnormality, especially one that may involve the basal ganglia as its anatomic focus, in the pathophysiology of OCD. Tics and "soft signs" suggestive of neurodevelopmental delay occur in a high percentage of children with OCD.[59] Moreover, in one series, choreiform movements occurred in about one-third of children with OCD.[59] The genetic relatedness of TS and OCD has already been discussed. OCD also has been described in patients with demonstrable basal ganglia lesions occurring, for example, after a wasp sting, carbon monoxide poisoning, and the encephalitis lethargica epidemic of 1916–1917.[59] A Positron Emission Tomography (PET) scan study observed increased glucose utilization in the caudate nuclei of 14 OCD patients with and without coexisting major depression, in comparison to a group of 14 unipolar depressed patients and 14 controls.[59] This PET scan result was not replicated in a group of 18 adults with childhood-onset OCD compared with 18 controls;[59] however, in the latter study, elevated metabolic rates were observed in frontal cortex and cingulate gyri of the OCD patient group.

There are known interconnections between the frontal cortex and basal ganglia, and their interruption may be the basis of the palliative effects of capsulotomy and cingulectomy in the neurosurgical treatment of severe OCD. The volume of the caudate nucleus was shown to be reduced bilaterally in a computerized tomographic (CT) scan study comparing 10 male patients with childhood-onset OCD and 10 male controls.[64] Finally, an association between Sydenham's chorea and OCD has provided further evidence of basal ganglia involvement in the pathophysiology of OCD.[65]

Pharmacologic studies suggest a selective behavioral supersensitivity of postsynaptic serotonin receptors in patients with OCD.[66] It has been postulated that the value of selective serotonin reuptake blockers in the pharmacotherapy of OCD may reside in their ability to "down-regulate" postsynaptic serotonin receptors with prolonged administration. Clinically, the anti-obsessional effects of selective serotonin-reuptake blockers emerge after several weeks, consistent with the time course of serotonin receptor down-regulation, whereas the inhibition of serotonin transport occurs immediately. The relevance of serotonergic transmission to the pathophysiology of OCD is supported by studies showing a lowered number of ^{3}H-imipramine binding sites on the platelets of untreated OCD patients, an inverse correlation between CSF 5-hydroxyindoleacetic acid (5-HIAA) concentrations and illness severity at baseline, and a correlation between reduction in platelet serotonin concentrations and clinical improvement with clomipramine treatment.[56, 66-68]

Treatment

In a double-blind controlled study with a crossover design, clomipramine was shown to be superior to placebo in the treatment of early-onset OCD in 19 patients.[69] The anti-obsessional effect required several weeks to emerge and appeared to be independent of depressive symptoms at baseline. Consistent with this latter impression, clomipramine was a more effective anti-obsessional agent than desipramine, a secondary tricyclic antidepressant, in the treatment of children and adolescents.[70, 71] Similarly, fluoxetine, a selective serotonin-reuptake blocker, was reported to be efficacious in the treatment of 4 out of 8 patients with early-onset OCD.[69] Although clomipramine can attenuate symptoms of OCD in short-term clinical trials, it is still too early to know if pharmacologic intervention alters the long-term prognosis of this disorder.

There is no relation between the anti-obsessional effect of clomipramine and its plasma concentrations or those of its metabolites.[56] After 5 weeks of active treatment with clomipramine (dose range 75–200 mg/day), plasma levels of the demethylated metabolite are about 2.5 times greater than the parent compound. The demethylated metabolite is capable of significant blockade of norepinephrine reuptake; thus, the actions of clomipramine *in vivo* may be less selective for serotonergic transmission. Whereas a decrease in platelet serotonin content was associated with a positive response to treatment with clomipramine, there was no association between a drug-induced decrease in platelet serotonin concentration and plasma tricyclic concentrations. These data argue against a simple pharmacokinetic explanation for the anti-obsessional effects of clomipramine. Moreover, in contrast to major depressive disorder, the monitoring of plasma clomipramine concentrations may not be helpful in the treatment of early-onset OCD.

Obsessive-compulsive behaviors occur commonly in as many as 50% of the patients with Tourette's syndrome.[72] In fact, the severity of these associated behaviors is often the major cause of functional impairment. In a naturalistic setting, fluoxetine was used on an open basis to treat the associated obsessive-compulsive behaviors in 30 patients with TS. The 30 patients (22 males and 8 females) ranged in age from 8 to 65 years old. The dosage range of fluoxetine was from 20 to 60 mg/day and the duration of treatment ranged from less than 3 months to more than 1 year. Moreover, the patients were taking a variety of concomitant medications to suppress their tics, including haloperidol, pimozide, sulperide, and clonidine. The primary outcome measure of efficacy for the treatment of the obsessive-compulsive behaviors was a clinical global impression of the severity of the symptomatology. After 6 and 12 weeks of treatment, 66% and 76% of the patients were reported to have some overall improvement, respectively; at both time points, 20% of the patients were rated "much improved." In 2 of the 14 children treated with fluoxetine, the emergence of aggressive behavior necessitated its discontinuation. The authors concluded that fluoxetine warranted further investigation for this specific indication.

ATTENTION-DEFICIT HYPERACTIVITY DISORDER

Clinical Aspects

In the latest revision of the *Diagnostic and Statistical Manual* (DSM-III-R, 3rd ed.) of the American Psychiatric Association, the behavioral syndrome referred to as Attention-Deficit Hyperactivity Disorder (ADHD) is characterized by developmentally inappropriate motor restlessness, impulsiveness, distractibility, and inattention. By definition, the onset of the disorder is before age 7; in fact, its recognition usually occurs when a child enters first grade and must conform to the demands of a structured classroom setting. A subtle neurological substrate is thought to account for the disorder in many children. Target behaviors should be observed in different situations.

The literature on this disorder is vast and has been plagued by inconsistent definitional criteria for its identification. The literature has referred to this behavioral syndrome as attention-deficit disorder with and without hyperactivity, hyperkinetic syndrome of childhood, and minimal brain disorder, among other designations. Depending on the investigation, these terms were more or less restrictive with respect to the diagnostic criteria used for enrolling study patients. For purposes of this review, both ADHD and attention-deficit disorder, with and without hyperactivity, will be employed consistent with the definitions appearing in the DSM-III-R and its earlier version, DSM-III, respectively.

The disorder is often associated with an academic skills disorder or other specific developmental disorders.

Pathophysiology

The initial enthusiasm that measurement of neurotransmitter metabolites in urine and plasma, especially urinary excretion of 3-methoxy-4-hydroxyphenylglycol (MHPG), would clarify the pharmacologic action of the psychostimulants in attention-deficit hyperactivity disorder (ADHD) has waned.[73,74] MHPG is a principal metabolite of norepinephrine, and its reduced urinary excretion in patients treated with dextroamphetamine focused attention on a possible pathophysiologic abnormality of noradrenergic transmission. Hypoperfusion of the striatal region in ADHD has been suggested.[75] Methylphenidate has been shown to increase striatal blood flow significantly. PET studies demonstrate the potential importance of a circuit involving the frontal cortex, caudate nucleus, globus pallidus, and thalamus in ADHD. Adults who have childhood histories of hyperactivity, who have persistent difficulty with inattention and restlessness as adults, and who are also the biologic parents of children with attention-deficit disorder with hyperactivity also demonstrated diminished glucose utilization.[76]

The two primary psychostimulants used in patients with ADHD, methylphenidate and d-amphetamine, are indirect-acting dopamine agonists releasing prejunctional stores of neurotransmitter. Although their clinical effects are similar, methylphenidate and d-amphetamine appear to act on two distinct pools of presynaptic dopamine. Methylphenidate releases dopamine from reserpine-sensitive vesicles, whereas d-amphetamine releases "newly synthesized" dopamine.

There appears to be a good positive correlation between levels of homovanillic acid (HVA) in the cerebrospinal fluid (CSF) of preadolescent boys with ADHD while on placebo and their teachers' ratings of hyperactivity. Furthermore, among preadolescent boys with ADHD, higher baseline CSF HFA values appear to predict a favorable response to psychostimulant medications, after controlling for the potentially confounding factors of age, height, and severity of symptoms at baseline. The authors attribute the therapeutic action of the stimulants to their ability to decrease dopamine turnover.[77] According to this view, dopaminergic transmission is dampened secondary to the stimulation of inhibitory presynaptic autoreceptors. In any event, the CSF data are consistent with a role for dopaminergic transmission in the pathophysiology of ADHD and therapeutic action of psychostimulant medications.

Treatment

Estimates suggest that as many as 700,000 American children receive stimulant medication; methylphenidate is most frequently prescribed for hyperactivity. Initially, there was enormous optimism that the measurement of methylphenidate blood concentrations and the clinical application of pharmacokinetic data would account for responders and nonresponders and reduce or eliminate toxicity, respectively. However, this has not proved to be true.

Absorption of the drug is essentially complete after an oral dose, although much of the parent compound is hydrolyzed before reaching the systemic circulation. Peak serum concentrations are attained in about 1–2 h, and elimination half-lives range from 2.3 to 4.2 h. In addition to its metabolism to ritalinic acid, which is inactive, methylphenidate is para-hydroxylated to an "active" metabolite; however, the significance of the para-hydroxylated metabolite is doubtful because of its low penetrability across the blood-brain barrier.[75, 78]

There is as much as fourfold inter-individual variability with respect to methylphenidate serum levels at 1, 2, and 3 h after an oral dose. Variability does not seem to be related to meals or activity levels, so methylphenidate can be administered with meals in order to avoid stomach aches and anorexia. In addition, serum methylphenidate levels vary within the same individuals on different days. Thus, marked intra-individual variability limits the clinical utility of serum concentrations. Serum concentrations obtained at various time intervals after an oral dose do not correlate with behavioral changes, as measured by teachers and parents or in the laboratory.[78, 79]

In a large study of children with attention-deficit disorder with hyperactivity (ADDH) evaluated in a normal classroom setting, methylphenidate (10–65 mg/d) was shown to "normalize" a variety of target behaviors at 4 and 8 weeks of treatment.[80] Methylphenidate also improves aspects of the mother-child interaction, even in preschool-age children with ADHD. In general, methylphenidate seems to diminish off-task and noncompliant behaviors of the children, while also diminishing the use of commands and directives by the mothers.[81]

An investigation comparing two dose concentrations of methylphenidate (0.3 and 1.0 mg/kg) found that the higher dose was optimal for effecting behavioral improvement, whereas the lower dose resulted in the greatest improvement in a short-term memory task performed in the laboratory.[82] These results heightened early concern that distinct methylphenidate dose-response relations existed for behavioral improvement, academic performance, and cognition. However, most clinical studies have suggested that academic performance and learning of most children does not worsen at doses of methylphenidate above 0.3 mg/kg.[83] In fact, dose-dependent positive effects of methylphenidate on academic performance (at doses of 0.15, 0.3, and 0.6 mg/kg) have been shown.[84]

Chronic treatment does not accelerate methylphenidate metabolism. Tolerance to the beneficial effects of methylphenidate on behavior is not observed. An upward adjustment of dose other than that needed to account for body growth is usually not required.[85]

The issue of stimulant-associated side effects is especially important in view of the fact that in some settings, 3–6% of school-age children are receiving this class of medication.[86] There have been serious concerns that behavioral side effects occurring in school interfere with learning and socialization. The rate of occurrence of side effects has been examined in 83 children who participated in a placebo-controlled crossover study of active dose concentrations of methylphenidate of 0.3 and 0.5 mg/kg twice a day.[86] Serious adverse effects, including tic, dizziness, headache, worsening hyperactivity, and "excessive speech and disjointed thinking," forced 3.6% of the children to terminate the protocol. Insomnia, decreased appetite, stomach aches and headaches occurred significantly more frequently in children receiving the drug. Parental ratings suggested that a small but significant number of children experienced decreased appetite and insomnia in the high-dose methylphenidate condition: 13% and 18% of the children were rated by parents as showing severe decreased appetite and insomnia in the 0.5 mg/kg condition, compared to 1% and 7% in the placebo condition, respectively.

Interestingly, according to the teacher ratings of a subsample of 53 of the 83 children, medication resulted in a decrease of the following "side effects": staring/daydreaming, sadness, and anxiety. Compared with placebo, fewer than half of the children experienced significant side effects. The study also demonstrated a high rate of occurrence of similar side effects in the children receiving placebo. There was no evidence to support concerns that behavioral side effects interfere with school performance. The data do, however, support the importance of clinical monitoring of the emergence of side effects. The higher dose (0.5 mg/kgBID) seemed appropriate for less than 25% of the sample, because of the accompanying side effects.

Symptoms of ADHD coexist frequently with those of TS. Because of theoretical and practical concerns regarding the ability of stimulant medications to either hasten tic onset or worsen coexisting tics, clonidine has been explored as an effective alternative medication in the setting of coexisting ADHD and tic disorder.[87] Initial experience supported the ability of clonidine to reduce impulsivity, motor activity, and attentional disturbances, as well as the severity of tics, in patients with TS. These results have encouraged the exploration of clonidine for the treatment of ADHD alone.

A retrospective review of clonidine's efficacy was performed in 54 children and adolescents with ADHD, 24 of whom fulfilled criteria for a comorbid tic disorder.[87] It is noteworthy that a significant subgroup of these patients received prior treatment with stimulant and antidepressant medications. Overall, 72% of the patients (39 out of 54) showed moderate to marked global improvement of their ADHD symptoms. The frequency of improvement was significantly greater among those children with coexisting tic disorder. The authors speculated that the lower response rate among the children without a comorbid tic disorder could be accounted for by a higher proportion of these children refractory to prior treatment with stimulant and antidepressant medications.[87] However, response rates to clonidine did not differ between those ADHD-alone patients with and without histories of prior treatment. The data support the moderate efficacy of clonidine in ADHD and suggest that clonidine may have a special role in the treatment of ADHD with a comorbid tic disorder. Clonidine was prescribed in a dose range of 0.025 to 0.6 mg/day (mean $= 0.19 \pm 0.02$ [SEM]). Sedation was the most significant limiting side-effect associated with this intervention.

Increasingly, tricyclic antidepressants (TCSs) are employed as effective alternative medications to the stimulants.[88] Because of their longer half-lives, they afford more flexible dosing schedules and are not associated with the same abuse liability. In a retrospective chart review of 58 children and adolescents with ADHD, nortriptyline was shown to be an effective and well-tolerated medication. Of note, all but two of the patients received prior pharmacotherapy on one or more occasions and either did not respond adequately or could not tolerate medication side effects. Moreover, 50 of the children had one or more comorbid psychiatric disorders, including mood disorders, oppositional defiant disorder, conduct disorder, anxiety disorder, developmental learning disorder, pervasive developmental disorder, and OCD.

Twenty-seven of the ADHD patients were treated with nortriptyline and a concurrent medication (i.e., stimulants, lithium carbonate, clonidine, neuroleptics, and anticonvulsants). Seventy-six percent of the patients responded to nortriptyline with moderate to marked improvement; although the study is limited by its retrospective design, the sample reflects the range of patients referred to a child psychiatry clinic in an academic setting.[88] Daily nortriptyline doses ranged between 20 mg and 200 mg and the mean weight-corrected daily dose was 1.94 ± 0.99 mg/kg. Of interest, significantly more patients whose serum levels were between 50 and 150 ng/mL were rated as "markedly improved" than those outside of this range (68% vs. 35%; $p < 0.03$). Medication was discontinued in only one child because of adverse effects. The most commonly occurring side effects were lethargy and gastrointestinal distress ($N = 5$ each). The authors advocated consideration of nortriptyline for treatment-resistant patients with ADHD.[88]

MAJOR DEPRESSIVE DISORDER

Clinical Aspects

From a developmental psychodynamic perspective, there has been controversy as to whether the necessary psychic structures, especially the superego, are developed sufficiently in children for them to manifest a full depressive syndrome. The controversy was resolved in the late 1970s, when it was reported that prepubertal children with major depression could be identified using unmodified adult criteria for the disorder.[89] The phenomenology of major depressive disorder (MDD) in prepubertal children is similar to that of adults; these children show persistence of dysphoria and loss of interest, depressive ideation, and objective symptoms of appetite and sleep disturbances.[90] The magnitude of the clinical problem is large. In one study, about 7% of pediatric inpatients and between 30% and 60% of outpatients attending a child psychiatry clinic met criteria for MDD.[91] A failure to recognize MDD and intervene therapeutically can have disastrous consequences for the development of these children.

Emerging data suggest a strong genetic contribution to the presentation of very early-onset affective disorder. Data suggest that an inverse relation may exist between age of onset and pedigree "loading".[92] Moreover, an earlier age of onset of MDD may be associated with recurrences and a more probable bipolar disorder outcome in adulthood. There has been no obvious Mendelian pattern to the inheritance of affective illness, nor is the nature of what is inherited known (i.e., single gene vs. polygenic influences).

Pathophysiology

Neuroendocrine investigations of prepubertal depressives confirm the existence of biological abnormalities; moreover, these abnormalities often persist following resolution of the depressive episode, suggesting that they may serve as genetic trait markers. The principal neurotransmitters which are implicated in the pathophysiology of depression are norepinephrine, serotonin, and acetylcholine. Abnormalities of growth hormone secretion (after stimulation tests) have also been noted.[93]

Treatment

The recognition of MDD in childhood stimulated systematic evaluation of the therapeutic efficacy of imipramine and other antidepressant medications. The results of these studies emphasize the potential importance of monitoring plasma levels of drug concentrations and pharmacokinetic considerations in the pharmacotherapy of these children. The relation between plasma drug concentration and imipramine efficacy has been documented.[94] A relation appears to exist between reduction in the severity of depression and both the concentration of total drug and desipramine in the plasma. There is not an obvious relationship between response and plasma concentrations of the parent compound alone.

However, the monitoring of plasma concentrations of imipramine and its metabolites has not resulted in improved strategies or guidelines for initial dosing. This is due to wide interindividual variability in steady-state plasma concentrations. Monitoring of plasma concentrations of imipramine and its demethylated metabolite confirms compliance and assists in dosage regulation, enabling the avoidance of subtherapeutic or "toxic" plasma concentrations. Plasma concentrations of imipramine and desipramine greater than 150 ng/mL are usually needed for response.[95] Drug concentrations above 400 ng/mL may result in a toxic-confusional state which may be difficult to distinguish from the depressive symptoms.[94] At times, dosage escalation to the therapeutic range is limited by prolongation of the PR interval, increased heart rate, orthostatic hypotension, irritability, chest pain, and a behavioral syndrome of forgetfulness and perplexity. There is some evidence to suggest that adolescents are less responsive than younger children.[96]

Nortriptyline, the demethylated metabolite of amitriptyline, is the other tricyclic antidepressant whose therapeutic efficacy in the treatment of prepubertal depression has been studied systematically.[97] Secondary demethylated metabolites are predominantly "blockers" of the presynaptic reuptake of norepinephrine. The selection of nortriptyline in these studies was guided, in part, by the data suggesting that desipramine, the secondary demethylated metabolite, was primarily responsible for imipramine's action. Other reasons for the selection of nortriptyline included its safety (especially cardiac safety) in the geriatric population when plasma concentrations are maintained within a "therapeutic" range, and the existence of predictive kinetics for establishing the effective maintenance dose in adults.

Plasma nortriptyline concentrations obtained 24 h after a single oral test dose can be used to predict the daily maintenance dose that would result in steady-state levels between 60 and 100 ng/mL in children and adolescents.[98] This dose range correlates best with response. This predictive approach, based on single-dose kinetics, is useful in identifying "slow" metabolizers who would be at risk for the development of toxic side effects. Plasma concentrations of nortriptyline of less than 100 ng/mL are associated with little cardiotoxicity.[98]

In general, in several open-label studies a relationship between plasma levels of tricyclic antidepressants and therapeutic response in prepubertal children with MDD appeared to exist.[98] However, two placebo-controlled studies involving prepubertal children failed to demonstrate a clear superiority of either imipramine or nortriptyline over placebo. Additionally, placebo-controlled clinical trials with adolescent MDD patients have failed to provide a clear indication of the superiority of medication over placebo. Explanations for the apparent discontinuity between MDD in children, adolescents, and adults have been sought. Possibilities include age-dependent differences in the brain's hormonal milieu, incomplete maturation of relevant neurotransmitter systems (e.g., noradrenergic), inclusion of patients whose illness evolves into bipolardisorder, and depressive phenocopies.[99]

Medication resistance has stimulated exploration of the ability of the lithium ion to "augment" the antidepressant efficacy of tricyclic antidepressants in adolescent MDD patients.[99, 100] In one study, lithium carbonate was added to the imipramine regimen of 24 adolescents who were classified as "nonresponders" after six weeks of monotherapy.[100] Lithium carbonate was initiated at a dose of 900 mg/day in three divided doses and serum levels were adjusted between 0.7 and 1.2 mEq/L; treatment efficacy was assessed after 3 weeks on the combined regimen. Ten of these patients were classified as at least "partial responders" to this regimen. Polyuria and tremor were the most commonly observed side effects and occurred in 7 patients whose serum lithium levels were in the "therapeutic" range. However, side effects did not result in discontinuation of therapy with the lithium ion. The authors concluded that lithium augmentation may be of modest therapeutic benefit in some medication-refractory patients with MDD.[100] Given the relatively common occurrence of refractoriness to tricyclic antidepressants, evaluation of the therapeutic efficacy of reuptake inhibitors is under active investigation.[99] Of course, compliance with a low-tyramine diet is a major limitation in the treatment of children and adolescents with monoamine oxidase inhibitors.

SUMMARY

In summary, a variety of therapeutic agents are used in child psychiatry. Their indications, desired therapeutic concentrations, and maintenance doses are given in Table 12–2.

TABLE 12–2. Therapeutic Profile of Commonly Used Agents in Child Psychiatry

Drug Class	Indication	Therapeutic Drug Concentration (ug/mL)	Maintenance Dose
Antidepressants			
Imipramine	Depression	0.125–0.225	Max. dosage 5 mg/kg/d
	Hyperactivity	N/A*	Mean dosage 80 mg/d
	Sleep Disorders	N/A*	10–50 mg at bedtime
	Pavor Nocturnus and Somnambulism	N/A*	
	Enuresis	N/A*	75 mg at bedtime
Nortriptyline	Depression	0.060–0.100	20–50 mg/d
Clomipramine	Obsessive-Compulsive Disorder	N/A*	75–200 mg/d
Desipramine	Hyperactivity	N/A*	Max. dosage 5 mg/kg/d
Stimulants			
Methylphenidate	Attention-Deficit Hyperactivity Disorder	Uninformative	10–60 mg/d
Dextroamphetamine	Attention-Deficit Hyperactivity Disorder	N/A*	2.5–40 mg/d
Alpha$_2$-Adrenergic Agonist			
Clonidine	Tourette's Syndrome	N/A*	0.05–0.6 mg/d
Neuroleptic Medication			
Haloperidol	Tourette's Syndrome	N/A*	0.5–10 mg/d
	Schizophrenia	N/A*	1.5–2.4 mg/d
	Pervasive Developmental Disorder, Infantile Autism	N/A*	0.5–3.0 mg/d
Pimozide	Tourette's Syndrome	N/A*	2.0–12.0 mg/d

*N/A = not applicable

REFERENCES

1. Scheuer ML, Pedley, TA. The evaluation and treatment of seizures. NEJM 1990;323:1468–74.
2. Commission on Classification and Terminology of the International League Against Epilepsy. Proposal for revised classification of epilepsies and epileptic syndromes. Epilepsia 1989;30:389–99.
3. Theodore WH, Dorwart R, Holmes, M, et al. Neuroimaging in refractory partial seizures: comparison of PET, CT, and MRI. Neurology 1986;36:750–9.
4. Delgado-Escueta AV, Ward AA, et al. New wave of research in the epilepsies. In: Delgado-Escueta AV, Ward AA, Woodbury DM, Porter RJ, eds. Advances in neurology. New York: Raven Press, 1986;44:3–55.
5. Fairgold CL, Browning RA. Mechanisms of anticonvulsant drug action: I. Drugs primarily used for generalized tonic-clonic and partial epilepsies. Eur J Ped 1987;146:2–7.
6. Faingold CL, Browning, RA. Mechanisms of anticonvulsant drug action: II. Drugs primarily used for absence epilepsy. Eur J Pediatr 1987;146:8–14.

7. Ramsey RE. The use of phenytoin and carbamazepine in the treatment of epilepsy. Neurology Clinics, Epilepsy 1986;4:585–600.
8. Woodbury DM. Absorption, distribution and excretion—Phenytoin. In: Levy RH, Dreifuss FE, Mattson RH, et al., eds. Antiepileptic drugs. New York: Raven Press, 1989:177–96.
9. Browne TR, LeDuc B. Phenytoin: chemistry and biotransformation. In: Levy RH, Mattson RH, Meldrum BS, eds. Antiepileptic drugs, 4th ed. New York: Raven Press, 1995:283–300.
10. Eldon MA, Loewen GR, Vioghtman RE, et al. Pharmacokinetics and tolerance of phenytoin and phenytoin administration intravenously to health subjects. Can J Neurol Sci 1993;20:5180.
11. Morselli PL. Absorption, distribution and excretion—Carbamazepine. In: Levy RH, Deifuss FE, Mattson RH, et al., eds. Antiepileptic drugs. New York: Raven Press, 1989:473–90.
12. Vining EPG. The use of barbiturates and benzodiazepines in the treatment of epilepsy. Neurology Clinics, Epilepsy 1986;4:617–32.
13. Farwell JR, Lee YJ, Hirtz DG, et al. Phenobarbital for febrile seizures: effects on intelligence and seizure recurrence. NEJM 1990;322:364–9.
14. Wallace SJ. Use of ethosuximide and valproate in the treatment of epilepsy. Neurology Clinics, Epilepsy 1986;4:601–16.
15. Levy RH, Shen, DD. Absorption, distribution and excretion—Valproate. In: Levy RH, Dreifuss FE, Mattson RH, et al., eds. Antiepileptic drugs. New York: Raven Press, 1989:583–600.
16. Harden CL. New antiepileptic drugs. Neurology 1994;44:787–95.
17. Kramer LD, Reife RA. Topiramate. In: Engel J Jr, Pedley TA, eds. Epilepsy: a comprehensive textbook. Philadelphia: Lippincott-Raven, 1997:1593–8.
18. Coulter DA, Sombati S, DeLorenzo RJ. Selective effects of topiramate on sustained repetitive firing and spontaneous bursting in cultured hippocampal neurons. Epilepsia 1993;34(S2):5–11.
19. Sombati S, Coulter DA, DeLorenzo RJ. Effects of topiramate on sustained repetitive firing and low Mg^{+2}-induced seizure discharges in cultured hippocampal neurons. Epilepsia 1995;36(Suppl 4):S38.
20. White HS, Brown SD, Skeen GA, Twyman RE. The investigational anticonvulsant topiramate potentiates GABA-evoked currents in mouse cortical neurons. Epilepsia 1995;36(Suppl 4):S34.
21. French JA, Bourgeois BFD, Dreifus FE, et al. An open-label multicenter study of topiramate in patients with the Lennox-Gastaut syndrome. Neurology 1995;45(S4):A250.
22. Gibson JP, Yarington JT, Loudy DE, et al. Chronic toxicity studies with vigabatrin, a GABA inhibitor. Tox Pathol 1990;18:225–38.
23. Leppik IE. Status epilepticus. Neurology Clinics, Epilepsy 1986;4:633–44.
24. Eldon MA, Loewen GR, Voightman RE, et al. Safety, tolerance and pharmacokinetics of intravenous fosphenytoin. Clin Pharmacol Ther 1993;53:212.
25. Olesen J. The classification and diagnosis of headache disorders. Neurology Clinics, Headaches 1996;8:793–9.
26. Prensky AL. Migraine and migrainous variants in pediatric patients. Pediatr Clin North Am 1976;23:461–70.
27. Moskowitz MA. Basic mechanisms in vascular headache. Neurologic Clinics, Headaches 1990;8:801–16.
28. Goadsby PJ, Edvinnson L. The trigeminovascular system and migraine: studies characterizing cerebrovascular and neuropeptide changes seen in humans and cats. Ann Neurol 1993;33:48–56.
29. Moskowitz MA. Neurogenic inflammation in the pathophysiology and treatment of migraine. Neurology 1993;43(Suppl 3):S16-20.
30. Moskowitz MA, Nozaki K, Kraig RP. Neocortical spreading depression provokes the expression of c-fos protein-like immunoreactivity within trigeminal nucleus caudalis via trigeminovascular mechanisms. J Neurosci 1993;13:1167–77.
31. Raskin NH. Modern pharmacology of migraine. Neurology Clinics, Headaches 1990;8:857–66.
32. Rall TW, Schleifer LS. Oxytocin, prostaglandins, ergot alkaloids and other drugs: tocolytic agents. In: Gilman AG, Goodman LS, Rall TW, Murad F, eds. Goodman and Gilman's the pharmacologic basis of therapeutics. New York: Macmillan, 1985:926–45.

33. The Oral Sumatriptan Dose-Defining Group. Sumatriptan: an oral, dose-defining study. Eur Neurol 1991;31:300–5.
34. Ryan R, Elkind A, Baker CC, et al. Sumatriptan nasal spray for the acute treatment of migraine: results of two clinical studies. Neurology 1997;49:1225–38.
35. The Oral Sumatriptan International Multiple-Dose Study Group. Evaluation of a multiple-dose regimen of oral Sumatriptan for the acute treatment of migraine. Eur Neurol 1991;31:306–13.
36. Ferrari MD, James MH, Bates D, et al. Oral Sumatriptan: effect of a second dose, and incidence and treatment of headache recurrences. Cephalalgia 1994;14:330–8.
37. Rapoport AM, Ramadan NM, Adelman JU, et al. Optimizing the dose of Zolmitriptan (Zomig, 311C90) for the acute treatment of migraine. Neurology 1997;49:1210–18.
38. Solomon GD, Cady RK, Klapper MA, et al. The clinical efficacy and tolerability of 2.5 mg Zolmitriptan for the acute treatment of migraine. Neurology 1997;49:1219–25.
39. Mathew NT, Asgharnejad M, Peykamian M, Laurenza A. Naratriptan is effective and well tolerated in the acute treatment of migraine: results of a double-blind, placebo-controlled, crossover study (performed by the Naratriptan S2WA3003 Study Group). Neurology 1997;49:1485–90.
40. Needleman P, Corr PB, Johnson EM. Drugs used for the treatment of aging: organic nitrates, calcium channel blockers, and β-adrenergic antagonists. In: Gilman AG, Goodman LS, Rall TW, Murad F, eds.Goodman and Gilman's the pharmacologic basis of therapeutics. New York: Macmillan, 1985:806–26.
41. Young AB, Penny JB. Neurochemical anatomy of movement disorders. Neurologic Clinics, Symposium on Movement Disorders 1984;2:417–33.
42. Fahn S, Jankovic J. Practical management of dystonia. Neurologic Clinics, Symposium on Movement Disorders 1984;2:555–70.
43. Caine ED, McBride MC, Chiverton P, et al. Tourette's syndrome in Monroe Country school children. Neurology 1988;38:472–5.
44. Chappell PB, Leckman JF, Pauls D, Cohen DJ. Biochemical and genetic studies of Tourette's syndrome: implications for treatment and future research. In: Deutsch SI, Weizman A, Weizman R, eds. Application of basic neuroscience to child psychiatry. New York: Plenum Publishing, 1990:241–60.
45. Swedo SE, Leonard HL, Mittleman BB, et al. Identification of children with pediatric autoimmune neuropsychiatric disorders associated with streptococcal infections by a marker associated with rheumatic fever. Am J Psychiatry 1997; 154:110–12.
46. Cohen DJ, Detlor J, Young JG, Shaywitz BA. Clonidine ameliorates Gilles de la Tourette syndrome. Arch Gen Psychiatry 1980;37:1350–7.
47. Hyde TM, Stacey ME, Coppola R, et al. Cerebral morphometric abnormalities in Tourette's syndrome: a quantitative MRI study of monozygotic twins. Neurology 1995; 45:1176–82.
48. Shapiro AK, Shapiro E, Eisenkraft GJ. Treatment of Gilles de la Tourette syndrome with pimozide. Am J Psychiatry 1983;140:1183–6.
49. Shapiro AK, Shapiro E, Fulop G. Pimozide treatment of tic and Tourette disorders. Pediatrics 1987;79(6):1032–9.
50. Baldessarini RJ. Drugs and the treatment of psychiatric disorders. In: Gilman AG, Goodman LS, Rall TW, Murad F, eds. Goodman and Gilman's the pharmacologic basis of therapeutics. New York: Macmillan, 1985:387–445.
51. Gould RJ, Murphy KMM, Reynolds IJ, Snyder SH. Antischizophrenic drugs of the diphenylbutylpiperidine type act as calcium channel antagonists. Proc Natl Acad Sci USA 1983;80:5122–5.
52. Berg R. A case of Tourette syndrome treated with nifedipine. Acta Psychiatr Scand 1985;72:400–1.
53. Alessi NE, Walden M, Hsieh PS. Nifedipine-haloperidol combination in the treatment of Gilles de la Tourette's syndrome: a case study. J Clin Psychiatry 1989;50:103–4.
54. Brunn RD, Budman CL. Risperidone as a treatment for Tourette's syndrome. J Clin Psychiatry 1996;57:29–31.

55. Sverd J, Gadow KD, Paolicelli LM. Methylphenidate treatment of attention-deficit hyperactivity disorder in boys with Tourette's syndrome. J Am Acad Child Adolesc Psychiatry 1989;28(4):574–9.
56. Sandyk R, Iacono RP, Crinnian C, et al. Effects of naltrexone in Tourette's syndrome (Abstract). Ann Neurol 1986b;20:437.
57. Bruun RD, Budman CL. Risperidone as a treatment for Tourette's syndrome. J Clin Psychiatry 1996; 57:29–31.
58. Silver AA, Shytle D, Philipp MK, Sanbert PR. Case study: long-term potentiation of neuroleptics with transdermal nicotine in Tourette's syndrome. J Am Acad Child Adolesc Psychiatry 1996; 35(12):1631–6.
59. Flament MF, Whitaker A, Rapoport JL, et al. Obsessive compulsive disorder in adolescence: an epidemiological study. J Am Acad Child Adolesc Psychiatry 1988;27(6):764–71.
60. Silver AA, Shytle D, Philipp MK, Sanberg PR. Case study: long-term potentiation of neuroleptics with transdermal nicotine in Tourette's syndrome. J Am Acad Child Adolesc Psychiatry 1996;35(12):1631–6.
61. Swedo SE, Rapoport JL. Neurochemical and neuroendocrine considerations of obsessive-compulsive disorders in childhood. In: Deutsch SI, Weizman A, Weizman R, eds. Application of basic neuroscience to child psychiatry. New York: Plenum Publishing, 1990:275–84.
62. Leonard HL, Rapoport JL. Pharmacoptherapy for childhood obsessive-compulsive disorder. Psychiatric Clinics of North America 1989;12(4):963–70.
63. Rapoport JL, Leonard HL, Swedo SE, Lenane MC. Obsessive compulsive disorder in children andadolescents: issues in management. J Clin Psychiatry 1993;54(6):27–9.
64. Luxenberg JS, Swedo SE, Flament MF, et al. Neuroanatomical abnormalities in obsessive-compulsive disorder detected with quantitative X-ray computed tomography. Am J Psychiatry 1988;145:1089–93.
65. Swedo SE, Rapoport JL, Cheslow DL, et al. High prevalence of obsessive-compulsive symptoms in patients with Sydenham's chorea. Am J Psychiatry 1989;146:246–9.
66. Zohar J, Mueller EA, Insel TR, et al. Serotonergic responsivity in obsessive-compulsive disorder: comparison of patients and healthy controls. Arch Gen Psychiatry 1987;44:946–51.
67. Weizman A, Carmi M, Hermesh H, et al. High-affinity imipramine binding and serotonin uptake in platelets of eight adolescent and ten adult obsessive-compulsive patients. Am J Psychiatry 1986;143:335–9.
68. Flament MF, Rapoport JL, Murphy DL, et al. Biochemical changes during clomipramine treatment of childhood obsessive-compulsive disorder. Arch Gen Psychiatry 1987;44:219–25.
69. Flament MF, Rapoport JL, Berg CJ, et al. Clomipramine treatment of childhood obsessive-compulsive disorder: a double-blind controlled study. Arch Gen Psychiatry 1985;42:977–83.
70. Leonard HL, Swedo S, Rapoport JL, et al. Treatment of childhood obsessive compulsive disorder with clomipramine and desmethylimipramine: a double blind crossover comparison. Psychopharm Bull 1988;24:93–5.
71. Liebowitz MR, Hollander E, Fairbanks J, Campeas R. Fluoxetine for adolescents with obsessive-compulsive disorder (letter). Am J Psychiatry 1990;147(3):370–1.
72. Eapen V. Trimble MR, Robertson MM. The use of fluoxetine in Gilles de la Tourette syndrome and obsessive compulsive behaviours: preliminary clinical experience. Prog Neuro-Psychopharmacol & Biol Psychiatr 1996; 20:727–43.
73. Zametkin AJ, Rapoport JL. Neurobiology of attention deficit disorder with hyperactivity: where have we come in 50 years? J Am Acad Child Adolesc Psychiatry 1987;26:676–86.
74. Elia J, Borcherding BG, Potter WZ, et al. Stimulant drug treatment of hyperactivity: biochemical correlates. Clin Pharmacol Ther 1990;48:57–66.
75. Lou HC, Henriksen L, Bruhn P, et al. Striatal dysfunction in attention deficit and hyperkinetic disorder. Arch Neurol 1989;46:48–52.
76. Zametkin AJ, Nordahl TE, Gross M, et al. Cerebral glucose metabolism in adults with hyperactivity of childhood onset. N Engl J Med 1990;323:1361–6.
77. Castellanos FX, Elia J, Kruesi MJP, et al. Cerebrospinal fluid homovanillic acid predicts behavioral response to stimulants in 45 boys with attention deficit/hyperactivity disorder. Neuropsychopharmacology 1996;14:125–37.

78. Gualtieri CT, Hicks RE. Neuropharmacology of methylphenidate and a neural substrate for childhood hyperactivity. Psychiatric Clinics of North America 1985;8(4):874–92.
79. Gualtieri CT, Wargin W, Kanoy R, et al. Clinical studies of methylphenidate serum levels in children and adults. J Am Acad Child Psychiatry 1982;21(1):19–26.
80. Abikoff H, Gittleman R. The normalizing effects of methylphenidate on the classroom behavior of ADDH children. J Abnormal Child Psychology 1985;13(1):33–44.
81. Barkley RA. The effects of methylphenidate on the interactions of preschool ADHD children with their mothers. J Am Acad Child Adolesc Psychiatry 1988;27:336–41.
82. Sprague R, Sleator E. Methylphenidate in hyperkinetic children: differences in dose effects on learning and social behavior. Science 1977;198:1274–6.
83. Rapport MD, Stoner G, DuPaul GJ, et al. Methylphenidate in hyperactive children: differential effects of dose on academic, learning, and social behavior. J Abnormal Child Psychology 1985;13(2):227–44.
84. Pelham WE, Bender ME, Caddell J, et al. Methylphenidate and children with attention deficit disorder: dose effects on classroom academic and social behavior. Arch Gen Psychiatry 1985;42:948–52.
85. Safer DJ, Allen RP. Absence of tolerance to the behavioral effects of methylphenidate in hyperactive and inattentive children. J Pediatr 1989;115:1003–8.
86. Barkley RA, McMurray MB, Edelbrock CS, Robbins K. Side effects of methylphenidate in childrenwith attention deficit hyperactivity disorder: a systemic, placebo-controlled evaluation. Pediatrics 1990:86:184–92.
87. Steingard R, Biederman J, Spencer T, et al. Comparison of clonidine response in the treatment of attention-deficit hyperactivity disorder with and without comorbid tic disorder. J Am Acad Child Adolesc Psychiatry 1993;32(2):350–3.
88. Wilens TE, Biederman J, Geist DE, et al. Nortriptyline in the treatment of ADHD: a chart review of 58 cases. J Am Acad Child Adolesc Psychiatry 1993;32(2):343–9.
89. Spitzer RL, Endicott J, Robins E. Research diagnostic criteria: rationale and reliability. Arch Gen Psychiatry 1978;35:773–82.
90. Puig-Antich J, Blau S, Marx N, et al. Prepubertal major depressive disorder: a pilot study. J Am Acad Child Psychiatry 1978;17:695–707.
91. Kashani J, Barber G, Bolander F. Depression in hospitalized pediatric patients. J Am Acad Child Psychiatry 1981;20:123–34.
92. Freimer N, Weissman MM. The genetics of affective disorder. In: Deutsch SI, Weizman A, Weizman R, eds. Application of basic neuroscience to child psychiatry. New York: Plenum Publishing, 1990:285–96.
93. Puig-Antich J, Goetz R, Davies M, et al. Growth hormone secretion in prepubertal major depressive children: II. Sleep related plasma concentrations during a depressive episode. Arch Gen Psychiatry 1984a;41:463–6.
94. Preskorn SH, Bupp SJ, Weller EB, Weller RA. Plasma levels of imipramine and metabolites in 68 hospitalized children. J Am Acad Child Adolesc Psychiatry 1989;28:373–5.
95. Puig-Antich J, Perel JM, Lupatkin W, et al. Imipramine in prepubertal major depressive disorders. Arch Gen Psychiatry 1987;44:81–9.
96. Ryan ND, Puig-Antich J, Cooper T, et al. Imipramine in adolescent major depression: plasma level and clinical response. Acta Psychiatr Scand 1986;73:275–88.
97. Geller B, Perel JM, Knitter EF, et al. Nortriptyline in major depressive disorder in children: response, steady-state plasma levels, predictive kinetics, and pharmacokinetics. Psychopharmacology Bulletin 1983;19:62–5.
98. Geller B, Cooper TB, Chestnut EC, et al. Child and adolescent nortriptyline single dose kinetics predict steady state plasma levels and suggested dose: preliminary data. J Clin Psychopharmacol 1985a;5:154–8.
99. Ryan ND. The pharmacologic treatment of child and adolescent depression. Psychiatric Clinics of North America 1992;15(1):29–40.
100. Strober M, Freeman R, Rigali J, et al. The pharmacotherapy for depressive illness in adolescence: II. Effects of lithium augmentation in nonresponders to imipramine. J Am Acad Child Adolesc Psychiatry 1992;31(1):16–20.

CHAPTER 13

Primary Immunodeficiency Diseases

Maria M. Chan, Ph.D.
Brett J. Loechelt, M.D.

INTRODUCTION

The diagnosis of immunodeficiency disorders is of prime importance in the first year of life. These disorders can be classified as primary and secondary according to the nature of the defect. The primary immunodeficiency diseases can be further subdivided into congenital or acquired. In congenital disorders, the defect is intrinsic to one or more components of the immune system: T lymphocytes, B lymphocytes, phagocytes, and complement proteins. T and B lymphocytes are involved in specific immunity whereas phagocytes and the complement system participate in innate immunity. Defects in these immune components affect host defenses against infections. If not appropriately diagnosed and treated, these disorders are often fatal. Recent advancements in DNA technology and gene cloning have contributed significantly to our understanding of the molecular basis of many of these deficiencies. With the identification of the putative gene(s) and molecule(s), development of new therapeutic and diagnostic strategies is now feasible.

The intent of this chapter is to review current knowledge in the area of primary immunodeficiency diseases. The first section provides an overview of general clinical presentation and laboratory approaches used for diagnosis of primary immunodeficiencies. The second section focuses on individual T and/or B cell disorders, with special emphasis on the genetics and immunobiology. Immunodeficiencies of the innate immune system and those secondary to infections, drugs, malnutrition, and other extrinsic factors are not addressed.

GENERAL CLINICAL PRESENTATION

The hallmark of primary immunodeficiency diseases is an increase in susceptibility to infection. Patients usually suffer from recurrent or chronic infections, often caused by opportunistic organisms. These infections can involve multiple organs or multiple sites of the same organ, and the outcome can be severe and sometimes fatal. The type of infectious agents and the location of the infection often give valuable insight into the nature of the immunological defect. For example, individuals with B cell deficiencies characteristically have increased susceptibility to infections with encapsulated pyogenic bacteria such as *Staphylococcus*, *Hemophilus influenzae*, and *Streptococcus pneumoniae*. They are also susceptible to enterovirus. On the other hand, patients with T cell deficiencies often suffer from fungal and viral infections; *Pneumocystis* infections are also common. Other important clinical manifestations are chronic diarrhea, malabsorption, and sometimes malnutrition, especially in infants and young children. These symptoms can be caused by infectious organisms such as *Giardia*, rotavirus, and *Cryptosporidium*, but can also be due to autoimmune or chronic inflammatory conditions such as inflammatory bowel disease and gluten-sensitive enteropathy. Hematological abnormalities such as anemia, thrombocytopenia, and leukopenia are common in immunodeficient patients. These abnormalities can be intrinsic to the immunologic defect; for example, thrombocytopenia exhibited by Wiskott-Aldrich patients is the result of abnormal platelet structure. In addition, it is not unusual to find autoimmune or rheumatic complications as part of the clinical presentation.

LABORATORY DIAGNOSIS AND EVALUATION

In order to determine the appropriate laboratory tests for evaluation of an immunocompromised patient, we have to take into consideration the patient's age, sex, family history, and clinical presentation. The initial evaluation should include screening tests for both humoral and cellular immunity. The screening tests should be relatively simple to perform, be readily available, and allow screening for more than one disorder at a time. An example of a screening test panel is shown in Table 13–1. Based on the test results, more advanced specialized testing will be needed to define the precise nature of the defect.

Screening Tests

Screening tests for humoral immunity consist of protein electrophoresis and quantitation of serum immunoglobulins. Protein electrophoresis is used for the detection of monoclonal gammopathies. Quantitative measurement of serum IgG, IgA, and IgM can identify patients with panhypogammaglobulinemia as well as patients with a selective deficiency of an individual isotype. It is important to remember that normal concentrations of IgG do not rule out IgG subclass deficiencies or defects in the production of specific antibodies.

TABLE 13–1. Screening Test Panel for Primary Immunodeficiency Diseases

WBC and Differential
Absolute neutrophil count
Absolute lymphocyte count
Platelet count
Serum Immunoglobulins
IgG, IgA, and IgM
Protein Electrophoresis
Functional Antibody Concentrations
Blood group antibodies
Antibodies to vaccine antigens
Delayed-type Hypersensitivity Skin Tests

A second category for evaluation of humoral immunity is assessment of specific antibody reactivity. This is often accomplished by measuring ABO blood group isohemagglutinins and antibodies to vaccine antigens such as diphtheria, pertussis, and tetanus. Other vaccine antigens recommended by the World Health Organization for humoral response evaluation include *Hemophilus influenzae* and *Neisseria meningitis* polysaccharides, bacteriophage ΦX174, and monomeric flagellin. If the patient's initial antibody titer to an immunized antigen is low, the patient should be reimmunized and retested.

For cell-mediated immunity assessment, the simplest screening test is a complete blood count (CBC). The CBC shows whether the patient is lymphopenic, granulocytopenic, thrombocytopenic, or has leukemia. An intradermal skin test is the only practical *in vivo* test available for determining the patient's cell-mediated immunity. This test primarily measures delayed type hypersensitivity (DTH) reactions. Antigens used are *Candida albicans*, tetanus, diphtheria, streptokinase/streptodornase (SK/SD), tuberculin (PPD), trichophyton, and proteus. Reactions should be read for induration 48–72 hours after inoculation. Many hospitals prefer the preloaded multipuncture device (multitest CMI) for performing skin tests. The advantages of the multitest CMI are a standardized antigen dose and ease of use. The major disadvantage is the limited number of antigens available for testing. For infants and very young children, skin testing is not recommended because of the high frequency of false-negative responses as a result of insufficient antigenic exposure. It is important to bear in mind that a negative skin test is not necessarily indicative of T cell dysfunction, since anergy can be induced in many disease and pathological states.

Advanced and Specialized Tests

Following screening, more specific tests for further evaluation of a presumed immune disorder can be conducted, such as those listed in Table 13–2.

TABLE 13–2. Advanced Tests for Evaluation of Primary Immunodeficiency Diseases

B cells	T cells
B lymphocyte quantitation	T lymphocyte quantitation Total T cells T helper cells T suppressor/cytotoxic cells
In vitro antibody production induced by pokeweed mitogen, protein A, or EBV	Proliferative responses to mitogens, antigens, and allogeneic cells
IgG subclass quantitation	Cytokine quantitation
Antibody response to polysaccharide antigens, e.g., pneumococcal antigen	Calcium (Ca^{++}) flux, protein phosphorylation, and phosphatidylinositol (PI) turnover
Isolation and biochemical analysis of defective molecules	Isolation and biochemical analysis of defective molecules

Flow cytometric immunophenotyping analysis with specific monoclonal antibodies is now a part of routine assessment of a patient's immune status. This test provides information on the distribution of lymphocyte subsets as well as their immunological state and stage of maturation. Table 13–3 is a basic panel used for screening. An extended panel, shown in Table 13–4, is often required for definitive diagnosis of some of the disorders. Table 13–5 illustrates phenotypic results of a representative group of primary T, B, and combined T and B cell deficiencies. A normal immunophenotyping result, however, does not preclude abnormal cell function.

Flow cytometry can also be used for assessment of functions such as cellular activation and signal transduction.

The most common cellular functional test is the *in vitro* lymphocyte proliferation assay. This assay is based on ^{3}H-thymidine uptake into DNA of activated lymphocytes after stimulation with mitogen(s) or antigen(s). The most widely used mitogens in a routine clinical laboratory are phytohemagglutinin (PHA), concanavalin A (ConA), and pokeweed mitogen (PWM). Responses to these mitogens are nonspecific and do not require prior *in vivo* or *in vitro* priming. Other nonspecific activators are phorbol myristate acetate (PMA) and superantigens such as staphylococcal enteroxins. PMA triggers T cells by activation of protein kinase C and bypass T cell receptor (TCR)/CD3 receptor system. Superantigens stimulate T cells by direct binding to the Vβ chain of the TCR and the conserved regions of the HLA Class II molecule. T cells can also be activated using anti-CD3 and anti-TCR monoclonal antibodies which can detect dysfunctional or abnormal TCR/CD3 receptor complexes.

Besides mitogens, antigens should be included as part of the evaluation panel. Unlike mitogen responses, specific antigenic responses require prior *in vivo* sensitization; hence, they are less useful for infants and very young children. Antigen responses also are less vigorous when compared to mitogenic responses. In cases of suspected chronic mucocutaneous candidiasis, stimulation with *Candida* is the crucial

TABLE 13–3. Basic Flow Cytometry Panel for Primary Immunodeficiency Disease Evaluation

Monoclonal Antibody Combination	Specificity
CD45/CD14	For gating of lymphocytes
IgG1/IgG2	Isotype control
CD3/CD4	T helper/inducer cells
CD3/CD8	T suppressor/cytotoxic cells
CD3/CD16/56	Natural killer cells
CD19/CD10	Mature and immature B cells

TABLE 13–4. Extended Flow Cytometry Panel for Primary Immunodeficiency Disease Evaluation

Monoclonal Antibody Combination	Specificity	Specific Defect
CD3/CD43	Sialophorin	Wiskott-Aldrich Syndrome
CD4/CD8	Immature T cells	SCID
CD4/CD38	Immature T cells	SCID
CD4/CD71	Immature T cells	SCID
CD20/sIg or κ/λ	Ig/ κλ chains	Selected Ig deficiencies
CD20/HLA-DR	MHC Class II	MHC Class II deficiency
CD3/HLA-ABC	MHC Class I	Bare Lymphocyte syndrome
CD3/TCRαβ	TCRαβ	Congenital TCR defect
CD4/CD45RA	Naive T cells	XLA
CD4/CD45RO	Memory T cells	Omenn's syndrome

TABLE 13–5. Immunophenotype in Primary T, B, or Combined T and B Cell Deficiencies

Disease	Primary Defect	T Cells			B Cells
		CD3	CD4	CD8	
X-linked hypogammaglobulinemia	Humoral	N/↑	↓	N	A/↓
Transient hypogammaglobulinemia of infancy	Humoral	N/↓	↓	N	N
Hyper IgM syndrome	Humoral	N/↑	N/↑	N	N[a]
Common variable immunodeficiency	Humoral	N/↓	↑/↓	N/↓	↑/↓
IgA deficiency	Humoral	N	N/↓	N/↑	↑/↓[b]
DiGeorge Syndrome	Cellular	A/↓	±	↓	N/↓
Chronic mucocutaneous candidiasis	Cellular	N	N	N/↑	N
Severe combined immunodeficiency	Combined	A/↓[c]	A/↓	A/↓	N/↑/↓
Adenosine deaminase deficiency	Combined	A	A	A	A
Omenn's Syndrome	Combined	N/↑	N/↑[d]	↓	↓
Ataxia-telangiectasia	Combined	↓[e]	↓[f]	N/↑	N
Wiskott-Aldrich syndrome	Combined	N/↓[g]	N/↓	N/↓	N

N = normal; A = absent
[a] IgM^+ B cells only; [b] IgA^+ B cells coexpress IgM and IgD; [c] express immature markers CD38 and CD71; [d] predominantly CD45RO and activated; [e] increase in $CD3^+TCR\gamma\delta^+$ T cells; [f] increase in $CD4^+CD8^+$ T cells; [g] decrease in $CD43^+$ expression

definitive test. Antigens commonly used in the laboratory are tetanus toxoid, *Candida* extract, pure protein derivative (PPD) and streptolysin-streptodornase. Proliferation to allogeneic cells as in mixed lymphocyte cultures (MLC) is another good method for assessing T cell function. Due to the complexity of this assay, it is not usually available in routine laboratories. Instead of using ^{3}H-thymidine uptake as an indicator of activation, surface activation markers (IL-2R, CD69, and HLA-DR) can be quantitated on stimulated T lymphocytes using flow cytometry. Other less commonly used methods for quantitation of activation include measurement of sIL-2R in the culture supernatant by enzyme linked immunoassay (ELISA) or detection of IL-2 mRNA by Northern blotting technique or by *in situ* hybridization on activated cells.

Defects in cytotoxic T cell (CTL) function can be assayed by release of ^{51}Cr from lysed target cells by specific CTLs. This test is not routinely used because of technical difficulty and the requirement of *in vitro* or *in vivo* priming.

For evaluation of B cell function, PWM, staphylococcus protein A, and Epstein Barr virus (EBV) are often used *in vitro* to induce polyclonal B cell proliferation and antibody production. PWM requires the presence of T cells whereas the other two do not. B cell proliferation is measured by H^3-thymidine uptake and production of immunoglobulins in the culture supernatants is quantitated by ELISA. An alternative method is the reverse or direct plaque-forming cell assay, which enumerates the number of antibody producing cells.

Depending on the suspected immunological problems, more complex tests such as cytokine production, signal transduction determination, and biochemical analysis might be required. For determination of specific cytokine produced in response to *in vitro* stimulation with mitogen/antigen, cytokine-dependent cell lines are induced to proliferate by cytokine in stimulated culture supernatants and proliferation is measured by H^3-thymidine uptake. Cytokine concentration can be quantitated by ELISA or radioimmunoassay. Another method of quantitation is measurement of cytokine mRNA in activated cells. Cytokine assays are not widely available in most routine laboratories.

Detection of signal transduction defects involves the measurement of calcium (Ca^{++}) flux, protein phosphorylation, and phosphatidylinositol (PI) turnover. Ca^{++} flux is measured on PMA- or Ca^{++} ionophore-activated cells by flow cytometric method using Indo-1 or Fluo-3 fluorescent dyes. Protein phosphorylation is measured by binding of anti-phosphorylated tyrosines to multiple substrates in whole cell lysates after electrophoresis and PI turnover is quantitated using radioactive phosphatidylinositol-4,5-diphosphate (PIP_2) after cell activation.

If the suspected immunodeficiency is due to structural changes in cellular molecules, isolation and biochemical analysis of the abnormal molecules have to be performed to confirm the diagnosis.

SPECIFIC IMMUNODEFICIENCY DISEASES

Since there are over 50 different primary immunodeficiency diseases, it is impossible to discuss each disease in depth. Selective disorders, as depicted in Table 13–6, are reviewed.

TABLE 13–6. Selected Primary Immunodeficiency Diseases

Disease	Immune Defect	Mode of Inheritance	Specific Abnormality
X-linked agammaglobulinemia	No B cells	X-linked	Defective or no Btk tyrosine kinase
Transient hypogammaglobulinemia of infancy	Defective immunoglobulin production	Unknown	Unknown
X-linked hyper IgM syndrome	No isotype switching	X-linked	Defective CD40 ligand
Common variable immunodeficiency	Defective antibody production	Autosomal recessive, autosomal dominant, unknown	Unknown
IgA deficiency	No IgA synthesis	Autosomal recessive, autosomal dominant, unknown	Unknown; isotype switch defect?
Selective IgG subclass deficiencies	No or low synthesis of specific IgG subclasses	Unknown	Unknown; isotype switch defect?
DiGeorge syndrome	No or low T cells	Autosomal dominant, autosomal recessive, unknown	Thymic aplasia
Chronic mucocutaneous candidiasis	No T cell response to *Candida*	Autosomal dominant, autosomal recessive, unknown	Unknown
X-linked SCID	No T and B cells	X-linked	IL-2Rγ chain deficiency
Alymphocytosis	No T and B cells	Autosomal recessive	Unknown
ADA deficiency	No T and B cells	Autosomal recessive	ADA deficiency
PNP deficiency	No T cells	Autosomal recessive	PNP deficiency
Omenn's syndrome	Abnormal T and low B cells	Autosomal recessive	Autoreactive T cells
Reticular dysgenesis	No T, B and granulocytes	Autosomal recessive	Unknown
CD3 chain deficiencies	Defective T cells	Unknown	Defective CD3γ and ε chains
MHC class II deficiency	No CD4 T cells	Autosomal recessive	Lack of class II expression
Bare lymphocyte syndrome	No CD8 T cells	Autosomal recessive	TAP mutations
Ataxia-telangiectasia	Defective cellular and antibody responses	Autosomal recessive	DNA fragility
Wiskott-Aldrich syndrome	Defective polysaccharide antibody response	X-linked	Defective O-glycosylation

Primary B Cell Immunodeficiencies

X-linked Agammaglobulinemia (Bruton's Disease)[1–8]

X-linked agammaglobulinemia (XLA), or Bruton's disease, was first described in 1952 by Bruton, who observed that affected male infants with recurrent pyogenic infections lacked detectable γ-globulins in their serum.

XLA is an X-linked recessive disease that occurs in 1 in 100,000 live births. The gene has been mapped to the long arm of the X chromosome at q21.2 to q22 by linkage analysis. Female heterozygous carriers are perfectly normal. Their B cells show a non-random X chromosome inactivation pattern, with their affected X chromosome being preferentially inactivated. On the other hand, their other cells, such as T and myeloid cells, are randomly inactivated. These findings indicate that this disease is confined to the B lymphocyte lineage, and that the defective gene is probably important in B cell development.

The putative gene has now been identified and characterized. This gene encodes for a B cell cytoplasmic tyrosine kinase, Bruton's tyrosine kinase (Btk). The cytoplasmic tyrosine kinases play an essential role in cell growth and differentiation and are classified into subfamilies which include Src, Abl, Fps, Syk/ZAP 70, and Jak. Btk is a member of the Src family, is a 77 kDa protein, and is expressed in B, myeloid, and erythroid lineages and mast cells, but not in T cells. Structurally, Btk contains the classical SH1, SH2, and SH3 domains. Unique to Btk is the N-terminal region, which contains a pleckstrin homology (PH) domain. The PH domain has been shown to bind IP4 (inositol 1,3,4,5-tetrakisphosphate), IP5 (inositol 1,3,4,5,6-pentkisphosphate, and IP6 (inositol 1,2,3,4,5,6-hexakisphosphate).[8] Mutations of the PH domain result in dramatic reductions in IP4 binding activity. Defective signal transduction results in maturation arrest of B cells in the pre-B stage, suggesting that B-cell differentiation is, in part, linked to the IP4 binding capacity of the PH domain of Btk. Another functional role for Btk may be in the regulation of apoptosis as Btk lies upstream of bcl-XL, a protein involved in regulation of apoptosis. Specific mutations identified to date include intragenic deletions, insertions, and point mutations. Severe XLA phenotype has been associated with Arg_{28}→Cys mutation, whereas milder forms of XLA have amino acid substitutions in the SH2 and kinase domains. In general, XLA patients exhibit low Btk activity and low to undetectable Btk mRNA concentrations.

Affected XLA male infants usually are well for the first 6–12 months of life. During this period, they are protected by passively transferred maternal IgG. Clinically, they often present with recurrent pneumonia, otitis media, sinusitis, and pyoderma. These infections are mainly caused by pyogenic encapsulated bacteria and can be controlled by antibiotics. About 20% of patients suffer severe diarrhea usually caused by *Giardia, Campylobacter*, and in some cases by *Cryptosporidia*. Infections by enteroviruses, particularly echoviruses, can cause fatal encephalitis.

XLA is diagnosed by the absence or presence of very few B lymphocytes in the peripheral blood. The small number of B cells found is of an immature phenotype $CD19^+CD38^+$. T cell number is normal but $CD4^+$ T cells are of naive phenotype ($CD45RA^+$). The bone marrow contains increased number of pre-B cells. Lymph nodes from XLA patients are small, with no germinal follicles in the cortex and no plasma cells in the medulla. The lymph nodes contain primarily T lymphocytes. Serum IgA and IgM concentrations are undetectable and serum IgG is usually less than 100 mg/dL. T cell functions such as delayed-type hypersensitivity and *in vitro* response to mitogens and specific antigens are normal.

XLA carriers have classically been diagnosed by analyzing the X chromosome inactivation pattern in B cells. Now, with the identification of the Btk gene, asymptomatic female carriers can be identified using DNA-based analyses such as restriction fragment length polymorphism (RFLP), polymerase chain reaction (PCR), and single-strand conformation polymorphism (SSCP). XLA patients can now be directly ascertained by assaying Btk enzyme activity or identifying mutations in the Btk gene.

Intravenous administration of γ-globulin is the current therapy for XLA. The usual dose is 400–700 mg/kg every 3 to 4 weeks. The optimal dose of γ-globulin needs to be established for each patient, since some require more frequent administration at higher dosages to be prophylactic. About 30% of patients on γ-globulin therapy experience rheumatoid-like arthritis with swelling of knee joints. Since the putative gene, Btk, has been cloned, gene therapy could be a possible future treatment modality.

Transient Hypogammaglobulinemia of Infancy (THI)[9, 10]

THI is a relatively common disorder affecting up to 20% of infants at 5–6 months of age. Infants show a delay in their immunoglobulin production with marked decrease in serum antibody. The condition persists beyond 6 months of age and the patient usually recovers after 1–2 years of age. In some patients, THI can persist until 5 years of age. The etiology of this order is unclear. Children with THI may develop respiratory tract infections and fever which is generally not life-threatening.

Laboratory findings that can distinguish THI from XLA include normal IgM concentrations, good antibody responses to immunized antigens such as tetanus and diphtheria, and a normal number of circulating B cells. The number of CD4 lymphocytes is decreased in some patients. It has been suggested that the decreased concentrations of immunoglobulins in THI may result from delayed CD4 T cell function. Most of these infants do not require intravenous immunoglobulin (IVIG).

Hyper-IgM Immunodeficiency Syndrome[11–20]

The hallmark of the hyper IgM immunodeficiency syndrome, previously termed "dysgammaglobulinemia type 1," is the inability to switch from one immunoglobulin isotype to another. Patients with this primary immune disorder usually present with recurrent bacterial infections and other opportunistic infections, most often *Pneumocystis carinii* pneumonia, in the first 2 years of life. Other clinical symptoms include recurrent neutropenia, lymphoid hyperplasia diarrhea, and, in some cases, autoimmune diseases.

There are two forms of hyper-IgM syndrome, one an inherited X-linked and the other an autosomal-recessive disorder. The underlying cause of the X-linked form is deficient expression and/or function of the T-cell molecule CD-40-ligand (CD40L), which specifically binds the B cell's molecule CD40 and drives the immunoglobulin isotype switch and B-cell proliferation.[11] The CD40L gene maps to the long arm of the X chromosome, Xq26.3-q27.1. The CD40L or gp39 glycoprotein is expressed on the surface of activated T cells. The interaction between CD40L and CD40 receptor on B cells induces B cells to proliferate. In the presence of appropriate cytokines such as IL-4, switching of IgM isotype to immunoglobulin isotype, IgE is promoted. In patients with hyper-IgM syndrome, at least 16 different point mutations or deletions have been found throughout the coding region of the CD40L gene. These genetic alterations result in the absence of CD40 binding activity and thus prevent isotype switching to occur.

Hyper IgM syndrome is diagnosed by normal or increased serum IgM and IgD concentrations but diminished concentrations or absence of IgG, IgA, and IgE. Patients have an apparently normal number of T and B lymphocytes, but B cells only express surface IgM and IgD and no IgG^+ or IgA^+ cells are found. Activated T cells from patients do not bind soluble CD40 antigen or anti-CD40L antibodies as determined by flow cytometry. Surface marker analyses confirm the presence of B cells with surface IgM and IgD but not IgG or IgA. The diagnosis of hyper IgM can now be confirmed by analysis of dinucleotide repeat polymorphism in the 3′ untranslated region of the CD40L gene.

Prenatal diagnosis of X-linked hyper-IgM syndrome has been deterred by the limited availability of polymorphic DNA probes for linkage analysis in the affected region of the X chromosome. With the identification the CD40L gene, screening for mutations in affected families could be feasible. Unfortunately, the number of mutations reported necessitates DNA sequencing, which is too complex to implement as a screening method. Recently DiSanto et al.[14] identified an intragenic microsatellite repeat in the CD40L gene (DXS255) which is highly polymorphic and informative in 80% of women tested. They have used this marker successfully for prenatal diagnosis of an affected fetus at 12 weeks of gestation.

Similar to XLA, the current therapy for hyper IgM syndrome is IVIG. Another therapeutic alternative is bone marrow transplant with an HLA-compatible donor. The identification of the CD40 ligand as the defective gene in X-linked hyper-IgM syndrome would permit the possibility of future treatment by gene replacement therapy.

Common Variable Immunodeficiency (Acquired Hypogammaglobulinemia)[21]

Common variable immunodeficiency (CVID) is a heterogenous group of immunological disorders with similar clinical presentation. CVID can occur in childhood but most often presents in early adult life. Patients suffer from recurrent bacterial infections and opportunistic infection such as *Pneumocystis carinii* pneumonia and recurrent herpes zoster. Other common clinical features are autoimmune diseases, lymphopenia, splenomegaly, lymphadenopathy, lymphoid hyperplasia in the bowel, and a high incidence of lymphoid and stomach malignancy. Multiple granulomas can be found in the spleen, abdominal lymph nodes, or lungs of some patients.

As for laboratory evaluation, the majority of CVID patients have a normal number of B cells in the peripheral blood, but plasma cells are reduced in number in the spleen and gut and the lymph nodes are usually small. Some B cells express an activated phenotype indicating a maturation defect. The serum immunoglobulin concentrations are variable. Usually, IgG is below 500 mg/dL and IgA is below 50 mg/dL; IgM can be normal or slightly decreased. These patients have severely reduced antibody responses when immunized with both T-dependent and T-independent antigens. As for their T cells, some patients have decreased $CD4^+$ cells with normal $CD8^+$ cells, while others have normal numbers of $CD4^+$ cells and increased numbers of $CD8^+$ cells. In about 30% of patients, the T lymphocytes show depressed proliferation *in vitro* following stimulation with mitogen, anti-CD3 monoclonal antibody, and phorbol-ionomycin, and *in vivo* fail to show delayed-typed hypersensitivity skin reactions.

The mechanisms proposed for CVID include an intrinsic B cell defect, excessive T suppressor cell activity, or suboptimal T-B cell interaction. B cells from CVID patients do proliferate and synthesize antibodies *in vitro*, indicating that the defect may be at the T cell level. This is supported by the fact that T cells of some CVID patients do not produce adequate levels of cytokines such as IL-2.

About 50% of patients share a common extended HLA haplotype with a high incidence of complement component 4A (C4A) and 21 hydroxylase A gene deletions and rare complement component 2 (C2) gene haplotypes. This information suggests a genetic basis for CVID and the possible involvement of complement gene(s) in the development of this deficiency.

Similar to XLA, treatment for CVID is immunoglobulin replacement therapy. Appropriate antibiotics should be used to treat recurrent infections.

Selective IgA Deficiency[22–24]

IgA deficiency is the most common immunodeficiency disease, with an incidence of about 1 in 700 in Caucasians. This disease is very rare in Africans and Japanese. Patients are usually clinically asymptomatic. About 20% of IgA-deficient patients have concomitant IgG subclass deficiency, especially IgG_2. This subgroup is more prone to recurrent respiratory infections. There is an increased incidence of allergy and autoimmune diseases, particularly rheumatoid arthritis, in IgA-deficient patients. A subset of patients also suffers from coeliac disease or gluten sensitive enteropathy. Skin disorders associated with this disorder include pyoderma gangrenosum, vitiligo, and trachyonychia. Patients with IgA deficiency reportedly have an increased risk of malignancies, especially gastric and colonic adenocarcinomas. About 50–70% of patients with hereditary ataxia telangiectasia are also IgA deficient. Patients with IgA deficiency make antibodies to IgA, which can result in an adverse reaction to transfusion.

Laboratory evaluation shows serum IgA concentrations of less than 5 mg/dL with normal concentrations of IgG and IgM. Secretions are also deficient in IgA. Patients have normal T and B cell phenotypes. However, IgA^+ B cells co-express surface IgM and IgD, suggesting failure of IgA^+ B cells to mature. IgA^+ B cells also do not respond to *in vitro* stimulation by PWM and EBV to differentiate into IgA-producing plasma cells. Other proposed mechanisms are defective helper T cell function or excessive suppressor function. The inheritance pattern of IgA deficiency is not clear but is possibly autosomal recessive. The predominant major histocompatibility complex (MHC) haplotypes found in IgA deficient patients are similar to those with CVID, suggesting that both disorders might have the same underlying genetic defect but represent either end of the disease spectrum.

In addition to genetic predisposition, environmental factors also play an important role in this disorder. It has been well established that congenital infections such as rubella, cytomegalovirus, and toxoplasma can cause transient IgA deficiency. Drugs can also lead to development of this disorder, as demonstrated in patients treated with phenytoin for seizure disorders.

Patients with recurrent sinopulmonary infections need immunoglobulin replacement therapy preferably, an IgA-depleted IgG preparation.

Selective Immunoglobulin G Subclass Deficiencies[25, 26]

Deficiencies in one or more IgG subclasses probably result from failure of isotype switch. There are four IgG subclasses: IgG_1, IgG_2, IgG_3, and IgG_4. IgG_1 accounts for 67% of total serum IgG, IgG_2 for 20–25%, IgG_3 for 5–10%, and IgG_4 for less than 5%.

Deficiency in IgG_1 subclass is not distinguishable from CVID. Patients with this defect often respond poorly to protein antigens such as diphtheria and tetanus toxoid and have recurrent infections. Besides IgA, IgG_2 deficiency is the most common deficiency and may occur in 1 in 1000 individuals. IgG_2 deficiency is associated with inability to respond to carbohydrate antigens, which leads to predisposition to infection by encapsulated organisms such as meningococci. Deficiency in IgG_2 can occur in association with deficiencies in IgA and IgG_4. Patients with this combination of defects tend to have more lung problems. IgG_3 deficiency is often observed in conjunction with IgG_1, and isolated IgG_3 deficiency can lead to recurrent bacterial infections; however, the pathophysiology is less well understood. Deficiency in IgG_4 does not have clinical consequences except when it is accompanied by IgG_2 deficiency.

Patients with IgG subclass deficiency can benefit from immunoglobulin replacement therapy.

T Cell Immunodeficiencies

Thymic Aplasia (DiGeorge Syndrome)[27–30]

In 1968, DiGeorge described a child with hypoparathyroidism and thymic aplasia as a result of congenital malformation of the third and fourth pharyngeal pouch. In addition to these abnormalities, almost all infants with this syndrome have congenital malformation of the heart, most often interrupted aortic arch, right-sided aortic arch, truncus arteriosus, and tetralogy of Fallot. Patients can have characteristic facial features with hypertelorism, micrognathia, low-set ears, and shortened philtrum of the upper lip. The thymus shadow may be absent from chest X-ray. The affected infants are hypocalcemic because of hypoparathyroidism. Immunological findings are very heterogenous. In most cases, there is absent or decreased numbers of circulating mature T lymphocytes, particularly in the $CD8^+$ subset. B cells are normal or increased in number, and natural killer (NK) cells are normal. Patients respond poorly to mitogen and allogeneic cell stimulation. Even though B cells can make antibodies, these antibodies are often not functional. In general, incidence of chronic cytomegalovirus and varicella infection is increased. Recurrent bacterial infections are unusual. Autoimmune diseases may be present.

DiGeorge syndrome usually occurs sporadically, but it may be inherited as an autosomal-dominant, autosomal-recessive, and X-linked condition. The incidence has been estimated at 1 in 20,000. Various chromosomal abnormalities have been reported in association with this syndrome, particularly monosomy 10p and deletion in chromosome 22q11. Patients with velo-cardio-facial syndrome have phenotypic characteristics that overlap those of DiGeorge syndrome, and it is important to differentiate them with specific DNA probes using fluorescent *in situ* hybridization (FISH) analysis. For patients with the severe form of the disease, in whom the thymus is completely absent, thymic transplant or fetal thymic epithelium implant is recommended. Bone marrow transplantation has also been successful in patients with DiGeorge syndrome with severe T-cell immunity.

Chronic Mucocutaneous Candidiasis[31, 32]

Chronic mucocutaneous candidiasis (CMC) is a clinical syndrome characterized by recurrent candida infections of the skin and superficial mucous membrane. Symptoms can occur in the first 2–3 months of life. The most common feature is oral lesions. Infections with other organisms can also be present. Recurrent upper and/or lower respiratory tract infections are most common. Systemic candidiasis is unusual. About 50% of patients have an endocrinopathy. Hypoadrenalism and hypothyroidism are the most frequently reported. Autoimmune hemolytic anemia and idiopathic thrombocytopenia have also been described.

It is estimated that about 20% of patients have a family history of CMC. The exact mode of inheritance has not been clearly established. CMC with endocrinopathy appears to be transmitted in an autosomal-recessive manner, while those forms without endocrinopathy are inherited as a dominant trait. The molecular basis for this disorder is unknown.

Immunologically, the patient's T lymphocytes respond normally to mitogens and allogeneic cells. Responses to antigens other than *Candida* are also normal. Similarly, the skin test to *Candida* is negative. B cell immunity is intact, as demonstrated by normal or increased concentrations of immunoglobulins. Increased concentrations of antibody to *Candida* are often found. Selective IgA deficiency has been reported in some patients. Isolated cases of abnormal neutrophil chemotaxis and macrophage function have been described. Phenotypically, patients have normal T and B cells.

Oral antifungal agents such as ketoconazole have been successfully used for treating CMC. Intravenous amphotericin B treatment also has a good outcome. Management of endocrinopathy, particularly hypoadrenalism, is most important, since Addison's disease is the major cause of death.

Combined T and B Cell Deficiencies

Severe Combined Immunodeficiency[33]

Infants with SCID have no cellular and humoral immunity. By 3 months of age, affected infants present with opportunistic infections. Other common symptoms are thrush, interstitial pneumonitis, and persistent diarrhea. Failure to thrive is another important feature of this disease. Affected infants are lymphopenic, with less than 3000 lymphocytes/mm^3. Mature T cells ($CD3^+$) are usually absent or depressed. In some infants, T cells are of maternal origin. Patient's lymphocytes are unresponsive to stimulation by mitogens, antigens, and allogeneic cells. The thymus may be absent or, if present, not well developed. All lymphoid tissue is poorly developed.

Severe combined immunodeficiency (SCID) represents a heterogenous group of disorders. It occurs in about 1 in 10^5 to 10^6 live births. SCID can be inherited as an X-linked or autosomal-recessive disorder. SCID can be further subdivided into: X-linked SCID (XSCID), Jak-3 deficiency, alymphocytosis of unknown origin, adenosine deaminase deficiency (ADA), purine nucleoside phosphorylase deficiency (PNP), ZAP-70 deficiency, Omenn's syndrome, reticular dysgenesis, CD3 chain deficiencies, and MHC class II deficiency.

X-Linked SCID (XSCID)[34–37]

XSCID is the most frequent form of SCID, accounting for 50–60% of cases. This deficiency is characterized by absence of mature T cells but with an increased or normal number of B cells. Precursor thymocytes are not detected in the thymuses of affected patients, indicating an early blockade in T cell differentiation. Proliferation to mitogens or allogeneic stimulation is absent. Even though SCID patients have a normal phenotype, their B cells and NK cells exhibit functional abnormalities. Serum concentrations of IgG and IgA are low, and IgM can be normal or low. Obligate carriers exhibit a skewed pattern of X chromosome inactivation only in their lymphocytes; other hematopoietic cell lineages are not affected.

Linkage analysis localized the putative locus to the long arm of the X chromosome at Xq13-13.3, which is the gene that encodes for the IL-2 receptor (IL-2R) γ-chain (γ_c). Point mutations in IL-2Rγ gene in DNA of XSCID patients resulted in truncated IL-2R γ-chain proteins. These defective proteins cannot function in signal transduction, which is vital in T cell maturation. In contrast, SCID patients with a deficiency in IL-2 production have relatively normal numbers of T cells in their peripheral blood, and the immune deficit can be corrected by administration of exogenous IL-2. The phenotype associated with IL-2Rγ deficiency is more severe because γ_c has been identified as the common subunit for IL-4, IL-7, and IL-13. Defective expression of γ_c would likely affect the production and function of these other cytokines. In the case of IL-7, γ_c is essential for T cell receptor V(D)J gene rearrangement. A defect in IL-7 can therefore block T cell development in XSCID. In the case of IL-4, γ_c is required for ligand-induced proliferation and ligand-induced tyrosine phosphorylation. Defective IL-4 signaling will affect B cell function. The identification of IL-2R γ-chain may allow gene therapy as a possible alternative treatment to bone marrow transplantation.

Jak-3 Deficiency[10, 38, 39]

A non-X-linked form of SCID characterized by a phenotype similar to that of XSCID, also known as SCID with B cells, has been known for some time. Mutations of the Jak-3 kinase gene have been associated with the autosomal form of SCID. The similarity of phenotype is due to the fact that the γ_c signal is mediated by Jak-3 activation. The putative gene for Jak-3 is located on chromosome 19p13.1. The identification of the Jak-3 gene may allow gene therapy as a possible alternative treatment to bone marrow transplantation.

Alymphocytosis of Unknown Origin

In 20–25% of SCID patients, mature T and B lymphocytes are absent while NK cells are functional and adenosine deaminase activity is normal. This form of SCID is inherited as an autosomal-recessive trait, but the molecular basis has not been clearly defined. If it is similar to murine SCID, it could be caused by defective recombination of V(D)J elements of the T cell receptor and immunoglobulin genes.

Adenosine Deaminase Deficiency (ADA)[40, 41]

The other common autosomal-recessive form of SCID is deficiency in the purine salvage enzyme adenosine deaminase (ADA). This form accounts for 20% of SCID. Clinical presentation of ADA deficiency can range from complete lack of ADA activity to partial deficiency. Patients with no ADA activity have very early onset of the disease and profound T and B lymphopenia, as compared to those with residual activity, who have later onset and a mild decrease in T cell number, with normal numbers of B cells and humoral responses. NK cell numbers can be decreased, normal, or increased. NK cell phenotype and function is variable. In most patients, there is marked increase in serum IgE. Eosinophilia is also common. Autoimmune symptoms such as autoimmune hypothyroidism and insulin-dependent diabetes mellitus has been described in some patients. Patients excrete large amounts of deoxyadenosine and adenosine in their urine and quantitation of these substances is used as a diagnostic test for ADA deficiency. Although the pathology of this disease is mainly limited to the immune system, some nonlymphoid organs are also affected. About 50% of ADA patients have bone abnormalities with cupping and flaring of the costochondral junctions. Renal and adrenal lesions as well as neurologic abnormalities are also found.

ADA is an enzyme present in all tissues. The highest activity is found in the thymus and the lowest in erythrocytes. ADA activity also varies among lymphocytes of different lineages and at different stages of differentiation. T cells express more activity than B cells, and thymocytes more than mature T cells. The function of ADA is to catalyze the deamination of adenosine and 2′-deoxyadenosine to inosine with production of ammonia. As a consequence of ADA deficiency, adenosine triphosphate (ATP) and deoxyadenosine triphosphate (dATP) accumulate in lymphoid cells. dATP is toxic to the enzyme ribonucleotide reductase, which is important for DNA synthesis. In addition, dATP inactivates S-adenosylhomocysteine hydrolase (SAH), which plays a role in DNA methylation.

The gene for ADA is mapped to human chromosome 20q13.11. Both point mutations and deletions have been identified. At least 16 different missense mutations have been reported; thirteen of these are at the mutational "hot spot," the CpG dinucleotides. A severe form of the disease is associated with mutations/deletions at the enzyme's catalytic site.

Untreated ADA deficiency is usually fatal. At the present time, there are three modes of therapy. Bone marrow transplantation is the treatment of choice if a histocompatible sibling donor is available. The best results are achieved if the transplant is performed before the patient acquires severe opportunistic infections. T cell-depleted haploidentical bone marrow transplantation is less successful. Enzyme replacement is another approach. The early form was by partial exchange blood transfusions. The majority of patients treated experienced no or minimal immunological improvement. Major drawbacks were increased risk of iron overload and transfusion transmitted infectious diseases. Nowadays, affected patients are treated with ADA conjugated to polyethylene glycol (PEG). About 80% of patients respond to treatment with improved immune function; however, efficacy is not long term. About one-fifth of patients treated with PEG-ADA show little recovery of immune function despite improvement in ADA concentrations. These patients might have irreversible damage to their lymphoid cells prior to treatment. Another recent form of treatment for ADA deficiency involving gene therapy has been described. Initial trials consisted of infusing patients every 6–8 weeks with IL-2 expanded peripheral T cells transfected with the ADA gene. More recently, similar techniques were employed to correct cord blood stem cells from three neonates with ADA deficiency.

ZAP-70 Deficiency[10, 39]

Other causes of autosomal forms of SCID include deficiency of ZAP-70, a protein kinase. This form of SCID is characterized by the presence of normal numbers of peripheral T cells with a deficiency of CD8+ T cells and a TCR signal transduction defect in peripheral CD4+ T cells. Although the patients have normal immunoglobulin levels, specific antibody formation may be impaired. The absence of CD8+ cells in the thymus and peripheral blood of these patients suggests that the positive selection process occurs at the transition of double-positive to single-positive cells. Down-regulation of Syk during T-cell maturation development or the absolute requirement for ZAP-70, or both, may explain why peripheral CD4+ T cells lacking ZAP-70 fail to transmit signal from the T-cell receptor normally.

The diagnosis, even the prenatal diagnosis, for this disease can be suggested by the family history, symptoms of SCID, and characteristic peripheral T-cell phenotype and function. As in other forms of SCID, bone marrow transplantation is curative for this disease. Identification of the gene may allow for future gene therapy correction.

Purine Nucleoside Phosphorylase (PNP) Deficiency[42]

PNP deficiency is rare, accounting for approximately 4% of SCID patients. To date, only 32 cases have been reported. Patients present with recurrent infections, failure to thrive, autoimmune disease, neurological impairment, and malignancies. The patient's total white blood cell count is usually within the normal range, but the percentage of lymphocytes is very low (< 10%). T cell numbers are very low and T cell responses to mitogens and allogeneic cells are very poor. The skin test to *Candida* is unreactive. T cell impairment usually is progressive, with normal proliferative responses occurring early in life and declining with age. B cell numbers are normal and function can be normal or hyperactive.

Like ADA, PNP is found in many tissues and its activity varies from tissue to tissue. PNP is an enzyme of the purine salvage pathway. Its function is to convert guanosine to guanine and inosine to hypoxanthine. Lack of PNP will result in the accumulation of deoxyguanosine triphosphate in thymocytes, which in turn inhibits ribonucleotide reductase and blocks DNA synthesis. Since deoxyguanosine is reportedly not toxic to T and B cells, the impaired immune function could be caused by low guanosine triphosphate (GTP) concentrations, which in turn affects G protein activation. Decrease in GTP also affects the production of cGMP, which is a crucial second messenger in immune responses. Inhibition of SAH inhibits methylation. The enzyme deoxynucleotidyl transferase is also affected in PNP deficiency, which could be responsible for abnormal gene rearrangements in T and B cells.

The gene for PNP is mapped to human chromosome 14q13.1. The pattern of inheritance is autosomal recessive. Point mutations in the PNP gene have been described as the basis for PNP deficiency. Several therapies have been used: red cell transfusions, oral guanine, oral uridine, deoxycytidine, plus tetrahydrouridine factors or fetal thymus transplants. However, none of these procedures has been found to be sufficient. Bone marrow transplantation is the recommended therapy. In the future, gene therapy could be a viable candidate.

Omenn's Syndrome[43–46]

In Omenn's syndrome, an unusual form of SCID, affected infants present with erythroderma, hepatosplenomegaly, histiocytosis, and hypereosinophilia. Other features are protracted diarrhea, failure to thrive, and life-threatening infections. It is usually fatal within the first year of life if not treated. Laboratory findings show increased serum IgE. Patients have a normal or increased number of circulating T cells but are deficient in B cells. In contrast, the lymph nodes and the thymus contain no lymphocytes. Peripheral blood T cells are predominantly of an activated mature phenotype expressing cell markers CD45RO and IL-2R. These T cells show poor function when stimulated *in vitro* with mitogens, antigens, and allogeneic cells. In addition, these T cells are oligoclonal, as demonstrated by limited T cell receptor repertoire and autoreactivity.

The syndrome is inherited as an autosomal-recessive trait. A possible mechanism is defective selection of T lymphocytes in the thymus, giving rise to autoreactive T cells which subsequently attack the immune system. Currently, bone marrow transplantation is the only treatment available.

Reticular Dysgenesis[47, 48]

Reticular dysgenesis is a form of SCID in which granulocytes are also absent. These infants die very rapidly unless treated with a bone marrow transplant. This disorder is inherited in an autosomal-recessive manner and accounts for < 1% of SCID.

CD3 Chain Deficiencies[48–52]

SCID can be caused by defective production or assembly of the CD3 antigen complex. The CD3 complex is found on the cell surface of mature T cells in conjunction with the TCR $\alpha\beta$ or $\gamma\delta$. It is composed of 4 chains, γ, δ, ε, and ζ. Its function is to regulate the assembly and signal transduction of TCR.

Two cases of CD3 chain deficiencies have been reported. One involved a defective CD3F128Mg chain and the other a defective CD3ε chain. Both disorders were inherited in an autosomal-recessive fashion. Point mutations in the CD3γ and CD3ε genes resulted in truncated and nonfunctional CD3γ and CD3ε proteins. T cells from the CD3γ^- individual express about half of the normal density of TCR/CD3 complex on their cell surface as compared to only 10% in the CD3ε^- cells. Mitogen and anti-CD3-induced proliferation of T cells are impaired in both defects; surprisingly, antigen-induced proliferation is either low or normal. T cell subset analysis showed that CD8$^+$ T cells were low in the CD3γ^- cells and normal in the CD3ε^- cells, whereas CD4$^+$ T cells were normal in the CD3γ^- cells and absent in the CD3ε^- cells. With the CD4 subset, CD45RA$^+$ (naive) were severely depleted in CD3γ deficiency, with CD45RO$^+$ being normal. Antibody response to protein antigens was normal while response to polysaccharides was defective in both defects. IgG$_2$ concentration was low in the CD3γ^- patient. The patient with CD3γ chain defect suffered from fatal viral infections, probably due to impaired CD8 cell function. Autoantibodies to erythrocytes and other organs were found in CD3γ^-. Possible therapy is bone marrow transplantation.

Major Histocompatibility Complex (MHC) Class II Deficiency and Bare Lymphocyte Syndrome[53–58]

In 1978, Touraine et al.[53] reported patients with defective expression of HLA Class I but normal Class II molecules on their cells. This immunodeficiency syndrome was called "Bare Lymphocyte Syndrome." Patients with this deficiency have no CD8 cells. The disease is inherited in an autosomal-recessive manner. The genetic defect is due to mutation in a TAP (transporter associated with antigen processing) gene. TAP proteins are involved in transporting short peptides from the cytosol into the endoplasmic reticulum (ER). In the ER, the peptides bind to newly synthesized MHC Class I molecules to complete their structure. TAP proteins are therefore required for proper expression of MHC Class I molecules. In the thymus, MHC Class I molecules are involved for the proper selection of CD8 T cells. The lack of MLC Class I will result in defective selection of CD8 T cells.

In 1980, Griselli et al.[57] identified a new immunodeficiency syndrome in which expression of HLA Class II antigens was abnormal. These patients had a normal number of T and B lymphocytes but abnormal cellular and humoral antigenic responses. This disease was named MHC Class II Deficiency. HLA Class I expression in these patients was also decreased but could be induced by interferon (IFN) α, β, and γ. Patients usually presented with severe bacterial and viral infections, protracted diarrhea, malabsorption with osteoporosis, and failure to thrive within the first year of life. Fungal infections by *Candida* and *Pneumocystis carinii* pneumonia are frequent. Autoimmune cytopenia is also present in some patients. Laboratory findings by flow cytometry showed surface expression of HLA Class I and β2-microglobulin on leukocytes and platelets of all patients. In some patients, expression was reduced. HLA Class II (DR, DQ, and DP) expression was abnormal or absent on B lymphocytes, monocytes, and activated T cells. In the thymus, very few HLA Class II positive dendritic and stromal cells were found. IFN-γ cannot induce Class II expression.

Phenotypically, patients have decreased numbers of $CD4^+$ lymphocytes with increased $CD8^+$ subset. Other surface markers are within the normal range. Immunologically, patients show an absence of delayed-type hypersensitivity which correlates with *in vitro* T cell response to recall antigens such as tetanus toxoid, diphtheria, PPD, or *Candida* extract. Patients respond normally to allogeneic cells in MLC and CTL activity. On the other hand, the patient's cells cannot stimulate in MLC. Responses to mitogens such as PHA, ConA, PWM, anti-CD3, or anti-CD2 are normal. The majority of patients are hypo- or agammaglobulinemic. Normal immunoglobulin concentrations and even increased IgM have been reported. Patients do not respond to vaccination with protein antigens. Isohemagglutinin is normal in 50% of patients. In some patients, the anti-*Candida* antibody is only of the IgM isotype. Patients can make antibodies to viruses—for example, cytomegalovirus or adenovirus—if chronically infected. The poor antibody response is probably attributable to impaired antigen presentation by HLA Class II deficient monocytes.

MHC Class II deficiency is inherited as an autosomal-recessive disorder. The primary defect is not due to deletion of Class II genes on chromosome 6, but to abnormal genes for transacting regulating factors regulatory factor X (RFX) and Class II transactivator (CIITA). RFX binds to conserved nucleic acid sequences in the promoter regions of the Class II structural genes. The gene(s) for RFX is mapped to the short arm of chromosome 19. CIITA is an essential mediator of induction of MHC Class II genes by IFN-γ and is regulated by IFN-γ itself. Gene complementation experiments showed that at least four independent genetic defects are involved, which could result in the failure to express HLA Class II gene products. With progress in characterization of the affected genes, gene therapy could be a possible alternative treatment to bone marrow transplantation.

Hereditary Ataxia Telangiectasia[59–64]

Hereditary ataxia telangiectasia (AT) is a rare, autosomal-recessive disease. Patients present with oculocutaneous telangiectasias, progressive cerebellar ataxia, and Purkinje cell degeneration. Recurrent respiratory infections, autoimmune disease, and malignancies (particularly T cell leukemia) are common. In 80% of patients, IgA, IgG_2, and IgE concentrations are decreased and cellular responses are poor. α-Fetoprotein is increased and is the most useful diagnostic test for AT. A hallmark of AT is DNA fragility with abnormal chromosomal translocation in lymphocytes, mainly involving T cell receptor and immunoglobulin gene loci. The patient's DNA is abnormally sensitive to ionizing radiation, which could be the cause of malignancies. At least four complementation groups have been defined. Three loci have been mapped to chromosome 11q23. The genes encoding the defect in group A and group

B patients have mapped between STMY and D11S385, and between NICAM/DRD2 and D11S132 respectively. The gene encoding the defect in group C patients is between D11S147 and D11S133. The candidate gene for the group D defect has been cloned, but gene identification has not been completed.

Lymphocyte phenotype studies show a decrease in total number of T cells, with a decrease in the CD4/CD8 ratio, cutaneous anergy, and an increase in immature T cells with increased γδ TCR expression. The number of B cells is usually normal; however, approximately 70% of patients have a selective IgA deficiency and more than half also have IgG2 subclass deficiency. NK cells are usually normal. The progressive ataxia associated with AT becomes apparent when the child begins to walk, whereas between 2 and 8 years of age telangiectasias develop on the bulbar conjunctivae, sun-exposed areas, and the flexor surfaces of the arms.

Therapy for AT consists of aggressive use of antibiotics for sinopulmonary infections, IVIG when deficiency in functional antibodies is documented, and treatment of associated endocrinopathies. The identification of the AT gene may allow the potential for gene therapy in the future.

Wiskott-Aldrich Syndrome[65–72]

The Wiskott-Aldrich syndrome (WAS) was first described by Wiskott in 1937 and subsequently by Aldrich et al. in 1954. The classical clinical presentation is immunodeficiency, thrombocytopenia, and eczema. However, many patients have only a partial or variant phenotype. Approximately 40% of patients suffer from autoimmune diseases and inflammatory infections. The most common autoimmune disease is autoimmune hemolytic anemia. Patients with autoimmune disease have higher risk of developing malignancies, in particular lymphoreticular tumors and leukemias.

Laboratory evaluation shows small platelet size (average diameter 1.82 μm compared to a normal diameter of 2.23 μm), but platelet counts can be variable, ranging from $< 10{,}000/mm^3$ to $> 100{,}000/mm^3$. Lymphopenia and eosinophilia can be found in 20–30% of patients. Quantitative immunoglobulins show increased serum IgA and IgE with decreased IgM and normal IgG. Patients are unable to make antibodies to polysaccharide antigens such as blood group substances or capsular polysaccharides of pneumococci and *Hemophilus influenzae.* T cell quantitation shows a gradual decline in T cell numbers, and CD8 cell counts are usually below normal. T lymphocytes have a characteristic morphology on scanning electron microscopy, appearing bald with lack of villous projections suggestive of abnormal cytoskeletal architecture. Lymphocyte function *in vitro* is variable. Many patients show normal responses to mitogens. Evidence of defective expression of CD43, a sialophorin (leucosialin) found on platelets and nucleated blood cells, has been reported. The synthesis of CD43 is normal in WAS T cells, but is more rapidly degraded. Since CD43 is involved in T cell activation and signal transduction, defects in CD43 could explain the poor T cell responses to antigenic stimuli. However, with the localization of the CD43 gene to the short arm of chromosome 16, the CD43 defect has been excluded as the basic defect in WAS.

WAS is an X-linked recessive disorder. Linkage analysis has mapped the gene at Xp11.22-p11.23. Obligate female heterozygous carriers are clinically normal and exhibit non-random inactivation of the X chromosome in cells of blood lineages. The primary defect is thought to be the regulation of O-glycosylation during development.

The most effective treatment strategy for WAS is bone marrow transplant, which corrects for both thrombocytopenia and immunodeficiencies. Splenectomy is used for treating thrombocytopenia but is not always effective in the long term. IVIG replacement therapy is sometimes included in management of thrombocytopenia and immunodeficiency, although its efficacy has not been well established. Due to the heterogenous clinical presentation and inconsistent laboratory abnormalities, the diagnosis of WAS still depends on a constellation of findings including small platelets, altered T or B cell function, and demonstration of the skewed X-chromosome inactivation.

Recently Derry et al.[65] isolated a novel gene, WASP, which was not expressed in the lymphoblastoid cells of four WAS patients. In one patient there was a single nucleotide deletion, resulting in a frame shift; in two others, there were point mutations. WASP encodes a 501 amino acid proline-rich protein, a structure common to transcription factors involved in signal transduction pathways. Identification of the defective WASP gene will provide a direct carrier detection test as well as contribute to gene replacement therapy for WAS patients.

SUMMARY

Primary immunodeficiency diseases are a heterogenous group of congenital disorders affecting infants and children. As a result of technological advances in molecular biology, the etiology of many of these deficiencies is now known. Most importantly, investigations of these disorders have provided insights into how the immune system functions—its various cellular and humoral components and its intricate network of controls and regulations.

REFERENCES

1. Bruton OC. Agammaglobulinemia. Pediatrics 1952;9:722–7.
2. Rawlings DJ, Saffran DC, Tsukada S, et al. Mutation of the amino-terminal unique region of Bruton's tyrosine kinase in murine X-linked immunodeficiency. Science 1993;358:358–61.
3. Rawlings DJ, Witte ON. Bruton's tyrosine kinase is a key regulator in B cell development. Immunol Rev 1994;138:105–19.
4. Thomas JD, Sideras P, Smith CIE, et al. Colocalization of X-linked agammaglobulinemia and X-linked immunodeficiency genes. Science 1993;261:355–8.
5. Tsukada S, Rawlings DJ, Witte ON. Role of Bruton's tyrosine kinase in immunodeficiency. Curr Opin in Immunol 1994;6:623–30.
6. Tsukada S, Saffron DC, Rawlings DJ, et al. Deficient expression of a B cell cytoplasmic tyrosine kinase in human X-linked agammaglobulinemia. Cell 1993;72:279–90.
7. Vetrie D, Vorechovsky I, Sideras P, et al. The gene involved in X-linked agammaglobulinemia is a member of the Src family of protein-tyrosine kinases. Nature 1993;361:226–33.

8. Smart BA, Ochs HD. The molecular basis and treatment of primary immunodeficiency disorders. Curr Opin in Pediatrics 1997;9:570–56.
9. McGeady SJ. Transient hypogammaglobulinemia of infants: need to reconsider name and definition. J Pediatr 1987;110:37–50.
10. Siegel RL, Issekutz T, Schwaber B, et al. Deficiency of T helper cells in transient hypogammaglobulinemia of infancy. N Engl J Med 1981;305:1307–13.
11. Shyur SD, Hill HR. Recent advances in the genetics of primary immunodeficiency syndrome. J Pediatrics 1996;129:8–24.
12. Allen RC, Armitage RJ, Conley ME, et al. CD40 ligand gene defects responsible for X-linked hyper-IgM syndrome. Science 1993;259:990–3.
13. DiSanto JP, Bonnefoy JY, Gauchat JF, et al. CD40 ligand mutations in X-linked immunodeficiency with hyper-IgM. Nature 1993;361:541–3.
14. DiSanto JP, Markiewicz S, Gauchat J-F, et al. Brief report: prenatal diagnosis of X-linked hyper-IgM syndrome. N Engl J Med 1994;330:969–73.
15. Foy TM, Durie FH, Noelle RJ. The expansive role of CD40 and its ligand, gp39, in immunity. Semin in Immunol 1994;6:259–66.
16. Fuleihan R, Ramesh N, Loh R, et al. Defective expression of the CD40 ligand in X chromosome-linked immunoglobulin deficiency with normal or elevated IgM. Pro Natl Acad Sci USA 1993;90:2170–3.
17. Klaus SJ, Berberich I, Shu G, Clark EA. CD40 and its ligand in the regulation of humoral immunity. Semin in Immunol 1994;16:279–86.
18. Korthauer U, Graf D, Mages HW, et al. Defective expression of T-cell CD40 ligand causes X-linked immunodeficiency with hyper-IgM. Nature 1993;361:539–41.
19. Mayer L, Kwan SP, Thompson C, et al. Evidence for a defect in switch T cells in patients with immunodeficiency and hyperimmunoglobulinemia M. N Engl J Med 1986;314:409–13.
20. Geha RS, Schneeberger E, Merle E, Rosen FS. Heterogeneity of "acquired" or common variable agammaglobulinemia. N Engl J Med 1974;291:1–6.
21. Spickett GP, Webster ADB, Farrant J. Cellular abnormalities in common variable immunodeficiency. Immunodefic Rev 1990;2:199–219.
22. Schaffer FM, Monteiro RC, Volanakis JE, Cooper MD. IgA deficiency. Immunodefic Rev 1991;3:15–44.
23. Schaffer FM, Palermos J, Zhu ZB, et al. Individuals with IgA deficiency and common variable immunodeficiency share polymorphisms of major histocompatibility complex class III genes. Proc Nat Acad Sci USA 1989;86:8005–9.
24. Volanakis JE, Zhu ZB, Schaffer FM, et al. Major histocompatibility complex class III genes and susceptibility to immunoglobulin A deficiency and common variable immunodeficiency. J Clin Invest 1992;89:1914–22.
25. Ferrante A, Beard LJ, Roberton DM. IgG subclass deficiency. Pediatr Allergy Immunol 1991;2:49–62.
26. Hanson, LA, Bjorkander J, Robbins JB, et al. IgG subclass deficiencies. Vox Sang 1986:51(suppl. 2):50–6.
27. Demaze C, Scambler P, Prieur M, et al. Routine diagnosis of DiGeorge syndrome by fluorescent in situ hybridization. Hum Genet 1992;90:663–5.
28. DiGeorge AM. Congenital absence of the thymus and its immunologic consequences: concurrence with congenital hypoparathyroidism. In: Bergsma D, McKusick FA, eds. Immunologic deficiency diseases in man. National Foundation-March of Dimes Original Article Series IV. Philadelphia: Williams & Wilkins, 1968;116–21.
29. Hong R. The DiGeorge anomaly. Immunodefic Rev 1991;3:1–14.
30. Scambler PJ. Deletions of human chromosome 22 and associated birth defects. Curr Opin in Genetics and Development 1993;3:432–7.
31. Dwyer JM. Chronic mucocutaneous candidiasis. Ann Rev Med 1981;32:492–7.
32. Staveren AM, Stiehm ER. Chronic mucocutaneous candidiasis: clinical immunologic and therapeutic considerations. In: Moss AJ, ed. Pediatric update. New York: Elsevier, 1986;93–110.
33. Weinberg K, Parkman R. Severe combined immunodeficiency due to a specific defect in the production of IL-2. N Engl J Med 1990;322:1718–23.

34. Gougheon ML, Drean G, LeDeist F, et al. Human severe combined immunodeficiency disease: phenotypic and functional characteristics of peripheral B lymphocytes. J Immunol 1990;145:2873–9.
35. Leonard WJ. The defective gene in X-linked severe combined immunodeficiency encodes a shared interleukin receptor subunit: implication for cytokine pleiotropy and redundancy. Curr Opin in Immunol 1994;6:631–5.
36. Leonard WJ, Noguchi M, Russell SM, McBride OW. The molecular basis of X-linked severe combined immunodeficiency: the role of the interleukin-2 receptor γ chain as a common γ chain, γ_c. Immunol Rev 1994;138:61–86.
37. Noguchi M, Yi H, Rosenblatt HM, Filipovich AH, et al. Interleukin-2 receptor γ chain mutation results in X-linked severe combined immunodeficiency in humans. Cell 1993;73:147–57.
38. Puck JM. Primary immunodeficiency diseases. JAMA 1997;278:1835–41.
39. Fischer A, Cavazzana-Calvo M, De Saint Basile G, et al. Naturally occurring primary deficiencies of the immune system. Annu Rev Immunol 1997;15:93–124.
40. Blaese RM. Development of gene therapy for immunodeficiency: adenosine deaminase deficiency. Pediatr Res 1993;33:549–55.
41. Hirschhorn R. Overview of biochemical abnormalities and molecular genetics of adenosine deaminase deficiency. Pediatr Res 1993;33:535–41.
42. Markert ML. Purine nucleoside phosphorylase deficiency. Immunodefic Rev 1991;3:45–81.
43. Businco L, Fazio AD, Ziruolo MG, et al. Clinical and immunological findings in four infants with Omenn's syndrome: a form of severe combined immunodeficiency with phenotypically normal T cells, elevated IgE and eosinophilia. Clin Immunol Immunopathol 1987; 44:123–33.
44. De Saint Basile G, LeDeist F, de Villartay JP, et al. Restricted heterogeneity of T lymphocytes in combined immunodeficiency with hypereosinophilia (Omenn's Syndrome). J Clin Invest 1991;87:1352–9.
45. Omenn GS. Familial reticuloendotheliosis with eosinophilia. N Eng J Med 1965;273:427–32.
46. Wirt DP, Brooks EG, Vaidy AS, et al. Novel T-lymphocyte population in combined immunodeficiency with features of graft versus host disease. N Engl J Med 1989;32:370–4.
47. DeVaal OM, Seynhaeve V. Reticular dysgenesis. Lancet 1959;ii:1123–5.
48. Levinsky RJ, Tiedman K, Successful bone-marrow transplantation for reticular dysgenesis. Lancet 1983;i:671–3.
49. Alarcon B, Regueiro JR, Arnaiz-Villena A, Terhorst C. Familial defect in the surface expression of the T-cell receptor-CD3 complex. N Engl J Med 1988;319:1203–8.
50. Arnaiz-Villena A, Timon M, Corell A, et al. Brief report: primary immunodeficiency caused by mutations in the gene encoding the CD3-γ subunit of the T-lymphocyte receptor. N Engl J Med 1992;327:529–33.
51. Perez-Aciego P, Alarcon B, Arnaiz-Villena A, et al. Expression and function of a variant T cell receptor complex lacking CD3γ. J Exp Med 1991;174:319–26.
52. Soudais C, de Villartay JP, LeDeist F, et al. Independent mutations of the human CD3ε genes resulting in a T cell receptor/CD3 complex immune deficiency. Nature Genet 1993;3:77–81.
53. Touraine JL, Betuel H, Souillet G. Combined immunodeficiency disease associated with absence of cell surface HLA-A and B antigens. J Pediatr 1978;93:47–51.
54. Van Kaer L, Ashton-Rickardt PG, Ploegh HL, Tonegawa S. TAP1 mutant mice are deficient in antigen presentation, surface class I molecules, and $CD4^-8^+$ T cells. Cell 1992;71:1205–14.
55. Clement LT, Plaeger-Marshall S, Haas A, et al. Bare lymphocyte syndrome: consequences of absent class II major histocompatibility antigen expression for B lymphocyte differentiation and function. J Clin Invest 1988;81:669–75.
56. De Preval C, Lisowska-Grospierre B, Loche M, et al. A trans-activating class II regulatory gene unlinked to the MHC controls expression of HLA class II genes. Nature 1985;318:291–3.
57. Griscelli C, Lisowska-Grospierre B. Combined immunodeficiency with defective expression in MHC class II genes. Immunodefic Rev 1989;1:135–53.
58. Reith W, Satola S, Sanchez SH, et al. Congenital immunodeficiency with regulatory defect

in MHC class II gene expression lacks a specific HLA-DR promoter binding protein, RF-X. Cell 1988;53:897–906.
59. Boder E, Sedgwick RP. Ataxia-telangiectasia: a familial syndrome and progressive cerebellar ataxia, oculocutaneous telangiectasia and frequent pulmonary infection. Pediatrics 1958;21:526–54.
60. Gatti RA, Berkel I, Boder E, et al. Localization of an ataxia-telangiectasia gene to chromosome 11q22-23. Nature 1988;336:577–80.
61. Jaspers NG, Gatti RA, Baan C, et al. Genetic complementation analysis of ataxia telangiectasia and Nijmegen breakage syndrome: a survey of 50 patients. Cytogenet Cell Genet 1988;49:259–63.
62. Kapp LN, Painter RB, Yu LC, et al. Cloning of a candidate gene for ataxia telangiectasia group. Am J Human Genet 1992;51:45–54.
63. Swift M. Genetic aspects of ataxia-telangiectasia. Immunodefic Rev 1990;2:67–81.
64. Waldmann TA, McIntire KR. Serum alpha-fetoprotein levels in patients with ataxia-telangiectasia. Lancet 1972;ii:1112–5.
65. Derry JM, Ochs HD, Francke U. Isolation of a novel gene mutated in Wiskott-Aldrich syndrome. Cell 1994;78:635–44.
66. Higgins EA, Siminovitch KA, Zhuang D, et al. Aberrant O-linked oligosaccharide biosynthesis in lymphocytes and platelets from patients with Wiskott-Aldrich syndrome. J Biol Chem 1991;266:6280–90.
67. Kwan S-P, Lehner T, Hagemann T, et al. Localization of the gene for the Wiskott-Aldrich syndrome between two flanking markers TIMP and DXS255 on Xp11.2-11.3. Genomics 1991;10:29–33.
68. Peacocke M, Siminovitch KA. Linkage of Wiskott-Aldrich syndrome with polymorphic DNA sequences from the human X chromosome. Proc Natl Acad Sci USA 1987;84:3430–3.
69. Remold-O'Donnell E, Rosen FS. Sialophorin (CD43) and the Wiskott-Aldrich syndrome. Immunodefic Rev 1990;2:151–74.
70. Rosenstein Y, Park JK, Hahn WC, Rosen FS, Bierer BE, Burakoff SJ. CD43, a molecule defective in Wiskott-Aldrich syndrome binds ICAM-1. Nature 1991;354:233–5.
71. Shelley CS, Remold-O'Donnell E, Davis III AE, et al. Molecular characterization of sialophorin (CD43), the lymphocyte surface sialoglycoprotein defective in Wiskott-Aldrich syndrome. Proc Natl Acad Sci USA 1989;86:2819–23.
72. Simon HU, Mills GB, Hashimoto S, Siminovitch KA. Evidence for defective transmembrane signalling in B cells from patients with Wiskott-Aldrich syndrome. J Clin Invest 1992;90:1396–1405.

ADDITIONAL READINGS

1. Aiuti F, Pandolfi F, Fiorilli M, et al. Monoclonal antibody analysis of T cell subsets in 40 patients with immunodeficiencies. J Clin Immunol 1982;2(suppl 3):81S–89S.
2. Buckley RH. Immunodeficiency diseases. JAMA 1992;268:2797–806.
3. Buckley RH, Gard S, Schiff RI, et al. T cells and T cell subsets in large population of patients with primary immunodeficiency. Birth Defects 1983;19:187–91.
4. Buckley RH, Schiff RI. The use of intravenous immune globulin in immunodeficiency diseases. N Engl J Med 1991;325:110–7.
5. Cournoyer D, Caskey CT. Gene therapy of the immune system. Ann Rev Immunol 1993;11:297–332.
6. Mensink EJB, Schuurman KB. Immunodeficiency disease genes on the X chromosomes. Disease Markers 1987;5:129–40.
7. Stiehm ER, ed. Immunological disorders in infants and children, 3rd ed. Philadelphia: W.B. Saunders, 1989.
8. Tedder TF, Crain MJ, Kubagawa H, et al. Evaluation of lymphocyte differentiation in primary and secondary immunodeficiency diseases. J Immunol 1985;135:1786–91.

CHAPTER 14

Autoimmune Disorders of Childhood

Robert N. Lipnick, M.D., F.A.A.P., F.A.C.R.

RHEUMATIC DISORDERS OF CHILDREN

There are over 50 different diseases that may affect the musculoskeletal system (joints, bones, and muscles), as well as internal organs and skin. In the United States, approximately 250,000 children suffer from juvenile rheumatoid arthritis (JRA), while systemic lupus erythematosus (SLE) and dermatomyositis follow in relative frequency.

This chapter deals with juvenile rheumatic diseases and their laboratory diagnosis, recognizing that most of these disorders are characterized not by specific laboratory tests, but by a constellation of signs and symptoms and by radiographic abnormalities of bones and joints.

PATTERNS OF PRESENTATIONS

1. Acute mono- or oligoarthritis (affecting one or a few joints)
2. Acute polyarthritis
3. Chronic mono- or pauciarthritis
4. Chronic polyarthritis
5. Non-articular "rheumatism" (symptoms arising from periarticular tissues or muscles)
6. Arthritis associated with skin disease
7. Arthritis associated with gastro-intestinal disease

8. Arthritis associated with pleuro-pulmonary disease
9. Arthritis associated with infection
10. Arthritis associated with hematologic and neoplastic disorders
11. Systemic disease associated with vasculitis
12. Arthritis associated with endocrine, biochemical, or metabolic disorders
13. Hereditary diseases of connective tissue

JUVENILE RHEUMATOID ARTHRITIS

JRA is the most common rheumatic disorder in the pediatric population. JRA may not represent a single disease but rather a syndrome of diseases. Current evidence implicates an autoimmune pathogenesis. Genetic, environmental, and immunoregulatory factors are believed to be involved in the pathogenic process. JRA is primarily a synovial disease (i.e., affecting the joint lining), with secondary pathological changes occurring in the synovial fluid, cartilage, periarticular tissues, and bone. The synovium becomes inflamed, causing pain and swelling in one or several peripheral joints. Fibroblasts, blood vessels, and chronic inflammatory cells proliferate, and the resulting granulation-tissue pannus extends over the surface of the articular cartilage, eroding and destroying it. The destructive changes may extend to articular and periarticular bone and to periarticular soft tissue, leading to joint deformities.

Information defining abnormalities of bone and mineral metabolism in JRA is limited. Reed and associates[9] reported decreased serum osteocalcin levels in children with inactive JRA. Bone mineral content (BMC) was normal in 16 patients with inactive disease, suggesting that decreased mineralization during active arthritis was reversible when inflammation resolved. Others have found decreased serum 25-hydroxy-vitamin D_3 levels and increased parathyroid hormone levels in patients with polyarticular and systemic JRA compared to controls. Children receiving glucocorticoids had significantly reduced bone mineral content which may be related to impairment of hepatic 25-hydroxy-glucocorticoid therapy. Future studies of BMC and bone metabolism should elucidate the mechanisms of decreased bone turnover in children with JRA, to determine whether dietary interventions such as calcium or vitamin D supplementation or intensive exercise programs might improve outcomes, or whether better suppression of the underlying inflammatory disease is required.

The pathogenic process may extend well beyond the border of synovial tissue and involve other tissues. Clinically, the patient may have overwhelming fatigue, morning stiffness lasting many hours, high fever, rash, swelling of joints, pericarditis, uveitis, and other signs of acute or chronic disease.

SYSTEMIC LUPUS ERYTHEMATOSUS

SLE is an episodic, multisystem disease characterized by widespread inflammation of the blood vessels and connective tissue and the presence of circulating autoantibodies. Its clinical manifestations are extremely variable, and its natural history is unpredictable. Untreated, SLE is often progressive and leads to death. SLE is regarded as a prototype of autoimmune diseases in humans. Although it remains a disease of uncertain etiology, many scientific observations are consistent with the hypothesis that SLE results from altered immunologic responsiveness on a background of a genetic predisposition to the disease.

The basic pathologic lesions of SLE are immune complex and autoantibody deposition in vessels and other tissues, resulting in fibrinoid necrosis, inflammatory cellular infiltrates, and sclerosis of collagen. The fibrinoid material is eosinophilic with hematoxylin-eosin stain and is deposited within the interfibrillar ground substance of the connective tissues. Vascular endothelial thickening is another characteristic of SLE. Capillaries, venules, and arterioles are all involved. Secondary changes include vascular obstruction and development of thrombosis.

Children with SLE may present with disease that ranges from an acute, rapidly fatal onset to an insidious onset with a long history of slowly unfolding exacerbations. There is enormous variability in the character and severity of the presenting signs and symptoms. Any organ in the body may be involved. A single system may be affected at onset; however, it is more usual to find multisystem disease. A lupus-like syndrome may be induced by many drugs, especially the following: anti-arrhythmics (procainamide, quinidine); anticonvulsants; antihypertensive agents (hydralazine, methyldopa); and D-Penicillamine.

NEONATAL LUPUS SYNDROME

Children of mothers who have SLE may develop manifestations of lupus in the neonatal period that are mediated by the transplacental passage of maternal IgG autoantibodies. The neonatal lupus syndrome (NLS) is more common in females than in males.

The affected infant demonstrates a transiently positive ANA and diminished serum complement concentrations. In the majority of these babies, there is no associated clinical disease and the serological abnormalities regress within several weeks to months after birth, in accordance with the normal half-life of maternal IgG (24–28 days). The clinical manifestations include rash, complete congenital heart block, hepatomegaly, thrombocytopenia, and neutropenia.

At least two specificities of Ro antigen have been identified. The highest risk for NLS appears to be associated with the presence of antibodies to the 48-kD La/SS-B polypeptide and the 52-kD Ro/SS-A polypeptide, but not to the 60-kD Ro antigen. Since ELISA currently does not differentiate between the two Ro antigens, care must be exercised in interpreting test results. The Ro antigen is widely distributed in the fetal conduction system and myocardium. Antibodies to Ro are bound to the conduction system of infants dying of complete congenital heart block.

IgG autoantibodies which cross the placenta and enter the fetal circulation are apparently responsible for the observed infant pathology. Anti-Ro antibodies are most characteristic of the syndrome, although anti-La antibodies may be found in some individuals. The latter infants usually do not have complete congenital heart block.

JUVENILE DERMATOMYOSITIS

Juvenile dermatomyositis (JDM) is a multisystem disease characterized by acute and chronic nonsuppurative inflammation of striated muscle and skin. Early in its course, the disease is marked by the presence of a vasculitis, and later by the development of calcinosis. The average age of onset is approximately 6 y, with a sex ratio of female to male of 1.7 to 1.

The etiology and pathogenesis of JDM remains unknown, although it is probably multifactorial in etiology. Potential pathogenic mechanisms include abnormalities of cellular immunity resulting in T-lymphocyte mediated destruction of striated muscle and deposition of immune complexes in muscle tissue. JDM has also been described in association with immunodeficiency and infection. Immunoglobulin G (IgG), immunoglobulin M (IgM), and the third component of complement (C3) can be found deposited in the vessel walls of skeletal muscle. A dermatomyositis-like disease has been described in some children with agammaglobulinemia in association with ECHO virus infection, and occasionally in patients with selective IgA deficiency and C2 deficiency. In addition, increased titers of serum antibodies to coxsackie virus B and toxoplasma have been reported.

Dermatomyositis usually presents in childhood with a combination of easy fatigue, malaise, muscle weakness, rash, and fever. Clinical expression and progression of the disease are variable.

The distinctive pathologic lesions of JDM involve the striated muscles, skin, and gastrointestinal tract. The main pathologic feature of the disease is muscle necrosis. Characteristic but nonspecific changes include disruption of the myofibril and tubular system, central nuclear migration, prominent nuclei, and basophilia. Concomitant degeneration and regeneration of muscle fibers result in variation in fiber size. Areas of focal necrosis are replaced during the healing phase by fibrous and fat tissue.

Routine laboratory studies are of little diagnostic help in the child with JDM. Nonspecific tests of inflammation such as the ESR and C-reactive protein tend to correlate with the degree of clinical inflammation or to be of no clinical usefulness.

Leukocytosis and anemia are uncommon at onset, except in the child with associated GI bleeding. Urinalysis is usually normal, although a few children have microscopic hematuria. There are no specific abnormalities of serum immunoglobulin concentrations. Children with JDM usually lack circulating rheumatoid factor. Antinuclear antibodies (ANAs) have been reported in patient serum at a frequency varying from 10 to 50%.

The three most helpful laboratory abnormalities are increased serum concentrations of the muscle enzymes, abnormal electromyographic changes, and specific histopathologic abnormalities on muscle biopsy. The serum muscle enzymes are important for diagnosis and for monitoring the effectiveness of therapy. Some individual variation in the pattern of enzyme increases occurs in JDM, and therefore it is recommended that CK, aspartate aminotransferase (AST), and aldolase be measured to provide a reliable baseline. The height of increase is variable but ranges from 20 to 40 times normal for CK and AST.

TABLE 14–1. Laboratory Abnormalities in the Rheumatic Diseases of Childhood

Abnormality	Juvenile Rheumatoid Arthritis: Polyarthritis	Juvenile Rheumatoid Arthritis: Oligoarthritis	Juvenile Rheumatoid Arthritis: Systemic Onset	Systemic Lupus Erythematosus	Dermatomyositis	Scleroderma	Vasculitis	Rheumatic Fever
Anemia	+	−	+	+	+	+	+	+
Leukopenia	−	−	−	+++	−	−	−	−
Thrombocytopenia	−	−	−	+	−	−	−	−
Leukocytosis	+	−	+++	−	+	−	+++	+
Thrombocytosis	+	−	+	−	+	−	+	+
Antinuclear antibodies	+	+	−	+++	+	+	−	−
Anti-DNA antibodies	−	−	−	+++	−	−	−	−
Rheumatoid factors	+	−	−	+	−	+	+	−
Anti-streptococcal antibodies	+	−	+	−	−	−	−	+++
Hypocomplementemia	−	−	−	+++	−	−	+	−
Elevated hepatic enzyme levels	+	−	+	+	+	+	+	−
Elevated muscle enzyme levels	−	−	−	+	+++	+	+	−
Abnormal urinalysis	+	−	+	+++	+	+	+	−

− = absent, + = minimal, ++ = moderate, +++ = severe

TABLE 14–2. Characteristics of Synovial Fluid in the Rheumatic Diseases

Group	Condition	Synovial Complement	Color/Clarity	Viscosity	Mucin Clot	WBC Count	PNM%	Miscellaneous Findings
Non-inflammatory	Normal	N*	Yellow/Clear	N	N	< 200	< 25	
	Traumatic arthritis	N	Xanthochromic//Turbid	N	N	< 2,000	< 25	Debris
	Osteoarthritis	N	Yellow/Clear	N	N	1,000	< 25	
Inflammatory	SLE	↓	Yellow/Clear	N	N	5,000	10	LE cells
	Rheumatic fever	N – ↑	Yellow/Cloudy	Å	Fair	5,000	10–50	
	Juvenile rheumatoid arthritis	N – ↓	Yellow/Cloudy	Å	Poor	15,000–20,000	75	
	Reiter's syndrome	↑	Opaque	Å	Poor	20,000	80	Reiter's cells
Pyogenic	Tuberculosis arthritis	N – ↑	Yellow/Cloudy	Å	Poor	25,000	50–60	Acid-fast bacteria
	Septic arthritis	↑	Serosanguinous/ Turbid	Å	Poor	80,000-200,000	75	Low glucose, bacteria

* N = Normal

Rarely, children have no increase in the serum concentration of CK during the acute phase of the disease, while other children have a persistent increase of this enzyme late in the course of disease, without any other clinical indication of muscle inflammation. In the latter instance, evaluation of serum CK in family members may reveal an unrelated, but unsuspected, genetic abnormality. Lactic dehydrogenase (LDH) and alanine aminotransferase (ALT) are increased in many children with JDM, but are less specific. Serum concentrations of all of these enzymes are increased in a wide variety of other conditions, such as muscle trauma, motor neuron diseases, vasculitis, metabolic disorders, toxins, and infections. Very large increases are most commonly associated with JDM and, to a somewhat lesser extent, with muscular dystrophy.

SPONDYLOARTHROPATHIES

The spondyloarthropathies (SAS) consist of a group of inflammatory arthropathies that affect the joints of the axial skeleton as well as peripheral joints. The four disorders classified as a spondyloarthropathy include juvenile ankylosing spondylitis (JAS), psoriatic arthritis, arthritis associated with inflammatory bowel disease, and Reiter's syndrome. They differ from JRA in many ways. Inflammation of the joints of the axial skeleton (spine and sacroiliac joints) and inflammation of the entheses (sites of attachment of ligaments and tendons on to bone) are common in children with a spondyloarthropathy, while uncommon in JRA. There is a high frequency of Human Leukocyte Antigen (HLA) B27 among patients with a spondyloarthropathy.

Juvenile Ankylosing Spondylitis

Juvenile ankylosing spondylitis is a chronic, progressive, inflammatory disorder of unknown etiology involving the sacroiliac joints, spine, and large peripheral joints. Ninety percent of cases occur in males, with the usual age at onset being the second or third decade of life. There is a strong genetic predisposition to ankylosing spondylitis, with several family members often involved. Ninety percent of patients with ankylosing spondylitis have HLA-B27. The gene that determines this specific cell surface antigen may be linked to other genes that determine pathologic autoimmune phenomena or that lead to an increased susceptibility to infectious or environmental antigens. There is no specific immunological diagnostic test.

The disease begins with the insidious onset of low back pain and stiffness, usually worse in the morning. Symptoms of the acute disease include pain and tenderness in the sacroiliac joints and spasm of the paravertebral muscles. Findings in advanced disease include ankylosis of the sacroiliac joints and spine, loss of lumbar lordosis, cervical kyphosis, and decreased chest expansion. Twenty-five percent of patients will have iritis. Carditis, with or without aortitis, is seen in 10% of patients.

Hypergammaglobulinemia, rheumatoid factors, and antinuclear antibodies are not present in the sera of patients with ankylosing spondylitis. During phases of active disease, elevated sedimentation rate and a mild anemia may be observed.

Juvenile Psoriatic Arthritis

Juvenile psoriatic arthritis (JPsA) is a chronic, recurrent, polyarthritis in children younger than 16 years, preceded by, accompanied by, or followed within 15 years by psoriasis. Psoriasis is a common disease, affecting 1 to 2 percent of the Caucasian population and has its onset in childhood in one-third of patients. Approximately 5–7% of patients with psoriasis have arthritis. The onset of arthritis may be acute or insidious and is often preceded by skin disease. The joints most commonly affected in patients with JPsA are knees, ankles, and wrists. Pitting of nails is seen in 75% of children, but onycholysis is uncommon. Other systemic manifestations may include uveitis, fever, pericarditis, and mitral valve prolapse.

In early disease, synovial histologic findings are indistinguishable from those of JRA. However, in chronic JPsA, histologic study shows increased fibrosis of capsule and arterial walls and less prominent synovial hypertrophy in comparison to JRA. Laboratory evaluation usually demonstrates an increased erythrocyte sedimentation rate, absence of rheumatoid factor, and ANA positivity in 17–50% of patients. Hyperuricemia is occasionally seen in patients with severe skin disease. Synovial fluid examination reveals a white blood cell count of 5000–40,000/mL; these are predominately polymorphonuclear cells (PMNs).

Reiter's Syndrome

Reiter's syndrome is classically defined as a clinical triad consisting of arthritis, urethritis, and conjunctivitis. However, the arthritis is frequently accompanied by only one of the other characteristic manifestations. Fever, malaise, and weight loss occur commonly with acute arthritis. The urethritis is nonspecific and often asymptomatic. The conjunctivitis is mild, but 20–50% of patients develop iritis. Balanitis circinata, painless oral ulcerations, and keratoderma blennorrhagicum (thick ketatotic lesions of the palms and soles) are mucocutaneous manifestations. Complications involve spondylitis and carditis.

Most patients have a mild leukocytosis. The urethral discharge is purulent, and smear and culture are usually negative for *Neisseria gonorrhea*. Synovial fluid is sterile, with a white cell count of 2,000–50,000/mL, mostly PMNs.

TABLE 14–3. Laboratory Abnormalities in the Common Forms of Spondyloarthropathy Compared to Juvenile Rheumatoid Arthritis

	Spondyloarthropathies			
Laboratory Abnormalities	Juvenile Ankylosing Spondylitis	Juvenile Psoriatic Arthritis	Reiter's Syndrome	**Juvenile Rheumatoid Arthritis**
Acute phase response	+	+	+	+++
Anemia	+	+	+	+++
Leukocytosis	–	+	+	+
Rheumatoid factors	–	–	–	+
Antinuclear antibodies	–	+	–	+++

– = absent, + = minimal, ++ = moderate, +++ = severe

The cause of Reiter's syndrome is not known. Some cases have been associated with sexual contact. Several infectious agents, including shigella, salmonella, gonococci, mycoplasma, chlamydia, yersinia, and campylobacter have been associated with Reiter's syndrome. Eighty percent of patients with Reiter's syndrome have HLA-B27.

INFLAMMATORY BOWEL DISEASE

Inflammatory joint disease constitutes one of the most common extraintestinal complications of both ulcerative colitis and Crohn's disease, occurring in 10–20% of such children.

There are two types of arthritis accompanying inflammatory bowel disease, one that is characteristically a nondeforming, nonerosive polyarthritis, and one in which inflammation of the sacroiliac joints occurs. The former is correlated with activity of the gut inflammation and occurs slightly more frequently in girls than in boys. The latter is independent of enteric disease activity, is associated with HLA-B27, and occurs most frequently in teenage boys. In a child with arthritis, in whom weight loss, unexplained fever, abdominal pain, hematochezia, marked abnormalities of the inflammatory indices, or hypoalbuminemia occur, the diagnosis of inflammatory bowel disease should be considered, because joint disease may precede other manifestations of bowel disease by many months.

Laboratory studies are of little assistance in differentiating JRA from the spondyloarthropathies, except that in the latter group RF is absent and HLA-B27 is frequently present. The high frequency of ANA in JRA contrasts with its corresponding low frequency in the spondyloarthropathies.

PROGRESSIVE SYSTEMIC SCLEROSIS

Progressive Systemic Sclerosis (PSS) is a disease of unknown cause characterized by abnormally increased collagen deposition in the skin and internal organs. The course is usually slowly progressive, but it can be rapidly progressive and fatal because of involvement of internal organs such as the lungs, heart, kidneys, and gastrointestinal tract. There may be vascular abnormalities in the lungs and kidneys.

Biopsy of involved skin reveals thinning of the epidermis with loss of rete pegs, atrophy of the dermal appendages, hyalinization and fibrosis of arterioles, and a striking increase of compact collagen fibers in the reticular dermis. Synovial tissue findings range from an acute inflammatory lymphocytic infiltration to diffuse fibrosis with relatively little inflammation. The histologic changes seen in muscle include interstitial and perivascular inflammatory infiltration followed by fibrosis and myofibrillar necrosis, atrophy, and degeneration.

In patients with renal involvement, the histologic appearance of the kidney is similar to that of malignant hypertensive nephropathy, with intimal proliferation of the interlobular arteries and fibrinoid changes in the intima and media of more distal interlobular arteries and of afferent arterioles.

Polyclonal hypergammaglobulinemia is frequently present in patients with progressive systemic sclerosis. The fluorescent antinuclear antibody test is positive in 70% of cases and shows a speckled or nucleolar pattern. A specific antinuclear antibody found only in PSS is anti-SCL 70.

VASCULITIS

The vasculitides represent a spectrum of pathologic and clinical disease ranging from acute, overwhelming necrotizing vasculitis to chronic, indolent vascular inflammation. No verifying pathogenetic mechanism has yet been defined for the vasculitides, but most are probably immunologically mediated disorders.

Polyarteritis nodosa represents one entity in a spectrum of inflammatory diseases involving arteries and veins. It is a multisystem disease characterized by acute inflammation and fibrinoid necrosis of small and medium-sized vessels. The etiology of the vascular inflammation is unknown, although infections and hypersensitivity mechanisms have been suggested because similar arterial lesions are seen in serum sickness-like illnesses following allergic reactions to drugs, after bacterial infections, and in patients who have circulating hepatitis B surface antigen (HBsAg).

The clinical manifestations of polyarteritis nodosa depend on the site and extent of arteries affected and may involve the brain, heart, kidneys, intestinal tract, or peripheral nerves. Aneurysm formation or thrombosis may occur, and the inflammatory process may involve adjacent veins. In the healing stage, fibrotic obliteration of vessel lumina may occur, leading to local and distal vascular insufficiency.

Polyarteritis may occur as a disease on its own. However, it is sometimes difficult to distinguish this disease from other forms of vasculitis, such as hypersensitivity angiitis, allergic granulomatous angiitis (with asthma and eosinophilia), or Wegener's granulomatosis (necrotizing granulomatosis of the respiratory tract, disseminated angiitis, and focal glomerulonephritis). Vasculitis also occurs in association with other rheumatic disorders, such as acute rheumatic fever and systemic lupus erythematosus. There are no characteristic diagnostic tests for this group of diseases, which are characterized by vascular inflammation, aside from *biopsy* of affected vessel. The biopsy will demonstrate the vascular involvement, initially with edema of the *intima* and adjacent media, with subsequent infiltration of acute inflammatory cells, fibrinoid necrosis, and disruption of the elastica. The diagnosis may be suggested by the following histologic clues: the size of the vessels involved, the presence of vascular lesions of the same or different ages, and the presence of giant cells.

SYSTEMIC AND JOINT DISORDERS ASSOCIATED WITH INFECTIONS

Many of the systemic arthritic disorders may be associated with as yet unrecognized infections in genetically susceptible individuals (e.g., juvenile rheumatoid arthritis, systemic lupus erythematosus). Ankylosing spondylitis has been linked to Klebsiella infection. Other disorders associated with clearly identified infectious agents are acute rheumatic fever (streptococcus) and the arthritis and tenosynovitis associated with Neisseria infections. In some disorders, arthritis may be present, but culture of synovial fluid or blood is unrewarding and serologic tests to determine exposure to infectious agents must be carried out.

The presence of specific infection may be established by finding antibodies to microorganisms such as the streptococcus, (i.e., antistreptolysin-O titer), hepatitis virus, or the spirochete *Borrelia burgdorferi* responsible for Lyme disease. Antibodies to this specific spirochete may be found in serum or synovial fluid. Erythema nodosum may be associated with systemic bacterial or fungal infections. Septic arthritis due to organisms within the joint may be diagnosed by appropriate culture of the synovial fluid. Some organisms, such as staphylococcus, streptococcus, and E. coli, are relatively easy to culture. *Neisseria gonorrhea* may be difficult to culture without appropriate laboratory precautions. Tuberculous infection of bones or joints may be difficult to diagnose without open biopsy and culture of synovium. Osteomyelitis or discitis (infection in the disc of the spine arising from vertebral end plate) may require culture by needle aspirate or bone biopsy.

ACUTE RHEUMATIC FEVER

Acute rheumatic fever (ARF) is a childhood rheumatic disease that many physicians believed had only historical significance. However, in 1985, this belief was contradicted unexpectedly when a series of epidemics was reported in several widely diverse geographic regions of the United States.

Acute rheumatic fever typically occurs in children age 4–9 y, although it may also occur in teenagers.The illness appears to be slightly more common in girls than in boys. The illness begins initially as a B-hemolytic streptococcal pharyngitis, followed two to three weeks later by migratory joint pain, fever, and palpitations or fatigue. Chorea may occur, but the onset is usually several months following the pharyngitis. The revised Jones Criteria provide diagnostic guidance (see Table 14–4). Treatment usually involves penicillin prophylaxis, non-steroidal anti-inflammatory drugs, and, for severe cases, steroids. Phenothiazides may be used in children with chorea.

Laboratory findings may be of great help in many cases of ARF, because approximately 40% of patients have an asymptomatic pharyngitis, and thus 2–4 w later, when the patient is first seen, a throat culture may show normal flora and no streptococci. In such cases, markedly increased antistreptolysin-O (ASO) and antistreptococcal deoxyribonuclease B titers which later return to normal provide supporting evidence of a recent streptococcal infection. Increased sedimentation rate or C-reactive protein is usually present. A prolonged PR interval on EKG is supportive evidence of rheumatic heart disease.

LYME DISEASE

Lyme disease was first recognized in 1975 as a distinct clinicopathologic entity by Steere et al. based on the investigation of a cluster of children with arthritis in Lyme,

TABLE 14–4. Jones Criteria (revised) for Diagnosis of Rheumatic Fever*

Major Manifestations	Minor Manifestations
Carditis	Fever
Polyarthritis	Arthralgia
Chorea	Previous rheumatic fever or rheumatic heart disease
Erythema Marginatum	Prolonged PR interval
Subcutaneous Nodules	Increased ESR or CRP
Plus: Supporting evidence of preceding streptococcal infection:	
Increased titers of antistreptolysin-O or other streptococcal antibodies	
Positive throat culture for group A Hemolytic streptococci	
Recent scarlet fever	

*A definite diagnosis is established with two major criteria or with one major and two minor criteria plus evidence of prior streptococcal infection.

Connecticut. Until 1983 there was no serologic test available to aid in the diagnosis. Since then, a spectrum of disease manifestations, including a characteristic skin lesion (erythema chronicum migrans), arthritis, and neurologic and cardiac abnormalities, has been shown to be associated with the tick-borne organism *Borrelia burgdorferi*. The serologic test for the antibody response to *B. burgdorferi* has been proposed as the best laboratory method for diagnosis of disease.

Initially, indirect immunofluorescent antibody (IFA) measuring both IgM and IgG was used, but most laboratories now use the enzyme-linked immunosorbent assay (ELISA), measuring both IgM and IgG. Some laboratories will perform Western Blot analysis to confirm an equivocal ELISA result. Several years ago, a group of investigators reported 17 patients with signs and symptoms of Lyme disease with negative serologic testing by IFA, ELISA, and Western Blot who had a specific T-cell blastogenic response to *B. burgdorferi*.

Antibodies to *B. burgdorferi* can be identified by either an indirect fluorescent antibody (IFA) test or an enzyme-linked immunosorbent assay (ELISA). ELISA testing is more objective than IFA and has generally replaced it in routine surveillance. Sensitivity is approximately 40–70 percent in early disease and 95 percent in late disease. Specific IgM titers to *B. burgdorferi* peak between the third and sixth weeks of the illness. IgG antibody is detected somewhat later, but may persist for years.

Cross-reactivity of antibodies with other species is a continuing problem. *Treponema pallidum* infection can be readily diagnosed by more specific tests. *Treponema denticola, Leptospiras,* and *Borrelia hermsii* may induce antibodies that cross-react with *B. burgdorferi*. Low-titer antibodies to *B. burgdorferi* occur in a variety of other rheumatic diseases (e.g., RA, SLE) and other illnesses (e.g., subacute bacterial endocarditis, infectious mononucleosis, mumps, meningitis, Rocky Mountain Spotted Fever, and other rickettsial diseases).

Western blot analysis is reserved as a confirmatory test in children with low-titer positive ELISA results or with atypical clinical manifestations. It is rarely positive when ELISA testing is normal or negative. However, criteria for interpretation of Western Blots have not been firmly established. Guidelines proposed currently include the presence of IgG reactivity to five of the following ten bands: 18-, 21-, 28-, 30-, 41-, 45-, 58-, 66-, 74-, and 93-kD.

Concern about interlaboratory variability of results and lack of standardization of assays for the detection of the antibody response to *B. burgdorferi* prompted one investigator to send serum specimens from 17 employees working in an area known to be infested with *Ixodes dammini*, the tick vector of *B. burgdorferi*,to four different laboratories in Minnesota. Six employees tested positive for antibodies to *B. burgdorferi* in at least one laboratory, with no employee testing positive in all four laboratories. There is a need for standardization of the assays and the availability of national reference material. The results of serologic testing should not be relied on as the sole criteria in making the diagnosis of Lyme disease.

ACUTE PHASE REACTANTS

Erythrocyte Sedimentation Rate (ESR)

The rate of fall in milliliters per hour of red blood cells (RBCs) by the Westergren Method (ESR) is frequently utilized to document inflammation and also in following the course of chronic rheumatic disorders such as JRA, SLE, JDM, and vasculitis. RBCs in inflammatory disorders tend to form stacks (rouleaux) that partly result from increased concentration of fibrinogen and thus sediment more rapidly. Falsely low sedimentation rates are found in sickle cell disease, anisocytosis, spherocytosis, polycythemia, and heart failure. Prolonged storage of blood or tilting of the calibrated tube will increase the ESR.

C-Reactive Protein (CRP)

CRP is an acute phase reactant serum protein that is present in low concentration in normal serum. It was originally identified by its ability to give a precipitin reaction with pneumococcal C-polysaccharide. CRP concentrations rise rapidly under an inflammatory stimulus and then fall when inflammation subsides. In systemic lupus erythematosus and scleroderma, CRP concentrations are inappropriately low unless infection is present. CRP testing may be performed on freeze-stored serum, its major advantage compared to ESR testing.

In summary, laboratory testing is very valuable in the differential diagnosis of rheumatic diseases in childhood.

The author would like to thank George C. Tsokos, M.D., for his critical review and Sterling McQueen for excellent assistance in the preparation of this manuscript.

TABLE 14–5. Pediatric Diseases Associated with a Positive Rheumatoid Factor

Rheumatic Diseases	Non-Rheumatic Diseases
JRA	Viral (e.g., EBV)
SLE	Chronic active hepatitis
Scleroderma	Chronic infections (e.g., TB, Malaria)
Vasculitis	Subacute bacterial endocarditis
	Malignancy (e.g., Leukemia, Lymphoma)
	Sarcoidosis
	Chronic pulmonary disease
	Post-vaccination

TABLE 14–6. Pediatric Diseases Associated with a Positive Antinuclear Antibody

Rheumatic Diseases	Non-Rheumatic Diseases
SLE	Drugs:
JRA	Anticonvulsants (e.g., Phenytoin)
Dermatomyositis	Anithypertensives (e.g., Hydralazine)
Scleroderma	Antiarrhythmics (e.g., Procainamide)
	Infections:
	Syphilis
	Hepatitis
	Mononucleosis
	Malignancy (e.g., Leukemia, Lymphoma)
	Inflammatory Bowel Disease

SUGGESTED READING

1. Lipnick RN, Tsokos GC. Immune abnormalities in the pathogenesis of juvenile rheumatoid arthritis. Clin Exp Rheum 1990;8:177–86.
2. Pachman LM. Juvenile Dermatomyositis. Pediatr Clin North AM 1986;33:1097–117.
3. Southwood TR, Petty RE, Malleson PN, et al. Psoriatic arthritis in children. Arthritis Rheum 1989;32:1007–13.
4. Petty RE, Malleson PN. Spondyloarthropathies of childhood. Pediatr Clin North AM 1986;33:1079–96.
5. Suarez-Almazor ME, Catoggio LJ, Maldonado-Cocco, et al. Juvenile progressive systemic sclerosis: clinical and serologic findings. Arthritis Rheum 1985;28:699–702.
6. Bisno AL. The resurgence of acute rheumatic fever in the United States. Annu Rev Med 1990;41:319–29.
7. Luger SW, Krauss E. Serologic tests for lyme disease. Arch Intern Med 1990;150:761–63.
8. Reed A, Haugen M, Pachman LM, Langman CB. 25-Hydroxyvitamin D therapy in children with active juvenile rheumatoid arthritis: short-term effects on serum osteocalcin levels and bone mineral density. J Pediatr 1991;119(4):657–60.
9. Steere AC, Malawista SE, Snydman DR, et al. Lyme arthritis: an epidemic of oligoarticular arthritis in children and adults in three Connecticut communities. Arthritis Rheum 1977; 20:7–17.

10. Cassidy JT, Petty RE. Textbook of pediatric rheumatology, 3rd ed. Philadelphia: Saunders, 1995.
11. Szer IS, Jacobs JC. Systemic lupus erythematosus in childhood. In: Lahita RG, ed. Systemic lupus erythematosus, 2nd ed. New York: Churchill Livingstone, 1992.
12. Watluck J. Bunyon JP. Autoantibody associated congenital heart block: outcome in mothers and children. Ann Intern Med 1994;120:544.
13. Pachman LM. Inflammatory myopathy in children. Rheum Dis Clin North Am 1994:919.
14. Burgos-Vargas R. Spondyloarthropathies and psoriatic arthritis in children. Current Opin Rheumatol 1993;5:634.
15. Ansell BM, Falcini F, Woo P. Scleroderma in childhood. Clin Dermatol 1994;12:299.
16. Ozean S, Besbas N, Saatci U, et al. Diagnostic criteria for polyarthritis nodosa in childhood. J Pediatr 1992;120:206.
17. Golightly MG. Lyme borreliosis: laboratory considerations. Seminars in Neurology 1997;17:11–17.

CHAPTER 15

The Laboratory and Adolescent Medicine

John T. Repke, M.D. Sue Ellen Carpenter, M.D.
Michele D. Wilson, M.D.

GENERAL ADOLESCENT MEDICINE

Introduction

In 1990 there were 33.8 million individuals between age 10 and 19 y in the United States, and it is expected that the number will reach 38.3 million in the year 2000. The American Academy of Pediatrics' Committee on Practice and Ambulatory Medicine recommends that a health assessment visit occur every two years during adolescence if the individual is healthy. Because of the multitude of physical, psychological, and social changes that occur during this age period, many adolescent medicine specialists suggest that assessments be performed yearly as a minimum. As part of the health assessment, a history and physical examination are performed. In addition, selected laboratory tests are routinely done.[1] Suggested routine laboratory testing includes: (1) hemoglobin or hematocrit, (2) sickle cell screening for those African-American adolescents who have not been tested, and (3) screening for sexually transmitted disease for those adolescents who are sexually active.

Hematology

Anemia

Iron-deficiency anemia is a common disorder during adolescence, occurring in approximately 8% of females and 3% of males. Several factors contribute to its high prevalence. Adolescents are growing rapidly and therefore have increased iron requirements. They often consume a diet of poor nutritional value and low iron content. Female adolescents lose iron with menstruation. Yet most teenagers with iron-deficiency anemia appear healthy, since the degree of anemia generally is not severe. They may have subtle difficulties such as behavior problems, decreased attention span, or poor school performance.

Screening for anemia is recommended as part of routine health care.[2] At minimum, a hemoglobin and/or hematocrit should be obtained at the initial visit with a teenager and again at the end of puberty. In order to screen for iron-deficiency anemia, ideally one would obtain a hemoglobin, hematocrit, red cell indices, and red cell distribution width. A hematocrit alone is often performed, since it can be performed easily in a physician's office or clinic. The test has an acceptably high sensitivity but a low specificity. Alternatively, the hematocrit can be measured by automated counting devices in the laboratory using venous blood. Hemoglobin can be measured by spectrophotometric methods. The mean cell volume can be determined directly by Coulter-type counter.

Iron stores can be markedly depleted without anemia. The iron stores decrease initially, as demonstrated by a low-serum ferritin. Next, the serum iron decreases, the iron-binding capacity increases, and the serum transferrin decreases. As the condition continues, erythrocytes become small, as evidenced by a low mean cell volume, and they have a low hemoglobin concentration. The red cell distribution width, which is a measure of the variability of the mean cell volume, increases and is a sensitive measure of iron deficiency states. Protoporphyrin accumulates when there is inadequate iron for heme synthesis. Thus, increased concentrations of erythrocyte protoporphyrin indicate iron depletion.

In determining reference ranges for hematologic values during adolescence, it is important to consider age, sex, race, and sexual maturity rating (see Table 15–1). Normal hemoglobin and hematocrit values for females remain fairly constant, while

TABLE 15–1. Changes in Hematocrit Values by Pubertal Stages and Race

		MALES		FEMALES	
Pubertal Stage	**Race**	**Mean (%)**	**SD (%)**	**Mean (%)**	**SD(%)**
STAGE 1	Black	37.7	2.5	37.3	2.6
	White	39.5	2.4	39.1	3.0
STAGE 2	Black	38.4	2.5	38.9	3.2
	White	39.8	3.0	39.2	2.1
STAGE 3	Black	39.7	2.4	39.0	3.7
	White	40.9	2.6	39.6	2.6
STAGE 4	Black	41.1	2.7	38.4	3.5
	White	42.3	2.5	39.2	2.4
STAGE 5	Black	42.7	3.1	38.7	2.8
	White	43.8	2.7	39.2	3.0

Adapted from Daniel, WA. Hematocrit: Maturity relationship in adolescence. Pediatrics, 1973:52:338.

the values for males are more dependent on sexual maturity rating. Hematocrit values for African-American versus Caucasian adolescents are 1%–3% lower on average.[3]

Sickle Cell Screening

If an African-American adolescent has not previously been screened, he or she should receive a sickle cell screening test during adolescence. An individual who is found to carry the trait should be fully informed of its significance prior to childbearing.

Cholesterol and Lipid Screening

Coronary artery disease is the major cause of death in the United States. The atherosclerotic process that leads to coronary artery disease begins early in life. Hyperlipidemia and hypercholesterolemia are important risk factors for the development of the disease.

The indications for cholesterol screening in children and adolescents has been the subject of debate. Cholesterol levels in childhood do not accurately predict cholesterol levels in adulthood. Studies have demonstrated that cholesterol levels during childhood and adolescence do not track consistently into adulthood. Unfortunately, targeted screening of individuals with a positive family history for hyperlipidemia or premature coronary heart disease does not identify many adolescents who have elevated cholesterol.[4] Thus, the controversy continues as to whether to screen adolescents in a selected manner or wait until age 20 to begin cholesterol testing.

Regardless of which strategy is adopted, all adolescents need education in maintaining a healthy life style that minimizes the risk factors for coronary heart disease.

Substance Use

Drug use commonly occurs during adolescence. The National Institute on Drug Abuse conducts a yearly survey of high school seniors to assess the prevalence of drug use among adolescents. For the class of 1993, 42.9% of high school seniors had used an illicit drug at some time and 18.3% had used an illicit drug in the last 30 days.[5] Substance use represents a range of usage from experimentation to drug addiction and dependency. Common complaints that alert the clinician to the possibility of substance abuse include poor school performance, personality change, family discord, legal problems, injuries, or physical effects secondary to acute or chronic drug use. The interview and the use of standardized screening questionnaires are important components of the assessment. Drug testing can prove useful in carefully selected situations. The indications for drug testing and the manner in which the sample is obtained remain controversial. One must carefully consider the ethical issues prior to undertaking drug testing. It is crucial to know which drugs the laboratory can detect and to what degree of accuracy.

There are many laboratory techniques available for drug testing. When drug testing is indicated, a screening test is usually done initially followed by a confirmatory test. Immunoassay techniques are used for screening purposes. This method employs a drug-specific antibody reaction. A limitation of this test is that antibodies can cross-react with related drugs and yield a false-positive result. Enzyme multiplied immunoassay (EMIT) is a commonly used screening test and is less costly than other tests. Radioimmunoassay (RIA) is also available, but has the disadvantages of requiring greater analysis time and using radioactive materials. The fluorescent polarization technique is an alternative screening method.

Confirmation of a positive screening test by a second, more specific measure—chromatography—is recommended. Chromatography involves separation of various components of the specimen followed by identification of the different substances. Thin-layered chromatography (TLC) can detect many drugs of abuse. Although this method is often used, interpretation of the results requires a very skilled individual. False-positive and false-negative results can occur. A combination of gas-liquid chromatography with mass spectrometry (GC/MS) is the gold standard for drug testing. It is a highly specific and sensitive method which requires very advanced technology. Substances present in the sample are ionized and separated. Drugs detected are compared to the mass spectra for known substances in a reference library.[6] The threshold concentrations of drugs used for screening and confirmation has been debated.[7]

Infectious Mononucleosis

Although many young children have subclinical or mild Epstein-Barr virus (EBV) infection, clinically apparent acute infectious mononucleosis (IM) develops most commonly in adolescents and young adults. EBV infection is more prevalent in lower socioeconomic status groups where 50–85% of children have positive serology by age 4 y, while only 14–50% of middle and upper socioeconomic status children have positive serology by college age. The incubation period for infectious mononucleosis is 5–7 w. Its common manifestations include fever, malaise, lymphadenopathy, tonsillopharyngitis, splenomegaly, hepatomegaly, and abdominal pain. Palatine petechiae, periorbital edema, and rash may also be present.[8] Hematologic findings of IM include lymphocytosis > 50% of the total white blood cell count and atypical lymphocytes > 10% of all leukocytes. Other laboratory abnormalities include neutropenia and moderate increases of serum transaminases.

Laboratory tests can corroborate the diagnosis of IM. Heterophile antibody tests are the standard means by which the diagnosis is made. The heterophile antibody test measures the titer of agglutinating antibody to sheep or horse (horse is more commonly used) erythrocytes after absorption with guinea pig kidney homogenate. These heterophile antibodies may be detected during the first week of infection but peak during the second and third week. Sheep and beef agglutination tests remain positive for 3–6 m; horse agglutination remains positive for as long as 18 m. The rapid slide test is the most frequently utilized heterophile test, and it is positive in over 90% of older children and adolescents with acute infectious mononucleosis.

When the patient has severe symptoms suggestive of IM but lacks heterophile antibodies, the clinician may decide to perform specific serologic tests for Epstein-Barr virus.[9] The presence of IgM antibody to EBV-capsid antigen can make the diagnosis of acute mononucleosis with good reliability, although cross-reactivity with the rheumatoid factor does arise. IgG antibody to EBV-capsid antigen is present in acute disease but remains positive for years and therefore cannot be used to distinguish acute from previous infection. Other tests include detection of early antigen antibody response to diffuse or restricted components of EBV-early antigen. Antibodies to EBV-nuclear antigen develop in the late phase of the disease. Laboratory techniques utilized in research studies include culture of saliva or mononuclear blood cells for EBV, *in situ* hybridization, or polymerase chain reaction.

Mycoplasma pneumoniae

Mycoplasma pneumoniae is a frequent cause of respiratory infections in teens, accounting for 30–50% of pneumonias in college-age populations. Illness may begin with fever, malaise, and headache. Cough usually develops 3–5 d later. Other signs and symptoms include chills, pharyngitis, chest pain, coryza, nausea, and vomiting. Physical exam shows lymphadenopathy, pharyngitis, and abnormal lung findings such as rales, rhonchi, and wheezing. The peak incidence occurs in early adolescence, between age 10 and 14 y.

The organism *Mycoplasma pneumoniae* can be recovered by culture technique from the nasopharynx or oropharynx. Because it takes 2–3 w for the organism to grow, cultures are not helpful clinically. The cold agglutinin reaction which demonstrates IgM autoantibodies that agglutinate red blood cells at 4°C may be increased to a titer > 1:32 in 75% of individuals with *Mycoplasma pneumoniae* but is not very specific. Complement fixation titers measure specific serum antibodies to *Mycoplasma pneumoniae* and will demonstrate a fourfold rise from the onset of illness until 1–3 w later. The treatment is oral erythromycin or tetracycline, 500 mg four times a day for 10 days.

Group A β-hemolytic Streptococci

Group A β-hemolytic streptococcal infection is frequent among teenagers. The clinical presentation can include high fever, exudative pharyngitis, tender anterior cervical lymph nodes, scarlatiniform rash, headache, vomiting, and abdominal pain. The diagnosis is more likely if there is a history of contact with an individual harboring streptococci. By contrast, Group A β-hemolytic streptococci is less probable if the patient has cough, coryza, and rhinitis.

Throat culture remains the gold standard for diagnosing streptococcal pharyngitis. As a useful adjunct to culture, many rapid diagnostic kits are now available that detect Group A β-hemolytic streptococcal antigen from throat swab samples. The tests require 5–60 min to perform. These tests use acid or enzyme extraction technique to remove the Group A carbohydrate from the throat swab sample, followed by latex agglutination. Rapid diagnostic tests are very specific so that false positives are unlikely. Nevertheless, they are less sensitive, so that false negatives occur in 15–40% of cases. Given the high specificity and relatively low sensitivity, some clinicians use the rapid diagnostic test first. It is generally recommended that if rapid diagnostic tests are used, positive results should result in prompt treatment. Thus, rapid diagnosis leads to rapid treatment and a quicker clinical response. If results are negative, culture should be performed, and need for treatment is based on culture results.[10, 11] Cultures are usually prepared on a blood agar plate with bacitracin disks. Latex agglutination, fluorescent antibody, coagglutination, and precipitation techniques as well as bacitracin-sensitivity disks differentiate group A from other β-hemolytic strep. Other rapid tests such as optical immunoassay and chemiluminescent DNA probes are on the horizon.

Serologic evidence occurs late in the disease process and therefore titers are beneficial in the diagnosis of late, nonsuppurative complications of Group A β-hemolytic streptococci but not in diagnosis of acute infection.

The recommended treatment of Group A β-hemolytic streptococcal infection is oral penicillin V, 125–250 mg three or four times a day for 10 d, or a single, intramuscular injection of benzathine penicillin G, 1.2 million units if the patient is over 60 lb. The alternative treatment for the penicillin allergic individual is oral erythromycin ethyl succinate, 40–50 mg/kg/d divided four times a day, or erythromycin estolate, 20–30 mg/kg/d in 2–4 divided doses (maximum daily dose of 1 gram). Use of oral cepholosporins in the "first generation" is also an acceptable treatment.

Male Reproductive Health

Screening sexually active teenage males for sexually transmitted diseases is a common, although not universal, practice. In the asymptomatic male, the first-catch urine specimen is a useful screening test for urethritis.[12, 13] The first-catch urine specimen consists of the initial 10–20 mL of voided urine. The finding of a positive leukocyte esterase test or more than 20 white blood cells on high-power (400×) field is significant pyuria and suggests the presence of urethritis. More specific confirmatory tests include cultures for *Neisseria gonorrhoeae* and either cultures of rapid diagnostic tests for *Chlamydia trachomatis.* Two recently manufactured tests, polymerase chain reaction (PCR) and ligase chain reaction (LCR) of male urine specimens are very sensitive and specific tools for detection of *Chlamydia* infection in symptomatic and asymptomatic men.[14, 15] In addition, yearly syphilis serology is recommended for high-risk males.

The decision as to whether to perform testing for hepatitis B will be based on consideration of the individual's risk factors and the prevalence of disease in the target population. In addition, hepatitis B immunization should be considered for all adolescents. The indications for human immunodeficiency virus (HIV) testing is controversial and should be done only with appropriate informed consent following discussion of risks and benefits.

Homosexual males are at increased risk for sexually transmitted diseases. Thus, urethral, rectal, and pharyngeal cultures for *Neisseria gonorrhoeae* and *Chlamydia trachomatis* should be obtained on a regular basis. An annual syphilis serology should be performed. Screening for hepatitis B is advocated and, if the individual is surface antibody and antigen negative, immunization is advised. One should consider HIV testing in homosexual teens. In addition, these individuals are at increased risk for intestinal infections, including *Shigella, Campylobacter, Entamoeba histolytica, Giardia lamblia*, cytomegalovirus, hepatitis A, hepatitis B, and hepatitis non-A and non-B.

Sexually active males may develop urethritis manifested by urethral discharge, dysuria, or pruritus at the distal urethra. *Neisseria gonorrhoeae, Chlamydia trachomatis,* and *Ureaplasma urealyticum* cause most infections. If a urethral discharge is present, gram stain of secretions is valuable. The finding of gram-negative diplococci on gram stain of urethral exudate is an extremely specific and sensitive test for *Neisseria gonorrhoeae.* When there is a urethra exudate, it can be sent for gonococcal culture. If not, one should insert a thin swab a minimum of 2 cm into the urethra to obtain culture material. The sample is inoculated onto selective media, typically modified Thayer-Martin media, and placed in a 5% or 10% CO_2 environment to grow. Growth of oxidase-positive, gram-negative diplococci with specific sugar fermentation pattern confirms the presence of *Neisseria gonorrhoeae.* Because of the emergence of increasing resistance, testing for antimicrobial susceptibility and β-lactamase production should be conducted.

The detection of *Chlamydia trachomatis* by culture technique requires that one obtain an endourethral sample. *Trichomonas vaginalis* is much less common in males than in females. If one suspects its presence, a wet preparation of secretions should be examined for the motile, flagellated protozoan.

ADOLESCENT GYNECOLOGY

Dysfunctional Uterine Bleeding

Sometimes adolescents present with heavy, prolonged, or very irregular periods. Most perimenarcheal cycles are anovulatory, but they are reasonably regular (21–45 d) and blood loss is modest. These cycles represent estrogen withdrawal bleeding. Follicular stimulating hormone (FSH) stimulates follicular growth and estradiol is produced. The negative feedback mechanism is intact, and as estradiol concentrations rise, FSH is suppressed and the follicle becomes atretic without ovulation. The estradiol concentration subsequently declines and withdrawal bleeding occurs.

The most common cause of dysfunctional uterine bleeding in early adolescence is delayed maturation of the negative feedback system which results in higher than normal FSH concentrations with prolonged estrogen stimulation of the endometrium and excessive proliferation. Irregular shedding of the heavily developed endometrium may lead to heavy uterine blood loss. However, this is a diagnosis of exclusion. Evaluation of the disorder includes pelvic examination to rule out pelvic infection, uterine anomalies or myomas, or a vaginal foreign body (i.e., tampon retention). The initial laboratory evaluation includes a hematocrit with reticulocyte count to assess the severity and chronicity of anemia. A serum human chorionic gonadotropin (HCG) assay is performed to exclude pregnancy as a cause of dysfunctional bleeding. At the time of pelvic examination, cervical cultures are performed for gonorrhea and *Chlamydia* if pelvic infection is considered a possible etiology.

Bleeding which is heavy enough to require hospitalization, particularly when it occurs in the first menstrual cycle, is more likely to be associated with a bleeding diathesis. In this case, there is usually a history consistent with a bleeding tendency.

Nonetheless, all patients should have a bleeding time, prothrombin time, activated partial thromboplastin time, and platelet count. Other endocrinologic disorders which can present as dysfunctional uterine bleeding include diabetes mellitus, thyroid disease, Cushing's syndrome, Addison's disease, hyperprolactinemia, chronic anovulation, and incipient ovarian failure as it progresses through anovulation prior to complete cessation of function (such as that associated with prior chemotherapy or radiation therapy). Therefore, glucose, thyroid stimulating hormone (TSH), thyroxine, T_3 resin uptake, luteinizing hormone (LH), FSH, prolactin, testosterone, dehydro-3-epiandrosterone sulfate (DHEAS), and progesterone concentrations should be obtained prior to therapy in order to make a specific diagnosis.

Oligomenorrhea

Patients who are more than two years from menarche and having fewer than six cycles per year, especially if ovulatory symptoms are not present, require a thorough endocrinologic evaluation. The laboratory evaluation usually includes serum prolactin, thyroid function tests, FSH, LH, and androgens if hirsutism is present. The most common cause of oligomenorrhea in later adolescence is chronic anovulation syndrome, also known as polycystic ovary syndrome (PCO).

Secondary Amenorrhea

Any adolescent with the abrupt loss of menstrual cycles for 4 m after regular cycles have been established should be evaluated. Stress and pregnancy are the most common causes of secondary amenorrhea. The possibility of pregnancy, severe weight loss or gain, increased athletic activity, disruption of the school or home environment, and oral contraceptive use should be sought historically. The laboratory evaluation includes FSH, LH, androgens, prolactin, thyroid function tests, and a pregnancy test.

Patients who have premature ovarian failure characterized by an FSH in a menopausal range on two occasions approximately 2 w apart must be screened for polyendocrine immune syndrome. This syndrome can include hypoadrenalism, hypoparathyroidism, thyroiditis, and pernicious anemia. Therefore, a screening laboratory evaluation including TSH, calcium, phosphorous, hemoglobin, and 8:00 AM and 4:00 PM serum cortisol is performed at the time of diagnosis and annually thereafter. Antimicrosomal antibodies, antithyroglobulin antibodies, adrenal antibodies, and parietal cell antibodies are available as adjunct screening for autoimmune disorders. Patients with secondary amenorrhea on the basis of anorexia nervosa should have a complete blood count and serum electrolytes as well as thyroid function tests if these were not included in the initial screening, as they are frequently abnormal.

Hirsutism

An adolescent who presents with a complaint of hirsutism should be assessed historically including recent changes in the amount of hair, location of new hair, relation of hair growth to the onset of puberty, presence of acne, anabolic steroid ingestion, weight gain, voice changes, changes in scalp hair distribution, and presence of acanthosis nigricans as well as family history of hirsutism, glucose intolerance, menstrual irregularity or infertility, and ethnic background. The degree of hirsutism is assessed and recorded in the physical examination. The Ferriman-Gallwey score is a useful tool for objective measurement.[16] The history of virilization should raise the question of the presence of an androgen producing tumor, adrenal enzyme deficiency, or intersex disorder. The abrupt onset of such changes increases the suspicion of a tumor. Signs of virilization include temporal hair recession, deepening of the voice, clitoral enlargement, or changes in body fat and muscle distribution.

The laboratory is utilized to define the etiology of the patient's hirsutism. The initial evaluation should include serum concentrations for testosterone, DHEAS, LH, FSH, and prolactin. A baseline concentration of 17-hyroxyprogesterone and progesterone obtained in the follicular phase in a menstruating patient is also recommended to rule out late-onset congenital adrenal hyperplasia. In adolescents, free testosterone is drawn because, at initial presentation, total testosterone concentrations are normal, but subtly increased testosterone production decreases circulating sex hormone binding globulin, and increased free testosterone can be measured before total testosterone becomes increased. If virilization is present or a tumor is suspected, serum concentrations of DHEA and androstenedione are added to the initial screening. DHEAS > 7 mg/mL (18.2 μmol/L), androstenedione > 500 mg/100 mL or testosterone > 200 ng/dL (6.94 nmol/L) (depending on the laboratory normal values) raises the suspicion of a tumor or intersex disorder.[17] Because of the possibility of ruling out androgen-secreting tumors which are extremely small, it is recommended that several measurements of the abnormal androgen be obtained that reach a value of 2.5 times greater than the upper limit of normal for the laboratory. Karyotyping is performed on adolescents with significant virilization, especially when associated with vaginal or uterine agenesis, a serum testosterone in the male range, or an increased FSH. Some patients with mild hirsutism have seemingly normal serum androgen concentrations. These patients probably have increased free testosterone as well as increased skin sensitivity to androgens. The degree of skin sensitivity may be reflected in the measurement of the concentration of the androstanediol glucuronide which, although not an androgen itself, is a metabolite of the conversion of testosterone to dihydrotestosterone. Dihydrotestosterone is the active androgen at the level of the skin.

If the stigmata of Cushing's syndrome are present, a 24-h urine specimen is collected for urinary free cortisol and an 8:00 AM serum cortisol concentration after a bedtime dose of 1 mg dexamethasone should be obtained. If the serum concentration of cortisol is not suppressed below 13.8 nmol/L (5 μg/dL) or urinary free cortisol is abnormal, formal dexamethasone suppression testing is performed.[18] If hyperprolactinemia is present, a pituitary adenoma should be excluded; however, some patients with chronic anovulation syndrome (PCO) have an associated increase in prolactin. Patients with a concentration of 17-hydroxyprogesterone measured in the follicular phase > 6.06 nmol/L (2 ng/mL) should have an adrenal corticotropic hormone (ACTH) stimulation test performed.[19] Baseline serum 17-hydroxyprogesterone and progesterone concentrations are measured, the patient is given 0.25 mg ACTH at time 0, and concentrations of 17-hydroxyprogesterone and progesterone are repeated at 30 min. The rise seen in late-onset congenital adrenal hyperplasia is typically > 6.5 ng/dL/min. In some referral populations, deficiency of 3-β-hydroxysteroid dehydrogenase has been found to be an important cause of hirsutism. The patients usually present with an increased baseline DHEAS, but with a normal testosterone. Detection of 3-β-hydroxysteroid dehydrogenase deficiency requires the measurement of baseline and 60 min 17-hydroxyprogesterone and dehydroepiandrosterone in comparison to the standards developed by Pang and colleagues.[20]

The diagnosis of PCO is made by exclusion of all other clinical entities associated with hirsutism. Reference values must be established within the individual laboratory; however, the LH-to-FSH ratio is above 2.5. An increased LH-to-FSH ratio may occur secondary to androgen excess of other causes. Intermittent sampling may also miss the abnormal gonadotropin ratio. The diagnosis is usually made based on the combination of increased testosterone, an increased LH to FSH ratio, history of anovulatory cycles, and signs of androgen excess. In clinical research centers, confirmatory dynamic testing for PCO may be obtained, such as exaggerated LH and normal FSH response to gonadotropic releasing hormone (GnRH) or an increased androstenedione or testosterone response to HCG stimulation; however, these stimulation tests are not required in usual clinical practice. As our understanding of the abnormalities in carbohydrate metabolism associated with chronic anovulation (HAIR-AN) syndrome increases, the demand for glucose tolerance testing and insulin concentrations will grow.

Anorexia Nervosa and Bulimia Nervosa

Anorexia nervosa is a common illness of adolescent girls. The illness does occur in boys, but is much more rare. The diagnosis of anorexia nervosa is based on the clinical presentation of (1) body weight 15% below what is expected, (2) intense fear of gaining weight or becoming fat, (3) a perceptual distortion that one's body is fat despite being obviously underweight.[21] In girls, the disease is invariably accompanied by amenorrhea. The amenorrhea sometimes precedes weight loss. Patients with other medical or neurologic reasons for extreme weight loss do not fear weight gain and do not have the perceptual disorder of anorexia nervosa.

Laboratory evaluation helps to assess the severity of the medical condition of patients with anorexia nervosa. Most patients, although they may appear emaciated and have cool cyanotic extremities, have undergone starvation over a long period of time. They tolerate dramatic physical and biochemical irregularities remarkably well due to adaptation over time. However, severe hypokalemic and alkalosis associated with self-induced vomiting or laxative and diuretic abuse can cause fatal arrhythmias. These patients often have increased serum bicarbonate, hypochloremia, and hypokalemia. Profound hypokalemia is an indication for emergency admission. On admission, an electrocardiogram and chest X-ray are mandatory for further evaluation of the patient's medical status.[22]

Most patients with anorexia nervosa have anemia of chronic illness characterized by a normocytic, hypochromic peripheral blood smear. This may be accompanied by other derangements of hematopoiesis, such as leukopenia and relative lymphocytosis. These abnormalities do not require specific treatment, as weight gain will correct them over time. Many anorexics will have low serum cholesterol, although most anorexic patients will have hypercholesterolemia, possibly secondary to hypothyroidism and/or hypoestrogenism. Carotinemia is also observed in malnourished, anoretic patients and is associated with excessive dietary intake of carrots or other yellow vegetables. Low serum albumin and calcium are other possible manifestations of malnutrition. Abnormal liver enzymes reflect fatty degeneration of the liver and can be observed in the emaciated phase as well as during refeeding.[23]

There are several endocrine manifestations of anorexia nervosa. The amenorrhea, whether primary or secondary, is hypothalamic in nature. It is characterized by very low FSH, LH, and estradiol. These values fall into the prepubertal range, and loss of pulsatility of GnRH and LH has been documented. In boys, testosterone drops dramatically and can be associated with azoospermia. Recovery occurs with weight gain and patients pass through the classic early pubertal phase of nighttime LH release before restoration of normal adult pulsatility. Return to ovulatory cycles often requires weight gain to 10% above the ideal body weight and seems to require relief of psychological stress as well. However, fertility is not impaired in patients who fully recover.

Cortisol and growth hormone may be normal or slightly increased. Abnormal thyroid function tests are characterized by low plasma T_3, increased reverse T_3, and low-normal T_4. No abnormalities in prolactin secretion have been described. The abnormalities in gonadotropin secretion, thyroid function, and cortisol secretion may suggest the presence of a primary hypothalamic defect. However, the return of normal pituitary function with successful therapy implies these abnormalities are secondary to weight loss.[24]

In adolescents who experience the onset of anorexia nervosa in early puberty, growth failure can occur. An X-ray for bone age is helpful in assessing growth potential. Patients who are chronically malnourished can develop osteoporosis due to hypoestrogenemia.[25] Bone densitometry is performed to assess the need for estrogen replacement therapy. Although it is preferable to allow menstrual cycles to resume spontaneously through nutritional rehabilitation, the development of osteoporosis warrants prompt intervention.

Bulimia nervosa is a disorder characterized by recurrent binge eating and purging. Purging can occur via self-induced vomiting, laxative or diuretic abuse, fasting, or rigorous exercise. These activities are accompanied by persistent overconcern with body shape and weight and a feeling of loss of control over the behavior involved.[26] Patients with isolated bulimia nervosa are not usually malnourished, as are patients with anorexia nervosa.

The biochemical abnormalities associated with vomiting and laxative or diuretic abuse include hypokalemia, increased serum bicarbonate, and hypochloremia. With laxative abuse, metabolic acidosis occasionally occurs instead. Fasting which produces dehydration can lead to aldosterone secretion and further renal loss of potassium. Patients who binge and vomit may have increased serum amylase due to parotid gland enlargement. Cardiomyopathy accompanied by increased liver enzymes and erythrocyte sedimentation rate is associated with ipecac intoxication.[27]

Pelvic Masses

Pelvic masses in adolescents may be detected by the patient due to increasing abdominal girth or present with abdominal pain due to adnexal torsion or cyst formation. Pelvic ultrasound and magnetic resonance imaging (MRI) yield the most useful radiologic information identifying the character of pelvic masses. Computed tomography (CT) of the abdomen is traditionally used to assess the upper abdomen and periaortic lymph nodes for ovarian tumor metastasis. Laboratory evaluation of pelvic masses includes a complete blood count with differential and an erythrocyte sedimentation rate (ESR) for patients with suspected tubo-ovarian abscess and an HCG to rule out intrauterine or ectopic pregnancy. Choriocarcinoma, hydatidiform mole, and benign or malignant germ cell tumors of the ovary also elaborate HCG. The endodermal sinus tumor and embryonal cell carcinoma may secrete α-fetoprotein. Struma ovarii, mature thyroid tissue, is sometimes present as a component of benign cystic teratoma and can cause hyperthyroidism. TSH and T_4 should be measured when symptoms are present. CA-125 was the first tumor marker to be defined with a monoclonal antibody against epithelial ovarian cancer. More than 80% of ovarian cancer patients have CA-125 antigen concentrations > 35 units/mL, compared with 1% of normal individuals.[28] CA-125 can be used to follow the progress of therapy in patients with epithelial tumors. However, CA-125 is particularly poor as a screening marker in adolescents because it can be positive in patients with endometriosis or pelvic inflammatory disease, and these entities are much more frequent than ovarian cancer in the adolescent population.

ADOLESCENT PREGNANCY

Adolescent pregnancy is a major health care issue in the United States. The United States has the highest adolescent pregnancy rate of industrialized nations. While some of the major problems relating to adolescent pregnancy are social and educational, a considerable part of our health care costs are in the area of actual clinical care. While the laboratory requirements for the management of adolescent pregnancy are not significantly different from those of adult pregnancy, certain areas require emphasis. The teenager who is pregnant carries with her many of the same pregnancy-related risks as her adult counterpart. Added to these, however, are not infrequently a deprived socioeconomic background leading to disorders of nutrition, as well as being epidemiologically in a group that is at increased risk for acquiring sexually transmitted diseases, having low-birth-weight infants, and developing preeclampsia.

Initial Laboratory Profile

Upon registration in an obstetric care facility, the pregnant teenage patient will find herself being screened in many ways. Part of this initial screening will include a Papanicolaou smear (Pap smear). While cervical cancer is not particularly prevalent in patients in this age, it is becoming increasingly clear that sexually active adolescents are at increased risk for exposure to human papilloma virus. Cytologic screening of the cervix can alert the clinician to the presence of this virus and, where indicated, lead to the performance of colposcopy and a more thorough investigation of cervical histology.

Also, sexually active adolescents not infrequently have more than one sexual partner, or have sexual partners who themselves have more than one sexual partner. This places the adolescent at greater risk for acquiring other sexually transmitted diseases, including syphilis, gonorrhea, *Chlamydia*, and HIV. A cervical sample can be used to screen for gonorrhea and *Chlamydia*, while a simple blood test can be used as an initial screen for exposure to syphilis. Screening for these diseases is particularly important, as all of them may be associated with adverse perinatal events. Gonorrhea has clearly been shown to be associated with increased rates of post-delivery infections, and while the significance of *Chlamydia* infections on pregnancy outcome are controversial,[29] there is no question that exposure to *Chlamydia* can result in conjunctivitis and pneumonia in the newborn.

The finding of positive syphilis serology is extremely important, as the ramifications of this finding for both mother and infant are significant. There is current controversy as to what the optimal method of screening should be and whether it should include not only first-trimester and third-trimester screening, but intrapartum screening and newborn screening as well. Also, based on recent findings, there is some question as to whether the rapid plasma reagin (RPR) test is sufficient, or whether a fluorescent Treponemal antibody test should become standard in high-risk populations.[30] This issue may not be settled for several years. Our current policy is to screen pregnant women at the time of their first prenatal visit and again in the third trimester. Women who have had no prenatal care are screened on arrival in Labor and Delivery.

Another very important part of prenatal screening now includes determination of HIV antibody status. In our institution, this is done only with the informed consent of the patient, and screening is offered to all individuals in our adolescent clinic. The decision to offer screening to all patients seeking prenatal care is well-founded epidemiologically.[31-34] While there is no cure for HIV infection, there are now convincing data supporting the use of Zidovudine during pregnancy and labor as being an effective method of reducing the mother-fetus vertical transmission rate of HIV from 30% to 9%.[35]

In addition to the above tests, other routine laboratory tests are ordered at the initial visit. A complete blood count is performed, with the most frequent finding being a low hemoglobin and hematocrit, suggestive of iron deficiency anemia. On occasion, this initial screening of hemoglobin and hematocrit has lead to the diagnosis of diseases such as immune thrombocytopenia or leukemia. In patients of African-American, Asian, or Mediterranean descent, special attention should be paid to blood cell morphology and indices, or a hemoglobin electrophoresis may be performed to rule out the possibility of sickle cell disease or thalassemia.

A serum specimen is sent to the blood bank for determination of blood group and Rh type, as well as for screening for atypical antibodies. This information is vitally important for the management of the remainder of the pregnancy. Atypical blood group antibodies have been responsible for repeated miscarriage and hydrops fetalis. Rh negative women must be evaluated very carefully to determine whether or not they will require antepartum administration of Rh immunoglobulin.

Also, at the first visit, immunity status with regard to rubella and occasionally other viral and protozoal illnesses may be determined.

Mid-Trimester Screening

In addition to the routine testing described above, other tests may be offered to women in the middle trimester of their pregnancy. The first of these is offered at approximately 16 w gestation and is the screening test for neural tube defects, namely maternal serum α-fetoprotein (MSAFP). The occurrence of neural tube defects does not seem to be age related, and therefore adolescents will benefit as much from this test as their adult counterparts. A single blood test may be drawn at approximately 16 w of gestation, and a result is generally reported as multiples of the mean (MOM). A result of less than 2.5 MOM, after correction for gestational age, is generally interpreted as normal. AFP concentrations may be lower among diabetics and in very obese individuals, and the laboratory should be able to adjust for these factors in calculating the final MOM result. Results coming back higher than this can be followed up with another serum specimen. If the second specimen is reported as normal, the screening procedure ends. If the second specimen also reveals an increase, then further evaluation using ultrasound and possibly amniocentesis with determination of amniotic fluid α-fetoprotein (AFAFP) may be required, though careful ultrasound fetal assessment may itself be sufficient.[36] Amniotic fluid acetylcholinesterase is also measured and is a much more specific test than AFAFP in detecting neural tube defects. Additionally, very low concentrations of α-fetoprotein have been associated with an increased incidence of Down syndrome.

To improve the specificity of the MSAFP test as it pertains to karyotypic abnormality screening, many centers now employ the "triple" screen, which consists of determination of MSAFP, human chorionic gonadotropin (HCG), and estriol (E_3). Utilization of the triple screen in conjunction with targeted ultrasound examination of the fetus may help to substantially reduce the number of patients who require amniocentesis.

First trimester and mid-trimester cytogenetic testing may also be available for those adolescents who have either a family history or a previous pregnancy history suggesting the need for such testing. Chorionic villus sampling (CVS), a procedure done in the first trimester, usually at approximately 10–11 w gestation, will allow for determination of fetal karyotype as well as detection of certain metabolic disorders. This may also be done via amniocentesis at approximately 16–17 w gestation. Early amniocentesis, done between 12–14 w gestation, may also be performed, with procedure-related risks similar to CVS. While it is rare that adolescents require such testing, it does occasionally happen, and the collaboration of Maternal and Fetal Medicine specialists with Laboratory Medicine personnel is crucial. Most recently, reports on the feasibility of first-trimester serum screening for Down syndrome have been published, and may offer an alternative to current mid-trimester approaches.[37]

Third Trimester Screening

In the routine, uncomplicated adolescent pregnancy, certain screening tests are repeated and others added as the patient approaches 28 w gestation. A repeat complete blood count is obtained in order to determine whether or not there has been adequate iron intake during the pregnancy or whether further iron supplementation is necessary. A repeat blood type and atypical antibody screen is sent as well. A follow-up serologic test for syphilis is also an important part of this screening procedure, as is a pelvic examination with culturing once again for the presence of gonococcal and/or *Chlamydia* infection. Not all centers routinely screen for *Chlamydia*; this depends primarily on the population of patients that they serve and the availability of relatively inexpensive test kits, utilizing either culture (most expensive) or fluorescent antibody slide test kits or enzyme assay kits.

Also at 28 w gestation, all adolescents are screened for gestational diabetes. There is some controversy as to whether this test is necessary as a routine screening test for women under age 25 y,[38] but since the test is relatively easy to do and relatively inexpensive, our clinic has chosen to employ it routinely. Also at this time, a screening test for hepatitis B is performed. While the issue of cost-effectiveness of routine hepatitis B screening has not been completely resolved, there are data to suggest that in high-risk populations it is a very worthwhile test,[39] and our current practice is to screen all pregnant women for the presence of hepatitis-B surface antigen. The information gained from such testing can be extremely important with respect to newborn management. All newborns in our hospital receive hepatitis B vaccine at birth, and those newborns of surface antigen positive women additionally receive hepatitis B immune globulin.

Finally, in the pregnant teenage patient whose pregnancy has remained uncomplicated throughout its term, one final series of tests is performed on arrival in Labor and Delivery. A hemoglobin and hematocrit is obtained once again, as is a blood group and antibody screen. This may be sent to the blood bank of the hospital, where it is held in the event that blood products would be needed during the patient's delivery process.

Pathologic Conditions

The above laboratory utilization applies to the uncomplicated teenage pregnancy. However, as mentioned at the beginning of this section, teenagers are more likely to be at risk for the development of infections and preeclampsia, and are at increased risk for preterm delivery.

Screening for infection can be initiated with the sexually transmitted disease screening described above. However, many adolescents will present in premature labor or with preterm premature rupture of membranes which may or may not be related to sexually transmitted diseases. Under these circumstances, it is very important that the patient be fully evaluated for evidence of intraamniotic infection or infection of other sites. Included would be cervical cultures and cultures of the amniotic fluid, looking specifically for sexually transmitted infections as well as Group B streptococcal infection or colonization. Group B streptococcal colonization is of great importance, since Group B streptococcal sepsis remains the leading cause of neonatal sepsis and death in nurseries within the United States. Culture remains the best test for Group B streptococcal colonization, although more rapid techniques are sorely needed. This is important because early identification of Group B streptococcal colonization in the absence of frank infection can lead to clinical intervention with antibiotics. This may result in prolongation of pregnancy or reduced morbidity from premature delivery. Additional information can be obtained from urinary culture, since urinary tract infections, particularly infections of the upper urinary tract, have been associated with an increased incidence of preterm delivery.

The issue of antepartum screening for group B streptococcal colonization is a controversial one. The American Academy of Pediatrics has advocated routine screening of all pregnant women at 28 w gestation. The American College of Obstetricians and Gynecologists does not advocate universal screening at this time, but has recommended adoption of the Centers for Disease Control and Prevention's guidelines for early onset Group B streptococcal disease prevention.[40, 41] Development of a reliable and rapid group B streptococcal screening test would significantly aid in the resolution of this management controversy.

In patients presenting close to term with suggestions of infection, an amniotic fluid sample may also be sent for analysis for fetal lung maturity. This most commonly consists of a request for a lecithin:sphingomyelin ratio and for presence or absence of phosphatidylglycerol. The availability of this test around the clock can significantly aid the clinician in making important decisions regarding delivery.

Premature labor is a clinical condition frequently encountered with teenage pregnancy. Since premature labor frequently can be secondary to infection, once again the utilization of the laboratory to rule out the possibility of infection as quickly and as accurately as possible is crucial to correct clinical decision making. The ability to rapidly determine the chemical evidence for probable fetal lung maturity can also play a crucial role in deciding how aggressively to try and prevent the continuation of uterine activity.

When the above information has been gathered, if a decision has been made to try to inhibit labor, the role of the laboratory will remain important. Magnesium sulfate, nifedipine, and betamimetic agents such as ritodrine hydrochloride or terbutaline sulfate are the most commonly employed agents (tocolytics) for the initial prevention of preterm labor. Each of these agents is metabolically active and can result in profound disturbances of electrolyte and chemistry profiles. Betamimetics can raise serum glucose, raise plasma insulin, and lower serum potassium. Magnesium sulfate may result in a profound drop in measurable serum calcium, sometimes making it difficult for the clinician to interpret true calcium balance. In this circumstance, availability of ionized calcium measuring techniques can be helpful, although they are rarely necessary.

Preeclampsia, formerly and perhaps more commonly called toxemia of pregnancy, is also a particularly important problem for teenagers. Epidemiologically, we know that younger women having their first child represent a high-risk group for the development of preeclampsia. Preeclampsia is defined as the development of hypertension with proteinuria, edema, or both, usually occurring after the 20th week of gestation. The clinical assessment of the patient with suspected preeclampsia is extremely important. However, also of great importance is the development of the laboratory profile of such a patient. The initial laboratory evaluation of the patient with preeclampsia would include a complete blood count, electrolytes, with specific attention to serum creatine and urea nitrogen, and a chemistry profile with specific attention paid to alanine amino transferase, aspartate aminotransferase, lactic acid dehydrogenase, and uric acid.

Some 24-hr urinary tests may also be helpful in assisting the clinician in making the diagnosis of preeclampsia and determining its severity. Specifically, these would include determination of urinary creatine clearance, total urinary protein per 24 h, and 24-h urinary calcium excretion. Each of these results will help the clinician better determine the nature and severity of the patient's illness. In mild preeclampsia, all of these values may be normal, with the exception of the urinary protein being slightly increased, usually > 300 mg/L/24 h. As disease severity increases, one can expect to see an increase in urinary protein, a decrease in creatine clearance, a rise in serum creatine with a rise in blood urea nitrogen, an increase in uric acid, and an increase in liver function tests. In very severe cases, thrombocytopenia and hypofibrinogenemia can also occur in the clinical setting of disseminated intravascular coagulation (DIC), and more sophisticated tests can be utilized.[42]

To make a correct diagnosis of preeclampsia is extremely important. Next in importance is determining its severity, since this will necessitate further decision making regarding timing of delivery. In the patient with severe preeclampsia, the general rules are for stabilization of the patient and her fetus, followed by attempts at expeditious delivery. Once this decision has been made, most patients are given magnesium sulfate for the purposes of preventing the progression of preeclampsia to eclampsia. Antihypertensive agents may also be required. During this critical period, close laboratory assessment of these patients is essential. This includes careful attention being paid to electrolytes and chemistries, as well as to coagulation factors. In patients receiving magnesium sulfate, serum magnesium concentrations are frequently followed at 6–12 h intervals as an adjunct to clinical assessment of the patient. In general, the patient in this clinical situation will be considered to have therapeutic serum magnesium concentrations at approximately 2–3 mmol/L (4–6 mEq/L).

In some cases, preeclampsia can be accompanied by premature separation of the placenta (abruptio placentae), which is an obstetric emergency. This can cause an acceleration of the disseminated intravascular coagulopathy process, which can result in significant fetal-maternal blood exchange. This can be of extreme importance in mothers who are Rh negative, requiring that a laboratory perform an assessment of the percentage of fetal cells in the maternal circulation so that an appropriate amount of Rh immunoglobulin can be given. In general, 300 μg of Rh immunoglobulin will be sufficient to cover a 30 mL fetal-maternal blood exchange (15 mL fetal red cells).

Cord Blood Banking

A final area which is relatively new to medicine, and in which the laboratory can play a critical role, is the area of umbilical cord blood banking. While previously used for routine laboratory tests, umbilical cord blood may now be used as a source of valuable hematopoietic stem cells. The first successful cord blood transplantation was performed in October of 1988 as part of the treatment of a child with Fanconi anemia. Today that child is alive and well. This first transplantation was based on results of a laboratory study suggesting the feasibility of using cord blood as a source of hematopoietic stem cells.[43] While the science of umbilical cord blood banking and cord blood transplantation has evolved rapidly and would be to detailed a topic to cover here, it is one area where biochemistry, molecular biology, and laboratory medicine have combined to bring forward a new technology and treatment of potential importance. Numerous cord blood banking services exist and are available for situations of need, or for storage for possible future need.

SUMMARY

The laboratory plays an important supportive role in general adolescent medicine, assisting the clinician in primary health care provision. The role of the laboratory has greatly expanded and, in fact, has become crucial in the management of simple and complicated endocrine disorders of adolescence. The laboratory evaluation of the pregnant patient can be as complicated as the patient herself. The adolescent, because of the high-risk nature of her pregnancy, has benefited from our expanded use of the clinical laboratory. As the clinician's ability to diagnose and manage various conditions improves, there is no doubt that the role of the laboratory as the physician's partner in clinical management will continue to expand.

REFERENCES

1. Marks A, Fisher M. Health assessment and screening during adolescence. Pediatr 1987;80 (suppl):135–58.
2. Cromer BA, McLean, CS, Heald FP. A critical review of comprehensive health screening in adolescents. J Adol Health 1992;13:1S–31S.
3. Friedman IM, Goldberg E. Reference materials for the practice of adolescent medicine. Pediatr Clin North Am 1980;27(1):198.
4. Steiner NJ, Neinstein LS, Pennbridger J. Hypercholesterolemia in adolescents: effectiveness of screening strategies based on selected risk factors. Pediatr 1991;88:269–75.
5. Johnston LD, O'Malley PM, Bachman JG. National survey results on drug use from the Monitoring the Future study, 1975–1993. Publication 94-3809. Rockville MD: National Institute on Drug Abuse, 1994.
6. Turner CE, Elsohly MA, Martin DM. Laboratory and psychiatric aspects of drug abuse testing. In: Giannini AJ, Slaby AE, eds. Drugs of abuse. Oradell, New Jersey: Medical Economics Co., 1989.
7. Soldin SJ, Morales AJ, D'Angelo L, et al. The importance of lowering the cut-off tests for benzoylecgonine/cocaine. Clin Chem 1991;37:993.
8. Sumaya CV, Ench Y. Epstein-Barr virus infectious mononucleosis in children: I. Clinical and general laboratory findings. Pediatr 1985;75:1003–10.
9. Sumaya CV, Ench Y. Epstein-Barr virus infectious mononucleosis in children: II. Heterophile antibody and viral-specific responses. Pediatr 1985;1011–9.

10. Centor RM, Meier FA, Dalton HP. Throat culture and rapid tests for diagnosis of group A streptococcal pharyngitis. Ann Int Med 1986;105:892–9.
11. Denny FW. Current problems in managing streptococcal pharyngitis. J Peds 1987; 111:797–806.
12. Adger H, Sweet RL, Shafer MA, Schachter J. Screening for *Chlamydia trachomatis* and *Neisseria gonorrhoeae* in adolescent males: value of first catch urine examination. Lancet 1984;2:944–5.
13. Shafer MA, Schacter J, Moncada J, et al. Evaluation of urine-based screening strategies to detect *Chlamydia trachomatis* among sexually active asymptomatic young males. JAMA 1992:2065–70.
14. Jaschek G, Gaydos C, Welsh LE, Quinn TC. Direct detection of *Chlamydia trachomatis* in urine specimens from symptomatic and asymptomatic men by using a rapid polymerase chain reaction assay. J Clin Microbiol 1993;31:1209–12.
15. Chernesky MA, Jang D, Lee H, et al. Diagnosis of *Chlamydia trachomatis* infections in men and women by testing first-void urine by ligase chain reaction. J Clin Microbiol 1994;32:2682–85.
16. Ferriman D, Gallwey JD. Clinical assessment of body hair growth in women. J Clin Endocrinol Metab 1961;21:1440.
17. Emans SJH, Goldstein DP. Pediatric and adolescent gynecology, 3rd ed. Boston: Little, Brown 1990:258.
18. Rebar RW. Practical evaluation of hormonal studies. In: Jaffe RB, Yen SSC, eds. Reproductive endocrinology, 2nd ed. Philadelphia: W.B. Saunders, 1986:683–733.
19. Azziz R, Zacur HA. 21-hydroxylase deficiency in female hyperandrogenism: screening and diagnosis. J Clin Endocrinol Metab 1989;69:577.
20. Pang S, Lerner A, Stoner E, et al. Late onset adrenal steroid 3-beta hydroxysteroid dehydrogenase deficiency: I. A cause of hirsutism in pubertal and prepubertal women. J Clin Endocrinol Metab 1985;60:428.
21. The American Psychiatric Association. DSM III-R. Washington, DC: The American Psychiatric Press, 1987:63.
22. Andersen AE. Practical comprehensive treatment of anorexia nervosa and bulimia. Baltimore: Johns Hopkins University Press 1985:67.
23. Halmi KA, Falk Jr. Common physiological changes in anorexia nervosa. Int J Eating Disorders 1981;1:16–27.
24. Frohman LA, Krieger DT. Neuroendocrine physiology and disease. In: Felig P, Baxter JD, Broadus AE, Frohman LA, eds. Endocrinology and metabolism, 2nd ed. New York: McGraw-Hill, 1987:234–5.
25. Brotman AW, Sturn TA. Osteoporosis and pathologic fractures in anorexia nervosa. Am J Psych 1985;142:495.
26. The American Psychiatric Association. DSM-III R. Washington, DC: The American Psychiatric Press, 1987:63.
27. Halmi KA, Eating disorders. In: Talbott JA, Hales RE, Yudofsky SC, eds. Textbook of psychiatry. Washington, DC: The American Psychiatric Press, 1988:761.
28. Bast RC Jr, Klug TL, St. John E, et al. A radio immunoassay using a monoclonal antibody to monitor the course of epithelial ovarian cancer. N Engl J Med 1983;309:883.
29. Investigators of the Johns Hopkins Study of Cervicitis and Adverse Pregnancy Outcomes. Association of *Chlamydia trachomatis* and *Mycoplasma hominis* with intrauterine growth retardation and preterm delivery. Am J Epidemiol 1989;129:1247–57.
30. Dorfman DH, Glaser JH. Congenital syphilis presenting in infants after the newborn period. N Engl J Med 1990;323:1299–302.
31. Barbacci M, Dalabetta GA, Repke JT, et al. Human immunodeficiency virus infection in women attending an inter-city prenatal clinic: ineffectiveness of targeted screening. Sexually Trans Dis 1990;17:122–6.
32. The Johns Hopkins–Georgetown Working Group on HIV Infection in Pregnant Women and Newborns. A policy proposal for information and testing. JAMA 1990;264:2416–20.
33. Repke JT, Townsend TR, Coberly JS, et al. Sero prevalence of human immunodeficiency virus type I among pregnant women. Am J Perinatol 1992;9:291–3.

34. Barbacci M, Repke JT, Chaisson RE. Routine prenatal screening for HIV infection. Lancet 1991;337:709–11.
35. Centers for Disease Control and Prevention. Zidovudine for prevention of HIV transmission from mother to infant. MMWR 1994;43:285–7.
36. American College of Obstetricians and Gynecologists. Alpha-fetoprotein. Technical Bulletin No. 228, September 1996.
37. Haddow JE, Palomaki BS, Knight GJ, et al. Screening of maternal serum for fetal Down's syndrome in the first trimester. N Engl J Med 1998;338:955–61.
38. Marquette GP, Klein VR, Repke JT, Neibyl JR. Cost effective criteria for glucose screening. Obstet Gynecol 1985;66:181–4.
39. McQuillan GM, Townsend TR, Johannes CB, et al. Prevention of perinatal transmission of hepatitis B virus: the sensitivity, specificity, and predictive value of the recommended screening questions to detect high risk women in an obstetric population. Am J Epidemiol 1987;126:484–91.
40. Centers for Disease Control and Prevention. MMWR 1996;45(RR-7):1–24.
41. American College of Obstetricians and Gynecologists. Committee opinion. 1996;173:1–8.
42. Proietti AB, Johnson MJ, Proietti FA, et al. Assessment of fibrin(ogen) degradation products in preeclampsia using immunoblot, ELISA and latex-bead agglutination. Obstet Gynecol 1991;77:696–700.
43. Boxmeyer HE, Douglas GW, Hangoc G, et al. Human umbilical cord blood as a potential source of transplantable hematopoietic stem/progenitor cells. Proc Natl Acad Sci USA 1989;86:3828–32.

CHAPTER 16

Clinical and Laboratory Approach to the Diagnosis of Inherited Genetic Disorders

Harvey J. Stern, M.D., Ph.D.

INTRODUCTION

The evaluation of the patient with an inherited genetic disorder remains among the most difficult problems in pediatrics and requires close cooperation and communication between the primary physician, geneticist/metabolic specialist, and clinical laboratory. Our ability to diagnose patients with a wide variety of genetic diseases has been enhanced by the development of new methodologies by which to study the biochemical and molecular basis of these disorders. Particularly, new techniques in molecular biology and specifically DNA analysis have provided sophisticated and powerful means for both diagnosis and primary research into the mechanism of human genetic disease.

This chapter provides an overview of the types of inherited genetic disorders and the clinical and laboratory approach to their diagnosis and treatment. Details on specific laboratory methodologies and metabolic diseases are presented in Chapter 17.

HISTORICAL PERSPECTIVE

At the turn of the century, Archibald Garrod initiated his studies of alkaptonuria and created his monograph, *Inborn Errors of Metabolism*.[1,2] Garrod observed that patients with alkaptonuria excreted excess quantities of homogentisic acid in their urine while other persons did not. He noted that this condition had a familial distribution and that frequently one or more siblings were affected while parents and more distant relatives were normal. He also observed a high incidence of consanguineous marriages among the parents of his patients.

After consulting William Bateson, a well-known geneticist at the time, Garrod realized that his observations could be easily explained if the defect were inherited as a recessive condition according to the recently rediscovered laws of Gregor Mendel. Later, from his studies of patients with alkaptonuria, albinism, cystinuria, and pentosuria, Garrod developed the concept that certain diseases arose because the ability to carry out a metabolic transformation was reduced or totally absent. This early theoretical construct of metabolic disorders was a remarkable achievement on Garrod's part, since at the time there was little or no understanding of human enzymology or metabolism. The idea that human genetic material (genes) directed the synthesis of protein enzymes would not be developed for another 35 years, when Beadle and Tatum described their "one gene, one enzyme" hypothesis.[3]

The period from 1948 to 1980 brought a series of new discoveries about the biochemical basis of many metabolic disorders, including methemoglobinemia,[4] glycogen storage diseases,[5] phenylketonuria,[6] and other amino acid disorders. The study of these diseases used the classical biochemical approach to studying intermediary metabolism or enzymology in various tissues. Krooth and Winberg,[7] in their studies of galactosemia, provided the first evidence that many (but not all) enzymes could be studied *in vitro* using human fibroblast cultures. This allowed more detailed and elegant biochemical studies to be performed than could previously be accomplished with small tissue biopsies or white blood cells whose enzymatic proteins often could not be stored and reassayed after removal from the body.

Another approach to understanding inborn errors of metabolism was through evaluation of metabolic intermediates which accumulate due to blockage of certain biochemical pathways. Early methods used crude and nonspecific chemical approaches to metabolic screening as well as the appearance of a characteristic color or odor in the urine of patients affected with various conditions. Some of these methods, such as the ferric chloride test, are still in use today as part of a rapid metabolic screening profile.

Gradually, more specific and sophisticated ways to study metabolic intermediates came into routine clinical laboratory use, such as automated amino acid analysis by high performance liquid chromatography (HPLC) or urine organic acid analysis by gas chromatography/mass spectrometry (GC/MS). These powerful and sensitive analytical methods are now employed by many clinical laboratories which evaluate and treat patients with inborn errors of metabolism. Even newer technologies to study more complex biological molecules, such as fast atom bombardment or tandem mass spectrometry, are now being used in mass spectrometry centers; because of their exquisite sensitivity, they have great potential as analytical tools.[8]

The "molecular era" of inherited genetic disorders began in 1949, when Linus Pauling provided evidence that the mutation in sickle cell disease led to the production of a structurally altered β-hemoglobin molecule.[9] This was confirmed by Ingram, who showed by peptide mapping that valine had been substituted for glutamic acid in the sixth position of the β-globin molecule.[10] Therefore, the early concepts of Garrod had progressed to the point where it was known that human mutation produces disease states by altering the primary amino acid sequence of protein molecules and presumably their catalytic function.

Although it was known from the early studies of Avery[11] that DNA was the primary genetic material, studies of nucleic acids lagged behind those of proteins and other macromolecules because of the difficulty in reproducibly manipulating the large DNA molecule. In 1970, Kelley and Smith[12] described the first restriction endonucleases, which finally provided reproducible means to produce specific fragments of DNA. Shortly thereafter, Kan and Dozy[13] performed the first DNA-based diagnosis of sickle cell disease using a restriction site polymorphism in the β-globin gene. Thus began the age of DNA-based diagnosis of genetic disorders.

This new technology had several advantages over the more traditional biochemical approaches to genetic disorders. First, DNA is present in every nucleated cell in the body, and therefore the problem of tissue-specific (limited) expression of certain enzymes is overcome. Second, DNA is relatively stable and once extracted can be stored indefinitely. Diagnostically useful DNA samples have been extracted from blood on newborn screening cards stored for over 30 years as well as from other sources such as tissue blocks.

The use of positional cloning (gene identification from chromosomal location) has enabled researchers to identify the basic pathophysiology of various diseases where little or no information existed previously. (The examples of cystic fibrosis and Duchenne/Becker muscular dystrophy are discussed later in this chapter.) With the development of polymerase chain reaction DNA amplification, extremely small samples (as little as one cell) can provide useful information on the presence of mutant genes. Even newer technologies such as automated DNA sequencing will help in further developing our understanding of the role of alterations in genetic material in inherited diseases and cancer. The Human Genome Project, an initiative to fully sequence the human genome, is expected to be completed by the year 2005. The information that will result from this study will greatly enhance our knowledge of the molecular basis of human disease.[14]

BIOLOGICAL BASIS OF HUMAN MUTATION

A mutation is a heritable change in the DNA sequence that can be passed from a cell onto its progeny. The altered nucleic acid sequence can be inherited from a parent or arise as a *de novo* event, either pre- or post conception. Some mutations are lethal and therefore are not passed on from one generation to another, while others permit survival of the organism under permissive conditions. From an evolutionary standpoint, mutation allows the generation of species diversity to allow survival in a changing environment.

Of the approximately 6000 genetic disorders described in McKusick's *Mendelian Inheritance in Man,* there are over 600 human diseases whose biochemical defects have been defined.[15] These include abnormalities of enzymes, receptor proteins, hormones, immunoglobulins, connective tissue components, and regulatory proteins. In the past, the biochemical basis of a disorder was elucidated by studying the metabolic derangements present in the disease state (pathophysiology) and relating these findings to identifiable alterations in cellular structure or metabolism. With the advent of DNA technology, another level of complexity is introduced, namely the molecular changes at the level of the gene. DNA analysis also adds a new dimension to the diagnosis of genetic disorders. For those diseases in which a biochemical defect is unknown or difficult to demonstrate, molecular diagnosis using DNA technology has proved to be a major advancement. This is particularly true for determining carrier status for a number of recessive disorders such as cystic fibrosis and Gaucher disease, for which biochemical testing for carriers is either impossible or unreliable.

There are situations, however, in which biochemical studies are still preferred over DNA-based methodologies as the method of choice for disease diagnosis. These occur most frequently when multiple mutations in a particular gene produce a common and easily identifiable biochemical phenotype. Unless the particular mutation of interest is known for a given family, it is more efficient to screen for the disorder by biochemical analysis since the result of most if not all mutations will be alteration in the biochemical phenotype. For example, in the case of cystic fibrosis (CF), over 600 mutations in the cystic fibrosis transmembrane conductance regulator protein (CFTR) have been described, yet these account for only 90% of all CF mutations. However, most patients with typical clinical features will demonstrate abnormal sweat electrolyte concentrations. For organic acidemias such as propionic and methylmalonic acidemia, or for amino acid disorders such as phenylketonuria, biochemical diagnosis by gas chromatography/mass spectrometry or amino acid analysis is still the method of choice, and it allows monitoring of therapy by following alterations in the critical or diagnostic metabolite.

Nevertheless, identification of the specific DNA mutation in a number of biochemical disorders is often useful, as it can provide some information about the prognosis and natural history for a particular patient and family when data regarding genotype-phenotype correlation exists. For example, it is known that cystic fibrosis patients who carry a particular CFTR mutation (R117H) are frequently pancreatic sufficient, even when they also carry the ΔF508 allele.[16] Information regarding the specific mutant alleles present in a patient is very useful for prenatal diagnosis of future pregnancies and for carrier screening of relatives of the index patient.

Therefore, in attempting to elucidate and understand the nature and history of any inherited genetic disease, three levels of understanding must be achieved:

1. *Patient phenotype*—clinical and pathophysiological features of the disease.
2. *Biochemical phenotype*—as defined by studies of intermediary metabolism and enzymology or physical changes identified in a structural protein molecule.
3. *Molecular (DNA) phenotype*—changes at the DNA level including phenotype/genotype correlation (the physiologic consequences of various mutations).

At the current time, it is convenient to consider inherited genetic disorders as belonging to one of two categories. For diseases in the first category, the biochemical phenotype has been well defined and is currently used in diagnosis and management. These are the classical inborn errors of metabolism as defined by the study of intermediary metabolism or enzymology. For diseases in the second category, the biochemical phenotype has not been defined or is difficult to demonstrate due to variable biochemical expression in different tissues (phenylketonuria, urea cycle defects, cystic fibrosis). In this group, the gene locus and mutant allele(s) of a particular disease have been identified by use of DNA technology.

INBORN ERRORS OF METABOLISM

Inherited metabolic disorders have become a more significant cause of morbidity and mortality in the newborn and young infant. Significant advances in obstetrical care as well as pre- and perinatal medicine have led to a decrease in disorders traditionally seen in this pediatric age group such as infections, respiratory disorders, and complications of perinatal asphyxia. The true incidence of metabolic disease remains unknown. Many patients with metabolic diseases die without a diagnosis being made, or their condition may be attributed to other causes such as sudden infant death syndrome (SIDS).[17] In the aggregate, biochemical disorders may occur as frequently as 1 in 5000 to 1 in 20,000 live births. Inborn errors may account for up to 20% of disease among full-term neonates who have no other risk factors such as neonatal asphyxia or prolonged rupture of the membranes.[18]

The difficulty in diagnosing biochemical defects can be attributed to many factors. The clinical signs and symptoms are usually nonspecific and overlap that of other conditions such as *in utero* or neonatal infections, central nervous system malformations, cardiac disease, and gastrointestinal disorders. Even findings on autopsy may be nonspecific, and in most cases the cause of death is attributed to sepsis. Clinicians are often unfamiliar with the types of tests used in biochemical screening and often do not consider inborn errors until other, more common diseases have been ruled out. In our institution, education of clinicians as to the optimal use of clinical information and laboratory studies in patients with metabolic disorders has increased the frequency of diagnosis in these often puzzling patients.

Pathogenesis of Inborn Errors of Metabolism

The pathogenesis of inborn errors of metabolism results from an abnormal flux of metabolic intermediates through a biochemical pathway. These disorders can be grouped into (1) enzyme or structural protein deficiencies; (2) defects in cellular membrane transport; (3) deficiency of cofactors or other substrates required for normal enzyme activity. Disease states in inborn errors of metabolism can be secondary to:

- *Abnormal transport of metabolites* in or out of cells (cystinuria, Menkes disease).
- *Accumulation of toxic precursors* proximal to a metabolic block (phenylketonuria, maple syrup urine disease).
- *Deficiency of products* distal to a metabolic block (albinism, collagen defects).

- *Induction of alternative pathways* of metabolism producing toxic metabolites (galactosemia).
- *Shunting of cofactors* to other pathways (gout).

Enzymatic or structural protein deficiencies constitute the largest group of inborn errors. They may be produced by decreased synthesis of a structurally normal protein (regulatory mutation) or by synthesis of an altered protein molecule with absent or decreased activity (structural gene defect). In many cases, persistence of some residual enzyme activity may alter or delay the appearance of clinical symptoms in affected patients. In many cases, these patients are apparently healthy until they experience a metabolic stress such as a common pediatric illness, at which time metabolic decompensation occurs and leads to the development of acute or life-threatening illness. The intermittent or intermediate form of maple syrup urine disease and X-linked ornithine transcarbamoylase deficiency in heterozygous female carriers are good examples of this type of episodic disorder.[19]

Transport defects can be due to abnormalities of renal tubular reabsorption or to defects in epithelial membrane transport. In renal tubular disorders, substances in the glomerular filtrate cannot be reabsorbed and are excreted in excess quantities in the urine. In cystinuria,[20] for example, excess urinary cystine can lead to renal stone formation. In addition, cellular transport of other substrates that share a common transport mechanism can also be affected. The dibasic amino acids ornithine, lysine, and arginine are also excreted in excess quantities in cystinuria. In Menkes syndrome, copper transport from epithelial cells is abnormal, leading to functional copper deficiency.[21] In general, the clinical consequences of transport abnormalities are dependent on the nature of the material and the magnitude of the defect.

Deficiencies of cofactors produce a clinical and biochemical phenotype similar to that of primary enzyme deficiencies. On enzymatic analysis, however, *in vitro* activity is often normal since the cofactor is supplied exogenously. For example, most cases of phenylketonuria are due to deficiency of the liver enzyme phenylalanine hydroxylase (Type I hyperphenylalaninemia). However, failure to synthesize or maintain adequate concentrations of the cofactor tetrahydrobiopterin produces Type IV (dihydropteridine reductase deficiency) and Type V (dihydrobiopterin synthase deficiency) hyperphenylalaninemia.[22]

Clinical Presentation of Inborn Errors of Metabolism

As noted above, the clinical features of inborn errors of metabolism are in most cases nonspecific and overlap that of the child with sepsis, severe viral infections (either pre- or postnatal), central nervous system disease (due either to infection, congenital anomaly, or tumor), and acute or chronic ingestion of a toxic substance. The typical newborn infant may be full-term, of normal birth weight, and apparently healthy upon initial examination. In many cases, however, after initiation of feeding shortly after birth, the infant becomes progressively more irritable and eventually lethargic. Projectile vomiting is common, as are seizures. Death often occurs shortly thereafter unless appropriate treatment is initiated.[23,24] Characteristic signs of metabolic disease in the newborn are shown in Table 16–1.

TABLE 16–1. Clinical Features of Metabolic Disease in the Newborn

Apparent sepsis
Hematologic abnormalities including thrombocytopenia, neutropenia, and anemia in the presence of a normal bone marrow
Poor feeding, projectile vomiting
Neurological abnormalities including seizures, coma, and myopathy
Dysmorphism (Menkes syndrome, pyruvate dehydrogenase deficiency, Zellweger syndrome, Glutaric acidemia type II)
Metabolic acidosis with an increased anion gap

Unusual odors in the diaper or isolette are often good clues to the presence of a metabolic disorder. These are produced by volatile organic intermediates. The nape of the neck and ear cerumen are good places to check for the presence of an unusual odor. Some of the well-described associations between odor and metabolic disorder are shown in Table 16–2.

Additional clues to the presence of a biochemical disorder include a family history of a sibling who died in the neonatal period of presumed sepsis, uncharacterized liver disease, or SIDS, but for whom no firm diagnosis was established. Such individuals should be considered to have a possible inborn error of metabolism. This is particularly true if the parents are consanguineous.

In the older child, clinical clues to metabolic disease (listed in Table 16–3) are also nonspecific. Frequently, the patient is evaluated for failure to thrive, nonspecific liver disease, mental retardation/developmental delay, or loss of previously attained motor or language skills.[25] Other significant presenting features include unexplained renal disease, cataracts, or an unusually severe response to a trivial illness such as an upper respiratory or ear infection.

TABLE 16–2. Characteristic Odors in Patients with Metabolic Disorders

Disorder	Odor
Maple syrup urine disease	Maple syrup (caramel)
Isovaleric acidemia	Sweaty feet
Phenylketonuria	Musty
Trimethylaminuria	Stale fish
Hypermethioninemia	Cabbage, rancid butter

TABLE 16–3. Clinical Features of Metabolic Disease in the Older Child

Unexplained mental retardation/developmental delay
Failure to thrive, poor growth
Inappropriately severe response to a usually minor pediatric illness, such as an upper respiratory or ear infection, resulting in coma or significant metabolic acidosis
Laboratory abnormalities including excessive or deficient ketosis, acidosis/lactic acidosis, hypoglycemia, or hyperammonemia
Hypopigmentation or abnormal hair
Cataracts, corneal clouding, or other ophthalmologic abnormalities
Hepatic dysfunction, especially "Reye syndrome-like" disorders including enlargement of the liver or spleen, fatty deposition in the liver or other tissues, or evidence of skeletal abnormalities on X-ray (dysostosis multiplex)
Loss of previously attained motor milestones, severe behavioral changes, difficulty with walking (ataxia)

Classification of Inborn Errors of Metabolism

Most frequently, inborn errors of metabolism are classified according to the chemical nature of the abnormal metabolite (amino acid disorders, organic acidemias) or organelles involved (lysosomal storage diseases, peroxisomal disorders). One such classification scheme is shown in Table 16–4. (More details on these disorders are given in Chapter 17.) This classification scheme is useful for laboratory evaluation, confirmation of diagnosis, and research purposes. Unfortunately, due to the lack of specificity and overlap of clinical features among the various inborn errors, this type of categorization is much less useful as a clinical guide to initial diagnosis.

One classification based on clinical presentation and initial laboratory evaluation has been proposed by Saudubray and Charpentier.[26] In this system, patients are divided into one of five types based on three major clinical presentations:

1. Neurological distress/intoxication type
2. Neurological distress/energy deficient type
3. Hypoglycemia with liver dysfunction

TABLE 16–4. Categories of Inborn Errors of Metabolism

Abnormalities of carbohydrate metabolism
Aminoacidopathies
Organic acidemias
Lysosomal storage disease
Peroxisomal abnormalities
Fatty acid oxidation defects
Mitochondrial disorders

TABLE 16–5. Clinical Classification of Inborn Errors of Metabolism

Type	Disorder
Type I. Neurological distress/intoxication type with ketosis	Maple syrup urine disease
Type II. Neurological distress with ketoacidosis	Organic acidemias: propionic, methylmalonic
Type III. Lactic acidosis with neurological distress/energy deficient type	Respiratory chain defects, primary lactic acidosis
Type IV(a). Neurological distress/intoxication type with hyperammonemia and without ketoacidosis	Urea cycle defects
Type IV(b). Neurological distress/energy deficient type without ketoacidosis or hyperammonemia	Peroxisomal disorders, non-ketotic hyperglycinemia
Type IV(c). Storage disorders without metabolic disturbances	Sialidosis, Niemann-Pick disease
Type V. Hypoglycemia with hepatomegaly and liver dysfunction	Glycogen storage disease (I, III)

Patients are also evaluated for the laboratory findings of ketosis, acidosis, lactic acidosis, and hyperammonemia. Combining the clinical presentation with initial laboratory data, patients are classified as described in Table 16–5. Examples of disorders in each category are also given. This classification scheme is helpful in guiding further laboratory testing in a focused rather than "shotgun" manner. It also underscores the importance of good communication between the clinician and laboratory for rapid, efficient diagnosis and optimal use of labor-intensive and expensive laboratory studies.

LABORATORY EVALUATION OF PATIENTS WITH SUSPECTED METABOLIC DISORDERS

Most patients with acute decompensation due to an inborn error of metabolism will present in the neonatal nursery or, in an older child, in a hospital emergency room. As part of an initial laboratory evaluation, all patients will probably undergo measurement of plasma or serum electrolytes, glucose, calcium, liver enzymes, complete blood count with differential, urinalysis, and blood gas. While these studies are not diagnostic for specific metabolic disorders, certain features may suggest the need for further testing. Specifically, neutropenia or evidence of marrow suppression, inappropriate ketosis (especially in young infants), hypoglycemia, unexplained increased liver enzymes, and a low serum bicarbonate and pH are all typical of inborn errors of metabolism. The anion gap ($Na^+ - [Cl^- + HCO_3^-]$) is a useful calculation; when increased (> 16 mmol/L [mEq/L]), it indicates the presence of excessive quantities of an acid of either physiologic or exogenous (ingested toxin) origin. For this reason, all patients presenting with metabolic acidosis should have a toxicology screen performed which includes osmolality, salicylates, methanol, ethanol, and ethylene glycol.

Additional testing is based on the clinical status of the patient and on the initial laboratory findings. Metabolic acidosis with an anion gap of > 25mmol/L (mEq/L) is suggestive of an organic acidemia and should prompt measurement of blood lactate and urine organic acid analysis by gas chromatography/mass spectrometry. Many of these patients present with a sepsis-like picture and show evidence of bone marrow suppression. Ketosis without acidosis in a newborn with lethargy/apnea is suggestive of maple syrup urine disease, and quantitative plasma amino acid analysis should be carried out. Although many laboratories still use paper chromatography of urine samples as a screening procedure, quantitative plasma amino acid analysis is the procedure of choice due to its speed and accuracy; it is certainly indicated in any patient for whom there is a high suspicion of an aminoacidopathy. To avoid false-positive values due to the recent ingestion of protein, blood specimens should be obtained after a 12-h fast in adults or at least 4–6 h in young children. While evaluation of urinary amino acid excretion is helpful in some disorders, such as cystinuria and argininosuccinic lyase deficiency, the wide variability of "normal" urine amino acid concentrations makes interpretation much more difficult than with plasma. Analysis of CSF glycine concentration is particularly useful in the diagnosis of non-ketotic hyperglycinemia.

A positive urine-reducing substance test, especially when the specific dipstick test for glucose is negative, indicates the possibility of galactosemia. This disorder is frequently seen in newborns with apparent liver disease and *E. coli* sepsis. Hypoglycemia with low or absent ketosis is seen in children with fatty acid oxidation defects. Cardiomyopathy, encephalopathy, or features of Reye syndrome are frequent clinical findings. The diagnosis may be made by organic acid analysis or study of carnitine esters. Hypoglycemia and hepatomegaly along with lactic acidosis may also be seen in glycogen storage diseases, gluconeogenic disorders, or disorders of pyruvate metabolism.

Neurological deterioration in a term infant after a variable symptom-free period should prompt measurement of plasma ammonia. In the absence of ketoacidosis, a urea cycle defect is likely. Plasma amino acid analysis, with particular attention to the concentration of citrulline, will help establish the diagnosis. Metabolic acidosis with hyperammonemia is most likely secondary to an organic acidemia and should be further evaluated by urine organic acid analysis. Neurological signs, especially loss of developmental milestones along with ataxia, visual changes, or organomegaly, suggest a lysosomal storage disease. Seizures and severe hypotonia can be seen in peroxisomal disorders. Encephalopathy and/or myopathy, especially in the presence of lactic acidosis, should lead to the consideration of a mitochondrial disorder. Measurement of the lactate/pyruvate ratio is often helpful, but a muscle biopsy is required for definitive diagnosis of many of these disorders.

Screening for Metabolic Disorders

The urine metabolic screen (metabolic urinalysis) consists of a series of rapid screening tests which often provide the first clue to the presence of a metabolic disorder.[27] The ferric chloride test is the best known of these, and is useful in the diagnosis of phenylketonuria, tyrosinemia, histidinemia, and alkaptonuria. The disorders, asso-

TABLE 16–6. Ferric Chloride Test

Disorder	Compound	Color Reaction
Phenylketonuria	Phenylpyruvic acid	Green
Tyrosinemia	4-hydroxyphenylpyruvate	Fading green
Maple syrup urine disease	Branch chain ketoacids	Green/gray
Histidinemia	Imidazolepyruvate	Gray
Alkaptonuria	Homogentisic acid	Blue/green
Ketosis	Acetoacetate	Red/brown
Salicylates	Salicylic acid	Purple
Phenothiazines	Phenothiazines	Gray/green
Acetaminophen	Acetaminophen	Green

ciated compounds, and color reactions observed are given in Table 16–6. Several drugs, including phenothiazines and salicylates, as well as the presence of conjugated bilirubin will yield a positive result with the ferric chloride reagent.

The 2,4-dinitrophenylhydrazine test detects 2-oxoacids and is useful in the diagnosis of maple syrup urine disease. Nitrosonaphthol reacts with tyrosine and its metabolites (tyrosinemia) and cyanide-nitroprusside detects sulfur amino acids (cystinuria, homocystinuria). Other tests often included in this panel consist of a spot test for urine sulphites (molybdenum cofactor deficiency), qualitative or quantitative tests for urinary mucopolysaccharides (mucopolysaccharide storage disease), and thin-layer chromatography of urinary oligosaccharides (oligosaccharide storage diseases). A positive result on any of these tests should often be repeated to confirm the initial finding. More specific biochemical testing (quantitative amino acid analysis, organic acid analysis or lysosomal enzyme screening) should be carried out on confirmed positive patients, or immediately if the patient's clinical manifestations are consistent with a metabolic disease.

Newborn Metabolic Screening

In 1963, Guthrie described a bacterial growth assay for measurement of blood phenylalanine concentration that could be performed on a small amount of whole blood which had been spotted on filter paper and dried.[28] Two years later, screening of newborns for phenylketonuria by the "Guthrie card" method became widespread in the United States and Europe. Subsequently, microbiological assays were introduced to screen for maple syrup urine disease, galactosemia, histidinemia, tyrosinemia, and homocystinuria. In 1966, testing for galactosemia was improved by an assay of enzyme activity known as the Beutler test.[29] In 1974, screening for congenital hypothyroidism by radioimmunoassay was introduced.[30] Today, nearly all states perform newborn metabolic screening, and the menu of tests has expanded to include such disorders as biotinidase deficiency, fatty acid oxidation defects, homocystinuria, and sickle cell disease.

The rationale behind newborn screening is that metabolic disorders, if identified early, can be treated by alteration of diet (phenylketonuria, maple syrup urine disease) or administration of cofactors or other substrates (biotinidase deficiency, betaine in homocystinuria). In the case of sickle cell disease, penicillin prophylaxis and pneumococcal vaccine are offered early to affected infants in an attempt to avoid infectious complications.

For newborn biochemical screening to be effective, the following criteria must be met:

1. The disease must be a significant cause of morbidity and mortality in affected patients.
2. A treatment exists which is readily available, easily administered, and effective in decreasing or aborting the serious medical complications of the disorder.
3. The screening test must be easily performed, accurate, and of reasonable cost.
4. The test should have few false positives and no false negatives.
5. Testing should be performed in a centralized laboratory to facilitate quality control and data collection.

When performing biochemical screening, certain precautions must be observed. Since galactosemia testing utilizes an enzymatic assay, heating of the sample in the summer months can result in a false-positive test. In newborns receiving transfusions, false-negative results for galactosemia and sickle cell disease may be obtained. In addition, for the aminoacidopathies, it is important that the infant has consumed a protein meal, preferably two to three feedings before the specimen is obtained, to ensure that increased concentrations of amino acids will be detected. Unfortunately, the trend of early discharge from the birth hospital, often within 24 hours of delivery, has led to the misdiagnosis of some affected newborns. For this reason, in newborns discharged within the first day of life, it is recommended that metabolic screening be repeated at the first pediatric visit to ensure identification of infants with amino acid disorders.

A new method of performing newborn genetic screening using electrospray tandem mass spectrometry has been developed and shows extraordinary promise. In addition to accurately determining the concentration of multiple amino acids, this methodology allows simultaneous detection of a number of fatty acid oxidation defects and organic acidemias. Data acquisition and analysis can be computerized and abnormal results automatically flagged. It is likely that the traditional Guthrie microbiological screen will be replaced by this powerful new technology within the next few years.[31]

DNA Diagnosis of Genetic Disorders

As discussed earlier, the application of the technologies of molecular biology and DNA analysis has greatly increased the power and scope of our abilities to diagnose inherited genetic disorders. DNA-based diagnosis allows determination of a person's genotype without the need for a biochemical/enzymatic assay. This is particularly useful when the gene of interest is:

1. Not expressed in cultured cells or leukocytes (phenylketonuria, sickle cell disease).
2. Does not provide a biochemically detectable phenotype (Duchenne muscular dystrophy).
3. The disease has a delayed onset of expression (Huntington disease, retinoblastoma).

In addition, recombinant DNA technology has allowed for rapid advances in biological research, many of which can be directly applied to the diagnosis as well as understanding of the pathogenesis of various genetic disorders. For example, over the past five years, a new class of genetic alteration called "dynamic mutations" has been described. It was found that a series of three nucleotides is repeated in tandem, usually 10 to 40 times, either within the coding sequence or in regulatory elements around functional genes. In some cases, these sequences become unstable and expand during gamete formation to hundreds or thousands of repeats which interfere with transcription of the gene. DNA triplet mutations have now been shown to cause a number of inherited genetic diseases, such as fragile X syndrome, myotonic dystrophy, and Huntington disease.[32]

As compared to biochemical analysis, DNA-based diagnosis has a number of distinct advantages that make this technology attractive even for small laboratories. The specimen requirements are extremely small, and sufficient DNA can be obtained from a drop of blood or even epithelial cells from cheek brushing or mouth washing. The relative stability of DNA also overcomes many of the problems of unstable or fastidious enzymes. On the other hand, DNA diagnosis remains a highly complex and labor-intensive undertaking which requires close supervision and excellent technique and quality control.

Types of Mutation Analysis

There are two basic approaches to DNA-based diagnosis: direct gene evaluation and linkage analysis. In the former, an alteration is detected in a particular gene, either from study of a previously affected family member or from population screening. For large defects such as those resulting from major deletions (e.g., Duchenne/Becker muscular dystrophy, α-thalassemia), Southern blotting techniques are very effective in following the transmission of the mutation. Smaller point mutations are more difficult to detect and are usually identified by allele-specific hybridization with labelled oligonucleotide probes. In many diseases, there are numerous mutations, all of which can cause the same disease phenotype. For example, in cystic fibrosis the common ΔF508 mutation accounts for 70% of CF chromosomes, while over 600 other mutations have been described, many of which are specific for an individual family (see discussion of cystic fibrosis in a later section). Yet despite this, only 90% of all CF mutations have been accounted for at this time. Therefore, for a given family, the exact mutation that produces the disease phenotype may not be identified without complete gene sequencing, which is technically impractical on a routine basis. In these cases, linkage analysis provides an alternative means for genetic diagnosis.

FIGURE 16–1. DNA-based Diagnosis by Linkage Analysis

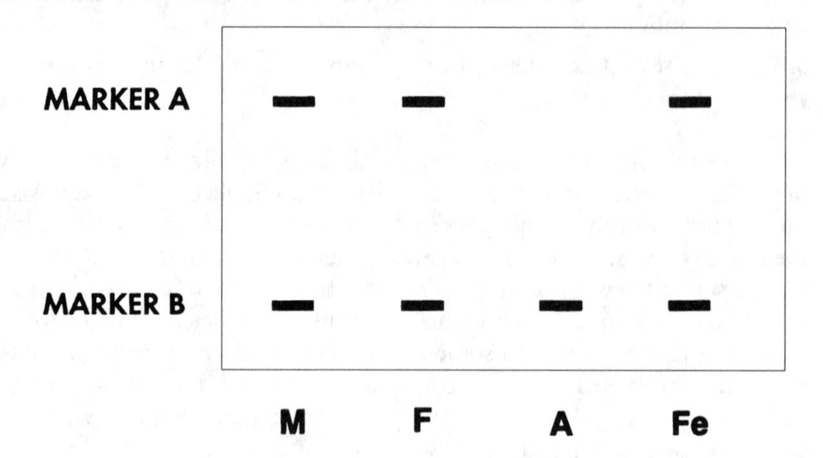

Linkage analysis is based on the concept of genetic recombination, which reflects the physical distance on the chromosome between a genetic marker (indicator) and disease locus.[33] Linked genes are located close to each other on the same chromosome and are less likely to be separated by the process of meiotic recombination. The most useful markers for linkage are those that show negligible recombination with the disease locus and are sufficiently informative that the contribution from either parent can be recognized in the correct phase (association with the disease locus).

An example of genetic diagnosis by linkage analysis is shown in Figure 16–1. In this family, both parents are heterozygous for the marker AB. Their child, who is affected with a recessive genetic disorder, such as cystic fibrosis, is homozygous for the B marker. This implies that in the parents, the chromosomes carrying the CF mutations also contain the B markers, and the normal alleles are associated with the A marker. This is what is meant by the phase. In the case of the fetus shown in the fourth lane, assuming no recombination, one would predict that this child will inherit one CF allele from one parent and a normal allele from the other, and thus be a CF carrier.

In most cases, linkage analysis is most useful as a backup technique in inherited disorders for which multiple mutant alleles exist, and when the specific mutation in a family cannot be identified due to time restrictions or technical difficulties. It should be noted that markers *within* a gene can also be used for linkage analysis, and these have the advantage of extremely low risk of meiotic recombination. Linkage analysis still is routinely used in diseases for which the abnormal gene has not yet been cloned but its chromosomal location is known. As information about the defective gene becomes available, diagnosis by direct gene analysis becomes preferable.

Polymerase Chain Reaction (PCR)

A number of technical developments have proved to be particularly important in the progress of the field of molecular genetics. The first was the characterization of restriction endonucleases, which resulted in a reproducible means to manipulate DNA. The cloning of a segment of DNA into a plasmid vector and its amplification in a biological system provided a way to obtain larger quantities of DNA from a defined chromosomal region for study. Southern blotting allowed examination of DNA fragments at the single gene level, and rapid sequencing techniques allowed pinpoint determination of the nature of mutation by examining the DNA sequence directly. Likewise, the development of the polymerase chain reaction has transformed our ability to study and understand the human genome by allowing us to rapidly amplify a DNA sequence a million-fold by a strictly chemical reaction.[34] This essentially allows "cloning" of any region of the genome without the need for a biological system and provides an extremely powerful analytical tool for the molecular geneticist. PCR is now becoming an important part of the clinical laboratory as more genetic tests are developed and population-based genetic screening programs become widespread. PCR has also become an important tool in the laboratory diagnosis of infectious diseases and identification of the molecular rearrangements seen in cancer.[35]

As compared to previous means of analysis, PCR offers multiple advantages in the diagnosis and study of genetic disorders. First, since only nanogram quantities of DNA sample are required, the analyses can be carried out with buccal washes, single hair bulbs, sperm, urinary sediment, and dried blood spots. Recently PCR has been successfully used in at-risk couples to provide genotype information for unfertilized human ova by analysis of extracted polar body DNA and in the early embryo by blastocyst biopsy at the 4–8 cell stage. A second advantage of PCR is that the DNA sample used in the initial amplification steps may be unpurified, substantially degraded, fixed in formalin or mercury-based fixatives, or embedded in paraffin, and still yield a satisfactory amplification product. In many cases, simply boiling a small amount of whole blood can produce a suitable template for PCR. DNA for PCR analysis has been obtained from stored screening cards which contain small circles of dried blood from newborns who died before their condition could be diagnosed. It is likely that this latter method will become a convenient way to transport patient samples for future analysis or to bank DNA on patients with unknown or uncharacterized genetic disorders.

As noted above, in many genetic diseases the defective gene product is expressed only in one or a limited number of tissues. Examples include the urea cycle defect ornithine transcarbamylase deficiency and phenylalanine hydroxylase deficiency. In both cases, enzyme activity is expressed only in liver. Prior to DNA analysis, prenatal diagnosis would have required a fetal liver biopsy, with a significant risk of fetal loss. PCR analysis of fetal DNA obtained by amniocentesis or chorionic villus biopsy provides a means for rapid, accurate diagnosis without the need to perform invasive tissue sampling or complex biochemical assays. PCR also is a superior method for determining carrier status for inborn errors of metabolism, since in these disorders there is often significant overlap of enzymatic activity between carriers and normal or even affected individuals, making genotype assignment difficult. DNA analysis allows direct determination of alleles at a given genetic locus and genotype assignment by DNA sequence, which is generally more accurate than carrier status determination by enzymatic activity.

Recently, a method for simultaneous detection of approximately 45,000 DNA sequence variations has been developed using high-density oligonucleotide arrays fixed to a glass "chip." Detection of hybridization after PCR is determined by a laser-assisted fluorescent scanner. This "gene chip" technology provides enormous potential for rapid screening of multiple alleles. The loci identified could provide information regarding an individual's genetic health or specific disease susceptibility including predisposition to cancer.[36]

Clinical Example: Cystic Fibrosis

Cystic fibrosis is one of the most common autosomal-recessive genetic disorders affecting Caucasians of Northern European ancestry, with an incidence of 1 in 2500 live births and a carrier frequency of 1 in 25.[37] CF is also seen in varying frequency among other racial and ethnic groups. Clinically, CF is a progressive multisystem disorder which shows prominent involvement of the lungs, pancreas, gastrointestinal tract, sweat glands, liver, and reproductive organs. Biochemically, patients have abnormal chloride conduction across apical endothelial cells, causing inspissated secretions in the respiratory tract, pancreas, and vas deferens, as well as an increased sweat chloride concentration, which is the basis of the sweat test used in laboratory diagnosis. Shwachman syndrome,[38] consisting of metaphyseal chondrodysplasia, pancreatic insufficiency, and neutropenia has a clinical presentation similar to CF in infants, but is distinguished by the usual absence of pulmonary disease and normal sweat chloride concentration.

The CFTR gene on chromosome 7 was discovered in 1989 and sequence data revealed that approximately 70% of Caucasian CF chromosomes carried a similar mutation which resulted in the deletion of a phenylalanine residue at position 508 (ΔF508).[39] Currently, over 600 different mutations in CFTR have been characterized. Although some occur with a frequency of 1–3% of CF chromosomes, the majority of the rare alleles have been described only in a single family.[40]

Multiple methodologies have been reported for the detection of mutations in CFTR, including polyacrylamide gel electrophoresis of PCR products, allele-specific hybridization using ^{32}P labelled probes, solid-phase minisequencing, restriction endonuclease mapping, generation of specific DNA methylation sites, and amplification refractory mutation system (ARMS) PCR with electrophoretic separation of PCR products. Allele-specific hybridization with a dot-blot format is the method most often used at the current time for detection of the ΔF508 and other CFTR mutations. This technique requires amplification of a specific area of the CF gene, which is then immobilized on a filter. Allele-specific probes labelled with either ^{32}P or a non-isotopic label are hybridized to the filter containing the amplified DNA and then the filters are washed under stringent conditions. The genotype is determined by identifying the positive hybridization signals. Another format called "reverse dot blot" uses oligonucleotides fixed to a membrane which are hybridized to a labelled PCR product. This format has the advantage that the genotype of a patient specimen can be read directly on a single strip of filter.[41]

The issue of population screening for CF has been controversial.[42] While it is universally agreed that carrier testing of individuals with a positive family history of

CF should be carried out, the role of general population screening is less clear. Recently, however, an NIH panel recommended offering screening for CF to all pregnant couples.[43] Due to the large number of mutations in the CFTR gene, it is difficult to identify all CF carriers in a cost-effective screening program. Currently the detection rate is approximately 90% in the Caucasian population and may not improve without a significant increase in the cost of testing. It therefore appears that population-based CF screening may begin in the near future.

Clinical Example: Duchenne/Becker Muscular Dystrophy

Duchenne muscular dystrophy (DMD) is a severe progressive muscular disorder that presents in infancy with delayed acquisition of motor milestones, weakness, and pseudohypertrophy of the calf muscles. Serum creatinine phosphokinase is highly elevated. Patients are generally wheelchair bound by 11–12 years of age and death due to respiratory insufficiency occurs in the late teens to early twenties. Mental retardation and cardiac and gastrointestinal abnormalities have also been reported. The incidence of DMD is approximately 1 in 3500 male births, with approximately one-third of cases representing new mutations.[44]

Becker muscular dystrophy (BMD) is a milder form of DMD associated with proximal muscle weakness, abnormal gait, and eventual involvement of pectoral muscles. Most patients are ambulatory until 20–30 years or later and death occurs in middle age. Creatinine phosphokinase is highly elevated, but there is little early involvement of the myocardium or mental deficiency. BMD is ten times less common than DMD.

Both disorders were known to be inherited as X-linked recessive traits and cytogenetic analysis of a number of unusual patients revealed abnormalities (translocation or deletions) in the Xp_{21} region of the X chromosome. By examining DNA from these patients carefully, Koenig and associates were able to identify a gene product that appeared to be abnormal in both DMD and BMD patients.[45] This protein, called dystrophin, was a component of the membrane cytoskeleton and was related to α-actin and spectrin. When antisera was raised against dystrophin, it was found that this component was localized to the inner face of the myofibril membrane. Muscle biopsies from DMD patients showed virtual absence of dystrophin staining, while biopsies from BMD patients had decreased and irregular staining. This provided proof that DMD and BMD, although very different clinically, were actually allelic disorders caused by different mutations in the same gene.

Dystrophin is the largest human gene that has been isolated with a 14kb RNA transcript and 2500 kb of genomic DNA spanning 70 exons.[45] The huge size of the gene explains the high mutation rate, with dystrophin presenting a large "target" for mutational events. Further studies have shown that nearly 65% of DMD and BMD patients had deletions in the gene, some of which span multiple exons. If the deletion results in alteration of the reading frame (the sequence of nucleic acids which are read into mRNA during transcription), then little or no functional dystrophin will be present and the patient will clinically be affected with DMD. If, on the other hand, the reading frame is maintained, then a truncated protein with some residual function will be synthesized and the patient will demonstrate the milder BMD phe-

FIGURE 16–2. Western Blot Analysis of Dystrophin from Patients with Muscular Dystrophy

Lanes 1, 3, and 5 show no dystrophin staining and are from DMD patients. Lanes 7 and 9 show a dystrophin which is smaller in size and decreased in quantity from a BMD patient. Lanes 11 and 13 show decreased amounts of normal-size dystrophin from a BMD patient. Samples in the evenly numbered lanes show normal size and quantity of dystrophin. *(Courtesy Genica Pharmaceuticals)*

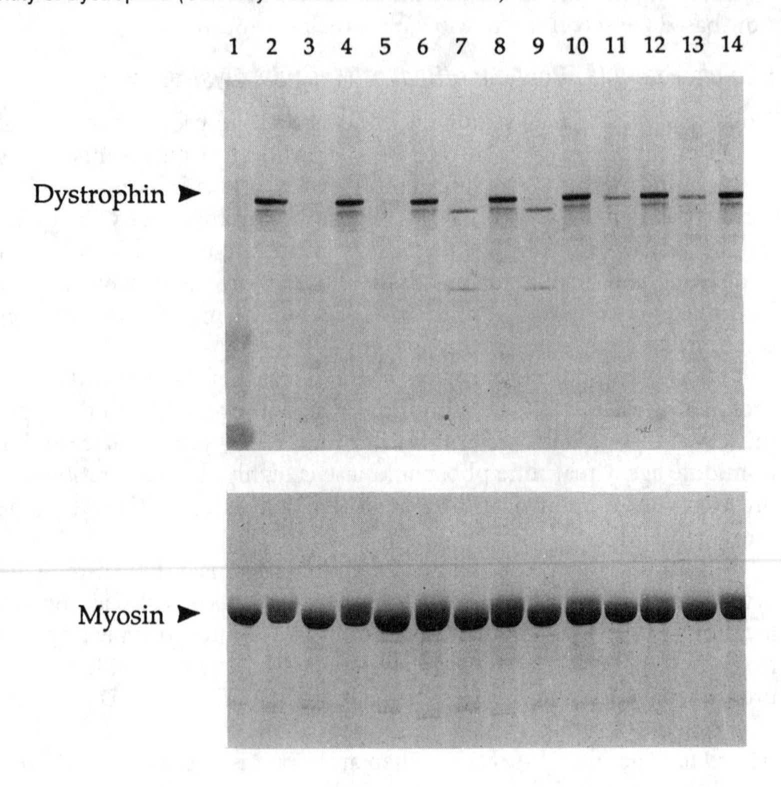

notype. By this means, the tools of molecular biology have provided the means to provide accurate diagnosis/prognosis as well as genetic testing and prenatal diagnosis for the majority of families with DMD/BMD.

At this time, two methodologies are used for testing for DMD/BMD (more appropriately called dystrophinopathies).[46] In the first, dystrophin is examined by Western blotting (immunoblotting) from samples of skeletal, cardiac, or smooth muscle using sheep anti-dystrophin and immunoperoxidase conjugated rabbit anti-sheep IgG followed by peroxidase development. (See Figure 16–2.) Myosin staining is used as a control. Duchenne muscular dystrophy patients show no immunoreactive dystrophin while BMD patients demonstrate either a decreased amount of dystrophin and/or a dystrophin molecule of larger or smaller size than normal. Despite the accuracy and sensitivity of the Western blot method, it cannot detect many carrier females. Direct immunohistochemistry of muscle biopsies in carrier females will show

FIGURE 16–3. Multiple PCR Analysis of the Dystrophin Gene

Shown are two sets of primers, each simultaneously amplifying 9 exons. The outer lanes are molecular weight markers and the two middle sets of 5 lanes are patient samples. On the left side, lanes 1, 3, and 5 are normal, each containing 9 bands of appropriate size. Lanes 2 and 4 each have a deletion of an exon. On the right side, lanes 2, 3, and 4 show deletions and lanes 1 and 5 shows the normal amplification pattern. *(Courtesy Genica Pharmaceuticals)*

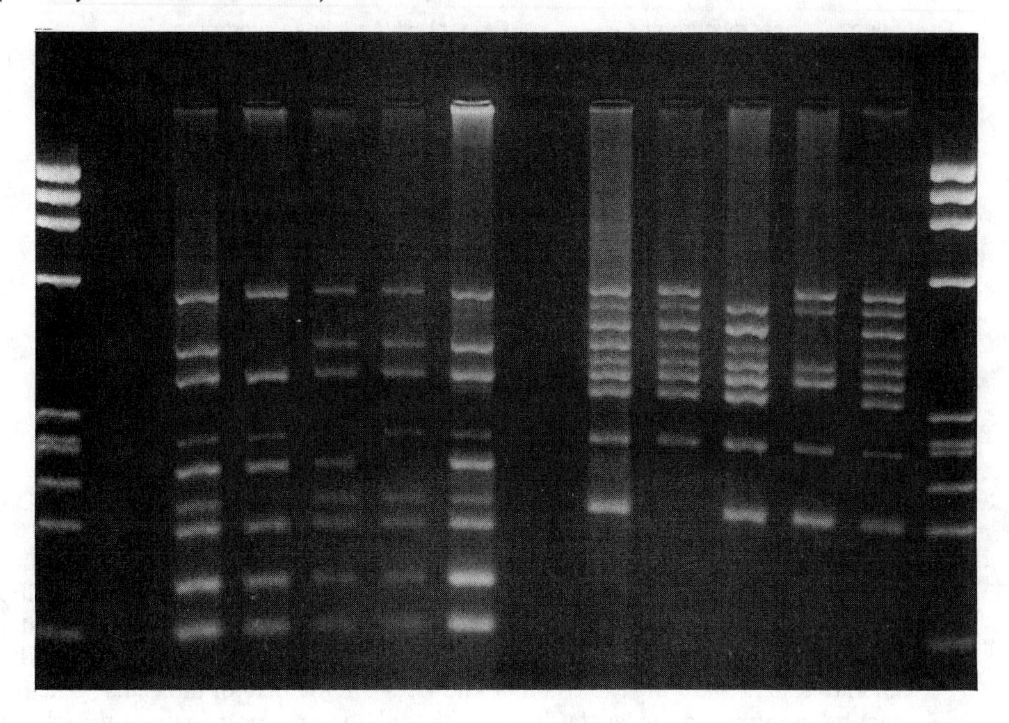

mosaic dystrophin staining following the pattern of random inactivation of the X chromosome containing the normal and abnormal dystrophin alleles.

DNA-based detection of dystrophin gene mutations can be performed using Southern blotting with cDNA probes. The use of multiple restriction enzyme-probe combinations allows detection of the approximately 65% of DMD/BMD patients who have gene deletions/duplications. The clustering of dystrophin gene mutations within a few selected regions of the gene has led to the development of a rapid multiplex PCR assay. Using two mixtures of PCR primers that simultaneously amplify 9 exons each, 98% of deletions/duplications detectable by Southern blotting can be identified by PCR. The major advantages of this latter methodology are in its speed (1–2 days compared to 1–2 weeks) and small sample requirement (0.5 mL blood vs. 20 mL). Figure 16–3 shows an example of a multiplex PCR analysis for DMD/BMD.

TABLE 16–7. Genetic Disorders Diagnosed by DNA Technology

Sickle Cell disease and other hemoglobinopathies	Autosomal dominant polycystic kidney disease
Hemophilia A and B	Medium-chain acyldehydrogenase deficiency
Cystic fibrosis	DiGeorge/Velo-cardio-facial syndrome
Duchenne muscular dystrophy	Prader Willi/Angelman syndrome
Gaucher disease	Neurofibromatosis 1
Fragile X syndrome	Marfan syndrome
Retinoblastoma	Phenylketonuria
α-1-antitrypsin deficiency	Chronic granulomatous disease
Myotonic dystrophy	Spinocerebellar ataxia
Huntington disease	Familial polyposis coli syndrome
Charcot-Marie-Tooth disease 1A	Familial breast and ovarian cancer syndrome
Spinal muscular atrophy	Various mitochondrial disorders

Diagnosis of Other Disorders

A number of other inherited genetic disorders can now be diagnosed with the aid of DNA technology, particularly PCR. Some of these conditions are listed in Table 16–7. In most of these diseases, the responsible gene has been mapped and cloned and the most common mutations identified. Even without knowledge of the specific abnormal allele in a given family, linkage analysis has been used for both prenatal diagnosis and carrier detection. The list of diagnosable disorders changes rapidly and is a testament to the explosion of knowledge in the field of molecular genetics that has occurred in the last few years. Although major concerns about the ethical use of DNA technology still exist (such as whether information on presymptomatic individuals' susceptibility to genetic disease should be released to insurance companies), there is no doubt that the knowledge gained by the use of molecular biology will forever change the way we approach the pathogenesis and diagnosis of human disease.

REFERENCES

1. Garrod AE. Croonian Lecture I: Inborn errors of metabolism. Lancet 1908;2:1–7,73–79, 142–148, 214–220.
2. Garrod AE. Inborn errors of metabolism. London: Oxford Press, 1923.
3. Beadle GW, Tatum EL. Genetic control of biochemical reactions in *Neurospora.* Proc Natl Acad Sci USA 1941;27:499–503.
4. Gibson QH. The reduction of methemoglobin in red blood cells and studies of the causes of idiopathic methemoglobinemia. Biochem J 1948;42:13–20.
5. Cori GT, Cori CF. Glucose-6-phosphatase of the liver in glycogen storage disease. J Biol Chem 1952;199:661–8.

6. Jervis GA. Phenylpyruvic oligophrenia: deficiency of phenylalanine oxidizing system. Proc Soc Exp Biol Med 1953;82:514–17.
7. Krooth RS, Winberg AN. Studies on cell lines developed from the tissues of patients with galactosemia. J Exp Med 1961;113:1155–60.
8. Chance DH, Hillman SL, Millington DS, et al. Rapid diagnosis of maple syrup urine disease in blood spots from newborns by tandem mass spectrometry. Clin Chem 1995;41(1):62–8.
9. Pauling L, Itano HA, Singer SJ, Wells IC. Sickle cell anemia: a molecular disease. Science 1949;110:543–8.
10. Ingram VM. A specific chemical difference between the globins of normal human and sickle cell anemia hemoglobin. Nature 1956;178:792–5.
11. Avery OT, MacLeod CM, MacCarty M. Studies on the chemical nature of the substance inducing transformation of pneumococcal types. J Exp Med 1944;79:137–58.
12. Kelly Jr. TJ, Smith HO. A restriction enzyme from *Hemophilus Influenza* II. Base sequence of the recognition site. J Mol Biol 1970;51:393–401.
13. Kan YW, Dozy AM. Polymorphism of DNA sequence adjacent to human β-globin structural gene: relationship to sickle mutation. Proc Natl Acad Sci USA 1978;75:5631–4.
14. Green ED, Cox DR, Myers RM. The human genome project and its impact on the study of human disease. In: Scriver CR, Beaudet AL, Sly WS, Valle D, eds. The metabolic and molecular basis of inherited disease, 7th ed. New York: McGraw-Hill, 1995:401–36.
15. McKusick VA. Mendelian inheritance in man: catalogs of autosomal dominant, autosomal recessive and X-linked phenotypes, 11th ed. Baltimore: Johns Hopkins University Press, 1994.
16. Tsui LC. Mutations and sequence variations detected in the cystic fibrosis transmembrane conductance regulator (CFTR) gene: a report from the Cystic Fibrosis Genetic Analysis Consortium. Hum Mutat 1992;1:197–203.
17. Holton JB, Allen JT, Green CA, et al. Inherited metabolic disease in the sudden infant death syndrome. Arch Dis Child 1992;66(11):1315–17.
18. Arn PH, Valle DL, Brusilow SW. Recognizing inborn errors of metabolism. Contemporary OB/GYN 1989;33:58–72.
19. Rowe PC, Newman SL, Brusilow SW. Natural history of symptomatic partial ornithine transcarbamylase deficiency. New Eng J Med 1986;314(9):541–6.
20. Segal S, Thier SO. Cystinuria. In: Scriver CR, Beaudet AL, Sly WS, Valle D, eds. The metabolic and molecular basis of inherited disease, 7th ed. New York: McGraw-Hill, 1995:3581–603.
21. Danks DM. Disorders of copper transport. In: Scriver CR, Beaudet AL, Sly WS, Valle D, eds. The metabolic and molecular basis of inherited disease, 7th ed. New York: McGraw-Hill, 1995:2211–37.
22. Scriver CR, Clow CL. Phenylketonuria and other phenylalanine hydroxylase mutations in man. Annu Rev Genetics 1980;14:179.
23. Goodman SI, Green CL. Inborn errors as causes of acute disease in infancy. Seminars in Perinatology 1991;1(1):31–4.
24. Burton BK. Inborn errors of metabolism: the clinical diagnosis in early infancy. Pediatrics 1987;79(3):359–69.
25. Wappner RS. Biochemical diagnosis of genetic diseases. Pediat Annals 1993;22(5):282–97.
26. Saudubray JM, Charpentier C. Clinical phenotypes: diagnosis/algorithms. In: Scriver CR, Beaudet AL, Sly WS, Valle D, eds. The metabolic and molecular basis of inherited disease, 7th ed. New York: McGraw-Hill, 1995:327–401.
27. Shih VE, Mandell R, Sheinhait I. General metabolic screening tests. In: Hommes FA, ed. Techniques in diagnostic human biochemical genetics. New York: Wiley-Liss, 1991:45–68.
28. Guthrie R, Susi A. A simple phenylalanine method for detecting phenylketonurics in large populations of newborn infants. Pediatrics 1963;32:338–43.
29. Beutler E, Baluda MC. A simple spot screening test for galactosemia. J Lab Clin Med 1966;68:137–41.
30. Dussault JH, Coulombe P, Laberge C, et al. Preliminary report on a mass screening program for neonatal hypothyroidism. J Peds 1975;86:670–4.
31. Rashed MS, Bucknall MP, Little D, et al. Screening blood spots for inborn errors of metabo-

lism by elecrospray tandem mass spectrometry with a microplate batch process and a computer algorithm for automated flagging of abnormal profiles. Clin Chem 1997;43:1129–41.
32. Stern HJ, Stanley WN. The fragile X syndrome. J Intl Fed Clin Chem 1994;6(2):42–47.
33. Donis-Keller H, Barker DF, Knowlton RG, et al. Highly polymorphic RFLP probes as diagnostic tools. Cold Spring Harb Symp Quant Biol 1986;L1:317–39.
34. Erlich H, Gelfand D, Sninsky J. Recent advances in the polymerase chain reaction. Science 1991;252:1643–51.
35. Schutzbank TE, Stern HJ. Minireview: principles and application of polymerase chain reaction DNA amplification. J Intl Fed Clin Chem 1993;5(3):96–105.
36. Southern EM. DNA chips: analyzing sequence by hybridization to oligonucleotides on a large scale. Trends in Genetics 1996;12/3:110–15.
37. Welsh MJ, Tsui L-C, Boat TF, et al. Cystic fibrosis. In: Scriver CR, Beaudet AL, Sly WS, Valle D, eds. The metabolic and molecular basis of inherited disease, 7th ed. New York: McGraw-Hill, 1995:3799–878.
38. Shwachman H, Diamond LK. The syndrome of pancreatic insufficiency and bone marrow dysfunction. J Pediatr 1964;65:645–8.
39. Kerem B, Rommens JM, Buchanan JA, et al. Identification of the cystic fibrosis gene: genetic analysis. Science 1989;245:1073–80.
40. Tsui LC. Mutations and sequence variations detected in the cystic fibrosis transmembrane conductance regulator (CFTR) gene: a report from the Cystic Fibrosis Genetic Analysis Consortium. Hum Mutat 1992;1:97–203.
41. Skogerboe KJ, West SF, Murillo MD, Tait JF. Development and evaluation of a simplified dot-blot method for detection of the ΔF508 mutation in cystic fibrosis. Clin Chem 1990;36:1984–6.
42. Williamson R. Universal community carrier screening for cystic fibrosis? Nature Genetics 1993;3:195–201.
43. National Institutes of Health. Genetic testing for cystic fibrosis. NIH Consensus Statement 1997[Apr 14–16];15(4):1–37.
44. Worton RG, Brooke MH. The X-linked muscular dystrophies. In: Scriver CR, Beaudet AL, Sly WS, Valle D, eds. The metabolic and molecular basis of inherited disease, 7th ed. New York: McGraw-Hill, 1995:4195–226.
45. Koenig M, Hoffman EP, Bertelson CJ, et al. Complete cloning of the Duchenne muscular dystrophy (DMD) cDNA and preliminary genomic organization of the DMD gene in normal and affected individuals. Cell 1987;50:509–17.
46. Beggs AH, Kunkel LM. Improved diagnosis of Duchenne/Becker muscular dystrophy. J Clin Invest 1990;85:613–9.

ADDITIONAL READINGS

1. Scriver CR, Beaudet AL, Sly WS, Valle D, eds. The metabolic and molecular basis of inherited disease, 7th ed. New York: McGraw-Hill, 1995.
2. Fernandes J, Saudubray J-M, Tada K, eds. Inborn metabolic diseases: diagnosis and treatment. Berlin: Springer-Verlag, 1990.
3. Hommes FA, ed. Techniques in diagnostic human biochemical genetics. New York: Wiley-Liss, 1991.

CHAPTER 17

Genetic Metabolic Disorders

Lawrence Sweetman, Ph.D.
Julian C. Williams, M.D., Ph.D.

INTRODUCTION

It is estimated that there are 10^5 genes in the human genome, and more than 5000 human genetic diseases have been delineated to date. In only 10% of these has the protein abnormality been identified. Until recently, with the advent of "reverse genetics," the vast majority of those with known protein defects have been characterized initially through analytic techniques on accumulated metabolites and are termed "inborn errors of metabolism." From a knowledge of the accumulated metabolite and biochemical pathways, the enzymatic defect has been subsequently proven. Thus, the identification and characterization process itself tends to select for defects in intermediary metabolism which are enzymatic and usually inherited as autosomal or sex-linked recessive traits. Hereditary abnormalities in structural, receptor, or developmental proteins are much more difficult to characterize at the protein level and are not routinely diagnosed by standard analytic or clinical chemistry techniques.

While 1–2% of all human births are afflicted by chromosomal or single gene disorders, a much smaller percentage are associated with inborn errors of metabolism. The incidence of individual diseases is only estimated, as in most cases true frequencies have not been determined by newborn screening programs or population studies of gene frequency. The estimated incidence ranges from about 1:10,000 for phenylketonuria (PKU) and medium-chain acyl-CoA dehydrogenase (MCAD) deficiency to 1:500,000–1:1,000,000 for the rare disorders. Nevertheless, the number of distinct diseases (approximately 600, with approximately 20–30 new diseases reported every year) makes for a rather large aggregate occurrence, especially in large medical centers.

The economic and social impact of these diseases on the health care system is several orders of magnitude larger in countries with well-developed programs for control of infectious disease and perinatal mortality, as patients with inborn errors of metabolism have a disproportionately high frequency of acute hospital admissions and chronic complications such as mental retardation.

Unfortunately, the clinical manifestations of genetic metabolic disease are extremely diverse, and without a high index of suspicion, the correct diagnosis is rarely made on the initial clinical presentation. Thus, as a rule *metabolic diseases are underdiagnosed.* If the patient is fortunate enough to survive the first illness, the diagnosis may be made upon repeated hospitalizations.

While it is impractical to list all known clinical symptoms of metabolic disease, some generalities can be enumerated:

1. Since inborn errors of metabolism are rare, the common diseases should be ruled out first. However, if the routine diagnostic tests are normal, the patients' symptoms not entirely congruent with the suspected diagnosis, or the response to treatment inappropriate, the possibility of inherited metabolic disease should be considered.
2. Mental retardation without a known history of perinatal morbidity, meningitis, or trauma is suspicious, and progressive retardation is due to metabolic errors until proven otherwise.
3. Failure to thrive, if not attributable to psychosocial deprivation, hormonal disturbances, or gastroenterologic/renal disease may be a manifestation of metabolic disorders.
4. Many of the hereditary enzyme deficiencies involve catabolic enzymes and, as detailed below, the normal catabolic response to infection/fasting will result in an exaggerated physiologic response. An inappropriately severe response to minor infection/fasting or failure to respond to appropriate treatment should be suspect, especially if associated with chemical abnormalities such as hypoglycemia, hyperammonemia, excessive ketoacidosis/lactic acidosis, or deficient ketosis.
5. Hepatosplenomegaly, multi-focal bone abnormalities, myopathy and/or muscle weakness, and hepatic dysfunction may be manifestations of genetic/metabolic disease.

Unfortunately, few of the inborn errors of metabolism can be diagnosed by routine clinical chemistry tests, although abnormalities, particularly in urinalysis or electrolyte balance, may suggest the need for further specific tests. Microscopic examination of tissue biopsies may be more helpful for some disorders, but again are not generally diagnostic. Specific diagnosis is dependent on two processes:

1. The use of sophisticated analytic techniques such as high-performance liquid chromatography (HPLC), gas chromatography (GC), gas chromatography/mass spectrometry (GCMS), or tandem mass spectrometry (MS-MS) for the identification of abnormal metabolites.
2. The specific assay of enzyme activity in tissue samples, or occasionally, body fluids.

These two processes are, with the exception of amino acid analysis by high-pressure ion exchange chromatography, not generally available in most hospitals, medical centers, or commercial laboratories. Diagnosis is dependent on the acumen of the clinician and the clinical pathologist or laboratory scientist and the referral of samples to the appropriate specialized laboratory. An essential requisite for diagnosis is the collection of appropriate samples with the recognition that the greatest accumulation of abnormal metabolites occurs at the height of catabolism, i.e., upon presentation and before the administration of intravenous glucose. Thus, blood and urine specimens should be collected and stored upon presentation, or as soon as possible thereafter, for future analysis.

The recent advent of molecular genetic techniques has altered this diagnostic schema for some diseases. For those disorders whose causative gene has been cloned or restriction fragment length polymorphisms (RFLPs) have been identified, molecular diagnosis may be utilized based on symptom recognition or the identification of abnormal metabolites in physiologic fluids. In the vast majority of metabolic diseases, multiple DNA mutations have been identified as causative for each disease; for example, more than 100 mutations are known in phenylketonuria. In many disorders, each family's mutation is unique and screening for disease in unrelated families by mutation analysis is impractical. However, if the specific mutation has been identified in a given family, DNA analysis is useful for screening family members and for heterozygote detection and prenatal diagnosis. Unfortunately, the initial identification of the mutation in a new patient/family is a research project and is not generally available. Although currently molecular tests are performed only generally in research laboratories, they soon will be generally available and are amenable to newborn screening programs.

Genetic metabolic diseases can be crudely categorized into those with chronic, slowly progressive manifestations and those with acute, life-threatening symptoms. Although the correspondence is imperfect, they also can be similarly divided into those diseases with the accumulation of large molecules which are endogenously synthesized (chronic diseases) and small molecules (acute diseases), many of which are derived from dietary components.

The catabolic effects of fasting/infection will increase the degradation of small molecules and the flux of their breakdown products. This is pronounced for those molecules (protein, triglycerides, and glycogen) which are the storage forms of the metabolic fuels (amino acids, fatty acids, and glucose, respectively) necessary for energy production. Those disorders which are due to a deficiency of an enzyme in the catabolic pathway of one of these small molecules will then manifest a sudden increase in the accumulation of toxic intermediates and, consequently, acute symptoms.

Treatment of those chronic, slowly progressive disorders which are due to the accumulation of large molecules is primarily symptomatic and supportive, without alteration of the inevitable, downhill course. Catabolic defects in the degradative pathways of small molecules are more amenable to therapeutic intervention. If the offending molecule is "essential," i. e., derived from the diet and not endogenously synthesized, dietary restriction of intake may be effective. Acute crises may be treated by dialysis of the accumulated, toxic small molecules. Catabolic increases of the flux of these small molecules resulting in accumulation of toxic metabolites may be suppressed by supplying exogenous fuel such as intravenous glucose. In some cases, such as the organic acidemias and urea cycle defects, endogenous detoxification mechanisms can be augmented by supplying exogenous glycine, carnitine, or benzoate.

LYSOSOMAL STORAGE DISEASES

The lysosomal storage diseases are due to genetic deficiencies of the hydrolases of the lysosome which normally degrade the complex macromolecules of the cell. Many of these macromolecules are glycoprotein and glycolipid components of cell membranes.[1,2]

The majority of lysosomal enzyme deficiencies involve exoglycosidic hydrolases which cleave a terminal carbohydrate residue. Failure to remove a terminal carbohydrate results in a block in degradation of the entire macromolecule and its accumulation within the lysosome. The resulting lysosomal hypertrophy presumably inhibits other lysosomal degradative processes, distorts intracellular structure and, upon lysis, results in cell death.

The majority of these diseases can be categorized into three groups, named for the stored materials: the mucopolysaccharidoses, glycolipidoses, and glycoproteinoses.[3] All of these disorders have slowly progressive symptoms; are inherited as autosomal recessive traits, with a few exceptions; and often can be prenatally diagnosed by enzyme assay. The incidence of each of these disorders averages about 1:100,000. They can occur in all ethnic groups, and some occur in very high incidence in specific groups, such as Gaucher and Tay-Sachs disease in Ashkenazi Jews. Tentative diagnosis is established by clinical symptoms and analysis of stored materials in urine and tissues. Diagnostic confirmation is by enzyme assay in fibroblasts, leukocytes, tissues, or, occasionally, body fluids.

The mucopolysaccharide storage diseases are due to the accumulation of mucopolysaccharides (MPS, also called glycosaminoglycans or GAGs) which are polymers of monosaccharides containing sulfate, amino, and carboxyl groups.[4] These macromolecules are predominantly synthesized in connective tissues and accumulation in these sites accounts for the symptoms of coarse facial features, dysostosis multiplex, and restriction of joint motion. Storage in other tissues accounts for hepatosplenomegaly, corneal clouding, and/or mental retardation. Table 17–1 lists the disorders, inheritance pattern, and symptoms, as well as the specific enzyme deficiency and accumulated metabolite.

In association with the correct symptoms, a tentative diagnosis can be assigned upon demonstration of MPS accumulation, usually in urine. An acid turbidity test or an MPS spot test with toluidine blue will indicate an increased MPS concentration. Thin-layer chromatography or electrophoresis (see Figure 17–1A) will allow identification of the MPS species and selection of the appropriate enzyme assay for specific diagnosis.

Hyaluronidase deficiency is a recently described mucopolysaccharidosis in which urinary mucopolysaccharides are normal.[5] Hyaluronan is elevated in plasma and hyaluronidase is completely deficient in plasma. Hyaluronan is an extracellular mucopolysaccharide present in high amounts in synovial fluid, cartilage, and skin, and the enzyme deficiency results in periarticular masses, short stature, and erosion of the acetabula.

The glycolipidoses present with more diverse symptoms.[6] In general, bone/joint abnormalities and corneal clouding do not occur. Organomegaly is present in some, but not all, disorders. Mental retardation and/or focal neurologic deficits are frequently, but not universally, present. Table 17–2 lists these disorders with their respective symptoms, stored material, and enzymatic deficiency. Although methods exist for analysis of the accumulated glycolipid in tissues, these techniques are not readily available and frequently lack sufficient sensitivity to be easily applied to the analysis of blood and urine. Thus, specific diagnosis is dependent on enzymatic assay of leukocytes, fibroblasts, tissues, or, in some cases, plasma/serum.

The glycoproteinoses are due to a deficiency of a glycosidase or aminohydrolase necessary for the degradation of the oligosaccharide chains of glycoproteins.[7] The clinical symptoms overlap those of the MPS storage disorders and the glycolipidoses. Presumptive diagnosis is based on analysis of the accumulated oligosaccharides in urine by thin layer-chromatography (see Figure 17–1B) or HPLC with confirmation by enzyme assay (Table 17–2).

CARBOHYDRATE DEFICIENT GLYCOPROTEIN SYNDROME (CDGS)

CDGS is a heterogeneous group of disorders with multi-system involvement first described in 1980 by Jaeken et al.[8] Clinical symptoms always include neurologic abnormalities such as psychomotor retardation, hypotonia, decreased reflexes, and ataxia. Olivopontocerebellar atrophy is usual in patients presenting early in life. Other features vary according to subtype (currently four clinical phenotypes are described[9]), but range from failure to thrive, cardiac failure, severe hepatic dysfunction, and lipodystrophy in infants, to an adult form with peripheral neuropathy, ataxia, short stature, scoliosis, non-progressive retardation, retinal degeneration, and failure to progress through puberty in females.[10]

The extreme variation in organ involvement, non-specificity of symptoms, and differences according to age of presentation make clinical diagnosis extremely difficult. Fortunately for diagnostic purposes, all patients have abnormalities in the carbohydrate side-chains of N-linked glycoproteins, i.e. commonly decreased sialic acid, galactose, and N-acetylglucosamine content. Recognition of this has led to a simple diagnostic test: isoelectric focusing of a serum glycoprotein, typically transferrin, demonstrating an abnormal pattern.[10] This has led to basic research to elucidate the underlying defects. A mutation in a phosphomannomutase (PMMM2) on chromosome 16p13 appears to cause the majority but not all of the severe, early infantile forms (type I).[11] A partial deficiency of dehydrodolichol reduction has been found in a few type I patients.[12] Type II, a late infantile and childhood form, has been shown to be due to mutations in the MGAT2 gene which encodes UDP-GlcNac: alpha-6-D-mannoside beta-1 2-N-acetylglucosaminyltransferase II, which is essential for synthesis of N-linked glycans.[13]

TABLE 17–1. Mucopolysaccharidoses (MPS)

Disorder	Urine Excretion of Mucopolysaccharides	Primary Enzyme Deficiency	Clinical Features
Hurler syndrome (MPS-I)	Dermatan sulfate Heparan sulfate	α-L-iduronidase	Excessive growth in infancy followed by severe dwarfing thereafter, hernias, hepatosplenomegaly, progressive clouding of cornea, limitation of joint mobility, deterioration of mental function and coarseness of facial features, rhinorrhea, hydrocephalus, deafness, cardiac murmurs. Death usually occurs in the first decade of cardiorespiratory causes.
Scheie syndrome (MPS I-S)			Progressive clouding of cornea and joint limitation, aortic insufficiency, normal intelligence, normal stature.
Hurler-Scheie Compound (MPS I-H/I-S)			Features intermediate between Hurler and Scheie syndromes.
Hunter Syndrome (MPS II) Severe	Dermatan sulfate Heparan sulfate	Iduronide sulfatase	Dwarfing, deafness, retinal degeneration, hepatosplenomegaly, hernias, progressive limitation of joint mobility and deterioration of mental function, cardiac murmurs, clear cornea, cutaneous nodules. Death usually occurs in the second decade.
Mild			Same general features as severe Hunter syndrome, but mental deterioration much slower. Survival well into adult life.
Sanfilippo syndrome A (MPS III-A) B (MPS III-B) C (MPS III-C) D (MPS III-D)	Heparan sulfate	Heparan N-sulfatase N-acetyl-α-D-glucosaminidase Acetyl CoA:α-glucosaminide-N-acetyl-transferase N-acetyl-α-D-glucosaminide-6-sulfatase	Clear cornea, severe deterioration of mental function prior to school age, minimal organomegaly and shortening of stature. No differences in clinical features between the various types.

TABLE 17–1 Continued

Morquio syndrome (MPS IV)	Keratan sulfate		
Morquio A		N-acetylgalactosaminide-6-sulfatase	Severe dwarfing, pectus carinatum, kyphoscoliosis, genu valgum (prominent joints, some of which may be lax), mild corneal clouding, normal intelligence. May have cervical cord compression because of cervical spine dislocation, thin enamel.
Morquio B		ß-galactosidase	Similar to Morquio A syndrome, but dysostosis multiplex is milder and enamel is normal.
Maroteaux-Lamy syndrome (MPS VI)	Dermatan sulfate	Arylsulfatase B (N-acetyl-galactosaminide-4-sulfatase)	
Severe			Normal or excessive growth during infancy followed by severe dwarfing, limitation of joint mobility, corneal clouding, coarsening of facies, hepatosplenomegaly, hernias, cardiac murmurs, deafness, normal intelligence.
Mild			Skeletal features and growth retardation less prominent than in severe Maroteaux-Lamy syndrome.
ß-Glucuronidase	Dermatan sulfate Heparan sulfate	ß-glucuronidase	Variable features including coarse facies, hepatosplenomegaly, hernias, corneal clouding, dysostosis multiplex and mental retardation.

Modified from Williams & Howell[4] with permission.

FIGURE 17–1A. Electrophoresis of Urinary Mucopolysaccharides (performed according to Wessler[48])

Lanes 1 and 5: Standards, top to bottom, heparan sulfate, dermatan sulfate, and chondroitin sulfate. **Lane 2:** Normal urine. **Lane 2′:** Normal urine with added dermatan sulfate. **Lane 3:** Urine from Sanfilippo with high heparan sulfate. **Lane 3′:** Same urine with added dermatan sulfate. **Lane 4:** Urine from Morquio with high keratan sulfate. **Lane 4′:** Same urine with added dermatan sulfate.

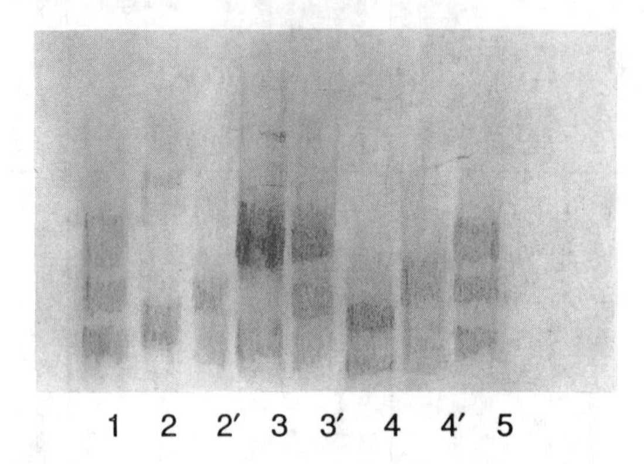

FIGURE 17–1B. Thin-layer Chromatography of Urinary Oligosaccharides (performed according to Humbel & Colart[49])

Lane 1: GM_1 gangliosidosis **Lane 2:** Glycogen storage disease type III **Lane 3:** Mucolipidosis type III **Lane 4:** Fucosidosis **Lane 5:** Mannosidosis

TABLE 17–2. Glycolipidoses and Glycoproteinoses

Disorder	Characteristic Clinical Features	Enzyme Deficiency	Enzyme Diagnosis in:	Confirmatory Tests
G_{M2}-gangliosidoses	Dementia, myoclonic seizures, blindness, and macular cherry-red spots predominate in early-onset forms; cerebellar ataxia and spinal muscular atrophy predominate in late-onset forms. Ashkenazi Jewish predilection (alpha-locus forms).	Hexosaminidase a. Alpha-locus disorders: Hexosaminidases A (and S) (Tay-Sachs disease and variants). b. Beta-locus disorders: Hexosaminidase A and B (Sandhoff disease and variants). c. Activator-locus disorders: Hexosaminidase A activator (AB-variant).	a. Serum, leukocytes, cultured skin fibroblasts, urine. b. Serum, leukocytes, cultured, skin fibroblasts, urine. c. Cultured skin fibroblasts.	Membranous cytoplasmic bodies in rectal ganglion cells (all types). Excessive urinary oligosaccharides in beta-locus disorders.
G_{M1}-gangliosidoses	Infantile form gives encephalopathy, hepatosplenomegaly, bone and joint involvement, often cherry-red spots; in a late-infantile form, encephalopathy predominates; in later onset form (Morquio type B), skeletal involvement predominates.	G_{M1}-ganglioside beta-galactosidase.	Leukocytes, cultured skin fibroblasts.	Excess urinary oligosaccharides in characteristic pattern.
Fabry disease	Purple 1- to 3-mm macular-maculopapular skin lesions, painful neuropathy, renal disease; X-linked (incompletely) recessive inheritance; vascular involvement may occur (lymphedema, stroke).	α-galactosidase A	Plasma or serum, leukocytes, cultured skin fibroblasts.	Characteristic histologic and histochemical appearance of biopsied skin lesions.

TABLE 17–2 Continued

Gaucher disease	Infantile form: severe hepatosplenomegaly and severe encephalopathy; juvenile form: milder nervous system involvement, variable splenomegaly; "adult" form (may begin in childhood): splenomegaly (thrombocytopenia), bone involvement, nervous system unaffected, Ashkenazi Jewish predilection.	Cerebroside beta-glucosidase (glucocerebrosidase)	Cultured skin fibroblasts, leukocytes.	Characteristic foam cells in bone marrow.
Niemann-Pick disease	Type A: severe infantile hepatosplenomegaly and severe encephalopathy, often cherry red spots, Ashkenazi Jewish predilection; Type B: hepatosplenomegaly in childhood without encephalopathy; Type C: Childhood encephalopathy with variable organ enlargement; Type D: infantile hepatosplenomegaly in Nova Scotia Acadians.	a. Sphingomyelinase (Deficient in types A, B; often partially deficient in "type C"). b. Abnormal cholesterol esterification in type C.	a. Cultured skin fibroblasts, leukocytes (Types A, B). b. Cultured skin fibroblasts.	Characteristic foam cells in bone marrow (all types). Types C and D: Characteristic membranous bodies by electron microscopy in rectal, skin, or conjunctival biopsy. Types C, D: Elevated sphingomyelin in liver biopsy.
Metachromatic leukodystrophy	Late infantile form: dementia, spasticity, optic atrophy, neuropathy,; juvenile forms: similar but later onset; adult form: dementia predominates; multiple sulfatase deficiency: infantile neurologic deterioration with seizures, ichthyosis, and mucopolysaccharidosis-like face and bone changes.	a. Arylsulfatase A (sulfatide sulfatase) (late-infantile, juvenile, and adult forms). b. Arylsulfatase A activator (usually resembles juvenile form clinically). c. Arylsulfatase A and at least ten other sulfatases (multiple sulfatase deficiency).	a. Serum, leukocytes, cultured skin fibroblasts, urine. b. Cultured skin fibroblasts. c. Cultured skin fibroblasts.	Metachromatic cells and demyelination by light microscopy, tuffstone bodies by electron microscopy in myelinated nerve from skin or sural nerve biopsy.
Krabbe leukodystrophy	Infantile encephalopathy, seizures, optic atrophy, neuropathy; rare later-onset forms.	Cerebroside beta-galactosidase (galactocerebrosidase).	Serum, leukocytes, cultured skin fibroblasts.	Demyelination and needle-like inclusions by electron microscopy on nerve biopsy.

TABLE 17–2 Continued

Farber disease	Early infantile painful arthropathy; subcutaneous nodules near joints, tendon sheaths, and pressure points; hoarseness; often hepatomegaly.	Acid ceramidase	Cultured skin fibroblasts, leukocytes.	Characteristic light and electron microscopic picture of biopsied skin lesions.
Fucosidosis	Infantile form: retardation, spasticity, seizures, coarse facies, hepatosplenomegaly, cardiomegaly, dysostosis multiplex, clear cornea. Juvenile form: retardation, coarse facies, dysostosis multiplex, minimal hepatosplenomegaly, angiokeratoma.	α-fucosidase	Plasma or serum, leukocytes, cultural skin fibroblasts.	Excess urinary oligosaccharides in characteristic pattern.
Mannosidosis α form	Mild and severe forms with earlier onset in the latter. Slightly coarse facies, hepatosplenomegaly, dysostosis multiplex, cataracts, hernias, progressive retardation.	α-mannosidase	Plasma or serum, leukocytes, cultured skin fibroblasts	Excess urinary oligosaccharides in characteristic pattern.
ß form	Mental retardation with delayed speech, scrotal angiokeratoma, mildly coarse facies, mild dysostosis multiplex. Few patients known and physical findings vary.	ß-mannosidase	Plasma or serum, leukocytes, cultured skin fibroblasts	Excess urinary excretion of a disaccharide in humans.

TABLE 17–2 Continued

Aspartylglycosaminuria	Early onset infections and diarrhea with childhood manifestation of speech delay and progressive retardation, cardiac murmurs, macroglossia, cataracts, hypotonia, loose joints and dysostosis multiplex.	Aspartylglycosaminidase	Plasma or serum, leukocytes, cultured skin fibroblasts.	Excess urinary aspartylglucosamine and complex glycopeptides.
Schindler disease	Mental retardation, progressive neurodegeneration with cortical blindness and myoclonic seizures.	α-galactosidase B (α-galactosaminidase)	Plasma or serum, leukocytes, cultured skin fibroblasts.	Excess urinary excretion of O-linked oligosaccharides.
Sialidosis				
Type I	Macular cherry red spot, punctate lens apacities, decreasing visual acuity, myoclonic seizures, ataxia, mild retardation, juvenile onset.	Neuraminidase	Plasma or serum, leukocytes, cultured skin fibroblasts.	Excess urinary excretion of oligosaccharides in characteristic pattern.
Type II	Earlier onset, coarse facies, increased head circumference, short stature, cataracts, corneal clouding, hepatosplenomegaly, hernias, dysostosis multiplex, moderate retardation.			
I-Cell disease				
Mucolipidosis II	Early onset of coarse facies, dysostosis multiplex, hernias, hepatosplenomegaly, clear corneas, cardiac murmurs, and progressive mental retardation. A later onset form with milder symptoms is termed mucolipidosis III_or pseudo-Hurler polydystrophy.	UDP-N-acetylglucosamine: glycoprotein N-acetylglucosaminylphos-photransferase.	Leukocytes and cultured skin fibroblasts	Increased plasma and urine lysosomal enzyme activities with a concomitant decrease in fibroblast lysosomal enzymes. Increased urinary oligosaccharides in a characteristic pattern.

Modified from Johnson[6] with permission.

Just as the clinical study of lysosomal storage diseases led to research revealing the enzymes of glycoprotein/glycolipid degradation and the mechanisms of lysosomal transport and function, further study of these complex CDGS clinical phenotypes will certainly teach us much about glycoprotein synthesis.

PEROXISOMAL DISORDERS

Peroxisomal disorders can be grouped according to whether there are greatly diminished number or absence of peroxisomes with multiple enzyme defects, as in group 1; normal peroxisomes with single enzyme deficiencies, as in group 2; and abnormal peroxisomes with more than one enzyme defect, as in group 3.[14] The disorders and some of their biochemical abnormalities are listed in Table 17–3.

Group I disorders show multiple biochemical abnormalities due to the general loss of peroxisomal function. These may include elevated very-long-chain fatty acids (VLCFA), elevated pipecolic acid, elevated phytanic and pristanic acids, elevated di- and trihydroxycholestanoic acid, and reduced or absent plasmalogen. There are multiple genetic complementation groups among the Group I disorders. More detailed descriptions of representative disorders from groups 1 and 2 follow.

TABLE 17–3. Peroxisomal Disorders

Group 1:	Multiple enzyme defects with reduced numbers or absence of peroxisomes	
	Zellweger cerebrohepatorenal syndrome	
	Neonatal adrenoleukodystrophy	
	Infantile Refsum disease	
	Hyperpipecolic acidemia	
Group 2:	Single enzyme defects with normal peroxisomes	
	X-linked adrenoleukodystrophy:	VLCFA acyl-CoA synthase deficiency with increased VLCFA
	Acatalasemia:	Catalase deficiency
	Hyperoxaluria type I:	Glyoxylate alanine aminotransferase deficiency with increased oxalic, glycolic, and glyoxylic acids
	3-Oxoacyl-CoA thiolase deficiency (Pseudo-Zellweger syndrome)	
	Acyl-CoA oxidase deficiency	
	Bifunctional enzyme deficiency	
	Refsum disease:	Phytanic acid alpha-hydroxylase deficiency with increased phytanic acid.
	Dihydroxyacetone phosphate acyltransferase deficiency	
Group 3:	More than one enzyme defect with abnormal peroxisomes	
	Rhizomelic chondrodysplasia punctata	

X-linked Adrenoleukodystrophy

This is an example of a group 2 single deficiency of very-long-chain fatty acid (VLCFA) acyl-CoA synthase in peroxisomes which are normal in structure and number. This enzyme is required for the catabolism of the VLCFA—i. e., straight-chain C24:0, C25:0, and C26:0 fatty acids—which occurs mainly in peroxisomes, and its deficiency results in increased VLCFA in plasma lipids.[15] The severe childhood form results in progressive demyelination and neurological deficit with adrenal insufficiency. The adult form presents with adrenal insufficiency and slowly progressive paraparesis. Although adrenal hormone replacement can correct the adrenal insufficiency, the neurological manifestations are not yet treatable, although some beneficial response has been seen with a diet low in fatty acids and supplemented with glycerol trioleate and trierucate. As an X-linked disorder, only males are severely affected. About 85% of female heterozygotes can be diagnosed by increased VLCFA.

Zellweger Syndrome

This is an example of a group 1 disorder in which peroxisomes are absent or greatly reduced in number, which results in multiple enzyme deficiency.[16] This is due to a number of different defects in the biogenesis of peroxisomes.

The classical Zellweger cerebrohepatorenal syndrome reflects the multiorgan effects of a deficiency of peroxisomes. Symptoms include dysmorphic features, severe muscular hypotonia, mental retardation, impaired liver function, eye abnormalities, renal cysts, and chondrodysplasia resulting in early death. The biochemical abnormalities include a combination of many of the abnormalities of the single enzyme defects. Among these are increased VLCFA in plasma lipids, decreased plasmalogen synthesis and concentrations in tissues, increased phytanic acid, increased intermediates of bile acid synthesis, and increased pipecolic acid.

Rhizomelic Chondrodysplasia Punctata

This is representative of group 3 disorders with peroxisomes present but with abnormal structures and more than one enzyme deficient. Plasmalogen synthesis is decreased and phytanic acid oxidation is impaired. The oxidation of VLCFA is normal.

CARBOHYDRATE DISORDERS

Numerous disorders affecting carbohydrate metabolism have been identified, including transport defects such as pentosuria and glucose-galactose malabsorption, the intestinal disaccharidase deficiencies of sucrase-isomaltase and lactase, erythrocyte abnormalities of anaerobic glycolysis, enzyme deficiencies resulting in the accumulation of toxic monosaccharide phosphates, disorders of glucose homeostasis, and those resulting in lactate accumulation.[17] Many are quite rare. The relatively more common diseases resulting in significant morbidity/mortality are described below.

The nervous system has obligate requirements for glucose and elaborate hormonal and enzymatic mechanisms have evolved for glucose homeostasis with fasting. Glucose is stored as glycogen for release when glucose concentrations diminish from the post-absorptive phase and, under most conditions, enough glycogen is available for 24 hours. Maintenance of glucose concentrations is then dependent on gluconeogenic synthesis from amino acids, lactate, and glycerol. Enzymatic deficiencies of glycogen synthesis and degradation and of gluconeogenesis may result in hypoglycemia with its associated effects. These disorders are inherited as autosomal recessive traits in general and occur with an approximate incidence of 1:100,000 in all ethnic groups, excepting certain inbred populations. Besides the obvious effects of hypoglycemia on the brain, symptomatology of the glycogen storage diseases (GSD) is directly manifested in liver, muscle, or both. Van Gierke disease (GSD I) is due to the hepatic deficiency of glucose-6-phosphatase, an enzyme necessary for the release of free glucose as the ultimate step in glycogen degradation. Symptoms include hepatomegaly, hypotonia, growth failure, and platelet dysfunction resulting in epistaxis, and easy bruising, and the neurologic effects of hypoglycemia. Metabolic abnormalities also include lactic acidosis, hypercholesterolemia, hypertriglyceridemia, and hyperuricemia. Untreated, hepatic adenomas are common, with progression to carcinoma frequently occurring in older patients. Diagnosis requires assay of glucose-6-phosphatase and/or its required transport proteins in liver tissue. Treatment is fairly simple and effective by avoiding fasting with frequent feedings, nocturnal nasogastric drip of carbohydrate or enteral formulas, and/or supplementation with complex carbohydrates such as starch. With treatment, the majority of symptoms and secondary metabolic abnormalities normalize or significantly improve.

Debrancher enzyme deficiency (GSD III) has similar but less severe symptoms, i.e., hepatomegaly, fasting hypoglycemia, and hypertriglyceridemia. Lactic acidosis and hyperuricemia do not occur, and the hypoglycemia appears only after longer fasting than in GSD I. Presumably, this is due to the availability of glucose released by phosphorylase from the termini of the glycogen molecule before it reaches a branch point. Many patients with debrancher deficiency also have muscle weakness with hypotonia and develop a chronic progressive myopathy in the later decades of life. Enzymatic diagnosis of this disorder can be accomplished in leukocytes, fibroblasts, and muscle and liver tissue.

Hepatic phosphorylase deficiency (GSD VI) and the deficiency of its activator enzyme, hepatic phosphorylase B kinase, have minimal symptomatology, with hepatomegaly being constant. Usually no treatment is necessary except for frequent feedings in those few patients with mild hypoglycemia in childhood. The rarest of the hepatic glycogenosis is brancher deficiency (GSD IV), with an incidence of about 1:500,000. Rather than hepatomegaly and hypoglycemia, the major symptom is progressive hepatic cirrhosis, resulting in failure to thrive and death at an early age. Enzyme deficiency can be confirmed in multiple tissues and the only available treatment is liver transplantation. Post-transplant, enzyme deficiency in non-hepatic organs such as skeletal and cardiac tissue continues and may result in myopathy with time.

Although muscle symptoms are minor manifestations of the aforementioned glycogen storage diseases, a major muscle glycogenesis is McArdle disease (GSD V), or muscle phosphorylase deficiency. Patients are usually asymptomatic until puberty for unknown reasons, and then present with severe muscle cramps and myoglobinuria with strenuous exercise. Myoglobinuria may result in renal failure. Avoidanceof strenuous exercise is the major treatment modality, although fructose and a diet high in protein have been suggested to be of benefit. In the fourth and fifth decades of life, a chronic progressive myopathy may occur.

Diagnosis is by the absence of lactate production in a forearm ischemic exercise test, abnormal muscle histology, or enzyme assay. Phosphofructokinase deficiency, a very rare disorder, has similar findings, with the added component of a mild hemolytic anemia. Pompe disease (GSD II), also known as α-glucosidase or acid maltase deficiency, differs from the other glycogenoses in that it is due to a defective lysosomal rather than a cytosolic enzyme. As such, symptoms are not related to a deficiency of glucose in affected tissues but to the progressive accumulation of glycogen inside lysosomes. Patients present with severe hypotonia and cardiomegaly in the first year of life and succumb to cardiac failure by age two. Milder variants may not manifest until adulthood, with a progressive skeletal myopathy.

Other disorders of glucose homeostasis are those affecting the gluconeogenic process. Deficiency of pyruvate carboxylase, which converts pyruvate to oxaloacetate as the first step in pyruvate's transformation to glucose, results in hepatomegaly and the neurologic sequelae of recurrent hypoglycemia, i.e., psychomotor retardation, seizures, and hypotonia. Metabolic abnormalities include increased pyruvate, lactate, alanine, and ketone bodies. Continuous provision of glucose corrects the metabolic abnormalities, as does the accepted treatment of avoiding fasting. Fructose-1, 6-diphosphatase deficiency has similar symptoms, abnormal laboratory findings, and treatment. The diseases can be separated by assay of the respective enzymes in liver, kidney, or intestinal tissue or, in the case of pyruvate carboxylase, also in fibroblasts and leukocytes.

Another mechanism of toxicity in defects of carbohydrate metabolism is the accumulation of monosaccharide phosphates. In hereditary fructose intolerance due to a deficiency of fructose-1-phosphate aldolase, ingestion of fructose results in emesis, hypoglycemia, seizures, coma, disseminated intravascular coagulation, and acute hypotension. Chronic symptoms include failure to thrive, hypotonia, hepatomegaly and cirrhosis, and a renal Fanconi syndrome. Strict avoidance of fructose corrects all abnormalities with an excellent prognosis. Although this disorder is very rare, accumulation of galactose-1-phosphate in galactosemia is more common, with an incidence of about 1:50,000. Unlike hereditary fructose intolerance, for which the defective enzyme must be measured in liver or intestinal tissue, in galactosemia the pertinent enzyme, galactose-1-phosphate uridyltransferase, can be measured in all tissues, including erythrocytes. Thus, it is amenable to newborn screening programs by direct assay or by measuring the accumulated metabolites galactose-1-phosphate, galactose, and galactitol. The symptoms are those of severe hepatic dysfunction, failure to thrive, renal Fanconi syndrome, susceptibility to *E. coli* sepsis, mental retardation, and cataracts. Treatment depends on elimination of galactose from the diet, predominantly in the form of lactose derived from milk products. With treatment from the neonatal period, outcome is good, although intelligence is minimally decreased and females have varying degrees of ovarian failure.

Unlike the previously discussed inborn errors of metabolism with secondary accumulation of lactic acid and pyruvate associated with low plasma glucose concentrations, the primary disorders of lactate and pyruvate accumulation have significant neuromuscular pathology not due to hypoglycemia.[18] Pyruvate dehydrogenase converts pyruvate to acetyl-CoA and is the entry point of glycolysis to the tricarboxylic acid cycle. Its deficiency causes pyruvate accumulation and the concomitant increase of lactate.

Complete deficiency results in early-onset psychomotor retardation, hypotonia with hyperreflexia, poor coordination, and optic atrophy. Partial deficiency may be manifested in childhood with intermittent ataxia, encephalopathy, and mild chronic motor dysfunction. Enzyme deficiency can be determined in multiple tissues. Unfortunately, there is no treatment with significant efficacy.

MITOCHONDRIAL DISORDERS

Another major group of diseases resulting in lactic acidosis are the mitochondrial myopathies due to defects in the respiratory chain enzymes which affect energy metabolism.[19, 20] Symptoms are extremely diverse and include abnormalities of muscle and brain function, short stature, cardiomyopathy, renal tubular dysfunction, endocrinopathy, and hepatic dysfunction. Various syndromes are part of this group, such as Leigh; Kearns-Sayre (KSS); Pearson; myoclonic epilepsy with ragged red fibers (MERRF); mitochondrial encephalomyelopathy, lactic acidosis, stroke-like episodes (MELAS); Leber hereditary optic neuropathy (LHON); maternally-inherited myopathy with cardiac involvement (MIMyCa); and maternally inherited sensory neuropathy, ataxia, retinitis pigmentosa, developmental delay, dementia, seizures and limb weakness (NARP). Some disorders have Mendelian inheritance because many mitochondrial proteins are encoded by the nuclear genome. Other disorders have a maternal inheritance because some of the mitochondrial proteins are encoded by the mitochondrial DNA which is inherited only via the mother.[20, 21] The abnormalities in mitochondrial DNA may be large-scale rearrangements as in Kearns-Sayre and Pearson syndromes, point mutations affecting mitochondrial tRNA as in MERRF, MELAS, and MIMyCa, or other point mutations as in LHON and NARP.[20, 22]

Diagnosis of the respiratory chain defects is difficult because of the diversity of the clinical features and the variable clinical presentation which may be due to heteroplasmy with different proportions of normal and mutated mitochondrial DNA in different individuals and even in different tissues. Diagnosis of these diseases may be aided by the dyad of lactic acidosis (which may be intermittent) and neuromuscular disfunction.[23] Diagnosis frequently involves muscle biopsy with abnormal muscle histology, mitochondrial electron microscopy, assay of various mitochondrial enzymatic activities, and analysis of mitochondrial DNA structure for point mutations, deletions, and rearrangements.[23–25] There is no known treatment which significantly alters symptoms or prognosis, although a low-carbohydrate diet is frequently advocated.

Defects in the beta oxidation of fatty acids can also be considered to be disorders of mitochondrial energy metabolism because their metabolism occurs in the mitochondria and feed reducing equivalents into the respiratory chain.[20, 23] These disorders, which are due to defects in the nuclear genome, are also related to the organic acidurias and will be described later.

AMINO ACID DISORDERS

These are defined as those inherited metabolic disorders with an abnormal concentration of one or more amino acids in physiologic fluids caused by either a deficiency of an enzyme or a defect in renal transport. A deficiency of an enzyme generally results in increases of an amino acid in plasma, urine, and/or cerebrospinal fluid.

Analysis of amino acids in plasma is more diagnostic than analysis of urine because the reference range of amino acid concentrations in plasma is relatively narrow and increases or decreases are readily quantified. Reference ranges of amino acid concentrations in urine are much wider, and since generalized amino acidurias are frequent in sick children, it is difficult to reliably detect specific increases of amino acids. A defect in renal transport results in excretion of increased amounts of amino acids in urine, while plasma amino acid concentrations are generally normal. For these disorders, analysis of urine is more informative than plasma. Analysis of amino acids in physiological fluids is most commonly done by cation exchange chromatography with post-column ninhydrin colorimetric detection.[26] Reference ranges for amino acids are age-dependent and have been extensively tabulated elsewhere.[27] New techniques for screening for the more common amino acid disorders are liquid secondary ion (also called fast atom bombardment or FAB) tandem mass spectrometry (MS-MS)[28] and electrospray ionization (ESI) MS-MS, which are well suited for newborn screening.[29]

Table 17–4 summarizes the abnormal concentrations of amino acids in plasma and/or urine that are diagnostic for a large number of amino acid disorders. The differential diagnosis frequently depends on a pattern of amino acid increases and/or decreases rather than on the concentration of a single amino acid. In addition to abnormal concentrations of amino acids, many of the disorders have abnormal excretions of organic acids derived from the amino acids, providing a complementary method of diagnosis (see Table 17–5). Six of the more important amino acid disorders in Table 17–4 are discussed in more detail below.

PKU and Hyperphenylalaninemia

The best known disorder of amino acid metabolism is classical PKU (phenylketonuria), with an incidence of about 1:10,000 in Caucasian newborns; it is very rare in black infants. PKU is due to a deficiency of phenylalanine hydroxylase, a liver-specific enzyme which converts phenylalanine to tyrosine. Phenylalanine is increased in plasma (> 1,200 μmol/L). Untreated PKU results in severe mental retardation.

TABLE 17–4. Amino Acid Disorders: Pathological Levels of Amino Acids

Disorder	Amino Acid	Abnormal Levels* Plasma	Urine
DISORDERS OF AROMATIC AMINO ACID METABOLISM			
Hyperphenylalaninemia			
Phenylketonuria (PKU): Phenylalanine Hydroxylase Deficiency	Phenylalanine	inc	inc
Biopterin Disorders	Phenylalanine	inc	inc
Tyrosinemia			
Transient Neonatal	Tyrosine	inc	inc
Hepatorenal (Type I)	Tyrosine	inc	inc
	Methionine	inc	
	Other amino acids		inc
Oculocutaneous (Type II)	Tyrosine	inc	inc
Nonspecific Liver Damage	Tyrosine	inc	inc
	Methionine	inc	inc
Hawkinsinuria	Tyrosine	inc	
	Hawkinsin		inc
DISORDERS OF NEUTRAL AMINO ACID METABOLISM			
Maple Syrup Urine Disease			
Classic	Valine	inc	inc
	Alloisoleucine	present	present
	Isoleucine	inc	inc
	Leucine	inc	inc
	Alanine	dec during severe episodes	
Intermittent, Variable, Intermediate, Thiamine-responsive	Above branch-chain amino acids increased during episodes, but may be normal to slightly increased between episodes.		
Dihydrolipoyl Dehydrogenase (E3) Deficiency	Branched-chain amino acids may be norm or slightly elevated.		
3-Hydroxyisobutyryl-CoA Deacylase Deficiency	S-(2-carboxypropyl-cysteine		inc
	S-(2-carboxypropyl)-cysteamine		inc
Non-ketotic Hyperglycinemia	Glycine	inc (also inc in CSF)	inc
Sarcosinemia	Sarcosine	inc	inc
Hartnup Disorder	Neutral amino aids	norm to dec	inc
DISORDERS OF BASIC AMINO ACID METABOLISM			
Hyperlysinemia	Lysine	inc	inc
	Pipecolic acid	inc	
Saccharopinuria	Lysine	inc	inc
	Saccharopine	inc	inc
Lysinuric Protein Intolerance	Lysine	norm to dec	inc
	Arginine	norm to dec	inc
	Ornithine	norm to dec	
	A number of amino acids	inc	

*inc = increased, dec = decreased, norm = normal

Continued

TABLE 17–4 Continued

Disorder	Amino Acid	Abnormal Levels* Plasma	Urine
Alpha-aminoadipic Aciduria	Alpha-aminoadipic acid	inc	inc
Hyperornithinemia-gyrate Atrophy	Ornithine	inc	inc
Hyperornithinemia-Hyperammonemia-Homocitrullinuria (HHH) Syndrome	Ornithine	inc	norm
	Homociturulline	norm	inc
Histidinemia	Histidine	inc	inc
DISORDERS OF UREA CYCLE			
Common finding: Glutamine and alanine increased when hyperammonemic.			
N-Acetylglutamate Synthetase	Amino acids	norm	norm
	Orotic acid	norm	norm
Carbamoyl Phosphate Synthase	Amino acids	norm	norm
	Orotic acid	norm	norm
Ornithine Carbamoyltransferase Deficiency	Amino acids	norm	norm
	Orotic acid		inc
Citrullinemia	Citrulline	inc	inc
	Orotic acid	inc	inc
Argininosuccinate Lyase Deficiency	Argininosuccinic acid	inc	inc
	Orotic acid		inc
Argininemia	Arginine	inc	inc
	Orotic acid		inc
	Lysine, ornithine, cystine		inc
DISORDERS OF IMINO ACID METABOLISM			
Hyperprolinemia			
Type I	Proline	inc	inc
	Hydroxyproline	norm	inc
	Glycine	norm	inc
Type II	Proline	inc	inc
	Hydroxyproline	norm	inc
	Glycine	norm	inc
	Δ'-pyrroline-5-carboxylic acid	inc	Inc
	Δ'-pyrroline-3-hydroxy-5 carboxylic acid		inc
Hyperhydroxyprolinemia	Hydroxyproline	inc	inc
Prolidase Deficiency	Iminodipeptides of proline and hydroxyproline		inc
Neonatal Iminoglycinuria	Proline, hydroxyproline, and glycine	norm	inc to age 6 mos
Familial Renal Iminoglycinuria	Proline		inc
	Hydroxyproline		inc
	Glycine		inc

* inc = increased, dec = decreased, norm = normal

Continued

TABLE 17–4 Continued

Disorder	Amino Acid	Abnormal Levels* Plasma	Urine
DISORDERS OF SULFUR AMINO ACID METABOLISM			
Homocystinuria			
Cystathionine Beta-Synthase Deficiency	Homocystine	inc	inc
	Cysteine-homocysteine mixed disulfide	inc	inc
	Methionine	inc	inc
	Cystine	norm to dec	
	Cystathionine	norm to dec	
Cobalamin Disorders: cblC, dblD, cblE & cblG and B12 deficiency	Homocystine	inc	inc
	Cysteine-homocysteine mixed disulfide	inc	inc
	Methionine	norm to dec	
	Cystathionine		norm to dec
5,10-Methylenetetrahydrofolate Reductase Deficiency	Homocystine	inc	inc
	Methionine	norm to dec	
	Cystathionine		norm to inc
Cystathioninuria	Cystathionine	norm to inc	inc
Hypermethioninemia	Methionine	inc	
	Methionine sulfoxides	Inc	
3-Mercaptolactic-Cysteine Disulfiduria	3-Mercaptolactic-cysteine mixed disulfide		inc
Sulfite Oxidase Deficiency	S-Sulfocysteine		inc
	Cystine	norm to dec	
Cystinuria	Cystine	norm	inc
	Dibasic amino acids (lysine, ornithine, arginine)	norm	inc
Cystinosis	Cystine	norm (inc in lysosomes of tissues)	norm
DISORDERS OF BETA- AND GAMMA-AMINO ACID METABOLISM			
Hyper-Beta-Alaninemia	Beta-alanine	inc	inc
Beta-Aminoisobutyric Aciduria	Beta-aminoisobutyric acid	norm to slightly inc	inc
Gamma-aminobutyric Acid Amino-transferase Deficiency	gamma-aminobutyric	inc	
	Beta-alanine	inc	
	Gamma-aminobutyric, beta-alanine, and homocarnosine also inc in CSF.		
Carnosinase Deficiency	Carnosine	inc	inc
	Anserine		inc
Homocarnosinosis	Homocarnosine	norm (inc in CSF)	norm

*inc = increased, dec = decreased, norm = normal

TABLE 17–5. Organic Acidurias: Pathological Excretions of Organic Acids

Disorder	Compound	Typical Abnormal Excretions (mmol/mol Creatinine)
DISORDERS OF AROMATIC AMINO ACID METABOLISM		
Phenylketonuria	Phenylpyruvic	300–1000
	Phenyllactic	200–1000
	2-Hydroxyphenylacetic	50–2000
Tyrosinemia		
Transient Neonatal, Oculocutaneous, and Hepatorenal Forms	4-Hydroxyphenylpyruvic	140–2000
	4-Hydroxyphenyllactic	100-5000
	4-Hydroxyphenylacetic	140–500
	N-acetyltyrosine	30–200
Hepatorenal Only	Succinylacetone	20–700
Hawkinsinuria	4-Hydroxycyclohexylacetic	10–70
	5-Oxoproline	1300–9000
	4-Hydroxyphenylpyruvic	170–1600
	4-Hydroxyphenyllactic	1000–5000
Alcaptonuria	Homogentisic	1000–5000
DISORDERS OF BRANCHED-CHAIN AMINO ACID METABOLISM		
Maple Syrup Urine Disease	2-Oxoisocaproic	400–4400
	2-Oxo-3-methylvaleric	500–2500
	2-Oxoisovaleric	300–800
	2-Hydroxyisovaleric	850–3600
	2-Hydroxyisocaproic	3–80
	2-Hydroxy-3-methylvaleric	60–400
Dihydrolipoyl Dehydrogenase (E3) Deficiency	Lactic	1000–30,000
	2-Oxoglutaric	150–1100
	2-Oxoisocaproic	0–200
	2-Oxo-3-methylvaleric	0–15
	2-Oxoisovaleric	0–3
	2-Hydroxyisovaleric	0–400
	2-Hydroxyisocaproic	0–70
	2-Hydroxy-3-methylvaleric	0–70
Isovaleric Acidemia	Isovaleryglycine	2000–9000
	3-Hydroxyisovaleric	1000–2000
	4-Hydroxyisovaleric	20–300
3-Methylcrotonyl-CoA Carboxylase Deficiency	3-Hydroxyisovaleric	1700–59,000
	3-Methylcrotonylglycine	400–1000
Biotin-Responsive Multiple Carboxylase Deficiency		
Holocarboxylase Synthetase Deficiency	3-Hydroxyisovaleric acid	250–3600
	3-Methylcrotonylglycine	30–260
	Methylcitric	15–200
	3-Hydroxypropionic	45–1300
	Lactic	100–75,000
Biotinidase Deficiency	Same as above, but generally smaller elevations.	
3-Methylglutaconic Aciduria		
3-Methylglutaconyl-CoA Hydratase Deficiency	3-Methylglutaconic	500–1000
	3-Hydroxyisovaleric	150–250
	3-Methyglutaric	5–10
Normal Hydratase	3-Methylglutaconic	25–600
	3-Methylglutaric	10–85
3-Hydroxy-3-Methylglutaric Aciduria	3-Hydroxy-3-methylglutaric	200–11,000
	3-Methylglutaconic	140–10,000
	3-Methylglutaric	14–1000
	3-Hydroxyisovaleric	60–4000
	3-Methylcrotonyglycine	0-400

TABLE 17–5 Continued

Disorder	Compound	Typical Abnormal Excretions (mmol/mol Creatinine)
3-Oxothiolase Deficiency		
Mitochondrial Branched-Chain 3-Oxothiolase Deficiency	2-Methyl-3-hydroxybutyric	200–4400
	2-Methylacetoacetic	0–650
	Tiglylglycine	0–1000
Cytosolic 3-Oxothiolase Deficiency or Succinyl-CoA: 3-Oxoacid-CoA Transferase Deficiency	3-Hydroxybutyric	Large
	Acetoacetic	Large
Propionic Acidemia	Methylcitric	150–2800
	3-Hydroxypropionic	20–2000
	Propionylglycine	0–450
	3-Hydroxyvaleric	0–1200
Methylmalonic Acidemia: Mutase Deficiency and Cobalamin Disorders	Methylmalonic	150–15,500
	(Plus same metabolites as propionic acidemia)	
Malonyl-CoA Decarboxylase Deficiency	Malonic	50–4000
	Methylmalonic	0–80
3-Hydroxyisobutyric Aciduria	3-Hydroxyisobutyric	130–400
DISORDERS OF DIBASIC AMINO ACID METABOLISM		
2-Oxoadipic Aciduria	2-Oxoadipic	20–220
	2-Hydroxyadipic	50–220
Glutaric Aciduria Type I	Glutaric	500–12,000
	3-Hydroxyglutaric	60–3000
	Glutaconic	0–360
Hyperornithinemia-Hyperammonemia-Homocitrullinuria (HHH) Syndrome	Orotic	30–500
Lysinuric Protein Intolerance	Orotic	1–640
DISORDERS OF THE UREA CYCLE		
N-Acetylglutamate Synthetase, Carbomoyl Phosphate Synthase, and Argininosuccinate Lyase Deficiency	No abnormalities or organic acids	
Ornithine Carbamoyltransferase Deficiency and Citrullinemia	Orotic	10–1300
	Uracil	30–500
Argininemia	Orotic	500–1000
DISORDERS OF PYRIMIDINE METABOLISM		
Orotic Aciduria	Orotic	1400–5600
Dihydropyrimidine Dehydrogenase Deficiency	Uracil	100–1100
	Thymine	35–850
DISORDERS OF FATTY ACID OXIDATION		
Long-chain Hydroxyacyl-CoA Dehydrogenase Deficiency	3-Hydroxydecanedioic	Increased
	3-Hydroxydodecanedioic	Increased
	3-Hydroxytetradecanedioic	Increased
	3-Hydroxy-unsaturated dicarboxylic, saturated and unsaturated dicarboxylic	Increased
Very-long-chain Acyl-CoA Dehydrogenase Deficiency	Suberic	0–20
	Sebacic	0–20
	Dodecamedioic and tetadecanedioic may be elevated	
Medium-Chain Acyl-CoA Dehydrogenase Deficiency	Octanoic	2–20
	5-Hydroxyhexanoic	15–700
	7-Hydroxyoctanoic	4–300
	Adipic	5–5200
	Suberic	6–5000

TABLE 17–5 Continued

Disorder	Compound	Typical Abnormal Excretion (mmol/mol Creatinine)
	Octenedioic	0–250
	Sebacic	0–5000
	Decenedioic	0–750
	Hexanoylglycine	2–730
	Phenylproionylglycine	1–90
	Suberylglycine	6–2200
Short-Chain Acyl-CoA Dehyrogenase Deficiency	Ethylmalonic	180–1150
	Methylsuccinic	20–60
	(Dicarboxylic aids variably elevated.)	
Multiple Acyl-CoA Dehydrogenase Deficiency (Glutaric Aciduria Type II)	Glutaric	0–22,000
	Ethylmalonic	10–1400
	Adipic	0–1600
	Suberic	0–200
	2-Hydroxyglutaric	180–8250
	Isovalerylglycine	0–1000
	Isobutyrylglycine	0–200
	2-Methylbutyrylgycine	0–200
	(Short-chain fatty acides may be elevated.)	
Normals Fed Medium-Chain Triglycerides	Adipic	200–320
	Suberic	10–620
	Sebacic	0–750
	5-Hydroxyhexanoic	0–220
	7-Hydroxyoctanoic	25–150
MISCELLANEOUS DISORDERS		
4-Hydroxybutyric Aciduria	4-Hydroxybutyric	130–7600
	3, 4-Dihydroxybutyric	5–225
Fumarase Deficiency	Fumaric	3000–4000
2-Oxoglutaric Dehydrogenase Deficiency	2-Oxoglutaric	150–1250
Mevalonic Aciduria	Mevalonolactone, mevalonic acid	1000–56,000
5-Oxoprolinuria	5-Oxoproline	4000–30,000
Canavan's Disease	N-Acetylaspartic	1000–7000
D-Glyceric Aciduria	D-Glyceric	10,000–20 ,000
Hyperoxaluria Type I	Oxalic	90–350
	Glycolic	> 100
	Glyoxylic	> 10
Hyperoxaluria Type II	Oxalic	90–350
	L-Glyceric	150–450
Glyceroluria	Glycerol	90,000–190,000
Lactic Acidemia	Lactic	100–30,000
	Pyruvic	50–10,000
	2-Hydroxybutyric	10–1000
	4-Hydroxyphenyllactic	50–500
Intestinal Bacterial Overgrowth	Lactic (D)	45–6000
	3-Hydroxypropionic	100–6400
	4-Hydroxyphenylacetic	100–2000
Ketosis	3-Hydroxybutyric	100–50,000
	Acetoacetic	50–20,000
	3-Hydroxyisobutyric	50–3000
	3-Hydroxyisovaleric	50–1000
	3-Hydroxy-2-methylbutyric	10–200
	Adipic	15–450
	Suberic	0–100

Pathological values from authors' experience and review of the literature.

With newborn screening and prompt treatment with a phenylalanine-restricted diet continuing lifelong,mental development is grossly normal although specific defects in spatial perceptual relationships and mathematic ability are found. Phenylalanine in plasma is routinely measured to monitor treatment. High concentrations of phenylalanine in maternal PKU cause severe fetal damage and therefore dietary treatment should be continued during pregnancy.

Hyperphenylalaninemia with modest increases of phenylalanine without phenylketonuria occurs with less severe deficiency of phenylalanine hydroxylase and generally may not require rigid dietary treatment except during pregnancy. Approximately 1–2% of hyperphenylalaninemia is caused by defects in the synthesis or metabolism of tetrahydrobiopterin, a cofactor for phenylalanine hydroxylase. The diagnosis requires analysis of urinary pteridines.

Tyrosinemia

Tyrosine is transaminated to 4-hydroxyphenylpyruvic acid, which is then further oxidized and cleaved to fumaric acid and acetoacetic acid in liver. The most common form of tyrosinemia is transient neonatal tyrosinemia, especially among premature infants, and resolves with time. The two major inherited disorders of tyrosine metabolism are hepatorenal (type I) and oculocutaneous (type II). A rare form of tyrosinemia, type III, is due to a deficiency of 4-hydroxyphenylpyruvate dioxygenase and does not have hepatorenal or oculocutaneous manifestations but may have neurological abnormalities.

The more severe form, hepatorenal tyrosinemia, is due to a deficiency of fumarylacetoacetate hydrolase, which cleaves the tyrosine catabolite fumarylacetoacetate. There is a secondary deficiency of 4-hydroxyphenylpyruvic acid oxidase, resulting in increased tyrosine and its phenolic acid metabolites. Fumarylacetoacetate is converted to succinylacetone, which is uniquely found in hepatorenal tyrosinemia and useful for differential diagnosis.

Other secondary abnormalities include increased methionine in plasma, a generalized amino aciduria, increased δ-aminolevulinic acid in urine, and increased α-fetoprotein in plasma. The amino acid pattern of increased tyrosine and methionine is not specific for hepatorenal tyrosinemia, but may also occur with severe liver damage due to a variety of causes, including galactosemia and hereditary fructose intolerance. The patients frequently present in infancy with chronic hepatic failure, and development of hepatomas is common. The preferred treatment is liver transplantation. A new treatment is the use of the drug NTBC, which inhibits 4-hydroxyphenylpyruvate dioxygenase, preventing the accumulation of succinylacetone and reducing its toxic effects on liver and kidney and on porphyrin synthesis.[30]

Oculocutaneous tyrosinemia presents with keratoses of the palms and digits and corneal ulcers, with highly increased tyrosine in the plasma. Some patients have mild mental retardation. This disorder is due to a deficiency of the soluble liver tyrosine aminotransferase, which prevents the normal formation of 4-hydroxyphenylpyruvic acid and its further catabolism in liver. Tyrosine is transaminated in peripheral tissues by aspartate aminotransferase, which results in excretion of the phenolic acid metabolites. Methionine is not increased in this form of tyrosinemia. Treatment with a diet low in phenylalanine and tyrosine can greatly reduce plasma tyrosine concentrations and reverse the oculocutaneous symptoms.

Maple Syrup Urine Disease (MSUD)

MSUD is caused by a deficiency of branched-chain α-ketoacid dehydrogenase, which decarboxylates the branched-chain α-ketoacids derived from transamination of valine, leucine, and isoleucine to acyl-CoA products. In addition to increases of the branched-chain keto and hydroxy acids, the branched-chain amino acids are also increased due to the reversibility of the transaminase reaction. The increased keto acid derived from isoleucine undergoes spontaneous keto-enol tautomerism to form a diastereoisomer which is also transaminated, forming alloisoleucine, which is elevated in MSUD. There is a range of severity in the deficiency of the complex, with classical MSUD having complete deficiency and severe life-threatening neonatal ketoacidosis, vomiting, lethargy, and hypotonia. Without treatment, this may progress to coma and death and, if not fatal, results in mental retardation. Treatment requires a special diet severely restricting the intake of the branched-chain amino acids and monitoring of plasma branched-chain amino acid concentrations. Partial enzyme deficiencies result in a range of milder symptoms presenting in infancy or childhood with ketoacidotic episodes and lesser, or even intermittent, increases of the branched-chain amino acids in plasma. These may be treated with mild protein restriction or, in the mildest forms, may require protein restriction only during acute episodes. Thiamine pyrophosphate is a cofactor for the dehydrogenase complex, and some patients are responsive to large doses of thiamine.

Nonketotic Hyperglycinemia

Glycine is normally metabolized to ammonia, carbon dioxide, and hydroxymethyl tetrahydrolfolate by the glycine cleavage system present in brain and liver. Deficiency of this system results in nonketotic hyperglycinemia with increased glycine in plasma, urine, and cerebrospinal fluid. The diagnosis is best made by determining the ratio of glycine in cerebrospinal fluid to that in plasma (normal = 0.03), which is increased tenfold to about 0.3 in this disorder. The diagnosis may be complicated by the existence of transient neonatal hyperglycinemia with increased cerebrospinal fluid to plasma glycine ratios which normalize with time. Nonketotic hyperglycinemia generally presents in the neonatal period with seizures and hypotonia and usually progresses to coma and death. Survivors have little psychomotor development, often develop spastic quadriparesis and die during the first year of life. No effective treatment has been found.

Homocystinuria

Deficiency of cystathionine synthase, which is the most common cause of homocystinuria, results in increased homocystine and cysteine-homocysteine mixed disulfide in plasma and urine with *increased* methionine and decreased cystine in plasma.

Common clinical symptoms are subluxation of the lenses, mental retardation, psychiatric disorders, thromboembolism, atherosclerosis, and osteoporosis. More than a third of the patients are responsive to large doses of pyridoxine, which decreases the homocysteine concentrations.

The relatively rare defects in homocysteine remethylation, such as the disorders of cobalamin metabolism listed in Table 17–4, result in increased amounts of homocystine and cysteine-homocysteine mixed disulfide in plasma and urine, with normal or decreased methionine in plasma.

Cystinuria

Cystinuria is a relatively common disorder of amino acid transport, affecting about 1:7,000. Cystine and the dibasic amino acids are transported in the renal tubule by a common transport mechanism. A deficiency results in normal concentrations of amino acids in plasma, but greatly increased cystine, lysine, ornithine, and arginine in urine (see Figure 17–2). Because of limited solubility, cystine forms renal stones. Treatment is aimed at minimizing stone formation through diluting the urine with a large water intake, alkalinizing the urine to increase cystine solubility, or treatment with penicillamine, which decreases urinary cystine by forming cysteine-penicillamine mixed disulfide, which is more soluble than cystine.

UREA CYCLE DISORDERS

The urea cycle detoxifies ammonia by forming urea and is required for the synthesis of arginine.[31] Deficiencies of any of the six enzymes of the cycle result in hyperammonemia, a low blood urea nitrogen, a secondary increase of glutamine and alanine and decreased arginine in plasma (except for argininemia). The clinical presentation may be acute illness in the first few days of life, with lethargy, vomiting, and coma. The onset may occur later with similar symptoms. Neurological damage often results from severe hyperammonemia. The differential diagnosis of the urea cycle disorders includes analysis of organic acids to rule out organic acidurias which can also cause hyperammonemia. The abnormalities of amino acids found in urea cycle disorders are listed in Table 17–4.

N-Acetylglutamate Synthetase and Carbamoyl Phosphate Synthetase

A deficiency of either of these first two enzymes of the urea cycle does not cause a specific abnormality of amino acid concentrations nor of orotic acid. Their tentative diagnosis depends on excluding other causes of hyperammonemia, and their definitive diagnosis requires assay for enzyme deficiency in liver biopsies.

Ornithine Carbamoyl Transferase Deficiency

This disorder also lacks specific abnormalities of amino acid concentrations, but may be associated with decreased citrulline concentration. Increased orotic acid and

FIGURE 17–2. Amino Acid Chromatogram of Urine from a Patient with Cystinuria (performed according to Slocum & Cummings[26])

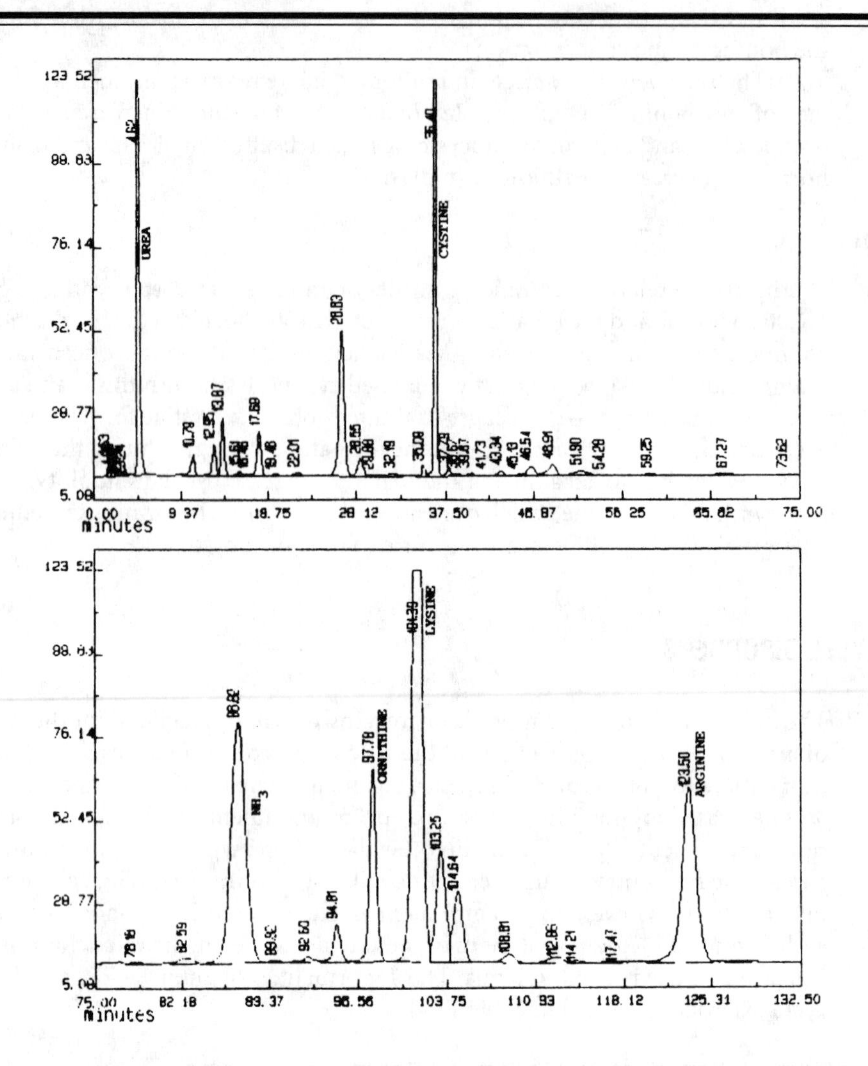

uracil excretion due to increased pyrimidine synthesis from accumulated carbamoyl phosphate is present. This is an X-linked disorder. Female heterozygotes for this deficiency may also present with symptoms of hyperammonemia. An interesting method of carrier detection is the finding of increased orotic acid and orotidine in urine after a single dose of allopurinol.

Citrullinemia

This disorder is characterized by large increases of citrulline in plasma and urine due to the deficiency of argininosuccinic acid synthase as well as increased orotic acid in urine.

Argininosuccinic Aciduria

A deficiency of argininosuccinase results in highly increased argininosuccinic acid in plasma and urine and, occasionally, increased orotic acid in urine. Argininosuccinic acid spontaneously forms two anhydrides, resulting in three peaks in the amino acid analysis which coelute with normal amino acids, making their quantification difficult. Citrulline is also moderately increased in this disorder.

Argininemia

A deficiency of arginase causes a large increase of arginine in plasma and urine as well as increased orotic acid in urine. The increased arginine in urine is accompanied by increased lysine, ornithine, and cystine due to competition in reabsorption of these amino acids.

The treatment of the urea cycle disorders involves restriction of dietary protein to reduce the formation of ammonia and supplementation with citrulline or arginine for carbamoyl phosphate synthetase and ornithine carbamoyl transferase deficiency, and arginine for citrullinemia and argininosuccinase deficiency to prevent arginine deficiency. Dialysis is of benefit during episodes of acute decompensation. Additional treatment with benzoate removes nitrogen as hippuric acid or treatment with phenylacetic acid removes nitrogen as phenylacetylglutamine.

ORGANIC ACID DISORDERS

Organic acids are defined as any acids that are not amino acids and thus encompass a very wide range of chemical functional groups, many different areas of metabolism, and hundreds of compounds found in physiological fluids.

Many of the amino acid disorders have abnormalities in organic acids as well as amino acids, and therefore analysis of organic acids gives diagnostic information that is complementary to the analysis of amino acids. For the general analysis of organic acids for diagnostic purposes, urine is the preferred physiological fluid, but there are areas of metabolism such as fatty acid oxidation that might be better diagnosed by analysis of organic acids in plasma. Analyses of organic acids generally have been done by organic solvent extraction of acidified urine, formation of trimethysilyl derivatives, and quantitative or semi-quantitative gas chromatographic or gas chromatography/mass spectrometric analysis.[32, 33] Because of the enormous complexity of organic acids in urine, it is very difficult to unambiguously identify acids by gas chromatographic retention times alone, and GCMS is essential. With the availability of relatively inexpensive bench-top GCMS, the preferred method is quantitative analysis using specific mass spectral fragment masses.[34] Quantification is more important because many compounds originally thought to be "abnormal" metabolites are now known to be metabolites normally present in small amounts. Diagnosis therefore frequently depends upon determining an increase of normal organic acids rather than the presence or absence of an organic acid.

In the diagnosis of the organic acidurias, it is generally a pattern of organic acids that is diagnostic rather than in increase of a single organic acid. This is especially true of many disorders of branched-chain amino acid metabolism where deficiencies of sequential enzymes in a pathway have many abnormal metabolite increases in common. Table 17–5 lists the typical diagnostic increased acids for a wide variety of organic acidurias. The degree of increase of many acids is very dependent on the clinical status of the patient, and when in good clinical control, the diagnostic acids may be minimally increased or even normal in some disorders. Reference ranges for the urinary organic acids of normal subjects are not well established and to some extent are dependent on the methods used, so each laboratory should establish its own reference ranges. Approximate reference ranges for children have been published,[34] as have age-related reference values in a healthy Turkish pediatric population.[35]

A useful new complementary diagnostic technique for some organic acidurias and especially disorders of fatty acid oxidation is the use of liquid secondary ion tandem mass spectrometry analysis of plasma acylcarnitines[36] and more recently electrospray (ESI) tandem mass spectrometric analysis of acylcarnitines in plasma or blood spots dried on filter paper.[29] The fatty acids and many organic acids are metabolized as Coenzyme A esters which are in equilibrium with acylcarnitines within cells. Disturbances of organic acid metabolism therefore result in elevations of diagnostic acylcarnitines.

Once a patient has been diagnosed with a specific organic aciduria, the role of the laboratory is to provide accurate determinations of specific organic acids in order to monitor therapy with diet or vitamins. In addition to the summary of diagnostic concentrations of urinary organic acids in Table 17–5, five of the more important organic acidurias are discussed in greater detail below.

Isovaleric Acidemia

This is a disorder of the catabolism of leucine caused by a deficiency of isovaleryl-CoA dehydrogenase, which normally metabolizes isovaleryl-CoA to 3-methylcrotonyl-CoA. The accumulated isovaleryl-CoA is hydrolyzed to some extent to free isovaleric acid, which can be increased in plasma and urine; its odor of "sweaty feet" may be quite noticeable during acute episodes. The most diagnostic finding is an increase in the metabolite isovalerylglycine, which is continuously excreted in very large amounts. When patients are clinically ill, additional diagnostic metabolites are 3-hydroxyisovaleric and 4-hydroxyisovaleric acids. Tandem mass spectrometry of acylcarnitines in plasma or dried blood spots also shows a characteristic elevation of a five-carbon acylcarnitine (isovalerylcarnitine).

About half of the patients present in the neonatal period with acute episodes of vomiting, ketoacidosis, and lethargy proceeding to coma and often death. Other patients present with intermittent episodes during the first year of life, often precipitated by infection or increased protein intake. Treatment during episodes includes procedures appropriate for many organic acidurias, namely glucose infusion to correct dehydration and to provide calories to reduce catabolism. Treatment during remission is generally with moderate restriction of normal dietary protein. Specific therapies that are beneficial are administration of carnitine, which reduces the toxic concentrations of isovaleryl-CoA by formation of isovalerylcarnitine and excretion in the urine, and/or treatment with glycine, which increases the detoxification of isovaleryl-CoA to isovalerylglycine. The management and clinical status of the patients can be monitored by the concentration of isovaleric acid in plasma.

Propionic Acidemia and Methylmalonic Acidemia

Propionic acid is derived from a variety of precursors, including isoleucine, valine, methionine, and threonine, odd-chain fatty acids and cholesterol, and from intestinal flora. It is metabolized by propionyl-CoA carboxylase to methylmalonyl-CoA, which in turn is metabolized to succinyl-CoA by methylmalonyl-CoA mutase. A deficiency of propionyl-CoA carboxylase causes propionic acidemia, while a deficiency of methylmalonyl-CoA mutase or a defect in the synthesis of its cobalamin cofactor, adenosylcobalamin, causes methylmalonic acidemia. The same increased metabolites occur in both propionic acidemia and methylmalonic acidemia, except that methylmalonic acid is highly increased only in the latter. The most diagnostic organic acid increased in propionic acidemia is methylcitrate, which is formed by citrate synthase. Another less specific metabolite is 3-hydroxypropionate. Propionylglycine is also increased during episodes. Tandem mass spectrometry of acylcarnitines in plasma or dried blood spots shows elevated propionylcarnitine in both propionic and methylmalonic acidemia.

The steps in isoleucine catabolism between tiglyl-CoA and propionyl-CoA are reversible, and during acute episodes a large number of intermediates and their secondary metabolites may be increased. These include tiglylglycine, 2-methyl-3-hydroxybutyric, and 3-hydroxyvaleric acids. In methylmalonic acidemia due to defects of cobalamin metabolism, the increase of methylmalonate is less than in mutase deficiency. The disorders cblA and cblB are defects in the synthesis of adenosylcobalamin. Disorders that affect the synthesis of both adenosylcobalamin and methylcobalamin, i. e., cblC, cblD, and cblF, result in combined methylmalonic acidemia and homocystinuria (See Table 17–4).

Additional biochemical abnormalities of propionic acidemia and methylmalonic acidemia include severe hyperammonemia and ketosis during episodes and a secondary increase of glycine. Most patients present with a severe acidotic episode in the neonatal period and/or with infections or excessive protein intake. Treatment consists of restriction of dietary precursors of propionic acid, namely the essential aminoacids valine and isoleucine, and administration of carnitine, which prevents secondary carnitine deficiency due to loss of carnitine as propionylcarnitine in urine. Some patients with methylmalonic acidemia due to cblA or cblB respond to high doses of vitamin B_{12} with decreased concentrations of methylmalonic acid in plasma and urine. Treatment of propionic acidemia is monitored by determining concentrations of propionic acid in plasma and urine, while that of methylmalonic acidemia is monitored by measuring methylmalonic acid in plasma.

Multiple Carboxylase Deficiency

This is due to either of two disorders of the metabolism of the vitamin biotin. Biotin is activated to biotinyl-AMP by holocarboxylase synthetase, which then attaches the biotin covalently to the epsilon-amino group of a lysine in all four biotin-dependent carboxylases: acetyl-CoA carboxylase, propionyl-CoA carboxylase, 3-methylcrotonyl-CoA carboxylase, and pyruvate carboxylase. When the carboxylases are degraded in normal protein turnover or when protein-bound biotin in the diet is digested, the product biocytin (biotinyl-lysine) is cleaved by biotinidase to free biotin, which can then be utilized for synthesis of new biotin-containing carboxylases.

A deficiency of holocarboxylase synthetase or biotinidase causes a deficiency of all four carboxylases. The most diagnostic metabolites are 3-hydroxyisovaleric acid and 3-methylcrotonylglycine, which result from the deficiency of 3-methylcrotonyl-CoA carboxylase. Acylcarnitine analysis of plasma or dried blood spots by MS-MS shows elevated 3-hydroxyisovalerylcarnitine. A modest increase of methylcitric and 3-hydroxypropionic acid results from the dysfunction of propionyl-CoA carboxylase, but these are generally much lower than in patients with propionic acidemia. Increased lactic acid results from the deficiency of pyruvate carboxylase. Patients with holocarboxylase synthetase deficiency generally present in the neonatal period with severe metabolic acidosis and ketosis. Those who present later and those with biotinidase deficiency have symptoms of biotin deficiency, such as an erythematous skin rash and alopecia. Biotinidase-deficient patients often have conjunctivitis and periorificial rashes, ataxia, developmental regression, nerve deafness, and optic nerve atrophy. All of the patients with biotinidase deficiency and most of those with holocarboxylase synthetase deficiency show normalization of organic acid metabolites and clinical symptoms with large doses of biotin (10 or more mg/day), making this a very effective treatment. Biotinidase deficiency can be detected by newborn screening for deficient activity in dried blood spots.

Glutaric Aciduria Type I

Glutaryl-CoA, derived from the catabolism of lysine, hydroxylysine, and tryptophan, is normally metabolized by glutaryl-CoA dehydrogenase to crotonyl-CoA. Patients with a deficiency of this enzyme have glutaric aciduria type I. Glutaric acid is usually highly increased in urine of these patients and is accompanied by a lesser increase of 3-hydroxyglutaric acid which is specific to this disorder (see Figure 17–3). However, some patients have little or no increase of glutaric acid. Glutaric aciduria type II is a defect in the transfer of electrons from a number of dehydrogenases, including glutaryl-CoA dehydrogenase and the fatty acid oxidation acyl-CoA dehydrogenases through electron transfer flavoprotein into the mitochondrial electron transport chain. That disorder may have an increase in glutaric acid, but it is not accompanied by 3-hydroxyglutaric acid but rather by 2-hydroxyglutaric acid, a number of dicarboxylic acids and acylglycines.

Glutaric aciduria type I causes severe neurological problems during the first year of life, with dystonia and dyskinesia due to neuronal degeneration of the caudate and putamen. Dietary restriction of lysine and tryptophan may be of some benefit prior to the onset of irreversible neurological symptoms.

FIGURE 17–3. ***Lower view:*** **Gas chromatography-mass spectrometry total ion chromatogram of urine from a patient with glutaric aciduria type 1 (performed according to Sweetman[34]).** ***Upper left view:*** **Mass spectrum of the diTMS derivative of glutaric acid.** ***Upper right view:*** **Mass spectrum of the triTMS derivative of 3-hydroxy-glutaric acid.**

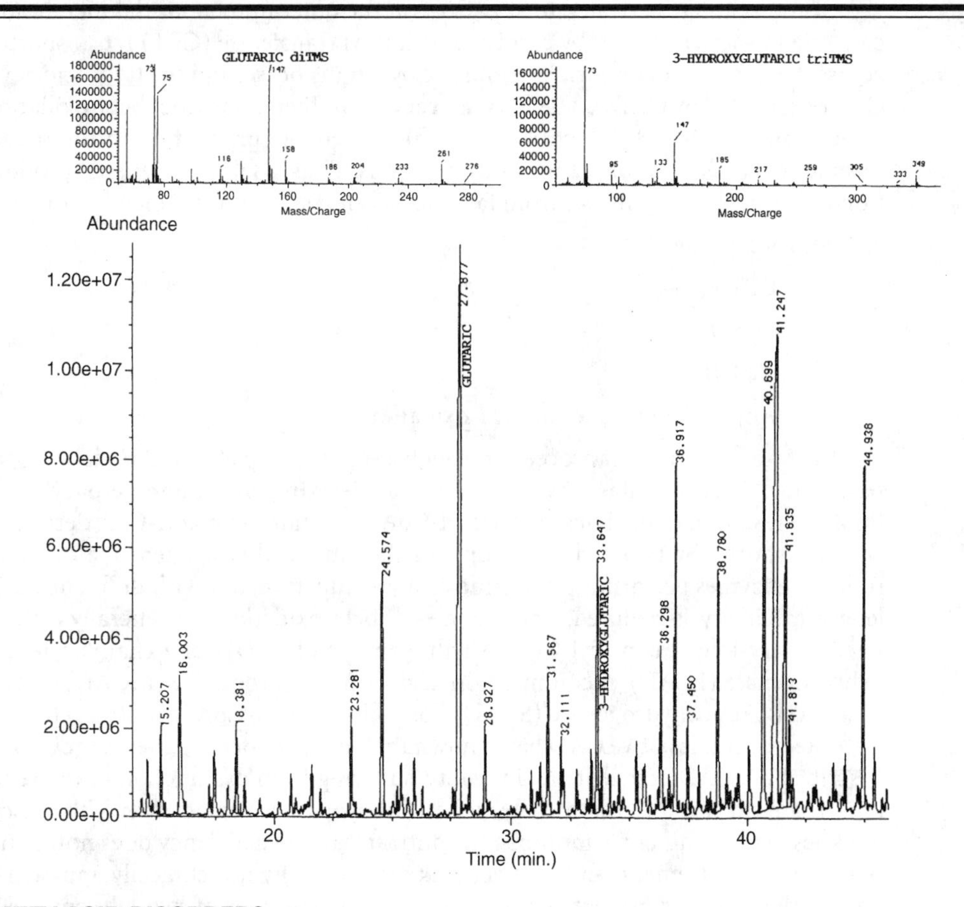

FATTY ACID DISORDERS

Long-chain fatty acids are a major substrate for energy production in skeletal and cardiac tissues under most physiologic conditions. During fasting, fatty acids and their metabolic products, ketone bodies, become a major fuel for most tissues. Even the normally glucose-dependent brain can adapt to ketone utilization after prolonged fasting induces the necessary enzyme.

Thus, logically one can predict that dysfunction of enzymes necessary for metabolism of fatty acids would manifest as two major symptom groups:

1. hypotonia, weakness, myopathy, cardiac failure, or cardiomyopathy
2. hypoglycemia, hepatic failure, or encephalopathy associated with fasting and indeed, at least a dozen inherited deficiencies have been characterized to date.[37, 38]

The major metabolic flux of long-chain fatty acids is through the beta-oxidation system of the mitochondria present in all cells except the mature erythrocyte. Access of the fatty acid to the beta-oxidation enzymes requires a carnitine-dependent transport system to cross the mitochondrial membrane.

Fatty acids are activated to acyl-CoAs at the outer mitochondrial membrane, converted to acylcarnitines by carnitine palmitoyl transferase (CPT) I, transported across the inner mitochondrial membrane by a translocase, and the fatty acid acyl-CoA regenerated by CPT II. The fatty acid acyl-CoA then undergoes beta-oxidation to generate acetyl-CoA, which is a substrate for energy production in the tricarboxylic acid cycle and for ketone body synthesis. Thus, a failure of energy production or ketone body synthesis from fatty acids can result from a deficiency of:

1. Carnitine
2. CPT I
3. Translocase
4. CPT II
5. Any of the enzymes of beta-oxidation.

Beta-oxidation itself proceeds through a series of steps (acyl-CoA dehydrogenase, enoyl-CoA hydratase, hydroxyacyl-CoA dehydrogenase, and ketoacyl-CoA thiolase) resulting in the release of acetyl-CoA and a fatty acid acyl-CoA derivative which is shorter by two carbon groups. As the fatty acid is shortened, a different series of enzymes performing the same catalytic function, but with different chain length specificity, is required. The enzymes of beta-oxidation are generally categorized as very-long-chain acyl-CoA dehydrogenase (VLCAD), long-chain acyl-CoA dehydrogenase (LCAD), medium-chain acyl-CoA dehydrogenase (MCAD), short-chain acyl-CoA dehydrogenase (SCAD), long-chain enoyl-CoA hydratase, etc.

Recent studies of VLCAD have shown that most, if not all, patients previously described as LCAD deficient are, in reality, suffering from dysfunction of the very-long-chain enzyme.[39] Cardiomegaly and cardiomyopathy in association with muscle weakness are prominent symptoms. In contrast, MCAD deficiency does not manifest cardiac involvement, and muscle weakness is usually not clinically apparent.[40] Rather, this disorder presents with recurrent acute episodes of hypoglycemia, encephalopathy, and apnea. These episode are brought on by fasting associated with intercurrent infections such as mild upper respiratory tract infections. Death or permanent neurologic damage occurs in a significant percentage of cases. MCAD deficiency is unique in that a single point mutation is found in 90% of the mutant alleles.[41] Affected children are predominately Caucasian, among whom the disease incidence is 1 in 20,000–30,000. The abrupt onset of symptoms and the high frequency of death with the first episode have prompted the suggestion that this disease is a significant cause of sudden infant death syndrome (SIDS). Molecular studies of SIDS cases have not substantiated this proposal.[42]

The disorders of energy production from fatty acids result in the intracellular accumulation of acyl-CoA derivatives. This is manifested by increased levels of urinary mono- and/or dicarboxylic acids, glycine conjugates, and acylated carnitines.[37]

Analysis of the acylcarnitines in plasma or dried blood spots by MS is an important technique for the diagnosis of fatty acid oxidation disorders.[29, 36, 43, 44]

There are no known genetic defects of carnitine biosynthesis, but low concentrations of carnitine can result from dietary deficiency, malabsorption, liver disease, or increased renal loss.[45, 46] Functional carnitine deficiency can also result when concentrations of total carnitine are normal but free carnitine is low, due to its sequestration in the acylated form. This secondary carnitine deficiency occurs when acyl-CoA accumulates as in the organic acidemias or enzymatic defects in the fatty acid oxidation.

Defects in carnitine transport across the plasma membrane are termed primary carnitine deficiency and classified into myopathic and systemic clinical presentations.[45, 46] The myopathic form manifests as progressive skeletal muscle weakness with a lipid storage. Serum carnitine is normal but muscle carnitine is low, suggesting an abnormality in a muscle transporter. Response to carnitine replacement is variable. Systemic carnitine deficiency is characterized by low serum and tissue carnitine concentrations and is very responsive to supplemental carnitine. Symptoms of cardiomyopathy, muscle weakness, hypotonia, hypoglycemia, hypoketonemia, and coma implicate a transporter deficiency in many tissues including heart, skeletal muscle, and liver.

Patients with a defective carnitine/acylcarnitine translocase have been identified.[47] Symptoms and signs included hypoglycemia, decreased ketogenesis, low serum free carnitine with increased long-chain acylcarnitine, hyperammonemia, muscle weakness, and mild hypertrophic cardiomyopathy.

SUMMARY

Although inborn errors of metabolism are individually rare, the large number of disorders and the referral patterns to tertiary care institutions result in these genetic diseases commonly being a part of differential diagnoses. As the signs and symptoms of metabolic disease are distressingly vague and routine clinical chemistry tests rarely indicative of a specific diagnosis, the clinician is frequently dependent on the guidance of specialists in laboratory medicine. It is their expertise in the newer technologies such as gas chromatography /mass spectrometry, high-performance liquid chromatography, enzymatic analysis, and recombinant DNA which is essential to the selection of appropriate tests and the interpretation of the results. This review does not discuss the technologies themselves, but rather focuses on the major groups of enzymatic deficiencies, their clinical manifestations, diagnostic tests, and interpretation of abnormalities.

The disorders of lysosomal and peroxisomal catabolic function primarily manifest with slowly progressive symptoms which may affect multiple organ systems or single tissues. Diagnosis is usually dependent on a specific enzymatic analysis of the suspected deficiency, although electron microscopic examination of tissues or analysis of accumulated metabolites may be useful. Treatment is supportive and specific interventional therapy rarely available. Conversely, enzymatic deficiencies of intermediary metabolism frequently manifest acutely due to their important role in physiologic homeostasis and the vastly changing flux of substrate through these pathways under catabolic conditions. These disorders may be classified according to substrate type, i. e., carbohydrate, fatty acid, or amino acid, the latter including amino acidopathies, organic acidemias/acidurias, and the urea cycle defects. Treatment of these diseases focuses on decreasing substrate flux through the affected pathway via dietary restriction or avoidance of catabolic states. Specific therapy with a vitamin cofactor or drugs increasing excretion of toxic metabolites is available in some instances. Diagnosis primarily depends on analysis of accumulated metabolites due to the enzymatic deficiency, which may then be confirmed by direct measurement. Extensive tables listing these metabolites, their usual values, and the corresponding enzyme have been provided to aid in interpretation and diagnosis.

REFERENCES

1. Scriver CR, Beaudet AL, Sly WS, Valle D. The metabolic and molecular basis of inherited disease, 7th ed. New York: McGraw-Hill, 1995.
2. Neufeld EF. Lysosomal storage disease. Ann Rev Biochem 1991;60:257–80.
3. Watts RWE, Gibbs WA. Lysosomal storage diseases: biochemical and clinical aspects. London: Taylor and Francis, 1986.
4. Williams JC, Howell RR. Mucopolysaccharidoses. In: Conn RB, ed. Current diagnosis, 7th ed. Philadelphia: WB Saunders, 1985:758–61.
5. Natowicz MR, Short MP, Wang Y, et al. Clinical and biochemical manifestations of hyaluronidase deficiency. N Eng J Med 1996;335:1029–33.
6. Johnson WB. Sphingolipidoses. In: Conn RB, ed. Current diagnosis, 7th ed. Philadelphia: WB Saunders, 1985:770–77.
7. Durand P, O'Brien JS. Genetic disorders of glycoprotein metabolism. Berlin: Springer-Verlag, 1982.
8. Jaeken J, Vanderschueren-Lodewyckc M, Lasaer P. Familial psychomotor retardation with markedly fluctuating serum prolactin, FSH and GH levels, partial TBG deficiency, increased arylsulfatase A and increased CSF protein: a new syndrome? Pediatr Res 1980;14:179.
9. Hagberg BA, Blenow G, Kristiansson B, Stibler H. Carbohydrate-deficient glycoprotein syndromes: peculiar group of new disorders. Pediatr Neurol 1993:9:255–62.
10. Jaeken J, Stibler H, Hagberg B. The carbohydrate-deficient glycoprotein syndrome. Acta Pediatr Scand 1991:375:5S–71S.
11. Matthijs G, Schollen E, Pardon E, et al. Mutations in PMMM2, a phosphomannomutase gene on chromosome 16p13 in carbohydrate deficient glycoprotein type I syndrome (Jaeken syndrome). Nature Genetics 1997;16:88–92.
12. Ohkura T, Fukushima K, Kurisaki A, et al. A partial deficiency of dehydrodolichol reduction is a cause of carbohydrate-deficient glycoprotein syndrome type I. J Biol Chem 1997;272:6868–75.
13. Tan J, Jaeken J, Schachten H. Mutations in the MGAT2 gene controlling complex N-glycan synthesis cause carbohydrate-deficient glycoprotein syndrome type II, an autosomal recessive disease with defective brain development. Am J Human Genetics 1996;59:810–17.
14. Naidu S, Moser HW. Peroxisomal disorders. In: Schaefer GB, Bodensteiner JB, eds., Neurologic clinics: pediatric neurogenetics (Vol. 12). Philadelphia: WB Saunders Co, 1994:727–39.
15. Moser HW, Moser AB. Measurement of saturated very long-chain fatty acids in plasma. In: Hommes FA, ed. Techniques in diagnostic human biochemical genetics: a laboratory manual. New York: Wiley-Liss, 1991:177–91.

16. Lazarow PB, Moser HW. Disorders of peroxisome biogenesis. In: Scriver CR, Beaudet AL, Sly WS, Valle D, eds. The metabolic basis of inherited disease, 6th ed. McGraw-Hill, 1989:1479–1509.
17. Williams JC, Howell RR. Hereditary disorders of carbohydrate metabolism. In: Conn RB, ed. Current diagnosis, 7th ed. Philadelphia: WB Saunders, 1985:752-58.
18. Zeviani M, Bonilla E, De Vivo DC, Di Mauro S. Mitochondrial diseases. Neurol Clin 1989;7:123–56.
19. DiMauro S, Bonilla E, Lombes A, et al. Mitochondrial encephalopathies. Neurol Clin 1990;8:483–506.
20. De Vivo DC. The expanding clinical spectrum of mitochondrial diseases. Brain & Devel 1993;15:1–22.
21. Shaffner JM, Wallace DC. Oxidative phosphorylation diseases: disorders of two genomes. In: Harris H, Hirschhorn K, eds. Advances in human genetics. New York: Plenum Press 1990;19:267–330.
22. Aprille JR. Mitochondrial cytopathies and mitochondrial DNA mutations. Curr Opin Pediatr 1991;3:1045–54.
23. Breningstall GN. Approach to diagnosis of oxidative metabolism disorders. Pediatr Neurol 1992;9:81–90.
24. Rustin P, Chretien D, Bourgeron T, et al. Biochemical and molecular investigations in respiratory chain deficiencies. Clin Chim Acta 1994;228:35–51.
25. De Vries DD, Ruitenbeek W, De Wijs IJ, Trijbels JMF. Enzymological versus DNA investigations in mitochondrial (encephalo-)myopathies. J Inherit Metab Dis 1993;16:534–6.
26. Slocum RH, Cummings JG. Amino acid analysis of physiological samples. In: Hommes FA, ed. Techniques in diagnostic human biochemical genetics: a laboratory manual. New York: Wiley-Liss, 1991:87–126.
27. Bremer HJ, Duran M, Kamerling JP, et al. Disturbances of amino acid metabolism: clinical chemistry and diagnosis. Baltimore: Urban & Schwarzenberg, 1981.
28. Millington DS, Kodo N, Terada N, et al. The analysis of diagnostic markers of genetic disorders in human blood and urine using tandem mass spectrometry with liquid secondary ion mass spectrometry. Int J Mass Spectrom & Ion Proc 1991;111:211–28.
29. Rashed MS, Bucknall MP, Little D, et al. Screening blood spots for inborn errors of metabolism by electrospray tandem mass spectrometry with a microplate batch process and a computer algorithm for automated flagging of abnormal profiles. Clin Chem 1997;43:1129–41.
30. Lindstedt S, Holme E, Lock EA, et al. Treatment of hereditary tyrosinemia type I by inhibition of 4-hydroxyphenylpyruvate dioxygenase. Lancet 1992;340:813–17.
31. Brusilow SW, Horwich AL. Urea cycle enzymes. In: Scriver CR, Beaudet AL, Sly WS, Valle D, eds. The metabolic and molecular basis of inherited disease, 7th ed. New York: McGraw-Hill, 1995;1187–1232.
32. Goodman SI, Markey SP. Diagnosis of organic acidemias by gas chromatography-mass spectrometry. Laboratory and research methods in biology and medicine (Vol. 6). New York: Alan R. Liss, Inc., 1981.
33. Chalmers RA, Lawson AM. Organic acids in man. London: Chapman and Hall, 1982.
34. Sweetman L. Organic acid analysis. In: Hommes FA, ed. Techniques in diagnostic human biochemical genetics: a laboratory manual. New York: Wiley-Liss, 1991:143–76.
35. Guneral F, Bachmann C. Age-related reference values for urinary organic acids in a healthy Turkish pediatric population. Clin Chem 1994;40:862–8.
36. Millington DS, Chace DH. Carnitine and acylcarnitines in metabolic disease diagnosis and management. In: Desiderio DM, ed. Mass spectrometry: clinical and biomedical applications (Vol. 1). New York: Plenum Press, 1992:299–318.
37. Hale DE, Bennett MJ. Fatty acid oxidation disorders: a new class of metabolic disease. J Pediatr 1992;121:1–11.
38. Suadubray JM, Mitchell G, Bonnefont JP, et al. Approach to the patient with a fatty acid oxidation disorder. In: Coates PM, Tanaka K, eds. New developments in fatty acid oxidation. New York: Wiley-Liss, 1992:271–88.

39. Yamaguchi S, Indo Y, Coates PM, et al. Identification of very-long-chain acyl-CoA dehydrogenase deficiency in three patients previously diagnosed with long-chain acyl-CoA dehydrogenase deficiency. Pediatr Res 1992;34:111–13.
40. Iafolla AK, Thompson RJ, Roe CR. Medium-chain acyl-coenzyme A dehydrogenase deficiency: clinical course in 120 affected children. J Pediatr 1994;124:409–15.
41. Zhang Z, Kolvraa S, Zhou Y, et al. Three RFLPs defining a haplotype associated with the common mutation in human medium-chain acyl-CoA dehydrogenase (MCAD) deficiency occur in Alu repeats. Am J Hum Genet 1993;52:1111–21.
42. Arens R, Gozal D, Jain K, et al. Prevalence of medium-chain acyl coenzyme A dehydrogenase deficiency in the sudden infant death syndrome. J Pediatr 1993;122:715–8.
43. Schmidt-Sommerfeld E, Penn D, Duran M, et al. Detection of inborn errors of fatty acid oxidation from acylcarnitine analysis of plasma and blood spots with the radioisotopic exchange–high-performance liquid chromatographic method. J Pediatr 1993;122:708–14.
44. Chace DH, Hillman SL, Van Hove JLK, Naylor EW. Rapid diagnosis of MCAD deficiency: quantitative analysis of octanoylcarnitine and other acylcarnitines in newborn blood spots by tandem mass spectrometry. Clin Chem 1997;43:2106–13.
45. De Vivo DC, Tein I. Primary and secondary disorders of carnitine metabolism. Int Pediatr 1990;5:134–41.
46. Breningstall GN, Carnitine deficiency syndromes. Pediatr Neurol 1990;6:75–81.
47. Stanley CA, Boxer J, Deleeuw S. Mitochondrial inner membrane acylcarnitine translocase deficiency in an infant with an inborn error of fatty acid oxidation. Pediatr Res 1991;29:1178.
48. Wessler E. Analytic and preparative separation of acidic glycosaminoglycans by electrophoresis in barium acetate. Anal Biochem 1968;26:439–44.
49. Humbel R, Collart M. Oligosaccharides in urine of patients with glycoprotein storage diseases. 1. Rapid detection by thin-layer chromatography. Clin Chim Acta 1975;60:143–45.

CHAPTER 18

Disorders of Lipid and Lipoprotein Metabolism in Children and Adolescents

Nader Rifai, Ph.D.
Peter O. Kwiterovich, Jr., M.D.

INTRODUCTION

Coronary heart disease (CHD), the leading cause of death in the western world, is responsible for more than 550,000 deaths in the United States each year. It has been estimated that the direct and indirect costs of CHD surpass $50 billion a year. This disease is multifactorial in nature. Epidemiologic findings such as those from the Framingham study have demonstrated that high blood pressure, cigarette smoking, and increased plasma total cholesterol and low density lipoprotein cholesterol (LDL-C) concentrations are determinant risk factors of CHD.[1] Other factors that associate with this disease include obesity, male gender, sedentary life style, stress, family history of early myocardial infarction, and decreased plasma high density lipoprotein cholesterol (HDL-C) concentration (< 0.91 mmol/L [35 mg/dL]).

Autopsies performed on young American soldiers killed in action in Korea[2] and Vietnam[3] revealed atherosclerotic lesions. These findings therefore indicated that atherosclerosis, the major cause of CHD, is a process that begins early in life and progresses silently for decades. In the International Atherosclerosis Project, coronary artery lesions were also found in aortas beginning at age 3 years[4] and in coronaries starting at age 10 years.[5] Findings from the Bogalusa heart study have demonstrated a correlation between systolic blood pressure, higher total and LDL cholesterol but lower HDL-C concentrations, and the degree of coronary and aortic atherosclerosis in children and adolescents.[6] In the Pathobiological Determinants of Atherosclerosis in Youth (PDAY) Study, post-mortem cholesterol and thiocyanate concentrations predicted the extent of coronary and aortic atherosclerosis, respectively, in autopsies of those aged 14 to 34 years.[7] Therefore, a direct relation between determinant risk factors and the extent of the atherosclerotic lesions in youth seems to exist.

Furthermore, children in countries with an increased incidence of CHD were reported to have higher cholesterol concentrations than children of countries with low incidence.[8] About 5% of American children 5 to 18 years of age have cholesterol concentrations > 5.18 mmol/L (200 mg/dL). In addition, findings from the Muscatine, Bogalusa, and Princeton School studies have demonstrated that serum cholesterol and lipoprotein cholesterol concentrations cluster in families and display a moderate degree of longitudinal tracking.[9–12] Therefore, those individuals who are in the highest rank order of the population for total and lipoprotein cholesterol concentrations tend to remain in a high rank. The identification of children with high risk of developing CHD at early age offers the possibility of early treatment and prevention of this disease.

The relation between lipids and lipoproteins and early CHD is particularly striking in families with premature CHD.[13] About one-third of the offspring born to parents from families with CHD before age 55 years have hypercholesterolemia or hypertriglyceridemia. Of those born to a parent with angiographically documented early CHD, about half will have a dyslipidemia. More recently, work from the Bogalusa heart study has indicated that measurements of apolipoprotein B-100 (apo B-100), the major protein of low density lipoproteins (LDL), and apo A-I, the major protein of high density lipoproteins (HDL), may be more sensitive indicators of identifying dyslipidemic children born to a parent with premature CHD.[14]

In patients with inherited dyslipidemia, clinical symptoms of CHD usually appear in the fourth or fifth decade of life. By the time most individuals develop the symptoms, the atherogenic process is far advanced and arterial blood flow is markedly diminished. However, clinical manifestations of CHD can develop in children and adolescents with the rare disease homozygous familial hypercholesterolemia.

This chapter describes lipoprotein composition and metabolism; disorders of lipoprotein metabolism, with special emphasis on hypercholesterolemia and increased LDL-C concentrations; screening; the role of the clinical laboratory in the diagnosis and follow-up of children with these disorders; and clinical management of these disorders.

LIPOPROTEIN COMPOSITION

Lipoproteins are particles that have in their core hydrophobic, non-polar lipids (triglyceride and cholesterol esters), which are coated with native surfactants (phospholipids and free cholesterol) and specific proteins called apolipoproteins.[15] The association of the core lipids with the phospholipid and protein coat is non-covalent, occurring primarily through hydrogen bonding and Van der Waals forces. This binding of lipid to protein is loose enough to allow the ready exchange of lipids between serum lipoproteins and between serum and cell membrane lipoproteins, yet tight enough to allow the native lipoprotein complexes to be separated by a variety of analytical techniques.

Lipoproteins are separated into six major classes according to their physical and chemical properties (Table 18–1). Lipoproteins separated by ultracentrifugation are classified by their densities as: (1) chylomicrons, (2) very low density lipoproteins (VLDL), (3) intermediate density lipoproteins (IDL), (4) LDL, and (5) HDL. Lipoprotein(a) [Lp(a)] is separated along with LDL and HDL. HDL can be further divided by density into two subpopulations, HDL_2 and HDL_3. As discussed later in this chapter, the two subfractions of HDL seem to differ in their metabolic roles and clinical significance.

Lipoproteins differ in density because they consist of different proportions of triglyceride, cholesterol, phospholipids, and apolipoproteins. In the fasting state, most of the plasma triglyceride is present in VLDL. In the non-fasting state, chylomicrons contribute significantly to the triglyceride level; LDL carry 70% of total plasma cholesterol while HDL contain the lowest amount of plasma triglyceride and about 20% of plasma cholesterol.

The lipoproteins also can be separated by electrophoresis on agarose, cellulose acetate, or paper.[16] At a pH of 8.6, HDL migrate with the α globulins, LDL with the β globulins, and VLDL and Lp(a) between the α and β globulins, the so-called pre-β globulins. IDL form a broad band between β and pre-β globulins. Chylomicrons stay at the point of application. The lipoproteins are still occasionally referred to by their electrophoretic locations, such as pre-β lipoprotein (VLDL).

Apolipoproteins are the protein components of lipoproteins. The characteristics of the major apolipoproteins are summarized in Table 18–2.[15,17,18] Each class of lipoprotein has a variety of apolipoproteins in differing proportions, with the exception of LDL which predominantly contain apo B-100. Apo A-I is the major protein in HDL. Apo C-I, -II, -III, and E are present in various proportions in all lipoproteins except LDL.

Apo A-I and apo A-II constitute about 90% of total HDL protein, with an apo A-I to A-II ratio of about 3:1. In addition to being an important structural component of HDL, apo A-I is a co-factor for lecithin cholesterol acyltransferase (LCAT), a plasma enzyme that transfers a fatty acid from phosphatidylcholine to cholesterol, forming cholesteryl ester and lysophosphatidylcholine. Some evidence suggests that apo A-II may inhibit LCAT and/or activate hepatic triglyceride lipase. Apo A-IV, is a component of newly secreted chylomicrons, but is not a major constituent of chylomicron remnants, VLDL, LDL, and HDL. The functions of apo A-IV and apo(a) are unknown.

Apo B exists in two forms: apo B-100 and apo B-48. The two proteins are known to be translation products of a single structural gene.[19] Apo B-100, a single polypeptide of over 4,500 amino acids, is a full-length translation product of the apo B gene. Apo B-100 is primarily made in the liver and excreted into plasma on VLDL. Apo B-100 is the major apolipoprotein of LDL, the product of VLDL catabolism. In the fasting state, most of the apo B is apo B-100. For each molecule of LDL or VLDL, there is one molecule of apo B-100. Apo B-48 contains 2151 amino acids and is homologous to the amino terminal portion of apo B-100. Apo B-48 results from the post-transcriptional modification of messenger RNA (mRNA), in which a single base substitution produces a stop codon corresponding to residue 2153 of apo B-100. Apo B-48 is made in the intestine and is the major apo B component of chylomicrons. Both apo B-100 and B-48 play an important role in regulating lipo-

TABLE 18–1. Characteristics of Human Plasma Lipoproteins

Variable	Chylomicron	VLDL	IDL	LDL	HDL	Lp(a)
Density, g/mL	< 0.95	0.95–1.006	1.006–1.019	1.019–1.063	1.063–1.210	1.040–1.130
Electrophoretic mobility	Origin	Pre-beta	Between beta and pre-beta	Beta	Alpha	Prebeta
Molecular weight	$0.4–30 \times 10^9$	$5–10 \times 10^6$	$3.9–4.8 \times 10^6$	2.75×10^6	$1.8–3.6 \times 10^5$	$2.9–3.7 \times 10^6$
Diameter, nm	> 70	25–70	22–24	19–23	4–10	25–30
Lipid-protein ratio	99:1	90:10	85:15	80:20	50:50	75:25–64:36
Major lipids	Exogenous triglycerides	Endogenous triglycerides	Endogenous triglycerides, cholesteryl esters	Cholesteryl esters	Phospholipids	Cholesteryl esters, phospholipids
Major proteins	A-I	B-100	B-100	B-100	A-I	(a)
	B-48	C-I	E	—	A-II	B-100
	C-I	C-II	—	—	—	—
	C-II	C-III	—	—	—	—
	C-III	E	—	—	—	—

VLDL = very low density lipoproteins, IDL = intermediate density lipoproteins, LDL = low density lipoproteins, HDL = high density lipoproteins, Lp(a) = Lipoprotein(a)

From: Rifai N. Lipoproteins and apolipoproteins: composition, metabolism, and association with coronary heart disease. Arch Path Lab Med 1986;110:694–702. Copyright 1986, American Medical Association. Reproduced with permission.

TABLE 18–2. Classification and Properties of Major Human Plasma Apolipoproteins

Apolipoprotein	Molecular Weight (d)	Chromosomal Location	Function	Lipoprotein Carrier(s)
Apo A-I	29,016	11	Cofactor LCAT	Chylomicron, HDL
Apo A-II	17,414	1	Not known	HDL
Apo A-IV	44,465	11	Activates LCAT(?)	Chylomicron, HDL
Apo B-100	512,723	2	Secretion of triglyceride from liver binding protein to LDL receptor	VLDL, IDL, LDL
Apo B-48	240,800	2	Secretion of triglyceride from intestine	Chylomicron
Apo C-I	6,630	19	Activates LCAT(?)	Chylomicron, VLDL, HDL
Apo C-II	8,900	19	Cofactor LPL	Chylomicron, VLDL, HDL
Apo C-III 0–2	8,800	11	Inhibits Apo C-II activator of LPL	Chylomicron, VLDL, HDL
Apo E	34,145	19	Facilitates uptake of chylomicron remnant and IDL	Chylomicron, VLDL, HDL
Apo(a)	187,000–662,000	6	?	Lp(a)

VLDL = very low density lipoproteins, IDL = intermediate density lipoproteins, LDL = low density lipoproteins, HDL = high density lipoproteins, LCAT = lecithin cholesterol acyltransferase, LPL = lipoprotein lipase, Lp(a) = lipoprotein(a)

From: Rifai N. Lipoproteins and apolipoproteins: composition, metabolism, and association with coronary heart disease. Arch Path Lab Med 1986;110:694–701. Copyright 1986, American Medical Association. Adapted with permission. Also Kwiterovich PO Jr. Diagnosis and management of familial dyslipoproteinemia in children and adolescents. Pediatr Clin North Am 1990;37:1489–523.

protein secretion (VLDL and chylomicrons, respectively). Apo B-100 is the ligand that enables LDL to be taken up by the LDL receptor (see also discussion below).

Apo C-I, C-II, and C-III are associated with all lipoproteins except LDL. Apo C-I, the smallest of the C apolipoproteins, is reported to activate LCAT *in vitro*. Apo C-II plays an important role in the metabolism of triglyceride-rich lipoproteins (VLDL and chylomicrons) by activating lipoprotein lipase (LPL), an enzyme that hydrolyses the triglyceride in the lipoproteins. Apo C-III exists in at least three polymorphic forms, due to differences in sialic acid content. The precise metabolic function of apo C-III is unknown, but it may inhibit LPL and/or activate LCAT.

Apo E is a constituent of chylomicrons, VLDL, and HDL. It is present in several polymorphic forms due to different amino acid substitutions. Apo E plays a central role in the metabolism of triglyceride-rich lipoproteins. It regulates and facilitates lipoprotein uptake in the liver through (1) the interaction of chylomicron remnants with chylomicron remnant receptors, and (2) the binding of VLDL remnants to the LDL (B, E) receptor.

LIPOPROTEIN METABOLISM

The pathways of lipoprotein metabolism are complex.[15, 20, 21] They can be divided conceptually into exogenous and endogenous systems that transport lipids of dietary and hepatic origin, respectively (Figures 18–1 and 18–2), the intracellular LDL receptor pathway (Figure 18–3), and reverse cholesterol transport (Figure 18–4).

Exogenous Pathway

In the intestine, triglyceride and cholesterol from the diet are incorporated into chylomicrons, which are secreted into lymph and from there enter the bloodstream (Figure 18–1). LPL is attached to the luminal surface of endothelial cells that line

FIGURE 18–1. Exogenous Lipoprotein Metabolism Pathway

TG = triglyceride, CE = cholesterol ester, FC = free cholesterol, PL = phospholipids, HDL = high density lipoproteins, FA = fatty acid, LPL = lipoprotein lipase, B = apolipoprotein B-48, A = apolipoprotein A-I, C = apolipoprotein C-II, E = apolipoprotein E.

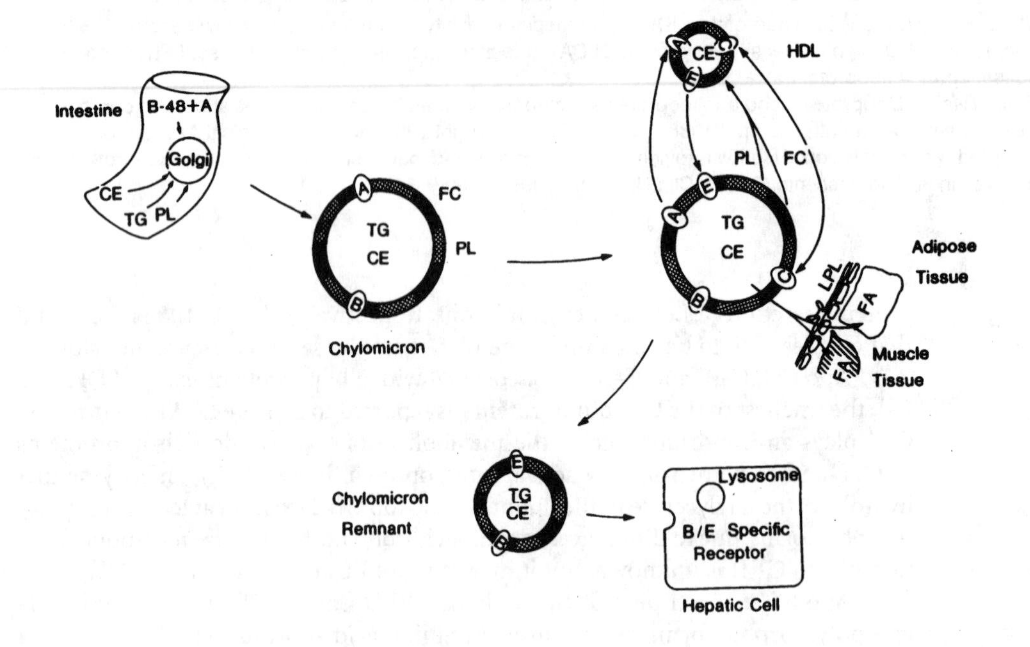

From: Rifai N. Lipoproteins and apolipoproteins: Composition, metabolism, and association with coronary heart disease. Arch Path Lab Med 1986;110:694-701. Copyright 1986, American Medical Association. Reproduced with permission.

FIGURE 18–2. Endogenous Lipoprotein Metabolism Pathway

TG = triglyceride, CE = cholesterol ester, FC = free cholesterol, PL = phospholipids, HDL = high density lipoproteins, LDL = low density lipoproteins, IDL = intermediate density lipoproteins, VLDL = very low density lipoproteins, FA = fatty acid, LPL = lipoprotein lipase, LCAT = lecithin cholesterol acyltransferase, B = apolipoprotein B-100, A = apolipoprotein A-I, C = apolipoprotein C-II, E = apolipoprotein E.

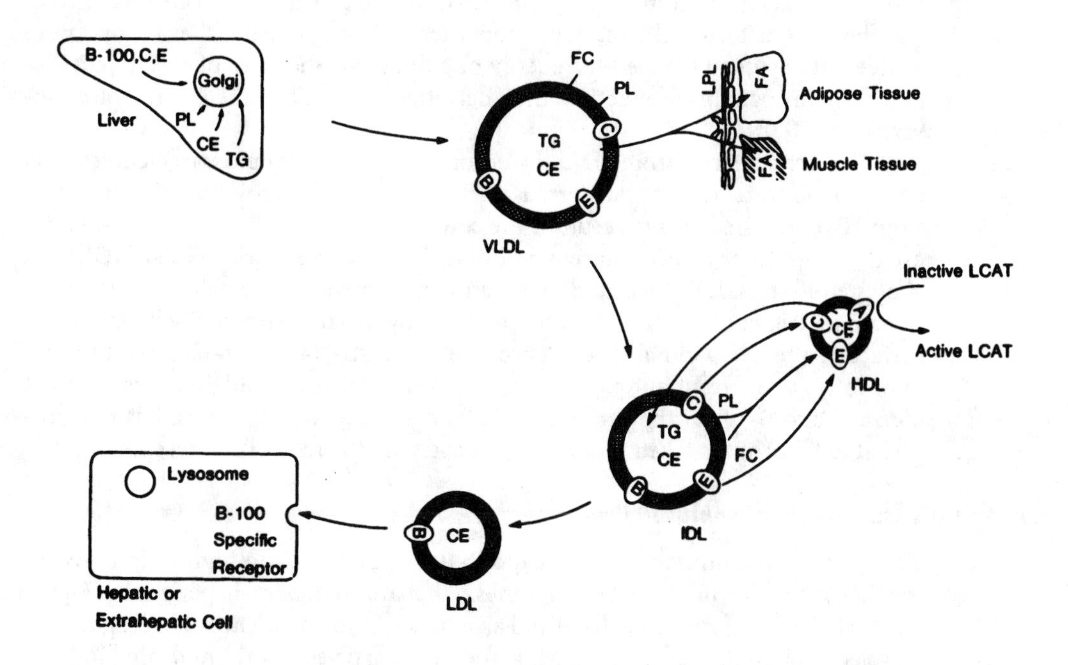

From: Rifai N. Lipoproteins and apolipoproteins: Composition, metabolism, and association with coronary heart disease. Arch Path Lab Med 1986;110:694-701. Copyright 1986, American Medical Association. Reproduced with permission.

capillaries of adipose and muscle tissue. Apo C-II is transferred from HDL to chylomicrons, where it enables LPL to hydrolyse chylomicron triglyceride, producing free fatty acids. The fatty acids may either be taken up into muscle cells, where they are used for energy, or into adipose cells, where they are resynthesized into triglyceride and stored for future use. As the triglyceride core in the chylomicron core is depleted, some of the surface material such as phospholipid, and apolipoproteins, are transferred to HDL, and a chylomicron remnant particle is produced. These remnants retain core cholesterol ester, apo B-48, and apo E. The remnants then bind via apo E to chylomicron remnant receptors to the surface of hepatic cells and are then internalized. The cholesterol from these remnants can down-regulate 3-hydroxy-3-methylglutaryl coenzyme A reductase (HMG-CoA reductase), the rate-limiting enzyme of cholesterol biosynthesis.

Endogenous Pathway

The liver synthesizes triglycerides from carbohydrates and fatty acids (Figure 18–2). When dietary cholesterol, derived from the receptor-mediated uptake of chylomicron remnants, is insufficient, the liver synthesizes its own cholesterol by increasing the activity of HMG-CoA reductase. The endogenously made triglycerides and cholesterol are then packaged into VLDL for export.

After excretion from the liver, the VLDL particles acquire apo C-II from HDL and then interact with LPL in tissue capillaries, releasing most of their triglycerides as free fatty acids to be used for energy or storage. As the sizes of VLDL particles diminish through this interaction, their densities increase and the particles are converted into IDL.

Surface material from IDL, including some phospholipids, free cholesterol, and apolipoproteins, are transferred to HDL, and cholesterol ester is transferred from HDL to IDL. The net result of the coupled lipolysis and the cholesterol ester exchange reactions is the replacement of much of the triglyceride core of IDL with cholesterol esters. IDL then undergoes a further conversion in which most of the remaining triglycerides are removed, probably by hepatic triglyceride lipase on the surface of the liver, and all apolipoproteins except B-100 are transferred to other lipoproteins. The resultant particles, which contain mostly cholesterol ester in the core and apo B-100 at the surface, are LDL. A variable fraction of IDL is not converted to LDL, but is taken up into hepatocytes via the LDL (B, E) receptors.

Low Density Lipoprotein Receptor Pathway

The lysine and arginine residues in apo B-100 of LDL bind to high-affinity receptors in coated pits on plasma membranes of hepatic and extra-hepatic cells (Figure 18–3).[21] LDL are then internalized and an endosome formed. The LDL receptors are recycled back to the cell surface, while the LDL particles in the endosome migrate toward the Golgi-endoplasmic reticulum-lysosome region. Once the LDL are delivered to the lysosomes, their apo B-100 component is degraded to small peptides and amino acids, and their cholesterol esters are hydrolyzed to free cholesterol and fatty acids. The free cholesterol has regulating functions in that it inhibits the activity of HMG-CoA reductase and down-regulates the production of LDL receptors. Both of these actions apparently occur through the interaction of a derivative of cholesterol, hydroxycholesterol, with specific (and homologous) areas in the regulatory portions of the reductase gene and the LDL receptor gene.

LDL can also be taken up and degraded by a low-affinity process. This mechanism is not saturable, and as the plasma LDL concentrations increase, more LDL are taken up by this route. The non-receptor mediated mechanism is not regulated, and LDL continue to enter, leading to an excess accumulation of cholesteryl esters. For example, when this happens in macrophages and in other scavenger cells, these cells may be converted to "foam cells," which are considered the earliest components of the atherosclerotic lesion. It has been estimated that normally about two-thirds of LDL are degraded by the high-affinity receptor pathway, with the remainder removed by the scavenger cell system.

FIGURE 18–3. Low Density Lipoprotein Receptor Pathway

LDL = low density lipoproteins, ACAT = acyl-CoA cholesterol acyltransferase, HMG-CoA reductase = 3-hydroxy-3-methylglutaryl coenzyme A reductase. Because of the presence of apolipoprotein B-100 on its surface, the LDL particle is recognized by a specific receptor in a coated pit and taken into the cell in a coated vesicle (top right). Coated vesicles fuse together to form an endosome. The acidic environment of the endosome causes the LDL particle to dissociate from the receptors, which return to the cell surface. The LDL particles are taken to a lysosome where apolipoprotein B-100 is broken down into amino acids and cholesterol ester is converted to free cholesterol for cellular needs. The cellular cholesterol level is self-regulated. Oversupply of cholesterol will lead to: (1) decrease rate of cholesterol synthesis by inhibiting HMG-CoA reductase, (2) increased storage of cholesteryl esters by activating ACAT, and (3) inhibition of manufacturing new LDL receptors by suppressing the transcription of the receptor gene into messenger RNA.

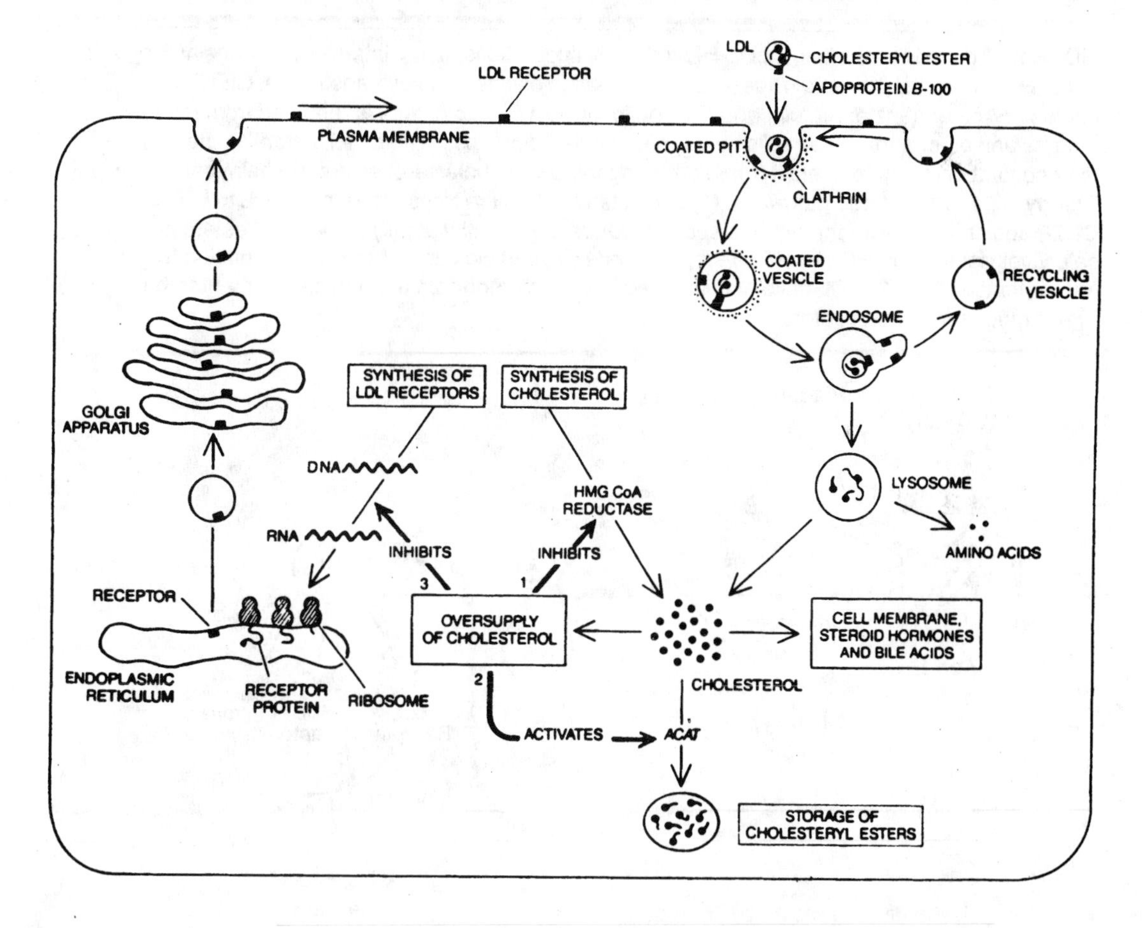

From: Brown MS and Goldstein JL. How LDL receptors influence cholesterol and atherosclerosis. Sci Am 1984;251:58-66.

Reverse Cholesterol Transport Pathway

HDL are secreted as nascent particles from either liver or intestine (Figure 18–4). These disc-like particles are round and flat and consist primarily of phospholipid in the core, surrounded by apo A-1.

Through the action of LCAT and its co-factor, apo A-1, free cholesterol is removed from peripheral tissues (Figure 18–4) and esterified by the transfer of a fatty acid from lecithin to cholesterol. In the process, HDL is converted from a disc to a sphere that contains cholesteryl ester in its core. The cholesteryl ester may be trans-

FIGURE 18–4. Reverse Cholesterol Transport Pathway

HDL = high density lipoproteins, LDL = low density lipoproteins, IDL = intermediate density lipoproteins, HTL = hepatic lipoprotein lipase, LCAT = lecithin cholesterol acyltransferase, CETP = cholesteryl ester transfer protein, apo E = apolipoprotein E. Cholesterol is removed from macrophages and other arterial wall cells by an HDL-mediated process. The LCAT esterifies the cholesterol content of HDL to prevent it from reentering the cells. Cholesterol esters are delivered to the liver by either one of three pathways: (1) cholesterol esters are transferred from HDL to LDL by CETP and enter the liver through the specific LDL receptor pathway; (2) cholesterol esters are selectively taken from HDL by HDL receptors and HDL particles are returned to circulation for further transport; or (3) HDL have accumulated apo E and therefore the particles can enter the liver through remnant receptors.

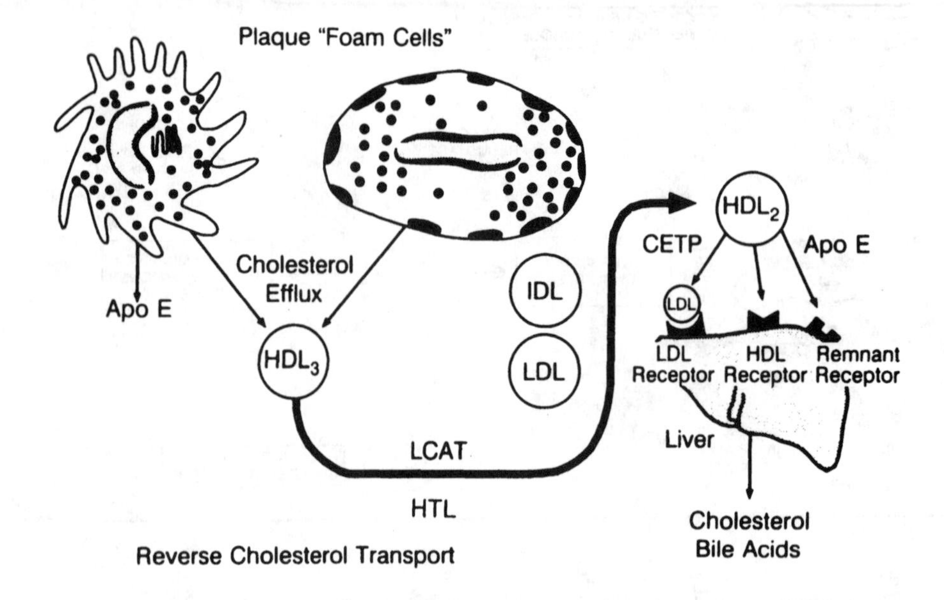

From: Gwynne JT. High density lipoprotein cholesterol levels as a marker of reverse cholesterol transport. Am J Cardiol 1989;64:10G-17G. Reproduced with permission.

ferred up to LDL by a cholesteryl ester transfer protein (CETP) or taken up directly by the liver by an HDL receptor.

While LDL are the major products resulting from the catabolism of VLDL, some conversion of HDL subfractions also occurs during this process. Surface material from the triglyceride-rich particles are transferred to HDL_3 circulating in the plasma, which are subsequently converted to cholesterol ester-rich HDL_2 by the action of LCAT. It has been shown that *in vitro* HDL_2 was converted back to HDL_3 in the presence of hepatic lipase.[22] HDL_2 can carry twice as many cholesterol molecules per unit of apolipoprotein compared to HDL_3. Thus, they can be viewed as a doubly efficient vehicle for the transfer of cholesterol from the peripheral tissues back to the liver.

PEDIATRIC LIPID AND LIPOPROTEIN CHOLESTEROL CONCENTRATIONS

As a result of their complex metabolism, the plasma concentrations of lipids, lipoproteins, and apolipoproteins are distributed over a wide range of values. Mean serum cholesterol concentration increases from about 1.71 mmol/L (66 mg/dL) at birth to about 4.02 mmol/L (155 mg/dL) at age 3. Approximately half of serum cholesterol at birth is carried in HDL. The LDL-C concentration increases rapidly in the first weeks of life as LDL become the major carrier of serum cholesterol. At age 5, LDL-C concentration is about 2.5 mmol/L (97 mg/dL) and HDL-C is about 1.4 mmol/L (54 mg/dL). Serum total and lipoprotein cholesterol concentrations of males and females in the first two decades of life are presented in Tables 18–3 and 18–4.[23] Later in life, males will have higher LDL-C but lower HDL-C than females, a lipoprotein profile that places males at greater risk of CHD.

TABLE 18–3. Serum Lipid Concentrations of Males and Females in the First Two Decades of Life (values in mmol/L [mg/dL])

	Cholesterol			Triglyceride		
Age/Sex	**5th**	**50th**	**95th**	**5th**	**50th**	**95th**
0–4 y						
Female	2.90 (112)	4.04 (156)	5.18 (200)	0.38 (34)	0.72 (64)	1.27 (112)
Male	2.95 (114)	4.01 (155)	5.26 (203)	0.33 (29)	0.63 (56)	1.12 (99)
5–9 y						
Female	3.26 (126)	4.25 (164)	5.31 (205)	0.36 (32)	0.68 (60)	1.19 (105)
Male	3.13 (121)	4.14 (160)	5.26 (203)	0.34 (30)	0.63 (56)	1.14 (101)
10–14 y						
Female	3.21 (124)	4.14 (160)	5.21 (201)	0.42 (37)	0.85 (75)	1.48 (131)
Male	3.08 (119)	4.09 (158)	5.23 (202)	0.36 (32)	0.75 (66)	1.41 (125)
15–19 y						
Female	3.11 (120)	4.09 (158)	5.26 (203)	0.44 (39)	0.85 (75)	1.49 (132)
Male	2.93 (113)	3.89 (150)	5.10 (197)	0.42 (37)	0.88 (78)	1.67 (148)

Data compiled from: Lipid Metabolism Branch, Division of Heart, Lung, and Blood Institute. The Lipid Research Clinics population studies data book, Vol I: The prevalence study. Bethesda, MD: National Institutes of Health, 1980. [NIH Publication No. 80-1527]

TABLE 18–4. Serum Lipoprotein Concentrations of Males and Females in the First Two Decades of Life (values in mmol/L [mg/dL])

	LDL-C			VLDL-C			HDL-C		
Age/Sex	5th	50th	95th	5th	50th	95th	5th	50th	95th
5–9 y									
Female	1.76 (68)	2.59 (100)	3.63 (140)	0.03 (1)	0.26 (10)	0.62 (24)	0.93 (36)	1.37 (53)	1.89 (73)
Male	1.63 (63)	2.41(93)	3.34 (129)	0	0.21 (8)	0.47 (18)	0.98 (38)	1.45 (56)	1.94 (75)
10–14 y									
Female	1.76 (68)	2.51 (97)	3.52 (136)	0.05 (2)	0.28 (11)	0.60 (23)	0.96 (37)	1.35 (52)	1.81(70)
Male	1.66 (64)	2.51 (97)	3.44 (133)	0.03 (1)	0.26 (10)	0.57 (22)	0.96 (37)	1.42 (55)	1.92 (74)
15–19 y									
Female	1.53 (59)	2.49 (96)	3.55 (137)	0.05 (2)	0.31 (12)	0.62 (24)	0.91 (35)	1.35 (52)	1.92 (74)
Male	1.61(62)	2.43 (94)	3.37 (130)	0.05 (2)	0.34 (13)	0.67 (26)	0.78 (30)	1.19 (46)	1.63 (63)

HDL = high density lipoproteins, LDL = low density lipoproteins, VLDL = very low density lipoproteins.
Data compiled from: Lipid Metabolism Branch, Division of Heart, Lung, and Blood Institute. The Lipid Research Clinics population studies data book, Vol I: The prevalence study. Bethesda, MD: National Institutes of Health, 1980. [NIH Publication No. 80-1527]

Frequency distributions for apo AI and apo B-100 in children have only recently become available (Table 18–5).[24] For apo B-100, values over the 75th and 90th percentile may represent borderline-high and increased values, respectively. For apo AI, values below the 25th and 10th percentile may represent borderline-low and decreased values, respectively.

TABLE 18–5. Serum Apolipoproteins AI and B-100 Concentrations Derived from the National Health and Nutrition Examination Survey III (values in mg/dL)

	Apo AI					Apo B-100				
Age (y)	10th	25th	50th	75th	90th	10th	25th	50th	75th	90th
Males										
4–5	112	122	132	149	159	62	69	79	89	98
6–11	117	126	141	155	168	61	69	76	89	99
12–19	106	116	128	141	153	58	67	75	85	98
Females										
4–5	111	118	130	140	155	64	72	82	91	99
6–11	117	125	135	145	157	61	70	81	90	101
12–19	111	120	132	146	165	58	67	79	92	104

From: Bachorik PS, Lovejoy KL, Carroll MD, Johnson CL. Apolipoprotein B and AI distributions in the United States, 1988-1991: results of the National Health and Nutrition Examination Survey III (NHANES III). Clin Chem 1997;43:2364–68.

DISORDERS OF LIPOPROTEIN METABOLISM

For the purpose of identifying children and adolescents more likely to have an inherited disorder of lipoprotein metabolism, the upper 95th percentiles have been used as cutpoints for increased cholesterol, LDL-C, and triglyceride, while the lower 5th percentile has been used for low HDL-C (Tables 18–3 and 18–4).

Primary versus Secondary Hyperlipidemia

Upon making the diagnosis of hyperlipidemia in a given child, the hyperlipidemic status should be evaluated as to whether it is primary or secondary to one of a variety of metabolic diseases. The diagnosis of primary hyperlipidemia can only be made after secondary causes are ruled out. The secondary causes of hyperlipoproteinemia in children and adolescents are listed in Table 18–6.[25] The secondary causes most commonly seen in the first year of life are glycogen storage disease and congenital biliary atresia. Hypothyroidism, nephrotic syndrome, and diabetes mellitus are more prevalent metabolic causes later in childhood. However, exogenous factors such as dietary and alcohol intake, oral contraceptives, pharmacological agents (steroids, isotretinoin [Accutane], beta-blockers, etc.) are the main secondary causes of hyperlipidemia in the first two decades of life.[17, 25]

Familial Dyslipoproteinemia

Historically, lipoprotein phenotypes reflecting lipoprotein metabolic disorders were classified according to Fredrickson and co-workers (Table 18–7). However, these disorders can now be approached based on the four metabolic pathways discussed above (Figures 18–1 to 18–4).[15, 17, 20] Defects in these pathways leading to hyperlipidemia may be related to (1) increased production of lipoproteins; (2) abnormal intravascular processing, e.g., enzymatic hydrolysis of triglyceride; and (3) defective cellular uptake of lipoproteins. Finally, a significant decrease in production and/or an increase in removal of lipoproteins can lead to a marked *reduction* in lipid concentrations.

Exogenous Triglyceride Pathway (Figure 18–1)

Deficiency in Lipoprotein Lipase Activity

A deficiency in the LPL activity causes severe hyperchylomicronemia (triglyceride as high as 113 mmol/L (10,000 mg/dL). The LPL is needed to hydrolyze triglyceride, and convert chylomicrons, the triglyceride-rich particles, to chylomicron remnants. The massive accumulation of chylomicrons in the bloodstream indicates the inability to catabolize dietary fat. VLDL-C concentration is usually normal and HDL-C and LDL-C concentrations are low (Type I lipoprotein pattern). The diagnosis of LPL deficiency is made by determining the enzyme activity in plasma after the administration of heparin. The concentration of apo C-II, the activator of LPL, in these patients is normal. Patients with this disorder generally present in the first decade of life with eruptive xanthomas, lipemia retinalis, and colicky abdominal pain. Overt pancreatitis can develop. LPL deficiency is an extremely rare autosomal

TABLE 18–6. Causes of Secondary Hyperlipidemia and Hyperlipoproteinemia in Children and Adolescents

Disorder	Cause
Exogenous	Drugs: corticosteroids, isotretinoin (Accutane®), thiazides, anticonvulsants, beta blockers, anabolic steroids, certain oral contraceptives)
	Alcohol
	Obesity
Endocrine and Metabolic	Acute intermittent porphyria
	Diabetes mellitus
	Hypopituitarism
	Hypothyroidism
	Lipodystrophy
	Pregnancy
Storage Disease	Cystine storage disease
	Gaucer disease
	Glycogen storage disease
	Juvenile Tay-Sachs disease
	Niemann-Pick disease
	Tay-Sachs disease
Renal	Chronic renal failure
	Hemolytic-uremic syndrome
	Nephrotic syndrome
Hepatic	Benign recurrent intrahepatic cholestasis
	Congenital biliary atresia
Acute and Transient	Burns
	Hepatitis
Others	Anorexia nervosa
	Idiopathic hypercalcemia
	Klinefelter syndrome
	Progeria (Hutchinson-Gilford syndrome)
	Systemic lupus erythematosus
	Werner syndrome

recessive disorder (< 1 in 100,000). Several insertions and deletions in the LPL gene that cause the deficiency in the activity of this enzyme have been described.[26]

Deficiency in Apolipoprotein C-II

Deficiency in the LPL cofactor apo C-II produces hypertriglyceridemia that ranges in severity from 9.04 mmol/L (800 mg/dL) to 113 mmol/L (10,000 mg/dL).[26] Total cholesterol concentration in these patients varies considerably, from 3.91 to 25.38 mmol/L (151 to 980 mg/dL). However, HDL-C and LDL-C concentrations are be-

TABLE 18–7. Classification of Hyperlipidemia

Frederickson Type	Lipid Elevation	Lipoprotein Elevation
I	Triglyceride	Chylomicrons
IIa	Cholesterol	Low-density lipoprotein
IIb	Cholesterol Triglyceride	Low-density lipoprotein Very-low-density lipoprotein
III	Cholsterol Triglyceride	Beta very-low-density lipoprotein (cholesterol-rich VLDL* remnant)
IV	Triglyceride	Very-low-density lipoprotein
V	Triglyceride Cholesterol	Very-low-density lipoprotein Chylomicrons

*VLDL, very-low-density lipoprotein

low the 5th percentile at approximately 0.93 mmol/L (36 mg/dL) and 1.68 mmol/L (65 mg/dL), respectively.[17, 26] The LPL activity is very low or absent, secondary to an almost undetectable concentration of apo C-II. As in LPL deficiency, patients with this disorder are not at risk of premature CHD, but recurrent pancreatitis in adulthood can be life threatening. Apo C-II deficiency is a rare disease and is inherited as an autosomal recessive. Several mutations in the apo C-II gene have been shown to produce this disorder.[26]

Endogenous Triglyceride Pathway: Overproduction of Very Low Density Lipoprotein (Figure 18–2)

Familial Combined Hyperlipidemia (FCH)

About 10–15% of patients with premature CHD (under the age of 55 years) have this disorder. The adult kindred members with FCH may have increased LDL-C alone (> 4.92 mmol/L [190 mg/dL]) (Type IIa), increased triglyceride alone (> 6.48 mmol/L [250 mg/dL]) (Type IV), or increases in both parameters (Type IIb).[17] The overproduction of VLDL-apo B-100 in these patients causes LDL-apo B-100 concentration to be increased. Therefore, even in patients with Type IV, who have normal LDL-C, the ratio of LDL-C to LDL-apo B-100 is decreased (small, dense LDL). Furthermore, FCH patients often have decreased HDL-C, particularly if hypertriglyceridemia is present. This disorder is inherited as an autosomal dominant, with an incidence of 1 in 100 individuals. There is a delayed expression of FCH before age 20, but children from families with premature CHD can present with increased cholesterol or triglyceride, or both lipids may be increased.

Hyperapobetalipoproteinemia

Up to a third of patients with premature CHD have a lipoprotein phenotype, hyperapobetalipoproteinemia (hyperapoB). This disorder is characterized by increased

LDL-apo B-100 concentrations with normal or moderately increased LDL-C values.[27] In these patients, total cholesterol and triglyceride concentrations are often normal but can be increased, and HDL-C and apo A-I are usually low. Although the exact defects have not yet been established, it appears that an increased hepatic synthesis of VLDL and apo B-100, which leads to the formation of small, dense LDL, and a decreased removal of dietary fat contribute to the formation of hyperapoB. The exact mode of inheritance and the prevalence of hyperapoB also remain uncertain. However, one third of children of a parent who had premature CHD and hyperapoB will also have hyperapoB. HyperapoB may also occur in families with FCH.

Familial Hypertriglyceridemia (FHT) (Type IV)

Production of large VLDL with an abnormally high triglyceride content is responsible for this disorder. Patients with FHT have increased VLDL cholesterol and triglyceride and normal LDL-C and apo B-100 serum concentrations; therefore, there is no increase in the conversion of VLDL to LDL. The HDL-C in FHT patients is decreased, probably secondary to the hypertriglyceridemia. Patients with FHT could develop glucose intolerance, hyperuricemia, obesity, and peripheral vascular disease later in life.[17] FHT is inherited in an autosomal dominant mode with a delayed expression; about 1 in 5 children born to affected parents manifest the phenotype early in life.

Both Exogenous and Endogenous Pathways (Figures 18–1 and 18–2)

Type V Hyperlipoproteinemia

Patients with this rare disorder have a marked hypertriglyceridemia resulting from increased chylomicrons and VLDL. Clinical findings include eruptive xanthomas, lipemia retinalis, pancreatitis, and abnormal glucose tolerance with hyperinsulinism.[17] Although this disorder is not usually expressed in childhood, several affected preadolescents have been described. The exact etiology of this disorder is unknown. It can either be due to an increased production or a decreased removal of VLDL or to a combination of both.

Dysbetalipoproteinemia (Type III)

This disorder is very rare in children and is caused by a defect in the removal of both chylomicron remnants and VLDL remnants.[17, 28] Serum cholesterol and triglyceride concentrations in dysbetalipoproteinemic patients are often increased to an equal degree and HDL-C and LDL-C are decreased.[17] The VLDL-C to serum triglyceride ratio in these patients is > 0.3 (normal: 0.15–0.25). Premature vascular disease and xanthomas can occur, but the yellow deposits in the crease of the palms are very characteristic of this disorder. This disease is caused by a defect in apo E resulting in faulty binding of apo E to both the chylomicron remnant and LDL (B, E) receptors on the hepatic cells; the increased concentration of triglyceride-rich particles is due to their faulty removal. As discussed earlier, apo E exists as three major isoforms: E_2, E_3, and E_4. Apo E_3 is the most common allele and apo E_2 is the rarest. Most patients with dysbetalipoproteinemia are homozygotic for the apo E_2 allele. The presence of the E_2E_2 phenotype is a necessary but insufficient cause of dysbetalipoproteinemia; overproduction of VLDL must also be present for the full-blown Type III syndrome to be expressed.

Low Density Lipoprotein Receptor Pathway (Figure 18–3)

Familial Hypercholesterolemia (Type IIa)

This disorder is inherited as an autosomal dominant and expressed in a heterozygous or homozygous mode with complete expression of high LDL-C at birth. Family studies to confirm the increased LDL-C concentration are essential to substantiate the diagnosis of familial hypercholesterolemia (FH). Heterozygous FH is a commonly seen genetic metabolic disorder with an incidence of 1 in 200–500 individuals in the United States. At birth, patients with heterozygous FH will have LDL-C concentrations higher than the 95th percentile (1.06 mmol/L [41 mg/dL]). After 1 year of age, FH heterozygotes often have total and LDL cholesterol concentrations over the 99th percentile (5.96 mmol/L [230 mg/dL] and 4.14 mmol/L [160 mg/dL], respectively). The HDL-C in these patients is often below average. Some develop tendon xanthomas during the second decade of life, but most heterozygous FH children are asymptomatic. CHD often occurs in the forties in men and in the fifties in women.

The prevalence of homozygous FH is 1 in 1,000,000. Patients will have cholesterol concentrations of 12.95–25.90 mmol/L (500–1000 mg/dL) and usually develop planar xanthomas by the age of 5 years. Angina pectoris, myocardial infarction, and aortic stenosis ordinarily occur before age 20.[17, 25]

FH is the result of a defect in the removal of LDL and therefore a large concentration of these particles accumulates in circulation. The defects include reduced or absent LDL binding because of defective or absent LDL receptors or defective internalization of the bound LDL particles. A number of different mutations in the LDL receptor gene which affect normal synthesis, transport, binding to LDL and internalization of the LDL receptor have been identified in FH.[29]

Familial Defective Apolipoprotein B-100

A mutation in the apo B-100 gene causes a substitution of glutamine for arginine at the residue 3500 in apo B-100 polypeptide, resulting in a reduced positive charge of the ligand and a decreased affinity of LDL to its negatively charged receptor. Therefore, patients with this disorder will have an increased LDL-C due to inadequate removal of LDL from circulation by normal receptors. The incidence of this disorder in children is unknown at present.

Reverse Cholesterol Transport Pathway (Figure 18–4)

Familial Hypoalphalipoproteinemia

Low HDL-C (below the 5th percentile) and normal lipid and LDL-C concentrations are the characteristics of this syndrome.[17] Although adult patients with this disorder are clinically normal, they are at increased risk of developing CHD. The exact etiology of this disorder is unknown; however, it may involve decreased production or increased catabolism of HDL or apo A-I. This disorder is relatively uncommon in children.

Defects in Decreased Synthesis of Apolipoprotein A-I

Mutations such as a rearrangement at the apolipoprotein gene locus that inactivates both apo A-I and C-III, a deletion of the entire locus, or an insertion in the apo A-I gene will lead to decreased synthesis and an abnormally low serum concentration of apo A-I.[30] Homozygotic patients have no detectable serum apo A-I and traces of HDL-C. Their risk of developing premature CHD is high and they have corneal clouding. Heterozygotes have HDL-C concentrations that are about 50% of normal.

Defects in Increased Catabolism of Apolipoprotein A-I (Tangier Disease)

This disorder is characterized by both a severely reduced serum concentration of HDL and abnormal HDL composition.[31] Apo A-I, which is also markedly decreased, is synthesized by intestinal cells but rapidly catabolized in plasma. The composition and concentration of the other lipoproteins are abnormal as well. Total and LDL cholesterol concentrations in these patients are below the 5th percentile (2.90 mmol/L [112 mg/dL] and 1.68 mmol/L [65 mg/dL], respectively) and triglyceride is normal or slightly increased. These patients have significant deposition of cholesteryl esters that results in relapsing peripheral neuropathy, splenomegaly and enlarged orange-yellow tonsils. Although the incidence of Tangier disease in children is very rare, children as young as 3 years have been diagnosed with this disorder.

SCREENING AND DIAGNOSIS ("WHO")

Traditionally, hypercholesterolemia in children and adolescents has been defined as a total or LDL cholesterol concentration higher than the 95th percentile (5.18 mmol/L [200 mg/dL] and 3.37 mmol/L [130 mg/dL], respectively). The National Cholesterol Education Program (NCEP) Expert Panel on Blood Cholesterol Levels in Children and Adolescents of the National Institutes of Health[32] and the American Academy of Pediatrics (AAP)[33, 34] used a similar definition of "high cholesterol" (≥ 5.18 mmol/L [200 mg/dL]) and high LDL cholesterol (≥ 3.37 mmol/L [130 mg/dL]) in children and adolescents from families with hypercholesterolemia or premature CHD. A "borderline" cholesterol concentration was defined as 4.40–5.15 mmol/L (170–199 mg/dL) and a "borderline" LDL-C concentration as 2.85–3.34 mmol/L (110–129 mg/dL). Borderline values are above the 75th percentile for both analytes.

The NCEP Expert Panel on Blood Cholesterol Levels in Children and Adolescents actually referred to cholesterol values < 4.40 mmol/L (170 mg/dL) and LDL-C values < 2.85 mmol/L (110 mg/dL) as "desirable." Children tend to have higher HDL-C concentrations than adults. Therefore, it is important to determine LDL-C and HDL-C concentrations before classifying the child as hypercholesterolemic.

Cholesterol screening to diagnose hypercholesterolemia is currently recommended for all adults in the United States.[35] However, for children, such a screening program remains highly controversial. According to the NCEP and the AAP,[32–34] only children above age 2 with a family history of hypercholesterolemia (≥ 6.22 mmol/L [240 mg/dL]) or early documented CHD (at 55 years of age or less), myocardial infarction, angina pectoris, peripheral vascular disease, cerebrovascular disease, or sudden cardiac death should be screened for hypercholesterolemia. However, several studies have demonstrated the deficiency of the selective approach and have advocated general screening for children.[36–40]

The results of the Bogalusa heart study actually demonstrated that by using the selective screening criteria, only 50% of white children and 20% of black children with high LDL-C concentration (above the 95th percentile, at about 3.37 mmol/L [130 mg/dL]) were detected.[36] Furthermore, it has been clearly shown that using parents' self-reported cholesterol values to determine the family risk history is an ineffective means of identifying children with high cholesterol.[40] Over 90% of children with total cholesterol over the 75th or 95th percentile were missed when physicians relied on parents' self-reported cholesterol values.[40] However, general screening is expensive, time consuming, and will generate a large amount of work in respect to follow-up. Furthermore, a significant number of children with high cholesterol concentrations will not remain hypercholesterolemic as adults.

Universal screening for those over 16 years of age has also been suggested on the basis of a finding that up to 66% of adolescents with increased LDL cholesterol are missed in a selective screening protocol.[41] Those hypercholesterolemic adolescents who are missed in the selective screening may not be identified until two decades later, when they usually start receiving their routine health examination. By that time, the atherosclerotic process is advanced and the dietary approach may not be sufficiently effective.

Another possible yet unpopular approach is not to do screening at all, but to recommend a prudent low-fat diet, such as the Step-One diet of the American Heart Association (AHA), for all children (Table 18–8).[32, 33] Such an approach would not engender anxiety, labeling, or overzealous treatment; however, it would miss completely those children with significant hypercholesterolemia, who are most at risk for adult CHD.

TABLE 18–8. Current Fat Intake in American Adults, Children, and Adolescents and the American Heart Association Step-One and Step-Two Diets

	Current Intake			
Nutrients	Adults	Children & Adolescents	Step One	Step Two
Total Fat				
(% of total calories)	35–36%	36%	< 30%	< 30%
Saturated Fat	14%	15%	< 10%	7%
Polyunsaturated Fat	6%	16%	10%	10%
Monounsaturated Fat	13–14%	15%	10–15%	10–15%
Cholesterol (mg/day)	193–296	400–500	< 300	< 200

Adapted from: National Cholesterol Education Program, Lipid Metabolism Branch, Division of Heart, Lung, and Blood Institute. The Report of the Expert Panel on Blood Cholesterol Levels in Children and Adolescents (draft). Bethesda, MD: National Institutes of Health, 1991.

Laboratory Methods for the Diagnosis and Management of Lipoprotein Disorders ("HOW")

The determination of lipid and lipoprotein concentrations is essential in the diagnosis and management of hyperlipoproteinemia. Furthermore, these tests are used in the assessment of CHD risk. Increased concentration of total cholesterol, LDL-C, and apo B-100 and decreased concentration of HDL-C and apo A-I are associated with increased risk of developing premature CHD. Furthermore, Lipoprotein(a) is shown to be higher in children from families with premature CHD and is not affected by dietary therapy.[42]

Accurate determination of serum lipids, lipoproteins, and apolipoproteins is dependent on the control of both analytical and preanalytical factors. Preanalytical variations result from differences in life style of patients, altered lipid metabolism due to disease or medication, source of the blood specimen, and conditions of specimen collection. Components of variation can be classified as biological, behavioral, clinical, variability in specimen collection and handling, and analytical.

The NCEP Laboratory Standardization Panel (LSP) issued specific recommendations to minimize the effect of preanalytical factors on lipid and lipoprotein testing.[43, 44] The panel recommends the following:

1. An individual's lipid and lipoprotein profile should only be measured when the individual is in a metabolic steady state.
2. Subjects should maintain their usual diet and weight for at least 2 weeks prior to the determination of their lipids or lipoproteins.
3. Multiple measurements within 2 months, at least 1 week apart, should be performed before making a medical decision about further action.
4. Patients should not perform vigorous physical activity within the 24-h period prior to testing.
5. Fasting or non-fasting specimens can be used for total cholesterol testing. However, a 12-h fasting specimen is required for triglycerides and lipoproteins.
6. The patient should be seated for at least 5 min before specimen collection.
7. The tourniquet should not be kept on more than 1 min during venipuncture.
8. Total cholesterol, triglyceride, and HDL-C concentrations can be determined in either serum or plasma. When EDTA is used as the anticoagulant, plasma should be immediately cooled to 2–4° C to prevent changes in composition and values should be multiplied by 1.03.
9. For total cholesterol testing, serum can be transported either at 4° C or frozen. Storage of specimens at –20° C is adequate for total cholesterol measurement. However, specimens must be stored frozen at –70° C or lower for triglyceride and lipoprotein and apolipoprotein testing.
10. Blood specimens should always be considered potentially infectious and therefore must be handled accordingly.

No specific recommendations were made by the panel concerning apolipoprotein testing. However, similar steps to those described should be taken to help minimize preanalytical sources of variation in apolipoprotein measurements.

The principles of the most commonly used methodologies in clinical laboratories for the determination of total, HDL, and LDL cholesterol, triglyceride, and apolipoproteins are briefly discussed in this chapter. Additional information is available in clinical chemistry textbooks.

Electrophoretic Separation of Lipoproteins

Electrophoresis separates lipoproteins according to their charges and allows the visual examination of their patterns.[16] Such an examination can be useful in the diagnosis of the various types of hyperlipoproteinemia. Although this technique is easily performed and requires simple equipment, it is a qualitative or a semi-quantitative method at best. In addition, lipoprotein electrophoresis cannot differentiate normal from abnormal lipid transport because only the ester bonds of triglyceride and cholesterol are stained; free cholesterol and phospholipids remain unstained. Therefore, patients with biliary cirrhosis would have a normal electrophoretic pattern in spite of a cholesterol concentration > 25.9 mmol/L (1000 mg/dL). In addition, certain lipoproteins have atypical mobility. For example, IDL and chylomicron remnants can smear between LDL and VLDL; Lp(a) generally migrates on agarose with slow pre-beta with, or near, VLDL; and beta-VLDL, when present, migrates with LDL.[45] Therefore, electrophoresis is not commonly used as a quantitative measure of lipoproteins. However, a newly introduced electrophoretic system appears to offer the potential for reliable quantitation.[46]

Measurement of Total Cholesterol Concentration

According to proficiency surveys (College of American Pathologists Comprehensive Proficiency Surveys), almost all clinical laboratories in the United States measure cholesterol enzymatically. This reaction first involves the hydrolysis of cholesterol ester by cholesterol esterase. Free cholesterol is then oxidized in the presence of cholesterol oxidase and hydrogen peroxide is generated. The hydrogen peroxide is coupled with an enzymatic reaction to form a colored oxidation product or a reduced pyridine nucleotide. The intensity of the generated color or the increase in absorbance is proportional to the cholesterol concentration. The cholesterol ester step is critical. Incomplete hydrolysis of cholesterol ester will lead to underestimation of the cholesterol concentration.

According to the NCEP, total cholesterol should be determined with bias and imprecision of less than 3%, which corresponds to total allowable error of about 9%.[47] The total acceptable error for cholesterol measurement set by the Clinical Laboratory Improvement Amendments of 1988 (CLIA '88) is presented in Table 18–9.[44]

A survey conducted by Children's Hospital revealed that 60% of pediatricians in the Washington, D.C., metropolitan area determine cholesterol concentration in their practice using a variety of desktop analyzers.[48] Most of these analyzers perform adequately in the hands of skilled laboratory personnel; however, when used

TABLE 18–9. National Performance Criteria for Lipid and Lipoprotein Measurement

	NCEP Performance Criteria		*CLIA Evaluation Criteria*	
Analyte	**Bias**	**Imprecision**[a]	**Total Error**	**Total Error**
TC	≤ 3% RV[b]	CV ≤ 3%	≤ 9%	±10%
TG	≤ 5% RV	CV ≤ 5%	≤ 15%	±25%
HDLC	≤ 5%RV	SD ≤ 1.7 at < 42 mg/dL CV ≤ 4% at ≥ 42 mg/dL	≤ 13%	
LDL-C	≤ 4%RV	CV ≤ 4%	≤ 12%	

Source: Federal Register, February 28, 1992
[a]CV = Coefficient of variation, SD = Standard deviation, TC = total cholesterol, TG = triglycerides
[b]Reference value assigned by the CDC reference methods

by poorly trained individuals, the results are usually less than desirable. A recent study showed that up to 20% of reported cholesterol values by 33 pediatric practices in Washington, D.C., exceeded the acceptable total allowable error of 9%.[48]

Since the diagnosis of hypercholesterolemia in children and adolescents will most likely be made in the pediatrician's or family practitioner's office, it is crucial that cholesterol concentration is measured correctly in these settings. At present, cholesterol testing in the physician's office is not as well regulated as that performed in clinical laboratories. State and federal regulatory agencies are beginning to deal with regulatory issues concerning physician's office testing. The NCEP-LSP, however, has recently issued recommendations regarding cholesterol testing outside the clinical laboratories.[43, 49] These recommendations include:

1. the use of accurate and precise analyzers (capable of determining cholesterol concentration within 3% bias of reference values and 3% imprecision);
2. the use of a properly trained operator (ideally, a trained medical technician or technologist);
3. the institution of a quality control system and the participation in proficiency surveys;
4. the use of a system of split-sample analyses to routinely compare cholesterol testing done in the physician's office to that done in a qualified laboratory; and
5. the use of a proper patient preparation procedure to minimize the preanalytical variations.

Such actions will ensure that the quality of testing done in the physician's office is comparable to that of a hospital or reference laboratory.

Measurement of Triglyceride Concentration

Serum triglyceride concentration is determined to establish the triglyceridemic status of an individual as well as to estimate LDL-C concentration (see the section below on estimation of low density lipoprotein cholesterol). Almost all clinical laboratories determine triglyceride concentration enzymatically. Triglycerides are hydrolyzed to glycerol in the presence of lipase. Complete triglyceride hydrolysis is essential for the accurate determination of this analyte. Glycerol is then coupled by one or more enzymatic reactions to generate either a colored dye or an ultraviolet light-absorbing chemical. The intensity of the produced color or the increase in absorbance is proportional to the triglyceride concentration.

Glycerol is a product of normal metabolic processes. Therefore, triglyceride concentration could be overestimated if not corrected for the endogenous glycerol.[50] In normal subjects, endogenous glycerol represents the equivalent of 0.11–0.22 mmol/L (10–20 mg/dL) triglyceride, which is a tolerable bias. However, in certain conditions, such as diabetes mellitus, emotional stress, intravenous administration of drugs or nutrients containing glycerol, contamination of blood collection devices by glycerol, and prolonged storage of whole blood under nonrefrigerated conditions, endogenous glycerol concentrations will be significantly higher and could complicate the interpretation of triglyceride values. In general, clinical chemists feel that the effect of endogenous glycerol will be minimized with careful specimen collection and storage. Furthermore, only minute fractions of samples analyzed in general clinical laboratories contain an appreciable quantity of endogenous glycerol. Therefore, only about 5% of all American clinical laboratories perform blank triglyceride measurements for endogenous glycerol.

The recommendations from the NCEP regarding the performance goals for triglyceride measurement and the acceptable criteria established by CLIA '88 are presented in Table 18–9.[51]

Separation of High Density Lipoprotein Fractions

The HDL fractions are separated from the other lipoproteins using precipitation techniques. Several precipitation reagents such as heparin-Mn^{++}, phosphotungstate, and dextran sulfate-Mg^{++} are commonly used to precipitate LDL and VLDL. The cholesterol concentration in the supernatant, which represents HDL-C, is then quantitated enzymatically.

The precipitation procedure selected to measure HDL-C should be assessed for analytical performance.[52] Besides assessing the precision and accuracy, the specificity of the assay should be determined. The precipitation techniques used are normally reproducible when performed with a sensitive and reproducible cholesterol assay. The accuracy of the HDL-C assay can be determined by a direct patient specimen comparison with the Centers for Disease Control and Prevention HDL-C procedure or other equivalent method with well-established accuracy. The specificity of the assay can be determined by the demonstration of complete precipitation of LDL and VLDL and/or no co-precipitation of HDL. This task can be established by:

1. lipoprotein electrophoresis of the supernatant and resolubilized precipitate; the supernatant should have an HDL or α band only and no β or pre-β band and the precipitate should have no HDL band.
2. measurement of apo A-I and B-100 in the supernatant; the supernatant should only have apo A-I and not apo B-100.

3. evaluation of the performance of the assay in the presence of high triglyceride concentration.

Recently, direct assays for the determination of HDL cholesterol have been introduced.[53–56] These methods are performed on-line with improved precision (CV of 1–2%), are less affected by increased triglycerides, and require less than 10 μL of sample. Unlike precipitation methods, soluble complexes with apo B-containing particles are formed in these assays. The cholesterol component of HDL is then determined using modified enzymes that have limited or no reactivity with cholesterol of the soluble complexes. These assays have shown to correlate highly with both the ultracentrifugation-dextran sulfate-Mg^{++} method and the CDC Designated Comparison Method and meet all performance criteria of regulatory agencies.[54, 55]

The recommendations from the NCEP regarding the performance goals for HDL-C measurement and the acceptable criteria established by CLIA '88 are presented in Table 18–9.[56]

Estimation of Low Density Lipoprotein Cholesterol

The NCEP guidelines require the use of LDL-C concentration in the diagnosis and management of hypercholesterolemia. LDL-C is not measured in most clinical laboratories but is estimated using the Friedewald equation:

LDL-C = Total cholesterol – (HDL-C + VLDL-C)

VLDL-C = Triglyceride/5 (for mg/dL or mg/L LDL-C values), or

VLDL-C = Triglyceride/2.22 (for mmol/L LDL-C values)

It has been shown that LDL-C values derived by the Friedewald formula correlate very highly with those determined by the reference method, the β quantification, when triglyceride concentrations are < 4.66 mmol/L (400 mg/dL).[57] Furthermore, 86% of LDL-C classifications based on NCEP cutpoints were shown to be concordant with those by measured LDL-C when triglyceride concentrations were < 4.66 mmol/L (400 mg/dL).[58]

Fasting specimens are required for the estimation of LDL-C by this formula. High triglyceride concentration can falsely overestimate VLDL-C and therefore underestimate LDL-C. Furthermore, patients with Type III hyperlipoproteinemia have VLDL that are enriched with cholesterol relative to triglyceride. The presence of these abnormal particles can result in an underestimation of VLDL-C and an overestimation of LDL-C. This can be especially problematic since a Type III patient can be misdiagnosed as having Type IIb hyperlipoproteinemia and the treatments for the two disorders are different.[5]

An immunologic assay for the direct determination of LDL-C has been introduced. Using monoclonal antibodies directed against apo A-I and apo E, HDL and VLDL particles are removed, leaving LDL in the supernatant. The cholesterol concentration of the LDL fraction is determined enzymatically. This assay presumably can be performed in non-fasting samples. Several investigators have demonstrated that this immunoprecipitation assay correlates with the reference method, the β quantification, in adults and children,[59, 60] but has some shortcomings. Recent studies have shown that this assay has limitations in the nonfasting state[61] and in correctly classifying children and adolescents into NCEP cutpoints.[62] A direct method for the determination of LDL cholesterol has recently been introduced.[63] However, the analytical and clinical performance of this assay is yet to be assessed.

The recommendations from the NCEP regarding the performance goals for LDL-C measurement are presented in Table 18–9.[64]

Measurement of Apolipoprotein Concentration

Apo A-I and B-100 are mainly measured in clinical laboratories by immunoturbidimetric or immunonephelometric assays. Other methods such as radioimmunoassay, radial immunodiffusion, and enzyme-linked immunosorbent assay are used in research settings and some specialized lipid laboratories.

Considerable effort has been expended over the past few years by national and international organizations in overcoming the problems of apo A-I and B-100 standardization. The International Federation of Clinical Chemistry, along with other organizations, embarked on the ambitious pursuit of developing a secondary serum reference material which can be used, without fear of matrix interaction, as a master calibrator for all current commercial assays.[65] This program has been successfully completed.[66, 67]

In order for these apolipoproteins to be used in routine patient care, more information regarding their clinical utility is needed. Dietary and drug intervention trials should be conducted to determine the extent of benefit expected in lowering CHD risk when apo B-100 is decreased and apo A-I is increased. Furthermore, clinically meaningful cut-off values for clinical decision making need to be established in children and adolescents.

Management of Children and Adolescents with Hypercholesterolemia

To lower serum cholesterol concentration in children and adolescents, the NCEP adapted a strategy that combines two complementary approaches, a population approach and an individualized approach.[32] A similar strategy has recently been adopted by the AAP.[68]

American children and adolescents have relatively high cholesterol concentration and high intake of saturated fatty acids and cholesterol (Table 18–8).[32] The population approach attempts to lower the mean cholesterol concentration by instituting population-wide modification in nutrient intake and eating habits. The AHA Step-One diet is recommended (Table 18–8). Even a modest decrease in mean cholesterol concentration in children and adolescents, if carried into adulthood, could conceivably have a significant impact on lowering CHD incidence. The panel did not recommend any dietary changes for infants from birth to 2 years of age. Toddlers 2 and 3 years of age should start making the transition to the recommended eating pattern. The NCEP also directed recommendations to schools, health professionals, government agencies, the food industry, and the mass media to help influence and modify the eating habits of children and adolescents.

The individualized approach aims to lower cholesterol concentration of children over the age of 2 and adolescents who were identified by the selective screening process and the risk assessment protocol (Figure 18–5).[32] Those with an average LDL-C concentration between 2.85–3.34 mmol/L (110–129 mg/dL) will be placed on the AHA Step-One diet, counseled about other CHD risk factors, and reevaluated after 1 year. Those with an average LDL-C concentration ≥ 3.37 mmol/L (130 mg/dL) are also placed on the AHA Step-One diet, evaluated for secondary causes, and their family members are screened. If after 3 months of initiating the dietary therapy the LDL-C concentration remains ≥ 3.37 mmol/L (130 mg/dL), the patient is placed on the AHA Step-Two diet that entails further reduction of the saturated fatty acid and cholesterol intake (Table 18–8).

The NCEP and AAP recommended drug therapy for children age 10 years and older if after careful adherence to dietary therapy (6 months to 1 year) the LDL-C

FIGURE 18–5. Risk Assessment Flowchart as Recommended by the National Cholesterol Education Program Expert Panel on Blood Cholesterol Levels in Children and Adolescents

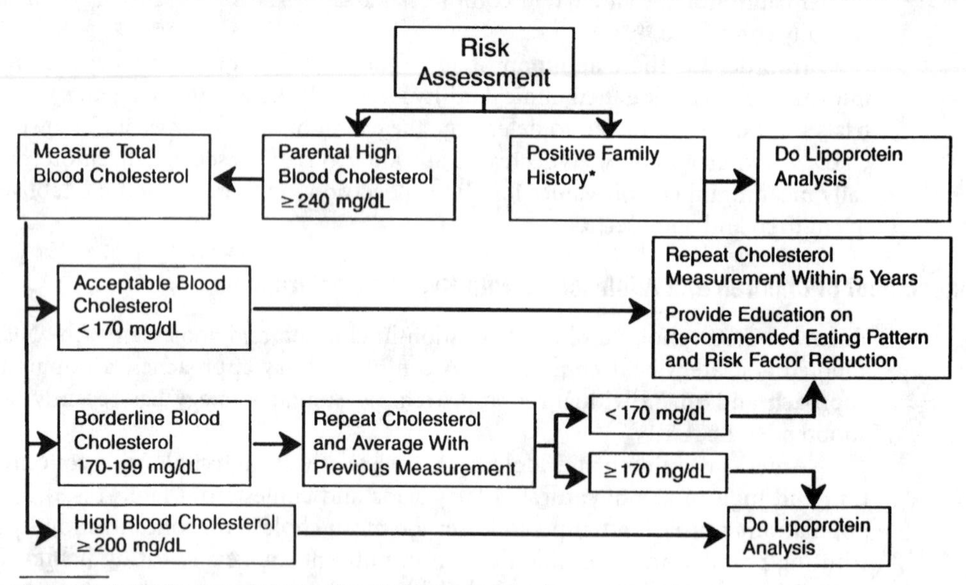

*Defined as a history of premature (before age 55 years) cardiovascular disease in a parent or grandparent

From: National Cholesterol Education Program, Lipid Metabolism Branch, Division of Heart, Lung, and Blood Institute. The Report of the Expert Panel on Blood Cholesterol Levels in Children and Adolescents (Draft), Bethesda, MD: National Institutes of Health, 1991.

concentration remains > 4.92 mmol/L (190 mg/dL) or LDL-C concentration remains > 4.14 mmol/L (160 mg/dL) and the patient has a positive family history of premature CHD or two or more other CHD risk factors. Only bile acid binding resins (cholestyramine and colestipol), which act by binding bile acids in the intestinal lumen, are currently recommended for use in children and adolescents. The acceptability, compliance, safety, and efficacy of these resins have recently been confirmed.[69, 70]

Other cholesterol-lowering drugs have no long-term proven efficacy or safety when used in children and adolescents; therefore, their use in this patient population is discouraged. Recent studies have demonstrated the short-term efficacy and safety of pravastatin and lovastatin in children and adolescents with familial hypercholesterolemia.[71, 72] However, until long-term safety has been shown, the routine use of these agents in the pediatric population is not recommended.

Most FH homozygotes are resistant to drug therapy. Plasmapheresis every 2 weeks is a viable alternative to surgery (partial ileal bypass or portacaval shunt) to lower total and LDL cholesterol in these patients.[25]

Management of Children and Adolescents with Hypertriglyceridemia

Patients with primary mild hypertriglyceridemia without hypercholesterolemia are advised to follow a Step-One Diet control their blood glucose, lose weight, and abstain from alcohol intake. Those with primary severe hypertriglyceridemia however are placed on a very low fat diet (10–15 g/day in a child). Since medium-chain triglycerides are absorbed directly from the portal vein, they can replace fat in food preparations for these patients. Drug therapy is seldom used in these patients unless hypertriglyceridemia is accompanied by hypercholesterolemia.[25]

SUMMARY

Atherosclerosis, the cause of CHD, is a process that starts in childhood and develops slowly and silently. The clinical manifestations of CHD usually appear in the fifth or sixth decade of life. Increased serum total and LDL cholesterol, apo B-100, and Lp(a) concentrations and/or decreased HDL-C and apo A-I concentrations correlate with increased risk of CHD. Children and adolescents of families with dyslipoproteinemia or premature CHD are at increased risk of developing this disease when they become adults. Therefore, the AAP and the NCEP have recommended screening all children over 2 years of age and adolescents with positive family history for hypercholesterolemia.

The physician must rule out the secondary causes of dyslipoproteinemia before making the diagnosis of a primary dyslipoproteinemia. The incidence, severity, and association with CHD risk vary significantly among the different types of dyslipoproteinemia. These disorders used to be classified according to Fredrickson. However, classification can now be better approached based on lipoprotein metabolic pathways.

Patients with hypercholesterolemia are treated with low-fat diet. Only children over 10 years of age with severe hypercholesterolemia will receive pharmacotherapy. Patients with hypertriglyceridemia are also treated with dietary means and advised to lose weight and abstain from alcoholic intake.

Since only a small fraction of patients with dyslipoproteinemia presents with clinical symptoms, the clinical laboratories are instrumental in making the initial diagnosis as well as monitoring the treatment of these patients.

REFERENCES

1. Gordon T., Kannel WB, Castelli WP, Dawber TR. Lipoproteins, cardiovascular disease, and death: The Framingham Study. Arch Intern Med 1981;141:1128–31.
2. Enos WF, Holmes RH, Beyer JC. Coronary disease among United States soldiers killed in action in Korea. JAMA 1953;152:1090–93.
3. McNamara JS, Molot MA, Stremple JF, et al. Coronary artery disease in combat casualties in Vietnam. JAMA 1971;216:1185–7.
4. Stary HC. The sequence of cell and matrix changes in atherosclerotic lesions of coronary arteries in the first forty years of life. Europ Heart J 1990;11(Supp E):3–19.
5. Strong JP, McGill HC Jr. The pediatric aspects of atherosclerosis. J Atherosclerosis Res 1969;40:37–49.
6. Berenson GS, Wattigney W, Tracy RE, et al. Atherosclerosis of the aorta and coronary arteries and cardiovascular risk factors in persons aged 6 to 30 years and studied at necropsy (The Bogalusa Heart Study). Am J Cardiol 1992;70:851–8.
7. PDAY Research Group. Relationship of atherosclerosis in young men to serum lipoprotein cholesterol concentrations and smoking. A preliminary report from the Pathobiological Determinants of Atherosclerosis in the Youth (PDAY) Research Group. JAMA 1990;264:3018–24.
8. Knuiman JT, Hermus RJ, Hautvast JG. Serum total and high density lipoprotein cholesterol concentrations in rural and urban boys from 13 countries. Atherosclerosis 1980;36:529–37.
9. Lauer RM, Clarke WR. Use of cholesterol measurements in childhood for the prediction of adult hypercholesterolemia: The Muscatine study. JAMA 1990;264:3034–8.
10. Laskarzewski P, Morrison JA, deGroot I, et al. Lipid and lipoprotein tracking in 108 children over a four-year period. Pediatrics 1979;64:584–91.
11. Khoury P, Morrison JA, Kelly K, et al. Clustering and interrelationships of coronary heart disease risk factors on schoolchildren, age 6–19. Am J Epidemiol 1980;112:524–38.
12. Webber LS, Srinivasan SR, Wattigney WA, Berenson GS. Tracking of serum lipids and lipoproteins from childhood to adulthood. Am J Epidemiol 1991;133:884–9.
13. Lee J, Lauer RM, Clarke WR. Lipoproteins in the progeny of young men with coronary artery disease: children with increased risk. Pediatrics 1986;78:330–7.
14. Freedman DS, Srinivasan SR, Shear CL, et al. The relation of apolipoproteins AI and B in children to parental myocardial infarction. N Engl J Med 1986;315:721–6.
15. Rifai N. Lipoproteins and apolipoproteins: composition, metabolism, and association with coronary heart disease. Arch Path Lab Med 1986;110:694–701.
16. Noble RP. Electrophoretic separation of plasma lipoproteins in agarose gel. J Lipid Res 1968;9:693–700.
17. Kwiterovich PO Jr. Diagnosis and management of familial dyslipoproteinemia in children and adolescents. Pediatr Clin North Am 1990;37:1489–523.
18. Mahley WR, Innerarity TL, Rall SC, et al. Plasma lipoproteins: apolipoprotein structure and function. J Lipid Res 1984;25:1277–94.
19. Kane JP, Havel RJ. Disorders of the biogenesis and secretion of lipoproteins containing the B apolipoproteins. In: Scriver CR, Beaudet AL, Sly WS, Valle D, eds. The metabolic and molecular bases of inherited diseases, 7th ed. New York: McGraw-Hill, 1995:1853–86.

20. Gwynne JT. High density lipoprotein cholesterol levels as a marker of reverse cholesterol transport. Am J Cardiol 1989;64:10G-7.
21. Brown MS, Goldstein JL. A receptor-mediated pathway for cholesterol homeostasis. Science 1986;232:34–47.
22. Patsch JR, Prasad S, Gotto AM Jr, et al. Post prandial lipemia: a key for the conversion of HDL2 into HDL3 by hepatic lipase. J Clin Invest 1984;74:2017–23.
23. Lipid Metabolism Branch, Division of Heart, Lung, and Blood Institute. The Lipid Research Clinics population studies data book. Vol I: The prevalence study. Bethesda, MD: National Institutes of Health, 1980. [NIH Publication No. 80-1527]
24. Bachorik PS, Lovejoy KL, Carroll MD, Johnson CL. Apolipoprotein B and AI distributions in the United States, 1988–1991: results of the National Health and Nutrition Examination Survey III (NHANES III). Clin Chem 1997;43:2364–68.
25. American Heart Association. Diagnosis and treatment of primary hyperlipidemia in childhood: a joint statement for physicians by the Committee on Atherosclerosis and Hypertension in Childhood of the Council on Cardiovascular Disease in the Young and the Nutrition Committee, American Heart Association. Circulation 1986;74:1181A–8.
26. Brunzell JD. Familial lipoprotein lipase deficiency and other causes of the chylomicronemia syndrome. In: Scriver CR, Beaudet AL, Sly WS, Valle D, eds. The metabolic basis of inherited diseases, 6th ed. New York: McGraw-Hill, 1989:1165–80.
27. Kwiterovich PO Jr. HyperapoB: a pleiotropic phenotype characterization by dense low-density lipoproteins and associated with coronary artery disease. Clin Chem 1988;34:B71–7.
28. Mahley RW, Rall SC Jr. Type III hyperlipoproteinemia (Dysbetalipoproteinemia): the role of apolipoprotein E in normal and abnormal lipoprotein metabolism. In: Scriver CR, Beaudet AL, Sly WS, Valle D, eds. The metabolic and molecular bases of inherited diseases, 7th ed. New York: McGraw-Hill, 1995:1953–80.
29. Hobbs HA, Leitersdorf E, Goldstein JL, et al. Multiple crm⁻ mutations in familial hypercholesterolemia: evidence for 3 alleles, including four deletions. J Clin Invest 1988;81:909–17.
30. Karathanasis SK, Ferris E, Haddad IA. DNA inversion within the apolipoprotein AI/CIII/AIV-encoding gene cluster of certain patients with premature atherosclerosis. Proc Natl Acad Sci USA 1987;84:7198–202.
31. Schaefer EJ, Blum CB, Levy RI, et al. Metabolism of high density lipoprotein, apolipoproteins in Tangier disease. N Engl J Med 1978;299:905–10.
32. National Cholesterol Education Program, Lipid Metabolism Branch, Division of Heart, Lung, and Blood Institute. The Report of the Expert Panel on Blood Cholesterol Levels in Children and Adolescents (Draft). Bethesda, MD: National Institutes of Health, 1991.
33. American Academy of Pediatrics Committee on Nutrition. Prudent life-style for children: dietary fat and cholesterol. Pediatrics 1986;78:521–5.
34. American Academy of Pediatrics Committee on Nutrition. Indication for cholesterol testing in children. Pediatrics 1989;83:141–2.
35. National Cholesterol Education Program Expert Panel. Report of the National Cholesterol Education Program Expert Panel on Detection, Evaluation and Treatment of High Blood Cholesterol in Adults. Arch Intern Med 1988;148:36–69.
36. Dennison BA, Kikucki DA, Srinivasan SR, et al. Serum total cholesterol screening for the detection of elevated low-density lipoprotein in children and adolescents: The Bogalusa Heart Study. Pediatrics 1990;85:472–9.
37. Dennison BA, Kikucki DA, Srinivasan SR, et al. Parental history of cardiovascular disease as an indicator for screening for lipoprotein abnormalities in children. J Pediatr 1989;115:186–94.
38. Garcia RE, Moodie DS. Routine cholesterol surveillance. Pediatrics 1989;84:751-5.
39. Griffin TC, Chistoffel KK, Binns HJ, et al. Family history evaluation as a predictive screen for childhood hypercholesterolemia. Pediatrics 1989;84:365–73.
40. Resnicow K, Cross D. Are parents' self-reported total cholesterol levels useful in identifying children with hyperlipidemia? An examination of current guidelines. Pediatrics 1993;92:347–53.
41. Rifai N, Neufeld E, Ahlstrom P, et al. Failure of current guidelines for cholesterol screening in urban African-American adolescents. Pediatrics 1996;98:383–8.

42. Kostner GM, Czinner A, Pfeiffer KH, Bihari-Varga M. Lipoprotein(a) concentrations as risk indicators for atherosclerosis. Arch Dis Child 1991;66:1054–6.
43. National Cholesterol Education Program. Recommendations for improving cholesterol measurement: a report from the Laboratory Standardization Panel of the National Cholesterol Education Program. Bethesda, MD: National Institutes of Health, 1990 [NIH Publication No. 90-2964]
44. Myers GL, Henderson LO, Cooper GR, et al. Standardization of lipid and lipoprotein measurements. In: Rifai N, Warnick GW, Dominiczak MH, eds. Handbook of lipoprotein testing. Washington, DC: AACC Press, 1997:223–50.
45. Bachorik PS. Measurement of low density lipoprotein cholesterol concentration. In: Rifai N, Warnick GR, Dominiczak MH, eds. Handbook of lipoprotein testing. Washington, DC: AACC Press, 1997:145–60.
46. Warnick GR, Leary ET, Goetsch J, Hicks D. Electrophoretic quantitation of LDL-cholesterol using the Helena REP. Clin Chem 1993;39:1122.
47. Naito HK, Bowers GN Jr, Baillie EE, et al. Current status of blood cholesterol measurement in clinical laboratories in the United States: a report from the Laboratory Standardization Panel of the National Cholesterol Education Program. Clin Chem 1988;34:193–201.
48. Rifai N, Iosefsohn M, Hicks JM. Cholesterol testing in the physician's office: accuracy assessment. Am J Dis Child 1991;145:1087–8.
49. National Heart, Lung, and Blood Institute. Recommendations regarding public screening for measuring blood cholesterol: a summary of a National Heart, Lung, and Blood Institute workshop. Bethesda, MD: National Institutes of Health. 1989. [NIH Publication No. 89-3045]
50. Cole TG. Glycerol blanking in triglyceride assays: Is it necessary? Clin Chem 1990;36:1267-8.
51. Stein EA, Myers GL. National Cholesterol Education Program Recommendations for triglyceride measurement: Executive Summary. Clin Chem 1995;41:1421–6.
52. Wiebe DA, Warnick GR. Measurement of high density lipoprotein cholesterol concentration. In: Rifai N, Warnick GW, Dominiczak MH, eds. Handbook of lipoprotein testing. Washington, DC: AACC Press, 1997:127–44.
53. Suguichi H, Yorshinori U, Okabe H, et al. Direct measurement of high density lipoprotein cholesterol in serum with polyethylene glycol-modified enzymes and alpha-cyclodextrin. Clin Chem 1995;41:717–23.
54. Harris N, Galpachian V, Thomas J, et al. Three generations of high density lipoprotein cholesterol assays compared with the ultracentrifugation-dextran sulfate-Mg^{++} method. Clin Chem 1997;43:816–23.
55. Rifai N, Cole TG, Iannotti E, et al. Assessment of interlaboratory performance in external proficiency testing programs with a direct HDL-C assay. Clin Chem 1998:in press.
56. Warnick GR, Wood PD. National Cholesterol Education Program Recommendations for measurement of high density lipoprotein cholesterol: Executive Summary. Clin Chem 1995;41:1427–33.
57. Warnick GR, Knopp RH, Fitzpatrick V, et al. Estimating low density lipoprotein cholesterol by the Friedewald equation is adequate for classifying patients on the basis of nationally recommended cut-points. Clin Chem 1990;36:15–9.
58. McNamara JR, Cohn JS, Wilson WPF, et al. Calculated values for low density lipoprotein cholesterol in the assessment of lipid abnormalities and coronary disease risk. Clin Chem 1990;36:36–42.
59. McNamara J, Cole T, Contois J, et al. Evaluation of an immunoseparation method for measuring LDL cholesterol directly from serum. Clin Chem 1995;41:232–40.
60. Harris N, Neufeld E, Newberger J, et al. Analytical performance and clinical utility of a direct LDL cholesterol assay in a hyperlipidemic pediatric population. Clin Chem 1996;42:1182–8.
61. Yu HH, Ginsburg GS, Harris N, Rifai N. Evaluation and clinical application of a direct low density lipoprotein cholesterol assay in normolipidemic and hyperlipidemic adults. Am J Cardiol 1997;80:1295–9.
62. Ticho BS, Neufeld EJ, Newberger JW, et al. Utility of direct measurement of LDL-cholesterol in dyslipidemic pediatric patients. Arch Child Adol Med 1998:in press.

63. Halloran P, Pisani T, Long S. A homogeneous assay for the direct measurement of LDL-cholesterol. Clin Chem 1997;43:S254.
64. Bachorik PS, Ross JW. National Cholesterol Education Program Recommendations for measurement of low density lipoprotein cholesterol: Executive Summary. Clin Chem 1995;41:1414–20.
65. Marcovina SM, Albers JJ. Apolipoprotein assays: standardization and quality control. Scan J Clin Lab Invest 1990;50:58–65.
66. Marcovina SM, Albers JJ, Henderson LO, Hannon WH. International Federation of Clinical Chemistry standardization project for measurements of apolipoproteins AI and B. III. Comparability of apolipoprotein AI values by use of international reference material. Clin Chem 1993;39:773–81.
67. Marcovina SM, Albers JJ, Kennedy H, et al. International Federation of Clinical Chemistry standardization project for measurements of apolipoproteins AI and B. IV. Comparability of apolipoprotein B values by use of international reference material. Clin Chem 1994;40:586–92.
68. American Academy of Pediatrics Committee on Nutrition. Cholesterol in childhood. Pediatrics 1998;101:141–7.
69. McCrindle BW, O'Neill MB, Cullen-Dean G, Helden E. Acceptability and compliance with two forms of cholestyramine in the treatment of hypercholesterolemia in children: a randomized, crossover trial. J Pediatr 1997;130:266–73.
70. Tonstad S, Knudtzon J, Sivertsen M, et al. Efficacy and safety of cholestyramine therapy in peripubertal and prepubertal children with familial hypercholesterolemia. J Pediatr 1996;129:42–9.
71. Lambert M, Lupien PJ, Gagne C, et al. Treatment of familial hypercholesterolemia in children and adolescents: effect of lovastatin. Pediatrics 1996;97:619–28.
72. Knipscheer HC, Boelen CCA, Kastelein JJP, et al. Short-term efficacy and safety of pravastatin in 72 children with familial hypercholesterolemia. Pediatr Res 1997;39:867–71.

CHAPTER 19

Diagnosis and Management of Pediatric Tumors

Guy Young, M.D., Karen L. Kaucic, M.D., Gregory H. Reaman, M.D.

INTRODUCTION

Over the past two decades, the clinical laboratory has become increasingly important in the diagnosis and treatment of pediatric malignancies. Not surprisingly, the laboratory's expanding role has paralleled advances in tumor biology, supportive clinical care, and anti-tumor therapy.

Today the clinical laboratory plays a vital role in the diagnosis, treatment, and supportive care of children with malignancies. This chapter focuses on the laboratory's contributions in each of these areas, specifically (1) biological markers in diagnosis and treatment, (2) supportive management, and (3) the clinical pharmacology of anti-neoplastic therapy. The most common pediatric malignancies are summarized in Figure 19–1.

BIOLOGICAL MARKERS

A biological marker can be broadly defined as a molecule, most often a protein or glycoprotein, present in blood, urine, or other body fluid, which is detectable or increased in the presence of a specific tumor or group of tumors. Biological markers may be intracellular or membrane-associated, biologically active or inert. They are frequently detectable in normal tissues, albeit in smaller quantities, and in other non-malignant disease states, and are thus generally considered to be tumor-associated rather than tumor-specific.[1] Tumor markers are most easily categorized based on their chemical structure

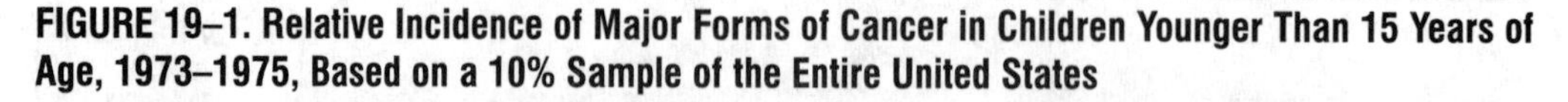

FIGURE 19–1. Relative Incidence of Major Forms of Cancer in Children Younger Than 15 Years of Age, 1973–1975, Based on a 10% Sample of the Entire United States

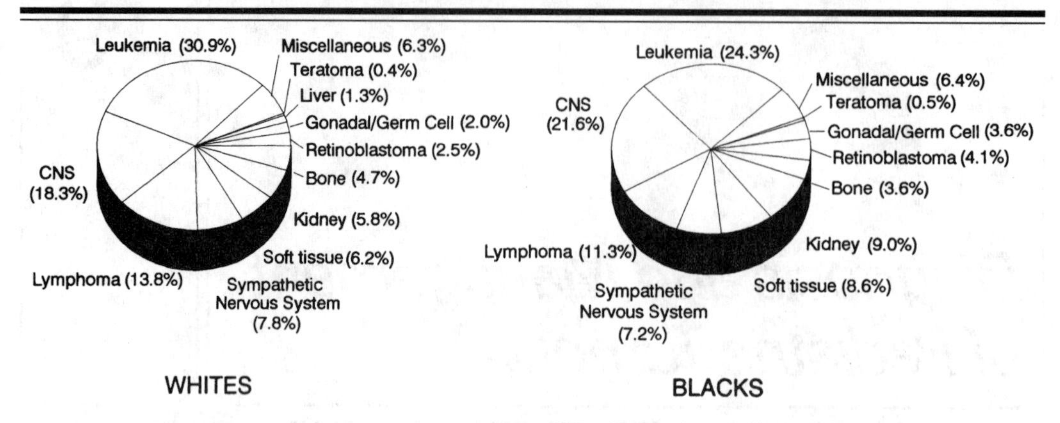

Adapted from Fernbach DJ, Vietti TJ. Clinical pediatric oncology. St. Louis: Mosby Year Book, Inc.

or biological function. Five major classes can be identified: carrier/storage proteins, antigens or membrane receptors, enzymes, hormones, and growth factors.[2]

Biological markers theoretically have four major roles in the diagnosis and management of pediatric malignancies: cancer screening, diagnostic confirmation, assessment of response to therapy, and early detection of relapse or recurrence.

With respect to screening, the low incidence of cancer in the pediatric population in general, and the relative lack of specificity of many biological markers for specific tumors, makes screening utilizing biological markers cost ineffective and clinically inefficient. The single exception is infant screening for neuroblastoma by measurement of urinary catecholamine metabolites, which is discussed in greater detail later in this chapter.

Biological markers are useful in the diagnosis of most pediatric malignancies as adjuncts to radiographic imaging and direct microscopic examination of tissue. They often aid in directing more invasive diagnostic testing and provide useful information in difficult diagnostic dilemmas. In addition, the quantitation of tumor markers often provides a means of assessing tumor bulk or the extent of disease. Biological markers are also useful as non-invasive adjuncts to radiographic studies in assessing response to therapy and screening for disease relapse. They are especially useful in situations in which there is no radiographically measurable disease, since detection of increased tumor marker concentrations may provide evidence of microscopic residual disease or microscopic recurrence, before bulk disease is evident on physical examination or radiographic studies. Ideally, baseline concentrations of tumor markers should be determined prior to surgical intervention or the initiation of radiation or chemotherapy, and then measured serially throughout treatment and post-therapy follow-up.

The biological markers relevant to the diagnosis and management of specific pediatric malignancies are discussed individually below. Table 19–1 summarizes the common pediatric tumor markers.

Carrier and Storage Proteins

α-Fetoprotein

Initially identified in 1944, α-fetoprotein (AFP) was the first circulating tumor-associated marker to be identified.[3] AFP is produced during fetal life by the liver, yolk sac, and gastrointestinal tract and can be detected in high concentrations in fetal serum. A glycosylated protein with structural and functional homology to human albumin, AFP is thought to perform physiological functions in the fetus similar to those of albumin in the adult.[2] Barely detectable in the serum of normal children and adults, its association with human tumors was first described in 1964, when increased concentrations were found in the serum of patients with hepatoma. Sub-

TABLE 19–1. A Summary of the Most Common Biological Markers Grouped by Disease and Their Role(s) in the Diagnosis and Management of Pediatric Malignancies

		Diagnosis	Prognosis	Screening	Follow-up	Not Defined
ALL	LDH		▲		▲	
	IL–2 Receptor	▲	▲			
	tDT	▲				
	GD3	▲				△
Non-Hodgkin's Lymphoma	LDH		▲			
	IL–2 Receptor	▲	▲			
	ß–2–Microglobulin		▲		▲	
	CRP		▲		▲	
	CEA				▲	
Hodgkin's Lymphoma	Ferritin		▲			
	ß–2–Microglobulin		▲		▲	
	CRP		▲		▲	
Neuroblastoma	Catecholamines	▲	▲	▲	▲	
	Cystathionine	▲	▲			
	Aminoisobutyric Acid	▲	▲			
	Ferritin		▲			
	NSE		▲		▲	
	CEA				▲	
	GD2	▲				△
Wilm's Tumor	Hyaluronic Acid	▲			▲	
	Erythropoietin	▲			▲	
	CEA				▲	
Hepatoblastoma	AFP	▲			▲	
	HCG	▲			▲	
	Ferritin				▲	
Germ Cell Tumors	AFP	▲			▲	
	HCG	▲			▲	
Soft Tissue Sarcomas	CK					△
	TAA					△
Osteosarcoma	Alkakine Phosphatase		▲		▲	
	TAA					△
Ewing's Sarcoma	LDH		▲			
CNS Tumors	NSE	▲				
	Polyamines	▲			▲	

sequently, increased serum concentrations of AFP were well documented in pediatric patients with hepatoblastoma, hepatocellular carcinoma, and gonadal and extra-gonadal germ cell tumors.[3–7] Other non-malignant conditions, such as hepatitis, cirrhosis, inflammatory bowel disease, ataxia telangiectasia, and tyrosinosis, also have been associated with increased serum concentrations of AFP.[3]

Initially, detection of AFP was accomplished utilizing bidimensional immunodiffusion or counterimmunoelectrophoresis. These detection methods are limited in their sensitivity and have been supplanted by radioimmunoassay[3] and fluorescence polarization immunoassay. Serum AFP concentrations peak during the 13th week of gestation, then decrease to approximately 30 µg/mL by term. By 6 months of age, serum concentrations generally are less than 50 ng/mL, and in normal children and adults rarely exceed 25 ng/mL.[2, 3]

Serum AFP is increased in 70–80% of patients with hepatocellular carcinoma. Available data suggest that increased concentrations are demonstrable in virtually all children with hepatoblastoma, and that the timing and magnitude of decline of AFP are predictors of outcome.[8] In addition, increased concentrations are observed in children with endodermal sinus (yolk sac) tumors. In patients with hepatic or germ-cell tumors, serum AFP concentrations typically range from 1,000 to 100,000 ng/mL; however, concentrations exceeding 200,000 ng/mL are not uncommon, and concentrations greater than 700,000 ng/mL have been reported.[2] There is evidence to suggest that the extent of AFP glycosylation, which is dependent on the concentration of glycosylase in hepatocytes, may be used in differentiating benign from malignant hepatic tumors. Complete glycosylation of AFP has been observed in benign hepatic neoplasms; however, the extent of glycosylation remains to be determined in patients with malignant tumors.[2]

New methods for the subfractionation of AFP depending on reactivity with lectins have been developed, and have allowed for classification of elevated AFP into three groups: yolk-sac type, hepatoblastoma type, and benign hepatic type. This technique is useful for the differential diagnosis of hepatic masses and AFP-positive tumors.[9]

Serum AFP concentrations decrease dramatically in patients with hepatoblastoma and gonadal germ-cell tumors following tumor resection. Transient post-operative increases (reflecting normal tissue regeneration) are sometimes observed following the resection of hepatic tumors. In patients with recurrent tumors, AFP concentrations often can be detected before clinical disease becomes evident. Hence, serial measurement of serum AFP provides a reliable, non-invasive means of assessing the response to therapy and screening patients for early evidence of disease recurrence.[2] A small subset of children with hepatic malignancies associated with precocious puberty or virilization demonstrate increased concentrations of both AFP and human chorionic gonadotropin (HCG). In these cases, AFP has been found to be a more reliable indicator than HCG of the extent of active disease (see discussion below).[6]

Ferritin

Ferritin is a protein-iron complex consisting of a cluster of 24 polypeptide chains, known as apoferritin, which form an outer shell around variable amounts of ferric hydroxyphosphate. It is found in erythroid progenitors in the bone marrow, hepatic parenchymal cells, and reticuloendothelial cells of the liver, spleen, and bone marrow. There are believed to be at least two structurally different types of polypeptide subunits, which are present in varying proportions in ferritins from different tissues and species, and which impart different electrophoretic mobilities to each of these isoferritins.[2]

In addition to intracellular ferritin, low concentrations of ferritin can be found in the serum of normal children and adults. Normal serum concentrations detected by radioimmunoassay, and more recently by enzyme immunoassay, vary considerably with different detection methods. In pediatric patients the normal range is 6–70 μg/L as determined by enzyme immunoassay.[10]

A sensitive indicator of total body iron stores, ferritin is decreased in the very early stages of iron deficiency. Conversely, it is increased in states of iron overload (hemosiderosis and hemochromatosis), when ferritin-containing hepatocytes undergo necrosis (hepatitis), and in chronic inflammatory conditions (chronic infection, rheumatoid arthritis, chronic renal disease).

In some malignant conditions, ferritin is produced by tumor cells, resulting in an increase in total body ferritin and an increase in serum ferritin. To date, increased concentrations of ferritin have been observed in patients with neuroblastoma, leukemia, Hodgkin's lymphoma, and hepatocellular carcinoma.[2] It is clinically most useful in patients with neuroblastoma, Hodgkin's disease, and hepatic malignancies.

In patients with localized tumors and those with Stage IVS neuroblastoma, serum ferritin concentrations are generally within the normal range, even when active disease is present. In contrast, approximately 50% of patients with advanced-stage disease (III and IV) have increased serum ferritin. In patients with disseminated neuroblastoma, serum ferritin is a reliable indicator of tumor burden and is therefore useful in following response to therapy. In addition, there is some evidence to suggest that ferritin concentrations at diagnosis are of prognostic value in advanced-stage disease. In one series, disease-free survival in patients with Stage III neuroblastoma and normal serum ferritin concentrations at diagnosis was 76%, compared to 23% in patients with increased ferritin concentrations. Survival in patients with Stage IV disease and normal ferritin concentrations was 27%, versus 3% in patients with Stage IV disease and increased ferritin concentrations.[11]

Both acidic and basic isoferritins can be identified in patients with neuroblastoma, and recent evidence suggests that they may exert inhibitory effects on both T-lymphocytes and granulocytes.[2] In the laboratory, transplantation of neuroblastoma into animal models has resulted in subsequent increase of serum ferritin. Ferritin production by neuroblastoma cells has also been observed *in vitro*.[2]

In patients with Hodgkin's disease, increased serum ferritin at diagnosis appears to be associated with an increased risk of relapse. In addition, the degree of increase correlates directly with disease stage (and therefore tumor burden).[12]

Serum ferritin is also a useful indicator of tumor burden and response to therapy in patients with hepatic malignancies, especially in the subset of patients with normal serum AFP concentrations. However, its utility as a prognostic tool has not been well defined in hepatic tumors.[2]

Enzymes

Alkaline Phosphatase

Alkaline phosphatase is a cell-membrane-associated enzyme present in all tissues. It is present in the greatest quantities in osteoblasts, renal tubular epithelium, intestinal epithelium, liver, and placenta. Several tissue-specific isoenzymes have been identified. Their exact functions have not been clearly elucidated; however, the bone-associated enzyme is thought to have some role in calcium deposition.[13]

Alkaline phosphatase activity is measured spectrophotometrically utilizing a chromogenic substrate. In normal children, maximum serum concentrations range from 100 to 500 U/L, depending on the child's age and the specific methodology employed. Maximum adult concentrations range from 50 to 100 U/L.[8, 13] Isoenzymes can be separated by electrophoresis, heat inactivation analysis, urea or chemical inhibition, or the use of specific antisera.

Alkaline phosphatase is increased in patients with intrahepatic and extrahepatic biliary obstruction, hepatocellular damage, or increased osteoblastic activity.[13] Increased concentrations of alkaline phosphatase can be demonstrated in both the serum and tumor tissue of patients with osteogenic sarcoma. Increased serum concentrations are observed in approximately 40% of patients,[14] although concentrations are not well correlated with tumor bulk, the extent of disease, or, interestingly, the degree of tumor calcification. Hence, measurement is not helpful in monitoring response to therapy.[2, 15] In addition, the clinical utility of serum alkaline phosphatase concentrations is limited in patients with underlying hepatic dysfunction or healing fractures, and in children and adolescents in phases of accelerated growth.

Alkaline phosphatase concentrations may be of prognostic significance in patients with osteogenic sarcoma. Data from several studies have suggested that the risk of disease recurrence is higher among patients with increased serum or tumor tissue concentrations of alkaline phosphatase. In one series, survival in patients with increased serum alkaline phosphatase concentrations was 19%, versus 54% among patients with normal serum alkaline phosphatase. In a study of tissue alkaline phosphatase concentrations in osteosarcoma, 17 of 19 patients (89%) with increased enzyme concentrations in the primary lesion developed recurrent disease, whereas relapse occurred in 1 of 6 patients (17%) with normal tumor alkaline phosphatase concentrations.[15]

Lactate Dehydrogenase

Lactate dehydrogenase (LDH) is a ubiquitous cytosolic enzyme which catalyzes the oxidation of lactate to pyruvate. The highest concentrations are found in cardiac and skeletal muscle, liver, kidney, and red blood cells. A tetrameric enzyme, LDH is composed of four polypeptide subunits. Polypeptide chains are of two types, designated M and H (or A and B). Five isoenzymes have been identified, corresponding to each of the five possible combinations of subunits, and denoted LDH-1 through LDH-5. LDH-1 and LDH-2 are found predominantly in kidney, cardiac muscle, and red blood cells; LDH-3 in a variety of tissues, including endocrine glands, spleen, lung, lymph nodes, and platelets; LDH-4 and LDH-5 in liver and skeletal muscle.[13]

LDH activity is measured spectrophotometrically. Reference values of 200–500 U/L typically are obtained in normal subjects; however, reference ranges can vary somewhat depending on the specific methodology employed.[10] Increased serum LDH concentrations have been observed in leukemia, lymphoma, rhabdomyosarcoma, Ewing's sarcoma, neuroblastoma, hepatoma, and germ-cell tumors.[2] Among leukemia patients, it appears that those with lymphoblastic leukemias demonstrate higher serum concentrations of LDH than those with myeloid leukemias.[16] Serum LDH concentrations appear to have prognostic value in acute lymphoblastic leukemia (ALL) and non-lymphoblastic non-Hodgkin's lymphoma, with higher serum concentrations of LDH at diagnosis associated with a poorer prognosis in both cases.[17] Similarly, in patients with non-metastatic Ewing's sarcoma, the rate of disease-free survival is greater among those patients with normal serum LDH concentrations at diagnosis.[18] LDH-1, which is not commonly increased in patients with malignant processes, has been found in increased concentrations in the serum of patients with endodermal sinus tumors.[19]

LDH is also increased in patients with hemolysis, as well as in those with muscle injury, inflammation, or infection. In general, the lack of specificity of LDH limits its usefulness as a diagnostic tool. It can, however, be used prognostically in some malignant processes, and, if increased at diagnosis, can serve as a non-invasive indicator of response to therapy.

Creatine Kinase

The reversible phosphorylation of adenosine diphosphate (ADP) by creatine phosphate to form adenosine triphosphate (ATP) is catalyzed by creatine phosphokinase (CK). CK is present mainly in myocardium, skeletal muscle, and brain, and functions in replenishing cellular stores of ATP following ATP-consuming processes such as muscle contraction. Three dimeric isoenzymes exist, each composed of a combination of M (muscle) and B (brain) subunits. CK-1 (BB) is found mainly in the brain and CK-2 (MB) and CK-3 (MM) in heart and skeletal muscle, with CK-3 the predominant isoenzyme.[13] Measured spectrophotometrically, the normal range in the pediatric population is 40–380 U/L.[10]

Increased concentrations of CK generally are observed in patients with inflammatory or degenerative muscle disorders, myocardial infarction, or damage to brain parenchyma (traumatic, ischemic, or inflammatory).[13] Immunohistochemical studies have demonstrated M and B CK subunits in neuroblastoma and rhabdomyosarcoma cells and B subunits in Ewing's sarcoma. Increased serum concentrations of CK-2 have been demonstrated in patients with rhabdomyosarcoma; however, its usefulness as a biological marker has not been widely explored.[2]

Enolase

Three dimeric forms of enolase, a glycolytic enzyme present in neural tissue, have been identified. Neuron-specific enolase (NSE), composed of two δ subunits, is found primarily in neuronal, endocrine, and neuroendocrine cells. Non-neuronal enolase (NNE), consisting of two α subunits, is found in glial cells. A third hybrid form (α, δ) has also been identified.[2]

Measured by RIA, normal concentrations range from 0 to 15 ng/mL. Presence of the enzyme can be detected in neural tissue by immunohistochemical staining. Increased serum concentrations of NSE have been demonstrated in patients with neuroblastoma, medulloblastoma, and retinoblastoma. Concentrations found in association with the latter two tumors are generally less than 100 ng/mL.[2]

In patients with neuroblastoma, disseminated (Stage III or IV) disease is strongly associated with increased concentrations of NSE. In one large, multi-institutional study, 117 of 121 patients (96%) were found to have increased concentrations of NSE at diagnosis. In this study, serum NSE greater than 100 ng/mL was predictive of a poor outcome in patients less than 2 years of age with Stage III disease, and in those less than 1 year of age with Stage IV disease, but not in older patients or those with lower stage disease.[20] Response to therapy is generally well correlated with a decrease in NSE concentrations;[20, 21] however, the utility of serum NSE as a predictive tool with respect to disease recurrence has not been extensively studied. As is also true of serum ferritin, serum NSE concentrations are not increased in patients with Stage IVS disease.[20]

Terminal Deoxynucleotidyl Transferase

Terminal deoxynucleotidyl transferase (tDT) is a DNA polymerase which is able to form single-stranded DNA from nucleotide monophosphates without a DNA template. It is thought to function in the normal state in immunoglobulin and T-cell receptor gene rearrangement. It can be detected in the nuclei of thymocytes and leukemic lymphoblasts by indirect immunofluorescence. It is not present in mature lymphocytes. Serum concentrations are measurable using quantitative enzyme assays or RIA. Increased concentrations are observed primarily in patients with T-cell and pre-B-cell ALL and CML.[22, 23]

Antigens

Carcinoembryonic Antigen

Carcinoembryonic antigen (CEA) is the best known of the tumor-associated antigens. A glycoprotein, it was initially identified as a cell-surface-associated antigen in patients with adenocarcinoma. It is believed to function in cell-to-cell interaction.[1] CEA is measured by RIA or enzyme immunoassay with normal concentrations ranging from 0 to 10 ng/mL.[24]

Increased concentrations are most often found in the sera of adult patients with gastrointestinal malignancies and can consistently be shown to decrease with successful therapy.[3] CEA has been identified in pediatric patients with a variety of malignancies, including Wilms' tumor, neuroblastoma, lymphoma, germ cell tumors, mesenchymal tumors, and retinoblastoma.[3, 25] The lack of specificity of CEA limits its utility as a diagnostic tool in differentiating pediatric tumors. However, if initially increased, CEA may be useful in monitoring response to therapy or as a non-invasive means of post-therapy follow-up in certain clinical situations.

Tumor-Associated Antigens

Tumor-associated antigens (TAAs) are thought to be normally occurring cellular substances expressed in relatively larger quantities by tumor cells. Proteins, carbohydrates, glycoproteins, and glycolipids have been identified in this structurally heterogeneous group of antigens. TAAs are thought to perform any of a number of cellular functions, including transport and inter- and intracellular signaling.

Utilizing monoclonal antibodies, a number of TAAs have been identified in patients with melanoma and carcinoma. In pediatric patients, TAAs have been detected in the urine of several children with sarcomas of soft tissues and bone. In one series of 50 sarcoma patients, 24 of 25 patients (96%) who developed recurrent disease after initial therapy demonstrated increased urinary TAA titers prior to clinical presentation, whereas 23 of 25 patients (92%) who remained disease-free had no increase of urinary TAAs.[26] While TAAs may be useful in post-therapy follow-up, their utility as biological markers requires further exploration.

β-2-Microglobulin

Considered an acute phase reactant, the peptide β-2-microglobulin (BMG) constitutes the light chain of the human leukocyte antigens (HLA). It is also found freely circulating in the serum. It is measured by RIA with serum reference range of 0.10–0.26 mg/dL.[24] Increased concentrations have been observed in association with advanced stage (III and IV) Hodgkin's and non-Hodgkin's lymphoma and appear to correlate with disease remission and response to therapy.[27]

Gangliosides

Gangliosides are glycolipid molecules containing a lipid core surrounded by sialic acid-containing oligosaccharide moieties. Two distinct gangliosides, GD_2 and GD_3, have been identified on the surfaces of neuroblastoma cells and T-cell ALL lymphoblasts, respectively. GD_2 is shed from cells and can be detected in the serum by HPLC or thin-layer chromatography, and increased concentrations have been demonstrated in patients with neuroblastoma. The utility of GD_2 and GD_3 as diagnostic and prognostic tools remains to be fully defined.[28, 29]

Interleukin-2 Receptor

A soluble form of the interleukin-2 receptor (IL2R), a membrane-associated cellular growth factor receptor, has been demonstrated in the serum by enzyme immunoassay. The reference range in normal children is 400–950 U/mL. Increased concentrations are observed in patients with ALL and non-Hodgkin's lymphoma and appear to correlate with increased LDH concentrations. Serum IL2R appears to correlate inversely with prognosis in both cases.[30, 31]

Hormones

Increased hormone concentrations can be detected in association with a number of malignancies. Tumor-associated hormones can be broadly classified into two groups:

those produced by primary endocrine malignancies and those produced by non-endocrine tumors. Primary endocrine malignancies are rare in the pediatric population, representing only 4–5% of all pediatric tumors. The tumors most commonly found are gonadal (45%), thyroid (30%), and pituitary (20%).[32] The majority of primary endocrine malignancies in children do not secrete hormones.

Neuroblastoma, germ-cell tumors, and hepatic tumors comprise the non-endocrine tumors that produce hormones in pediatric patients. The hormones most often secreted by these non-endocrine malignancies are human chorionic gonadotropin and the catecholamines.

Human Chorionic Gonadotropin

Human chorionic gonadotropin (HCG), a heterogeneous glycoprotein dimer, is normally produced by the trophoblastic cells of the placenta. It is structurally similar to the other dimeric gonadotropins produced by the anterior pituitary, follicle-stimulating hormone and luteinizing hormone. Composed of one α and one β subunit, the α subunits are identical among the three hormones. Their unique functional and antigenic properties are imparted by structurally distinct β subunits.[33]

HCG is detected by radioimmunoassay, utilizing an antibody directed against the β subunit. Less than 5 IU/mL is detected in the serum of normal males and non-pregnant females.[2] Increased concentrations are detected in gravid females. In pathologic states, increased concentrations are observed most consistently in association with choriocarcinoma and nonseminomatous germ-cell tumors[33, 34] and, less frequently, in association with seminomatous germ-cell tumors and hepatomas.[2, 4, 6, 33]

The half-life of HCG in the serum is 12–20 h. It is therefore a useful indicator of response to therapy, with a dramatic decrease in serum concentrations often demonstrable within several hours of complete resection of a HCG-secreting tumor.[2] Persistently increased HCG concentrations are reliably associated with residual or recurrent disease, except in children with virilizing hepatic tumors. AFP may be a more reliable indicator of disease status in this small group of patients; however, few patients have been studied extensively.

Catecholamines

The catecholamines epinephrine, norepinephrine, and dopamine are produced by cells of neural crest origin in the adrenal medulla. Epinephrine is secreted in large quantities, and norepinephrine to a much lesser degree, in response to pain, emotional stress, and hypoglycemia. They act primarily on the sympathetic nervous system to increase mean arterial blood pressure and myocardial contractility, and they induce glycogenolysis, resulting in increased serum glucose. Serum concentrations of catecholamines are virtually undetectable in the resting state.

Although rare in children, pheochromocytoma, a malignant transformation of the chromaffin cells of the adrenal medulla, is characterized by high circulating concentrations of epinephrine and norepinephrine, resulting in classical clinical symptoms including tachycardia, hypertension, weight loss, and flushing. Increased concentrations of epinephrine and norepinephrine can be detected in the serum, and their metabolites, vanillylmandelic acid (VMA) and the metanephrines, can be detected in the urine. It is necessary to assay for all intermediates in the catecholamine pathway, since pheochromocytomas may secrete a single intermediate.

Neuroblastoma, one of the most common tumors seen in the pediatric age group, also arises from cells of neural crest origin. In contrast to patients with pheochromocytoma, serum concentrations of epinephrine and norepinephrine are normal or minimally increased in children with neuroblastoma. However, catecholamine metabolites VMA and 3-methoxy-4-hydroxyphenoglycol (MHPG), the major metabolites of norepinephrine, and homovanillic acid (HVA), the major metabolite of dopamine, are excreted in the urine in large amounts.[35]

MHPG is measured by gas-liquid chromatography or high-performance liquid chromatography, with normal urinary excretion of 1–2 mg per day. VMA can be measured spectrophotometrically, and both VMA and HVA by high-performance liquid chromatography (HPLC). Both metabolites can be measured simultaneously utilizing bi-directional paper chromatography.[2, 36] Results generally are reported in terms of urine collection time or urine creatinine. Most commonly, HVA and VMA are measured in 24 h urine collections. Normal urinary excretion is less than 10 mg per day each for HVA and VMA. Reference ranges expressed in terms of creatinine are 1–40 micrograms HVA per mg creatinine and less than 7 micrograms VMA per mg creatinine.[36]

Because they can be measured utilizing less complex methodologies, urinary HVA and VMA are the most frequently assayed metabolites and the laboratory tests of choice in the diagnosis of neural crest tumors.[37] Reported rates of catecholamine metabolite excretion in neuroblastoma patients have ranged from 75 to 95% for VMA and 80 to 95% for HVA.[38, 39] In a recent study employing improved HPLC techniques, no overlap was observed between the reference ranges for urinary VMA and the VMA concentrations in patients with neural crest tumors. Patients with neuroblastoma also had urinary HVA concentrations above the 100th percentile.[40] In one study of 94 patients with neuroblastoma, the absolute value of the urinary VMA concentration and the ratio of VMA to HVA was found to correlate directly with prognosis. That is, patients with higher ratios of VMA to HVA tended to have better prognoses. No correlation was observed between the absolute urinary concentration of HVA and prognosis. The same authors also studied the excretion patterns of three other catecholamine metabolites—vanillactic acid (VLA), normetanephrine (NMN), and vanilglycol (VG)—and found that, in general, the presence of the dopamine metabolite VLA correlated with a poorer prognosis, but the presence of the epinephrine and norepinephrine metabolites NMN and VG did not. They postulated that increased urinary dopamine metabolites (VLA) may be observed in patients with poorly differentiated (and therefore more aggressive) tumors which lack dopamine β-hydroxylase, the enzyme which catalyzes the conversion of dopamine to norepinephrine.[39]

In Japan, mass screening of 6- to 7-month-old infants using a spot test for VMA has resulted in the detection of pre-clinical disease as well as an increase in the number of patients detected earlier in the course of the disease (that is, at a lower clinical stage). An Austrian study of 115,000 infants screened for neuroblastoma by

EIA of spot urines for catecholamine metabolites confirmed this previous finding.[41] The greater proportion of patients detected with localized disease has reportedly resulted in improved outcome since the implementation of mass screening.[42] Verification of these findings is in progress in North America using the Quebec Genetic Screening Program.

Growth Factors

Erythropoietin

Erythropoietin is a hematopoietic growth factor which is produced by the kidney and regulates erythropoiesis. A glycoprotein, it is measured by RIA and ELISA and is normally detectable in minute amounts in the serum and urine.

Erythropoietin has been detected in large amounts in both the serum and urine of patients with Wilms' tumor. Of note, increased concentrations of erythropoietin in these patients are not associated with erythrocytosis, suggesting that the erythropoietin produced by this neoplasm is functionally defective. In one study of 37 patients with Wilms' tumor and increased erythropoietin, concentrations were observed to fall dramatically after resection of the primary mass in patients with localized disease, but to remain persistently increased in patients with metastatic disease.[2]

Thrombopoietin

Thrombopoietin is the primary regulator of thrombopoiesis and is synthesized constitutively in the liver, kidney, and bone marrow.[43] It is assayed by a sandwich EIA utilizing polyclonal rabbit anti-human thrombopoietin antibodies.[44] Elevated levels are seen in thrombocytopenic conditions caused by decreased platelet production such as aplastic anemia, chemotherapy-induced thrombocytopenia, and congenital marrow failure syndromes.[45, 46] There is also evidence that the thrombocytosis associated with hepatoblastoma is caused by elevated thrombopoietin levels; however, its use as a tumor marker requires further investigation.[47, 48]

Other Markers

A number of other substances have been identified in increased quantities in children with malignant neoplasms. They include carbohydrate, protein, and nucleic acid constituents or metabolites. Several of these markers are of importance in pediatric patients: C-reactive protein, hyaluronic acid, cystathionine, aminoisobutyric acid, and the polyamines.

C-Reactive Protein

C-reactive protein (CRP) is an acute-phase reactant so named for its ability to react with the C-polysaccharide on the cell wall of *Streptococcus pneumoniae*. It is a pentameric structure consisting of five polypeptide subunits which associate in a ring-like fashion. Functionally, CRP can initiate opsonization and phagocytosis, and the classical complement cascade. It can be measured by RIA, radioimmunodiffusion, and rate nephelometry. The reference range using one of the latter two methods is 80–800 μg/dL.[24] Increased concentrations of CRP are observed in association with infection, inflammation, trauma, and malignancy. Increased concentrations of CRP have been observed in association with advanced-stage lymphomas (Hodgkin's and non-Hodgkin's).[27]

Hyaluronic Acid

The glycosaminoglycan, hyaluronic acid, is a large polysaccharide chain which associates with other glycosaminoglycan and protein subunits to form macromolecules called proteoglycans, the major constituents of cartilage and other connective tissue. It has been detected qualitatively by acetic acid precipitation and quantitatively by hyaluronidase degradation with colorimetric assay of disaccharide degradation products. It has been observed in the serum of several patients with Wilms' tumor, inducing hyperviscosity in some cases. Preoperative levels correlate well with clinical staging, and a rapid decrease in serum concentrations has been demonstrated in patients whose tumors are completely resected.[49–51] While measurement of serum hyaluronic acid concentrations may be of benefit in assessing response to therapy in Wilms' tumor, its utility is currently limited by complex assay methodology and limited patient data and clinical correlation.

Cystathionine and Aminoisobutyric Acid

Cystathionine and aminoisobutyric acid are amino acids that have been found in concentrations in the urine of patients with neuroblastoma. Both can be measured by bi-directional paper chromatography, ion exchange, or HPLC. Increased concentrations of cystathionine have been demonstrated in approximately 60% of all patients with neuroblastoma (Stages I–IV) and in up to 75% of patients with Stage III and IV disease. Comparable rates for aminoisobutyric acid are reported to be 75% and 70%, respectively.[39]

Polyamines

Polyamines such as spermidine, spermine, and putrescine are cationic molecules which function in nucleic acid metabolism. Polyamines are known to be both growth factors and inhibitors of immune function. They can be measured by ion-exchange chromatography and HPLC. Reference values in CSF have been established in patients with non-malignant neurological disorders and in healthy adults (spermidine 77–293 pmol/mL, putrescine 58–278 pmol/mL). Polyamines are produced in increased quantities by rapidly dividing tumors with high DNA turnover. Increased polyamine concentrations have been demonstrated in the urine, serum, and cerebrospinal fluid (CSF) of patients with central nervous system (CNS) malignancies, especially medulloblastoma. Increased CSF concentrations have been demonstrated in several patients with recurrent CNS tumors before clinical or radiographic evidence of relapse was evident.[52–54] The polyamine N1, N12-diacetylspermine has been shown to be a diagnostic marker of leukemia, and its level correlates with tumor burden.[55]

SUPPORTIVE MANAGEMENT OF PEDIATRIC CANCER PATIENTS

The clinical chemistry laboratory is essential to the diagnosis and appropriate management of patients with biochemical abnormalities resulting from tumor therapy. Metabolic derangements during treatment most commonly result from rapid lysis of tumor cells or the direct effects of chemotherapeutic agents on hepatic, renal, or pancreatic tissues.

Tumor Lysis Syndrome

Acute tumor lysis syndrome (TLS) results from the cytolysis of tumor cells and subsequent release of phosphate and potassium, as well as xanthine, hypoxanthine, and uric acid, the products of nucleic acid degradation.

TLS is observed in association with very large or rapidly dividing tumors and is most often encountered in patients with lymphoma or ALL.[56–58] Patients particularly at risk are those with Burkitt's lymphoma[59] and T-cell leukemia, both of which have particularly short doubling times. TLS also has been described in association with chronic myelogenous leukemia, recurrent non-Hodgkin's lymphoma,[60] and metastatic medulloblastoma.[61]

The classical metabolic triad of hyperuricemia, hyperphosphatemia, and hyperkalemia characterizes TLS. Phosphate and uric acid are freely filtered by the kidney and, if present in excessive quantities in the serum, can exceed their solubility in urine and precipitate in the renal collecting ducts. In addition, the solubility of uric acid (pKa 5.4) is decreased in the acid environment of the nephron, thus increasing even further the risk of uric acid precipitation. Urate and/or phosphate nephropathy may result in renal dysfunction and oliguria, and ultimately renal failure. Less frequently, excessive uric acid excretion results in the formation of urate stones. Hyperphosphatemia induces hypocalcemia as a result of precipitation of calcium phosphate crystals and sequestration of calcium in bone and other tissues; tetany or seizures may result. Increased serum potassium may induce electrocardiographic abnormalities, including fatal cardiac arrhythmias.

Since it occurs when cellular degeneration is greatest, TLS usually is observed at diagnosis or within the first several days after the initiation of therapy and has been reported to reappear in patients with recurrent tumors (see Figure 19–2). Routine screening of patients at diagnosis, especially those with malignancies in which there is an increased frequency of TLS, is essential in establishing baseline metabolic parameters and in identifying patients with chemical evidence of TLS without clinical manifestations. The laboratory evaluation should include measurement of electrolyte, calcium, phosphorus, and uric acid concentrations, as well as those of blood urea nitrogen and serum creatinine. Routine measurement of these parameters should continue through the initial phases of therapy, with the frequency of measurement tailored to the degree of metabolic derangement.

Therapy of TLS is aimed at correcting metabolic abnormalities such as hyperkalemia and hypocalcemia and decreasing the risk of renal impairment by minimizing renal deposition of phosphate and urate crystals. The latter is accomplished by vigorous hydration to maintain brisk urinary diuresis; administration of bicar-

FIGURE 19–2. A Typical Profile of the Metabolic Derangements Observed in a Patient with ALL and Acute Tumor Lysis Syndrome

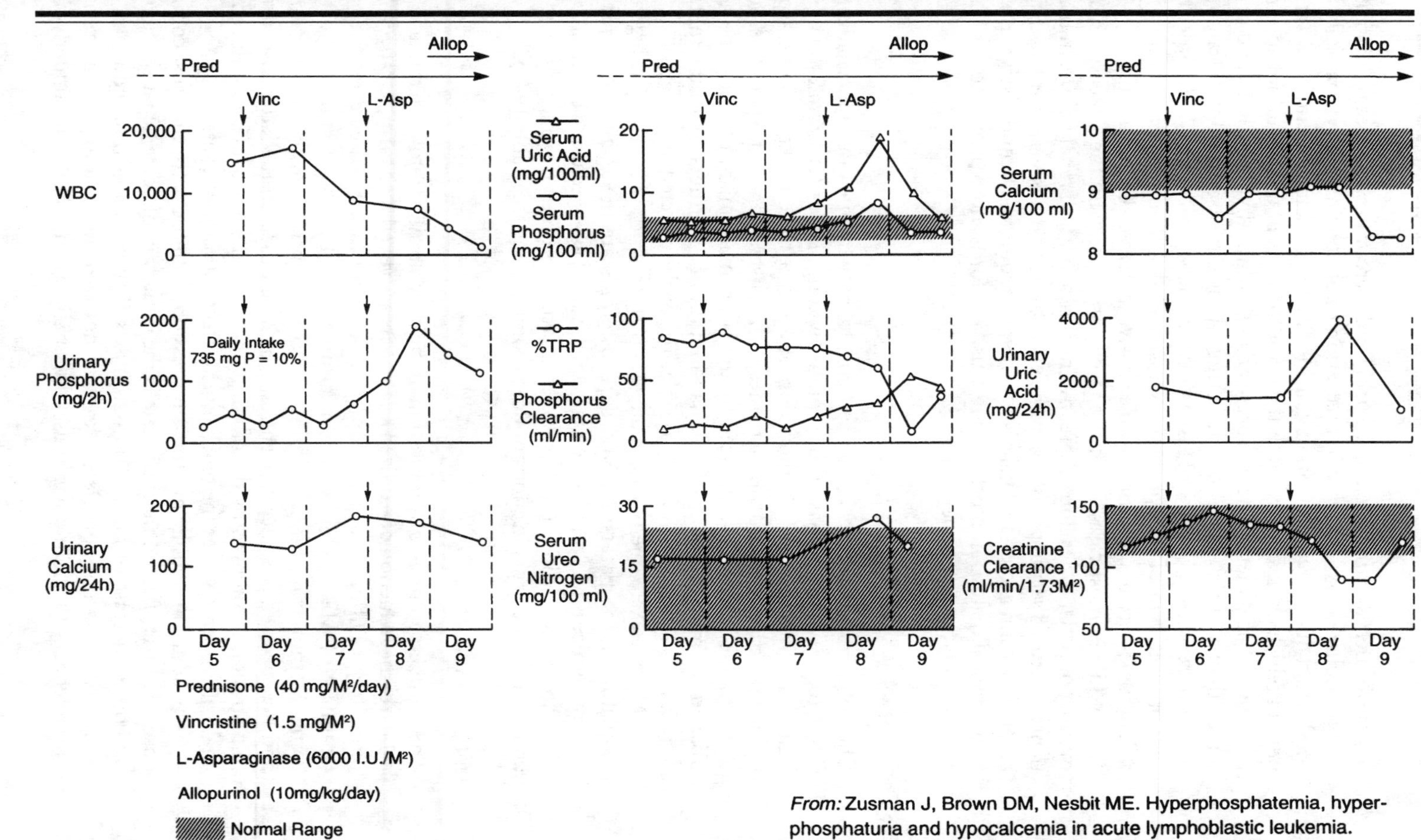

From: Zusman J, Brown DM, Nesbit ME. Hyperphosphatemia, hyperphosphaturia and hypocalcemia in acute lymphoblastic leukemia. N Eng J Med 1973;289:1335-40. Reprinted by permission.

bonate to effect alkalinization of the urine and thereby prevent precipitation of urate and phosphate crystals; and administration of allopurinol, which partially blocks production of uric acid from its oxypurine precursors, xanthine and hypoxanthine, both of which are also excreted in the urine. As a result of allopurinol administration, nucleic acid metabolites are excreted as xanthine, hypoxanthine, and uric acid rather than as uric acid alone, resulting in an increase in the total amount of oxypurine excreted. Urinary pH is maintained between 7.0 and 7.5 in order to prevent precipitation of phosphate in excessively alkaline urine and to minimize the risk of hypocalcemia resulting from excessive systemic alkalinization.

While in most cases TLS can be well controlled with these measures, a small number of patients develop progressive nephropathy and renal failure. In these patients, increased serum potassium induced by tumor cytolysis is exacerbated by poor renal potassium excretion. Dialysis is generally required. Hemodialysis is preferred to peritoneal dialysis in most cases because it affords more precise control of fluid and electrolyte management.

Assessment of Drug Toxicity

Chemotherapeutic agents induce systemic toxicity by one of two mechanisms: (1) interference with cell division in rapidly dividing tissues (gastrointestinal epithelium, bone marrow); or (2) induction of a direct toxic effect on some aspect of cellular function in non-dividing tissues such as liver, kidney, and pancreas. Surveillance for the toxic effects induced by the latter mechanism often can be accomplished by measurement of cellular metabolic products or other metabolic constituents in the serum which are specific for the affected target organ.

Methotrexate, the purine analogues (6-mercaptopurine and 6-thioguanine), *cis*-platinum, L-asparaginase, and corticosteroids are the agents which most frequently induce direct cellular damage which can be assessed using chemical parameters. Routine screening of such parameters facilitates timely treatment of toxic effects and appropriate drug deletions or dose modifications (see Table 19–2).[62–64]

Methotrexate

This antimetabolite acts by inhibition of the enzyme dihydrofolate reductase, which catalyzes the reduction of oxidized folate to its active reduced form, tetrahydrofolate, ultimately resulting in the cessation of purine synthesis. It is used extensively in the treatment of ALL in children and is also employed in the treatment of osteosarcoma. Methotrexate can be administered orally, intravenously, and intrathecally, and may be used at either conventional or high doses. In the latter case, drug administration is followed by the administration of the leucovorin, a reduced folate analogue which reverses the biochemical effects of methotrexate.

In addition to bone marrow suppression and mucositis, the most commonly observed toxic effect of methotrexate is the induction of acute hepatitis, characterized by an increase of hepatic transaminases. The mechanism of induction of hepatic toxicity is not completely known; however, it is thought to be related to interference with choline synthesis. Older patients and those with underlying liver

TABLE 19–2. Antineoplastic Agents which Induce Hepatic or Renal Toxicity or Require Dose Modification in Patients with Underlying Hepatic or Renal Dysfunction

	Induces Renal Dysfunction	Induces Hepatic Dysfunction	Altered Pharmacokinetics in Renal Dysfunction	Altered Pharmacokinetics in Hepatic Dysfunction
Anthracyclines				■
Cis–Platinum	□		■	
Methotrexate	□	□	■	
6–Mercaptopurine /6–Thioguanine		□		
5–Fluorouracil				■
Cyclophosphamide	□			■
Ifosfamide	□			■
Melphalan				■
Nitrosoureas	□			
Dacarbazine				■
Etoposide				■
Vincristine	□			■

disease are at greatest risk. High-dose therapy reliably induces an acute increase of hepatic enzymes, with a return to normal concentrations within 1 week. In addition, hyperbilirubinemia is sometimes observed in association with high-dose therapy. Chronic oral administration of lower dose methotrexate, employed in maintenance therapy for ALL, may induce an acute increase of hepatic enzymes, but less predictably than that observed in high-dose therapy. In this situation, temporary suspension of oral therapy or dosage reduction frequently results in return of enzyme concentrations to normal. Chronic hepatic dysfunction is infrequently observed in children. In general, assessment of liver function in patients receiving long-term therapy with methotrexate should be performed monthly and should include measurement of alanine aminotransferase, aspartate aminotransferase, alkaline phosphatase, and bilirubin.

Renal dysfunction, as reflected by blood urea nitrogen (BUN) and creatinine, is induced by the deposition of methotrexate and 7-hydroxymethotrexate in renal tubules. It is observed in association with high-dose therapy. Drug administration in this situation is accompanied by hydration and systemic alkalinization to facilitate renal excretion and reduce precipitation of methotrexate and its metabolites. The assessment of BUN and creatinine is essential prior to therapy and during drug administration.

6-Mercaptopurine and 6-Thioguanine

The purine analogues 6-mercaptopurine and 6-thioguanine (6-TG), which act both by inhibition of *de novo* nucleotide biosynthesis and incorporation into DNA, are important components of ALL and AML therapy in children. 6-MP induces hepatic cholestasis and hepatocellular necrosis, resulting in an increase of hepatic transaminases, alkaline phosphatase, and bilirubin. 6-TG has been associated with similar laboratory findings, albeit much less frequently. The risk of hepatotoxicity is increased in patients receiving concomitant therapy with other hepatotoxic agents such as methotrexate.

Cis-Platinum

Cis-platinum (*cis*-diaminedichloroplatinum or CDDP) is an alkylating agent which acts by induction of DNA crosslinks and interference in DNA synthesis. It is currently used in the treatment of brain tumors, lymphoma, osteosarcoma, and neuroblastoma. Its major non-hematologic side effect is nephrotoxicity, induced by direct cellular damage to the epithelium of the distal tubules and collecting ducts. The major clinical effects are progressive decrease in the glomerular filtration rate and magnesium wasting. The risk of renal damage is decreased with vigorous hydration during CDDP administration.

Routine screening of renal function with BUN and creatinine is essential throughout the duration of therapy and often for several months thereafter. In addition, glomerular function must be assessed prior to the administration of each course of CDDP. The determination of creatinine clearance based on a 24 h urine collection is employed in older children and adolescents who can cooperate with urine collection. Radiologic evaluation utilizing radioisotope renal scanning is necessary in younger children. Dose modification or deletion of CDDP is required with progressive decline in renal function.

Frequent monitoring of serum magnesium concentrations is also necessary during CDDP therapy. Many patients require chronic oral magnesium replacement during and often for several weeks following treatment with repeated courses of CDDP. Asymptomatic hypomagnesemia is most frequently encountered. Rarely, muscle cramping or frank tetany occurs.

L-Asparaginase

The enzyme L-asparaginase is a mainstay of therapy in childhood ALL and lymphoma in children. It acts by catalyzing the conversion of L-asparagine to aspartate, thus depleting cellular stores of L-asparagine and ultimately resulting in the inhibition of protein synthesis. The spectrum of its toxicities includes allergic reactions, coagulopathy, acute pancreatitis, and hepatotoxicity. Pancreatic toxicity is manifested by non-ketotic hyperglycemia, requiring assessment of serum and urine glucose concentrations, especially when therapy is initiated. Insulin is occasionally required to control hyperglycemia, especially in those patients also receiving steroid therapy. Death from acute pancreatitis in this setting is rare. Hepatotoxicity, manifested by increased concentrations of hepatic transaminases, is also rarely observed.

Corticosteroids

Although steroid therapy is employed as primary therapy for leukemia and lymphoma in children, its mechanism of action is not well understood. It is also used in patients with central nervous system tumors who have clinical evidence of intracranial pressure. Short courses of steroid therapy, even when administered in high doses, are generally without clinical effects. In contrast, prolonged steroid therapy may have a number of untoward clinical and biochemical effects, including increased appetite, obesity, poor growth, poor wound healing, salt and water retention, hypertension, and hyperglycemia.

Serum glucose must be assessed routinely in patients requiring prolonged steroid therapy and in patients who require concomitant therapy with L-asparaginase, such as those in the initial phases of therapy for ALL or lymphoma.

Miscellaneous Toxicities

A number of other chemotherapeutic agents which induce systemic biochemical toxicity are either less frequently employed in pediatric chemotherapy regimens or less frequently associated with toxicities.

The oxazophosphorine alkylating agents, cyclophosphamide and ifosfamide, are both associated with renal dysfunction. Cyclophosphamide, which is employed in the treatment of lymphoma, leukemia, neuroblastoma, and sarcoma, acts on the renal tubules to induce water retention and secondary hyponatremia in small numbers of patients. Hydration is required during cyclophosphamide administration to minimize morbidity from drug-induced hemorrhagic cystitis. Therefore, frequent assessment of serum electrolytes and urine specific gravity is warranted during cyclophosphamide administration. Ifosfamide, an agent employed in the treatment of sarcomas, has been reported to induce renal insufficiency as a result of direct renal tubular damage.

The alkylating agents, lomustine (CCNU) and carmustine (BCNU), are nitrosoureas which are used in the therapy of lymphomas and central nervous system tumors. High cumulative doses have been associated with the late development of renal dysfunction.

Finally, vincristine, a plant alkaloid which acts by mitotic inhibition, is widely used in the treatment of leukemia, lymphoma, and various solid tumors. Rarely observed in pediatric patients, it has been associated with inappropriate antidiuretic hormone secretion resulting in water retention and hyponatremia.

CLINICAL PHARMACOLOGY AND ANTINEOPLASTIC THERAPY

Therapeutic Drug Monitoring

Therapeutic drug monitoring (TDM) is defined as the measurement of a drug or its metabolite(s) in the serum or another body fluid for the purpose of tailoring systemic drug therapy to provide maximum therapeutic effect and minimal toxicity. The application of TDM to the clinical use of a specific drug requires that (1) its pharmacologic properties are well defined; (2) it can be measured using a reliable, simple, and inexpensive methodology with adequate sensitivity and specificity; and (3) serum or body fluid concentrations can be correlated both with the drug's desired clinical and biological effects and its toxic effects.[64]

The application of TDM to the clinical management of anticonvulsant, antibiotic, and anti-asthmatic therapy is well known. However, despite the extensive use of systemic drug therapy in the treatment of human malignancies, TDM has not been widely implemented with respect to most antineoplastic agents.

Several factors specific to antineoplastic therapy account for the limitations of TDM in this setting.[64] First, the distribution characteristics, metabolic properties, and pharmacokinetics of many neoplastic agents have yet to be fully defined. For some agents, like bleomycin and procarbazine, biologically active metabolites have not been completely identified. For other drugs, such as vincristine, distribution properties are not well characterized.

Secondly, the biological response of tumors to specific chemotherapeutic agents cannot be universally determined. While toxic drug concentrations may be determined with certainty if all active metabolites can be identified and measured, therapeutic concentrations must be assessed for each histologically distinct tumor. The assessment of therapeutic effect is complicated further by the functional heterogeneity of tumors of the same histologic type with respect to their biological response to antineoplastic drugs. This tumor heterogeneity can be subdivided into three subtypes: clonal, cell kinetic, and physical heterogeneity. Clonal heterogeneity refers to the development of genetic mutations within neoplasms, which render tumor cells drug-resistant. Cell-kinetic heterogeneity results from non-synchronous cell division within tumors, which results in non-uniform susceptibility to the effects of a chemotherapeutic agent on a neoplasm. Also, the location of cells within solid tumors relative to their blood supply affects both cellular accessibility and susceptibility to antineoplastic agents. This physical heterogeneity within tumors results in variability in the degree to which individual cells are exposed to both therapeutic drug concentrations and cellular nutrients.

Thirdly, the evaluation of the therapeutic and toxic effects of antineoplastic agents is difficult in the setting of multi-drug or multi-modality antineoplastic therapy. While *in vitro* data is essential in assessing a drug's therapeutic effect, *in vivo* drug effects do not always correlate with measurable concentrations. Furthermore, when multi-drug therapy is employed clinically, it becomes difficult, if not impossible, to attribute therapeutic or biologic effects to a single agent. Similarly, many drugs used in combination therapy have overlapping toxicities, which limits the clinical correlation between drug concentration and toxicity for individual agents.

Despite current limitations, the utility of TDM in the treatment of malignancies is promising. The potential applications of TDM in antineoplastic therapy include (1) the assessment of compliance; (2) the measurement of bioavailability; (3) the evaluation of efficacy and toxicity in specialized therapy such as high-dose, continuous infusion, regional, and adjuvant chemotherapy; (4) the assessment of dose modifications in patients with underlying organ dysfunction; and (5) the establishment of standard toxic ranges for agents with cumulative dose-limiting toxicities.[64]

Because its pharmacokinetic properties have been well established in both plasma and CSF (see Figure 19–3), TDM in antineoplastic therapy has been most successfully applied to systemic high-dose methotrexate therapy, where lethal doses of methotrexate are administered by continuous infusion over a 6–24 h period, fol-

FIGURE 19–3. Methotrexate Gradient from Plasma to Cerebrospinal Fluid during Constant Intravenous Infusion

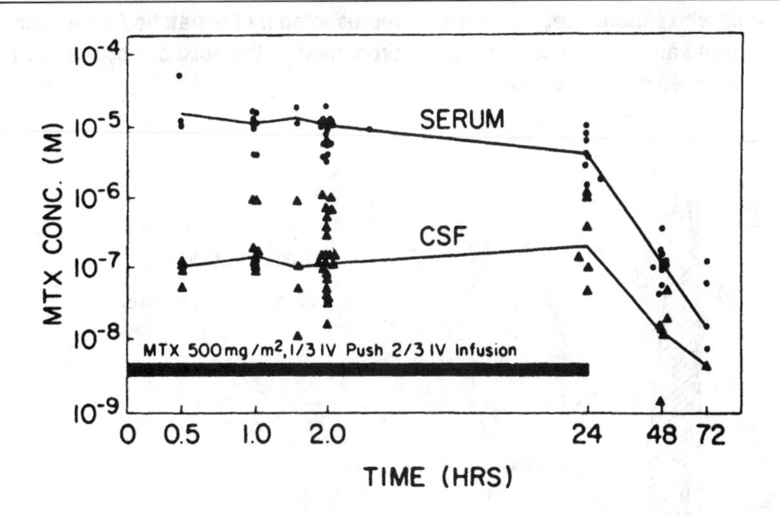

From Freeman AI, Wang JJ, Sinks LF. High-dose methotrexate in acute lymphocytic leukemia. Cancer Treat Rep 1977;61:727-31.

lowed by "rescue" therapy with leucovorin. High-dose methotrexate is employed both as a systemic treatment modality (osteosarcoma) and as a means of effecting treatment of or prophylaxis against malignant CNS disease (leukemia and lymphoma). Concentrations can be easily measured in serum and other body fluids by RIA, competitive protein binding, enzyme inhibition assay, immunoassay, or HPLC.[63, 64] The relationship between plasma methotrexate concentration and toxicity has been well established, and the measurement of serum concentrations can be used to tailor leucovorin "rescue" therapy (see Figure 19–4). In contrast to the widely accepted use of TDM in high-dose methotrexate therapy, drug levels are not useful in managing oral methotrexate therapy for several reasons. First, oral methotrexate is used in the pediatric population primarily in the maintenance treatment of ALL, where it is administered on a once-weekly basis. Since peak levels of orally administered methotrexate occur 30 minutes to 5 hours following ingestion, the use of random drug levels to monitor compliance is not feasible. Second, there is no correlation between drug levels and rates of relapse for childhood ALL.[65]

More recently, the measurement of serum of 6-mercaptopurine concentrations by HPLC in a small series of children receiving oral maintenance therapy for ALL revealed that patients who relapsed had significantly lower mean systemic exposure to 6-mercaptopurine compared to patients who did not relapse.[66] Recent evidence suggests a role for intravenous 6-mercaptopurine in the treatment of childhood ALL. Studies assessing its efficacy are underway. These clinical trials include monitoring of drug levels in an attempt to correlate systemic drug exposure and clinical outcome.[67]

FIGURE 19–4. Methotrexate Plasma Disappearance Curves in Patients Receiving Six-Hour Infusions (50–250 mg/kg), followed by Leucovorin Rescue

Levels for patients who experienced no toxicity is represented by the hatched area. Non-toxic patients who received additional leucovorin are represented by the solid circles. Levels for toxic patients are represented by open circles.

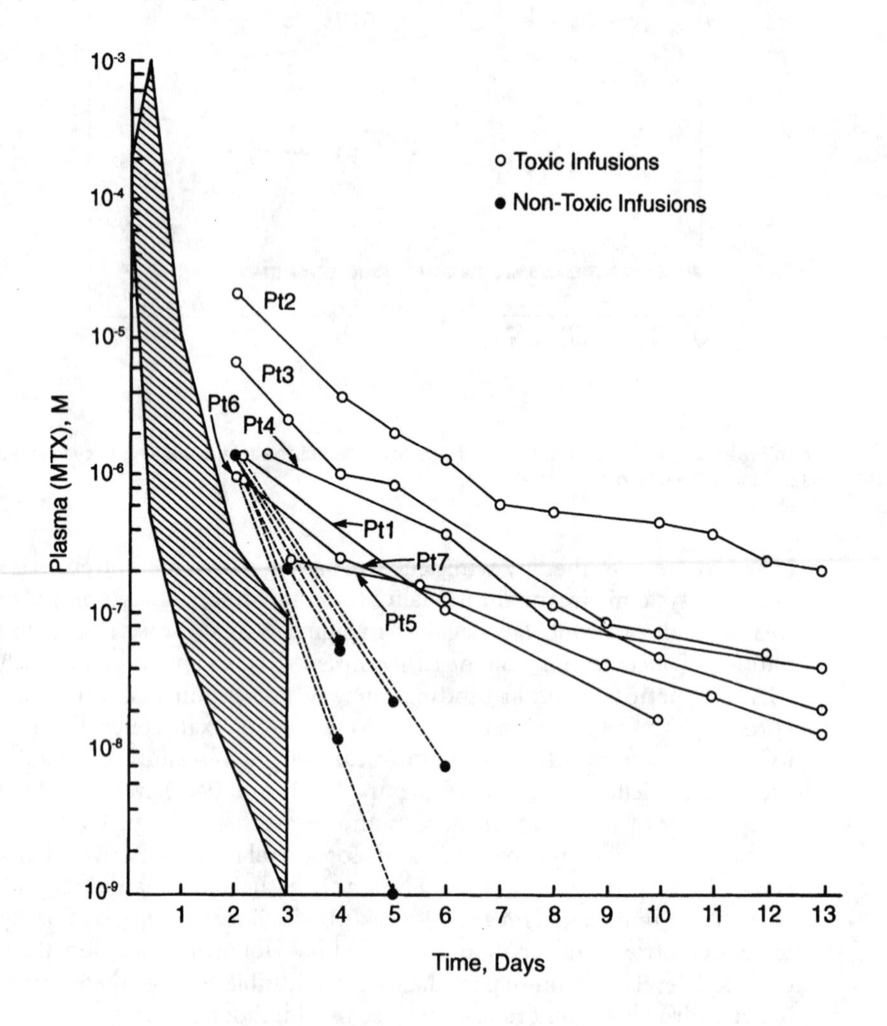

From Stoller RG, Hande KR, Jacobs SA, Rosenberg SA, and Chabner BA. Use of plasma pharmacokinetics to predict and prevent methotrexate toxicity. N Engl J Med 1977;297:630-34. Reprinted by permission.

CONCLUSION

The clinical laboratory provides rapid identification and measurement of tumor-associated markers in the blood, urine, and other body fluids, assisting the clinician in the diagnosis of many pediatric malignancies. In addition, in many cases the measurement of tumor markers provides a non-invasive means of assessing response to therapy and detecting early disease relapse or recurrence. The toxic effects of antineoplastic agents, specifically renal, hepatic, and pancreatic dysfunction, can be non-invasively detected and monitored in the clinical laboratory. The laboratory is also essential to the diagnosis and clinical management of TLS, a condition characterized by electrolyte and mineral derangements which result from the rapid and massive lysis of tumor cells in the early phases of therapy. Finally, the development of drug monitoring technologies has resulted in their clinical application to antineoplastic therapy. While currently limited to methotrexate and 6-mercaptopurine, the application of TDM to other chemotherapeutic agents is promising.

REFERENCES

1. Herlyn M, Menrad A, Koprowski H. Structure, function, and clinical significance of human tumor antigens. J Natl Cancer Inst 1990;82:1883–89.
2. Ortega JA, Siegel SE. Biological markers in pediatric cancer. In: Pizzo PA, Poplack DG, eds. Principles and practice of pediatric oncology, Philadelphia: Lippincott, 1989:149–62.
3. Mann JR, Lakin GE, Leonard JC, et al. Clinical applications of serum carcinoembryonic antigen and alpha-fetoprotein concentrations in children with solid tumors. Arch Dis Child 1978;53:366–74.
4. Perlin E, Engeler JE, Edson M, et al. The value of serial measurement of both human chorionic gonadotropin and alpha-fetoprotein for monitoring germinal cell tumors. Cancer 1976;37:215–19.
5. Talerman A, Haije WG. Alpha-fetoprotein and germ cell tumors: a possible role of yolk sac tumor in production of alpha-fetoprotein. Cancer 1974;34:1722–26.
6. Nakagawara A, Ikeda K, Tsuneyoshi M, et al. Hepatoblastoma producing both alpha-fetoprotein and human chorionic gonadotropin. Cancer 1985;56:1636–42.
7. Tsuchida Y, Saito S, Ishida M. Yolk sac tumor (endodermal sinus tumor) and alpha-fetoprotein: a report of three cases. Cancer 1973;32:917–21.
8. Van Turnout JM, Buckley JD, Quinn JJ, et al. Timing and magnitude of decline in alpha-fetoprotein levels in treated children with unresectable or metastatic hepatoblastoma are predictors of outcome: a report from the Children's Cancer Group. J Clin Onc 1997;15:1190–7.
9. Tsuchida Y, Terada M, Honna T, et al. The role of subfractionation of alpha-fetoprotein in the treatment of pediatric malignancies. J Pediatr Surg 1997;32:514–7.
10. Meites S, Buffone GJ, Cheng MH, et al., eds., Pediatric clinical chemistry, 3rd ed. Washington, DC: AACC Press, 1989.
11. Hann H, Evans A, Seigel S, et al. Prognostic importance of serum ferritin in patients with stage III and IV neuroblastoma: the CCSG experience. Cancer Res 1985;45:2843–48.
12. Hann HL, Lange BJ, Stalhut MW, McGlynn KA. Serum ferritin and prognosis of childhood Hodgkin's disease (abstract). Proc Am Soc Clin Oncol 1987;6:190.
13. Moss DW, Henderson AR, Kachmar JF. Enzymes. In Tietz NW, ed. Textbook of clinical chemistry. Philadelphia: Saunders, 1986:763–74.
14. Scranton PE, DeCicco FA, Totten RS, Yunis RJ. Prognostic factors in osteosarcoma: a review of 20 years' experience at the University of Pittsburgh Health Center Hospitals. Cancer 1975;36:2179–91.

15. Levine AM, Rosenburg SA. Alkaline phosphatase levels in osteosarcoma are related to prognosis. Cancer 1979;44:2291–93.
16. Kornberg A, Polliack A. Serum lactic dehydrogenase (LDH) levels in acute leukemia: marked elevations in lymphoblastic leukemia. Blood 1980;56:351–55.
17. Pui CH, Dodge RK, Dahl GV, et al. Serum lactic dehydrogenase level has prognostic value in childhood acute lymphoblastic leukemia. Blood 1985;66:778–82.
18. Glaubiger DL, Makuch R, Schwarz J, et al. Determination of prognostic factors and their influence on therapeutic results in patients with Ewing's sarcoma. Cancer 1980;45:2213–19.
19. Kinumaki H, Takeuche H, Nakamura K. Serum lactate dehydrogenase isoenzyme-1 in children with yolk sac tumor. Cancer 1985;56:178–81.
20. Zeltzer PM, Marangos PJ, Evans AE, Schneider SL. Serum neuron-specific enolase in children with neuroblastoma: relationship to stage and disease course. Cancer 1986;57:1230–34.
21. Ishiguro Y, Kato K, Ito T, et al. Nervous system-specific enolase in serum as a marker for neuroblastoma. Pediatrics 1983;72:696–700.
22. Poplack DG. Acute lymphoblastic leukemia. In: Pizzo PA, Poplack DG, eds. Principles and practice of pediatric oncology. Philadelphia: Lippincott, 1989:323–66.
23. Hutton JJ, Coleman MS, Moffitt S, et al. Prognostic significance of terminal transferase activity in childhood acute lymphoblastic leukemia: a prospective analysis of 164 patients. Blood 1982;60:1267–76.
24. Silverman LM, Christenson RH, Grant GH. Amino acids and proteins. In: Tietz NW, ed. Textbook of clinical chemistry. Philadelphia: Saunders, 1986:619–762.
25. Frens DB, Bray PF, Wu JT, Lahey ME. The carcinoembryonic antigen assay: prognostic value in neural crest tumors. J Pediatr 1976;88:591–94.
26. Huth JF, Gupta RK, Eilber FR, Morton DL. A prospective postoperative evaluation of urinary tumor-associated antigens in sarcoma patients. Cancer 1984;53:1306–10.
27. Child JA, Spati B, Illingworth S, et al. Serum beta 2 microglobulin and c-reactive protein in the monitoring of lymphomas. Cancer 1980;45:318–26.
28. Ladisch S, Wu ZL. Circulating gangliosides as tumor markers. Prog Clin Biol 1985;175:277–84.
29. Schulz G, Cheresh DA, Varki NM, et al. Detection of ganglioside G in tumor tissue and sera of neuroblastoma patients. Cancer Res 1984;44:5914–20.
30. Pui CH, Ip SH, Kung P, et al. High serum interleukin-2 levels are related to advanced disease and a poor outcome in childhood non-Hodgkin's lymphoma. Blood 1987;70:624–28.
31. Pui CH, Ip SH, Behm FG, et al. Serum interleukin 2 receptor levels in childhood acute lymphoblastic leukemia. Blood 1988;71:1135–37.
32. Chrousos GP. Endocrine tumors. In: Pizzo PA, Poplack DG, eds. Principles and practice of pediatric oncology, Philadelphia: Lippincott, 1989:733-57.
33. Altman AJ, Schwartz AD, eds., Malignant diseases of infancy, childhood and adolescence, 2nd ed. Philadelphia: Saunders, 1983.
34. Bosl GJ, Lange PH, Nochomovitz LE. Tumor markers in advanced nonseminomatous testicular cancer. Cancer 1981;47:572–76.
35. Gitlow SE, Dziedzic LB, Strauss L, et al. Biochemical and histological determinants in the prognosis of neuroblastoma. Cancer 1973;32:898–905.
36. Chattoraj SC, Watts NB. Endocrinology. In: Tietz NW, ed. Textbook of clinical chemistry. Philadelphia: Saunders, 1986:997–1171.
37. Soldin SJ, Hill JG. Liquid chromatographic analysis for urinary VMA and HVA and its use in the investigation of neural crest tumors. Clin Chem 1981;27:502–3.
38. Gitlow SE, Bertani LM, Rausen A, et al. Diagnosis of neuroblastoma by qualitative and quantitative determination of catecholamine metabolites in the urine. Cancer 1970;25:1377–83.
39. Laug WE, Siegel SE, Shaw KNF, et al. Initial urinary catecholamine metabolite concentrations and prognosis in neuroblastoma. Pediatrics 1978;62:77–83.
40. Soldin SJ. Applications of liquid chromatography in a children's hospital. In: Hawk GE, ed. Biological/biomedical applications of liquid chromatography. M. Dekker, 20:135–44.
41. Kerbl R, Urban CE, Ambros PF, et al. Screening for neuroblastoma in late infancy by use of EIA (enzyme-linked immunoassay) method: 115000 screened infants in Austria. Eur J Cancer 1996;32A:2298–305.

42. Sawada T, Kidowaki T, Sakamoto I, et al. Neuroblastoma: mass screening for early detection and its prognosis. Cancer 1984;53:2731–35.
43. Kaushansky K. Thrombopoietin: the primary regulator of platelet production. Blood 1995: 86:419–31.
44. Marsch JCW, Gibson FM, Prue RL, et al. Serum thrombopoietin levels in patients with aplastic anemia. Br J Haematol 1996:95:605–10.
45. Meng YG, Martin TG, Peterson ML, et al. Circulating thrombopoietin concentrations in thrombocytopenic patients, including cancer patients following chemotherapy, with or without peripheral blood progenitor cell transplantation. Br J Haematol 1996;95:535–41.
46. Mukai HY, Kojima H, Todokoro K. Serum thrombopoietin levels in patients with amegakaryocytic thrombocytopenia are much higher than those with immune thrombocytopenic purpura. Thromb Haemost 1996;76:675–8.
47. Yamaguchi H, Ishii E, Hayashida, et al. Mechanisms of thrombocytosis in hepatoblastoma: a case report. Pediatr Hematol/Oncol 1996;13:539–44.
48. Komura-Naito E, Matsumura T, Swada T, et al. Thrombopoietin in patient with hepatoblastoma [letter]. Blood 1997;90:2849–50.
49. Lin RY, Argenta PA, Sullivan KM, et al. Urinary hyaluronic acid is a Wilm's tumor marker. J Pediatr Surg 1995:30:304–8.
50. Powars DR, Allerton SE, Beierle J, Butler BB. Wilms' tumor: clinical correlation with circulating mucin in three cases. Cancer 1972;29:1597–1605.
51. Wu AHB, Parker OS, Ford, L. Hyperviscosity caused by hyaluronic acid in serum in a case of Wilms' tumor. Clin Chem 1984;30:914–16.
52. Russell DH, Levy CC, Schimpf SC, Hawk IA. Urinary polyamines in cancer patients. Cancer Res 1971;31:1555–58.
53. Marton LJ, Hruby O, Levin VA, et al. The relationship of polyamines in cerebrospinal fluid to the presence of central nervous system tumors. Cancer Res 1976;36:973–77.
54. Marton LJ, Edwards MS, Levin VA, et al.. Predictive values of cerebrospinal fluid polyamines in medulloblastomas. Cancer Res 1979;39:993–97.
55. Lee SH, Suh JW, Chung BC, Kim SO. Polyamine profiles in the urine of patients with leukemia. Cancer Lett 1998;122:1–8.
56. Boles JM, Dutel JL, Briere J, et al. Acute renal failure caused by extreme hyperphosphatemia after chemotherapy of an acute lymphoblastic leukemia. Cancer 1984;53:2425–29.
57. Zusman J, Brown DM, Nesbit ME. Hyperphosphatemia, hyperphosphaturia and hypocalcemia in acute lymphoblastic leukemia. N Engl J Med 1973;289:1335–40.
58. Kelly KM, Lange B. Oncologic emergencies. Pediatr Clin North Am 1997;44:809–30.
59. Cohen LF, Balow JE, Magrath IT, et al. Acute tumor lysis syndrome: a review of 37 patients with Burkitt's lymphoma. Am J Med 1980;68:486–91.
60. Boccia RV, Longo DL, Lieber ML. Multiple recurrences of acute tumor lysis syndrome in an indolent non-Hodgkin's lymphoma. Cancer 1985;56:2295–97.
61. Tomlinson GC, Solberg LA. Acute tumor lysis syndrome with metastatic medulloblastoma: a case report. Cancer 1984;53:1783–85.
62. Balis FM, Holcenberg JS, Poplack DG. General principles of chemotherapy. In: Pizzo PA, Poplack DG, eds. Principles and practice of pediatric oncology. Philadelphia: Lippincott, 1989:165–205.
63. Chabner BA. Clinical pharmacokinetics and drug monitoring. In: Chabner BA, ed. Pharmacologic principles of cancer treatment. Philadelphia: Saunders, 1982:100–8.
64. Moore MJ, Erlichman C. Therapeutic drug monitoring in oncology: problems and potential in antineoplastic therapy. Clin Pharm 1987;13:205–27.
65. Pearson ADJ, Amineddine HA, Yule M, et al. The influence of serum methotrexate concentrations and drug dosage on outcome in childhood acute lymphoblastic leukaemia. Br J Cancer 1991;64:169–73.
66. Koren G, Ferrazini G, Sulh H, et al. Systemic exposure to mercaptopurine as a prognostic factor in acute lymphocytic leukemia in children. N Engl J Med 1990;323:17–21.
67. Camitta B, Leventhal B, Lauer S, et al. Intermediate dose intravenous methotrexate and mercaptopurine therapy for non-T, non-B acute lymphocytic leukemia of childhood: a Pediatric Oncology Group study. J Clin Oncol 1989;7:1539–44.

CHAPTER 20

Disorders of Porphyrin Metabolism

George H. Elder, B.A., M.D., F.R.C.P., F.R.C. Path.

INTRODUCTION

The porphyrias are a group of disorders of heme biosynthesis in which characteristic clinical features occur in association with specific patterns of overproduction of heme precursors. There are two main types of clinical disease: skin lesions, caused by photosensitization of the skin by accumulated porphyrins, and acute neurovisceral attacks, which typically consist of severe abdominal pain which may be accompanied by peripheral neuropathy, mental disturbances, and convulsions.

The main types of porphyria, their clinical features and prevalence are shown in Table 20–1. Only two of the main types of porphyria, erythropoietic protoporphyria (EPP) and congenital erythropoietic porphyria (CEP), are disorders of childhood. Symptoms in the other types usually do not appear until adult life, even though all porphyrias, except for some forms of porphyria cutanea tarda (PCT), are inherited disorders with biochemical defects present from birth. In particular, the life-threatening acute attacks that occur in acute intermittent porphyria (AIP) and the other acute hepatic porphyrias (see Table 20–1) are very rare before puberty.

When porphyrias are encountered in pediatric practice, it is usually for one of two different reasons. First, symptoms may suggest a diagnosis of porphyria. Usually these will be dermatological because those types of porphyria that typically present during childhood—CEP, EPP, and rare homozygous variants of the acute porphyrias—mainly affect the skin. Second, advice may be sought about a child who, although asymptomatic, has a family history of porphyria. This chapter fo-

TABLE 20–1. The Main Types of Porphyria

Disorder	Acute Attacks	Skin Lesions	Estimated Prevalance of Overt Cases (all ages)
1. PBG-synthase deficiency porphyria	+	–	—
2. Acute intermittent porphyria	+	–	1–2:100,000
3. Congenital erythropoietic porphyria	–	+	Less than 1:10^6
4. Porphyria cutanea tarda	–	+	1:25,000
5. Hereditary coproporphyria	+	+	Less than 1:250,000
6. Variegate porphyria	+	+	1:250,000
7. Erythropoietic protoporphyria	–	+	1:200,000

In hereditary coproporphyria and variegate porphyria, skin lesions and acute attacks may occur together or separately.

cuses on these two aspects, as comprehensive general descriptions of the porphyrias are provided by a number of reviews.[1–3]

Abnormalities of porphyrin metabolism occur in several disorders apart from the porphyrias, notably in iron deficiency and some other anemias, in lead poisoning, in cholestasis, and in inherited hyperbilirubinemias.[4, 5, 6] These conditions are not discussed here, except in relation to the differential diagnosis of porphyria.

BIOSYNTHESIS OF HEME

The pathway of heme biosynthesis is outlined in Figure 20–1. Formation of the first committed precursor, 5-aminolevulinate (ALA), from succinyl-CoA and glycine is catalyzed in mitochondria by ALA synthase. A series of condensation reactions then leads to the formation of the linear tetrapyrrole, hydroxymethylbilane, which is then cyclized with reversal of one pyrrolic unit to form the asymmetric tetrapyrrolic macrocycle, uroporphyrinogen III. An alternative fate for hydroxymethylbilane, non-enzymatic cyclisation to the symmetrical porphyrinogen isomer, uroporphyrinogen I, accounts for less than 1% of the metabolism of hydroxymethylbilane in normal circumstances, but may be enhanced in pathological conditions where hydroxymethylbilane accumulates. Uroporphyrinogen is then decarboxylated to coproporphyrinogen by a reaction that is not isomer-specific.

Subsequent side chain modifications and aromatization to form protoporphyrin IX are restricted to the isomer III series. Heme is then formed by enzymatic chelation of ferrous iron (see Figure 20–1). The porphyrinogen intermediates of this pathway are unstable and readily autoxidize to the corresponding porphyrins within tissues and during excretion.

Normal adults synthesize about 7 μmol/kg body weight of heme each day, 80–85% of which is used for hemoglobin formation, while the rest is used, mainly in the liver, for the formation of cytochromes and other hemoproteins. At least 50% of the heme made in the liver is incorporated into cytochromes of the P450 series that

FIGURE 20–1. The Pathway of Heme Biosynthesis

The reactions are catalyzed by 5-aminolevulinate (ALA) synthase (1), porphobilinogen (PBG) synthase (2), PBG deaminase (3), uroporphyrinogen III synthase (4), uroporphyrinogen decarboxylase (5), coproporphyrinogen oxidase (6), protoporphyrinogen oxidase (7), and ferrochelatase (8.)

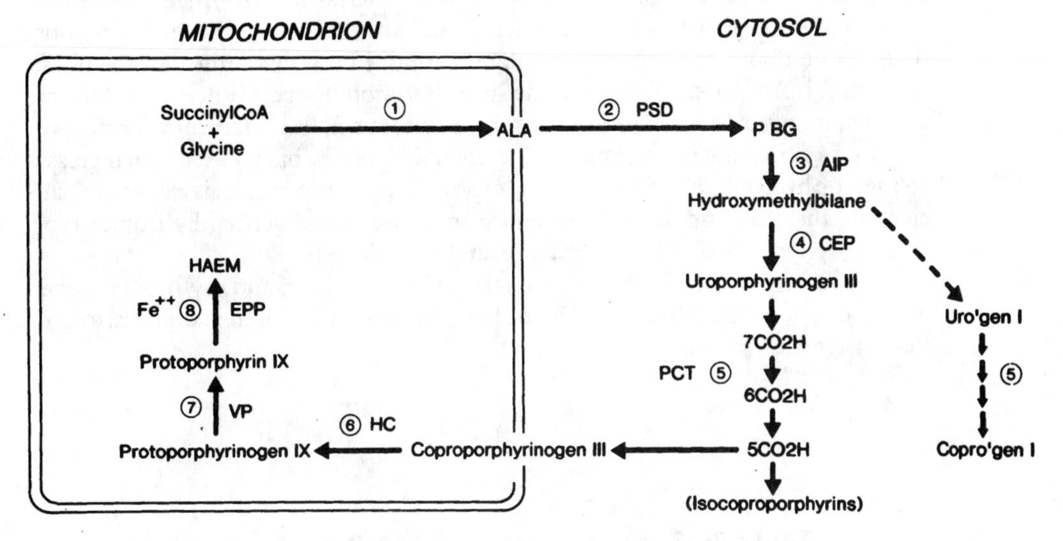

catalyze the oxidative metabolism of a wide range of endogenous compounds and xenobiotics, including many drugs.

The regulation of the rate of heme biosynthesis in mammalian cells has been studied extensively.[7] The ALA synthases of human liver and erythroid cells are encoded by separate genes on chromosome 3 and the X chromosome, respectively, and factors influencing their activities in these tissues are different.[7] In the liver, ALA synthase activity determines the rate of heme synthesis. Activity is controlled by negative feedback regulation by heme of the rate of synthesis of mature mitochondrial enzyme. The short half-life of the enzyme allows the cell to respond rapidly to changes in the demand for heme, for example, in response to administration of a drug that induces cytochrome P450 synthesis.

Heme for the formation of hemoproteins is believed to come from a regulatory heme pool. Depletion of this pool through combination of heme and apoprotein leads to derepression of the synthesis of ALA-synthase and hence to replenishment of the heme pool. This type of mechanism is consistent with an important feature of hepatic heme synthesis: the readiness with which changes in ALA synthase activity occur in response to a wide range of external stimuli, including many drugs that induce cytochrome P450. In contrast, few compounds affect ALA synthase activity in erythroid cells. In these cells, mechanisms for the regulation of heme synthesis are complex and an integral part of the process of progressive differentiation of erythroid cells.[7]

METABOLISM OF HEME PRECURSORS

The close regulation of heme biosynthesis and the kinetics of the intermediate reactions ensure that losses from the pathway are normally small. Intermediates that are not converted into heme are not metabolized by alternative routes, although hydroxymethylbilane and porphyrinogens may undergo non-enzymatic conversion to porphyrins, which accumulate in tissues and are excreted unchanged. The route of excretion under normal and pathological conditions is determined by the physicochemical properties of the intermediate. Porphobilinogen (PBG) and ALA are excreted in urine, as is the most hydrophilic porphyrin, the octacarboxylic uroporphyrin. As the number of carboxylic side-chains decreases, biliary excretion increases so that the hydrophobic, dicarboxylic porphyrin, protoporphyrin, is excreted exclusively in the bile. The route of excretion may also be influenced by isomer type, coproporphyrin I being preferentially excreted in the bile.

Reference ranges for heme precursors in urine, feces, and erythrocytes from adults are shown in Table 20–2. Use of these ranges for children is unlikely to produce diagnostic problems.

TABLE 20–2. Heme Precursor Concentrations

Heme Precursor	Urine		Feces		Erythrocytes
ALA	0–34	μmol/L	–		
PBG	0–8.8	μmol/L	–		
Total porphyrin	20–320	nmol/L	10–200	nmol/g dry wt*	0.4–1.7 μmol/L**
Porphyrin fractions					
Uroporphyrin	0–40	nmol/day			
Coproporphyrin	0–280	nmol/day	0–46	nmol/g dry wt	
Protoporphyrin			0–220	nmol/g dry wt	
Ether-insoluble porphyrin***			0–24	nmo/g dry wt	
Individual porphyrins					
Uroporphyrin	0–24	nmol/L	< 2% total		
Hepta ($7CO_2H$)	0–4	nmol/L	< 2% total		
Hexa ($6CO_2H$)	0–3	nmol/L	< 2% total		
Penta ($5CO_2H$)	0–5	nmol/L	< 2% total		
Isocoproporphyrin			< 0.5% total		
Coproporphyrin	23–115 nmol/L (60–70%)		2–33% total (10–20%)		
Protoporphyrin			60–98% total		

Note: Figures in parentheses give percentage of isomer type III
* Ether-soluble porphyrin only
** More than 90% of total porphyrin erythrocytes is zinc-protoporphyrin
*** Includes uroporphyrin, heptacarboxylic porphyrin, X-porphyrin
Source: Elder GH, Smith SG, Smyth SJ. Laboratory investigation of the porphyrias. Ann Clin Biochem 1990:27;395-412.

BIOCHEMICAL GENETICS

Each of the main types of porphyria results from partial deficiency of one of the enzymes of heme biosynthesis (Table 20–3). In recent years, the human genes for all these enzymes have been cloned (see Table 20–3), and molecular genetic methods are now being used to identify and characterize mutations and define the extent of heterogeneity at the DNA level in these conditions.[2, 8]

Five of the enzyme deficiencies listed in Table 20–3 are inherited as autosomal-dominant traits. In all except EPP, enzyme activity is decreased by close to 50% and mainly reflects expression of the normal gene allelic to the mutant gene.[1–3] In EPP, activity may be decreased by 70–80% in symptomatic individuals, which suggests that some additional factor may modify enzyme activity in this disorder. The two remaining porphyrias, CEP and PBG synthase deficiency porphyria, are both autosomal recessive conditions. In all of these conditions, apart from an uncommon form of AIP in which the erythroid isoenzyme of PBG deaminase is unaffected,[8] the inherited enzyme deficiencies are present in all tissues, although the mitochondrial enzyme defects are absent from mature erythrocytes.

In normal cells, the concentrations of the intermediates of heme biosynthesis appear to be lower than the K_ms of the enzymes that metabolize them. A partial enzyme deficiency can therefore be compensated and the rate of formation of heme maintained by increasing the concentration of the substrate of the defective enzyme.

TABLE 20–3. The Porphyrias: Enzyme Deficiencies and Inheritance

Disorder	Enzyme Deficiency	Inheritance	Chromosomal Location	Human cDNA/gDNA Cloned
PBG-synthase deficiency	PBG-synthase	Autosomal recessive	9q34	yes
Acute intermittent porphyria	PBG-deaminase*	Autosomal dominant	11q24.1–24.2	yes
Congenital erythropoietic porphyria	Uroporphyrinogen III synthase	Autosomal recessive	10q25.2–26.3	yes
Porphyria cutanea tarda				
Type I (sporadic)	Uroporphyrinogen decarboxylase	Polygenic		
Type II (familial)	Uroporphyrinogen decarboxylase	Autosomal dominant	1p34	yes
Toxic	Uroporphyrinogen decarboxylase	Not inherited		
Hereditary coproporphyria	Coproporphyrinogen oxidase	Autosomal dominant	3q12	yes
Variegate porphyria	Protoporphyrinogen oxidase	Autosomal dominant	1q21–23	yes
Protoporphyria	Ferrochelatase	Autosomal dominant	18q21.3	yes

*Synonyms: hydroxymethylbilane synthase, uroporphyrinogen-I-synthase.

This increase is achieved by raising the activity of ALA synthase through operation of the regulatory mechanisms described above. These compensatory changes do not occur to the same extent in all tissues. Thus, in all the autosomal dominant porphyrias except EPP, they are restricted to the liver, whereas in EPP and CEP, ALA synthase activity and tissue porphyrin concentrations are increased in erythroid cells.

There are also wide intra-individual differences between the extent of the compensatory changes. These differences are important clinically because symptomatic porphyria does not occur in the absence of demonstrable overproduction of heme precursors. At least 80% of individuals who inherit one of the autosomal dominant enzyme deficiencies remain asymptomatic throughout life and are considered to have latent porphyria. Many of these persons may show no evidence of heme precursor overproduction. It is not clear why these phenotypic differences in response to the same degree of enzyme deficiency occur. Although drugs and other acquired factors are known to precipitate symptoms in certain types of porphyria, interactions of this type do not provide a full explanation. In general, enzyme activities are lower in the autosomal recessive conditions.[1–3] Individuals are clinically affected and symptoms tend to start at a young age and persist, although there are some exceptions which will be described below.

Overproduction of heme precursors can be divided into two main symptom-associated groups. First, acute neurovisceral attacks are always associated with increased excretion of the porphyrin precursor ALA, accompanied by PBG except in the very rare condition, PBG synthase deficiency porphyria.[2] Acute attacks do not occur in porphyrias in which neither PBG nor ALA excretion is increased (see Table 20–1). Possible mechanisms for the neurological basis of the acute attacks have been reviewed.[1–4] Second, skin lesions in porphyria are the consequence of overproduction of porphyrins, which, except in EPP, are derived from oxidation of accumulated porphyrinogens. They are not seen in the two conditions, AIP and PBG synthase deficiency porphyria (see Table 20–1), in which the enzyme deficiencies do not lead to porphyrin overproduction. The mechanism by which the photodynamic action of porphyrins in light-exposed areas of skin produces photosensitivity and skin lesions has been investigated extensively.[2]

CUTANEOUS PORPHYRIAS IN CHILDREN

Congenital Erythropoietic Porphyria

Congenital erythropoietic porphyria (CEP), or Günther's disease, is an uncommon cutaneous porphyria in which massive overproduction of porphyrins, mainly within the erythropoietic system, produces a severe photodermatosis, hemolytic anemia, and marked porphyrinuria.[9, 10] It was the first of the porphyrias to be described (by Schultz in 1874) and remains the most striking and severe in its cutaneous manifestations.

Clinical Features

CEP occurs worldwide and with equal frequency in both sexes. It usually presents in infancy, where the first symptom is often red discoloration of the diapers that is noticed at or soon after birth. Such infants may be photosensitive and develop erythema and bullae in areas of skin exposed to sunlight either directly or through window glass. Severe cutaneous reactions to phototherapy for hyperbilirubinemia have been reported in CEP. By the second year of life, most affected children have characteristic porphyric lesions on light-exposed skin: subepidermal bullae, hypertrichosis, and superficial erosions resulting from increased mechanical fragility. Rarely, the onset of symptoms is delayed until later in childhood or even adult life.

In older children and adults, there is often extensive scarring of the skin due to repeated infection of blisters and erosions, with atrophy and extensive areas of sclerodermatous change. Together, these lesions may progress to severe photomutilation with atrophy of ears, nose, and digits, while damage around the eyes may lead to corneal ulcerations and blindness.

Almost all patients have erythrodontia, with both the deciduous and permanent teeth being colored reddish-brown due to deposition of porphyrins. The teeth show bright red fluorescence on exposure to long-wave ultraviolet light. Porphyrin also accumulates in erythrocytes, and accelerated destruction of photo-damaged erythrocytes in the spleen probably explains the hemolysis and splenomegaly that is present in many patients, the latter usually appearing as the disease progresses. The hemolytic anemia is characteristically intermittent and is usually mild or moderate in severity, only rarely becoming life-threatening.

Most patients with the classical, childhood-onset form of CEP do not survive beyond age 40. In recent years, careful screening from sunlight and the prevention of secondary infections with antibiotics has been effective in preventing severe photomutilation. It remains to be seen whether the overall prognosis is also improved.

Biochemical Findings

Uroporphyrinogen III synthase activity is decreased by 70–90% in CEP patients and is intermediate between this range and normal in obligatory carriers.[1] Over 20 point mutations have now been identified in the uroporphyrinogen III synthase gene, for which patients are either homozygous or compound heterozygous.[8,11,12] Most of these mutations are restricted to one or a few families, but one, C73R, is present on nearly 40% of alleles in patients of European descent and, particularly in homozygotes, is associated with severe disease and a poor prognosis.[11,12] Accumulation of hydroxymethylbilane proximal to the defective enzyme results in the formation of excessive amounts of uroporphyrin I and coproporphyrin I which are excreted in urine and feces and accumulate in erythrocytes (Table 20–4). Protoporphyrin is also increased in erythrocytes, but usually only to the moderate degree seen both in other homozygous porphyrias and in other hemolytic anemias, and is present mainly as the zinc chelate.

Treatment

Treatment of CEP is unsatisfactory. Skin damage may be lessened by minimizing exposure to sunlight, prompt treatment of secondary infection, and antioxidants.[8,10] Hypertransfusion and intravenous hematin both provide short-term suppression of porphyrin production, but neither is suitable for use over long periods of time. Allogeneic bone marrow transplantation is emerging as the treatment of choice for

TABLE 20–4. The Porphyrias: Diagnostic Patterns of Overproduction of Heme Precursors

Disorder	Urine PBG/ALA	Porphyrins	Feces Porphyrins	Erythrocytes Porphyrins
PBG-synthase deficiency*	ALA	Copro III	Not increased	Zn-proto
Acute intermittent porphyria	PBG > ALA	(Porphyrin mainly from PBG)	Normal, occas. slight increase (copro, proto)	Not increased
Congenital erythropoietic porphyria	Not increased	Uro I > Copro I	Copro I	Zn-proto,copro, uro
Porphyria cutanea tarda	Not increased	Uro > Hepta***	Isocopro, Hepta***	Not increased
Hereditary coproporphyria	PBG > ALA**	Copro III (Porphyrin from PBG)	Copro III	Not increased
Variegate porphyria	PBG> ALA	Copro III (Porphyrin from PBG)	Proto IX > Copro III X-porphyrin	Not increased
Protoporphyria	Not increased	Not increased	± Protoporphyrin	Protoporphyrin

*Lead poisoning produces an identical overproduction pattern.
**PBG and ALA excretion may be normal when only skin lesions are present.
***Hexa- and pentacarboxylic prophyrins and coproporphyrin are increased to a smaller extent.

children with severe disease, provided bone marrow or cord blood stem cells is available from an HLA-compatible sibling donor.[13] In the future, gene transfer therapy may provide an alternative treatment when a suitable donor is unavailable.[14] Patients with severe hemolytic anemia and hypersplenism may benefit from splenectomy.[9, 10]

Prenatal Diagnosis

CEP is probably the only porphyria in which prenatal diagnosis with a view to termination of pregnancy may be justifiable. For this purpose, measurement of porphyrins in amniotic fluid and uroporphyrinogen III synthase in amnion cells[3] is likely to be superseded by recombinant DNA methods for direct detection of mutations.[10]

Uroporphyrinogen Decarboxylase Deficiency Disorders

Two types of cutaneous porphyria result from decreased activity of uroporphyrinogen decarboxylase: porphyria cutanea tarda (PCT) and hepatoerythropoietic porphyria (HEP).[2] PCT is mainly a disease of adults. Its features have been reviewed,[1, 2, 3, 15] and hence it is only discussed briefly here.

Porphyria Cutanea Tarda in Children

Less than 1% of patients with PCT first develop skin lesions during childhood, and these may appear as early as the second year of life. The lesions are much less severe than in CEP and similar to those seen in adults with PCT; skin fragility, sub-epidermal bullae, and hypertrichosis on the backs of the hands, face, and other sun-exposed areas are the usual findings. Photosensitivity is not usually a prominent feature. In contrast to adults with PCT, evidence of co-existent liver disease is uncommon.

Decreased uroporphyrinogen decarboxylase activity in the liver leads to a characteristic pattern of porphyrin overproduction (Table 20–4). Uroporphyrin and other porphyrins with acetic acid substituents (see Figure 20–1) accumulate in the liver and are excreted in excess. In urine, the main porphyrins are uroporphyrin I and III and heptacarboxylic porphyrin III, while isocoproporphyrin and heptacarboxylic porphyrin are usually the most prominent in feces.[16] Erythrocyte porphyrin concentrations are normal.

PCT is a heterogeneous disorder.[15] It is probable that all affected children have the type II or familial form of PCT in which uroporphyrinogen decarboxylase deficiency is present in all tissues and is inherited in an autosomal dominant fashion (see Table 20–3). Most individuals who inherit the gene for type II PCT are asymptomatic and therefore it is not unusual for patients to be the only clinically affected member of their families. The diagnosis of type II PCT can be established by demonstrating a 50% decrease in erythrocyte uroporphyrinogen decarboxylase.[1, 2, 3, 15] Children, like adults with PCT, may be homozygous for the hemochromatosis C282Y mutation and should be screened for its presence, particularly if they are of northern European descent.[17]

PCT in children, as in adults, can be treated either by depleting iron stores by repeated venesection or, preferably, with "low-dose" chloroquine at an appropriately lower dose than for adults.[2, 3] Both treatments produce clinical and biochemical remission which may persist for many years, even throughout life. Remission may also occur without treatment, and if skin lesions are mild, no treatment may be required. In girls, iron depletion following menarche may produce spontaneous remission.

Toxic Cutaneous Porphyria

In the late 1950s, there was a widespread outbreak of cutaneous porphyria in southeastern Turkey following the consumption of bread made from wheat seed that had been dressed with the fungicide hexachlorobenzene.[18] This compound was later shown to inactivate hepatic uroporphyrinogen decarboxylase and "porphyria turcica" is now regarded as a form of PCT. Many of the affected individuals were children, and hypertrichosis was a prominent clinical feature. Follow-up studies have been published.[17]

Hepatoerythropoietic Porphyria

Hepatoerythropoietic porphyria (HEP) is a rare form of cutaneous porphyria that results from severe uroporphyrinogen decarboxylase deficiency.[1, 2, 3, 19] About 30 patients have been reported. Skin fragility and blisters, often accompanied by hypertrichosis and clinically indistinguishable from the lesions of PCT and CEP, are usually first noticed between the ages of 2 and 5. The skin lesions are usually more severe than in PCT and, with progression, may come to resemble those of CEP with photomutilation. Other clinical features of CEP are usually absent. Porphyrinuria is less marked and may not be sufficient to color the urine; erythrodontia is infrequent and hemolytic anemia with splenomegaly has been reported in only two patients.[20]

Urinary and fecal porphyrin excretion patterns resemble those of PCT. Although small differences have been reported,[20] these are not sufficiently consistent to reliably distinguish HEP from PCT. In contrast to PCT, the erythrocyte porphyrin concentration is invariably raised, largely due to increased zinc-protoporphyrin concentrations.[20]

Differentiation between PCT and HEP depends on measurement of uroporphyrinogen decarboxylase. In erythrocytes, enzyme activity is decreased by at least 70% and usually by close to 90%. These low activities, together with the finding that both parents of affected individuals have enzyme activities around 50% of normal, suggest that patients with HEP may be homozygous for the enzyme defect that causes type II PCT. Immunochemical and molecular genetic investigations have led to the identification of several different mutations in both HEP and type II PCT, but only one mutation common to both diseases has yet been identified.[19, 21]

There is no specific treatment for HEP. Both venesection and chloroquine are ineffective. Management of the skin lesions is therefore symptomatic and similar to that recommended for CEP.

Other Blistering Cutaneous Porphyrias in Children

Kushner et al.[22] have described a patient with partial uroporphyrinogen decarboxylase deficiency, dyserythropoietic anemia, and severe skin lesions, resembling CEP, that started at the age of 4. A similar decrease in enzyme activity was present in asymptomatic relatives, suggesting that interaction between this defect and the dyserythropoietic anemia was responsible for the severe porphyria. Co-existence of two enzyme defects in the heme biosynthetic pathway may also modify the clinical picture, as in an infant with severe photosensitization who was found to have co-existent CEP and hereditary coproporphyria.[23]

Erythropoietic Protoporphyria

Erythropoietic protoporphyria (EPP)[24] is the third most common porphyria (see Table 20–1) and by far the most common form of porphyria in children; indeed, onset of EPP after childhood is uncommon. The condition is produced by accumulation of protoporphyrin IX secondary to decreased ferrochelatase activity with most of the porphyrin coming from the erythropoietic system. Although the mechanism of photosensitization is the same as in other cutaneous porphyrias, the most prominent feature is acute photosensitivity and the condition is clinically distinguishable from all other cutaneous porphyrias. The main diagnostic problem is differentiation of EPP from other causes of acute photosensitivity.

Clinical Features

Patients present with acute photosensitivity that usually starts in early childhood, often before age 2 y.[24] An intense pricking, itching, burning sensation usually occurs within 5 to 30 minutes of exposure to sunlight, but is sometimes delayed for several hours, and blends into burning pain. Erythema and edema with occasional later crusting and petechiae follow, but usually have resolved within a day or two. Uncommonly, small vesicles and acute photo-oncolysis may occur.

Particularly in young children who have had few episodes of photosensitivity, there may be little to suggest EPP apart from the history, and it is probably for this reason that the diagnosis is often delayed. After repeated attacks, the skin may become thickened, waxy, and pitted with small circular or linear scars, especially over the bridge of the nose, around the mouth, and over the knuckles. However, the changes are rarely marked and may be missed on superficial examination. About 25% of patients have a mild hypochromic microcytic anemia that is not caused by iron-deficiency and may result from the enzyme defect. Older patients may develop pigmented protoporphyrin gallstones.

As in other autosomal dominant porphyrias, carriers of the EPP gene are often asymptomatic. Thus, affected individuals may have no relatives with overt EPP, and the risk that a child of a patient with EPP will ever develop symptoms has been estimated at less than 5%.

Progressive hepatic failure is an uncommon but well-recognized complication that appears to result from liver damage caused by accumulation of protoporphyrin in hepatocytes.[25] Over 30 patients in whom liver disease was either fatal or required transplantation have been reported.[24] Onset is usually after age 30 y, but fatal liver damage has been reported in children. Up to 35% of all patients may have biochemical evidence of liver dysfunction at some stage, but not all of these show protoporphyrin deposition or hepatocyte necrosis and fibrosis.[24] Liver disease does not occur in asymptomatic gene carriers.

Biochemical Findings

The diagnosis of EPP is established by demonstrating an increased concentration of free protoporphyrin in erythrocytes[16] (see Table 20–4). Protoporphyrin concentration may also be increased in plasma and, less frequently, in feces. Urinary porphyrin concentrations are normal, except when liver disease leads to secondary coproporphyrinuria. Ferrochelatase activities are decreased to 10–30% of normal in lymphocytes and other nucleated cells.[1] Detection of asymptomatic gene carriers may require enzyme measurement or DNA analysis, as erythrocyte protoporphyrin concentrations are often normal in such individuals. Over 30 mutations of the ferrochelatase gene have now been identified in EPP.[8, 26] Most are inherited in an autosomal-dominant pattern. Recent evidence suggests that inheritance of a severe ferrochelatase mutation of this type does not produce clinically overt disease unless the other ferrochelatase allele carries a mutation outside the coding region, which leads to low expression of structurally normal enzyme.[27] In addition, a minority of patients with overt disease may be homoallelic or heteroallelic for severe mutations.[26] It has been suggested that inheritance of two disabling ferrochelatase mutations may predispose to liver disease in EPP.[26]

Prediction of liver disease is difficult. Liver function should be assessed regularly by standard biochemical tests and persistent abnormalities investigated by biopsy. Very high and increasing erythrocyte porphyrin concentrations (greater than 20–30 μmol/L), high plasma porphyrin concentrations, and relatively low fecal protoporphyrin excretion reflect impaired biliary secretion and thus suggest liver disease.

Treatment

Skin damage may be minimized by avoiding sunlight, by using sunscreen ointments or by building up a protective layer of β-carotene in the skin.[1,2] Sufficient oral carotene should be given to produce a serum concentration of 6–8 mg/L. At this concentration, the skin turns yellowish-orange and contains sufficient β-carotene to block photo damage by acting as a singlet oxygen trap. In patients with evidence of liver damage, further accumulation of porphyrin may be discouraged either by suppressing synthesis or interrupting the enterohepatic circulation of protoporphyrin. The latter may be achieved by giving oral cholestyramine or activated charcoal. Hypertransfusion or intravenous hematin may be useful for short-term suppression of heme synthesis, for example, prior to liver transplanation.[24] For hepatic failure, liver transplantation has been successful, although it leads to little decrease in protoporphyrin production and porphyrin may reaccumulate in the liver.[24,26]

PEDIATRIC ASPECTS OF ACUTE PORPHYRIA

Episodic acute attacks of neurovisceral dysfunction occur in four types of porphyria (see Table 20–1). Of these, the autosomal recessive disorder, PBG synthase deficiency porphyria, is very rare; one of the six patients reported to date was a child.[19] The autosomal dominant acute hepatic porphyrias—acute intermittent porphyria (AIP), hereditary coproporphyria (HC), and variegate porphyria (VP)—are essentially adult diseases. In all three disorders, detectable overproduction of heme precursors and symptoms are very uncommon before puberty. The biochemical basis of prepubertal latency is not understood.

Acute illness, clinically similar to acute porphyria and associated with overproduction of ALA, may also occur in children with hereditary tyrosinemia.[28]

Overt Acute Porphyria in Children

Acute attacks of AIP, HC, or VP may occur around the age of puberty but are uncommon earlier in childhood. They are very rare, although a number have been reported, the youngest patient being 4 months old.[29–31] In several cases, the attacks appear to have been precipitated by anticonvulsants. The clinical features and treatment are the same as for adults and have been reviewed in detail.[1–3,32] The diagnosis depends on demonstration of excess PBG in urine, followed by analysis of fecal porphyrins to distinguish between AIP, HC, and VP[16] (see Table 20–4). Onset of VP or HC with skin lesions in the absence of acute porphyria does not appear to have been reported in children before puberty.

Detection and Management of Gene Carriers before Puberty

It is important that relatives of patients with AIP, HC, or VP be screened to detect asymptomatic individuals so that they can be advised to avoid various drugs and other factors that can precipitate acute attacks.[1–3] Screening should be applied to children as well as adults, because, although the risk of an acute attack in children is much less, it does exist. Affected parents are often anxious to know whether their children have inherited porphyria.

Since PBG and porphyrin excretion are invariably normal in children, detection of carriers of the genes for AIP, VP, or HC requires measurement of the activities of the defective enzymes (Table 20–3) or DNA analysis. Measurement of erythrocyte PBG deaminase will detect gene carriers in the majority of families with AIP, but there is some overlap between enzyme activities in normal and affected individuals and the method has other limitations.[3, 16] In particular, PBG deaminase activity is dependent on the age distribution of circulating erythrocytes, being highest in the least mature cells, which complicates interpretation in young infants and individuals who are not hematologically normal. For this reason, detection of carriers by PBG deaminase measurement should not be attempted until after age 6–8 m. More precise identification of carriers at any age can be obtained by recombinant DNA methods.[8, 33] Over 120 disease-specific mutations have now been identified in the PBG deaminase gene, most of which are restricted to one or a few families.[33] Thus, the use of methods based on direct detection of mutations for screening the families of patients with AIP is complicated by the need to first identify the mutation in each family.

Enzymatic detection of carriers of the VP and HC genes during childhood depends on measurement of protoporphyrinogen and coproporphyrinogen oxidases, respectively. Both measurements require nucleated cells, such as lymphocytes or lymphoblastoid or fibroblast cell lines, are technically difficult, and do not always distinguish between affected and unaffected individuals. DNA methods are now becoming available for both conditions.[8, 34] In South Africa, where the high prevalence of VP among persons of African descent is caused by a founder effect, most patients have the same mutation (R59W) in the protoporphyrinogen oxidise gene.[34] Elsewhere, VP shows the extensive allelic heterogeneity that is characteristic of AIP, HC, and other porphyrias.[8]

Children who are known or suspected carriers of the genes for AIP, VP, or HC should be managed in a similar fashion to adult carriers.[1–3] They or their parents should ensure that drugs known to precipitate acute porphyria are avoided. In addition, they should wear a bracelet or necklace indicating that they have porphyria to prevent, for example, administration of an inappropriate anesthetic after an accident.

Homozygous Forms of the Acute Autosomal Dominant Porphyrias

During recent years, homozygous forms of AIP, VP, or HC have been described.[1, 2, 19] All the affected individuals have been children with enzyme deficiencies of 80% or more and patterns of overproduction of heme precursors resembling those of the corresponding autosomal dominant disorders. Typical acute attacks of porphyria are unusual. None have had an anemia attributable to defective heme biosynthesis, although erythrocyte zinc-protoporphyrin concentrations are increased, as in other homozygous porphyrias.[35] Both parents have the biochemical features of the autosomal dominant counterpart and there is an increased incidence of consanguinity. Either a parent or other close relative may have overt porphyria.

Homozygous AIP

This condition is the most severe of the homozygous variants of the autosomal dominant porphyrias.Four children with homozygous AIP have been described.[19] All had excessive excretion of PBG from birth with PBG deaminase activities of less than 20% of normal. Clinically, the condition is characterized by progressive neurological deterioration with leucodystrophy and, in most patients, convulsions and bilateral cataracts. Three of the children, from two families, have been shown to be compound heterozygotes for mutations in exon 10 of the PBG deaminase gene.[19]

Homozygous VP

At least 12 children with this condition have been reported.[19] All developed skin lesions of varying severity early in childhood, usually before the age of 1 year, with blisters, skin fragility, hypertrichosis, and skeletal abnormalities of the hands as prominent features. Other clinical features that have been present in more than one family, but not in all cases, include mental retardation, convulsions, and short stature. The combination of short stature and hypertrichosis may provoke extensive endocrine investigation if the other skin changes, which may be minimal, are overlooked. Acute attacks of porphyria have not yet been reported in this condition.

Homozygous HC

Two types of homozygous HC have been described.[1, 19] In two unrelated children, short stature, skin lesions, and attacks of acute porphyria were associated with excessive excretion of coproporphyrin III. The other type, known as harderoporphyria, has been identified in only two families and is characterized by excretion of harderoporphyrin, a tricarboxylic intermediate of the coproporphyrinogen oxidase reaction (see Figure 20–1). Affected children have severe hyperbilirubinemia and hemolytic anemia at birth, often accompanied by blisters caused by porphyrin-induced photosensitization. Mild photosensitivity and compensated hemolytic anemia may persist after the neonatal period.

ROLE OF THE LABORATORY IN THE INVESTIGATION OF PORPHYRIA IN CHILDREN

None of the porphyrias have clinical features that are sufficiently distinctive to enable the diagnosis to be made without laboratory investigations. These are essential both to distinguish porphyria from other disorders with similar clinical presentation and to identify the type of porphyria. For most laboratories the former objective is the more important. In adults, and even more so in children, the majority of tests for suspected porphyria will be negative, and it is important not to miss patients at this stage by using inappropriate screening tests. This aspect is discussed below. The second stage in diagnosis—identification of the type of porphyria—requires definition of the pattern of heme precursor overproduction (see Table 20–4). In children, enzyme measurements may also be needed. Methods and diagnostic strategies have been reviewed.[16, 36]

PBG and porphyrins are moderately unstable in biological samples. Fresh, random samples of urine should be used for their measurement and results expressed per liter or per mg/creatinine. Twenty-four-hour collections delay analysis and rarely give additional diagnostic information. Porphyrins in feces should be analyzed as soon as possible after collection. In practice, diagnostically important changes in the PBG or porphyrin content of urine or feces are unlikely to occur in samples kept at room temperature for 24–36 h, provided they are shielded from light. Porphyrins are stable in EDTA-anticoagulated blood for several days.

Children with Suspected Acute Porphyria

Older children, particularly, may present with the typical features of an attack of acute porphyria, but this is rare. It is much more usual for the laboratory to be asked to exclude AIP, HC, or VP as the cause of unexplained recurrent attacks of abdominal pain or convulsions, perhaps accompanied by behavioral disturbances. The essential investigation is examination of urine for excess PBG. Screening tests, such as the Watson-Schwartz test, which depend on the reaction of PBG with p-dimethylaminobenzaldehyde in acid to form a red color which is insoluble in organic solvents, have been criticized because of poor sensitivity,[37] but if carefully carried out can detect as little as 35–50 μmol PBG/L.[16] If this test is negative while symptoms are present, the child is very unlikely to have an acute porphyria.[16, 36] If doubt remains or if the child is seen between recurrent attacks and the screening test is negative, PBG should be measured by a quantitative method.[16]

A normal PBG concentration excludes AIP. In VP and HC, PBG may return to normal after an acute attack, but fecal porphyrin excretion remains high; these conditions can be excluded by measuring fecal and plasma porphyrins.[16] An increase in fecal porphyrin concentration without any other evidence of heme precursor overproduction is almost always explained by an increased concentration of heme in the gut, either from the diet or from occult gastrointestinal bleeding, the heme being metabolized to porphyrins by bacteria.[16]

Measurement of urinary porphyrins is usually unhelpful. If PBG excretion is increased, it does not differentiate between AIP, VP, or HC; fecal and plasma porphyrin measurements are required for this purpose.[16, 36] If PBG concentration is normal, the most frequent cause of increased urinary porphyrin excretion is coproporphyrinuria.[16, 36] The usual cause is cholestasis, but occasionally lead poisoning or hepatic enzyme induction due, for example, to long-term treatment with anticonvulsants may be responsible.

TABLE 20–5. Porphyrias Presenting in Childhood with Skin Fragility, Blisters, and Hypertrichosis

Condition	Inheritance
Congenital erythropoietic porphyria	Autosomal recessive
Porphyria cutanea tarda (Type II)	Autosomal dominant
Hepatoerythropoietic porphyria	Homozygous UROD defect
Homozygous hereditary coproporphyria	Homozygous form of HC
Harderoporphyria	(Autosomal recessive?)
Homozygous variegate porphyria	Homozygous form of VP

Children with Suspected Cutaneous Porphyria

Photosensitivity

EPP should be excluded as a possible cause in all children who present with a history of unexplained acute photosensitivity without skin fragility, blisters, or hypertrichosis. The simplest and most reliable method is to measure total erythrocyte porphyrin by a quantitative fluorometric micromethod.[16] Screening tests based on solvent extraction or fluorescence microscopy may give false-negative results and should not be used. A normal erythrocyte porphyrin concentration excludes EPP. If the concentration is increased, the diagnosis of EPP should be confirmed by showing that the increase is caused by free protoporphyrin.[16] In other causes of raised erythrocyte porphyrin concentrations, such as iron deficiency and lead poisoning, zinc-protoporphyrin is increased.[4, 16, 36]

Other Cutaneous Porphyrias

Blisters, skin fragility, and hypertrichosis are features of all the other cutaneous porphyrias of childhood. This is a complex group of rare disorders (Table 20–5). The skin lesions are characteristic of porphyria and detailed investigation of urinary, fecal, plasma, and erythrocyte porphyrins is usually required from the start. Final diagnosis may depend on enzyme measurement. If exclusion of porphyria is required, demonstration of normal total porphyrin concentrations in urine and feces by a spectrophotometric or fluorometric method is adequate.[16, 36]

REFERENCES

1. Nordmann Y, Deybach J-C. Human hereditary porphyrias. In: Daley H, ed., Biosynthesis of heme and chlorophylls. New York: McGraw-Hill, 1990:491–542.
2. Kappas A, Sassa S, Galbraith RA, Nordmann Y. The porphyrias. In: Scriver CR, Beaudet AL, Sly WS, Valle D, eds., The metabolic and molecular basis of inherited disease, 7th ed. New York: McGraw-Hill, 1995:2103–59.
3. Anderson K. The Porphyrias. In: Zakim D, Boyer TD, eds. Hepatology: a textbook of liver disease. Philadelphia: WB Saunders, 1995:417–63.

4. Moore MR, McColl KE, Rimington C, Goldberg A. Disorders of porphyrin metabolism. New York: Plenum Press, 1987.
5. Frank M, Doss MO. Relevance of urinary coproporphyrin isomers in hereditary hyperbilirubinemias. Clin Biochem 1989;22:221–22.
6. Poh-Fitzpatrick MB, Zaider E, Sciales C, et al. Cutaneous photosensitivity and coproporphyrin abnormalities in the Alagille syndrome. Gastroenterology 1990;99:831–5.
7. Ponka P. Tissue-specific regulation of iron metabolism and heme synthesis: distinct control mechanisms in erythroid cells. Blood 1997;89:1–25.
8. Elder, GH. Genetic defects in the porphyrias: types and significance. Clin Dermatol 1998, in press.
9. Nordmann Y, Deybach J-C. Congenital erythropoietic porphyria. Semin Dermatol 5:106–14.
10. Fritsch C, Bolsen K, Ruzicka T, Günter G. Congenital erythropoietic porphyria. J Am Acad Dermatol 1997;36:594–610.
11. Warner CA, Yoo H-W, Roberts AG, Desnick RJ. Congenital erythropoietic porphyria: identification and expression of exonic mutations in the uroporphyrinogen III synthase gene. J Clin Invest 1992;89:693–700.
12. Fontanellas A, Bensidhoum M, De Salamanca RE, et al. A systematic analysis of the mutations of the uroporphyrinogen III synthase gene in congenital erythropoietic porphyria. Eur J Hum Genet 1996;4:274–82.
13. Zix-Kieffer I, Langer B, Eyer D, et al. Successful cord blood stem cell transplantation for congenital erythropoietic porphyria (Günther's disease). Bone Marrow Transplantation 1996;18:217–20.
14. Moreau-Gaudry F, Ged C, de Verneuil H. Gene therapy for erythropoietic porphyria. Gene Therapy 1996;3:843–44.
15. Elder, GH. Porphyria cutanea tarda. Seminars in Liver Disease 1998;18:67–75.
16. Elder GH, Smith SG, Smyth SJ. Laboratory investigation of the porphyrias. Ann Clin Biochem 1990;27:395–412.
17. Elder GH, Worwood M. Mutations in the hemochromatosis (HFE) gene, porphyria cutanea tarda and iron overload. Hepatology 1998;27:289–91.
18. Cripps DJ, Peters HA, Gocmen A, et al. Porphyria turcica due to hexachlorobenzene: a 20 to 30 year follow-up study on 204 patients. Brit J Dermatol 1984;111:413–22.
19. Elder GH. Hepatic porphyrias in children. J Inher Metab Dis 1997;20:237–46.
20. Smith SG. Hepatoerythropoietic porphyria. Semin Dermatol 1986;5:125–37.
21. Roberts AG, Elder GH, De Salamanco RE, et al. A mutation (G281E) of the human uroporphyrinogen decarboxylase gene causes both hepatoerythropoietic porphyria and overt familial porphyria cutanea tarda. J Invest Dermatol 1995;104:500–2..
22. Kushner JP, Pimstone NR, Kjeldsberg CR, Pryor MA, Huntley A. Congenital erythropoietic porphyria: diminished activity of uroporphyrinogen decarboxylase and dyserythropoiesis. Blood 1982;59:725–37.
23. Nordmann Y, Amram D, Deybach J-C, Phung LN, Lesbros D. Coexistent hereditary coproporphyria and congenital erythropoietic porphyria (Günther's disease). J Inher Metab Dis 1990;13:687–91.
24. Todd DJ. Erythropoietic protoporhyria. Brit J Dermatol 1994;131:751–66.
25. Rank JM, Straka JG, Bloomer JR. Liver in disorders of porphyrin metabolism. J Gastroent Hepatol 1990;5:573–85.
26. Cox TM. Erythropoietic protoporphyria. J Inher Metab Dis 1997;20:258–69.
27. Gouya L, Deybach J-C, Lamoril J, et al. Modulation of the phenotype in dominant erythropoietic protoporphyria by a low expression of the normal ferrochelatase allele. Am J Hum Genet 1996;58:292–99.
28. Mitchell G, Larochelle J, Lambert M, et al. Neurologic crises in hereditary tyrosinemia. New J Med1990;322:432–37.
29. Barclay N. Acute intermittent porphyria in childhood: a neglected diagnosis? Arch Dis Child 1974;49:404–5.
30. Beauvais P, Klein M-L, Denave L, Martel C. Porphyria aigue intermittente a l'age de quatre mois. Arch Franc Ped 1976;33:987–92.

31. Day RS. Variegate porphyria. Semin Dermatol 1986;5:138–54.
32. Mustajoki P, Nordmann Y. Early administration of heme arginate for acute porphyric attacks. Arch of Int Med 1993;153:2004–08.
33. Puy H Deybach JC, Lamoril J et al. Molecular epidemiology and diagnosis of PBG deaminase gene defects in acute intermittent porphyria. Am J Hum Genet 1997;60:1373–83.
34. Hirsch RE, Meissner PN, Hift R. Variegate porphyria. Seminars in Liver Disease 1998;18:33–40.
35. Kordac V, Martasek P, Zaman J, Rubin A. Increased erythrocyte protoporphyrin in homozygous variegate porphyria. Photodermatology 1985;2:257–59.
36. Bonkovsky H, Barnard G. Diagnosis of porphyric syndromes. In: Seminars in Liver Disease, in press.
37. Deacon AC. Performance of screening tests for porphyria. Ann Clin Biochem 1988;25:392–7.

CHAPTER 21

Therapeutic Drug Monitoring and Clinical Toxicology in a Pediatric Hospital

Steven J. Soldin, Ph.D., F.A.C.B., F.C.A.C.B.
Tai C. Kwong, Ph.D., F.A.C.B.

THERAPEUTIC DRUG MONITORING

General Considerations

Based on theoretical and practical knowledge, a physician attempts to choose the ideal drug for treatment of an identified disease or pathophysiologic process. This search for optimal pharmacotherapy is made more difficult by the growing awareness of immense genetically, environmentally, and age-determined variations in drug response.[1] Some investigators appear biased toward the prediction of pharmacokinetic behavior and the monitoring of drug concentrations in biological fluids as an end in itself. Such measurements in the absence of clinical assessment of pharmacologic or therapeutic effects are likely to prove pointless. Recent indications are that approximately 12% of all drugs prescribed in the United States are for children under age 9 y.[2] A review of drug-dosing habits in neonatal intensive care units has shown that the average number of drugs administered to premature infants under 1000 g varies from institution to institution but is usually in the 15–20 range, while infants over 2500 g usually receive 4–10 drugs during their hospital stay.

Physicians have a responsibility to be informed adequately about the risks, limitations, and use of drugs they prescribe, to acquaint their patients with possible adverse effects, and to ensure that patients are being optimally treated. For certain drugs, this necessitates their measurement in plasma or serum, followed by appropriate dosage adjustments if required.

The use of any drug carries with it a risk that is often not precisely established. When the rate of drug-induced disease is reported as 1 in every 20,000 to 200,000 patients (e.g., the devastating aplastic anemia caused by chloramphenicol); the recognition of a causal relationship is sometimes difficult and delayed.[3]

Some Basic Pharmacokinetic Considerations

An in-depth discussion of pharmacokinetics is beyond the scope of this chapter. However, a brief review of some concepts and definitions is important for a better understanding of therapeutic drug monitoring.

Pharmacokinetics is a tool that serves to describe in quantitative terms what happens to a drug in the body. The primary goal of therapeutic drug monitoring is to optimize drug administration with such information. To reach the required steady-state blood concentrations in a particular patient receiving a drug chronically, it is necessary to establish parameters such as:

- *Apparent Volume of Distribution* (Vd). The volume in which the drug appears to be distributed if it were present throughout the body at the concentration in which it is found in the blood. A very large (greater than the total body water) Vd, e.g., Digoxin (Vd = 5–10 L/Kg), indicates significant tissue binding.
- *Plasma Half-Life:* the time it takes for the plasma drug concentration to decrease by 50% (see Figure 21–1).
- *Total Body Clearance* (CI): the volume of vascular fluid in which the drug is measured and from which the drug is irreversibly removed per unit of time.
- *Bioavailability* (F): The fraction of the administered dose reaching the systemic circulation intact.

The above parameters can be estimated using average population data, or established more precisely for a patient by analyzing suitably collected blood samples after a trial dose.

When a drug is administered intravenously, it undergoes a distribution phase followed by an elimination phase. The elimination process follows exponential first-order kinetics, i.e., a constant fraction of the drug in the body is eliminated per unit of time (Figure 21–1). The elimination phase half-life is an important parameter often quoted in the literature. If the elimination phase line is extended back to the *Y* axis, the point of intersection with the *Y* axis provides the "zero-time" drug concentration. Dividing the dose administered by the zero-time concentration provides the apparent volume of distribution, Vd.

The relationship between elimination half-life, apparent volume of distribution, and clearance is $t_{1/2} = 0.693\ (Vd/Cl)$.

Based upon the available information, it is possible to recommend the dose (D) and frequency of administration (T) needed to achieve the desired average steady-state blood concentration (C_{ss}) using the relationship in Equation 1, where TBC is the total body clearance.

Thus, either the available dosage form is used to calculate the required interval (Equation 2), or a convenient frequency of administration is made to dictate the amount of drug to be administered (Equation 3).

FIGURE 21–1. Plasma Drug Concentration versus Time Profile for a Drug Administered Intravenously

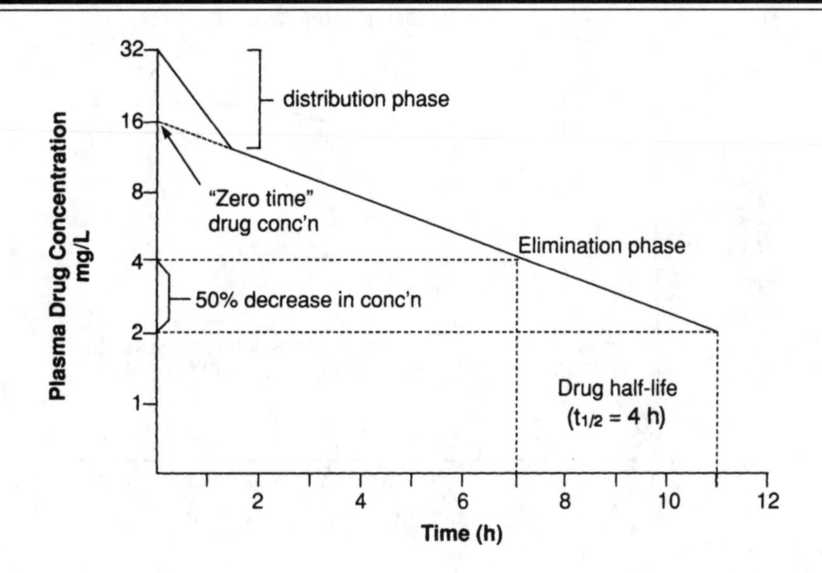

$$C_{ss} = \frac{F \cdot D}{TBC \cdot T} \quad \text{Equation 1}$$

$$T = \frac{F \cdot D}{C_{ss} \cdot TBC} \quad \text{Euqation 2}$$

$$D = \frac{C_{ss} \cdot TBC \cdot T}{F} \quad \text{Equation 3}$$

About 90% of the eventual steady-state concentration will be reached in 3.3 times the $t_{1/2}$ after initiation of the selected dosage regimen, with steady-state concentration being achieved after approximately 5 times the half-life.

Time of Sampling

The interpretation of drug concentrations depends not only on the dosage regimen, but also on the time of the last dose relative to the time of blood sampling. For a drug administered orally at intervals equal to its half-life (say, 4 h), it takes 4 to 5 times the half-life to achieve steady-state plateau concentrations (Figure 21–2). For most drugs, there is an excellent correlation between the dose and the steady-state serum concentration, e.g., doubling the dose will also double the steady-state concentration. Exceptions to the rule include those drugs undergoing saturation kinetics (e.g., phenytoin, ethanol, and salicylate). Therefore, specimens for analysis should not be drawn until sufficient time has elapsed to enable steady-state concentrations to be achieved (unless, of course, toxicity is suspected at an earlier stage).

FIGURE 21–2. Plasma Drug Concentration versus Time Profile for a Drug Administered Orally at Intervals Equal to the Drug's Elimination Half-life

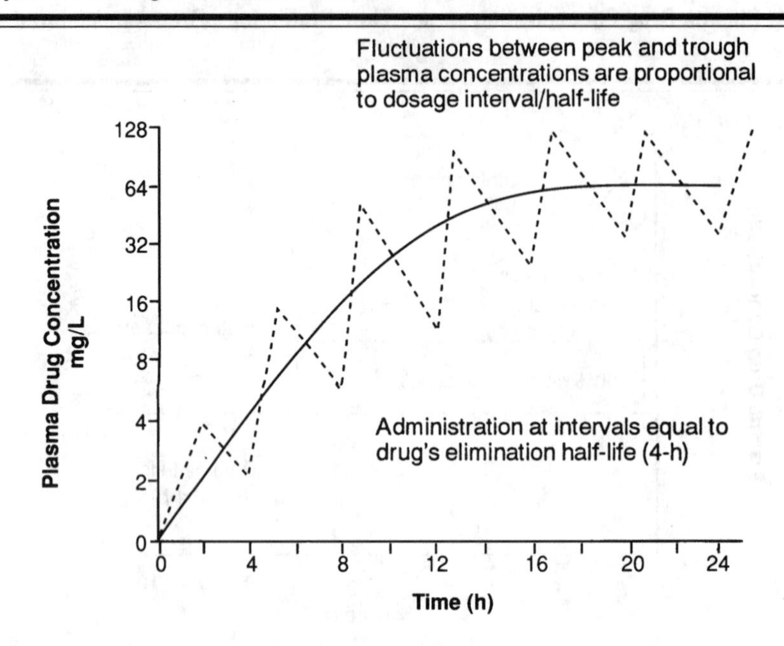

For drugs with a long half-life, such as phenobarbital, which are administered at intervals shorter than the half-life, there is little difference between steady-state peak and trough drug concentrations. However, for drugs with a short half-life, such as the aminoglycosides, theophylline, and primidone, differences between peak and trough concentrations may be considerable, and it is often advisable to measure both. As a general rule, however, the ideal sample is one that would provide the steady-state trough serum concentration. This is the sample drawn just before the next dose.

Steady-state drug concentrations can be achieved more rapidly by administering oral, intramuscular, or intravenous loading doses of a drug. Loading doses circumvent the necessity of waiting 5 half-lives to achieve a serum concentration plateau and a maximum therapeutic effect. For a drug administered intravenously (e.g., digoxin), it is necessary to wait a fixed time interval after loading to allow for drug distribution to occur. In the case of digoxin, distribution may take 6 h.

In general, concentration measurements should be made 0.5–1 h after intravenous administration of medication. For example, a specimen representing the "peak" serum concentration for gentamicin is most appropriately drawn 30 min after the end of drug infusion, after distribution is complete.

THE RATIONALE FOR THERAPEUTIC DRUG MONITORING

For most drugs, the intensity and duration of the given pharmacological response is proportional to the drug concentration at the receptor site. This drug concentration depends on many factors, including drug dose and the pharmacokinetic properties of the drug administered. Some of the factors affecting the pharmacokinetics of drugs include genetic differences in drug metabolism, disease, age, drug interactions, and diet. For many drugs, extreme interindividual variation makes it impossible to predict a serum concentration for any given dose based on a weight relationship.

For most drugs, there is a plasma concentration below which the clinical response is unsatisfactory (subtherapeutic). At higher concentrations, the drug elicits a therapeutic effect. At still higher concentrations, unwanted toxic side effects can occur. The aim of drug dosage design is to maintain the plasma concentration in the therapeutic range, as represented in Figure 21–3.

For therapeutic monitoring to be useful in the clinical management of patients, it is necessary that the drugs of interest fulfill certain requirements:

1. The relationship between serum concentration and pharmacological effect must be good. This usually implies a strong correlation between serum concentration and concentration in the target tissue.[4]
2. A reliable and rapid method for drug analysis must be available.
3. A narrow margin should exist between serum concentrations which provide therapeutic effects and those which cause toxic effects, e.g., as observed with digoxin, theophylline, and aminoglycoside antibiotics.
4. There should be a poor correlation between serum concentration and drug dosage due to interindividual differences in drug absorption, metabolism, and excretion. Such poor correlation has been shown with clomipramine used in treatment of enuresis.[5]
5. Pharmacological effects should not be readily measurable, e.g., anticonvulsant drugs in which the suppression of seizure activity is difficult to monitor clinically.

For therapeutic drug monitoring to be regarded as having established value, there should be a better correlation between the plasma drug concentration and the pharmacological effect than between the drug dosage and the pharmacological effect.

FIGURE 21–3. Relationship between Serum Drug Concentration and Clinical Effect

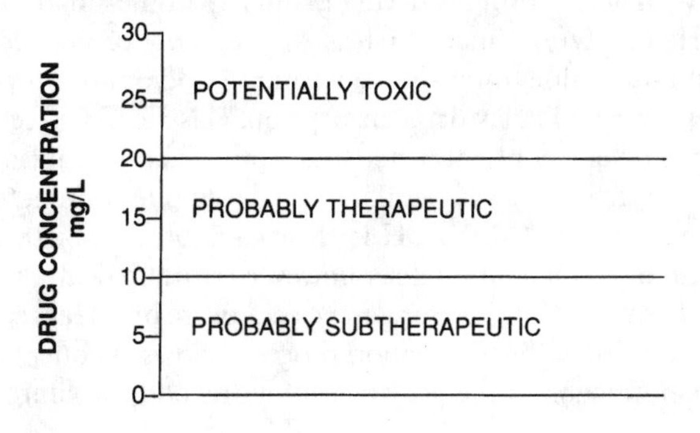

The need for therapeutic drug monitoring through measurement of serum concentrations also implies the lack of any clear, objective clinical marker of drug effect.

Although the problems listed above pertain to both adult and pediatric populations, there are nevertheless important differences between the two groups:

1. Absorption is altered for many drugs in the neonatal period due to changes in gastric pH and gastric emptying time.
2. There are differences in the apparent volume of distribution due to differences in body composition (the neonate has proportionately less body fat and more body water than children and adults).
3. The clearance of drugs is often low in premature infants and neonates due to immature hepatic and renal function.
4. Biotransformation of many drugs is slow in the premature infant and neonate due to immaturity of the enzymes responsible for drug metabolism (the hepatic microsomal enzyme system). In contrast, the activity of this system is often greater in children than in adults, requiring a higher milligram/kilogram body weight dosage in the former to achieve steady-state concentrations comparable to those found in adults. A more detailed discussion of these variables follows.
5. Protein binding may be somewhat decreased in the neonate.

Absorption

Drug absorption is affected by numerous factors, including route of administration, drug formulation, age of recipient, and concomitant administration of other drugs or food. Administration by the intravenous route provides rapid availability, with absorption being quantitative. In contrast, absorption of some drugs, such as phenytoin or diazepam, after intramuscular administration is slower and less complete. Intramuscular dosing with such drugs should be avoided whenever possible. Many drugs are, however, administered orally, and factors that influence the amount of drug absorbed from the gastrointestinal tract (the bioavailability of a drug) include drug formulation, drug solubility and pK, concomitant administration of other drugs, and simultaneous ingestion of food.

Most drugs are absorbed from the gastrointestinal tract by a process of passive diffusion, with absorption occurring primarily in the small intestine. Variables include gastric emptying time, which is considerably prolonged in the neonate and approaches adult values only after age 6 m.[5,6] Food or any other factor which delays gastric emptying will delay drug absorption. Gastric pH affects the state of ionization of some drugs and hence their absorption across lipid membranes. Erythromycin and ampicillin are acid labile, and delayed retention in the stomach results in decreased absorption. Gastric pH is close to neutral at birth and falls to approximately 2 within several hours; it does, however, return to neutrality by 24 h and remains neutral for 1–2 w. Adult values for gastric acidity are only reached after age 2 y.[7]

For most drugs, the elimination process follows exponential first-order kinetics, i.e., a constant fraction of the drug present in the body is eliminated per unit of time.

However, three important drugs undergo dose-dependent or saturation kinetics: phenytoin (discussion follows), salicylate, and ethanol.

Drug Metabolism

Drug metabolism is influenced by genetic and dietary factors, and also by age and the activity of drug-metabolizing enzymes. In addition, altered hepatic, renal, and cardiac function can markedly affect biotransformation and may lead to serious drug accumulation if dosage regimens are not tailored accordingly.

Studies by Vesell and Page[8] indicate the magnitude of genetic control over rates of drug metabolism. In these studies, identical twins were found to have very similar plasma half-lives for antipyrine.

Isoniazid and procainamide are metabolized by acetylation in the liver. The capacity of rapid acetylation occurs in families as a Mendelian dominant gene. Persons lacking the dominant gene for this acetyltransferase display a reduced capacity for metabolism of these drugs, i.e., they are slow acetylators (approximately 50% of the people in North America are slow acetylators), and as a result plasma concentrations of drugs normally acetylated are higher and remain increased longer than in the fast-acetylator group.[9]

Humans are exposed to many chemicals, and some of these have been shown to alter the rates of drug biotransformation by enhancing the activity of the hepatic microsomal enzyme system. For example, the half-life of theophylline is considerably shorter in smokers than in nonsmokers.[10, 11] Also, theophylline half-life decreases in patients on long-term theophylline therapy who are fed a charcoal-broiled beef diet.[12] The ratio of protein to carbohydrate in the diet can also affect the rate of drug metabolism. For example, the half-life of both antipyrine and theophylline is markedly reduced when the diet is changed from a low-protein, high-carbohydrate to a high-protein, low-carbohydrate content.[13] Phenobarbital is a well-known inducer of the hepatic microsomal system, while cimetidine inhibits the same system.

The hepatic microsomal enzymes are active at birth, although their titers are considerably reduced in comparison with adult values. Activity increases with advancing fetal and postnatal age and then begins to decrease with the onset of puberty until adult values are reached. Children on chronic drug treatment (e.g., epileptics and asthmatics) should be followed very closely as they progress through puberty, as the drug dose probably will need to be adjusted downward to maintain therapeutic drug concentrations. The theophylline half-life in premature infants has been quoted as 14.4–57.7 h, whereas the half-life in children age 1–4 y has been reported as 1.9–5.5 h.[14] In contrast, theophylline half-life in adults is 3.0–9.5 h.[15]

Protein Binding

The extent of protein binding can significantly affect drug elimination. Usually it is the "free" drug which is thought to be pharmacologically active. In disease states characterized by hypoalbuminemia (e.g., hepatic or renal failure, nephrotic syndrome, protein-losing enteropathy), the concentration of the free active drug will be higher at any given total drug concentration. This may give rise to toxicity in patients who nonetheless have a total serum concentration of the drug within the therapeutic range. Since enhanced protein binding slows the elimination of drugs that are removed from the serum by glomerular filtration or diffusion into the liver, it may increase the duration of action of such drugs. Quantitative and qualitative differences in serum proteins in the newborn period frequently alter drug disposition.

In addition to albumin, various blood constituents such as red blood cells and α1-acid glycoprotein are capable of binding drugs. The concentration in plasma of α1-acid glycoprotein, a protein which binds many basic drugs,[16] increases with infectious, inflammatory, and malignant diseases and after surgery. Clearly, the binding of drugs such as propranolol and chlorpromazine to α1-acid glycoprotein is dependent on the concentration of this protein in serum.[16] It is interesting to note that the concentration of α1-acid glycoprotein in serum is low in the neonate, and consequently a number of drugs show reduced binding in neonatal serum. In a study by Piafsky and Mpamugo,[17] the binding of both lidocaine and propranolol was shown to be significantly reduced in cord serum as compared to binding in serum obtained from 14 healthy adult controls.

Free Drug Concentration

The routine measurement of free drug concentrations may be desirable, but this is still an unrealized ideal. Equilibrium dialysis is time-consuming, and the various membranes available commercially (e.g., Millipore Ultra-Free Membrane System) which allow the free drug concentration to be measured following generation of protein-free ultrafiltrate are costly. Both of the above procedures demand large sample volumes, and this requirement is always a problem in a pediatric population. Nevertheless, in many situations measurement of the non-protein-bound drug should allow a more meaningful evaluation of dosage requirements, and probably will slowly replace the now-accepted correlation of total serum drug concentration with clinical effect.

Knowledge of the free drug concentration is most important in those instances where the drug is strongly protein bound, e.g., phenytoin, valproic acid, and the tricylic antidepressants. For many drugs with a high pKa value (phenytoin, primidone, ethosuximide, carbamazepine, etc.), the concentration in saliva has been shown to approximate the free serum drug concentration. This has led to the suggestion that in many instances saliva should be substituted for the plasma sample. Since saliva is collected by non-invasive techniques,[18] there is further advantage in this approach; it is, however, impractical in neonates and infants.

In the author's experience, the clinician's request for a free drug measurement occurs most frequently with phenytoin. As already mentioned phenytoin is strongly (90%) protein bound. Any disease causing a decrease in serum protein binding of phenytoin can be associated with a large increase in free phenytoin concentration leading to phenytoin toxicity. This is known to occur in patients with renal failure who may have signs of phenytoin toxicity at serum concentrations in the therapeutic range (10–20 mg/L). In these instances the free phenytoin concentration should be adjusted to provide a free phenytoin concentration between 1–2 mg/L.[19]

The protein binding of valproic acid is variable and dependent on many factors, including the concentration of valproic acid in serum, e.g., at 10–60 mg/L there is approximately 5% free drug, while at 145 mg/L there is approximately 20% free drug. Therefore, measurement of free valproic acid concentration may occasionally be requested.[19]

Although digoxin is only slightly protein bound (20–40%), measurement of free digoxin is being increasingly requested in patients receiving either Digibind® for treatment of digoxin toxicity or in patients with digoxin-like immunoreactive factors (DLIFS) such as in neonates, patients with renal and/or liver disease, and women in the third trimester of pregnancy being treated with digoxin.[19] Digoxin-like factors are strongly protein bound and measurement of digoxin in the ultrafiltrate provides the free digoxin concentration and separates it from the cross-reactive DLIFS. In this way the physician can evaluate the patient's digoxin status even the presence of Digibind or DLIFS. By multiplying the conventional therapeutic range of 0.8–2.0 ng/mL by 0.8, one arrives at a therapeutic range for free digoxin of 0.6–1.6 ng/mL. Finally, patients receiving Digibind will have very high plasma or serum concentrations of digoxin when measured by most methods. This is because the Fab antibody Digibind draws digoxin out of skeletal muscle and heart tissue. This Fab-bound digoxin is not pharmacologically active digoxin, and for this reason measurement of free digoxin in the ultrafiltrate is strongly recommended.[20–23]

An in-depth review of free drug measurement has recently been published.[24]

Patient Noncompliance

When a patient fails to follow a prescribed medication regimen, the effectiveness of the therapy is likely to be less than desirable. Unsuspected noncompliance can lead to unnecessary tests, additional medications, or increased and sometimes dangerous dosing. Hospital admissions that might have been prevented can occur. Unused drugs may accumulate in homes and present a risk to others, especially small children.

Noncompliance is particularly problematic in the pediatric population. Bergman and Werner[25] found noncompliance in 82% of children on short-term penicillin therapy. In children, noncompliance is generally due to parental neglect and unwillingness to follow the prescribed regimen. Hence, strategies to improve compliance in children must be directed toward parents.

PRACTICAL ASPECTS OF THERAPEUTIC DRUG MONITORING

Optimal timing for taking of the sample is imperative. For this reason, a service is recommended which includes a venipuncture team or similar personnel whose sole task is to ensure that blood specimens are drawn at appropriate time intervals relative to the drug dose. Also necessary is a special drug-monitoring requisition listing the patient's age, sex, weight, and height; dose, time of last dose, and time of sampling; clinical status, especially with regard to renal, hepatic, and cardiac function; and a list of other medications received by the patient. There must also be a means to convey the sample rapidly to the laboratory for analysis. Shown in Figure 21–4 is the requisition used at Children's Hospital in Washington, D.C., for both therapeutic drug monitoring and requesting a therapeutic drug monitoring consultation.

FIGURE 21–4. Therapeutic Drug Monitoring Requisition and Report Form

Date of Requisition: ____________

COLLECTION TIMES	DOSE: ____	ROUTE	INFUSION DATA	
❑ 1600 h ❑ 1800 h ❑ 2000 h ❑ 2200 h ❑ 2400 h ____________ Consultation Requested: ❑ Yes ❑ No	q 4h ❑ q 6h ❑ q 8h ❑ q 12h o q 24h o Other: ____ ________	IV ❑ IM ❑ SC ❑ PO ❑ Other: ________	Start Time: ________ Finish Time: ________ Flush Time: Initials:	ADDRESSOGRAPH

ANALYSIS WILL NOT BE PERFORMED UNLESS ALL INFORMATION IS PROVIDED

✔	DRUG REQUESTED	RESULT	✔	DRUG REQUESTED	RESULT	✔	DRUG REQUESTED	RESULT
	Amikacin (Amikin) TROUGH	ug/mL		Digoxin (Lanoxin)	ng/mL		Primidone	ug/mL
	Amikacin (Amikin) PEAK	ug/mL		Ethosuximide (Zarontin)	ug/mL		Theophylline	ug/mL
	Caffeine	ug/mL		Gentamicin TROUGH	ug/mL		Tobramycin TROUGH	ug/mL
	Carbamazepine (Tegretol)	ug/mL		Gentamicin PEAK	ug/mL		Tobramycin PEAK	ug/mL
	Chloramphenicol (Chloromycetin) TROUGH	ug/mL		Pentobarbital	ug/mL		Valproic Acid (Depakene)	ug/mL
	Chloramphenicol (Chloromycetin) PEAK	ug/mL		Phenobarbital	ug/mL		Vancomycin TROUGH	ug/mL
	Cyclosporine	ng/mL		Phenytoin (Dilantin)	ug/mL		Vancomycin PEAK	ug/mL
	REQUESTING PHYSICIAN: PRINT: BEEPER:			TIME DRAWN: DRAWN BY:			OTHER* (please write in): *Interpretation not availabile	

INTERPRETATION AND RECOMMENDATION	PHARMACOKINETIC PARAMETERS
	Volume of Distribution (V_d) Elimination Rate Constant (K_e) Half-Life ($T_{1/2}$) New Dose New Dosing Interval Predicted Cp max Cp min
PHARMACIST INTERPRETATION:	DATE:

THERAPEUTIC RANGES

DRUG REQUESTED	THERAPEUTIC RANGE	DRUG REQUESTED	THERAPEUTIC RANGE	DRUG REQUESTED	THERAPEUTIC RANGE
Amikacin - Send to AML (Amikin) TROUGH	5–10 ug/mL	Digoxin (Lanoxin)	0.8–2.0 ng/mL	Primidone	5–12 ug/mL
Amikacin - Send to AML (Amikin) PEAK	20–35 ug/mL	Ethosuximide (Zarontin)	40–100 ug/mL	Theophylline	10–20 ug/mL
Caffeine	5–30 ug/mL	Gentamicin TROUGH	0–2 ug/mL	Tobramycin TROUGH	0–2 ug/mL
Carbamazepine (Tegretol)	8–12 ug/mL	Gentamicin PEAK	5–10 ug/mL	Tobramycin PEAK	5–10 ug/mL
Chloramphenicol (Chloromycetin) TROUGH	0–10 ug/mL	Pentobarbital Send to AML	1–5 ug/mL	Valproic Acid (Depakene)	50–100 ug/mL
Chloramphenicol (Chloromycetin) PEAK	10–25 ug/mL	Phenobarbital	15–40 ug/mL	Vancomycin TROUGH	5–10 ug/mL
Cyclosporine WHOLE BLOOD Specific / Non-specific Kidney 100-250 ng/mL / 400-800 ng/mL Liver 200-400 ng/mL / 500-1100 ng/mL Heart 200-400 ng/mL / 600-1200 ng/mL Bone Marrow 80-150 ng/mL / 200-450 ng/mL		Phenytoin (Dilantin)	10–20 ug/mL	Vancomycin PEAK	20–40 ug/mL
Tacrolimus (FK-506)	3-15 ng/mL				

Selection of Analytical Procedure for Drug Measurement

The ideal analytical procedure chosen for drug measurement would be accurate and precise, rapid, easy to perform, readily automated, and inexpensive. No single analytical technique consistently meets all of these requirements. For example, high-performance liquid chromatography and gas liquid chromatography probably provide the most accurate and precise analysis of many drugs, but they require specialized and expensive equipment and trained personnel, and even today they cannot be regarded as easy to perform. Nevertheless, provided the laboratory workload is sufficiently high, the reagent cost per analysis with these techniques is significantly lower than with the alternative methodologies: enzyme immunoassay, fluorescence immunoassay, fluorescence polarization immunoassay, radioimmunoassay, radioenzymatic assay. Furthermore, gas-liquid and high-performance liquid chromatographic techniques often allow for the simultaneous analysis of several drugs or drug metabolites in a single sample, an advantage not offered by any of the immunoassay techniques.

In contrast, drug assays performed by the enzyme multiplied immunoassay system (EMIT, Syva Diagnostics, Palo Alto, CA) and fluorescence polarization immunoassay (FPIA, Abbott Diagnostics, Abbott Park, IL) are straightforward and provide adequate specificity, sensitivity, accuracy, and precision. For smaller laboratories, the increased reagent cost per analysis is offset by the ease of drug quantitation and the ability to provide a fairly comprehensive drug analytic service with minimal technical expertise and equipment cost. Radioreceptor assays may be the method of choice for drugs which are extensively metabolized to both active and inactive metabolites, e.g., digoxin and cyclosporine. This subject was recently reviewed.[26]

Once the analysis has been performed, it is imperative that the results be rapidly conveyed to the requesting physician. Ideally, an interpretative arm of the drug monitoring service would link the laboratory and the wards to ensure that the appropriate adjustments in drug regimen have been made as a result of the analytic service provided. Such a function can best be carried out in a cost-effective fashion by clinical pharmacists supported by a clinical pharmacology service. The official report form should include the drug concentration found, the desired therapeutic concentration range, and recommendations as to how the latter can be achieved. In special instances, it may be desirable to carry out more detailed pharmacokinetic studies to derive parameters necessary to guide dosage adjustment for optimal patient management. The use of a clinical pharmacology consultative service greatly improves outcomes.[27,28]

Anticonvulsant Drugs

Phenytoin exhibits dose-dependent kinetics, i.e., the concentration of phenytoin increases linearly with dose until a point is reached at which the metabolizing pathways are saturated. Any slight further increase in drug dose can give rise to a large increase in serum concentration and drug toxicity. It is important to note that although phenytoin is effective in suppressing seizures at serum concentrations of 40–80 μmol/L (10–20 mg/L), the drug has been known to produce an exacerbation of seizures at serum concentrations > 160 μmol/L (40 mg/L). Phenytoin is strongly protein bound; therefore, any disease causing a decrease in binding can be associated with a large increase in the free phenytoin concentration, leading to phenytoin toxicity. This is known to occur particularly in patients with renal failure who may have signs of phenytoin toxicity at serum concentrations of 40–80 μmol/L (10–20 mg/L), the usual therapeutic range. In these instances, the measurement of free phenytoin concentrations is recommended, the free concentration being most easily obtained by quantitating the concentration of phenytoin in saliva. The dosage regimen should then be adjusted appropriately to provide a free concentration of 4–8 μmol/L (1–2 mg/L).

Phenobarbital and carbamazepine are potent inducers of the hepatic microsomal enzyme system and can markedly affect the half-life of other drugs metabolized by this route.

The protein binding of valproic acid is variable and dependent on many factors, including the concentration of valproic acid in serum. For example, at 140–420 μmol/L (20–60 mg/L), there is approximately 5% free drug; at 560 μmol/L (80 mg/L), there is approximately 8% free drug; and at 1015 μmol/L (145 mg/L), there is approximately 20% free drug.[29] Furthermore, there is competition for binding sites between valproate and phenytoin, resulting in initial increased free concentrations of both drugs.[30] Removal of phenytoin, carbamazepine, or phenobarbital from a drug regimen including valproic acid has been known to give rise to large increases in valproic acid serum concentrations.[31] Clearly, any change in the drug regimen should be followed shortly thereafter by drug concentration measurement and appropriate adjustment of the drug regimen if required.

Primidone is converted to phenobarbital and phenylethylmalonamide, and anticonvulsant properties have been attributed to all three compounds. Therefore, phenobarbital concentrations should always be measured in patients on primidone therapy. Although the serum primidone concentration is very dependent on the time of sampling relative to the time of drug ingestion, owing to its short half-life, this is not the case for phenobarbital. Hence, adjustments in the primidone dosing schedule are sometimes more appropriately made on the measured phenobarbital concentration.

Finally, the measurement of anticonvulsant drug concentrations is always useful in the detection of patient noncompliance with a prescribed regimen. Table 21–1 lists serum concentrations associated with various toxic signs and symptoms.

Digoxin

Digoxin does not meet many of the criteria for therapeutic drug monitoring. There are major problems in accurately measuring concentrations of digoxin with currently available immunoassays. This is especially so in newborn infants, in hypertensive patients, in states of renal and hepatic insufficiency, and in pregnancy, where the existence of endogenous digoxin-like substances (EDLS) may lead to falsely increased values of the glycoside.[32–35]

In a recent study,[36] an association between age and the apparent digoxin readings caused by EDLS was documented in newborn infants. When adding true digoxin to these sera, there was an additive effect upon the measurable digoxin concentration.

TABLE 21–1. Clinical Manifestations of Toxicity for Anticonvulsant Drugs

Drug	Serum Concentration		Clinical Manifestations of Toxicity
Phenobarbital*	172-258 μmol/L	(40-60 mg/L)	Slowness and ataxia
	258-474 μmol/L	(60-110 mg/L)	Comatose, reflexes present
	> 474 μmol/L	(110 mg/L)	No deep tendon reflexes
Phenytoin	80-120 μmol/L	(20-30 mg/L)	Nystagmus
	120-160 μmol/L	(30-40 mg/L)	Nystagmus, ataxia
	> 160 μmol/L	(40 mg/L)	Nystagmus, ataxia, and lethargy
	Chronic use		Gum hypertrophy, hirsutism
Primidone	> 64 μmol/L	(14 mg/L)	Nystagmus, vertigo, ataxia, vomiting, dysarthria
Ethosuximide	> 708 μmol/L	(100 mg/L)	Sedation, nausea, vomiting, pancytopenia
Carbamazepine	> 38 μmol/L	(9 mg/L)	Nystagmus, drowsiness, nausea, vomiting, headache
Valproic acid	> 875 μmol/L	(125 mg/L)	Rare, but include anorexia, nausea, vomiting, and hair loss

*Tolerance to the sedative effect of phenobarbital is marked. Many patients may have serum concentrations as high as 75 mg/L (323 μmol/L) and show no clinical signs of toxicity.

There is no accurate definition of a "therapeutic window" for digoxin or digitoxin. Few blind, controlled studies have tried to prove digitalis' efficacy in congestive heart failure. More importantly, sparse information exists on the correlation of serum concentrations of cardiac glycosides with inotropic effects. More information exists on the putative correlation between serum concentrations of digoxin and its antiarrhythmic effects. Some investigators have observed a correlation, whereas others have not.[37–40]

Most authorities regard the therapeutic range of digoxin to be 0.6–2.4 nmol/L (0.5–2.0 ng/mL). At concentrations above 2.4 nmol/L (2 ng/mL), there is an increased risk of digitalis toxicity, presenting as nausea, vomiting, anorexia, yellow vision, malaise, and cardiac arrhythmias. However, there is a wide "gray zone" of concentrations that may be toxic in one individual and nontoxic in another. In a recent study, Koren and Parker[41] demonstrated that even at serum concentrations above 6 nmol/L (5 ng/mL), about one-third of pediatric patients would not show symptoms or signs of toxicity. The risk of toxicity of digitalis glycosides increases in a variety of clinical conditions, including hypokalemia, hypocalcemia, hypomagnesemia, and chronic heart disease.

Despite the limitations outlined above, the therapeutic monitoring of digoxin concentrations is indicated in routine therapy, for several reasons:

1. *To assess patient compliance.* Here, therapeutic drug monitoring may be an important guideline for the assessment of therapeutic failures.
2. *To determine an optimal dosing schedule.* If a patient receives a given dose of digitalis in the hospital, does not respond clinically, and is found to have a

steady-state serum concentration of < 1.2 nmol/L (1.0 ng/mL), the clinician can safely increase the dose without achieving potentially toxic concentrations.

3. *To confirm a clinical impression of toxicity.* Many of the symptoms and signs of digitalis toxicity (anorexia, cachexia, nausea, vomiting, arrhythmias) may be caused by the underlying cardiac condition. The only available way to differentiate between these two diagnostic possibilities is by measuring the serum concentration of the glycoside. If the measured concentration is, for example, 0.8 nmol/L (0.7 ng/mL), it is very unlikely that drug toxicity caused the symptoms; if, however, the measured concentration is 4.6 nmol/L (3.8 ng/mL), it is conceivable that drug-related toxicity has occurred.

During the last decade, several drugs that are commonly coadministered with digoxin have been shown to interfere with the disposition of cardiac glycosides and to cause potentially toxic serum concentrations.[42] Quinidine, verapamil, and amiodarone may cause a significant increase in the serum concentration of digoxin, which is often associated with signs of digoxin toxicity. Spironolactone has been shown to decrease digoxinclearance, but no cases of toxicity have been reported.

Digoxin Toxicity. The concept of using hapten-specific antibodies to reverse the toxic effects of a drug has been previously advanced.[43] More recently, digoxin-specific Fab antibody fragments have been purified and used to treat patients with advanced, life-threatening toxicity.[44] In such circumstances, an immunologic approach is feasible, can be life-saving, and has been used experimentally for over 10 years. Fab antibody fragments recently have become commercially available. The fascinating side of this new approach is that it can neutralize the pharmacologic effects of a drug with a very large distribution volume that cannot be effectively removed by hemodialysis or hemoperfusion. The use of Fab antibody fragments affects the quantitation of digoxin by most immunoassay procedures. These problems can be largely overcome by measurement of "free" digoxin concentrations in a plasma ultrafiltrate.

Theophylline, Caffeine, and Doxapram

Theophylline is used widely in the treatment of bronchial asthma and neonatal apnea. The drug is a smooth muscle relaxant, possibly because of effects on adenosine receptors, and is also an inhibitor of phosphodiesterase, at least *in vitro*. This produces a buildup of intracellular cyclic AMP and consequent smooth muscle relaxation. In addition to its effect on smooth muscle, theophylline is a cardiac muscle stimulant. Theophylline also has a narrow therapeutic index, and progressively more serious side effects have been noted beginning at serum concentrations of 110 μmol/L (20 mg/L). Intersubject variability in theophylline metabolism is large, due to factors such as genetic variation, age, diet, etc., as was already discussed. For this reason, the optimal dosage regimen cannot be readily predicted, and drug monitoring plays a central role in aiding the clinician to optimize therapy. Note that the theophylline half-life is short, and this requires either the use of long-acting theophylline preparations or a regimen in which the drug is administered four times daily.

We recommend measurement of trough (predose) and peak (approximately 2 h post-dose) concentrations. Side effects include irritability, insomnia and headache, and gastrointestinal effects such as nausea, vomiting, and gastric irritation. Serum concentrations greater than 220 μmol/L (40 mg/L) have, on occasion, been associated with seizures.

Today, caffeine is preferred over theophylline for the treatment of neonatal apnea. Approximately 30–50% of premature infants suffer from apnea, generally defined as cessation of respiration for more than 20 sec, with or without bradycardia, cyanosis, or both. For infants < 29 w gestational age, the incidence increases to > 90%. Reasons for preferring caffeine to theophylline include its wider therapeutic index, slower excretion, and reduced toxicity, and the fact that, in the neonate, substantial amounts of theophylline are metabolized to caffeine, giving rise to the problem of necessitating monitoring of both drugs. The therapeutic range for caffeine is 25–150 μmol/L (5–30 mg/L).

Doxapram is an effective drug in the treatment of idiopathic apnea of prematurity that is refractory to xanthine (theophylline, caffeine) therapy. In general, infants respond to doxapram at serum concentrations of 4.0–10.6 μmol/L (1.5–4.0 mg/L). Concentrations > 13.2 μmol/L (5 mg/L) are associated with toxicity.

Aminoglycosides

This class of drugs includes gentamicin, tobramycin, and amikacin, which are used for serious gram-negative infection such as pneumonia, meningitis, and UTI. Gentamicin is not a pure chemical substance and consists of several components, all of which appear to have similar antimicrobial activity. These drugs have poor gastrointestinal absorption and are usually administered intravenously. The methods of choice for analysis of gentamicin are enzyme multiplied immunoassay, fluorescence immunoassay, fluorescence polarization immunoassay, and radioimmunoassay. Serum concentration monitoring of aminoglycosides is generally accepted for its clinical utility because these drugs are both nephrotoxic and ototoxic. For gentamicin and tobramycin, peak concentrations (drawn 30 min after the end of an intravenous infusion) should be 5–10 mg/L and trough concentrations (drawn just before the next dose) should be < 2 mg/L. Adverse reactions include allergic reactions, transient agranulocytosis, and increases in serum transaminases in addition to renal and cochlear or vestibular damage. The incidence of these reactions is low. The nephrotoxicity of gentamicin results in proximal tubular damage manifested by rising serum creatinine concentrations, proteinuria, and enzymuria.[45] A rather unique toxic reaction—muscular paralysis and apnea resulting from neuromuscular blockade—has been attributed to various aminoglycosides[46] and is a particular problem in low-birth-weight infants requiring anesthesia.

Antineoplastic Drugs

Progress in this area of therapeutic drug monitoring has been extremely slow, for numerous reasons. Most antineoplastic drugs inhibit the S-phase of the cell cycle, which is that phase in which DNA synthesis/replication occurs. If all tumor cells were in this S-phase, these drugs would be effective; however, the growth fraction or percentage of cells in the tumor that are in the "active" cell cycle varies greatly from one tumor to the next. In general, small tumors tend to have large growth fractions, while larger tumors have a greater number of cells in the quiescent Go (null) phase of the cell cycle. Most antineoplastic drugs are ineffective against cells in the Go phase.

Some cells within the tumors may also become tolerant to the drug being used. This has led to the widespread use of multidrug therapy. Multiple drug resistance (MDR) cells are able to maintain a lowered intracellular drug concentration via the increased activity of an energy-dependent drug efflux mechanism. P-glycoprotein expression correlates with both the decrease in intracellular drug accumulation and the observed degree of drug resistance in many MDR cell lines.[47]

A number of drugs have been found to reverse the MDR effect. These include calcium antagonists such as verapamil and the immunosuppressant cyclosporine.

The time of day that drugs are given can have a profound effect upon their pharmacokinetics and pharmacodynamics, e.g., Rivard et al.[48] showed that the outcome in children with acute lymphocytic leukemia (ALL) who received their maintenance 6-mercaptopurine (6MP) dose at night was better than in those who received their dosage regimen in the morning. Langevin et al.[49] subsequently showed that the area under the serum concentration versus time curve was 1.5 times greater in children with ALL if they received their 6MP dosage at night rather than in the morning. A recent study of the relationship between area under the serum concentration versus time curve for 6MP in children with ALL and outcome[50] indicated that therapeutic drug monitoring may well play an increasing role in the optimization of the drug regimen in these patients. For a review of chronopharmacology, the reader is referred to a recent article by Marks.[51]

The use of methotrexate serum concentrations to identify and treat patients with a high probability of manifesting toxicity when the drug is given at high doses has been a significant contribution to decreasing drug toxicity. The relationship between methotrexate concentrations and clinical toxicity has been well documented.[52] Folinic acid rescue has been used effectively to treat patients and thereby prevent methotrexate toxicity. In many high-dose methotrexate protocols, folinic acid (leucovorin) rescue is continued until methotrexate concentrations drop below 2×10^{-8} M.

Immunosuppressive Drugs

Cyclosporine is currently one of the main drugs used to suppress the immune response in patients receiving a transplanted organ. This drug is extensively metabolized to both active and pharmacologically inactive metabolites. Measurement of the parent drug concentration employing monoclonal immunoassays or high-performance liquid chromatography (HPLC) will not measure the pharmacologically active metabolites, while measurement of cyclosporine blood concentrations employing non-specific polyclonal immunoassays is problematic because it allows measurement of inactive metabolites which cross-react in the assay. Also, the active metabolites do not necessarily cross-react in a manner proportional to their pharmacologic activity. Use of a radioreceptor assay which hypothetically interacts with only "active" metabolites may be the method of choice in the future.[53–55]

Following are therapeutic ranges for the different transplant types, using the whole blood nonspecific immunoassay (Abbott TDx) and the specific assay (Incstar, HPLC).

	Specific	*Non-specific*
Liver	200–400 µg/L	500–1100 µg/L
Heart	200–400 µg/L	600–1200 µg/L
Bone Marrow	80–150 µg/L	200–450 µg/L
Kidney	100–250 µg/L	350–875 µg/L

The therapeutic range varies not only with the transplant type but also with the time since transplant.For a complete review, see Oellerich, Armstrong, Kahan et al.[56]

Tacrolimus (FK-506), another important immunosuppressive drug, has recently been approved by the FDA for use in liver transplant recipients. Several methods are available for its measurement. Once again, whole blood is the specimen of choice and the therapeutic range currently used is 3–15 ng/mL.[57]

Tables 21–2 and 21–3 provide drug monitoring information for some frequently used drugs, including major active metabolites, bioavailability, protein-binding, recommended dose, therapeutic and toxic concentrations, plasma half-life, time to peak plasma concentration, and apparent volume of distribution.

TABLE 21–2. Drug Monitoring Information

		Plasma Half-Life of Active Metabolite (h)			
Drug	**Major Active Metabolite**	**Neonates**	**Children**	**Adults**	**Dose Dependent Kinetics**
Acetylsalicylic acid	Salicylic acid	4.5–11.5	2–3	2–4.5	Yes (salicylic acid)
Amitriptyline	Nortriptyline			14–93	
Carbamazepine	10,11-Epoxide			5–6	
Desipramine	2-Hydroxydesipramine				
Disopyramide	N-Desisopropyldisopyramide				
Imipramine	Desipramine 2-Hydroxyimipramine 2-Hydroxydesipramine				
Methotrexate	7-Hydroxymethotrexate				
Phenytoin					Yes
Primidone	Phenobarbital Phenylethylmalonamide (PEMA)			50–120 29–36	
Procainamide	N-Acetylprocainamide			6	
Propranolol	4-Hydroxypropranolol				
Quinidine	3-Hydroxyquinidine				
Theophylline					Yes

TABLE 21–3. Parameters of Interest for Commonly Used Drug

Drug	% of Oral Dose Absorbed	Route of Administration	% of Protein Bound	Maintenance Dose (mg/kg/d)				Effective Plasma Concentration (mg/L)	Toxic Plasma Concentration (mg/L)	Half-Life (h) of Parent Drug				Time (h) to Peak Plasma Concentration	Apparent Volume of Distribution (L/kg)
				Neonates	Infants	Children	Adults			Neonates	Infants	Children	Adults		
Acetaminophen	100	oral/PR	20–30			20–40	17–34	n/a	>25			2–4	2–4	0.5–1.0	0.8–1.0
Acetylsalicylic acid	80–100	oral/PR	50–80			14–25	30–70	Antipyretic 20–100 Antiinflammatory 100–250	>300			0.25–0.35	0.25–0.35	1.0–2.0	
Amikacin	not absorbed orally	IM/IV	10	10–15		10–15	10–15	15–25	>30 peak, >5 trough	variable			2–3	0.5–1	0.05–0.7
Carbamazepine	70–80	oral	65–83			15–20	7–15	4–12	>12	8–28		5–30	5–30	3	0.8–1.9
Chloramphenicol	75–90	oral/IV	60–80	25		50	50–100	10–25	>25	8–15	15–22	2.4–3.4	1.5–5.0	2	0.6
Digoxin	50–93	IV/oral	20–40	0.010	0.015	0.01	0.008–0.012	0.8–2.0 μg/L	>2.4 μg/L	20–76	36–180	12–42	33–51	0.5–5.0	5.0–10.0
Disopyramide	80	oral/IV	10–80				8.6	2–5	>5				5–6	0.5–3.0	0.8
Ethosuximide	100	oral	0			15–40	15–30	40–100	>100			30–50	40–60	2–4 capsule, 1–2 syrup	0.7–0.9
Gentamicin	not absorbed orally	IM/IV	0–30			6–7.5	3–5	5–10	>12 peak, >2 trough			2–3	2–3	0.5–1	adults, 0.15–0.25; children, 0.07–0.7
Imipramine	29–77	oral/IM					0.7–1.4	0.150–0.250	>0.5				9–24	0.5–2	10–20
Lidocaine		IM/IV	60–80			0.02–0.05 (per min)	1–3 (per min)	1.5–5.0	>5.0				1–2	0.25–0.5	1.7
Methotrexate	variable	IV/oral	50–70			variable	variable	Depends on therapeutic regimen	24 h, $>10^{-5}$ M; 48 h, $>10^{-6}$ M; 72 h, $>10^{-7}$ M			variable	variable	1–2	0.75
Phenobarbital	80–100	IV/IM/oral/PR	45–50			3–8	2–4	15–40	>40	67–99	40–70	40–70	50–120	6–18	0.7–1 adults
Phenytoin	90	IV/IM/oral	87–93	3–5	3–5	5–15	5–10	10–20 (adults) 5–20 (children)	>20	17–60*	75 ± 64.5	12–22*	18–30*	4–8	0.5–0.8
Primidone	80–90	oral/IM	0–20			10–25	10–20	5–12	>12			10–12	10–12	2–4	0.6–1.0
Procainamide	70–95	IV/oral	15				2.8–3 (per h)	4–10	>10				2–4	1–2 oral, 0.5 IM	1.7–2.4
Propranolol	90	oral/IV	85–96				1.1–9	0.05–0.10	variable				2–6	1–4	2.0–64
Quinidine	40–98		80–90			5–30	10–30	2–5	>5				4–7	1–2 sulfate	3 ± 0.25
Theophylline	95–100	PR/oral/IV	55–65			16–24	13–18	10–20	>20	24–30	14.4–57.7	1–10	3.6–12.0	2–3 oral	0.3–0.7
Tobramycin		IM/IV	0–10	3		3–5	3–5	5–10	>12 peak, >2 trough				2–3	1 IM	0.22
Valproic acid	85–100	oral	90–95			15–100	15–45	50–100	>100			6–15	8–15	0.5–4.0	0.15–0.40

*Exhibits saturation kinetics. Half-life therefore dependent on serum concentration.

CLINICAL TOXICOLOGY

Acetaminophen

Acetaminophen (paracetamol in Great Britain) is an effective analgesic and antipyretic drug which lacks anti-inflammatory action. It presents less risk for producing gastrointestinal ulceration and hemorrhage than aspirin and other nonsteroidal anti-inflammatory drugs. With the reported link of Reye's syndrome to aspirin use, usage of over-the-counter acetaminophen medication in recent years has surpassed that of aspirin. Unfortunately, the popularity of acetaminophen and the general belief that the drug is not toxic have made accidental acetaminophen overdose a common toxicological problem. In the United States in 1995, more than 58,000 acetaminophen-only poisoning cases involving patients age 19 y and younger were reported to poison control centers; 72% of those patients were under age 6 y.[58]

Acetaminophen is available as drops, chewable tablets, and elixir, packaged in child-resistant safety bottles. Acetaminophen is a safe drug when administered in typical pediatric doses of 40–480 mg every 4 h. At higher doses, acetaminophen is hepatotoxic, although the toxic dosage is variable. Single doses of 7.5 g or greater in healthy adults or 150 mg/kg in children are used to define risk for liver damage.[59]

After a therapeutic dose, acetaminophen is more than 90% metabolized by the liver and eliminated as glucuronide and sulfate conjugates. Neither the drug nor these metabolites are toxic. Approximately 4% of the dose is converted by the cytochrome P-450 mixed function oxidase system to a reactive intermediate, N-acetyl-p-benzoquinoneimine (NAPQI). This metabolite, thought to be normally detoxified by endogenous glutathione, is excreted into the urine as mercapturic acid and cysteine conjugates. After an overdose, excessive NAPQI not detoxified by glutathione reacts with and destroys hepatocytes. As hepatocellular damage ensues, hepatic insufficiency and fulminant necrosis may follow.[60]

Acetaminophen is rapidly adsorbed, with peak plasma concentration reached within 30–120 min after therapeutic doses; however, delayed peaks may occur following large doses, due to slower gastric emptying. Clinically, patients overdosed on acetaminophen follow a course that can be divided into four phases.[59] In the initial phase, lasting 0–24 h after ingestion, the patient usually exhibits gastrointestinal irritability, nausea, and vomiting. Some patients may be asymptomatic. Adults who do not develop symptoms within 24 h after ingestion rarely show clinical toxicity, although toxicity in young children (< 6 y) always presents with vomiting within 1 h, regardless of their initial serum concentration.[61] Central nervous system, cardiovascular, respiratory, or metabolic toxicity generally is not present in phase 1. If these symptoms are present, other illnesses or drug ingestion must be suspected.

During the second phase (24–72 h), the patient may feel reasonably well while liver enzymes and bilirubin become abnormal and prothrombin time is prolonged. Oliguria may occur but without increased blood urea nitrogen as a result of decreased hepatic formation. If significant hepatic necrosis has occurred, the third phase (72–96 hours) is characterized by the sequelae of hepatic necrosis including coagulopathy, jaundice, encephalopathy, and renal failure. If the patient survives phase 3 with damage which is not irreversible, complete resolution of hepatic dysfunction will occur within 4 days to 2 weeks.

Children (≤ 12 y) are less susceptible to the hepatotoxic effects of acetaminophen despite concentrations that are toxic in adults. Emesis may also play a role in decreasing toxicity, since children are likely to vomit soon after toxic ingestion.[61]

N-acetylcysteine (NAC) is an effective antidote. In the United States, the standard oral regimen consists of a loading dose of 140 mg/kg followed by 17 doses of 70 mg/kg every 4 h. Protection against hepatotoxicity by NAC is most successful when started within 8 h of ingestion, regardless of the initial plasma acetaminophen concentrations.[61] The effectiveness of oral NAC appears to extend to those high-risk patients who are treated as late as 16–24 h post-ingestion.[62] In Canada and Europe, intravenous administration of 300 mg/kg over a 20 h period is the standard therapy.[63] This protocol of NAC usually has been well tolerated, although anaphylactoid reactions have been reported and it may have no value 16 h post-ingestion.[62] A recent experimental protocol for a 48 h intravenous NAC regimen reportedly was as efficacious as other NAC regimens when treatment was started within 10 h.[64] When treatment was initiated 10–24 h after overdose, it was as effective as the 72 h oral protocol and more effective than the 20 h intravenous treatment.

A nomogram relating time since ingestion and plasma drug concentration has been constructed to predict the risk of hepatotoxicity and is used in evaluating the need for N-acetylcysteine treatment (Figure 21–5).[65] It requires that a blood concentration be obtained at least 4 h after ingestion. Samples drawn before 4 h may not represent peak concentrations. An acetaminophen plasma concentration is in the potentially toxic range if it is above (or to the right of) the toxic line (solid line) of the nomogram which connects 1322 µmol/L (200 µg/mL) at 4 h with 330 µmol/L (50 ug/mL) at 12 h. The nomogram has a lower broken line which is plotted 25% below the solid line to allow for some uncertainty of the time of ingestion. Patients whose plasma concentrations are higher than the broken line are given the entire course of NAC treatment. Since early treatment is critical to a favorable outcome, the initial plasma drug concentration is a crucial factor in deciding to initiate therapy. Providing prompt and reliable plasma acetaminophen concentrations is an important emergency toxicology service.

Numerous methods are available for the analysis of acetaminophen. Colorimetric tests such as the cresol-ammonia spot test or the quantitative Glynn and Kendal[66] method are fast and sensitive but not specific; the Glynn and Kendal method is interfered with by salicylates. Colorimetric methods based on the prior hydrolysis of acetaminophen *and* its conjugated metabolites to indophenol are not recommended, since the above-mentioned nomogram is based on serum concentration of unconjugated acetaminophen only.[67] HPLC procedures, though simple and rapid, are not as convenient as the fluorescence polarization immunoassay and enzyme immunoassay methods which are available in most clinical laboratories.

Salicylates

Salicylate is one of the least expensive and most widely used drugs. The main therapeutic uses of salicylate to reduce pain, fever, and inflammation are well known. It is

FIGURE 21–5. Nomogram Relating Plasma or Serum Acetaminophen Concentration and Time Since Ingestion

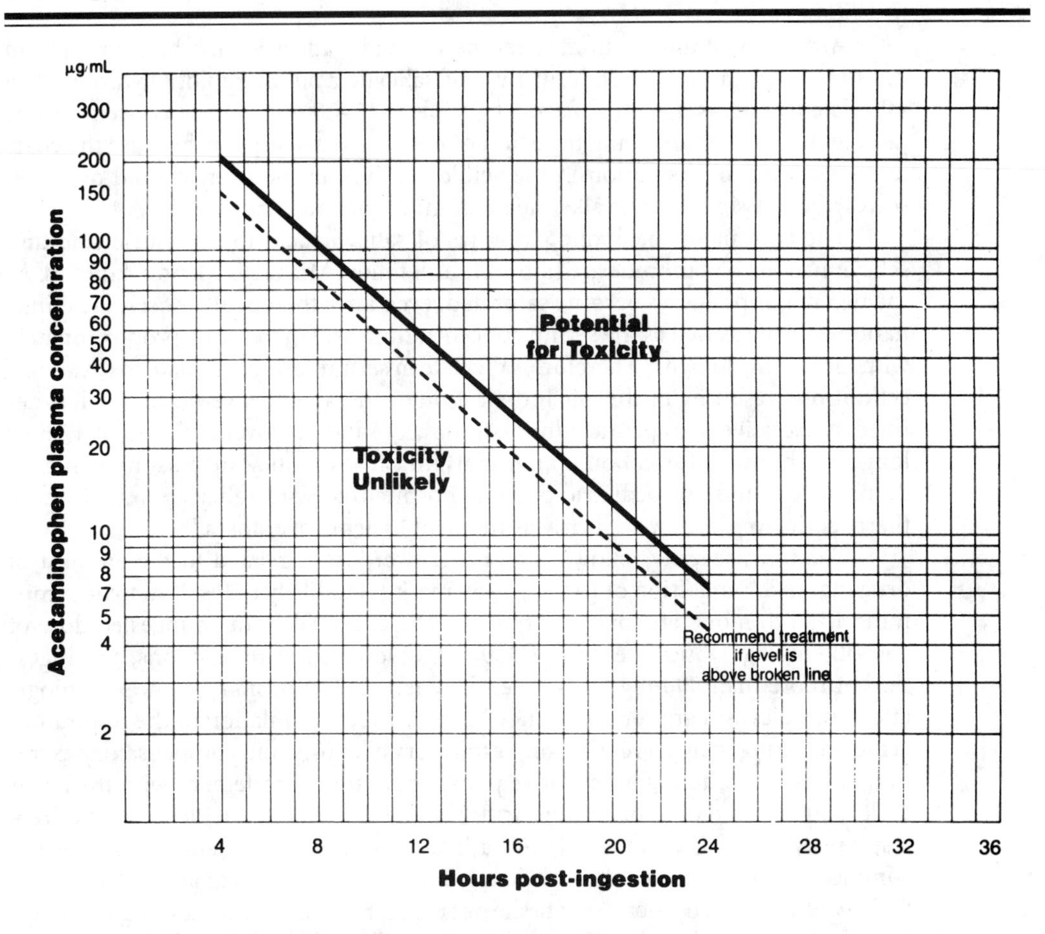

also commonly used to treat juvenile rheumatoid arthritis. A large number of different preparations of salicylates are in use, many of which are available as nonprescription medications.[68] The prevalence of salicylate as a household item has resulted in many accidental ingestions. For many years, aspirin and other salicylate-containing over-the-counter medications were the leading cause of childhood accidental poisoning. A number of safety measures enacted resulted in a decline in the incidence of salicylate poisoning in children.[68] In 1995, there were 4951 reports to poison control centers of salicylate poisoning of children under age 6 y.[58]

The most important derivative of salicylic acid is acetylsalicylic acid, which is aspirin. Other derivatives include sodium salicylate, magnesium salicylate, choline salicylate, choline magnesium trisalicylate, and salicylsalicylic acid, which is a salicylate derivative that on hydrolysis yields two molecules of salicylate. Benorylate is an acetaminophen ester of aspirin that is hydrolyzed to acetaminophen and aspirin in the gastrointestinal tract. Diflunisal, a recently introduced drug, is a difluorophenyl derivative of salicylic acid that lacks the acetyl group and is not metabolized to salicylate.

After oral administration, salicylate is rapidly adsorbed by the stomach and intestine. Aspirin and other derivatives of salicylic acid are rapidly hydrolyzed to salicylate by esterases, with a plasma half-life of 15–20 min. Serum concentrations peak up to 2 h later following ingestion of enteric-coated aspirin, because the coating is resistant to dissolution in the acidic medium in the stomach and only dissolves after passing into the alkaline medium of the intestine.

The two major metabolic pathways of salicylic acid to salicyluric acid and salicylphenolic glucuronide are saturable and follow Michaelis Menten kinetics. As the two major pathways become saturated, even after therapeutic doses, the elimination half-life as well as the serum concentrations will increase disproportionately with increasing dosage.[69] Therefore, salicylate in serum can accumulate to toxic concentrations, resulting in chronic intoxication or therapeutic overdose, which is defined as excessive therapeutic administration of salicylate over a period of 12 h or longer.[70] Chronic intoxication is an important cause of salicylate poisoning in children. In one study of pediatric patients hospitalized with salicylate intoxication, therapeutic overdoses were nearly as frequent as acute overdoses.[71]

The toxic severity following an acute overdose is related to the amount of drug ingested.[62] Ingestion of less than 150 mg/kg is unlikely to result in toxic symptoms. Mild to moderate toxic reactions can be expected from an ingested dose of 150–300 mg/kg. Doses in excess of 300 mg/kg lead to severe reactions, and ingestion of more than 500 mg/kg is potentially lethal. The primary pathophysiologic effects of salicylism are complex. They include direct stimulation of the respiratory center, resulting in hyperventilation, respiratory alkalosis, and compensatory excretion of base, uncoupling of oxidative phosphorylation, interference with the Krebs cycle, and accumulation of organic acids leading to metabolic acidosis. In children, respiratory alkalosis is transient, and a late-stage dominant metabolic acidosis is common. Acidemia favors the non-ionized form of salicylic acid and enhances the toxicity of salicylate by increasing tissue uptake of the drug. Thus, neurological symptoms such as confusion, delirium, and coma usually are associated with severe metabolic acidosis.

Acute salicylate intoxication in children is usually not difficult to diagnose. If sufficient quantity of salicylate has been ingested, the typical symptoms of salicylate intoxication will be evident. In addition, children are frequently found ingesting the tablets, and circumstantial evidence such as finding the container nearby often helps in the diagnosis. A diagnosis of salicylate intoxication is readily confirmed by measuring serum salicylate concentration. Thus, the availability of a salicylate assay on an emergency basis is critical.

Diagnosis of chronic salicylate intoxication is much more difficult without a high degree of suspicion. Salicylate is such a common household medication that parents of intoxicated children do not realize the hazard of their seemingly harmless drug therapy and do not typically disclose salicylate intake unless specifically questioned. They may not even be aware that the over-the-counter products being used contain aspirin. This leads to delay in reaching the correct diagnosis, which accounts for the more severe clinical picture that is associated with chronic intoxication. Because of the difficulty in recognizing chronic salicylate intoxication clinically, documentation of increased serum salicylate concentrations becomes very important in the differential diagnosis.

Treatment of salicylate intoxication involves correction of fluid and electrolyte depletion and acid-base imbalance. Alkalinization to enhance urinary excretion of the drug should be considered when the serum salicylate concentrations exceeds 2.5 mmol/L (350 µg/mL), and hemoperfusion or hemodialysis when the serum concentration is 7.2 mmol/L (1000 µg/mL) or greater.[70]

A nomogram (Done nomogram) is helpful in the interpretation of salicylate concentrations at different times following ingestion to predict the severity of intoxication[73] (Figure 21–6). The greatest clinical value of the nomogram lies in the early estimation of the severity of the intoxication for appropriate patient disposition and in identifying those high-risk patients who may require prompt alkalinization therapy or hemoperfusion. The nomogram is not useful in predicting the rate of salicylate elimination or future serum salicylate concentrations. Furthermore, this nomogram is applicable only to assessment of acute ingestion, not chronic intoxication.

FIGURE 21–6. Done Nomogram for Salicylate Poisoning

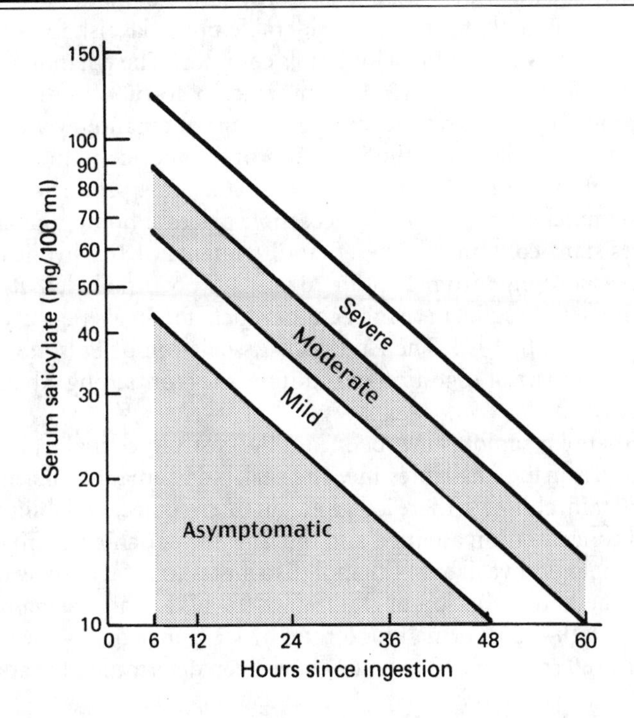

If enteric coated or sustained-release salicylate is ingested, absorption of salicylate and the increase of serum salicylate concentration will be delayed. A patient suspected of ingesting these salicylate formulations should be observed and the serum salicylate determination repeated because the peak salicylate concentration may not be attained until 60–70 h after ingestion. The Done nomogram should not be used, because an ingestion time-serum concentration relationship different from that for regular tablets is involved.

While most clinical chemistry laboratories provide serum salicylate concentrations on a STAT basis, simple qualitative screening tests such as ferric chloride, Trinder's reagent, and Phenistix for urine salicylate are useful for quick confirmation of salicylate overdose if quantitation of serum concentrations is not available immediately.[68] These screening tests are not specific for salicylate; therefore, all positive screening results should be confirmed using quantitative assays and serum samples.

Colorimetric assays based on the reaction of salicylic acid with ferric ion to give a purple color are not specific, and some assays have high serum blanks. Of these assays, Trinder's method with serum blank values less than 10 µg/mL has proved useful in the diagnosis of salicylate intoxication.[74] Fluorescence polarization immunoassay provides a rapid and accurate assay for serum salicylate. Other approaches to salicylate measurement are HPLC and enzymatic; the latter uses the enzyme salicylate hydrolase (EC 1.14.13.1) purified from *Pseudomonas cepacia*.[68]

Alcohols

Ethanol is such a widely used social drug and alcoholic beverages are so readily available at home that there is considerable potential risk for accidental ingestion. Ethanol intoxication among children is common. The ethanol content in beverages ranges from 3.6% in beer, 10–12% in wine, to 40–50% in distilled beverages. The term "proof" means two times the percentage of ethanol by volume. An additional risk for young children is the ingestion of ethanol-containing mouthwashes, cologne, perfume, and aftershaves.[75,76] These consumer products are commonly available to families, are kept in easily accessible places at home, and are not packaged in child-resistant containers. The ethanol contents of the five leading name-brand mouthwashes range from 14% to 26.9%.[75] A potentially lethal dose of ethanol is approximately 3 mg/kg in a small child, which, for an average 2-year-old, is 6–10 oz of mouthwash. In 1995, The American Association of Poison Control Centers reported 3598 cases of ingestion of mouthwashes containing ethanol in children under age 6 y.[58]

Ethanol is rapidly absorbed from the gastrointestinal tract, 20% in the stomach and 80% in the small intestine. The peak blood ethanol concentration is achieved in 30–60 min, although there is significant inter-subject variability in the peak blood alcohol concentration attained and the time for its achievement due to food intake and physiological variables. Ethanol distributes to total body water with an apparent volume of distribution in children of 0.7 L/kg. The plasma/blood ratio of 1.18 (range of 1.10–1.35), urine/blood ratio of 1.3 (range of 0.3–2.6), and breath/blood ratio of 2180 (range of 1837–2863) have been determined for adults.[77]

Ethanol is metabolized mostly (> 90%) by liver alcohol dehydrogenase to acetaldehyde. The proportion excreted unchanged in breath and urine is relatively small (< 5% at 17.4 mmol/L [80 mg/dL]) but assumes more significance at higher concentrations. Elimination follows first-order kinetics at low concentrations (< 4.4 mmol/L [20 mg/dL]). At higher concentrations and when absorption is essentially completed, metabolism generally is believed to proceed at zero-order kinetics, which is dependent on biological variability, history of use, and dose. In adults, the rate of elimination varies from 1.7–8.6 mmol/L/h (8–39 mg/dL/h),[78] the average being approximately 3.5 mmol/L/h (16 mg/dL/h). In children, elimination may be more rapid; the mean rate has been described as 6.2 mmol/L/h (28.4 mg/dL/h), almost twice that of adults.[79]

Ethanol toxicity in children has been described.[79] Gastrointestinal irritation may result in nausea and vomiting. Ethanol produces central nervous system toxicity, and clinical symptoms are generally consistent with blood ethanol concentrations. Blood alcohol concentrations < 11 mmol/L (50 mg/dL) are unlikely to be associated with symptoms. Exuberance, giddiness, talkativeness, mild incoordination, and visual impairment are noticeable with blood alcohol concentrations up to 33 mmol/L (150 mg/dL). Concentrations of 33–66 mmol/L (150–300 mg/dL) result in verbal confusion, ataxia, exaggerated emotional states, and muscular incoordination. Concentrations in excess of 66 mmol/L (300 mg/dL) are associated with blurred vision, stupor, coma, and compromised cardiorespiratory functions, and death has been reported with concentrations > 88 mmol/L (400 mg/dL).[80]

Other clinical findings include hypothermia secondary to peripheral vasodilatation, CNS depression, and metabolic acidosis in young children. Dehydration may occur because ethanol is a competitor of anti- diuretic hormone, and severe, acute intoxication may result in considerable fluid loss. Hypoglycemia is a serious complication, and the patient may present in a coma or convulsion, with blood alcohol concentrations that may be below 22 mmol/L (100 mg/dL).[81] The hypoglycemic effect of ethanol is the leading cause for childhood hypoglycemic coma. Thus, in the management of a child who has ingested ethanol, the potential for life-threatening hypoglycemia must be considered, and serum glucose concentrations need to be monitored closely.

Many analytical methods for alcohol analysis are in use in clinical laboratories. The most frequently used are assays based on enzymatic oxidation using alcohol dehydrogenase (ADH). The specificity of an enzymatic assay depends on the source of ADH, and interference by methanol and isopropanol varies substantially among kits. Laboratories using the enzymatic assay must be prepared to investigate ingestion of alcohols other than ethanol or the coingestion of ethanol and another alcohol. Gas chromatographic methods can identify ethanol as well as methanol, and isopropanol, and direct inspection of diluted plasma or serum makes it suitable for emergency analysis.

In small hospital laboratories with no facility for either gas chromatographic or enzymatic analysis, the serum osmolarity gap between the measured osmolality and calculated serum osmolarity can serve as an indirect approximation.[82] A formula to calculate serum osmolarity is:

$$1.86 \cdot Na\ (mmol/L) + \frac{Glucose\ (mg/dL)}{18} + \frac{GUN\ (mg/dL)}{2.8}$$

The measured osmolality should be determined by a freezing point depression instrument, not by a vapor pressure osmometer. The expected contribution by ethanol at 21.7 mmol/L (100 mg/dL) is 21 mOsm/kg. Ethanol is the most common cause for elevation of serum osmolarity.

Methanol, Isopropanol, and Ethylene Glycol

Methanol, isopropanol, and ethylene glycol are important industrial chemicals which are also available as household items—methanol and ethylene glycol as a constituent of some antifreeze and windshield washer solutions, and isopropanol as a disinfectant (30–99.9% solution) or as rubbing alcohol (70% solution). Childhood (< 6 y) intoxication with methanol and isopropanol due to accidental ingestion is not uncommon, with more than 13,208 isopropanol and 206 methanol ingestions reported to poison control centers in 1995.[58]

Methanol, isopropanol, and ethylene glycol are readily absorbed following ingestion, although food in the stomach may delay absorption. They are metabolized by hepatic alcohol dehydrogenase at rates one-tenth or less than that of ethanol and follow zero-order kinetics even at relatively low concentrations.

Methanol is oxidized to highly toxic formaldehyde and its metabolite, formic acid. Formic acid is much more toxic than methanol and accounts for the profound anion gap in metabolic acidosis and ocular toxicity.[83] Single ingestion of as little as 10 mL of methanol has caused permanent blindness in adults, and the fatal dose for children is 1–2 mL/kg. Since methanol is a CNS toxin, symptoms may develop within 20–30 min and may include inebriation, headache, dizziness, seizure, and coma. Nausea, vomiting, stiff neck, abdominal pain, and malaise are also common complaints. There may be a latent period of up to 8–12 h when there is a deceiving lack of severe toxic manifestation until products of metabolism begin to appear, but during which appropriate treatment is critical. Young children are susceptible to hypoglycemia.

Isopropanol is metabolized to acetone, which accounts for the CNS effects and ketonemia. There is no metabolic acidosis. Hemorrhagic tracheobronchitis and gastritis are characteristic findings. An acute, lethal ingested dose of isopropanol has been estimated to be 2–3 mL/kg for a child.[84]

Ethylene glycol is metabolized to glycolaldehyde, glycolic acid, glyoxylic acid, formic acid, and oxalic acid. Clinically, the patient appears drunk 30 min to 12 h post-dose and may have nausea, vomiting, metabolic acidosis, renal failure, muscle paralysis, convulsions, and coma. The presence of oxalic acid crystals in urine is not a very sensitive indicator of ethylene glycol poisoning.

The main method of treatment of methanol, isopropanol, and ethylene glycol poisoning is hemodialysis to reduce blood levels of these chemicals.[83, 84] Since the toxicity of methanol and ethylene glycol is due to the toxic metabolites generated by alcohol dehydrogenase, a concentration (22–33 mmol/L [100–150 mg/dL]) of ethanol, the preferred substrate, is administered to inhibit alcohol dehydrogenase activity on methanol and ethylene glycol. At the same time, hemodialysis is performed to remove methanol or ethylene glycol (and their toxic metabolites) until they reach undetectable levels. Ethanol administration to inhibit isopropanol metabolism has not been used to the same extent because the metabolite (acetone) is not as toxic.

Gas chromatography is the method of choice for identification and measurement of methanol, isopropanol, and ethylene glycol. The methods for ethanol are generally applicable to methanol and isopropanol if acetone is adequately resolved from the alcohols.[85]

The popular enzymatic assay for ethanol is not applicable for methanol and isopropanol because of the weak enzyme activity when these alcohols are substrates. However, toxic serum concentrations of these osmotically active substances will result in a significant osmolal gap between measured and calculated serum osmolarity, thus allowing the evaluation of an acute situation when specific assays for methanol, isopropanol, and ethylene glycol are not available.

Lead

The toxic effects of long-term exposure to lead have been known for a long time. Lead poisoning is recognized as a public health problem because its environmental sources are widespread.[86] The greatest risk is posed for young children, as their developing brain and nervous system are particularly susceptible to the deleterious effects of lead.[87] There are many sources and pathways to exposure, but lead-based paint is the most common high-dose source for preschool children, who become poisoned by ingesting paint chips or paint-contaminated dust or soil. A thumbnail-size paint chip may contain 50–200 ug of lead, and ingestion of a few chips a day is a significant toxic dose. Although exterior and interior lead-based paint for residential use has been banned, it has been estimated that 74% of privately owned occupied housing units in the United States built before 1980 contain lead-based paint.[88] Of particular concern is the decrepit housing in economically depressed inner-city areas, where many young children live. Childhood lead poisoning has also resulted from exposure to lead-contaminated dust during renovation or remodeling of older homes.[89] Lead poisoning is not a problem limited to lower socioeconomic families, however; lead in water has been associated with lead poisoning in infants fed home-reconstituted formulas.

Once absorbed, lead is distributed to blood, soft tissues, and bone. It is the lead in blood and soft tissues that causes symptoms of lead poisoning. Chronic exposure results in hypermineralization of bone, which is evident radiographically. Severity of lead intoxication is not directly proportional to total body burden, but to lead concentrations in blood and soft tissues. Doubling of the body burden of lead only increases blood lead concentration by a few ug/dL. Lead is excreted very slowly.

Lead is known to interfere with the various steps of the biosynthetic pathway of heme biosynthesis.[87] Lead produces feedback derepression (stimulation) of delta-aminolevulinic acid (ALA) synthetase and inhibition of ALA dehydratase and co-

FIGURE 21–7. Effects of Lead on Heme Biosynthesis (X indicates inhibitory action of lead)

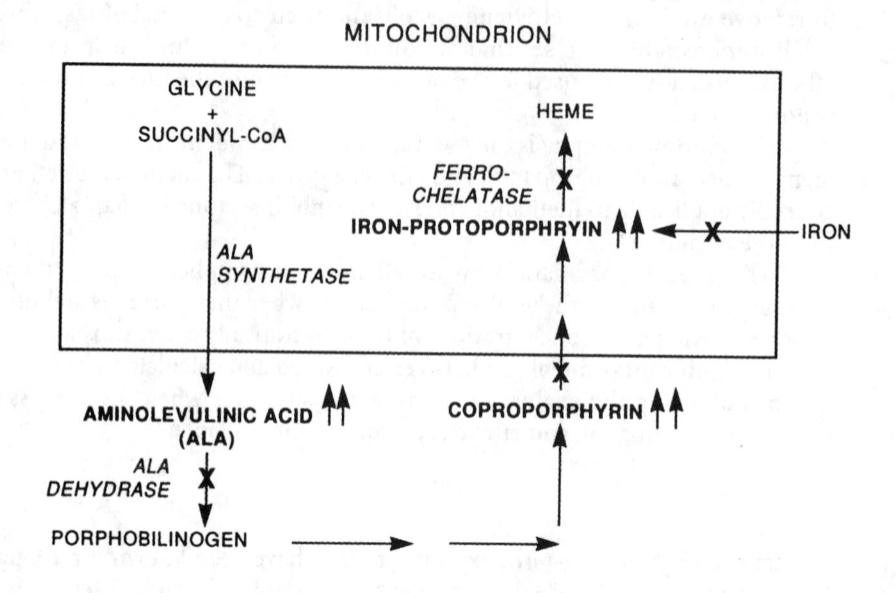

proporphyrin decarboxylase (Figure 21–7). The resulting accumulation of ALA and coproporphyrin (CP) in urine is evidence of lead poisoning. Lead can also block the insertion of iron into protoporphyrin IX to form heme, causing the accumulation of protoporphyrin and the increase of protoporphyrin in erythrocytes (EP), which also serves as a not-too-sensitive marker for lead poisoning. Since the final step of heme biosynthesis occurs in the mitochondria, the increase in EP not only indicates impaired heme biosynthesis, but also suggests general mitochondrial injury which may impair a variety of processes, including cellular energetics and calcium homeostasis.[87] The most evident hematological defect is anemia from reduced heme synthesis. Since nutritional iron deficiency is common among children from the lower socioeconomic levels who are also at risk for lead poisoning, childhood anemia is frequently caused by both nutritional iron deficiency and lead poisoning. Anemia caused by lead poisoning alone is quite rare.[90] A finger-stick erythrocyte protoporphyrin and hematocrit are two screening tests for lead poisoning, although the former is no longer recommended due to its lack of sensitivity.[88]

The neurotoxic effect of lead in children is due to the sensitivity of the developing CNS to lead exposure.[87] Chronic exposure to subclinical doses can have a harmful effect on behavioral and intellectual skills in children whose blood lead concentrations are less than "toxic" and do not cause distinctive symptoms.[87, 88, 91] Therefore, the recognized concentration for lead toxicity has progressively shifted downward. The 1985 intervention concentration of 1210 nmol/L (25 ug/dL) recommended by the Centers for Disease Control (CDC) has been revised to 480 nmol/L

(10 ug/dL). This has been prompted by a number of recent studies on low-level lead exposure and child development.[88] The CDC has issued a set of recommended guidelines for dealing with children, with blood lead concentrations of 10–25 μg/dL involving scheduled retesting, environmental investigations, and medical follow-up.[88]

Children with blood concentrations of 1210–2420 nmol/L (25–50 ug/dL) may be asymptomatic, although their urinary ALA may be increased. Concentrations of 2420–3860 nmol/L (50–80 ug/dL) may be associated with mild, nonspecific complaints when urinary ALA, CP, and EP are all increased. Symptomatic lead poisoning is characterized by lethargy, anorexia, vomiting, colic and constipation, and is usually associated with increased blood concentrations of at least 3380 nmol/L (70 ug/dL), although occasionally cases have been associated with concentrations as low as 2420 nmol/L (50 ug/dL). Lead encephalopathy, characterized by the above-mentioned symptoms in addition to seizures and coma, is almost always associated with blood lead concentrations exceeding 4830 nmol/L (100 ug/dL). Occasionally, though, it has been reported at concentrations as low as 3380 nmol/L (70 ug/dL).

A child presenting with symptoms of lead poisoning accompanied by an increased blood lead concentration constitutes a medical emergency. The possibility of lead encephalopathy should be considered in the differential diagnosis of children presenting with coma and convulsions of unknown etiology. Damage to the CNS caused by lead is irreversible, and children surviving acute poisoning episodes with or without encephalopathy suffer neurological sequelae.

The blood lead concentration is the most reliable indicator of exposure. The two most frequently used techniques for determination of blood lead concentrations are anodic stripping voltametry and atomic absorption spectrometry.[92] These methods are capable of achieving detection limits of < 97–240 nmol/L (2–5 ug/dL), which are below the 480 nmol/L (10 ug/dL) cutoff recommended by CDC. Accuracy and precision in determination of low concentrations of lead, however, will require meticulous attention to the details of analysis. The ubiquity of lead in the environment requires that specimens be collected with care to avoid contamination. Since collection of capillary blood by finger stick is more prone to contamination than venipuncture, a positive result should be confirmed by testing venous blood, which is the preferred specimen.[88] Special lead-free evacuated tubes are available for blood collection, but standard tubes containing EDTA (lavender caps) or heparin (green caps) can be acceptable if each lot of tubes is screened for lead before being put into use.

Blood lead determination is difficult and expensive to perform. Therefore, it is not a screening test. Erythrocyte protoporphyrin (EP) has been used historically as an inexpensive alternate to screening for blood lead. EP is a direct measurement of the toxic effect on heme synthesis. At blood lead concentrations higher than 1930 nmol/L (40 ug/dL), the EP concentration rises exponentially. An increase in a few nmol/L of lead is associated with a much larger increase of EP. Therefore, an increased EP concentration is a sensitive index for identifying children with excessive lead exposure and high blood lead concentrations, and is the basis for further evaluation for lead poisoning.[93] EP concentrations, however, correlate poorly with low blood lead concentrations. Using the current recommended EP cutoff of 0.6 μmol/L

(35 ug/dL), EP was shown to be a poor predictor of blood lead concentration ≥ 1210 nmol/L (25 ug/dL); the true positive and false positive rates of EP were 0.23 and 0.04.[94] In another study, the sensitivity of EP (≥ 0.6 μmol/L [35 ug/dL]) dropped from 73% to 37% when the blood lead cutoff was reduced from 1210 to 720 nmol/L (25 to 15 ug/dL). Therefore, screening of children for blood lead concentrations using the most recent recommended cutoff of 480 nmol/L (10 ug/dL) will require direct measurement of blood lead concentration, not EP.[95,96]

EP concentration can be measured fluorometrically using a hematofluorometer. Most protoporphyrin in erythrocytes (> 90%) is zinc protoporphyrin (ZnP), the fraction measured by hematofluorometers. Methods involving an extraction will strip Zn-protoporphyrin of its zinc and will measure zinc-free erythrocyte protoporphyrin (FEP). On a weight basis, EP, ZnP, and FEP are roughly equivalent. All increased EP results should be followed by a venous blood lead test.

Treatment of lead poisoning is by chelation therapy using BAL (dimercaprol) calcium disodium ethylenediamine tetraacetate (CaNa2EDTA), and D-penicillamine (not FDA approved, but used in some centers). Succimer (meso-2,3-dimercaptosuccinic acid) was approved by the FDA in 1991.

Symptomatic patients, or those with blood lead > 2170 nmol/L (45 ug/dL) should be treated with chelation therapy immediately. Asymptomatic patients with initial concentrations of 1210–2170 nmol/L (25–45 ug/dL) are given the $CaNa_2EDTA$ challenge test to assess the burden of lead. The ratios of lead excreted in urine per dose of $CaNa_2EDTA$ dose (ug Pb/mg $CaNa_2EDTA$) are calculated. An 8 h challenge test is considered positive if the ratio is > 0.6. Children with blood concentrations of 1210–2130 nmol/L (25–44 ug/dL) and a positive challenge test should undergo a 5-day course of chelation. Chelation treatment may be repeated if blood lead remains or rebounds 2420 nmol/L (50 ug/dL) or higher.

Iron

Many iron pills are brightly colored and are attractive to young children. Children under age 6 y accounted for over 84% of the accidental iron ingestions reported.[58]

Many iron salts are available. Ferrous sulfate, the cheapest, is the most frequently involved (Table 21–4). An estimation of the amount of elemental iron in the formulation is important in assessing potential toxicity of an acute ingestion. A dose of less than 20 mg of elemental iron/kg has little risk of toxicity. An ingestion of 20–60 mg/kg can cause mild gastrointestinal distress and poses moderate risk, whereas a dose greater than 80 mg/kg has high risk for toxicity.[97]

Abdominal x-ray may reveal undissolved adult-strength tablets or fragments as long as 6 h or more after ingestion of the tablets. Pediatric preparations, which are chewable iron supplements, dissolve rapidly in 30–60 min and are not always seen.[98] A screening test on gastric fluid is useful in confirming iron ingestion.[99] Addition of deferoxamine causes an immediate color change if iron ingestion has occurred. A negative test obtained within 2 h of ingestion indicates the patient needs no further evaluation. A negative test obtained more than 2 h after ingestion does not rule out iron ingestion because absorption of ingested iron may have been completed.

TABLE 21–4. Iron Salts and Elemental Iron Equivalents

Iron Salt	% Iron	mg Iron/Tablet*
Sulfate	20	65
Gluconate	12	38
Fumarate	33	106
Lactate	19	—
Chloride	28	—
Ferrocholinate	13	—

*325 mg tablet

A qualitative test to predict potential for toxicity is the deferoxamine challenge. A sufficiently large deferoxamine dose is given to bind toxic free iron in plasma to form the reddish feroxamine complex, the appearance of which in urine within 4–6 h post-ingestion implies potential toxicity. This test is useful when measurement of serum iron concentration is not readily available. False-negative results of this test have been reported, and a negative challenge test should not rule out toxicity.[100]

Serum iron concentrations > 63 μmol/L (350 ug/dL) are associated with toxicity, although a lower concentration does not rule out toxicity. Serum iron concentrations within the 63–90 μmol/L (350–500 μg/dL) range may require chelation therapy if these concentrations exceed total iron binding capacity (TIBC) and if the patient is exhibiting signs of systemic toxicity. Serum toxicity and death have been reported in cases with serum concentrations > 90 μmol/L (500 ug/dL). Theoretically, a serum iron value greater than the TIBC implies toxic free-circulating iron is present. TIBC has been reported to rise and remain above serum iron concentrations following the ingestion of a clinically toxic dose, with symptoms of toxicity occurring.[101] Sampling of blood should be 4–6 h post-ingestion of adult formulation and 2 h following ingestion of pediatric preparations. A repeat determination is valuable due to variability in formulation, dissolution, and absorption.

Management of acute iron poisoning includes removal of residual iron in the gastrointestinal tract by emesis or lavage and standard life-support therapy.[97] Deferoxamine chelation therapy is used to chelate free serum iron for excretion and to render the chelated iron unavailable for binding to effect toxicity.

Results from colorimetric methods for serum iron concentrations using bathophenanthroline, ferrozine, tripyridyltriazine (TPTZ), or other proprietary dyes are interfered with by deferoxamine, which functions as a competing chelator to falsely lower results.[102] Therefore, blood should be drawn prior to deferoxamine chelation therapy. Atomic absorption spectroscopy for measurement of serum iron concentrations is impractical, but it is a method that can be used in the presence of deferoxamine.

Drugs of Abuse

At Children's Hospital between 1986 and 1991, the positivity of cannabinoid metabolites (THC), phencyclidine (PCP), and cocaine/benzoylecgonine was found to be 9.3 → 2.2%, 9.9 → 1.8%, and 0.8 → 7.7%, respectively. All three drugs are first screened in urine employing immunoassay techniques, with all positive screens being confirmed for the presence of the drug in question by gas chromatography/mass spectrometry. Note that while the incidence of urine testing positive for THC and PCP is on the decline in the Washington area, between 1986 and 1991, there was an approximately ten-fold increase in urines testing positive for cocaine/cocaine metabolite.

Cocaine (benzoylmethylecgonine) is an alkaloid extracted from the leaves of the *Erythroxylon coca* plant and is a powerful CNS stimulant. In recent years, the abuse of cocaine has reached epidemic proportions, especially since "crack" became available. "Crack" (so named because of the crackling sound made by the crystals when heated) is a freebase form of cocaine prepared by precipitation from heated cocaine HCl solution made alkaline with baking soda or ammonia. Crack is relatively pure cocaine (80–90%) and is vaporized rather than pyrolysed when heated. Therefore, it can be smoked, unlike cocaine hydrochloride, which is snorted or used intravenously. Cocaethylene (ethylbenzoylecgonine) is a metabolite formed through a hepatic carboxyesterase mediated transesterification of cocaine when cocaine and ethanol are used concurrently.[103] It is neuroactive and has many neurochemical properties in common with cocaine. Its presence in the newborn has been reported.[104]

Because many cocaine users are women of child-bearing age, many babies are exposed to cocaine *in utero* and could be born with medical, developmental, and behavioral problems.[105] These include low birth weight, microcephaly, pre-term delivery, cerebral infarction, and withdrawal syndrome, which consists of abnormal sleep patterns, visual function disturbances, tremors, poor feeding, hypertonia, and higher pitch crying. Cocaine babies incur significantly higher hospital costs.[106] A study conducted at Children's Hospital found that approximately 13% of the neonates in the Neonatal Intensive Care Unit tested positive for cocaine metabolite in the urine and that clinical suspicion would have detected only about half of those infants.[107] A set of guidelines for testing newborns for drugs of abuse has been proposed.[108]

Clinically, early identification of cocaine-affected infants is not easy. Neither the signs and symptoms of cocaine withdrawal nor the medical problems commonly associated with intrauterine exposure to cocaine are specific. Therefore, testing newborn urines for the cocaine metabolite benzoylecgonine (BE) is an objective means to identify these babies. Urine testing has limitations and is an insensitive test for a number of reasons,[109] including late collection of urine due to delayed appearance of withdrawal symptoms, difficulty in obtaining urine specimens, and low drug concentrations in urine.

Hair or meconium have been proposed as alternative specimens.[110,111] The following issues should be considered when performing hair analysis of the newborn:

1. It does not detect exposure that occurs shortly before birth.

2. Low drug concentration in hair means a lot of hair (25 mg and up for some procedures) is needed. Many newborns do not have enough hair for analysis.

3. Analytical problems such as washing, digestion, sensitivity, and lack of appropriate standards and controls.

Meconium seems promising because it is easy to collect, drug concentration is relatively high and the window of detectability is longer (which is helpful if testing is not done immediately after birth). In a study of meconium specimens collected from 1237 consecutive live births, meconium analysis for benzoylecgonine identified 33% more *in utero* exposed infants than urine testing.[111] The disadvantage of meconium is that it is an unfamiliar matrix.

Immunoassays (RIA, EMIT, FPIA) are used routinely to screen urines for drugs of abuse such as benzoylecgonine (BE), cannabinoid metabolites (THC), and phencyclidine (PCP). Typically, the thresholds used in forensic urine drug testing (BE, 300 ng/mL; THC, 100 ng/mL; PCP, 25 ng/mL) for designating a urine as positive are adopted for clinical testing. Lower thresholds are more appropriate for clinical testing, as the number of positive urines is much higher when the thresholds are lowered.[112] An immunoassay positive result is a presumptive result and should be confirmed using one of the chromatographic techniques, preferably by gas chromatography / mass spectrometry.

Other Toxic Agents

Also encountered in pediatric hospitals, although with less frequency, are patients with herbicide, tricyclic antidepressant, amphetamine, barbiturate, ethchlorvynol, and phenothiazine toxicity.

REFERENCES

1. Vesell ES. On the significance of host factors that affect drug disposition. Clin Pharmacol Ther 1982;31:1–7.
2. Kennedy DL, Forbes MB. Pediatric drug prescribing: a preliminary report presented at the American Society of Hospital Pharmacists mid-year clinical meeting, San Francisco, December 1980.
3. Yunis AA. Chloramphenicol toxicity. In: RH Girdwood, ed. Blood disorders due to drugs and otheragents. Amsterdam: Exerpta Medica, 1973:107–26.
4. Gorodischer R, Jusko WJ, Yaffe SJ. Tissue and erythrocyte distribution of digoxin in infants. Clin Pharmacol Ther 1976;19:256–63.
5. Smith CA. The physiology of the newborn infant, 2nd ed. Springfield: Charles C Thomas 1951:180–98.
6. Morselli PI. Clinical pharmacokinetics in neonates. Clin Pharmacokinet 1976;1:81–98.
7. Weber WW, Cohen SN. Aging effects and drugs in man. In: Gillette JR, Mitchell JR, eds. Concepts in biochemical pharmacology, Vol. 28. Berlin: Springer 1975:213–33.
8. Vessell ES, Page JG. Genetic control of the phenobarbital-induced shortening of plasma half-lives in man. J Clin Invest 1969;48:2202–9.
9. Vessell ES. The role of pharmacogenetics in therapeutic drug monitoring. In: Basic Principles of Therapeutic Drug Monitoring. Presented at the Second Annual Pine Mountain Conference of the American Association for Clinical Chemistry, March 28–April 1, 1976:27–29.
10. Jusko WJ. Influence of cigarette smoking on drug metabolism in man. Drug Metab Rev 1979;9:221–36.
11. Jenne J, Nagasawa H, McHugh R, et al. Decreased theophylline half-life in cigarette smokers. Life Sci 1975;17:195–8.
12. Alvares AP, Pantuck EJ, Anderson KE, et al. Regulation of drug metabolism in man by environmental factors. Drug Metab Rev 1979;9:185–205.

13. Kappas A, Anderson KE, Conney AH, et al. Influence of dietary protein and carbohydrate on antipyrine and theophylline metabolism in man. Clin Pharmacol Ther 1976;20:643–53.
14. Aranda JV, Sitar DS, Parson WD, et al. Pharmacokinetic aspects of theophylline in premature newborns. NEJM 1976;295:413–6.
15. Jenne JW, Wyze E, Rood FS, et al. Pharmacokinetics of theophylline: Application to adjustment of the clinical dose of aminophylline. Clin Pharmacol Ther 1972;13:349–60.
16. Piafsky KM, Buda A, MacDonald I, et al. Clinical significance of drug binding to orosomucoid. Reta Pharm Suec 1980;17:99.
17. Piafsky KM, Mpamugo L. Dependence of neonatal drug binding on α-acid glycoprotein concentration. Clin Pharm Ther 1981;29:272.
18. Danhof M, Breimer DD. Therapeutic monitoring in saliva. Clin Pharmacokinet 1978;3:39–57.
19. Soldin SJ. Therapeutic drug monitoring in pediatric practice. In: MacLeod SM, Raddle IC, eds., Textbook of pediatric clinical pharmacology. PSE Publishing Co., 1985.
20. Berkovitch M, Akilesh MR, Rocco G, et al. Acute digoxin overdose in a newborn with renal failure: use of digoxin immune Fab and peritoneal dialysis. Ther Drug Monit 1994;16:531–33.
21. Ujhelyi MR, Green PJ, Cummings DM, et al. Determination of free digoxin concentration in digoxin toxic patients after administration of digoxin Fab antibodies. Ther Drug Monit 1992;14:147–54.
22. Ujhelyi MR, Cummings DM, Green P, et al. Effects of digoxin Fab antibodies on five digoxin immunoassays. Ther Drug Monit 1990;12:288–92.
23. Christenson RH, Studenberg SD, Beck-Davis S, Sedor FA. Digoxin-like immunoactivity eliminated from serum by centrifugal ultrafiltration before fluorescence polarization immunoassay of digoxin. Clin Chem 1987;53:606–8.
24. Kwong TC. Free drug measurements: methodology and clinical significance. Clin Chem Acta 1985;151:193–216.
25. Bergman A, Werner R. Failure of children to receive penicillin by mouth. NEJM 1963;268: 1334–8.
26. Soldin SJ. Receptor assays in the clinical laboratory. Clin Biochem 1996;29:439–44.
27. Hicks JM, Corson M, Alessi RM, Soldin SJ. Therapeutic drug monitoring: does it benefit the patient? Proc. of the 7th Asian-Pacific Congress of Clinical Biochemistry, September 17–22, 1995, Bangkok, Thailand, pp. 211–14.
28. Koren G, Soldin SJ, MacLeod SM. Organization and efficacy of a therapeutic drug monitoring consultation service in a pediatric hospital. Ther Drug Monitor 1985;7:295–8.
29. Cramer JA, Mattson RH. Valproic acid: In vitro plasma protein binding and interaction with phenytoin. Ther Drug Monit 1979;1:105–16.
30. Friel PN, Leal KW, Wilensky AJ. Valproic acid—phenytoin interaction. Ther Drug Monit 1979;1:243–8.
31. Johannessen SI. Antiepileptic drugs: pharmacokinetic and clinical aspects. Ther Drug Monit 1981;3:17–37.
32. Graves SW, Brown B, Valdes R. An endogenous digoxin-like substance in patients with renal impairment. Ann Int Med 1983;99:604–8.
33. Koren G, Farine D, Maresky D, et al. Significance of the endogenous digoxin-like substance in infants and mothers. Clin Pharmacol Ther 1984;36:759–64.
34. Nanji AA, Greenway RC. Falsely raised plasma digoxin concentrations in liver disease. Br Med J 1985;290:432–3.
35. Soldin SJ. Digoxin: Issues and controversies. Clin Chem 1986;32:5–12.
36. Ford AR, Aronson JK, Grahame-Smith DG, et al. Changes in cardiac receptor sites, 86-Rubidium uptake and intracellular sodium concentrations in the erythrocytes of patients receiving digoxin during the early phases of treatment of cardiac failure in regular rhythm and of atrial fibrillation. Br J Clin Pharmacol 1979;8:125–34.
37. Belz GG, Aust PE, Munkes R. Digoxin plasma concentrations and nifedipine. Lancet 1981;i: 844–5.
38. Jogestrand T, Ericsson R, Sundquist K. Skeletal muscle digoxin concentration during digitalization and during withdrawal of digoxin treatment. Eur J Clin Pharmacol 1981;19:97–105.

39. Kim YI, Noble RJ, Zipes DP. Dissociation of inotropic effects of digitalis from its effects on atrioventricular conduction. Am J Cardiol 1975;36:459–67.
40. Shapin W, Narahara K, Taubert K. Relationship of plasma digitoxin and digoxin to cardiac response following intravenous digitalization in man. Circulation 1970;42:1065–72.
41. Koren G, Parker R. Interpretation of excessive serum concentrations of digoxin in children. Am J Cardiol 1985;55:1210–4.
42. Koren G. Interaction between digoxin and commonly coadministered drugs in children. Pediatrics 1985;75:1032–7.
43. Butler VP Jr, Chen JP. Digoxin-specific antibodies. Proc Natl Acad Sci USA 1967;57:71–8.
44. Smith TW, Butler VP Jr, Haber E, et al. Treatment of life-threatening digitalis intoxication with digoxin-specific Fab antibody fragments. NEJM 1982;307:1357–62.
45. Kumin GD. Clinical nephrotoxicity of tobramycin and gentamicin: a prospective study. JAMA 1980;224:1808–10.
46. Pittinger CB, Eryasa Y, Adamson R. Antibiotic-induced paralysis. Anesth Analg 1970; 49:487–501.
47. Endicott JA, Ling V. The biochemistry of p-glycoprotein-mediated multidrug resistance. Ann Rev Biochem 1989;58:137–71.
48. Rivard GE, Hoyoux C, Infante-Rivard C, Champagne J. Maintenance chemotherapy for childhood acute lymphoblastic leukemia: Better in the evening. Lancet 1985;ii:1264–6.
49. Langevin AM, Koren G, Soldin SJ, Greenberg M. Pharmacokinetic case for giving 6-mercaptopurine maintenance doses at night. Lancet 1987;ii:505–6.
50. Koren G, Ferrazini G, Sulh H, et al. Systemic exposure to mercaptopurine and a prognostic factor in acute lymphocytic leukemia in children. NEJM 1990;323:17–21.
51. Marks V, English J, Aherne W, Arendt J. Chronopharmacology. Clin Biochem 1985;18:154–7.
52. Stoller RG, Hande KR, Jacobs SA, et al. Use of plasma pharmacokinetics to predict and prevent methotrexate toxicity. NEJM 1977;297:630–4.
53. Russell R, Donnelly J, Palaszynski E, Chan M, Soldin SJ. A preliminary study to evaluate an in vitro assay for determining patient whole blood immunosuppressive cyclosporine A and metabolite activity: Comparison with cytosolic binding assays using cyclophilin, a 50KDa binding protein, and the Abbott TDx™ cyclosporine A parent and parent and metabolites assays. Ther Drug Monit 1991;13:32–6.
54. Soldin SJ, Murthy JN, Chen Y et al. Correlation of two radioreceptor assays and the specific and non-specific fluorescence polarization immunoassays for cycloserine with immunosuppression as measured by the mixed lymphocyte culture assay. Transplan Proc 1994, 26, 2814–7.
55. Soldin SJ. Receptor assays for immunosuppressive drugs. Ther Drug Monit 1995;17:574–6.
56. Oellerich M, Armstrong VW, Kahan B, et al. Lake Louise Consensus Conference on Cyclosporin Monitoring in Organ Transplantation: Report of the Consensus Panel. Ther Drug Monitor 1995;17:642–54.
57. Soldin SJ, Morales A. Assessment of current tacrolimus (FU-506) assay methods to monitor a pediatric transplant population. (Abstract). Clin Chem 1996;42:S308.
58. Litovitz TL, Felberg L, White S, Slein-Schwartz W. 1995 Annual Report of the American Association of Poison Control Centers Toxic Exposure Surveillance System. Am J Emerg Med 1996;14:487–537.
59. Linden CH, Rumack BH. Acetaminophen overdose. Emerg Med Clin North Am 1984;2:103–19.
60. Cocoran GB, Mitchell JR, Vaishnav YN, Horning EC. Evidence that acetaminophen and N-hydroxyacetaminophen form a common arylating intermediate, N-acetyl-p-benzoquinoneimine. Mol Pharmacol 1980;18:536–42.
61. Rumack BH. Acetaminophen overdose in young children: treatment and effects of alcohol and other additional ingestant in 417 cases. Am J Dis Child 1984;138:428–33.
62. Smilkstein MJ, Knapp GL, Kulig KW, Rumack BH. Efficacy of oral N-acetylcysteine in the treatment of acetaminophen overdose. N Engl J Med 1988;319:1557–62.
63. Prescott LF, Illingwork RN, Critchley JA, et al. Intravenous N-acetylcysteine: The treatment of choice for paracetamol poisoning. Br Med J 1979;2:1097–100.

64. Smilkstein MJ, Bronstein AC, Linden C, Angenstein WL, Kulig KW, Rumack BH. Acetaminophen overdose: a 48-hour intravenous N-acetylcysteine treatment protocol. Ann Emerg Med 1991;20:1058–63.
65. Rumack BH, Matthew H. Acetaminophen poisoning and toxicity. Ped 1975;55:871–6.
66. Glynn JR, Kendal SE. Paracetamol measurement. Lancet 1975;i:1147–8.
67. Stewart MJ, Chambers AM, Watson ID. Letter to the Editor. Clin Chem 1984;30:1885.
68. Kwong TC. Salicylate measurement: Clinical usefulness and methodology. CRC Critical Reviews in Clin Lab Med 1987;25:137–59.
69. Paulus HE, Siegel M, Morgan E et al. Variations of serum concentrations and half-life of salicylate in patients with rheumatoid arthritis. Arthritis Rheum 1971;14:527–32.
70. Proudfoot AT. Toxicity of salicylates. Am J Med 1983;75(suppl 5A):99–103.
71. Gaudreault PI, Temple AR, Lovejoy FH. The relative severity of acute versus chronic salicylate poisoning in children: a clinical comparison. Ped 1982;70:566–9.
72. Temple AR. Acute and chronic effects of aspirin toxicity and their treatment. Arch Int Med 1981;14:354–9.
73. Done AK. Salicylate intoxication: significance of measurements of salicylate in blood in cases of acute ingestion. Ped 1960;26:800–7.
74. Trinder P. Rapid determination of salicylate in biological material. Biochem J 1954;57:301–3.
75. Weller-Fahy ER, Berger LR. Mouthwash: a source of acute ethanol intoxication. Ped 1980; 66:302–5.
76. Scherger DL, Wsuk KM, Kulig KW, Rumack BH. Ethyl alcohol (ethanol)-containing cologne, perfume, and aftershave ingestions in children. Am J Dis Child 1988;142:630–2.
77. Basalt RC, Cravey RH. Disposition of toxic drugs and chemicals in man (4th ed.). Chicago: Year Book Medical Publishers 1989;293–4.
78. Forrest ARW. Non-linear kinetics of ethyl alcohol metabolism. J Forensic Sci Soc 1986;26: 121–3.
79. Leung AKC. Ethyl alcohol ingestion in children. Clin Ped 1986;25:617–9.
80. Lovejoy FH. Ethanol intoxication. Clin Tox Rev 1981;4:1–2.
81. Ricci LR, Hoffman SA. Ethanol-induced hypoglycemic coma in a child. Ann Emerg Med 1982;11:202–4.
82. Geller RJ, Spyker DA, Herold DA, Bruns DE. Serum osmolal gap and ethanol concentration: A simple and accurate formula. Clin Toxicol 1986;24:77–84.
83. McCoy HG, Cipolle RJ, Ehlers SM, et al. Severe methanol poisoning. Am J Med 1979;67: 804–7.
84. Lacouture PG, Wason S, Abrams A, Lovejoy, Jr FH. Acute isopropyl alcohol intoxication: Diagnosis and management. Am J Med 1988;75:680–6.
85. Gadsden RH, Terry CS, Thompson BC. Alcohols in biological fluids by gas chromatography (automated head-space method). In: Frings CS, Faulkner WR, eds. Selected methods of emergency toxicology. Washington: AACC Press 1986:40–43.
86. Mushak P, Crocetti AF. Determination of number of lead-exposed American children as a function of lead source: Integrated summary of a report to the U.S. Congress on childhood lead poisoning. Environ Res 1989;50:210–29.
87. Muschak P, Davis JM, Crocetti AF, Grant LD. Prenatal and postnatal effects of low-level lead exposure: integrated summary of a report to the U.S. Congress in childhood lead poisoning. Environ Res 1989;50:11–36.
88. Centers for Disease Control. Preventing lead poisoning in young children: a statement by the Centers for Disease Control. Atlanta, Georgia, U.S. Health and Human Services, 1991.
89. Friedman JA, Weinberger HL. Six children with lead poisoning. Am J Dis Child 1990;144: 1039–44.
90. Mahaffey KR, Annest JL, Roberts J, Murphy RS. National estimates of blood lead levels, United States, 1976–1980: Association with selected demographic and socioeconomic factors. N Engl J Med 1982;207:573–9.
91. Agency for Toxic Substances and Disease Registry. The nature and extent of lead poisoning in children in the United States: a report to Congress. Atlanta, Georgia, U.S. Health and

Human Services, 1988.

92. Tabor MW. Lead. In: Pesce A, Kaplan LA, eds. Methods in clinical chemistry. St. Louis: CV Mosby 1987;394–404.
93. Piomelli S, Davidow B, Guinee V, Young P, Giselle G. The FEP (free erythrocyte porphyrin) test: A screening micromethod for lead poisoning. Ped 1973;51:254–9.
94. DeBaum MR, Sox HC Jr. Setting the optional erythrocyte protoporphyrin screening decision threshold for lead poisoning: A decision analytical approach. Ped 1991;88:121–31.
95. McElvaine MD, Orbach HG, Binder S, Blanksma LA, Macs EF, Kreig RM. Elevation of the erythrocyte protoporphyrin test as a screen for elevated blood lead levels. Ped 1991;119: 548–50.
96. Turk DS, Schonfeld DJ, Cullen J, Rainey P. Sensitivity of erythrocyte protoporphyrin as a screening for lead poisoning. N Engl J Med 1992;326:137–8.
97. Schauben JL, Augenstein WL, Cox J, Sato R. Iron poisoning: Report of three cases and a review of therapeutic intervention. J Emerg Med 1990;8:309–19.
98. Everson GW, Oudjhane K, Young LW, Krenzelock EP. Effectiveness of abdominal radiographs in visualizing chewable iron supplements following overdose. Am J Emerg Med 1989;7:459–63.
99. McGuigan MA, Lovejoy FH, Marino SK, Propper RP, Goldman R. Qualitative deferoxamine color test for iron ingestion. J Ped 1979;94:940–2.
100. Proudfoot AT, Simpson D, Dyson EH. Management of acute iron poisoning. Med Toxicol 1986;1:83–100.
101. Burkhart KE, Kulig KW, Hammond KB, Piearson JR, Ambruso D, Rumack BH. The rise in the total iron binding capacity after iron overdose. Annals Emerg Med 1991;20:532–5.
102. Helfer RE, Rodgerson DO. The effects of deferoxamine on determination of serum and iron binding capacity. J Ped 1966;68:804–6.
103. Jatlow P. Cocaethylene: Pharmacologic activity and clinical significance. Ther Drug Monit 1993;15:533–6.
104. Wu AH, Onigbinde TA, Johnson KG, Wimbish GH. Alcohol-specific cocaine metabolites in serum and urine of hospitalized patients. J Anal Tox 1992;16:132–6.
105. Giacola GP. Cocaine in the cradle: A hidden epidemic. South Med J 1990;83:947–51.
106. Phibbs CS, Bateman DA, Schwartz RM. The neonatal costs of maternal cocaine use. JAMA 1991;266;1521–6.
107. Rifai N, Morales A, MacDonald MG, Soldin SJ. Prevalence of cocaine in a neonatal intensive care unit: the impact of staff education. Pediatric AIDS and HIV infection: Fetus to Adolescent, 1991;2:137–8.
108. Kwong TC, Ryan RM. Detection of intrauterine illicit drug exposure by newborn drug testing. Clin Chem 1997;43:235–42.
109. Osterlolh JD, Lee BL. Urine drug screening in mothers and newborns. Am J Dis Child 1989;143:791–3.
110. Koren G. Measurement of drugs in neonatal hair: a window to fetal exposure. Forensic Sci Int 1995;70:77–82.
111. Ryan RM, Wagner CL, Schultz JM et al. Meconium analysis for improved identification of infants exposed to cocaine in utero. J Ped 1994;125:435–40.
112. Hicks JM, Morales A, Soldin SJ. Drugs of abuse in a pediatric outpatient population. Clin Chem 1990;36:1256–7.

CHAPTER 22

Assessment of Nutritional Status: The Role of the Laboratory

Clodagh M. Loughrey, M.D., M.R.C.P. (U.K.), Dip.R.C.Path.
Christopher Duggan, M.D., M.P.H.

INTRODUCTION

Despite significant advances in the diagnosis and management of nutritional disorders over the past two decades, the incidence of both acute and chronic malnutrition in hospitalized pediatric patients remains unacceptably high. A recent study found that approximately one quarter of a North American pediatric inpatient population demonstrated at least some degree of malnutrition, with severe protein-energy malnutrition existing in every disease category.[1] The association between illness and malnutrition is complex: Malnutrition is not only a consequence of disease, but also predisposes to disease. It has been shown that severity of malnutrition also predicts occurrence of disease complications in inpatients, an association not explained by potentially confounding variables such as age and severity of disease.[2]

With the technology currently available, including parenteral and ever-expanding forms of enteral nutrition, even ill patients need not now be nutritionally deprived. Objective measures are required, however, in order to determine exactly when nutritional intervention is required, as well as precisely which specific nutrients should be given. It may be equally important for the health of the nation to be aware of the nutritional status of "well" children, particularly in underprivileged communities where marginal underfeeding may be more common. It is incumbent upon health workers to promote optimal nutritional status by early and accurate detection of nutritional deficiencies and appropriate intervention. This chapter focuses on the role of the hospital laboratory in attaining these objectives.

ASSESSMENT OF NUTRITIONAL STATUS

Despite the proliferation of laboratory tests used in screening for individual nutritional deficiencies, there is no single laboratory test that gives a satisfactory picture of the global nutritional status of the individual. Initial screening should therefore be based primarily on non-laboratory procedures (Table 22–1).[3] Accurate clinical assessment is a mandatory first step and may be augmented by detailed dietary evaluation. Anthropometric assessment provides objective data for comparison with readily available age- and sex-standardized values. However, these measures may be less useful in hospitalized patients, especially the critically ill, due to confounding factors such as edema and fluid shifts, as well as logistical difficulties in the accurate recording of height.[4]

The laboratory plays a role complementary to these procedures in providing:

1. objective and quantitative confirmation of nutritional deficiencies suggested by non-laboratory assessment, as well as diagnosis of those not yet apparent;
2. diagnosis of specific nutritional deficiencies which may not ever be clinically evident;
3. baseline data which, in conjunction with anthropometric data and clinical assessment, is used to more precisely monitor response to nutritional intervention;
4. clues to the underlying cause of growth failure, which may be related solely to undernutrition (e.g., malabsorption) or have additional or alternative explanations (e.g., chronic kidney disease, endocrine disorders);
5. objective and reproducible information of value to epidemiologists and researchers.

TABLE 22–1. Non-Laboratory Assessment of Nutritional Status

Clinical Assessment
Clinical history
Subjective global assessment
Physical examination
Dietary Assessment
24-hour recall
Typical day recall
72-hour recall
Food Frequency Questionnaire
Anthropometric Assessment
Height-for-age percentiles (or Z scores)
Weight-for-age percentiles (or Z scores)
Weight-for-height percentiles (or Z scores)
Triceps skinfold and mid-arm circumference and percentiles

Source: Modified from Lo C. Laboratory assessment of nutritional status. In: Walker WA, ed. Nutrition in pediatrics: basic science and clinical applications. BC Decker, 1996:29–43.

LIMITATIONS OF THE LABORATORY'S ROLE IN NUTRITIONAL EVALUATION

Correct interpretation of any test result is facilitated by awareness of potential sources of biological or analytical test variability which can influence a test outcome. If it is not possible to control these factors, it is important at least to recognize and to consider their possible effects in evaluation of laboratory data. General issues such as sample collection and handling were discussed in Chapter 1. Issues that may be of particular relevance in the assessment of nutritional parameters are emphasized here.

Biological Variation

Inter-individual variation refers to differences in *true* concentrations of any nutrient between individuals. These may be dependent on several parameters unrelated to nutrition (Figure 22–1). Age is one such factor: Use of an appropriate age-matched reference range is obviously of particular importance. Other factors that may influence analytes important in nutritional assessment include:

- effect of disease on some plasma proteins and protein-bound substances (e.g., calcium and copper);
- sex differences (lower serum iron and hematocrit in menstruating females);
- genetic predisposition to elevated blood cholesterol and/or triglycerides;
- physiological factors such as the reliance of vitamin E for transport on low-density lipoprotein (LDL) cholesterol. Vitamin E levels are strongly correlated with cholesterol concentrations, and it is thus appropriate to correct for these.[5] Diminished tissue stores of specific nutrients may also be masked by physiological factors when blood levels are maintained by homeostatic mechanisms (e.g., calcium).

Analytes that are significantly influenced by factors that cannot be controlled will be unreliable indicators of adequate intake. The following factors *can* be controlled to some extent and analytes influenced solely or mainly by these factors may

FIGURE 22–1. Factors that Influence Inter-individual Nutrient Levels

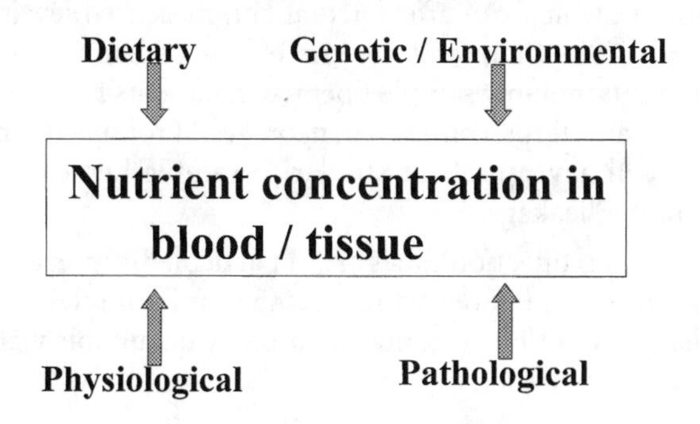

make better nutritional indicators. An awareness of the potential influence of these factors on test outcome is necessary for correct interpretation of test results.

Intra-individual variation refers to temporal differences in *true* concentrations of any nutrient in one individual and may relate to time of sampling in relation to factors such as meals, time of day, season. When making day-to-day comparisons, specimens ideally should be taken at the same time of day. Factors that can affect nutritional status evaluation include:

- diurnal variation of serum iron and growth hormone;
- seasonal variation of some vitamins, particularly vitamin C;
- postprandial elevation of plasma triglycerides and some amino acids (particularly branched-chain);
- exercise, which can affect blood lipids, free fatty acids, blood urea nitrogen, creatinine and urine constituents, depending on duration and intensity;[6]
- potential elevation of serum calcium due to prolonged application of a tourniquet;
- postural effect on plasma volume: Upright position causes increased concentration of all plasma proteins, including enzymes, hormones, and protein-bound compounds; bed rest results in fluid retention and has the opposite effect.

Pre-analytical variation refers to differences in *measured* level of an analyte due to factors which may influence this at any stage from when the sample is obtained to its entrance into an analyzer system, e.g., sample collection, transport, or storage.

- Stress associated with blood drawing, particularly in children, may result in elevated blood glucose, growth hormone, and cortisol. Higher blood lactate and lower pH may also be noted. Physical restraint may cause increased muscle enzyme activity.[6]
- Sample collection proximal to the site of an intravenous infusion ("drip-arm sample") will result in dilution of the blood with the constituents of the infusion and can result in, for example, low sodium, high glucose, high potassium. Ideally, an alternative limb should be selected and, if practical, the infusion should be shut off for 3 minutes prior to obtaining the specimen.
- Capillary blood collection or a very fine-bore needle can result in sample hemolysis, which can affect actual and measured levels of many blood constituents. (See Chapter 1 for the effects of hemolysis and other analytical interferents, notably sample lipemia, in patients receiving fat emulsion preparations, and icterus, common in neonates.) Prolonged time before sample separation will have an effect similar to sample hemolysis, due to erythrocyte membrane "leakage."
- Appropriate collection tubes are of particular importance in the estimation of blood trace metal levels which, being of micromolar concentrations, are particularly susceptible to contamination by unsuitable vial constituents, including glass and rubber.

- Some analytes, such as ammonia, blood gases, gastrin, parathyroid hormone, lactate, and pyruvate, are unstable at room temperature and require the blood sample to be transported on ice and separated as soon as possible. This is facilitated by advance notice to the laboratory that the sample is being collected. Vitamin A is light-sensitive, so samples need to be transported rapidly to the laboratory while being shielded from light to inhibit degradation.

Analytical variation refers to differences in *measured* levels of an analyte due to factors involved in the actual biochemical analysis, such as fluctuations in ambient temperature or automated fluid dispensing. Advances in instrumentation and methodology have led to improved precision and sensitivity and have considerably reduced much of the random error associated with biochemical analysis. This is generally the smallest source of error relating to a given analysis, with a coefficient of variation of less than 5% for most automated assays. Rigorous checks are made by laboratory staff to ensure that results are not issued unless control specimens fall strictly within an acceptable range of values.

Analytical variation also includes *bias:* differences in analyte values due to different laboratories, instruments, or methods. Alkaline phosphatase measurement is a noteworthy example. Bias may result in different reference ranges between laboratories and should be considered when comparing results issued by different institutions, but should not otherwise affect clinical practice.

Communication between clinicians and laboratory staff allows for meaningful discussion regarding test availability, response time, or clinical utility of newer tests to meet clinical and budgetary needs. Clinicians should be aware of any limitations posed by the specific methodologies and instrumentation utilized by a particular laboratory. Turnaround time (the elapsed time from when sample is collected to when the test result is issued) is more important in some situations than in others, and laboratory staff need to be aware of those instances when a shorter turnaround time is desirable. Appropriate liaison between clinical and laboratory staff allows more effective use of laboratory services.

SPECIFIC TESTS OF NUTRITIONAL STATUS

Essential nutrients are categorized as macronutrients if they are required in large amounts as sources of energy, for formation of cellular structures, or for synthesis of enzymes, hormones, or transport molecules. This group comprises carbohydrate, protein, and fat. Micronutrients include vitamins, minerals, and trace elements and generally function as cofactors or coenzymes in metabolic reactions. They are required in much smaller amounts, often being of micromolar concentrations in blood, and sophisticated technology is employed in their analysis.

Although measurement of a nutrient in a single blood sample at a single point in time may not always be representative of its body stores, distribution, or functional metabolic significance, it is still the most practical means of evaluating availability of many nutrients. Various other approaches have been employed, including measurement of red cell, white cell, or other tissue stores; assessment of stores via metabolic balance techniques; and functional assays based on measurement of activity of an enzyme which is dependent on a specific micronutrient.

Energy

Quantitative assessment of energy status of an individual is largely an exercise in metabolic balancing in that an estimation of energy requirements, based on measured expenditure, is compared to dietary calorific intake. It is also informative to have some perception of which specific nutrients the body is using for energy sources and the interpretation of this requires an understanding of how energy is normally provided.

Energy Production from Nutrients

In humans, all energy is supplied by the hydrolysis of phosphate bonds in adenosine triphosphate (ATP). This is provided by three related biochemical pathways, the latter two mechanisms supplying the most ATP:

1. glycolysis (Embden-Meyerhof pathway);
2. tricarboxylic acid (Krebs) cycle;
3. electron transport (respiratory chain).

The substrate for glycolysis is glucose, either exogenous, from dietary carbohydrate, or derived from the breakdown of glycogen stores. The usual substrate for the Krebs cycle is pyruvate derived from glycolysis, and the Krebs cycle provides substrate for ATP production via respiratory chain reactions. However, glycerol and some amino acids, derived respectively from fatty acid and protein catabolism, can also enter the Krebs cycle when in surplus to requirements or if there is a deficit in glucose availability through dietary insufficiency or depletion of glycogen stores. The main source of energy in a normal, healthy diet is glucose derived from carbohydrate, with a smaller contribution from fat-derived glycerol and a minor contribution from protein. Diets consisting of excess fat or protein in relation to carbohydrate will provide a greater proportion of energy in the form of glycerol and some amino acids. Inadequate provision of energy from dietary sources triggers the mobilization of fat stores and nitrogen wasting for energy production.

Estimates of Energy Requirements

Plasma glucose, which is normally regulated by insulin, among other factors, is not a good indicator of energy status. Hypoglycemia in childhood is not a nutritional disorder but an indication for metabolic investigation. Hyperglycemia, which may be accompanied by glycosuria, may be due to frank diabetes mellitus or to a more temporary state of insulin resistance, not infrequently noted in acute metabolic stress and/or in association with parenteral feeding.

In estimating whether an individual's energy intake meets requirements, it is generally more helpful to use non-laboratory-based procedures to assess energy expenditure. Total energy expenditure (TEE) equals the sum of energies of physical activity, growth, obligatory losses of energy in stool and urine, diet-induced thermogenesis, and the basal metabolic rate (BMR). In healthy adults, the Harris-Benedict equation, which is based on height, weight, age, and sex, is frequently used to calculate BMR, which is then used to estimate TEE.[7] Guidelines are also available which give age- and sex-specific recommended daily caloric intake for children, based on the average needs of healthy people, with a 30–50% excess as a margin of error.[8] True estimates of TEE may be obtained by isotopic dilution studies of doubly-labeled water.

Estimates of TEE, however, are of limited value in critically ill patients,[9] in whom formal assessment of resting energy expenditure (REE), which approximates BMR, is likely to be of most relevance. Indirect calorimetry (IC) estimates resting energy expenditure based on oxygen consumption and carbon dioxide production using the Weir equation,[10] or as modified by Cunningham.[11] Unlike other approximations of energy expenditure, IC provides a real-time, reproducible measurement on an individual patient with an acceptable degree of accuracy. Meticulous attention must be paid to potential confounding factors, particularly in ventilated patients.[12] This procedure can be carried out at the bedside in a few minutes using portable gas analyzers.

Calculation of the respiratory quotient (RQ), which is the ratio of carbon dioxide production to oxygen consumption, also helps to predict energy balance in addition to giving some insight into the type of fuel being utilized for energy production. Specific fuels have specific and constant respiratory quotients. Oxidation of glucose yields an RQ of 1.0 whilst oxidation of fat and proteins yield RQs of 0.7–0.8. With lipogenesis, the RQ can exceed 2.0; therefore any measured RQ > 1.0 suggests that calories are being provided in excess of requirements.

Protein-Energy Malnutrition

Macronutrient deficiency has classically been categorized into syndromes of marasmus and kwashiorkor. Marasmus is generally characterized by cachexia with fat and muscle loss and relative sparing of visceral proteins. In kwashiorkor, deficiency of proteins is typically predominant, with edema, ascites, and characteristic changes in skin and hair.[13–15] On a practical level, there is considerable overlap between these syndromes, and the term "protein-energy malnutrition" (PEM) is now in more common usage.

Children, and particularly infants, are more susceptible than adults to PEM due to the additional macronutrient intake required to support growth and development. Inadequate protein and energy intake is manifest by a fall-off in growth curves; growth is therefore the gold standard for assessment of the adequacy of nutritional delivery in the healthy, non-stressed child. Since lack of weight gain, or weight loss, is generally an earlier feature than inadequate gain in height, ratios of these parameters give some indication of the chronicity of suspected PEM. Recognition and quantification of PEM is the first step in the management of malnourished patients who may be at risk of increased morbidity and mortality. It may also be helpful to further categorize PEM into "starvation" due solely to deficient macronutrient intake (e.g., anorexia nervosa), and "hypermetabolism," malnutrition occurring in critical illness (e.g., trauma and sepsis).[16]

Although the human body stores energy mainly in the form of fat, normal diets supply most of the energy required as carbohydrate (50–55%), with a smaller contribution from fat (35–40%), and only 10% or less from protein. In starvation, the body tries to compensate for a lack of nutrient intake by reducing energy expenditure in order to divert substrate into maintaining essential functions such as the central nervous system. Initially, energy is provided by glycogen stores and amino acids derived from proteins, but the fuel source then switches primarily to fatty acids, ketones, and glycerol, with reduced protein catabolism to conserve lean body mass. This results in marked production of ketone bodies, with a less significant urinary nitrogen loss. Indirect calorimetry would give a low respiratory quotient of 0.6–0.7, indicating that the primary fuel source is fat. In contrast, however, in a hypermetabolic state, energy expenditure may be dramatically increased and catabolism may be rampant, with indiscriminate concurrent breakdown of glycogen stores, body fat, and lean body mass. This state is indicated biochemically by significant urinary nitrogen losses with relatively less dramatic ketone body production. A higher RQ of 0.8–0.9 would indicate a mixed fuel source.

Over-Feeding Syndrome

Post-operative stress, sepsis, trauma, burns, and chronic disease are all associated with a hypermetabolic state in which resting energy expenditure may be considerably increased. However, the nature of the metabolic stressor causes a variable response, even among subjects for the same type of injury,[17] and any increased energy demands may be offset by decreased physical activity. Accurate assessment of requirements is required, not only to meet increased needs with the aim of limiting protein catabolism for energy production, but also to avoid causing hyperglycemia, which is often apparent in hypermetabolic patients, particularly in those receiving carbohydrate supplementation.[18] This results in lipogenesis, as evidenced by a high RQ (> 1.0), and causes substantially increased CO_2 production.[17] Overfeeding has been implicated in respiratory compromise, causing ventilatory dependence,[19] hepatic steatosis,[20] and increased risk of mortality. Patients with severe injury and those at extremes of life, i.e., infants, especially preterm infants, and the elderly, are at particular risk.[17]

Proteins

Approximately 15% of total body mass consists of protein. This is distributed in two relatively discrete pools: "somatic protein," which is abundant in muscle, and "visceral proteins," which originate in the liver, circulate in plasma, and have metabolic functions. Although these protein pools are influenced by different factors, there is some interchange and, generally, significant changes in one pool are likely to be reflected in the other. Thus, generalized muscle wasting due to protein malnutrition may be accompanied by diminished concentrations of circulating proteins.

A primary aim of nutritional therapy is to ensure that the protein proportion of total body mass is preserved. The role of the laboratory in achieving this objective generally relies on the monitoring of selected plasma proteins. However, although more than 100 plasma proteins have been identified thus far, very few have been shown to have significant direct association with protein nutritional status. As with assessment of energy reserves, the metabolic effects of illness also render the investigation of protein status less straightforward.

Metabolic Stress and Proteins

Following the onset of metabolic stress, such as sepsis, trauma, or surgery, particularly when endotoxin is present, there is early release of cytokines, notably tumor necrosis factor (TNF-α, "cachectin"), interleukins 1 (IL-1), 2 (IL-2), and 6 (IL-6), and interferon γ (IFN-γ).[21] The direct metabolic effects of these mediators include promotion of muscle catabolism; decreased muscle uptake and increased hepatic uptake of amino acids; decreased synthesis of visceral hepatic proteins and increased synthesis of acute-phase proteins (see later discussion); and increased ACTH secretion, hypozincemia, and hypoferremia.[22–25] This phase is followed by a surge in "counter-regulatory" hormones, including glucocorticoids, adrenaline, and glucagon, which counter-regulate the anabolic effects of insulin and growth hormone.[21] The overall outcome is catabolism of visceral and somatic protein, which provides amino acids to convert to substrate for a fuel source, as well as for the *de novo* synthesis of acute-phase proteins (see Figure 22–2). Laboratory indicators of this process include:

1. increased blood urea nitrogen due to deamination of amino acids;
2. increased breakdown products of somatic protein (e.g., 3-methylhistidine), which may be detected in the urine;
3. decreased concentrations of some visceral proteins due to proteolysis, increased transcapillary escape, and the fluid shifts that accompany this state.

Visceral Proteins

The ideal blood marker for evaluation of protein nutritional status would be rapidly synthesized and would exhibit a measurable change in plasma concentration in response to protein status changes only. It would have a short biologic half-life with a constant catabolic rate and the total body pool would be small.[26] Unfortunately, no such marker is known to exist, and all of the plasma proteins currently employed in diagnosing protein deficiency states have inherent properties that can make interpretation of changes in their plasma levels difficult. One such problem is the response of plasma proteins to acute disease: Some, termed positive acute-phase reactants (or simply "acute-phase proteins"), are preferentially secreted by the liver; others, known as negative acute-phase reactants, fall due to decreased hepatic synthesis or fluid shifts (see Table 22–2).

The plasma proteins albumin, prealbumin, retinol-binding protein (RBP), and transferrin constitute labile protein stores which are catabolized early in starvation or injury.[21] (Such is the relationship between protein and energy status that visceral protein measurement is also a reasonably good indicator of energy reserves.)

Albumin remains the protein most commonly used in the assessment of protein status, due at least in part to the fact that it is the most abundant protein in blood and is the cheapest and quickest to measure. Hypoalbuminemia has been shown to be a good predictor of morbidity and mortality in hospitalized patients.[27] However, it is neither sensitive nor specific enough to be a useful marker of short-term protein nutrition. It has a large body pool, over 60% of which is extravascular, and this component can be mobilized in protein depletion. The daily exchange of albumin between these two

FIGURE 22–2. The Effects of Acute Injury on Protein Metabolism

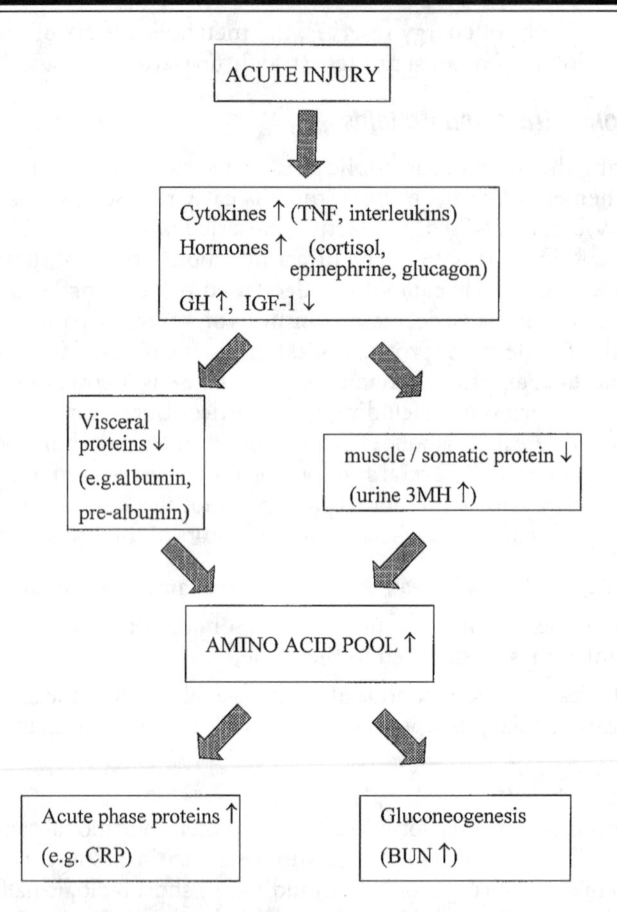

Source: Adapted from Chwals WJ. Metabolism and nutritional frontiers in pediatric surgical patients. Surg Clin North Am 1992;72:1237–66.

compartments is 10 times its synthesis rate, and acute disease increases its transcapillary escape, thereby lowering plasma levels. Acute illness also results in decreased hepatic synthesis of albumin, and thus it is a negative acute-phase reactant. Moreover, its biologic half-life is long (20 days), and day-to-day changes in total body protein will not be

TABLE 22–2. Visceral Proteins Influenced by Acute Illness

Positive Acute-Phase Reactants	Negative Acute-Phase Reactants
C-reactive protein	Albumin
Fibrinogen	Prealbumin
Ferritin	Retinol-binding protein (RBP)
Ceruloplasmin	
Alpha-1-antitrypsin	
Alpha-1-glycoprotein	

accurately reflected by plasma albumin concentrations. Plasma albumin is nonetheless a good indicator of chronic protein deficiency.

Prealbumin, so named because of its proximity to the albumin peak on an electrophoretic strip, is a transport molecule for thyroxine; hence its alternative name, transthyretin. It circulates in a complex with retinol-binding protein (RBP) in a 1:1 molar ratio. It has a small body pool and a short half-life (2 days). It has a high proportion of essential to non-essential amino acids, and also a high content of tryptophan, which initiates protein synthesis.[28] Levels fall quickly in protein-energy malnutrition, possibly as early as 3 days (whereas albumin levels may not fall even after 3 weeks[4]), and respond quickly to nutritional support. For these reasons, prealbumin is a better indicator of visceral protein status than albumin.

RBP has similar properties to prealbumin, having a short half-life of 12 hours, a small body pool, and a rapid response time to protein-energy deprivation. Their association in plasma means that levels of these proteins tend to mirror one another. Both proteins are catabolized to some extent in the kidney; however, the glomerular filtration and subsequent reabsorption of RBP in the tubules, where it is catabolized, results in extremely high levels in kidney failure. This is in contrast to prealbumin, which displays only moderately elevated levels even in advanced renal impairment. In hepatic failure, synthesis of all plasma proteins is impaired; however, prealbumin is not affected as early or to the same extent as the other proteins, particularly RBP. RBP is also influenced by vitamin A levels and, like prealbumin and albumin, is a negative acute-phase reactant.[29]

Transferrin has an intermediate half-life of 8 days and has been used as a nutritional indicator in some population studies. However, it is subject to influence not only by hepatic failure (due to decreased synthesis) and nephrotic syndrome (increased glomerular loss, being a relatively small molecule), but also by iron deficiency and neoplasia. It is therefore not a useful marker of nitrogen balance in individuals. Similarly, *ferritin,* which is a positive acute-phase protein and can be elevated in various inflammatory states, particularly hepatic disease (due to liver storage), poorly reflects protein nutrition.

Of the plasma proteins currently being evaluated as markers of nutritional status, *insulin-like growth factor 1* (IGF-1) mediates the anabolic effects of growth hormone (GH), but its concentration in plasma is independent of GH and depends on nutritional intake. Unlike GH, it displays no diurnal variation and the half-life of its bound form is 2–4 hours. Although its binding proteins are subject to variability in hepatic and renal disease, its levels do generally correlate well with nitrogen balance, falling with protein starvation and rising with refeeding.[30] Its measurement by immunoassay has an unacceptably long turnaround time, and its clinical use as a nutritional marker is not yet routine, but it shows promise.

Another new plasma protein, *fibronectin,* has a half-life of 15 hours and has the advantage of not being synthesized exclusively in the liver. It has shown potential as a short-term nutritional marker in a study of infants receiving nutritional support.[31]

Of the plasma proteins currently in routine use as nutritional markers, prealbumin appears to be the most sensitive and specific. It must be remembered that in critical illness, the levels of most of these visceral proteins tend to fall as part of the acute-phase response. Preferential hepatic synthesis of some acute-phase reactants, such as C-reactive protein (CRP) and fibrinogen, occurs, although the magnitude of this is to some extent modulated by nutrition status.[32] Measurement of visceral proteins must be accompanied by some assessment of the acute-phase response (e.g., CRP) to facilitate clinical interpretation.

Somatic Protein

Assessment of lean body mass is most readily carried out by anthropometric measures, such as mid-arm muscle circumference. The laboratory has also been utilized for this purpose. Muscle creatine is directly metabolized to creatinine, which is freely excreted in urine and has been used as an indicator of total muscle mass. Analysis of 24-hour excretion of creatinine is compared to height-standardized reference values to give a creatinine-height index (CHI).[4] This quick and inexpensive test has been widely used since 1905 as a marker of muscle protein status.[33] The amino acid 3-methylhistidine is also a muscle breakdown product which is excreted in urine and has been correlated with muscle-protein turnover.[34] However, both of these parameters are subject to interference by factors that cause increased protein catabolism and by impaired renal function.

Nitrogen Balance

Protein turnover is most commonly assessed by estimating daily nitrogen intake and subtracting measured losses, or more commonly, measured urine excretion plus a factor to allow for losses from feces, skin, hair, and nails.[35] Urine nitrogen is most accurately assayed by the laborious Kjeldahl method or by expensive chemiluminescence; however, in practice, it is most frequently estimated from measured urinary urea (UUN):

$$\text{Nitrogen balance} = \frac{\text{24-hr protein intake (g)}}{6.25} - \text{24-hr UUN (g)} - F$$

where F = Factor to account for unmeasured gastrointestinal and cutaneous losses, usually 2–4 g.

Healthy young children are generally in positive nitrogen balance, whereas in adults the value approaches zero. In acute illness, decreased nutritional intake combines with endogenous protein breakdown to effect a net negative nitrogen balance. Upon recovery from illness, with adequate nutritional support, the nitrogen balance should become positive, as accelerated or "catch-up" growth becomes apparent in children whose growth was retarded during a period of illness.

One limitation of this test is the considerable inter- and intra-individual variation in the amount of nitrogen excreted as urinary urea; another is potential contamination or infection of the urinary tract with urease-containing bacteria, which results in falsely low levels. The most common and preventable source of error is inaccuracy or incompleteness of timed urine collections. The assumptions required (e.g., normal total body water, normal kidney function) are not valid in patients with severe stress, sepsis, or any degree of nephropathy.

Amino Acid Profiles

Quantitative amino acid analysis can be carried out by laboratories that possess an amino acid analyzer. In practice, actual amino acid concentrations in plasma are not as helpful in practice as they might seem in theory, since individual amino acids are subject to a wide range of physiological variation and their levels poorly reflect release or uptake by tissues. However, levels of the essential branched-chain amino acids (leucine, isoleucine, and valine) tend to be lower in protein-energy malnutrition and relatively higher in infection and injury. This may reflect the fact that branched-chain amino acids, unlike most others, are only minimally metabolized by the liver and are therefore available for muscle protein synthesis, which is not prominent in infection and injury.

A ratio of plasma levels of non-essential amino acids (NEAAs) to essential amino acids (EAAs) may be formulated and used as an indicator of protein status:

$$\text{NEAA:EAA} = \frac{\text{glycine} + \text{serine} + \text{glutamine} + \text{taurine}}{\text{leucine} + \text{isoleucine} + \text{valine} + \text{methionine}}$$

Normally, this ratio is less than 3 and this is ratio can be seen in marasmus. A ratio greater than 3 is associated with kwashiorkor.[36]

Lipids

Plasma lipids and lipoproteins are strongly influenced by genetic and environmental factors. Although plasma lipid levels tend to rise, albeit inconsistently, in obesity, elevations are also associated with some disease states, notably hepatic, renal, and thyroid disorders, as well as diabetes mellitus. In addition, plasma low-density lipoprotein, which transports cholesterol, falls in response to acute metabolic stress, with an accompanying drop in plasma total cholesterol. Hence, these parameters are poor indicators of nutritional status. Normal and abnormal lipid metabolism is discussed in Chapter 18.

Measures of body composition have been used to assess fat status and lean body mass, but as yet have little application in routine clinical laboratories. They include measurement of total body potassium using the radioisotope ^{40}K, which determines lean body mass and gives an indirect estimate of body fat composition. Adipose tissue also has a low water content, and radiolabelled water (with deuterium, tritium, or ^{18}O) can be similarly used. Plethysmography, dual photon absorptiometry, and bioelectric impedance can all differentiate between fat and lean body tissue and have also been employed in the assessment of fat stores; however, all of these procedures have limitations in hospitalized patients.

Essential Fatty Acids

In addition to supplying important substrate for energy, lipid metabolism also supplies fatty acids required for synthesis of cholesterol, cell walls, fat-soluble vitamins, and prostaglandins. Long-chain fatty acids (LCFAs), which are between 12 and 20 carbon atoms in length, are the most common fatty acid configuration found in nature. Saturated LCFAs (e.g., stearic acid, C18:0), which have no double bonds, and monounsaturated LCFAs (e.g., oleic acid, C18:1) can be synthesized *in vivo* from medium-chain fatty acids and are found in large quantities in adipose tissue triglycerides, representing an important energy reserve.[37] Although long-chain polyunsaturated fatty acids also can be mobilized to meet energy requirements, their main physiological functions are structural and metabolic.

LCFAs are characterized into members of the ω-9 (omega-9, n-9), ω-6, or ω-3 series, depending on the number of carbon atoms between the terminal methyl group and its nearest double bond. The human organism has the capacity to introduce double bonds in the ω-9 position but not in the ω-6 or ω-3 positions; therefore, ω-6 and ω-3 fatty acids must be supplied preformed in diet, and thus are essential nutrients.

The clinical importance of essential fatty acids (EFAs) in the diet was first noted in 1963, when formula-fed infants given differing amounts of fat and linoleic acid (C18:2 ω-6) displayed inadequate growth and desquamative skin lesions.[38] Improvement was noted when the formula was altered to provide 1% total energy in the form of linoleic acid. A subsequent report of a child who for several months received total parenteral nutrition which was rich in linoleic acid but low in linolenic acid (C18:3 ω-3) highlighted resultant neurological difficulties which reversed upon administration of an infusion rich in linolenic acid.[39] By chain elongation and saturation steps, these C-18 fatty acids can act as substrate for the endogenous synthesis of fatty acids with longer carbon chains, including arachidonic acid (C20:4 n-6), which is a precursor of eicosanoids. Arachidonic acid, along with docosahexaenoic acid (C22:6 n-3), comprises the main lipid moiety of neural membrane structure; nutritional deficiencies of these fatty acids have been implicated as causative agents in defective intra-uterine visual development and are also important in normal maturation of the central nervous system, particularly in preterm infants.[40] It is not difficult to envisage that complete absence of their precursor molecules from diet for a prolonged period results in neurological problems, even though the requirement comprises less than 1% of total caloric intake.[40, 41]

The capacity for endogenous synthesis of longer chain polyunsaturated fatty acids from linoleic and linolenic acid is limited in preterm infants, and perhaps in term infants as well, and these may be considered conditionally essential nutrients in these groups.[42] Arachidonic acid and docosahexaenoic acid are both present in the lipid fractions in human breast milk, and in 1992 the British Nutrition Foundation's Task Force on Unsaturated Fatty Acids recommended that both these LCPs should be included preformed in the feeds of term infants and especially preterm infants. However, studies in the United States have been less encouraging, having shown that feeding very low birth weight infants with formulas supplemented with marine oil, which is rich in these fatty acids, resulted in less optimal growth.[43]

Laboratory assessment of fatty acid status is complex. It seems logical that the best markers of dietary intake would be tissue levels of fatty acids which cannot be synthesized endogenously, and until recently, most studies were concerned with the relative proportions of oleic acid (unessential) to linoleic acid (essential). Technological advances have resulted in improved extraction of various plasma fractions by gas chromatography, and now most individual fatty acids can be measured by high-performance liquid chromatography (HPLC). Results are normally expressed as percentages of total fatty acid and should be interpreted as indicating relative rather than absolute patterns of fatty acid intake. A complicating factor is that different plasma fractions, as well as erythrocytes, platelets, and adipose tissue, exhibit markedly different proportions of individual fatty acids in a single subject; hence, care is needed in interpretation. More research is required before recommendations can be made as to which specific measurement best reflects fatty acid status. However, for day-to-day comparisons, the relative proportions of fatty acids in plasma triglyceride are likely to be most informative; for other studies, the slow turnover of adipose tissue implies that its fatty acid composition should best reflect dietary intake over the longer term.[5] Elevation of nonessential eicosatrienoic acid (20:3, a triene) relative to essential arachidonic acid (20:4, a tetraene) in a ratio > 0.5 has been considered diagnostic of EFA deficiency.[44]

Carnitine

Carnitine (3-hydroxy, 4-*N*-trimethylaminobutyric acid) is a small, water-soluble molecule now recognized to play an important metabolic function in higher animals. It has two major physiological roles:

1. facilitating the transport of long-chain fatty acids, as acylcarnitines, into the mitochondrion for generation of energy by β-oxidation of fatty acids in liver, heart, and skeletal muscle;
2. facilitating the removal of short-chain and medium-chain fatty acids which accumulate inside the mitochondrion under conditions of normal and abnormal metabolism.

The main dietary sources of carnitine are red meat and dairy products, but it can be synthesized endogenously from peptide-bound lysine and methionine; in strict vegetarians this latter source provides more than 90% total available carnitine.[45] It is stored mainly in skeletal and cardiac muscle (98%); liver stores comprise 1.6%, and a very minor proportion of total body carnitine exists in extracellular fluid.[46] Carnitine is excreted unchanged by the kidney, although it is normally highly conserved, with more than 90% tubular reabsorption.

Carnitine is generally considered a conditionally essential nutrient, although a clinical deficiency state has not yet been well defined in subjects who do not possess one of the rare primary inherited carnitine defects. The carnitine transport disorders have only recently been defined; these patients present variably with nonketotic hypoglycemia, myopathy with myoglobinuria, cardiomyopathy, and encephalopathy. Hereditary carnitine deficiency can also occur in organic acidurias, where it is secondary to increased excretion of acylcarnitines.

Acquired carnitine deficiency is most likely to develop where there is reduced intake, reduced synthesis, increased requirements, or increased excretion, although in these conditions symptoms directly attributable to low carnitine are rare and anecdotal. Both strict and lact-ovo vegetarian children have lower plasma carnitine than their omnivorous peers (about 30% and 20% respectively), but no metabolic derangements have been demonstrated.[45] Newborn infants, who depend heavily on lipids as a concentrated fuel source for rapid growth in early life, also have relatively low plasma and tissue carnitine, probably due to immature synthetic pathways and a lower renal threshold for excretion.[47] This may be of particular relevance in preterm infants, whose carnitine stores are very low compared to term infants.[48] Critical illness has been reported to result in increased carnitine excretion,[49] and parenteral nutrition formulas do not normally contain carnitine. Thus, the preterm sick infant on exclusive intravenous feeding is likely to be at greatest risk for functional carnitine deficiency, which may manifest as defective energy-dependent processes. Hypoglycemia, infection, respiratory distress, delayed growth, and developmental delay may conceivably result. Administration of carnitine to very low birth weight infants has been shown to result in improved ketogenesis and increased weight gain compared to controls.[50] Increased urinary loss of carnitine has been reported in renal tubular Fanconi syndrome, due to defective reabsorption, and in treatment with sodium valproate and some penicillins, where there is increased excretion of acylcarnitines.

The interpretation of low plasma or tissue carnitine is not always straightforward. Plasma carnitine, constituting a minute proportion of total body stores, does not necessarily reflect tissue levels, although on a practical level plasma and urine are the most amenable to sampling. In both plasma and tissue, carnitine is present both as free carnitine and bound to fatty acids as acylcarnitine esters. Both total and free carnitine must be measured, since quantitative reductions in total and/or acylcarnitines, as well as alterations in acyl:free ratios, have been described in both hereditary and acquired carnitine deficiencies. The recent advent of tandem-mass spectrometry has enabled the identification of abnormal acylcarnitines, which will be of value in newborn screening[51] and may also help broaden our understanding of disordered carnitine metabolism.

Micronutrient Status

The metabolic functions, clinical deficiency states, and laboratory assessment of most of the vitamins are now relatively well defined and are summarized in Table 22–3. In comparison, the minerals and trace elements are generally less well understood; their functions, clues to clinical deficiency, and approach to assessment are summarized in Table 22–4. Micronutrient deficiencies might be anticipated in certain clinical situations, including intestinal, liver, or kidney disease; dialysis; abnormal diet (e.g., parenteral/enteral nutrition, metabolic formula); and treatment with medications that interfere with metabolism, which include some anticonvulsants and many chemotherapeutic agents. Many micronutrients are cofactors or coenzymes in enzyme-catalyzed reactions and, where possible, measurement of enzyme activity should be utilized in their functional assessment.

It is now recognized that some micronutrients have important functions as antioxidants, including vitamins C and E, which are potent free-radical scavengers in the aqueous and lipid phases respectively, and selenium, which is an integral component of the antioxidant metalloenzyme glutathione peroxidase. Recently, assays have been developed and aggressively marketed which purport to assess "total antioxidant activity" of body fluids. These measurements, however, include *in vitro* antioxidant activity due to serum constituents which may or may not be physiologically important, such as urate, bilirubin, and albumin, and the clinical value of these analyses has yet to be established.[52] For the present, any laboratory assessment of antioxidant status of an individual should rely on measurement of the individual nutrients known to have major antioxidant functions.

As with laboratory assessment of nutrition generally, care is required in the interpretation of micronutrient assays obtained during metabolic stress. It is widely accepted that acute illness results in redistribution of vitamins and trace elements for various reasons, including acute-phase response of their carrier molecules.[53] For example, sepsis and surgery result in increased serum copper and decreased iron and zinc. The rise in serum copper is due to increased serum levels of its carrier protein, ceruloplasmin, while the decline in iron and zinc is partly due to the negative acute-phase response of their respective carriers, transferrin and albumin. There is also significant tissue redistribution, particularly of zinc from plasma to liver, mainly due to metallothionein induction by IL-6.[54] The plasma levels of vitamins C, A, E, and B6 also tend to fall during acute illness.[53] Monitoring the trends and magnitude of the acute-phase response (e.g., by measuring CRP concentrations) will facilitate interpretation of blood micronutrient levels under these circumstances.

Whether an anabolic or catabolic state predominates also strongly influences blood levels of the important intracellular constituents potassium, magnesium, and phosphate. Hyperkalemia and hyperphosphatemia are well-recognized complications of situations associated with profound cell breakdown, such as tumor lysis syndrome and rhabdomyolysis. The reverse is frequently noted in conditions associated with rapid cell division and growth, as in the refeeding syndrome. In this instance, the provision of macronutrients after a period of starvation, particularly when complicated by metabolic stress, results in insulin secretion which drives potassium, magnesium, and phosphate into cells. Hypokalemia, hypophosphatemia, and hypomagnesemia, which may be associated with weakness, myopathy, ventilatory dependence, and cardiac arrhythmias, are well-documented features of this syndrome.

Other Laboratory Indicators of General Nutritional Status

Reference ranges for these and many of the previously discussed tests commonly performed in nutritional evaluation are listed in Table 22–5.

Hematological Tests

A complete blood count is quick and inexpensive to perform. It may indicate anemia, and red cell indices may suggest chronic disease or deficiencies in iron, vitamin B12, or folate. The product of the total white blood cell count (WBC) and percentage of lymphocytes seen on a peripheral blood film will also give a total lymphocyte count (TLC), which has been correlated with general nutritional status. TLC is calculated as follows:

$$\text{TLC} = \text{WBC} \times \text{lymphocytes \%}$$

TABLE 22–3. Laboratory Tests for Assessment of Vitamin Status

Vitamin	Function	Clinical Deficiency State	Laboratory Assessment
Vitamin A Retinol (beta-carotene is dietary precursor)	Retinal in rhodopsin and iodopsin Carbohydrate transfer to glycoprotein Maintains epithelial integrity Required for cell proliferation	Night blindness Xerophthalmia Bitot spots Keratomalacia	Plasma retinol (HPLC) Plasma retinol-binding protein Relative dose response Dark adaption test Liver biopsy concentration
Vitamin D Cholecalciferol D_3 (endogenous) Ergocalciferol D_2 (synthetic)	Regulates calcium and phosphate gut absorption, excretion by kidney and bone resorption	Rickets/osteomalacia Dental caries Hypocalcemia/hypophosphatemia Increased alkaline phosphatase Phosphaturia, aminoaciduria	Plasma 25-hydroxyvitamin D (HPLC) Serum alkaline phosphatase, calcium and phosphate Radiography Bone densitometry
Vitamin E Alpha-tocopherol	Cell membrane antioxidant Inhibits polyunsaturated fatty acid oxidation	Anemia/hemolysis Neurological deficit (ocular palsy, wide-based gait, decreased reflexes) Altered prostaglandin synthesis	Plasma tocopherol (HPLC) (corrected for total or LDL-cholesterol) Hydrogen peroxide hemolysis
Vitamin K Phylloquinone Menadione (synthetic)	Carboxylation of clotting factors Affects bone formation	Coagulopathy Abnormal bone matrix synthesis	Prothrombin time (prolonged) Plasma phylloquinone Clotting factor levels Proteins induced by vitamin K absence or antagonists-II (PIVKA-II)
Vitamin B_1 Thiamine	Oxidative phosphorylation Pentose phosphate shunt Aldehyde transferase Triosephosphate isomerase	Beriberi ("wet" or "dry") Cardiac failure/ neuropathy Korsakoff's syndrome Wernicke's encephalopathy Lactic acidosis	Red cell transketolase activity Whole blood level (HPLC) Urine thiamine:creatinine ratio
Vitamin B_2 Riboflavin	Oxidation/reduction reactions	Seborrhoeic dermatitis/cheilosis/glossitis Decreased fatty acid oxidation Altered B_6 activation to coenzyme Decreased tryptophan to niacin conversion	Red cell glutathione reductase activity (EGR) Red cell flavine adenine dinucleotide Urine riboflavin:creatinine ratio
Vitamin B_6 Pyridoxine	Aminotransferase reactions	Dermatitis/cheilosis/glossitis Microcytic anemia/weight loss Decreased serum transaminases	Red cell aminotransferase activity Plasma pyridoxal phosphate (HPLC) Tryptophan loading test

Continued

TABLE 22–3 *Continued*

Vitamin	Function	Clinical Deficiency State	Laboratory Assessment
		Peripheral neuritis/irritability/convulsions Irritability/convulsions Decreased tryptophan to niacin conversion	Urine 4-pyridoxic acid
Vitamin B12 Cyanocobalamin	Methyl group donor Sulfur amino acid conversion Branched-chain amino acid catabolism	Megaloblastic anemia Hypersegmented neutrophils Demyelination / posterior spinal column changes Methylmalonic acidemia Hyperhomocysteinemia	Plasma level (RIA or microbiologic) Schilling test Plasma homocysteine Deoxyuridine suppression test
Vitamin C Ascorbate	Reducing agent (regenerates Vit. E) Cofactor for hydroxylators Noradrenaline/carnitine synthesis? Cholesterol synthesis? Leukocyte function	Scurvy Perifollicular/petechial hemorrhages Hematologic abnormalities Poor wound healing Impaired collagen synthesis Psychological disturbances	Plasma level (enzyme assay/HPLC) Leukocyte concentration (longer-term) Whole blood concentration Urine concentration
Folic Acid	Methyl group donor DNA/RNA synthesis Amino acid metabolism	Megaloblastic anemia, neutropenia Altered amino acid metabolism Impaired growth Diarrhea	Plasma level (RIA/microbiologic) Red cell level
Biotin	Coenzyme for carboxylases, decarboxylases and transcarboxylases	Multiple carboxylase deficiency Organic acidemia/acidosis Dermatitis/alopecia CNS: seizures/ataxia/depression	Plasma (microbiologic assay) Plasma lactate Urine organic acids Lymphocyte carboxylase
Niacin	Dehydrogenase activity	Pellagra: diarrhea/dermatitis/dementia Glossitis/stomatitis/vaginitis Impaired absorption of fat, carbohydrate and vitamin B12 Achlorhydria	Urine ratio of metabolites (N-methyl nicotinamide: 2-pyridone) Tryptophan load Red cell NAD or NAD:NADP ratio
Pantothenic Acid	Pyruvate dehydrogenase cofactor Carrier of acyl groups Acetylation of alcohol/amines	Postural hypotension Anorexia and vomiting Reduced acetylation Neuromuscular defects/hyperreflexia	Urine excretion Whole blood level (RIA/microbiologic)

Source: Modified from Merritt RJ, Rock CL. Nutritional requirements and assessment. In: Walker WA, Durie PR, Hamilton JR, et al., eds. Pediatric gastrointestinal disease: pathophysiology, diagnosis, and management. St Louis: Mosby, 1996:1860–83.

TABLE 22–4. Laboratory Test for Assessment of Mineral and Trace Element Status

Mineral/Trace Element	Function	Clinical Deficiency State	Laboratory Assessment
Calcium	Bone structure Cell metabolic regulator Nerve excitation threshold	Bone demineralization Tetany/seizures Cardiac arrythmias	Plasma total calcium Plasma free calcium in altered protein binding e.g. hypoalbuminemia, acidosis Radiographs CT and photon densitometry
Chromium	Glucose tolerance factor Metabolism of nucleic acids ? iodine/thyroid function	Glucose intolerance Neuropathy/encephalopathy Altered nitrogen metabolism Increased free fatty acids	Plasma chromium Glucose tolerance
Copper	Cofactor for several enzymes including superoxide dismutase, tyrosinase, ferrochelatase, cytochrome C oxidase	Hypochromic anemia, neutropenia Skin depigmentation Dyslipidemia CNS problems	Plasma copper Plasma ceruloplasmin (ferrochelatase) Liver biopsy concentration Superoxide dismutase activity
Iodide	Component of thyroid hormones	Goiter Cretinism	Thyroid hormones, TSH Urinary iodide/creatinine ratio
Iron	Heme synthesis Component of cytochromes	Hypochromic microcytic anemia Altered oxidative phosphorylation Diminished concentration Decreased exercise tolerance	Plasma iron and ferritin Total iron-binding capacity Hemoglobin/hematocrit, red cell indices RBC zinc protoporphyrin:heme ratio Bone marrow aspirate stain
Magnesium	Cofactor for hexokinase and phosphokinase Alters ribosomal aggregation in protein synthesis Increases nerve excitation threshold	Cardiac dysrhythmias Neuromuscular excitability Decreased PTH level/activity Hypocalcemia/hypokalemia Convulsions	Plasma total or free magnesium Magnesium loading test
Manganese	Mucopolysaccharide synthesis Cholesterol synthesis Cartilage/bone formation Pyruvate carboxylase cofactor Superoxide dismutase cofactor	Dermatitis Decreased clotting factors Decreased nail/hair growth ?Hair color change	Plasma level Whole blood level Mitochondrial superoxide dismutase

Continued

TABLE 22–4 *Continued*

Mineral/Trace Element	Function	Clinical Deficiency State	Laboratory Assessment
Phosphorus	Bone structure Cell membrane structure Energy utilization Glycogen deposition Acid-base balance: buffering Oxygen release (2,3 deoxyribonucleic acid)	Tissue hypoxia Respiratory failure (ventilatory dependence) Hemolytic anemia Rickets CNS abnormalities	Plasma concentration Alkaline phosphatase activity Radiography Densitometry Renal tubular excretion threshold
Selenium	Glutathione peroxidase constituent Thyroid hormone metabolism	Myositis Cardiomyopathy Nail bed changes Macrocytic anemia?	Plasma concentration Glutathione peroxidase acitivity Nail/hair selenium
Zinc	Co-factor for > 70 enzymes Immune function Cell replication Vision	Skin lesions/poor wound healing Immune dysfunction (esp. T-cell) Anorexia/dysgeusia Growth failure/nitrogen wasting Hypogonadism/delayed puberty Diarrhea	Plasma concentration Alkaline phosphatase activity Urinary excretion Leukocyte concentration

Source: Modified from Merritt RJ, Rock CL. Nutritional requirements and assessment. In: Walker WA, Durie PR, Hamilton JR, et al., eds. Pediatric gastrointestinal disease: pathophysiology, diagnosis, and management. St. Louis: Mosby, 1996:1860–83.

TABLE 22–5. Reference Ranges for Analytes Measured in Nutritional Evaluation*

Analyte	Units	0.5–2 y	2–12 y	12–18 y	Notes
Hematocrit	%	30.9–37.2	31.7–39.6	34.0–43.9	Higher in neonates; male > female
Hemoglobin	g/dL	10.3–12.4	10.5–13.3	11.2–14.8	
Mean cell volume (MCV)	fL	70.5–81.8	72.7–87.6	77.9–91.0	
Mean cell hemoglobin (MCH)	pg	23.2–27.6	24.1–29.6	25.8–31.7	
Lymphocyte count	$\times 10^3$/µL	1.2–7.0	1.3–3.5	1.0–2.8	

Analyte	Units	1–18 y	Notes
Total protein	g/dL	5.7–8.0	lower in neonates/infants
Albumin	g/dL	2.9–4.7	lower in neonates/infants/females
Prealbumin (transthyretin)	mg/dL	14–45	lower in small children, esp. infants
Retinol-binding protein	mg/dL	1.0–9.2	lower in neonates
Ferritin	µg/L	6–320	lower in small children/females; inter-laboratory variation
Transferrin	g/L	1.96–4.16	
Insulin-like growth factor 1 (IGF-1)	nmol/L	1.6–47.3	highly age-specific
Glucose	mg/dL	70–126	lower in neonates/young infants
Aspartate aminotransferase (AST)	U/L	15–45	
Alanine aminotransferase (ALT)	U/L	5–45	
Alkaline phosphatase (ALP)	U/L	65–530	Highest at puberty; significant inter-laboratory variation
Bilirubin (conjugated)	µmol/L	< 2	Can be < 10 in neonates
Bilirubin (total)	µmol/L	< 17	
Gamma-glutamyl transferase (GGT)	U/L	2–42	Significant inter-laboratory variation
Lactate dehydrogenase	U/L	105–395	Significant inter-lab. variation; higher in small children, esp. neonates
Ammonia	µmol/L	< 35	< 50 in neonates
Sodium	mmol/L	134–143	
Potassium	mmol/L	3.7–5.0	
Urea nitrogen (BUN)	mg/dL	3–20	lower in small children and in breast-fed infants
Creatinine	mg/dL	0.4–1.4	lower in small children; higher in neonates
Cholesterol	mg/dL	85–234	lower in young children
Triglycerides	mg/dL	27–140	
Free fatty acids	mmol/L	0.2–1.1	(for age 7–15 yr)
Carnitine (total)	µmol/L	28–84	Total minus free = esterified; free normally 60–80% of total[1]
Carnitine (free)	µmol/L	22–66	

(continues)

TABLE 22–5 *(Continued)*

Analyte	Units	1–18 y	Notes
Calcium	mmol/L	2.17–2.66	
Magnesium	mmol/L	0.62–0.99	
Phosphate	mmol/L	1.00–1.60	higher in infants
Parathyroid hormone (PTH)	pg/mL	9–52	Intact hormone
Vitamin D (25-hydroxy)	μg/L	1.8–48.9	higher in young children; seasonal variation
Iron	μmol/L	4.5–24.7	falls with acute-phase response
Total iron binding capacity (TIBC)	μmol/L	29.0–69.8	lower in infants
Transferrin saturation	%	0.07–0.44	(= iron [μmol/L] / TIBC)
Selenium	μmol/L	1.22–2.35	significant geographical variation
Glutathione peroxidase	U/L	554–1153	
Zinc	μmol/L	9.2–18.1	
Copper	μmol/L	10.1–25.2	
Vitamin A	μmol/L	0.7–2.5	
Vitamin B_{12}	pmol/L	134–1038	
Vitamin E	μmol/L	7–24	
Folic acid	nmol/L	2.7–35.6	higher in young children and infants

Source: Soldin SJ, Brugnara C, Gunter KC, Hicks JM. Pediatric reference ranges. Washington, DC: AACC Press, 1997, unless otherwise indicated.

*This table is intended to be used only as a guide. Where separate male and female reference ranges exist, these have been amalgamated into one range, as have some of the more specific age-range groups. For sex- and age-specific reference ranges, refer to source. To ensure complete accuracy, obtain reference range based on specific laboratory method. For more specialized tests requiring a local reference range, refer to laboratory.

[1]From: Rebouche CJ. Carnitine function and requirements during the life cycle. FASEB J 1992;6:3379–86.

A decrease in TLC to < 1500/mm^3 is frequently, although not invariably, noted in malnourished individuals. It has been suggested that a TLC of 800–1200/mm^3 represents a moderate nutritional deficit, while TLC < 800/mm^3 is indicative of severe malnutrition.[55] However, TLC can be affected by factors other than nutritional status, including steroid treatment and sepsis.

Immunological Tests

Delayed-type hypersensitivity is tested by subcutaneous administration of one or more skin test antigens, such as *Candida albicans*, tetanus, diphtheria, tuberculin, and mumps. Skin induration of at least 5 mm diameter 24–48 hours after testing is considered a positive response to recall antigens. Cutaneous anergy, delayed or absent response, is a consistent finding in moderate to severe malnutrition and has been associated with an increased risk of complications of surgery. However, the relationship is not specific. Attenuated or lack of response to skin testing also has been noted during immunosuppression, irradiation, and post-surgery.[56] It has been suggested that skin testing is of most value when performed serially in identifying and monitoring progress of severely malnourished individuals.[57]

T-lymphocyte response to mitogens such as concanavalin A and phytohemagglutinin has also been studied in malnourished patients, in whom the rate of proliferation is generally blunted. In a study of 85 patients with gastric carcinoma, lymphocyte mitogenesis was diminished in all patients post-operatively and returned to normal only in those patients whose standard enteral feed was supplemented with arginine, RNA, and ω-3 fatty acids.[58] This suggests that T-cell proliferative response to mitogens may prove to be a useful marker of nutritional status.

The observation that certain dietary constituents can exert a variety of positive effects on the immune system has led to much research on the potential role of "nutritional immunomodulation" in ill patients.[59, 60] As a result, immune function tests, whose lack of specificity makes them poor general nutritional markers, may become more significant in assessing the effects of dietary manipulation on immune response.

CONCLUSION

The influence of malnutrition on outcome of illness is now well accepted. Theories have recently been proposed which imply that nutrition in early infancy may also impact on health in adult life. Large epidemiological studies have associated low birth weight with a higher incidence of disease conventionally thought to be of adult onset, including coronary artery disease, stroke, cancer, and diabetes mellitus.[61, 62] It has been postulated that this relates to a high sensitivity to nutritional deprivation during a period of enormously rapid growth and development: any influence on cell size, number, and function at this time might have significant repercussion in later life. Extrapolation of this hypothesis of "nutritional programming" leads to the implication that optimal nutrition in early infancy, when growth and development are in a relatively accelerated phase, might play a protective role in the pathogenesis of adult degenerative disease.

The laboratory plays an integral role in the assessment of nutritional status of an individual in that it provides objective, quantitative, and specific measures that assist in diagnosis and monitoring of deficiencies. The ever-growing list of potential biochemical markers of nutrition makes possible earlier and more appropriate intervention in malnutrition. However, it also increases the risk of extensive diagnostic testing in situations where this may be inappropriate. In a study of 185 children under 3 years of age who were admitted to hospital for investigation of growth failure, of a total of 2607 laboratory tests performed, only 36 (1.4%) were helpful in making the diagnosis. Furthermore, all 36 positive results were suspected from clinical evaluation.[63]

As with any clinical laboratory analysis, correct interpretation of a result depends on awareness of the potential effects of both analytical and pathophysiological factors. As emphasized throughout this chapter, the clinical state of the individual has a significant influence on many of the analytes commonly employed as nutritional indicators, an influence which is frequently independent of the state of nutrition. Thus, nutritional evaluation must remain primarily a clinical assessment which includes both dietary and anthropometric data, supplemented and complemented where necessary by measurement of selected laboratory parameters which are interpreted in the context of the current clinical milieu.

REFERENCES

1. Hendricks KM, Duggan C, Gallagher L, et al. Malnutrition in hospitalized pediatric patients. Arch Ped Adol Med 1995;149:1118–22.
2. Naber THJ, Schermer T, de Bree A, et al. Prevalence of malnutrition in nonsurgical hospitalized patients and its association with disease complications. Am J Clin Nutr 1997;66:1232–9.
3. Lo C. Laboratory assessment of nutritional status. In: Walker WA, ed. Nutrition in pediatrics: basic science and clinical applications. BC Decker, 1996:29–43.
4. Green CJ, Campbell IT, McClelland P, et al. Energy and nitrogen balance and changes in mid upper-arm circumference with multiple organ failure. Nutrition 1995;11:739–46.
5. Hunter D. Biochemical indicators of dietary intake. In: Willett W, ed. Nutritional epidemiology. New York: Oxford University Press, 1990:143–216.
6. Young DS, Bermes BW. Specimen collection and processing: sources of biological variation. In: Burtis CA, Ashwood ER, eds. Tietz textbook of clinical chemistry. Philadelphia: Saunders, 1994:59–101.
7. Harris JA, Benedict TG. Biometric studies of basal metabolism in man. Washington, DC: Carnegie Institute, 1919.
8. Subcommittee on the Tenth Edition of the RDAs, Food and Nutrition Board, Commission on Life Sciences, National Research Council. Recommended Dietary Allowances. Recommended dietary allowances, 10th ed. Washington, DC: National Academy Press, 1989.
9. Coss-Bu JA, Jefferson LS, Walding D, et al. Resting energy expenditure in children in a pediatric intensive care unit: comparison of Harris-Benedict and Talbot predictions with indirect calorimetry values. Am J Clin Nutr 1998;67:74–80.
10. Weir JBdV. New methods for calculating metabolic rate with special reference to protein metabolism. J Physiol 1949;109:1–9.
11. Cunningham JJ. Calculation of energy expenditure from indirect calorimetry: assessment of the Weir equation. Nutrition 1990;6:222–3.
12. Weissman C, Kemper M. Metabolic measurements in the critically ill. Crit Care Clin 1995;11:169–97.
13. Latham MC. The dermatosis of kwashiorkor in young children. Semin Dermatol 1991; 10:270–2.
14. McLaren DS. Skin in protein energy malnutrition. Arch Dermatol 1987;123:1674a–6a.
15. Bradfield RB, Jelliffe DB. Hair-colour changes in kwashiorkor (letter). Lancet 1974;1 (7855):461–2.
16. Barton RG. Nutrition support in critical illness. Nutr Clin Pract 1994;9:127–39.
17. Chwals WJ. Overfeeding the critically ill child: fact or fantasy? New Horizons 1994;2:147–55.
18. Schears GJ, Deutschman CS. Common nutritional issues in pediatric and adult critical care medicine. Crit Care Clin 1997;13:669–90.
19. Askanazi J, Weissman C, LaSala PA, et al. Effect of protein intake on ventilatory drive. Anesthesiology 1984;60:106–110.
20. Payne-James JJ, Silk DB. Hepatobiliary dysfunction associated with total parenteral nutrition. Dig Dis 1991;9:106–124.
21. Chwals WJ. Metabolism and nutritional frontiers in pediatric surgical patients. Surg Clin North Am 1992;72:1237–66.
22. Zamir O, Hasselgren PO, James H, et al. Effect of tumor necrosis factor or interleukin-1 on muscle amino acid uptake and the role of glucocorticoids. Surg Gyn Obstet 1993;177:27–32.
23. Flores EA, Bistrian BR, Pomposelli JJ, et al. Infusion of tumor necrosis factor/cachectin promotes muscle catabolism in the rat: a synergistic effect with interleukin 1. J Clin Invest 1989;83:1614–22.

24. Warren RS, Starnes HF, Jr., Gabrilove JL, et al. The acute metabolic effects of tumor necrosis factor administration in humans. Arch Surg 1987;122:1396–400.
25. Dinarello CA. Interleukin-1 and interleukin-1 antagonism. Blood 1991;77:1627–52.
26. Spiekerman AM. Proteins used in nutritional assessment. Clin Lab Med 1993;13:353–69.
27. Seltzer MH, Bastidas JA, Cooper DM, et al. Instant nutritional assessment. J Paren & Enter Nutr 1979;3:157–9.
28. Ingenbleek Y, Van Den Schrieck HG, De Nayer P, De Visscher M. Albumin, transferrin and the thyroxine-binding prealbumin/retinol-binding protein (TBPA-RBP) complex in assessment of malnutrition. Clin Chim Acta 1975;63:61–7.
29. Duggan C, Colin AA, Agil A, et al. Vitamin A status in acute exacerbations of cystic fibrosis. Am J Clin Nutr 1996;64:635–9.
30. Clemmons DR, Underwood LE, Dickerson RN, et al. Use of plasma somatomedin-C/insulin-like growth factor I measurements to monitor the response to nutritional repletion in malnourished patients. Am J Clin Nutr 1985;41:191–8.
31. Yoder MC, Anderson DC, Gopalakrishna GS, et al. Comparison of serum fibronectin, prealbumin, and albumin concentrations during nutritional repletion in protein-calorie malnourished infants. J Ped Gastroent Nutr 1987;6:84–8.
32. Cruickshank AM, Hansell DT, Burns HJ, Shenkin A. Effect of nutritional status on acute phase protein response to elective surgery. Brit J Surg 1989;76(2):165–8.
33. Viteri FE, Alvarado J. The creatinine height index: its use in the estimation of the degree of protein depletion and repletion in protein calorie malnourished children. Pediatrics 1970;46:696–706.
34. Young VR, Munro HN. N-methylhistidine (3-methylhistidine) and muscle protein turnover: an overview. Federation Proceedings 1978;37:2291–300.
35. Spiekerman AM. Laboratory tests for monitoring total parenteral nutrition (TPN). Clin Chem 1987;27:1–11.
36. Munro HN. Fifth annual Jonathan E. Rhoads lecture. Metabolic integration of organs in health and disease. J Paren & Enter Nutr 1982;6:271–9.
37. Giovannini M, Riva E, Agostoni C. Fatty acids in pediatric nutrition. Ped Clin No Am 1995;42:861–77.
38. Hansen AE, Wiese HF, Boelsche AN, et al. Role of linoleic acid in infant nutrition: clinical and chemical study of 428 infants fed on milk mixtures varying in kind and amount of fat. Pediatrics 1963;31:171–92.
39. Holman RT, Johnson SB, Hatch TF. A case of human linolenic acid deficiency involving neurological abnormalities. Am J Clin Nutr 1982;35:617–23.
40. Phylactos AC, Ghebremeskel K, Costeloe K, et al. Polyunsaturated fatty acids and antioxidants in early development: possible prevention of oxygen-induced disorders. Eur J Clin Nutr 1994;48(Suppl 2):S17–23.
41. Cuthbertson WF. Essential fatty acid requirements in infancy. Am J Clin Nutr 1976;29:559–68.
42. Decsi T, Koletzko B. Polyunsaturated fatty acids in infant nutrition. Acta Paed 1994;83 (Suppl):31–7.
43. Carlson SE, Cooke RJ, Werkman SH, Tolley EA. First year growth of preterm infants fed standard compared to marine oil n-3 supplemented formula. Lipids 1992;27:901–7.
44. Holman RT, Johnson SB, Mercuri O, et al. Essential fatty acid deficiency in malnourished children. Am J Clin Nutr 1981;34:1534–9.
45. Rebouche CJ. Carnitine function and requirements during the life cycle. FASEB J 1992;6:3379–86.
46. Engel AG, Rebouche CJ. Carnitine metabolism and inborn errors. J Inher Metab Dis 1984;7(Suppl 1):38–43.
47. Walter JH. L-Carnitine. Arch Dis Child 1996;74:475–8.
48. Shenai JP, Borum PR. Tissue carnitine reserves of newborn infants. Ped Res 1984;18:679–82.
49. Tanphaichitr V, Leelahagul P. Carnitine metabolism and human carnitine deficiency. Nutrition 1993;9:246–54.
50. Bonner CM, DeBrie KL, Hug G, et al. Effects of parenteral L-carnitine supplementation on

fat metabolism and nutrition in premature neonates. J Ped 1995;126:287–92.
51. Van Hove JL, Zhang W, Kahler SG, et al. Medium-chain acyl-CoA dehydrogenase (MCAD) deficiency: diagnosis by acylcarnitine analysis in blood. Am J Hum Genet 1993;52:958–66.
52. Schofield D, Braganza JM. Shortcomings of an automated assay for total antioxidant status in biological fluids. Clin Chem 1996;42:1712–4.
53. Manning EM, Shenkin A. Nutritional assessment in the critically ill. Crit Care Clin 1995;11: 603–34.
54. Schroeder JJ, Cousins RJ. Interleukin 6 regulates metallothionein gene expression and zinc metabolism in hepatocyte monolayer cultures. Proceedings of the National Academy of Sciences of the United States of America. 1990;87:3137–41.
55. Blackburn GL, Bistrian BR, Maini BS, et al. Nutritional and metabolic assessment of the hospitalized patient. J Paren & Enter Nutr 1977;1:11–22.
56. Forse RA, Christou N, Meakins JL, et al. Reliability of skin testing as a measure of nutritional state. Arch Surg 1981;116:1284–8.
57. Meakins JL, Pietsch JB, Bubenick O, et al. Delayed hypersensitivity: indicator of acquired failure of host defenses in sepsis and trauma. Ann Surg 1977;186:241–50.
58. Daly JM, Lieberman MD, Goldfine J, et al. Enteral nutrition with supplemental arginine, RNA, and omega-3 fatty acids in patients after operation: immunologic, metabolic, and clinical outcome. Surgery 1992;112:56–67.
59. Barbul A. Arginine and immune function. Nutrition 1990;6:53–8.
60. Kulkarni AD, Fanslow WC, Rudolph FB, Van Buren CT. Effect of dietary nucleotides on response to bacterial infections. J Paren & Enter Nutr 1986;10:169–71.
61. Barker D. Intrauterine programming of coronary heart disease and stroke. Acta Paed 1997;423(Suppl):178–82.
62. Michels K, Trichopoulos T, Robins J, et al. Birthweight as a risk factor for breast cancer. Lancet 1996;348:1542–6.
63. Sills RH. Failure to thrive: the role of clinical and laboratory evaluation. Am J Dis Child 1978;132:967–9.

CHAPTER

23

The Biochemical Basis of Red Blood Cell Disorders

Jeanne A. Lumadue, M.D., Ph.D.
Carlo Brugnara, M.D.

INTRODUCTION

It is appropriate that any text reviewing the biochemical basis of pediatric disease devote a chapter to red blood cell disorders, for they are among the most frequent and best understood of all human diseases. Approximately 5% of the world's population are genetic carriers for a hemoglobin disorder, and approximately 300,000 severely affected persons are born each year.[1] The globin genes were among the first eukaryotic genes to be cloned and sequenced. Pioneering research on mutations in these genes lead not only to our understanding of the hemoglobinopathies, but laid the foundation for a broader understanding of the structure, function, and regulation of all eukaryotic genes. Similarly, enzymatic deficiency of glucose-6-phosphate dehydrogenase (G6PD) is the most common inborn error of metabolism in the world population. It not only serves as an excellent example of how a biochemical defect can produce a particular clinical phenotype, but also demonstrates how the multifunctional effects of a mutation can lead to the establishment of the gene in particular gene pools. Our understanding of the red blood cell membrane and the various defects in its protein structure provides useful correlation between the biochemical basis of disease and the dramatic changes in morphology which they can produce. Since all of these disorders most frequently present in early childhood or adolescence, it is particularly important for pediatricians to have an understanding of their pathogenesis.

THE MOLECULAR BASIS OF THE HEMOGLOBINOPATHIES

Genetic Structure and Synthesis of Normal Hemoglobins

The molecular structure and expression of the hemoglobin genes has been reviewed in greater detail elsewhere.[2,3] Hemoglobin is best considered a family of protein molecules which all serve the crucial role of supplying oxygen to the tissues. Hemoglobin gene expression is under developmental regulation, accounting for the different biochemical forms of hemoglobin that exist between the human embryo, the fetus, and the adult. All hemoglobin molecules are heterotetramers, composed of two alpha-like and two beta-like protein chains with a total molecular weight of 64,500 Daltons. Alpha (α) hemoglobin and zeta (ζ) hemoglobin are the two alternative alpha-like chains, both 141 amino acids long. The genes encoding these proteins map to the short arm of chromosome 16 (16p13.3).[4,5] Beta (β), delta (δ), gamma (γ), and epsilon (ε) are the beta-like chains of hemoglobin. These proteins are 146 amino acids in length and the genes that encode them are clustered on the short arm of chromosome 11 (11p15.5).[6,7] The amino acid sequences are conserved between all hemoglobin proteins, suggesting they are evolutionarily derived from the duplication and divergence of a single ancestral gene (see Table 23–1).[2]

Hemoglobin genes are expressed at different levels during development, and the change in molecular forms is referred to as hemoglobin switching.[2,8,9] (See Figure 23–1.) The embryonic hemoglobins, which are produced in the yolk sac between the third and eighth weeks of gestation, are composed of different combinations of α, ζ, γ, and ε chains. The three major forms are Gower 1 ($\zeta_2\varepsilon_2$), Gower 2 ($\alpha_2\varepsilon_2$), and Portland ($\zeta_2\gamma_2$). Because ζ and ε are abundant only during this brief developmental period, they are referred to as the embryonic chains. Of note, however, trace amounts (0.3%) of ζ subunits may be detected in fetuses until the time of birth.[10]

At approximately 8 weeks gestational age, hematopoiesis shifts from the yolk sac to the liver, and with this shift comes a switch in the expression of the hemoglobin genes. Fetal hemoglobin becomes the predominate form. Fetal hemoglobin (Hb F) is a heterotetramer of two alpha and two gamma chains ($\alpha_2\gamma_2$). The gamma chains have two distinct forms, and are encoded by two distinct genes within the beta globin cluster. Gamma ^{A} (γ^A) contains an alanine at amino acid residue 136, whereas gamma ^{G} (γ^G), which represents approximately two-thirds of the gamma chains at the time of birth, has a glycine.[11] In adults, approximately 1% of the total hemoglobin is Hb F, which is restricted to a small population of red cells, the F cells.[12]

Over 95% of the hemoglobin in a normal adult is Hb A, which is composed of two alpha and two beta hemoglobin chains. Hb A_2 ($\alpha_2\,\delta_2$)is the second most abundant form, accounting for about 2–2.5%. The remainder of the adult hemoglobin variants is composed of chemically modified forms of Hb A, such as A_{1c}.

The genetic structure of the globin genes has been molecularly dissected, and has several layers of complexity. The globin genes, like other genes, synthesize RNA in a particular direction in relationship to the DNA molecule, from the 5′-deoxynucleotide end of the molecule to the 3′-deoxynucleotide end. Their chromosomal arrangement follows a similar pattern, in that they are organized in the order

TABLE 23–1. Primary Structure of the Major Human Hemoglobins

HELIX	α	ζ	HELIX	β	δ	γ	ε
NA1	1 Val	Ser	NA1	1 Val	Val	Gly	Val
			NA2	2 His	His	His	His
NA2	2 Leu	Leu	NA3	3 Leu	Leu	Phe	Phe
A1	3 Ser	Thr	A1	4 Thr	Thr	Thr	Thr
A2	4 Pro	Lys	A2	5 Pro	Pro	Glu	Ala
A3	5 Ala	Thr	A3	6 Glu	Glu	Glu	Glu
A4	6 Asp	Glu	A4	7 Glu	Glu	Asp	Glu
A5	7 Lys	Arg	A5	8 Lys	Lys	Lys	Lys
A6	8 Thr	Thr	A6	9 Ser	Thr	Ala	Ala
A7	9 Asn	Ile	A7	10 Ala	Ala	Thr	Ala
A8	10 Val	Ile	A8	11 Val	Val	Ile	Val
A9	11 Lys	Val	A9	12 Thr	Asn	Thr	Thr
A10	12 Ala	Ser	A10	13 Ala	Ala	Ser	Ser
A11	13 Ala	Met	A11	14 Leu	Leu	Leu	Leu
A12	14 Trp	Trp	A12	15 Trp	Trp	Trp	Trp
A13	15 Gly	Ala	A13	16 Gly	Gly	Gly	Ser
A14	16 Lys	Lys	A14	17 Lys	Lys	Lys	Lys
A15	17 Val	Ile	A15	18 Val	Val	Val	Met
A16	18 Gly	Ser					
AB1	19 Ala	Thr					
B1	20 His	Gln	B1	19 Asn	Asn	Asn	Asn
B2	21 Ala	Ala	B2	20 Val	Val	Val	Val
B3	22 Gly	Asp	B3	21 Asp	Asp	Glu	Glu
B4	23 Glu	Thr	B4	22 Glu	Ala	Asp	Glu
B5	24 Tyr	Ile	B5	23 Val	Val	Ala	Ala
B6	25 Gly	Gly	B6	24 Gly	Gly	Gly	Gly
B7	26 Ala	Thr	B7	25 Gly	Gly	Gly	Gly
B8	27 Glu	Glu	B8	26 Glu	Glu	Glu	Glu
B9	28 Ala	Thr	B9	27 Ala	Ala	Thr	Ala
B10	29 Leu	Leu	B10	28 Leu	Leu	Leu	Leu
B11	30 Glu	Glu	B11	29 Gly	Gly	Gly	Gly
B12	31 Arg	Arg	B12	30 Arg	Arg	Arg	Arg
B13	32 Met	Leu	B13	31 Leu	Leu	Leu	Leu
B14	33 Phe	Phe	B14	32 Leu	Leu	Leu	Leu
B15	34 Leu	Leu	B15	33 Val	Val	Val	Val
B16	35 Ser	Ser	B16	34 Val	Val	Val	Val
C1	36 Phe	His	C1	35 Tyr	Tyr	Tyr	Tyr
C2	37 Pro	Pro	C2	36 Pro	Pro	Pro	Pro
C3	38 Thr	Gln	C3	37 Trp	Trp	Trp	Trp
C4	39 Thr	Thr	C4	38 Thr	Thr	Thr	Thr
C5	40 Lys	Lys	C5	39 Gln	Gln	Gln	Gln
C6	41 Thr	Thr	C6	40 Arg	Arg	Arg	Arg
C7	42 Tyr	Tyr	C7	41 Phe	Phe	Phe	Phe
CE1	43 Phe	Phe	CD1	42 Phe	Phe	Phe	Phe
CE2	44 Pro	Pro	CD2	43 Glu	Glu	Asp	Asp
CE3	45 His	His	CD3	44 Ser	Ser	Ser	Ser
CE4	46 Phe	Phe	CD4	45 Phe	Phe	Phe	Phe
			CD5	46 Gly	Gly	Gly	Gly
CE5	47 Asp	Asp	CD6	47 Asp	Asp	Asn	Asn
CE6	48 Leu	Leu	CD7	48 Leu	Leu	Leu	Leu
CE7	49 Ser	His	CD8	49 Ser	Ser	Ser	Ser
CE8	50 His	Pro	D1	50 Thr	Ser	Ser	Ser
			D2	51 Pro	Pro	Ala	Pro
			D3	52 Asp	Asp	Ser	Ser
			D4	53 Ala	Ala	Ala	Ala
			D5	54 Val	Val	Ile	Ile
			D6	55 Met	Met	Met	Leu
CE9	51 Gly	Gly	D7	56 Gly	Gly	Gly	Gly
E1	52 Ser	Ser	E1	57 Asn	Asn	Asn	Asn
E2	53 Ala	Ala	E2	58 Pro	Pro	Pro	Pro
E3	54 Gln	Gln	E3	59 Lys	Lys	Lys	Lys
E4	55 Val	Leu	E4	60 Val	Val	Val	Val
E5	56 Lys	Arg	E5	61 Lys	Lys	Lys	Lys
E6	57 Gly	Ala	E6	62 Ala	Ala	Ala	Ala
E7	58 His	His	E7	63 His	His	His	His
E8	59 Gly	Gly	E8	64 Gly	Gly	Gly	Gly
E9	60 Lys	Ser	E9	65 Lys	Lys	Lys	Lys
E10	61 Lys	Lys	E10	66 Lys	Lys	Lys	Lys
E11	62 Val	Val	E11	67 Val	Val	Val	Val
E12	63 Ala	Val	E12	68 Leu	Leu	Leu	Leu
E13	64 Asp	Ser	E13	69 Gly	Gly	Thr	Thr
E14	65 Ala	Ala	E14	70 Ala	Ala	Ser	Ser
E15	66 Leu	Val	E15	71 Phe	Phe	Leu	Phe
E16	67 Thr	Gly	E16	72 Ser	Ser	Gly	Gly
E17	68 Asn	Asp	E17	73 Asp	Asp	Asp	Asp
E18	69 Ala	Ala	E18	74 Gly	Gly	Ala	Ala
E19	70 Val	Val	E19	75 Leu	Leu	Ile,Thr	Ile
E20	71 Ala	Lys	E20	76 Ala	Ala	Lys	Lys
EF1	72 His	Ser	EF1	77 His	His	His	Asn
EF2	73 Val	Ile	EF2	78 Leu	Leu	Leu	Met
EF3	74 Asp	Asp	EF3	79 Asp	Asp	Asp	Asp
EF4	75 Asp	Asp	EF4	80 Asn	Asn	Asp	Asn
EF5	76 Met	Ile	EF5	81 Leu	Leu	Leu	Leu
EF6	77 Pro	Gly	EF6	82 Lys	Lys	Lys	Lys
EF7	78 Asn	Gly	EF7	83 Gly	Gly	Gly	Pro
EF8	79 Ala	Ala	EF8	84 Thr	Thr	Thr	Ala
F1	80 Leu	Leu	F1	85 Phe	Phe	Phe	Phe
F2	81 Ser	Ser	F2	86 Ala	Ser	Ala	Ala
F3	82 Ala	Lys	F3	87 Thr	Gln	Gln	Lys
F4	83 Leu	Leu	F4	88 Leu	Leu	Leu	Leu
F5	84 Ser	Ser	F5	89 Ser	Ser	Ser	Ser
F6	85 Asp	Glu	F6	90 Glu	Glu	Glu	Glu
F7	86 Leu	Leu	F7	91 Leu	Leu	Leu	Leu
F8	87 His	His	F8	92 His	His	His	His
F9	88 Ala	Ala	F9	93 Cys	Cys	Cys	Cys
FG1	89 His	Tyr	FG1	94 Asp	Asp	Asp	Asp
FG2	90 Lys	Ile	FG2	95 Lys	Lys	Lys	Lys
FG3	91 Leu	Leu	FG3	96 Leu	Leu	Leu	Leu
FG4	92 Arg	Arg	FG4	97 His	His	His	His
FG5	93 Val	Val	FG5	98 Val	Val	Val	Val
G1	94 Asp	Asp	G1	99 Asp	Asp	Asp	Asp
G2	95 Pro	Pro	G2	100 Pro	Pro	Pro	Pro
G3	96 Val	Val	G3	101 Glu	Glu	Glu	Glu
G4	97 Asn	Asn	G4	102 Asn	Asn	Asn	Asn
G5	98 Phe	Phe	G5	103 Phe	Phe	Phe	Phe
G6	99 Lys	Lys	G6	104 Arg	Arg	Lys	Lys
G7	100 Leu	Leu	G7	105 Leu	Leu	Leu	Leu
G8	101 Leu	Leu	G8	106 Leu	Leu	Leu	Leu
G9	102 Ser	Ser	G9	107 Gly	Gly	Gly	Gly
G10	103 His	His	G10	108 Asn	Asn	Asn	Asn
G11	104 Cys	Cys	G11	109 Val	Val	Val	Val
G12	105 Leu	Leu	G12	110 Leu	Leu	Leu	Met
G13	106 Leu	Leu	G13	111 Val	Val	Val	Val
G14	107 Val	Val	G14	112 Cys	Cys	Thr	Ile
G15	108 Thr	Thr	G15	113 Val	Val	Val	Ile
G16	109 Leu	Leu	G16	114 Leu	Leu	Leu	Leu
G17	110 Ala	Ala	G17	115 Ala	Ala	Ala	Ala
G18	111 Ala	Ala	G18	116 His	Arg	Ile	Thr
G19	112 His	Arg	G19	117 His	Asn	His	His
GH1	113 Leu	Phe	GH1	118 Phe	Phe	Phe	Phe
GH2	114 Pro	Pro	GH2	119 Gly	Gly	Gly	Gly
GH3	115 Ala	Ala	GH3	120 Lys	Lys	Lys	Lys
GH4	116 Glu	Asp	GH4	121 Glu	Glu	Glu	Glu
GH5	117 Phe	Phe	GH5	122 Phe	Phe	Phe	Phe
H1	118 Thr	Thr	H1	123 Thr	Thr	Thr	Thr
H2	119 Pro	Ala	H2	124 Pro	Pro	Pro	Pro
H3	120 Ala	Glu	H3	125 Pro	Gln	Glu	Glu
H4	121 Val	Ala	H4	126 Val	Met	Val	Val
H5	122 His	His	H5	127 Gln	Gln	Gln	Gln
H6	123 Ala	Ala	H6	128 Ala	Ala	Ala	Ala
H7	124 Ser	Ala	H7	129 Ala	Ala	Ser	Ala
H8	125 Leu	Trp	H8	130 Tyr	Tyr	Trp	Trp
H9	126 Asp	Asp	H9	131 Gln	Gln	Gln	Gln
H10	127 Lys	Lys	H10	132 Lys	Lys	Lys	Lys
H11	128 Phe	Phe	H11	133 Val	Val	Met	Leu
H12	129 Leu	Leu	H12	134 Val	Val	Val	Val
H13	130 Ala	Ser	H13	135 Ala	Ala	Thr	Ser
H14	131 Ser	Val	H14	136 Gly	Gly	Gly,Ala	Ala
H15	132 Val	Val	H15	137 Val	Val	Val	Val
H16	133 Ser	Ser	H16	138 Ala	Ala	Ala	Ala
H17	134 Thr	Ser	H17	139 Asn	Asn	Ser	Ile
H18	135 Val	Val	H18	140 Ala	Ala	Ala	Ala
H19	136 Leu	Leu	H19	141 Leu	Leu	Leu	Leu
H20	137 Thr	Thr	H20	142 Ala	Ala	Ser	Ala
H21	138 Ser	Glu	H21	143 His	His	Ser	His
HC1	139 Lys	Lys	HC1	144 Lys	Lys	Arg	Lys
HC2	140 Tyr	Tyr	HC2	145 Tyr	Tyr	Tyr	Tyr
HC3	141 Arg	Arg	HC3	146 His	His	His	His

Source: Bunn H F, Forget, BG. Hemoglobin: molecular, genetic and clinical aspects. Philadelphia, Saunders, 1986.

FIGURE 23–1. Organization and Expression of Hemoglobin Genes

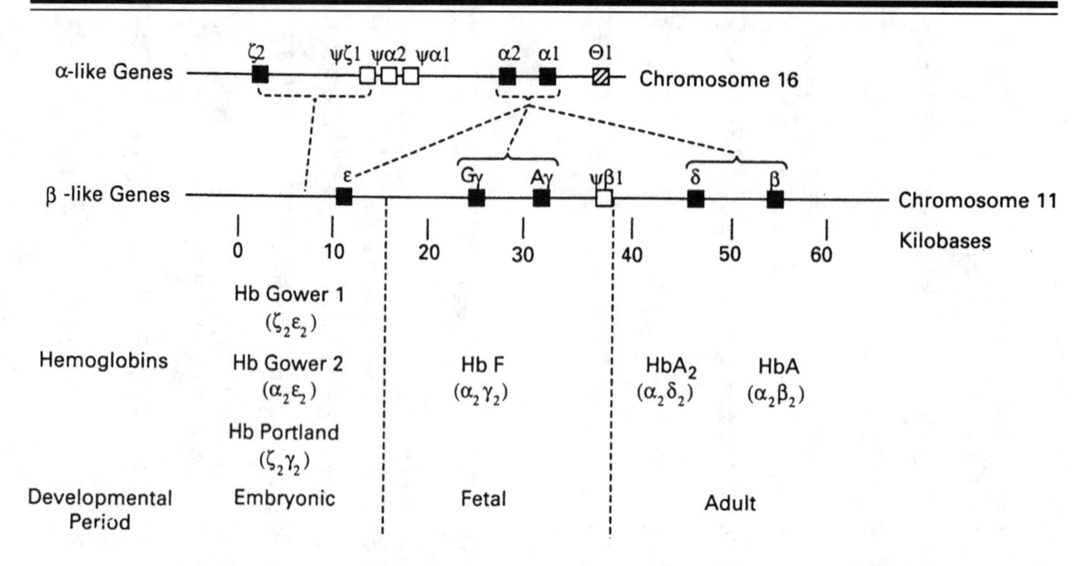

Source: Orkin SH, Nathan DG. The thalassemias. In: Nathan DG, Orkin SH, eds. Hematology of infancy and childhood. Philadelphia: W. B. Saunders, 1986. Reprinted by permission.

in which they are developmentally expressed, in the 5′ to 3′ direction. Thus, the zeta gene lies to the 5′ end of the two alpha chain genes (alpha 1 and alpha 2),[13,14] while the beta-like chains are arranged in the order of epsilon, gamma, delta, and beta in the 5′ to 3′ direction.[2,15,16] (See Figure 23–1.)

DNA sequences flanking the 5′ end of the genes, where RNA transcription begins, are required for proper gene expression.[2,17] The ATA box, located about 30 bases upstream of the gene, localizes the precise initiation site for transcription and is required for abundant transcription. A CCAAT sequence (about 70–80 bases upstream) and a CACCC-rich region (80–100 bases upstream) also function to regulate transcription. Other regions of DNA upstream from the complexes are believed to modulate chromatin secondary structure and regulatory protein binding and are crucial to globin gene expression. Approximately 10–20 kb upstream of the ε globin gene is a DNA sequence known as the locus control region (LCR), which confers high-level tissue-specific expression of the beta globin complex.[18,19] The importance of these sequences is demonstrated by the fact that patients who lack the LCR DNA sequences but retain the globin genes fail to express the genes.[20] The alpha globin genes contain an equivalent region approximately 40 kb upstream from the ξ gene. This site, known as HS-40, is thought to be the major regulatory sequence for the alpha globin complex.[21,22]

Like most eukaryotic genes, the globin genes also have intervening sequences of DNA (introns) embedded within the coding (translated) sequences of the gene. These intervening sequences must be eliminated or "spliced" out of the transcript in order for accurate translation to occur. All globin genes possess two introns in identical positions relative to the coding sequences but of variable length. Consensus sequences at both the 5′ (C/AAG↓GUA/GAGU) and 3′ (U/CXC/UAG↓G) ends of the introns direct the accurate splicing of the transcript; mutations in either sequence result in an unstable message.[23] Sequences at the 3′ end of the transcript are rich in adenine nucleotides and are required for the addition of the poly A tail, which functions to stabilize the message during this processing.

The clusters of globin genes on chromosomes 16 and 11 have an additional level of complexity in that the gene complex contains not only the structural genes that encode the globin proteins, but a number of other DNA sequences related to the globin genes, which have no known function. The genetic sequence of these so-called "pseudogenes" has been determined. While the DNA sequences are clearly related to those of the globin genes, and are actually thought to have been evolutionarily derived from them, the sequences are diverged enough that they are unable to support RNA synthesis. Some of the pseudogenes are only partial segments of the globin genes and some contain DNA sequences which, because of point mutations, insertions, or deletions, cause an early termination or a gross alteration in RNA synthesis.

A single β globin pseudogene is located at the 5′ end of the delta gene, while a pseudogene of ζ and two pseudogenes for α globin are located at the 5′ end of the alpha gene complex[2, 14] (Figure 23–1). It should be mentioned that the alpha complex additionally contains a theta (θ) sequence, localized at the 3′ end of the alpha genes. While there is evidence that the theta message exists at low levels within the cell (< 1% of all alpha transcripts), the predicted protein sequence suggests that the protein is dysfunctional.[24, 25]

Assembly of the Hemoglobin Molecule

In the native state, approximately 80% of the hemoglobin molecule is in an alpha helical configuration.[26] The charged amino acid residues are oriented toward the outer aqueous environment of the cell, whereas the uncharged amino acid residues are oriented toward the less hydrophilic interior of the molecule. Each individual protein chain contains either seven (alpha globin) or eight (beta globin) helical segments which are evolutionarily conserved between the two different molecules. Oxygen binding to hemoglobin is mediated by heme. The iron containing heme moiety (ferroprotoporphyrin IX) covalently binds to histidine residues within a strongly conserved helical region located at near the middle of each chain. This corresponds to amino acid residue number 87 of the alpha chain and number 92 of the beta chain. Of note, all hemoglobins sequenced to date have a histidine residue at these respective sites.[26]

The quaternary structure of hemoglobin involves a number of considerations. Most of the strong interactions between the individual protein chains are limited to interactions between dissimilar chains; there is relatively little contact between the like chains, and this contact is limited primarily to short interfaces. The unlike chains, on the other hand, have molecular associations in two regions of the dimer: an area of relatively weak hydrogen bonding which results in a "sliding" contact, and another which results in a "packing" contact. The packing contact is a strong charge association requiring high salt or urea for disruption. When a hemoglobin molecule is disrupted by such conditions, alpha-beta dimers are produced. The tetramer is ultimately assembled with the polypeptides folded upon themselves such that the heme molecule lies in internal clefts of the molecule, equidistant from each of the individual amino acid chains.[26]

Hemoglobin's primary function is to bind oxygen for delivery to tissues while at the same time clearing these tissues of the metabolic waste product CO_2. It has evolved to bind oxygen allosterically, with a sigmoidally shaped binding curve (see Figure 23–2).[2] The binding of the oxygen molecule induces a conformational change based on the dissociation of salt bonds which function to stabilize the tetramer in the deoxygenated state. At low oxygen tensions, hemoglobin has a relatively low affinity for oxygen. As the molecule begins to bind oxygen molecules, the affinity

FIGURE 23–2. The Hemoglobin Dissociation Curve Showing the Effects of Ph, DPG, and Temperature on the Binding of Oxygen to Hemoglobin

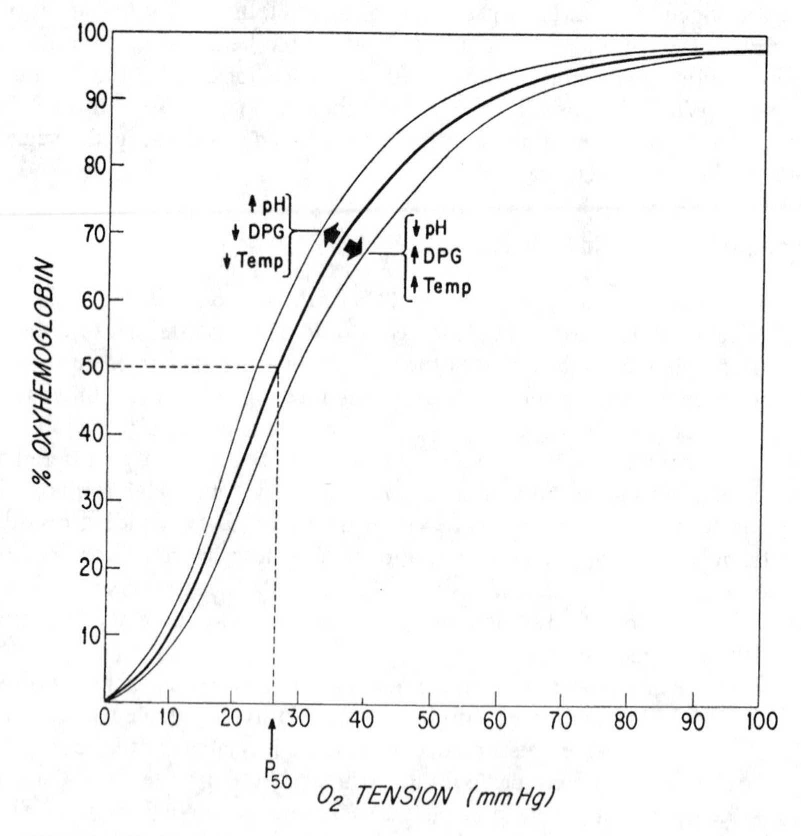

Source: Bunn, HF, Forget BG. Hemoglobin: molecular, genetic and clinical aspects. Philadelphia: W. B. Saunders, 1986. Reprinted by permission.

for oxygen increases, and the oxygen binding curve becomes steep. Biologically, this ensures that if a hemoglobin molecule is oxygenated, it is fully oxygenated, and there are relatively few molecules of partially oxygenated hemoglobin *in vivo.*

Numerous biologic factors are known to influence the binding of oxygen to the hemoglobin chains, but the three most physiologically important ones are pH, temperature, and the concentration of 2-diphosphoglycerate (2DPG). The effect of pH on the oxygen binding curve was first detailed in 1904 by Bohr and colleagues, and is accordingly known as the Bohr effect.[27] Originally described as a decreased oxygen affinity associated with increasing pCO_2, it was later recognized that the effect was actually dependent on the pH of the system. Between pH values of 6 and 8.5, oxygen affinity varies directly with pH: that is, the lower the pH, the lower the affinity for oxygen. This is clearly advantageous from a physiological standpoint. The Bohr effect accounts for the desirable effect of oxygen being released at physiological sites where the pH is lowest (and the metabolic rate is highest), and additionally accounts for the efficient binding of oxygen in the lungs, where the pCO_2 is lowest and the pH is highest.

Temperature is another parameter which is known to effect the oxygen binding curve. As temperatures increase, the binding of O_2 decreases and the oxygen binding curve shifts to the right. Once again, this makes sense physiologically, since it is clearly advantageous to have oxygen released to those areas of the tissue which are metabolically most active and hence have a higher microtemperature.[2, 26]

The third major factor affecting the binding of hemoglobin to red cells is the small organic molecule 2-diphosphoglycerate (2DPG).[2, 26] Normal human erythrocytes contain approximately 5 mmol of 2DPG in 1 L of fresh packed cells—a concentration approximately four times that of ATP. The reason for this elevated concentration was originally unclear, but has since been determined to be secondary to the molecule's function as a strong modulator of oxygen binding. As the concentration of 2GPD increases within an erythrocyte, the affinity of the erythrocyte for oxygen decreases. This has particularly important clinical implications for persons receiving red cell transfusions. As erythrocytes age in storage, the intracellular concentrations of 2DPG decrease, and the erythrocytes have an increased affinity (decreased release) for oxygen. While this has never been shown to definitely have an adverse effect on individuals being transfused, it remains a consideration in small infants receiving red cells and also in persons undergoing massive transfusion. Studies have shown that the transfused red cells reaccumulate 2DPG quickly: levels are 50% of normal within 3–8 hours.[28]

Hemoglobinopathies

The hemoglobinopathies are a diverse group of disorders which fall into three overlapping groups: the structural variants, which have altered hemoglobin binding affinities or other biochemical alterations which affect function; the thalassemias, in which there is a reduced amount or complete lack of production of one or more globin proteins; and the so-called hereditary persistence of fetal hemoglobin (HPFH) syndromes, in which the fetal hemoglobins persist beyond their appropriate developmental period.

Structural Hemoglobin Variants

Over 700 structural variants in hemoglobin have been identified.[29] The majority of these are the result of single point mutations in the gene, but may also be due to so-called fusion products which are derived from portions of the β and δ or β and γ gene products. Only some of those variants associated with clinical sequelae are detailed in this chapter; exhaustive lists of all known structural mutations in the hemoglobins are available elsewhere.[2, 29]

The structural variants of hemoglobin can be molecularly categorized into four major types:[26]

- The first (and most common) type of variant is the result of a single base mutation in the gene, giving rise to a single amino acid substitution in the protein. A few variants with two separate mutations have been documented.
- A second type of variant has been described in which the hemoglobin protein is longer than normal. This may result from a single base mutation in the termination codon of the gene, a frameshift mutation in the coding region, a tandem repeat sequence, or a mutation which alters amino terminus protein processing.
- A third category of mutants results in a shortened hemoglobin protein chain, usually resulting from gene deletions, or in rare cases, missense mutations that cause early termination of protein synthesis.
- A fourth category is the result of nonhomologous recombination (unequal crossover) of the hemoglobin genes, giving rise to an array of hybrid genes and fusion hemoglobins.

Variants of hemoglobin are also classified by their clinical manifestations. Some variants result in a chronic hemolytic anemia (e.g., the sickling disorders, unstable variants of hemoglobin), others have altered oxygen binding (the low or high oxygen affinity variants), and others result in ineffective production or marked instability. The last group is best considered variants of the thalassemia syndromes. As will be discussed, the presence of compound heterozygotes in the affected population adds an additional level of complexity to the categorization of these disorders.

Most clinically significant hemoglobin variants are detected with hemoglobin electrophoresis or isoelectric focusing. Anemia may indicate the presence of a thalassemia syndrome (discussed later) or an unstable hemoglobin variant. Tests on the chemical stability of hemoglobin (thermal or isopropanol stability) and measurement of the oxyhemoglobin dissociation curve are helpful in the diagnosis of these variants. Final identification of many hemoglobin variants can be achieved with nucleotide sequencing of the coding regions for the alpha and beta globin genes.

The Sickling Disorders

The sickling disorders are characterized genetically by one or more alleles for Hb S at the β globin locus. This includes sickle cell anemia (homozygosity for Hb S), sickle cell trait (heterozygosity for Hb S), or any other heterozygous state in which Hb S is associated with another β globin variant or β thalassemia allele.

Hb S is the result of a single Adenine to Thymine (A→T) base mutation which substitutes valine (Val) for glutamic acid (Glu) at amino acid residue 6 of the β globin protein. It is a common mutation in African populations, where the gene frequency parallels the incidence of malaria. Indeed, the presence of the gene is felt to provide some level of resistance to infection by *T. falciparum;* however, the mechanism for this resistance remains unknown.

The mechanism by which Hb S undergoes sickling is complex and not entirely understood. It is a polymerization reaction which converts deoxyhemoglobin S molecules in solution into gelled aggregates of molecules: a so-called sol-gel transition.[30,31] (See Figure 23–3.) Kinetically, the reaction is explained by a *double nucle-*

FIGURE 23–3. A Model for the Polymerization and Alignment of Deoxyhemoglobin S

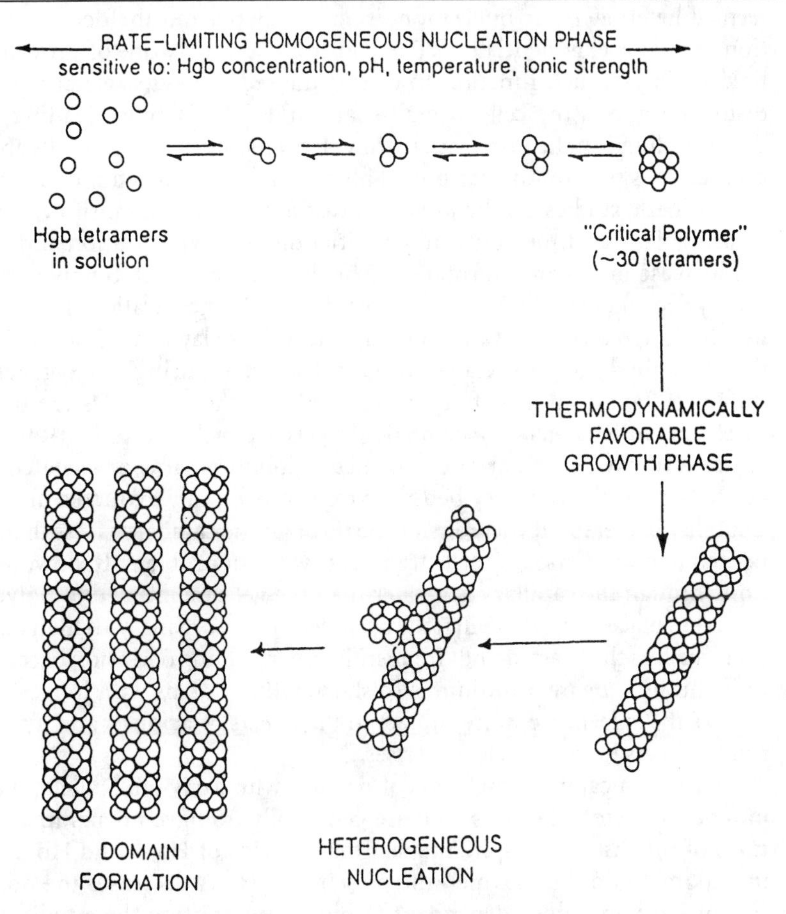

Source: Dover GJ, Platt OS. Sickle cell disease. In: Nathan DG, Larkin SH, eds. Hematology of infancy and childhood. Philadelphia: W. B. Saunders, 1998. Reprinted by permission.

ation reaction.[31] Hemoglobin molecules are stable in solution up to certain concentrations; however, perturbations in the microenvironment of the solution can alter their solubility, prompting the formation of short polymers. This is the rate-limiting step in the reaction, the equilibrium of which is shifted by environmental parameters. Oxygen content is the most important parameter affecting polymer formation: molecules which are completely oxygen saturated are totally soluble in solution. As the oxygen content decreases, or as other parameters which can affect oxygen binding change, polymerization (gel formation) is favored. Factors such as increased hemoglobin concentration, increased pH, increased temperature, ionic strength, and increased levels of 2DPG have all been shown to promote polymerization of deoxy S molecules.[30–32]

Once the polymers reach a critical size of approximately 30 molecules—the critical nucleus—addition of further molecules is thermodynamically favored and the polymer chains enlarge. This elongation increases the surface area for more polymerization, prompting the second nucleation phase of the reaction. This phase, termed heterogeneous nucleation, is autocatalytic, and the degree of polymerization increases exponentially.[31] The end result is a network of growing and cross-linking fibers which function to distort the red cell cytoskeletal membrane. This distortion affects the cells' overall shape and deformability, leading to their tendency to sludge in the microvasculature. Irreversibly sickled red cells are the slender, pointed cells seen on the peripheral blood smear of afflicted individuals.[32]

Kinetic studies on the *double nucleation* reaction have shown that there is a measurable delay time between the initiation of polymerization and the exponential increase in polymer formation. The delay time for Hb S polymerization is inversely dependent to the 20th–30th power of Hb S concentration. Thus, small changes in cellular Hb S concentration greatly affect the delay time. This explains, in part, the pathophysiology associated with the disease. In the highly oxygenated alveoli of the lungs, hemoglobin is fully oxygenated and the molecules are in solution. At these oxygen tensions, any hemoglobin gels are melted rapidly (< 0.5 sec). As the red cells transverse the arteries, the hemoglobin remains oxygenated; however, as the cells enter the capillary beds, the oxygen is rapidly extracted and hemoglobin solubility decreases. If the transit time through the capillary is less than the gel time needed to polymerize, the cells transverse without problem. If, however, the transit time through the capillary is greater than the gel time needed to polymerize, sickling takes place and the capillary is occluded. Thus, organs with high oxygen extractions, such as the heart, do not frequently suffer sickling occlusion because the transit time through the myocardium is so short. Other organs with longer transit times, such as the spleen, are more subject to the effects of acidosis and hypoxia, and are prime targets for vasoocclusive crises.[32]

The clinical manifestations of persons who carry Hb S allele(s) depend on a number of factors. Persons who are genetically AS have no significant manifestations of the disease. Despite the fact that hybrids of Hb A and Hb S ($\alpha_2\beta^A\beta^S$) can incorporate into the polymer, the presence of Hb A decreases the polymerization rate of Hb S in a dose-dependent fashion, thus shifting the equilibrium towards solubilization. Hb F functions to solubilize Hb S to an even greater degree.[33, 34] This explains the milder severity of persons heterozygous for Hb S and a globin mutation which is associated with higher fetal hemoglobin levels (as in HPFH syndromes). New therapies for sickle cell anemia employ agents such as hydroxyurea in order to increase the intracellular levels of Hb F.[35]

Persons homozygous for Hb S have sickle cell anemia and suffer the clinical sequelae associated with that disease. Sickle cell anemia is a chronic hemolytic anemia which results from the increased clearance of sickled cells in the microvasculature of the reticuloendothelial system, primarily the spleen. Children with sickle cell disease have a propensity for infections, suffer splenic sequestration syndromes, painful vasoocclusive crises, and the clinical sequelae of long-term damage to the microvasculature, including renal papillary necrosis and, most devastatingly, cerebral infarctions.

Other mutations in the β globin locus and even the α globin locus can alter hemoglobin sickling. The most prevalent of these alleles is Hb C, which, like Hb S, has a single amino acid substitution at amino acid residue 6 (Glu→Lys). Persons heterozygous for Hb A and Hb C have no hematological abnormalities, with the exception of an increased number of target cells on their peripheral blood smear. Persons homozygous for Hb C have a mild hemolytic anemia and splenomegaly, with nearly 100% target forms on peripheral smear.[36] Because Hb C is less soluble than Hb A, it has a tendency to form intracellular crystals, which are favored in the oxygenated state over the deoxygenated state.[37]

Hb C has pathologic manifestations when complexed with Hb S, at which time it results in a sickling disorder. While initial studies on the polymerization of Hb S and Hb C suggested that these mixtures were less soluble than mixtures of Hb S and Hb A, this is currently not felt to be the case *in vivo.* Rather, it appears that the pathogenicity associated with the SC phenotype is secondary to the levels of the mutant forms within the cells: There is relatively more Hb S in the red cells of patients with SC disease than in those of persons with AS. Moreover, the overall hemoglobin concentration appears to be higher in these cells,[38] probably as a result of an effect of Hb C on the red cell membrane which leads to K loss and dehydration.[39]

Other common variants of hemoglobin which deserve mention are Hb D, which is, in fact, a heterogeneous group (class) of hemoglobin variants which have a similar electrophoretic mobility as Hb S on alkaline gels. The most common type is Hb $D_{\text{Los Angeles}}$ (Hb D_{Punjab}; β121 Glu→Gln).[2]

This variant has a slightly increased O_2 affinity. D homozygotes have normal hemoglobin levels and a tendency for increased target forms on their peripheral smears. Heterozygotes are clinically normal. Persons who are compound heterozygous for Hb S and Hb D tend to have a moderate hemolytic anemia and may have crises. Hb O-Arab is a hemoglobin variant which can also be associated with a sickle syndrome. Individuals who are heterozygous for Hb S or Hb O-Arab have a clinical picture identical to that of sickle cell anemia.[2]

Additional variant hemoglobins which can result or affect sickling have been tabulated and are reviewed in detail elsewhere.[2]

Hb E is the result of a Glu→Lys mutation at residue 26 of the β globin chain.[40] It is one of the most common variants, if not the most common variant, in the world population, with high incidence in the Chinese, Indonesian, and Southeast Asian populations. Heterozygotes are clinically normal with a mild microcytosis and hypochromasia. Hb E homozygotes are normal or slightly anemic, with a pronounced microcytosis and hypochromasia. When combined with the β thalassemia allele, Hb E is pathologic, with a broad clinical spectrum ranging from mildly affected to severe disease. (Thalassemia is discussed in a later section.)

The clinical spectrum seen in these compound heterozygotes is due to the variations in the amounts of Hb A produced (from the thalassemic gene), combined with the fact that Hb E is produced at levels only about 30–35% that of Hb A.[40]

Unstable Hemoglobin Variants

Congenital Heinz body hemolytic anemia (CHBA) is caused by any one of a number of unstable hemoglobin variants. Clinically, it is an important category of hemolytic diseases which can produce a variable degree of anemia and are typically associated with the presence of a specific type of red cell inclusion, the so-called Heinz body, which is seen on the peripheral smear after staining with rhodanile blue or methyl violet dyes. This disorder typically presents in childhood with hemolytic anemia (which may be aggravated by fever or medication), jaundice, and splenomegaly.

Over 100 unstable variants which can cause CHBA have been characterized.[26, 41] They are inherited as autosomal-dominant traits, with the mutant hemoglobin only constituting about 10–30% of the total hemoglobin protein.[26] The majority of the mutations are single amino acid substitutions in the β chain, many of which are located in the region which associates with the heme molecule. It is speculated that the mutations alter the configuration of the hydrophobic interior of the molecule, interfere with the secondary structure of the protein, or prevent the binding of the heme moiety to the hemoglobin protein. As would be expected from such dramatic alterations, much of the red cell destruction takes place in the marrow, before the cells enter the peripheral circulation. *In vitro*, the unstable hemoglobin variants precipitate readily when heated to 50° C or when incubated in isopropanol. The red blood cells typically manifest this instability in the form of a coccoid precipitate which has come to be known as the Heinz body. These have been shown to contain α and β hemoglobin chains (in approximately equal number) and a normal proportion of heme. The demonstration of Heinz bodies is valuable in establishing the diagnosis of CHBA, as is hemoglobin electrophoresis (which is frequently abnormal) and thermal instability studies.[26]

Variants which warrant particular mention are Hb Zurich (β63 His→Arg), which efficiently binds O_2 and is mildly unstable. Hb Zurich is stabilized by carbon monoxide; thus, individuals with this variant who smoke have considerably less hemolysis than individuals who do not.[26] The use of oxidative drugs by carriers of Hb Zurich may precipitate severe hemolytic episodes. Other variants are characterized by Hb instability, decreased oxygen affinity, and severe hemolysis and anemia requiring chronic transfusion. A few variants (Hb Indianapolis, Hb Geneva, Hb Cagliari, and Hb Showa-Yakushiji) are so unstable that they degrade rapidly and cannot be found in the peripheral circulation.[26]

Hemoglobin Variants with Altered Oxygen Affinities

A number of hemoglobin variants associated with altered affinity for oxygen have been described. Variants such as Hb Chesapeake (α92 Arg $\rightarrow$Leu) have an increased affinity for oxygen, resulting in a functional left shift to the oxygen dissociation curve with a relative decrease in the unloading of oxygen to the tissues. These persons have a compensatory erythrocytosis and a tendency to a ruddy complexion, but are otherwise clinically unremarkable. Diagnosis is based on family history, hemoglobin electrophoresis, and measurements of oxygen affinity.[42, 43]

Over 50 stable hemoglobin variants with high oxygen affinity have been identified. Individuals heterozygous for these variants typically have erythrocytosis. An additional 50 hemoglobin variants with a mildly increased oxygen affinity have also been characterized; these heterozygotes are normal and exhibit only mild erythrocytosis. Other hemoglobin variants included in this category include Hb Bethesda and Hb Kempsey.[26]

A number of hemoglobin variants with a decreased affinity for oxygen have also been characterized. The decreased affinity of the hemoglobin for oxygen results in a decreased Bohr effect which clinically produces cyanosis and, in some instances, mild hemolysis. These, too, are diagnosed using hemoglobin electrophoresis. Most of these variants are due to mutations in the β chain of Hb, including Hb Kansas (β102 Asn$\rightarrow$Thr). Only a few alpha variants with decreased oxygen affinity have been identified. Hb M_{Boston} (α58 His$\rightarrow$Tyr) and Hb M_{Iwate} (α87 His$\rightarrow$Tyr) are associated with significant cyanosis.[26]

Other groups of hemoglobin variants are characterized by a relative excess of methemoglobin (ferric hemoglobin, which is subsequently reduced to deoxyhemoglobin) in the red cells; these are the M variants of hemoglobin.

Hb M variants display familial cyanosis, which is inherited in an autosomal-dominant pattern. As described above, some of the α-chain M hemoglobins have decreased oxygen affinity, whereas some of the β variants have normal oxygen affinity (Hb $M_{Saskatoon}$ and Hb $M_{Hyde\ Park}$).[26] The definitive diagnosis of Hb M is made based on the absorption spectra abnormalities and by isoelectric focusing. Ferricyanide may be used to oxidize the hemoglobin to the Fe^{+++} state, improving the resolution of the detection.

The Thalassemia Syndromes

Thalassemia is a group of syndromes characterized by decreased or absent synthesis of one or more globin chains. Alpha and beta thalassemia refer to clinical syndromes caused by a deficiency in the respective globin chains. The molecular genetic defects that produce these syndromes are extremely varied and require review of the normal globin gene structure and hemoglobin switching pattern. In general, the severity of the syndromes is directly related to how much functional hemoglobin molecules are synthesized. This, in turn is dependent on the severity of the mutation and whether any functional protein chains can be synthesized. Any allele that produces a small amount of functioning protein (α+ or β+ alleles) typically results in a less severe phenotype than that seen with alleles that produce no functional protein (α^0

or β^0 alleles). As with all hemoglobinopathies, there is considerable clinical overlap due to the variation in established mutations and the presence of compound heterozygotes in the population.

Alpha Thalassemia

As outlined previously, there are normally four functioning α globin genes, the products of which are found in fetal and adult hemoglobin. The α thalassemia syndromes vary in clinical severity depending on the number of normally functioning α globin genes present. Persons who have a mutation in one copy are *silent carriers* with no clinical anemia, normal red cell morphology, and normal levels of Hb A. Persons who carry two mutated α globin genes are said to have *alpha thalassemia trait,* with mild anemia and red cell morphology which shows moderate to marked hypochromic and microcytic features. Because of the relative excess in γ chains being synthesized *in utero*, persons with thalassemia trait will have tetramers of γ hemoglobin (γ_4; Hb Bart's) at birth: this comprises only 5–10% of the total hemoglobin and disappears in the neonatal period.[44] Hb A is the pattern typically seen in older infants, children, and adults.

The presence of three mutated α genes results in a syndrome known as *hemoglobin H disease.* Hb H is a β_4 tetramer, which results from the disproportional synthesis of β globin chains. The β_4 tetramer may represent as much as 30% of the total hemoglobin present. Hb H disease is associated with a moderately severe hypochromic, microcytic anemia, with abundant fragmented red cell forms. Hemoglobin values can range from as low as 3 g/dL to as high as 10 g/dL. The major complications of Hb H disease are primarily related to the severe, ongoing hemolysis and include jaundice, splenomegaly, nutritional deficiencies, gall stones, and impaired immune function.

Inheritance of four mutated α globin genes causes severe intrauterine anemia which results in *hydrops fetalis* or fetal death *in utero.* This is associated with a predominance of Hb Bart's (γ_4), which is produced because of the lack of functional α globin chains.[44]

Beta Thalassemia

There is considerable clinical variation in the β thalassemia syndromes as well, but the variation is less dependent on the number of abnormal genes and more dependent on the nature of the specific mutations. This may not seem logical at first, since there are two fewer copies of each β globin gene (one copy per chromosome); however, the expression of the four additional γ globin genes which can be recruited for fetal hemoglobin production can serve as critical modulators of phenotypic expression.

In general, there are four clinical categories of the β thalassemia syndromes. *Silent carriers* are hematologically normal. *Beta thalassemia trait* is associated with a mild microcytic, hypochromic anemia. These individuals have modest increases in the relative amounts of Hb F and Hb A_2 produced.

Thalassemia intermedia is a microcytic, hypochromic anemia of moderate severity. Individuals with thalassemia intermedia may occasionally require transfusion therapy, but are not transfusion dependent. There is an associated significant increase in the levels of Hb A_2 and Hb F.

Thalassemia major is a severe anemia which requires regular transfusion therapy. The red cell morphology changes are striking, with microcytes, fragments, teardrops, nucleated red cells, and abundant variations in red cell size and shape.[44] Hemoglobin electrophoresis shows marked elevations in Hb A_2 and Hb F and a marked relative decrease in the level of Hb A. In its most severe form, thalassemia major presents a clinical picture of severe anemia, growth retardation, and bone deformities which is known as Cooley's anemia. These patients require chronic transfusion therapy and ultimately may be treated with bone marrow transplantation.

Mutations Causing the Thalassemia Syndromes

Molecular cloning and sequence analysis of the globin genes has led to the categorization of the types of mutations which give rise to the thalassemia syndromes. The mutations are numerous and are molecularly diverse. They produce a range of phenotypes and have been well established in the gene pools of certain ethnic populations. Alpha thalassemia alleles range in frequency from 5–10% in the Mediterranean regions,[45] to 20–30% in West Africa,[46] to 60–70% in areas of Southeast Asia. [47] Beta thalassemia alleles are common in North Africa, Southeast Asia, India, and the Mediterranean region.[44] As in the case of sickle cell anemia, it has been hypothesized that these mutations provide some selective advantage in malaria infection.

A number of single nucleotide mutations causing both α and β thalassemia have been characterized. These mutations are best understood by thinking of them with respect to the normal steps that occur as the hemoglobin molecule is produced: Defects can occur as the gene is transcribed, as the message is processed, as the mRNA is translated, or as the hemoglobin molecule is assembled. This discussion highlights and provides examples of the major categories of these mutations; for more complete compilations, the reader is referred to other references.[2, 44, 48]

Point Mutations Causing Defects in Message Transcription, Stability, and Processing

Point mutations in the promoter sequences of the β globin genes frequently act to decrease the affinity of DNA binding proteins which are necessary for normal transcription to occur. The majority of these mutations are located either in the so-called ATA box or in the CACCC-rich domains which lie 5′ to the coding sequences.[49, 50] One variant characterized has a defect in the RNA cap site which alters the stability of the transcribed message.[51] The result is a normal RNA sequence but a marked decrease in the quantity of mRNA produced (β^+ thal), which is clinically associated with a thalassemia intermedia phenotype.

A variety of point mutations alter the splicing of the RNA transcript, which in turn has deleterious effects on message processing, stability, and translation. Point defects in the 5′ splice donor (GT) and 3′ splice acceptor (AG) sites of introns have been described as causing many variants of thalassemia.[52]

Point mutations in the nucleotide sequences surrounding the junctions of the intervening sequences have varying effects on message stability, and have been reported as causing a β^+ thalassemic phenotype.[53] A number of point mutations have been described which alter the sequence of an exon or intron, producing new donor or acceptor splice sites. These newly formed splice sites alter the normal processing of the RNA, causing insertions, deletions, and frameshift mutations (and the ultimate lack of normally translated product). Depending on the exact mutation, these can result in a β^0 or β^+ phenotype.[54, 55] Variants with decreased mRNA stability have been shown to be caused by point mutations in the pre-mRNA cleavage and/or polyadenylation site (AAUAAA).[56] This causes inefficient processing with a number of "run-on" transcripts which terminate downstream of the gene. As would be expected, this results in a decreased level of normal translated product and can cause an α^+ or a β^+ phenotype.

Point Mutations Causing Alterations in Protein Translation

Point mutations can also affect the normal translation of the protein product. Mutations which alter the normal AUG translation initiation codon decreases and typically abolishes translation. Mutations of this type have been shown to produce an α^+, α^0, or β^0 phenotype.[48, 57, 58] Several nonsense mutations in the coding region of the gene have also been described. These produce stop codons (UAG, UUA, UGA) that halt translation of the message and lead to the production of a truncated peptide. The vast majority of these mutations produce no appreciable levels of globin protein (α^0 or β^0 phenotype).[59, 60] A final type of mutation affecting protein translation alters the normal UAA termination codon of the gene, and causes run-on gene products which are terminated at the next downstream in frame stop codon. These mutations give rise to rather well known hemoglobin variants: Hb Constant Spring, an α chain thalassemia variant prevalent among Chinese;[61] Hb Tak, a β chain thalassemia variant;[62] and Hb Cranston, a β chain variant which does not produce a thalassemia syndrome.[63]

Mutations Affecting Globin Chain Stability

Soon after the α and β globin protein chains are synthesized, they bind to a heme molecule, associate into $\alpha\beta$ dimers, and subsequently form tetramers. This assembly is highly dependent on the electrostatic charges on the associating faces of the hemoglobin molecules. Should mutations arise which alter these electrostatic charges, the globin monomers are degraded by proteolysis. Several α and β variants have been identified. Unstable α chain variants, such as Hb $\alpha_{\text{Quong Sze}}$ (α125 Leu→Pro), have mutations which make the monomeric forms of the protein extremely unstable, although stable when incorporated into a hemoglobin tetramer (α^+ thalassemia).[64] Several unstable β globins have been characterized as well, all of which result in a thalassemic syndrome. These are the results of point mutations and frameshift mutations (which produce a β^+ phenotype) and a single early termination mutation (which causes a β^0 thalassemia).[44]

In addition to point mutations within the genes, a number of thalassemia variants have arisen which are the results of larger scale mutations within the α or β gene clusters. Most variants which give rise to an α thalassemia phenotype are caused by large deletions within the α globin gene cluster. Deletions within the large, distant regulatory element HS-40 have been shown in heterozygotes to cause an α thalassemia variant in which no ζ or α gene products are produced.[20] Other α globin variants are the result of deletions of one or more α globin structural genes. Since there are two α globin genes on each chromosome, the sequence of which are highly conserved, unequal crossing over during meiosis can give rise to chromosomes which have a single copy (α) and three copies ($\alpha\alpha\alpha$) of the α globin genes, which are subsequently passed on to the offspring. These variants are common in the Asian populations.[2, 44] There are, in addition, variants of α thalassemia which are the result of events which remove both copies of the α globin genes. These mutations result from nonhomologous recombination within the α globin cluster which gives rise to an α^0 chromosome; persons heterozygous for this chromosome have an α^+ thalassemia phenotype, while individuals homozygous for the chromosome have Hb H disease and hydrops fetalis. In parts of Southeast Asia, the incidence of the $\alpha^0\alpha^0$ genotype is as high as 3%.[65]

While the vast majority of mutations giving rise to β thalassemia are point mutations, larger scale genetic alterations have also been shown to cause the syndrome. Deletions within the β globin cluster give rise to a β thalassemia which is frequently associated with a significant increase in the production of Hb F, a finding that distinguishes this type from the more common forms of β thalassemia.

The first such mutation characterized was Hb Lepore.[66] Hb Lepore is a variant which is the result of nonhomologous recombination between the δ globin and β globin loci. It is actually a hybrid molecule of $\delta\beta$ hemoglobin, which is produced at low levels because it is under the regulatory control of the δ globin promoter. (Interestingly, an anti-Lepore locus which has normal copies of δ and β hemoglobin and a $\beta\delta$ hybrid gene also has been found). Heterozygotes for Hb Lepore have predominately Hb A with about 2–5% of Hb Lepore and Hb F. Homozygotes for Hb Lepore have approximately 90% Hb F, 10% Hb Lepore, and no Hb A or A_2, but are clinically similar to thalassemia major.[67] A similar phenomenon gave rise to Hb Kenya, which is the product of nonhomologous recombination between the γ^A gene and the β globin gene.[68]

So called "silent deletions" within the β globin complex have been described, although, as might be predicted, they are rare. These are typically the result of a deletion in one of the γ genes or the single δ gene.[44] Many deletions in the β globin gene have been characterized, all of which result in a β^0 phenotype. These are typically associated with elevations in Hb A_2 and, in cases where the β globin gene promoter is deleted, elevations in Hb F.[2, 44]

Deletions in the δ and β genes give rise to $\delta\beta$ thalassemia, which in the heterozygous form results in a microcytic hypochromic anemia. Approximately 5–15% of the total hemoglobin produced in heterozygotes is Hb F. Individuals homozygous for $\delta\beta$ thalassemia have 100% Hb F and exhibit a β^0 *thalassemia intermedia* phenotype. The deletion of the $\gamma^A\delta\beta$ genes gives rise to $\gamma^A\delta\beta$ thalassemia which has similar hemoglobin production and clinical features.[8, 44] Even larger deletions within the β globin complex give rise to $\gamma\delta\beta$ thalassemia, which in heterozygous form gives rise to a thalassemia syndrome and in the homozygous form is likely incompatible with life.[69]

Hereditary Persistence of Fetal Hemoglobin

As discussed above, several mutations in the β globin complex result in a thalassemia syndrome and are associated with elevations in the level of Hb F produced. Many other deletions within the complex give rise to hereditary persistence of fetal hemoglobin (HPFH), which can be described as an abnormally high level of Hb F in individuals without associated red cell abnormalities. Many are caused by deletions in the region 3′ to the γ^A gene (which do not affect a known γ gene enhancer) and extend for variable lengths, in some cases encompassing the entire β globin cluster. Heterozygotes produce up to 30% Hb F in all cells and are not anemic. Homozygotes contain 100% Hb F, are clinically well, and may be slightly polycythemic (because of the slightly increased oxygen affinity for Hb F). Other HPFH mutations are not the result of deletions. These tend to result from point mutations in the promoter region(s) of either γ gene which alter the affinity for regulatory DNA binding proteins and result in an increased expression. Levels of Hb F range from 4–30% in heterozygotes. Many of these mutations are detected during hemoglobinopathy screening and have been shown to modulate the phenotypic severity of sickle cell disease and β thalassemia.[2, 44]

Laboratory Diagnosis of the Hemoglobinopathies

Routine newborn screening is the means by which most infants with sickle cell anemia are initially diagnosed. This screening does not, however, identify individuals with other hemoglobinopathies. Moreover, hematologists and pediatricians are still called upon to confirm and in some cases interpret test results. A systematic approach to the diagnosis of a hemoglobinopathy is of critical importance.

The evaluation of any individual who is suspected of having a hemoglobinopathy begins with a clinical history and, in particular, a detailed family history. A hemoglobin and hematocrit with red cell indices and red cell morphology is the next step in the procedure. Persons who are heterozygous for Hb S may have no anemia and may have normal findings on the peripheral smear. It is important that these individuals be identified, because they will transmit the affected gene to about half of their offspring. Many reliable "quick screens" for the detection of fetal hemoglobin are available and serve as an initial screening for the presence of Hb S. Those individuals who test positive should have a confirmatory hemoglobin electrophoresis. Of note, individuals who have alleles for Hb C or other variants will not be detected with these quick screens. Anyone with a family history of a hemoglobin variant other than Hb S or target cells on the peripheral smear should be evaluated by electrophoresis.

Persons who have abnormal red cell morphology with hypochromic, microcytic features must be further evaluated. Many persons will be tested initially for iron deficiency or lead poisoning—two alternative causes of microcytic, hypochromic anemia. Laboratory evaluation for a hemoglobinopathy should include hemoglobin electrophoresis (often under both alkaline and acid conditions) and quantitations of the percentages of Hb A_2 and Hb F. In some cases, family studies may be necessary to sort out inheritance patterns. Genetic analysis of the mutations is feasible, largely due to our understanding of the molecular biology of the hemoglobinopathies. Although these genetic studies are available at some institutions, they are not performed in routine diagnosis.[70]

RED CELL MEMBRANE DEFECTS

Structure of the Red Cell Membrane

The red cell membrane is a dynamic structure composed of approximately equal proportions of proteins and lipids. The lipids, which are predominately phospholipid and cholesterol, are arranged in a planar bilayer into which integral membrane proteins are inserted or completely transverse. The integral membrane proteins are in turn laminated to an underlying two-dimensional network of submembranous proteins, known as the "red-cell membrane skeleton." This design renders the red blood cell flexible and deformable enough to transverse a capillary bed, and concomitantly strong and durable enough to withstand the shear forces of the circulation.

The red cell membrane skeleton is the insoluble protein meshwork that remains following treatment of red cells with Triton X-100 detergent. It contains as a protein core the spectrins, actin, protein 4.1, and dematin (protein 4.9). Additional proteins associated with the skeleton include tropomyosin, tropomodulin, adducin, ankyrin, band 3 (anion exchange 1 [AE1]), pallidin, and band 7 proteins. (See Figure 23–4.)

Spectrin is the major skeletal protein and accounts for about 50–75% of the skeletal mass.[71] It is composed of two very large protein subunits, the α chain (protein 1; 281 kD) and β chain (protein 2; 246 kD)[72] which are encoded for by two separate genes on chromosomes 1 and 14, respectively.[73, 74] The two subunits have a common structural organization in that they both contain a repeated segment of approximately 106 amino acids which folds into an alpha helical structure. The amino acid residues between these repeats are non-helical segments. The α and β chains further associate in an antiparallel arrangement with respect to their terminal ends. Side-to-side assembly between the two different chains occurs in a zipperlike fashion: Nucleation sites at the carboxy terminus of the α chain and the amino terminus of the β chain associate, inducing additional conformational changes which are propagated down the entire length of the molecules. The spectrin dimers further associate by the head-to-head binding of the dimeric molecules into tetramers (which tends to be the predominate species on the intact red cell membrane) and higher oligomers. By electron microscopy, the molecule appears as slender, twisted forms arranged in a variety of conformations which likely correlate with red cell membrane plasticity.[75]

Ankyrin is a 206 kD protein, 1880 amino acids in length, which provides the primary linkage between the spectrin-based skeletal membrane and the plasma membrane of the cell.[76] It has three structural and functional domains: the 89 kD amino terminus which binds to band 3 protein, a 62 kD spectrin binding domain, and a 55 kD carboxy terminus which functions as a regulatory region.[77] The association between ankyrin, the β chain of spectrin, and the cytoplasmic domain of band 3 are mediated by high-affinity linkages, which, if destroyed, markedly decrease red cell membrane stability.[78]

FIGURE 23–4. A Schematic Model of the Red Cell Membrane (not drawn to scale)

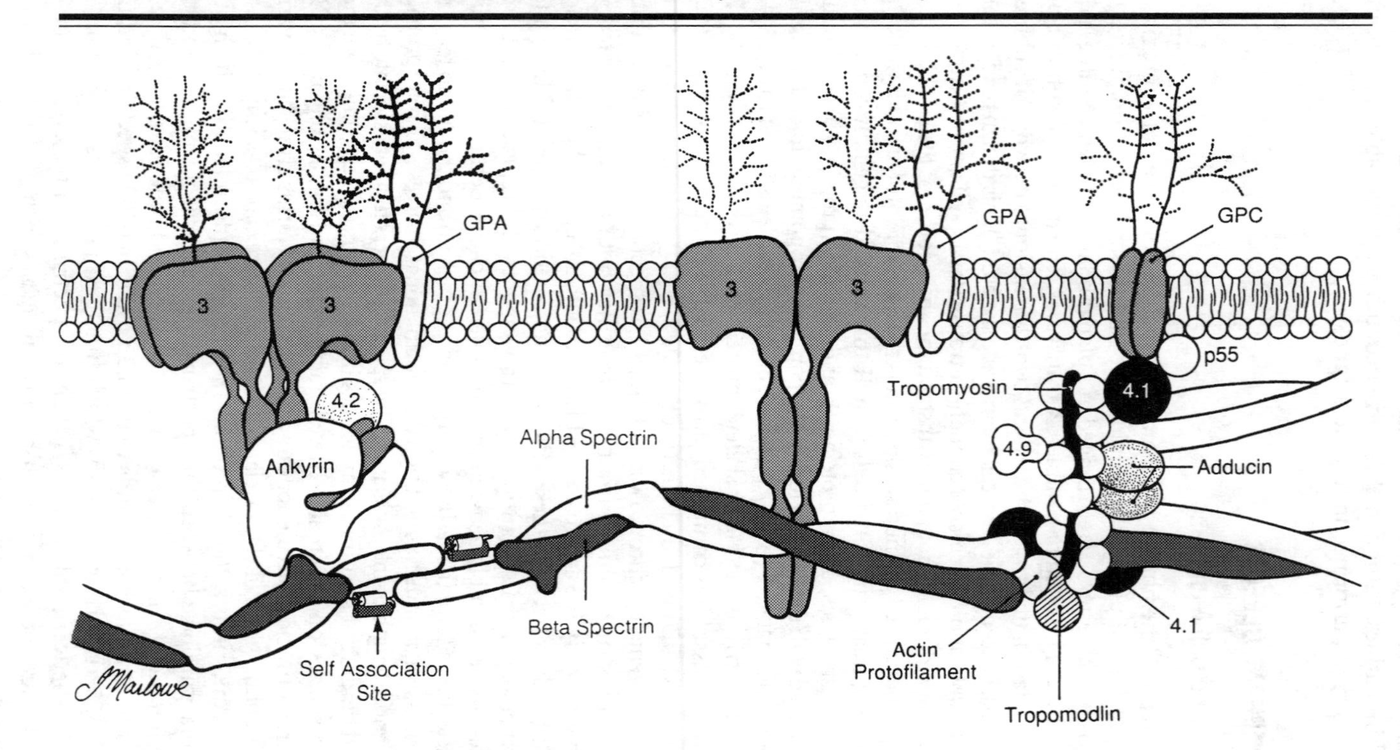

GPA = glycophorins; 3 = band 3; 4.2 = protein 4.2; 4.1 = protein 4.1
Source: Lux SE, Palek J. Disorders of the red cell membrane. In: Handin RI, Lux SE, Stossel TP, eds. Blood: principles and practice of hematology. Philadelphia: Lippincott, 1995. Reprinted by permission.

Band 3, which is also referred to as the erythrocyte anion exchange protein (AE1), is the most abundant red cell membrane protein. It is 911 amino acids in length and contains two distinct structural and functional domains: a 43 kD amino terminus which serves as an association site for several cytoplasmic and skeletal erythrocyte proteins, and a 52 kD carboxy terminus which functions in ion transport (primarily the essential exchange between Cl and HCO_3).[75]

Protein 4.1 is a 66–80 kD protein which binds tightly to spectrin to enhance its interaction with actin. It also binds to the overlying lipid bilayer and serves as a secondary attachment site for its interaction with the plasma membrane.[79] Protein 4.2 is a 78 kD peripheral membrane protein which functions to link the membrane skeleton to the lipid bilayer, binding both to band 3 and ankyrin to enhance their interactions.[80] The structure and functions of other red cell integral membrane and cytoskeletal proteins are reviewed elsewhere.[75, 81]

Hereditary Defects of the Red Cell Membrane

Hereditary Spherocytosis

Hereditary spherocytosis (HS) is a congenital hemolytic anemia caused by an intrinsic red cell membrane defect. It is a disorder with heterogeneous etiologies, the clinical severity of which can range dramatically. In milder forms of HS, there is a persistent destruction of the red cells for which the marrow can compensate. These individuals may be asymptomatic for years, only suffering anemia when exposed to stresses of infection, pregnancy, or bleeding. A more typical case of HS will present with jaundice and anemia with splenomegaly in childhood, often after an infection. More severe forms of HS have a severe, underlying hemolysis with bouts of life-threatening anemia. The severe forms are frequently associated with growth retardation. All variants of HS are prone to the most serious complication of the disease, which is aplastic crisis due to parvovirus B19 infection. These crises may be quite severe, and may be the first manifestation of the condition.[75]

In all cases, HS is associated with characteristic changes on the peripheral blood smear. The abnormal cell membrane is less durable than the normal membrane and is prone to fragmentation as it transverses the microvasculature. There is an ongoing loss of membrane surface area which, in turn, causes the cells to become smaller and increasingly fragile. Ultimately, the cells are detained within the splenic cords where they are finally destroyed. This process is manifested on the peripheral blood smear by a spherocytic red cell morphology, with smaller than normal erythrocytes which additionally lack the typical central pallor of the biconcave disc.[75]

HS is particularly common in Northern Europeans, in whom the frequency is estimated to be 1 in 5000 individuals.[82] It occurs in African-Americans and Southeast Asians but is less common. In the majority of cases (75%), hereditary spherocytosis is inherited as an autosomal-dominant trait, and heterozygotes for the disorder are clinically affected. Approximately 5–10% of these persons have normal parents and likely represent spontaneous mutations. There have been no reports of individuals who are genetically homozygous for these mutations, which strongly suggests that in homozygous form the mutations are lethal.[82] In 20–25% of cases the pattern of inheritance is more typical of a recessive disorder.[83] In these families there is an affected proband, but the parents have only subtle clinical abnormalities which suggest a carrier state. These cases tend to either be associated with an extremely mild phenotype (that of an asymptomatic carrier) or a clinically severe phenotype.

The suspicion of HS typically arises when the characteristic morphologic changes on the peripheral blood smear are observed. The most sensitive test for diagnosis is the direct measurement with flow cytometry of the volume and hemoglobin concentration of erythrocytes. This identifies the presence of dense, dehydrated microspherocytes which is the hallmark of this disease.[84]

The classic osmotic fragility test is abnormal in HS only when there is a reduction in the surface area/volume ratio, which occurs in two-thirds of HS patients. One-third of the patients present only with a reduced surface area, reduced volume (normal ratio), and normal osmotic fragility. In these patients, the osmotic fragility tests should be repeated after incubation of the cells at 37° C for 24 h (incubated osmotic fragility). Under these conditions, HS erythrocytes lose membrane area, increase cell volume (reduced ratio), and exhibit increased osmotic fragility. However, some HS patients have normal incubated osmotic fragility. Flow cytometric studies of HS erythrocytes have indicated that the percentage of microcytic cells is the best indicator for the severity of the disease.[85]

HS is etiologically diverse. The primary molecular defect resides in the membrane skeletal proteins, particularly those involved in the interactions with the phospholipid bilayer: spectrin, ankyrin, band 3, and protein 4.2. The variants, seen in European and American populations, tend to be mutations in spectrin and ankyrin, while a fewer number have defects in band 3 or 4.2.[82]

Alpha Spectrin Defects

Defects in α spectrin are inherited as autosomal recessive traits.[82] This results from the fact that the synthesis of α spectrin chains is approximately 3–4 times that of β spectrin chains. Thus, the rate of β chain synthesis controls the amount of spectrin oligomers in the cell, and a defect in one of the α genes does not cause a decrease in this total mass. Even in the severe recessive forms, heterozygotes show no spectrin deficiency. When in the homozygous form, these mutations are associated with a marked decrease in spectrin (20–40% normal) and a severe[83] HS.

Beta Spectrin Defects

Defects in the β spectrin chain are limiting for the formation of mature spectrin and are therefore inherited as autosomal-dominant traits. A number of variants have been identified, including an unstable product which cannot bind to protein 4.1 (and actin). This mutation results from a point mutation, but an array of different mutations have been detailed which include deletions, splicing mutations, nonsense mutations, and frameshift mutations.[82, 86]

Ankyrin Defects

Defects in the ankyrin protein have been implicated in both typical[87] and severe cases[88] of HS and can be inherited as autosomal-dominant or recessive mutations.

Dominant forms of the mutation appear to be associated with a structural defect in the protein,[89] while the recessive forms that have been characterized are defective in the regulatory or promoter regions of the gene.[87]

The majority of the ankyrin defects are private, which means that each kindred examined has a different mutation identified. In some cases the decrease in ankyrin is associated with a concomitant deficiency in the total amount of spectrin.[82, 88]

Band 3 Defects

Defects in the band 3 protein are inherited as autosomal-dominant forms of HS and account for approximately one-third of these cases.[90] These individuals have 20–40% of the normal levels of band 3 and protein 4.2 and tend to have a moderate degree of hemolysis.[90, 91] A variety of mutations in band 3 have been described. These include frameshift mutations, chain termination mutations, duplications, and non-sense mutations which alter mRNA stability.[82]

Protein 4.2 Defects

Defects in the 4.2 protein are inherited in an autosomal-recessive pattern.[92] Mutations which alter mRNA processing and binding with band 3 have been described.[91, 92]

Hereditary Elliptocytosis

Hereditary elliptocytosis (HE) is characterized by the presence of oval or elliptical erythrocytes on the peripheral blood smear. HE and the related disorder hereditary pyropoikilocytosis (HPP) are heterogeneous disorders with a spectrum of clinical severity, inheritance patterns, and biochemical etiologies. HE is most common in persons of African and Mediterranean descent.[93, 94] In the U.S. population it occurs with a frequency of 1 in 2000 to 1 in 4000 individuals.[82] HE is inherited in an autosomal-dominant pattern and is clinically classified into three categories: common HE, spherocytic HE, and Southeast Asian ovalocytosis.

Common (Mild) HE

The most common form of HE is designated mild HE. These patients tend to be asymptomatic, with no anemia. They may present with mild splenomegaly and a mild compensated hemolysis with reticulocytosis. The red cell morphology shows a predominance of elliptocytes, ranging in frequency from 30–100% of the red cell forms.[94] Infants who have the trait may be born with a moderately severe hemolytic anemia, occasionally warranting exchange transfusion.[95] The red cell abnormalities can be dramatic, with budding and fragmented forms. In some cases, it may be necessary to examine the parents' peripheral blood smears to exclude other causes of poikilocytosis in the newborn period (sepsis, infantile pyknocytosis, or hemolytic disease of the newborn).

More severe variants of HE exist. These individuals have significant clinical hemolysis with its associated clinical features. The peripheral smear may show bizarre forms with budding cells, fragments, and poikilocytosis. These variants are sometimes associated with a coinherited defect in a spectrin gene.[96]

Hereditary pyropoikilocytosis (HPP) is a subtype of HE which warrants particular attention. It is an uncommon disorder which presents in infancy or early childhood with a severe, hemolytic anemia. Red cell abnormalities are marked, with budding forms, fragments, spherocytes, and other bizarre forms but a relative paucity of elliptocytes. Osmotic fragility studies in these patients are markedly abnormal and the mean cell volume (MCV) is extremely low.[94] A characteristic feature of this disorder is the remarkable thermal instability of these cells, with fragmentation occurring after short periods (10–15 minutes) of heating to temperatures of 45–46° C (normal 49°).[97] It is thought that individuals with HPP represent double mutations in that they are homozygous deficient or compound heterozygous deficient for structural defects in the spectrin protein.[82]

Spherocytic HE

Spherocytic HE has a phenotype intermediate between HE and HS. It is typically associated with a mild to moderate degree of hemolysis. It is inherited as an autosomal-dominant disorder, but the genetic defect responsible for the phenotype is unknown. Diagnosis is based on family studies, the peripheral smear (which shows a variable number of elliptocytes and spherocytes), and a positive osmotic fragility test.[82]

The majority of the aforementioned variants of HE are due to mutations in either α or β spectrin. These tend to be mutations in the regions of the protein which are associated with self-association between the protein chains. Defects in protein 4.1 are seen in both the heterozygous form, which produces a clinically mild HE, and in the homozygous form, which produces a clinically more severe form.

Southeast Asian Ovalocytosis

A variant of HE which deserves additional mention is that of Southeast Asian ovalocytosis. This condition is inherited as an autosomal-dominant trait[98] and is observed in the aboriginal populations of Malaysia, the Philippines, and Indonesia, where a significant proportion of the population is affected.

The defect is caused by a mutation in the band 3 protein, which results in abnormally tight binding between band 3 and ankyrin.[98] The variant is associated with an inability to transport anions and a decrease in membrane fluidity. Morphologically the trait is manifested by rounded elliptocytes on the peripheral smear. Clinically there tends to be little, well compensated hemolysis. It is generally believed that the decreased fluidity (increased rigidity) is associated with a resistance to malarial infection, accounting for the high prevalence of the allele in the population.[99]

ERYTHROCYTE ENZYMOPATHIES

Hereditary Defects in the Glycolytic Pathway

Human erythrocytes, which lack a nucleus, mitochondria, and other organelles, are unable to synthesize proteins or carry out oxidative phosphorylation; they rely exclusively on the glycolytic pathway to meet their energy requirements. Enzyme defects in the glycolytic pathway have adverse effects on red cell survival and usually result in a hemolytic anemia of variable severity. Although relatively uncommon, an erythrocyte enzymopathy should be considered in any patient with unexplained hemolysis. A thorough patient history is crucial, with particular attention to family history and medications. Initial diagnostic testing for any hemolytic anemia should include a complete blood count with red cell indices, blood film for morphologic examination, and a reticulocyte count. Depending on the patient's ethnic background and family history, additional testing may include hemoglobin electrophoresis with quantitation of the percentages of Hb F and Hb A_2, osmotic fragility, and Heinz body stain and G6PD quantitation. A direct antiglobulin test (DAT or Coombs test) should be done to eliminate the possibility of an autoimmune etiology. Definitive diagnosis is dependent on erythrocyte enzyme analysis or in some cases, genetic marker studies.

An abbreviated diagram of the glycolytic pathway is shown in Figure 23–5. Since pyruvate kinase deficiency serves as a prototype for this type of disorder, it will be discussed first.

Pyruvate Kinase Deficiency

Pyruvate kinase (PK) catalyzes the conversion of phosphoenolpyruvate to pyruvate, generating a molecule of ATP from ADP in the next to the last step of glycolysis. Humans have several isoenzyme forms of PK, the result of transcriptional, splicing, and post-translational modifications of the products of two different autosomal genes. PK-M forms are derived from a gene that maps to 15q22.[100] The two different forms are the result of alternative slicing and are found in skeletal muscle and brain (PK-M1) and in white blood cells, platelets, lung, spleen, kidney, and adipose tissues (PK-M2).[101] The other isozymes are derived from a gene which maps to 1q21.[102] Tissue-specific promoters result in two different transcripts, the PK-L and PK-R forms. PK-L forms are found in the liver and gut, while the PK-R forms undergo post-translational modifications and are found in the erythroid precursors (PK-R1) and mature red cells (PK-R2).[103]

PK deficiency, which was the first red cell glycolytic enzymopathy described, accounts for about 90% of these disorders.[104–106] Approximately 400 cases have been reported.[107] The deficiency is commonly seen in individuals of Northern European descent, but has been widely documented in all geographic regions of the world and in many ethnic groups.

Clinically, PK deficiency results in a chronic hemolytic anemia of variable severity. Exacerbations may be seen with infections and pregnancy. Some individuals are well compensated, with only an underlying shortened RBC survival, mild jaundice, and splenomegaly. More severely affected persons have severe, chronic hemolysis with lifelong transfusion requirements. In most cases, the clinical sequelae are apparent in infancy or early childhood. More severe cases may present in the newborn period with neonatal anemia and jaundice requiring exchange transfusions.[106]

PK deficiency is inherited as an autosomal-recessive trait. Individuals who are homozygous or compound heterozygous for mutant alleles have anywhere from 5–25% of normal levels of activity and are clinically affected. Individuals who are het-

FIGURE 23–5. The Glycolytic Pathway

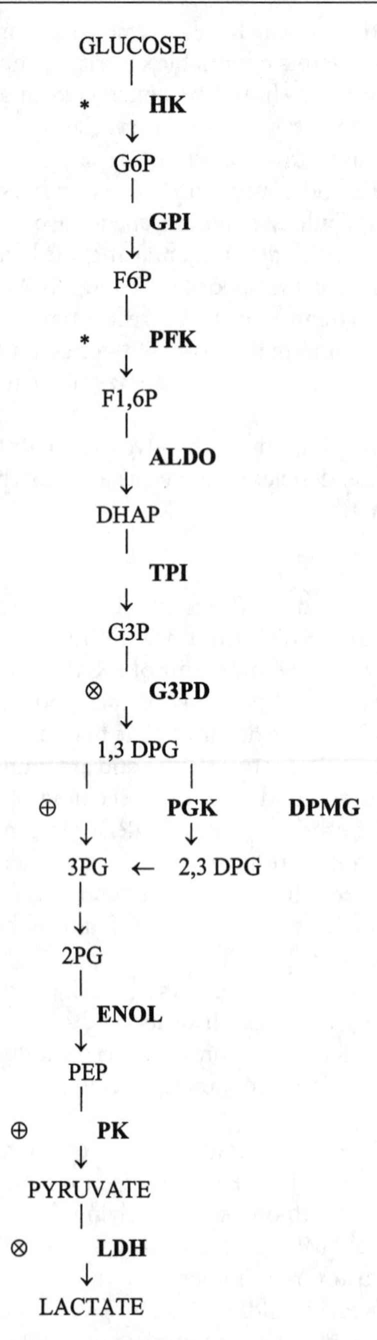

HK = hexokinase; GPI = glucosephosphate isomerase, PFK = phosphofructokinase; aldo = aldolase; TPI = triosephosphate isomerase; G3PD = glucose-3-phosphate dehydrogenase; PGK = phosphoglycerate kinase; DPGM = diphosphoglycerate mutase; ENOL = enolase; PK = pyruvate kinase; LDH = lactate dehydrogenase. ⊕ indicates ATP requiring steps; ⊗ indicates ATP generating steps, and indicates NADH producing steps.

erozygous for a single mutant allele usually have about 40–60% of normal enzyme activity and are hematologically normal. In rare cases, individuals heterozygous for PK deficiency have been shown to have clinical manifestations related to decreased activity of the enzyme.[107]

PK-deficient red cells have a decreased glycolytic rate. The decreased enzyme activity leads to a secondary accumulation of glycolytic intermediates, most notably 3-phosphoglycerate and 2,3 DPG. The concentration of the latter can increase from two- to fourfold over normal levels, shifting the oxygen dissociation curve to the right, in favor of dissociation (tissue oxygenation). While this may serve to compensate for the chronic anemia, it may also inhibit alternative energy-generating pathways (such as the hexose monophosphate shunt), contributing to hemolysis, particularly during periods of stress.[106, 107]

Hexokinase Deficiency

Hexokinase (HK) catalyzes the initial energy dependent step of glycolysis, converting glucose to glucose-6-phosphate. Four isozymes exist, with type I being the predominant red cell form. HK activity is age dependent: Levels of activity are the highest in the youngest red cells (reticulocytes) but decrease with senescence.[108]

Hexokinase deficiency in red cells was first described as one of the multiple anomalies in Fanconi syndrome, but was later described as an inborn error of metabolism. It is inherited as an autosomal-recessive trait. HK deficiency is rare, with only about 20 cases reported in the literature. There is considerable variation in the severity of symptoms, but in general the disorder results in a moderate degree of anemia which usually does not require transfusion therapy.[107] The hexokinase gene maps to 10p11.2.[109]

Glucosephosphate Isomerase Deficiency

Glucosephosphate isomerase (GPI) converts glucose-6 phosphate to fructose-6 phosphate. GPI deficiency is probably the second most common of the erythrocyte glycolytic pathway defects. It causes a hemolytic anemia of variable severity, ranging from quite mild to very severe.[106] Tissue-specific isozymes do not seem to exist, and persons who are deficient for the enzyme are deficient in all tissue types, possibly accounting for the clinical associations of mental retardation, myopathy, and granulocyte dysfunction which have been reported in association with hemolytic anemia.[110]

GPI maps to chromosome 19,[111] and its deficiency is inherited as an autosomal-recessive disorder. The mutant forms which have been characterized are thermally labile.[112]

Phosphofructokinase

Phosphofructokinase (PFK) catalyzes the phosphorylation of fructose-6-phosphate to fructose 1,6-diphosphate. It is a tetrameric protein, the subunits for which are encoded by three structural loci which map to chromosomes 1, 10, and 21.[113–115] Different protein forms are expressed differentially in tissues: M in muscle, L in liver, and P in platelet. Red cells, which express the M and L subunits, through random tetramerization contain 5 different isozyme forms: M_4, M_3L_1, M_2L_2, M_1L_3, and L_4 .[116]

PFK deficiency is inherited as an autosomal-recessive trait. Defects in the M form of the protein represent severe cases of PFK deficiency and are associated with a myopathy. The deficiency has been classified as glycogen storage disease type VII because of the deposition of glycogen in muscle.[117] Approximately 35 cases have been reported, all of whom showed a moderate compensated hemolysis and a prominent myopathy with muscle weakness, cramps, and exercise intolerance. Occasionally, defects in the L form of the protein are found; these are characterized by a hemolytic anemia with no apparent myopathy.[106]

Aldolase Deficiency

Aldolase catalyzes the conversion of fructose 1,6 diphosphate to dihydroxyacetone and glyceraldehyde-3-phosphate. There are three isoforms, originating from a single gene on 16.[118] Aldolase deficiency is very rare; it has been reported in only two families. It is inherited as an autosomal-recessive trait and clinically results in a moderate hemolytic anemia.[107]

Triosephosphate Isomerase Deficiency

Triosephosphate isomerase (TPI) catalyzes the reversible isomerization between dihydroxyacetone phosphate and glyceraldehyde 3-phosphate. It has a high level of endogenous activity, and its deficiency is one of the most clinically severe of the red cell enzymopathies. TPI deficiency affects all tissues of the body, producing a multisystem disorder with hemolytic anemia, neurologic dysfunction, cardiomyopathy, and increased susceptibility to infection. It is usually fatal in early childhood. Approximately 30 cases are reported in the literature.[107]

TPI deficiency is inherited as an autosomal-recessive trait with the gene mapping to the short arm of chromosome 12.[119] Heterozygotes have approximately 50% normal activity but are clinically normal. Despite the rare frequency of homozygous deficiency, null alleles (alleles of the gene with no activity and no protein or related protein synthesis) are relatively common: 0.37–0.48% in whites and 4.7% in African Americans.[120, 121] This may indicate that fetuses with TPI deficiency are prone to an increased incidence of fetal wastage.

Phosphoglycerate Kinase

Phosphoglycerate kinase (PGK) catalyzes the conversion of 1,3 diphosphoglycerate to 3-phosphoglycerate. It is the only X-linked enzyme in the glycolytic pathway, mapping to Xq13.[122] PGK deficiency is seen primarily in males and produces neurologic defects including behavioral abnormalities, mental retardation, lability, movement disorders, seizures, and aphasia. There is an associated hemolytic anemia of moderate severity. Because of random X chromosome inactivation (Lionization), heterozygous females have populations of red cells which lack the enzyme and therefore may have a low level of hemolysis. Neurologic abnormalities in females have not been reported.[123]

Diphosphoglycerate Mutase Deficiency

Diphosphoglycerate mutase (DPGM) is a multifunctional enzyme which primarily catalyzes the formation and, to a lesser extent, the degradation of 2,3 DPG. Thus, this enzyme regulates the intracellular levels of 2,3 DPG, which has profound effects on the dissociation of oxygen from hemoglobin.[124]

DPGM deficiency is very rare. Clinically it is associated with an erythrocytosis and a ruddy cyanosis, with no evidence of hemolysis. Erythrocyte 2,3 DPG levels were < 3% of normal.[124] DPGM maps to 7q22-34, and the deficiency is inherited in an autosomal-recessive manner.[125]

Enolase Deficiency

Enolase catalyzes the conversion of 2-phosphoglycerate to phosphoenolpyruvate. Three isoforms of the enzyme exists, each a homodimeric protein composed of α, β, or γ subunits. The $\alpha\alpha$ form predominates in all tissues, and the gene has been mapped to the short arm of chromosome 1.[126]

Enolase deficiency is rare, and our understanding of the disorder is based on only a few pedigrees. It appears to have an autosomal-dominant mode of inheritance with variable clinical expression. Individuals from the same kindred with half normal levels of the enzyme may have a compensated hemolysis or may be normal. In one pedigree examined, the hemolytic anemia was associated with a spherocytosis on the peripheral smear.[106]

Lactate Dehydrogenase Deficiency

Lactate dehydrogenase (LDH) converts pyruvate to lactate in the last step of glycolysis. LDH is a tetramer composed of two subunits, H and M, which map to chromosomes 12 and 11 respectively.[127, 128] Deficiency of the H subunit has been well documented, is inherited in a recessive fashion, and is not associated with anemia or hemolysis.[129] Deficiency of the M subunit has also been reported. M deficiency is associated with a myopathy without hemolysis and is inherited as a recessive disorder as well.[130]

Glucose 6-Phosphate Dehydrogenase (G6PD) Deficiency

G6PD deficiency is the most common inborn error of metabolism in humans, affecting approximately 400 million persons worldwide.[131] It was initially discovered during the investigation into why some persons, but not others, develop a hemolytic anemia when administered primaquine for the treatment of malaria.[132] Since then, it has been identified as a potential cause of chronic hemolysis (so-called congenital nonspherocytic hemolytic anemia [CNSHA]). Other offending drugs have been implicated with hemolysis (Table 23–2) in addition to infections and the ingestion of fava beans (fauvism).

G6PD is a ubiquitous enzyme found in prokaryotes and eukaryotes and in plants and animals alike. G6PD catalyzes the first step in the hexose monophosphate shunt, the oxidation of glucose-6-phosphate to 6-phosphogluconolactone with

TABLE 23–2. Drug Use in G6PD Deficiency

Drugs and Chemicals That Should Be Avoided by Persons With G6PD Deficiency	
Acetanilid	Primaquine
Furazolidone	Sulfacetamide
Methylene Blue	Sulfamethoxazole
Nalidixic acid	Sulfanilamide
Naphthalene	Sulfapyridine
Niridazole	Thiazolesulfone
Isobutyl nitrite	Toluidine blue
Naphthalene	Trinitrotoluene
Nitrofurantoin	Urate oxidase
Phenazopyridine	Phenylhydrazine

Some Common Drugs That Can Safely Be Administered in Therapeutic Doses* to G6PD-Deficient Subjects without Nonspherocytic Hemolytic Anemia	
Acetaminophen	Acetophenetidin
Acetylsalicylic acid (aspirin)	Aminopyrine
Actazoline	Antipyrine
Ascorbic acid (vitamin C)*	Benzhexol
Chloramphenicol	Chlorguanidine
Chloroquine	Colchicine
Diphenylhydramine	Isoniazid
L-Dopa	Menadione sodium bisulfite
Menapthone	p-Aminobenzoic acid
Phenylbutazone	Phenytoin
Probenecid	Procainamide hydrochloride
Pyrimethamine	Quinidine
Quinine	Streptomycin
Sulfacytine	Sulfadiazine
Sulfaguanidine	Sulfamerazine
Sulfamethoxypyridazine	Sulfisoxazole
Tiaprofenic acid	Trimethoprim
Tripelennamine	Vitamin K

*Very high "therapeutic" doses (1–~80 g administered intravenously) have precipitated severe, even fatal, hemolysis.

Source: Beutler E. G6PD deficiency. Blood 1994;84:3613–36.Reprinted by permission.

the concomitant reduction of NADP to NADPH. It is the erythrocyte's only source of NADPH, which is necessary for the production of glutathione and the subsequent inactivation of peroxides and other reactive oxygen molecules. The enzyme, therefore, is crucial in protecting the erythrocyte from oxidative damage.[133] Although not completely understood, unchecked oxidative damage is felt to be the mechanism by which drugs and fava beans produce hemolysis in G6PD-deficient individuals.

The protein monomer is 514 amino acids in length with a molecular weight of 59 kD.[134] The active form is either a homodimer or a homotetramer,[135] the assembly of which requires the binding of two molecules of NADP.[136] The coenzyme and substrate specificities of G6PD are exquisite, in that there is virtually no activity of the molecule with NAD or with other hexose monophosphates. The enzyme is under tight regulation, and any oxidative event that increases the concentration of NADP within the cell will function to increase G6PD activity.[133] G6PD has a half-life of about 60 days;[137] since erythrocytes cannot synthesize new protein, activity is approximately 5 times greater in the young reticulocytes than in senescent red cells.[138]

The gene for G6PD is 20 kb in length and maps to Xq28.[139] The enzyme and its mutations are inherited in an X-linked pattern. Hemizygous males are deficient. There is a tendency for heterozygous females to have intermediate levels of the enzyme activity in hemolysates; however, there is a broad range of activity due to random X chromosome inactivation (Lionization). Two percent of females will have less than 5% of either the sufficient or deficient cell population and are regarded as having a G6PD "extreme phenotype." Such extreme phenotypes are thought to arise because of close genetic linkage with a different gene which has a particular selective advantage (a so-called hitchhiking effect).[140]

Over 300 distinct variants of the G6PD polymorphism have been identified based on biochemical data, and 60 different mutations have been characterized at the genetic level. A more detailed review of these mutations exists elsewhere.[133] The mutations giving rise to G6PD deficiency have been classified into two types based on the clinical picture they produce and the level of enzyme activity. WHO class I mutations are sporadic mutations that occur at a very low rate, have a worldwide distribution, and tend to be clinically heterogeneous. They often have a more severe clinical syndrome, producing a chronic, nonspherocytic hemolytic anemia (CNSHA) with reticulocytosis, hyperbilirubinemia, splenomegaly, and a variable anemia. The condition is prone to exacerbation by usual agents promoting oxidative damage.[133, 140]

WHO class II and III mutations are inherited as genetic polymorphisms within certain ethnic groups. Individuals with these variants tend to be less severely affected, are asymptomatic in the normal steady state, but suffer acute hemolytic anemia (AHA) in association with ingestion of certain drugs, infection, or eating fava beans (fauvism). The anemia may be moderate to severe, with associated hyperbilirubinemia and hematuria.[133, 140]

The incidence of deficiency varies greatly in the world population: 1–7% of the southern Italian population are deficient,[141] as are 2–16% of Chinese,[142] up to 26% of Africans,[143] and as many as 70% of Kurdish Jews.[144] Early studies correlated the high incidence of G6PD deficiency with the worldwide distribution of malaria;

this hypothesis has been borne out by epidemiological studies.[145, 146] While the mechanism is not clearly understood, clinical studies have shown that heterozygous females have, on average, a lower percentage of parasitemia than homozygous normal females.[147] Additionally, *in vitro* studies have shown that while normal and deficient cells are infected at similar rates, there is impaired schizogony of the parasite during the first several cycles of replication in deficient cells.[148]

It appears that total deficiency of G6PD is incompatible with life, since all mutations show some low level of enzyme activity. Thus, the majority of variants characterized are missense point mutations, with fewer numbers of deletions in multiples of three nucleotides (so as not to result in a frameshift). A single splicing mutation has also been characterized. The distribution of mutations along the length of the coding region is not random. The point mutations which result in the class I mutants (those associated with CNSHA) are clustered in two regions, which correspond to substrate and cofactor binding domains of the protein. The clinical severity of any particular variant depends not only on the amino acid residue affected, but on the biochemistry of the substitution.[133, 140]

Well established mutations causing the polymorphic variants of G6PD deficiency predominate in particular ethnic groups. Many geographic regions have a single (or several) characteristic mutations which have been established in the gene pool. G6PD Mediterranean is the most prevalent variant in the Mediterranean, Middle East, Iran, and parts of India. It is felt to result in somewhat more severe hemolysis. G6PD Mahidol is seen in Thailand and Southeast Asia and can have a similar severity. G6PD A- is the variant which predominates in the African population, and in general produces a syndrome less severe than that seen with the Mediterranean and Mahidol forms.[140]

G6PD deficiency frequently presents in the neonatal period with otherwise unexplained jaundice. Neonatal jaundice is associated with class I, II, or III variants of G6PD deficiency, but only a proportion of these newborns develop jaundice. It may be that a subset of these infants merely have an exaggerated course of physiologic jaundice of the newborn. Alternatively, hemolysis may be secondary to the exposure of some undetected agent or possibly infection.

The diagnosis of G6PD deficiency requires careful attention to family and ingestion histories. The peripheral smear often shows significant red cell abnormalities, with variable sizes and shapes of red cells. There may be "bite cells" and irregularly contracted red cells ("hemighosts" or double-colored RBCs) on the peripheral blood smear. The hemolytic picture is frequently associated with the presence of Heinz bodies (particles of denatured protein attached to the RBC membrane), and frequently there is reticulocytosis. Definitive diagnosis is based on G6PD enzyme quantitation, which measures the rate of formation of NADPH through its maximum absorption peak. The red cell activity must always be expressed in International Units (micromoles of NADPH produced) per gram of hemoglobin or per microliter of RBCs. Care must be exercised to ensure that white cells, which have higher levels of G6PD, have been completely removed. The test must always be interpreted with caution in the acute hemolytic setting, where a relative degree of reticulocytosis often exists.

REFERENCES

1. WHO Working Group. Hereditary anemias: genetic basis, clinical features, diagnosis and treatment. Bull World Health Organ 1982;60:643–60.
2. Bunn H F, Forget BG. Hemoglobin: molecular, genetic and clinical aspects. Philadelphia: W. B. Saunders, 1986.
3. Weatherall, DJ. Toward an understanding of the molecular biology of some common inherited anemias: the story of thalassemia. In: Wintrobe MM, ed. Blood, pure and eloquent. New York: McGraw-Hill, 1980.
4. Deisseroth A, Nienhues A, Turner P, et al. Localization of the human α-globin structural gene to chromosome 16 in somatic cell hybrids by molecular hybridization. Cell 1977;12:205–18.
5. Nicholls RD, Jonasson JA, McGee JO, et al. High resolution mapping of the human α-globin locus. J Med Genet 1987;24:39–46.
6. Deisseroth A, Nienhius A, Turner P, et al. Chromosomal localization of human β globin gene in human chromosome 11 somatic cell hybrids. Proc Natl Acad Sci 1978;75:1456–60.
7. Sanders-Haigh L, Anderson WF, Francke U. The β-globin gene is on the short arm of chromosome 11. Nature 1980;283:683–6.
8. Weatherall DJ, Clegg JB. The thalassemia syndromes, 3rd ed. Oxford: Blackwell Scientific Publications, 1981.
9. Orkin, SH. Globin gene regulation and switching: circa 1990. Cell 1990;63:665–72.
10. Chui DH, Mentzer WC. Human embryonic zeta-globin chains in fetal and newborn blood. Blood 1989;74:1409–14.
11. Schroeder WA, Huisman THJ, et al. Evidence of multiple structural genes for γ chain of human fetal hemoglobin. Proc Natl Acad Sci 1968;60:537–44.
12. Boyer SH, Belding TK, et al. Fetal hemoglobin restricted to a few erythrocytes (F-cells) in normal human adults. Science 1975;188:361–3.
13. Lauer J, Shen C-KJ, Maniatis T. The chromosomal arrangement of human α-globin genes: sequence homology and α-globin gene deletions. Cell 1980;20:119–30.
14. Higgs DR, Vickers MA, et al. A review of the molecular genetics of the human alpha-globin gene cluster. Blood 1989;73:1081–104.
15. Lawn RM, Fritsch, EF, Parker RC, et al. The isolation and characterization of linked δ and β globin genes from a cloned library of human DNA. Cell 1978;15:1157–74.
16. Fritsch EF, Lawn RM , Maniatis T. Molecular cloning and characterization of the human β-globin gene cluster. Cell 1980;19:959–72.
17. Collins FS, Weissman SM. The molecular genetics of human hemoglobin. Prog Nuc Acid Res Mol Biol 1984;31:315–462.
18. Grosveld F, Blom van Assendelft G, Greaves DR, Kollias G. Position independent, high level expression of the human β-globin gene in transgenic mice. Cell 1987;51:975–85.
19. Forrester W, Thompson C, Elder JT, Groudine M. A developmentally stable chromatin structure in the human β-globin gene cluster. Proc Natl Acad Sci 1986;83:1359–63.
20. Driscoll MC, Dobkin CS, Alter BP. γδβ Thalassemia due to a de novo mutation deleting the 5′ β-globin locus activating region hypersensitivity sites. Proc Natl Acad Sci 1989;86:7470–4.
21. Hatton CS, Wilkie AOM, Brysdale HC, et al. Alpha thalassemia caused by a large (62 kb) deletion upstream of the human α-globin gene cluster. Blood 1990;76:221–7.
22. Higgs DR, Wood WG, Jarman AP, et al. A major positive regulatory region located far upstream of the human alpha-globin gene locus. Genes Dev 1990;4:1588–601.
23. Green MR. Pre mRNA splicing. Ann Rev Genet 1986;20:671–708.
24. Hsu S-L, Marks J, Shaw JP, et al. Structure and expression of the human θ globin gene. Nature 1988;331:44–46.
25. Clegg JB. Can the product of the θ gene be a real globin? Nature 1987;329:465–6.
26. Bunn FH. Human hemoglobins: normal and abnormal. In: Nathan DG, Orkin SH, eds. Hematology of infancy and childhood. Philadelphia: W. B. Saunders,1998:729–61.

27. Bohr C, Hasselbach L, Krogh A. Ueber einen in biologischer Beichung wichtigen Einfluss den die Kohlensaurespannung des Blutes auf dessen Sauerstoffbindung ubt. Skan Arch Physiol 1904;16:402.
28. Buetler E, Muel A, Wood LA. Depletion and regeneration of 2,3 diphosphoglyceric acid in stored red blood cells. Transfusion 1969;9:109–14.
29. Huisman THJ, Carver MFH, Efremov GD. A syllabus of human hemoglobin variants. Atlanta, GA: The Sickle Cell Anemia Foundation, 1996.
30. Hofrichter J, Ross PD, Eaton WA. Supersaturation in sickle cell hemoglobin solutions. Proc Natl Acad Sci 1976;73:3035–9.
31. Ferrone FA, Hofrichter J, Eaton WA. Kinetics of sickle hemoglobin polymerization. II. A double nucleation mechanism. J Mol Biol 1985;183:611–31.
32. Dover GJ, Plat OS. Sickle cell disease. In: Nathan DG, Orkin SH, eds. Hematology of infancy and childhood, 5th ed. Philadelphia: W. B. Saunders, 1998.
33. Goldberg, MA, Husson MA, Bunn HF. Participation of hemoglobins A and F in polymerization of sickle hemoglobin. J Biol Chem 1977;252:3414–21.
34. Benesch RE, Edalji R, Benesch R, et al. Solubilization of hemoglobin S by other hemoglobins. Proc Natl Acad Sci 1980;77:5130–4.
35. Charache S. Treatment of sickling disorders. Curr Opin Hematol 1996;3:139–44.
36. Charache S, Conley CL, Waugh DF, et al. Pathogenesis of hemolytic anemia in homozygous hemoglobin C disease. J Clin Invest 1967;46:1795–1811.
37. Fitzgerald PDM, Love WE. Structure of deoxy hemoglobin C (β6 Glu$\rightarrow$Lys) in two crystal forms. J Mol Biol 1979;132:603–19.
38. Bunn HF, Noguchi CT, Hofrichter J, et al. Molecular and cellular pathogenesis of hemoglobin SC disease. Proc Natl Acad Sci 1982;79:7527–31.
39. Brugnara C, Kopin A, Bunn HF, et al. Regulation of cation content and cell volume in erythrocytes from patients with homozygous hemoglobin C disease. J Clin Invest 1985;75:1608–17.
40. Weatherall DJ, Clegg JB, Higgs DR, et al. The hemoglobinopathies. In: Scriver CR, Beaudet AL, Sly WS, et al., eds. The metabolic and molecular bases of inherited disease. New York: McGraw Hill, 1995.
41. Nagel RL. Disorders of hemoglobin function and stability. In: Handin RI, Lux SE, Stossel TP, eds. Blood: principles and practices of hematology. Philadelphia: Lippincott, 1995:1591–1644.
42. Charache S, Weatherall DJ, Clegg JB. Polycythemia associated with a hemoglobinopathy. J Clin Invest 1966;45:813–22.
43. Nagel RL, Gibson QH, Charache S. Relation between structure and function in hemoglobin Chesapeake. Biochemistry 1967;6:2395–402.
44. Orkin SH, Nathan DG. The thalassemias. In: Nathan DG, Orkin SH, eds. Hematology of infancy and childhood. Philadelphia: W. B. Saunders, 1998:811–86.
45. Kanavakis E, Tzot zos S, Liapaki A, et al. Frequency of alpha-thalassemia in Greece. Am J Hematol 1986;22:225–32.
46. Falusi AG, Esan GJ, Ayyub H, et al. Alpha-thalassaemia in Nigeria: its interaction with sickle-cell disease. Eur J Haematol 1987;38:370–75.
47. Flint J, Hill AV, Bowden DK, et al. High frequencies of alpha-thalassaemia are the result of natural selection by malaria. Nature 1986;321:744–50.
48. Kazazian H. The thalassemia syndromes: molecular basis and prenatal diagnosis in 1990. Seminars Hematol 1990;27:209–28.
49. Antonarakis SE, Irkin SH, Cheng TC, et al. Beta thalassemia in American blacks: novel mutations in the TATA box and an acceptor splice site. Proc Natl Acad Sci USA 1984;81:1154–8.
50. Fei YH, Stoming TA, Efremov GD, et al. Beta-thalassemia due to a T$\rightarrow$A mutation within the ATA box. Biochem Biophys Res Comm 1988;153:741–7.
51. Wong C, Dowlin CE, Saiki RK, et al. Characterization of beta-thalassemia mutations using direct genomic sequencing of amplified single copy DNA. Nature 1987;330:384–6.
52. Gonzalez-Redondo JM, Stoming TA, Lanclos KD, et al. Clinical and genetic heterogeneity in black patients with homozygous beta-thalassemia from the southeastern United States. Blood 1988;72:1007–14.

53. Kazazian HH, Boehm CD. Molecular basis and prenatal diagnosis of beta-thalassemia. Blood 1988;72:1107–16,
54. Metherall JE, Collins FS, Pan J, et al. Beta zero thalassemia caused by a base substitution that creates an alternative splice acceptor site in an intron. Embo J 1986;5:2551–7.
55. Cheng TC, Orkin SH, Antonaraki SE, et al. Beta thalassemia in Chinese: use of *in vitro* RNA analysis and oligonucleotide hybridization in systematic characterization of molecular defects. Proc Natl Acad Sci USA 1984;82:2821–5.
56. Higgs DR, Goodbourn SE, Lamb J, et al. Alpha-thalassemia caused by a polyadenylation signal mutation. Nature 1983;306:398–400.
57. Pirastu M, Sagli G, Chang JC, et al. Initiation codon mutation as a cause of alpha thalassemia. J Biol Chem 1984;259:12315–17.
58. Morle F, Starck J, Godet J. Alpha-thalassemia due to the deletion of nucleotides -2 and -3 preceding the AUG initiation codon affects translation efficiency both *in vitro* and *in vivo*. Nucleic Acids Res 1986;14:3279–92.
59. Liebhaber SA, Coleman MB, Adams JG, et al. Molecular basis for nondeletion alpha-thalassemia in American blacks: alpha 2(116GAG→UAG). J Clin Invest 1995;80:154–9.
60. Chang JC, Kan YW. Beta zero thalassemia, a nonsense mutation in man. Proc Natl Acad Sci USA 1979;76:2886–90.
61. Milner PF, Clegg JB, Weatherall DJ. Haemoglobin H disease due to a unique haemoglobin variant with an elongated alpha chain. Lancet 1971(April 10);1:729–32.
62. Flatz G, Kinderlerer JL, Kilmartin JV, et al. Haemoglobin Tak: a variant with additional residues at the end of the beta-chains. Lancet 1971(April 10);1:732–3.
63. Bunn HF, Schmidt GJ, Haney DN, et al. Hemoglobin Cranston, an unstable variant having an elongated beta chain due to non-homologous cross over between two normal beta chain genes. Proc Natl Acad Sci USA 1975;72:3609–12.
64. Goossens M, Lee KY, Liebhaber SA, et al. Globin structural mutant alpha 125 Leu→Pro is a novel cause of alpha thalassemia. Nature 1982;296:864–5.
65. Liang ST, Wong VC, Soo WW, et al. Homozygous alpha-thalassemia: clinical presentation, diagnosis and management. A review of 46 cases. Br J Obstet Gynaecol 1985;92:680–84.
66. Flavell RA, Kooter JM, De Boer E, et al. Analysis of the beta delta globin gene loci in normal and Hb Lepore DNA: direct determination of gene linkage and intergene distance. Cell 1978;15:25–41.
67. Duma H, Efremov G, Sadikario A, et al. Study of nine families with hemoglobin Lepore. Br J Haematol 1978;15:161–72.
68. Ojwang PJ, Nakatsuji T, Gardiner MB, et al. Gene deletion as the molecular basis for the Kenya-G gamma-HPFH condition. Hemoglobin 1983;7:115–23.
69. Kan YW, Forget BG, Nathan DG. Gamma-beta thalassemia: a cause of hemolytic disease of newborns. N Eng J Med 1972;286:129–34.
70. Oski FA, Brugnara C, Nathan DG. A diagnostic approach to the anemic patient. In: Nathan DG, Orkin SH, eds. Hematology of infancy and childhood. Philadelphia: W. B. Saunders, 1997:375–84.
71. Sheetz MP. Integral membrane protein interaction with Triton cytoskeletons of erythrocytes. Biochem Biophys Acta 1979;557:122–34.
72. Dunn MJ, Kemp RB, Maddy AH. The similarity of the two high-molecular weight polypeptides of erythrocyte spectrin. Biochem J 1978;173:197–205.
73. Huebner K, Palumbo AP, Isobe M, et al. The alpha-spectrin gene is on chromosome 1 in mouse and man. Proc Natl Acad Sci USA 1985;82:3790–94.
74. Prachal JT, Morley BJ, Yoon SH, et al. Isolation and characterization of cDNA clones for human erythrocyte beta spectrin. Proc Natl Acad Sci USA 1987;84:7468–72.
75. Becker PS, Lux SE. Hereditary spherocytosis and hereditary elliptocytosis. In: Scriver CR, Beaudet AL, Sly WS, et al., eds. The metabolic and molecular bases of inherited disease. New York: McGraw Hill, 1995.
76. Lambert S, Yu H, Prachal JT, et al. cDNA sequence for human erythrocyte ankyrin. Proc Natl Acad Sci USA 1990;87:1730–34.

77. Lux SE, John KM, Bennett V. Analysis of cDNA for human erythrocyte ankyrin indicates a repeated structure with homology to tissue-differentiation and cell-cycle control proteins. Nature 1990;344:36–42.
78. Bennett V, Stenbuck PJ. Association between ankyrin and the cytoplasmic domain of band 3 isolated from the human erythrocyte membrane. J Biol Chem 1980;255:6424–32.
79. Tyler JM, Reinhardt BN, Branton D. Associations of erythrocyte membrane proteins: binding of purified band 2.1 and 4.1 to spectrin. J Biol Chem 1980;255:7034–9.
80. Cohen CM, Dotimas E, Korsgren C. Human erythrocyte membrane protein band 4.2 (pallidin). Semin Hematol 1993;30:85–137.
81. Liu S-C, Derick LH. Molecular anatomy of the red cell membrane skeleton: structure-function relationships. Semin Hematol 1992;29:231–43.
82. Gallagher PG, Forget BG, Lux SE. Disorders of the erythrocyte membrane. In: Nathan DG, Orkin SH, eds. Hematology of infancy and childhood. Philadelphia: W. B. Saunders, 1998.
83. Agre P, Orringer EP, Bennett V. Deficient red-cell spectrin in severe, recessively inherited spherocytosis. N Eng J Med 1982;306:1155–61.
84. Gilsanz F, Ricard MP, Millan E. Diagnosis of hereditary spherocytosis with dual-angle differential light scattering. Am J Clin Pathol 1993;100:119–22.
85. Cynober T, Narla M, Tchernia G. Red cell abnormalities in hereditary spherocytosis: relevance to diagnosis and understanding of the variable expression of clinical severity. J Lab Clin Med 1996;128:259–69.
86. Goodman SR, Shiffer KA, Casoria LA, et al. Identification of the molecular defect in the erythrocyte membrane skeleton of some kindreds with hereditary spherocytosis. Blood 1982;60:772–84.
87. Coetzer TL, Lawler J, Liu SC, et al. Partial ankyrin and spectrin deficiency in severe, atypical hereditary spherocytosis. N Eng J Med 1988;318:230–34.
88. Savvides P, Shalev O, John KM, et al. Combined spectrin and ankyrin deficiency is common in autosomal dominant hereditary spherocytosis. Blood 1993;82:2953–60.
89. Jarolim P, Rubin HL, Brabec V, et al. A nonsense mutation 1669 Glu→Ter within the regulatory domain of human erythroid ankyrin leads to a selective deficiency of the major ankyrin isoform (band 2.1) and a phenotype of autosomal dominant hereditary spherocytosis. J Clin Invest 1995;95:941–7.
90. Jarolim P, Rubin HL, Brabec V, et al. Mutations of conserved arginines in the membrane domain of erythroid band 3 lead to a decrease in membrane-associated band 3 and to the phenotype of hereditary spherocytosis. Blood 1995;85:634–40.
91. Takaoka Y, Ideguchi H, Matsuda M, et al. A novel mutation in the erythrocyte protein 4.2 gene of Japanese patients with hereditary spherocytosis (protein 4.2 Fukuoda). Br J Haematol 1994;88:527–33.
92. Matsuda M, Hatano N, Ideguchi H, et al. A novel mutation causing an aberrant splicing in the 4.2 gene associated with hereditary spherocytosis (protein 4.2 Notame). Hum Mol Genet 1995;4:1187–91.
93. Palek J, Lux SE. Red cell membrane skeletal defects in hereditary and acquired hemolytic anemias. Semin Hematol 1983;20:189–224.
94. Palek J. Hereditary elliptocytosis and related disorders. Clin Haematol 1985;14:45–87.
95. Austin RF, Desforges JF. Hereditary elliptocytosis: an unusual presentation of hemolysis in the newborn associated with transient morphologic abnormalities. Pediatrics 1969;44:196–200.
96. Coetzer T, Sahr K, Prachal J, et al. Four different mutations in codon 28 of α spectrin are associated with structurally and functionally abnormal spectrin α I/74 in hereditary elliptocytosis. J Clin Invest 1991;88:743–9.
97. DePalma L, Luban NL. Hereditary pyropoikilocytosis: clinical and laboratory analysis in eight infants and young children. Am J Dis Child 1993;147:93–95.
98. Liu SC, Zhai S, Palek J, et al. Molecular defect of the band 3 protein in Southeast Asian ovalocytosis. N Eng J Med 1990;323:1530–38,
99. Mohandas N, Lie-Injo LE, Friedman M, et al. Rigid membranes of Malayan ovalocytes: a likely genetic barrier against malaria. Blood 1984;63:1385–92.

100. Tani K, Yoshid MC, Satoh H, et al. Human M_2 type pyruvate kinase: cDNA cloning, chromosomal assignment, and expression in hepatoma. Gene 1988;73:509–16.
101. Hance AJ, Lee J, Feitelson M. The M_1 and M_2 isozymes of pyruvate kinase are the products of the same gene. Biochem Biophys Res Comm 1982;106:492–9.
102. Tani K, Fujii H, Nagata S, et al. Human liver type pyruvate kinase: cDNA cloning and chromosomal assignment. Biochem Biophys Res Comm 1987;143:431–8.
103. Nijhof W, Wierenga PK, Staal GEJ, et al. Changes in activities and isozyme patterns of glycolytic enzymes during erythroid differentiation *in vitro*. Blood 1984;64:607–13.
104. Tanaka KR, Valentine WN, Miwa S. Pyruvate kinase (PK) deficiency hereditary non-spherocytic hemolytic anemia. Blood 1962;19:267–72.
105. Sullivan DW, Glader BE. Erythrocyte enzyme disorders in children. Ped Clin North Am 1980;27:449–62.
106. Tanaka KR, Zerez CR. Red cell enzymopathies of the glycolytic pathway. Semin Hematol 1990;27:165–85.
107. Tanaka KR, Paglia DE. Pyruvate kinase and other enzymopathies of the erythrocyte. In: Scriver CR, Beaudet AL, Sly WS, et al., eds. The metabolic and molecular bases of inherited disease. New York: McGraw Hill, 1995.
108. Stocchi V, Magnani M, Canestrari F, et al. Multiple forms of human red blood cell hexokinase: preparation, characterization and age dependence. J Biol Chem 1982;257:2357–64.
109. Danesino C, Lo Curto F, Bonfant G, et al. Deficiency 10p: report of a case and exclusion mapping of the hexokinase 1 locus to band 10p12. Ann Genet 1984;27:162–6.
110. Pagli de, Valentine WN. Hereditary glucosephosphate isomerase deficiency: a review. Am J Clin Pathol 1974;62:740–51.
111. McMorris FA, Chen TR, Ricciuti F, et al. Chromosome assignments in man of the genes for two hexosephosphate isomerases. Science 1973;179:1129–31.
112. Magnani M, Stocchi V, Cucchiarini L, et al. Hereditary nonspherocytic hemolytic anemia due to a new hexokinase variant with reduced stability. Blood 1985;66:690–97.
113. Vora S, Durham S, De Martinville B, et al. Assignment of the human gene for muscle type phosphofructokinase (PFKM) to chromosome 1 (region cen→q32) using somatic cell hybrids and monoclonal anti-M antibody. Somat Cell Genet 1982;8:95–104.
114. Vora S, Miranda A, Hernandez E, et al. Regional assignment of the human gene for platelet type phosphofructokinase (PFKP) to chromosome 10p: novel use of poly-specific rodent antisera to localize human enzyme genes. Hum Genet 1983;63:374–9.
115. Vora S, Francke U. Assignment of the human gene for liver type 6-phosphofructokinase isozyme (PFKL) to chromosome 21 by using somatic cell hybrids and monoclonal anti-L antibody. Proc Natl Acad Sci USA 1981;78:3738–42.
116. Kahn A, Meienhofer MC, Cottreau D, et al. Phosphofructokinase (PFK) isozymes in man. I. Studies of adult human tissues. Hum Genet 1979;48:93–108,
117. Brown BI, Brown DH. Glycogen storage diseases: types I, III, IV, V, VII and unclassified glycogenoses. In: Dickens F, Rankle PJ, Whelan WJ, eds. Carbohydrate metabolism and its disorders. New York: Academic Press, 1968.
118. Kukita A, Yoshid MC, Fukushige S, et al. Molecular gene mapping of human aldolase A (ALDOA) gene to chromosome 16. Hum Genet 1987;76:20–26.
119. Jongsma AP, Los WR, Hagemeijer A. Evidence for synteny between the human loci for triosephosphate isomerase, lactate dehydrogenase B and peptidase B and the regional mapping of these loci on chromosome 12. Cytogenet Cell Genet 1974;13:106–7.
120. Eber SW, Dunnwald M, Heinemann G, et al. Prevalence of partial deficiency of red cell triosephosphate isomerase in Germany: a study of 3000 people. Hum Genet 1984;67:336–9.
121. Mohrenweiser HW, Fielek S. Elevated frequency of carriers for triosephosphate isomerase deficiency in newborn infants. Pediatr Res 1982;16:960–63.
122. Willard HF, Goss SJ, Holmes MT. Regional localization of the phosphoglycerate kinase gene and pseudogene on the human X chromosome and assignment of a related DNA sequence to chromosome 19. Human Genet 1985;71:138–43.
123. Valentine WN, Paglia DE. Erythrocyte enzymopathies, hemolytic anemia and multisystem disease: an annotated review. Blood 1984;64:583–91.

124. Rosa R, Prehu M-O, Beuzard Y, et al. The first case of a complete deficiency of diphosphoglycerate mutase in human erythrocytes. J Clin Invest 1978;62:907–15.
125. Barichard F, Joulin V, Henry I, et al. Chromosomal assignment of the human 2,3 biphosphoglycerate mutase gene (BPGM) to region 7q34→7q22. Hum Genet 1987;77:283–5.
126. D'Ancona GG, Chern CJ, Benn P, et al. Assignment of the human gene for enolase 1 to region p*ter* in equilibrium p36 of chromosome 1. Cytogenet Cell Genet 1977;18:327–32.
127. Boone C, Chen T-R, Ruddle FH. Assignment of three human genes to chromosomes (LDH-A to 11, TK to 17 and IDH to 20) and evidence for translocation between human and mouse chromosomes in somatic cell hybrids. Proc Natl Acad Sci USA 1972;69:510–14.
128. Mayeda K, Weiss L, Lindahl R, et al. Localization of the human lactate dehydrogenase B gene on the short arm of chromosome 12. Am J Hum Genet 1974;26:59–64.
129. Kitamura M, Iijima N, Hashimoto F, et al. Hereditary deficiency of subunit H of lactate dehydrogenase. Clin Chim Acta 1971;34:419–23.
130. Kanno T, Sudo K, Takeuchi I, et al. Hereditary deficiency of lactate dehydrogenase M-subunit. Clin Chim Acta 1980;108:267–76.
131. Mason PJ. New insights into G6PD deficiency. Fr. J Haematol 1996;94:585–91.
132. Carson PE, Flanagan CL, Ickes CE, et al. Enzymatic deficiency in primaquine sensitive erythrocytes. Science 1956;124:484–5.
133. Beutler E. G6PD deficiency. Blood 1994;84:3613–36.
134. Camardella L, Damonte G, Carratore V, et al. Glucose 6 phosphate dehydrogenase from human erythrocytes: identification of N-acetyl alanine at the N terminus of the mature protein. Biochem Biophys Res Comm 1995;207:331–8.
135. Cohen P, Rosemeyer MA. Subunit interactions of human glucose-6-phosphate dehydrogenase from human erythrocytes. European J Biochem 1969;8:8–15.
136. Deflora A, Morelli A, Giulian F. Human erythrocyte G6PD: content and bound enzyme. Biochem Biophys Res Comm 1974;59:406–13.
137. Piomelli S, Corash LM, Davenport DD, et al. *In vivo* lability of glucose-6-phosphate dehydrogenase in GdA and Gd Mediterranean deficiency. J Clin Invest 1968;47:940–48.
138. Marks PA, Johnson AB. Relationship between the age of human erythrocytes and their osmotic resistance: a basis for separating young and old erythrocytes. J Clin Invest 1958;37:1542–9.
139. Mason PJ, Bautista J, et al. Human red cell glucose 6 phosphate dehydrogenase is encoded only on the X chromosome. Cell 1990;63:9–10.
140. Luzzatto L. Glucose-6-phosphate dehydrogenase deficiency and hemolytic anemia. In: Nathan DG, Orkin SH, eds. Hematology of infancy and childhood. Philadelphia: W. B. Saunders, 1998.
141. Calabro V, Giaccobbe A, Vallone D, et al. Genetic heterogeneity at the glucose 6 phosphate dehydrogenase locus in southern Italy: a study on a population from the Matera district. Human Genet 1990;86:49–53.
142. Chiu D, Zuo L, Chao I, et al. Molecular characterization of glucose 6 phosphate dehydrogenase (G6PD) deficiency in patients of Chinese descent and identification of new base substitutions in the human G6PD gene. Blood 1993;81:2150–54.
143. Luzzatto L, Battistuzzi G. Glucose 6 phosphate dehydrogenase. Adv Hum Genet 1985;14:217–329.
144. Cohen T. Genetic markers in migrants to Israel. Israeli J Med Sci 1971;7:1509–14.
145. Luzzatto L. Genetic factors in malaria. Bull WHO 1974;50:195–202.
146. Motulsky AG. Metabolic polymorphisms and the role of infectious diseases in human evolution. Hum Biol 1960;32:28–36.
147. Bienzle U, Ayeni O, et al. Glucose 6 phosphate dehydrogenase deficiency and malaria: greater resistance of females heterozygous for enzyme deficiency and of males with non-deficient variant. Lancet 1972;1:107–10.
148. Roth EF Jr, Raventos-Suarez C, et al. Glucose 6 phosphate dehydrogenase deficiency inhibits *in vitro* growth of *Plasmodium falciparum*. Proc Nat Acad Sci USA 1983;80;298–9.

Index

Abnormal targeted growth, 128t, 134, 134t
Absorption, of food
- abnormal, 111-112
- normal, 107-111, 108f, 109t, 110t

Abuse, drugs of, 563-565
Acetaminophen
- clinical toxicology of, 551-552, 553f
- described, 550t
- liver damage in older children due to, 103, 103t

N-Acetylglutamate synthetase, 438t, 441t, 445
Acetylsalicylic acid, 553-554
- described, 550t
- therapeutic drug monitoring of, 549t

Acid(s)
- amino. *See* Amino acid(s)
- organic, defined, 447
- titratable, in proximal tubule, 52

Acid phosphatase, hemolysis effects on, 7t
Acidemia
- isovaleric, 440t, 448-449
- lactic, 442t
- methylmalonic, 441t, 449
- propionic, 441t, 449

Acidosis, renal tubular, in renal diseases, 53
Aciduria
- α-aminoadipic, 438t
- argininosuccinic, 447
- 3-hydroxy-3-methylglutaric, 440t
- 3-hydroxyisobutyric, 441t
- 4-hydroxyisobutyric, 442t
- 3-methylglutaconic, 440t
- mevalonic, 442t
- organic, 440t-442t
- orotic, 441t
- 2-oxoadipic, 441t

Acquired heart disease, 136-150. *See also* Heart disease, acquired
Acquired hypogammaglobulinemia, 345t, 348-349
ACTH deficiency. *See* Adrenocorticotropic hormone (ACTH), deficiency of
ACTH stimulation tests, 235
Action potentials, cardiac, 147-149, 148f
Acute autosomal dominant porphyrias, homozygous forms of, 527-528
Acute glomerulonephritis, 65
Acute intermittent porphyria, 526-528
- enzyme deficiencies in, 519t
- gene carriers and, 527
- homozygous forms of, 527-528
- inheritance of, 519t
- overproduction of heme precursors in, diagnostic patterns of, 522t
- overt, 526
- suspected, laboratory investigation of, 529

Acute interstitial nephritis, 65
Acute liver failure, in older children, 105
Acute lymphocytic leukemia (ALL), biological markers in, 491t
Acute phase reactants, 374
Acute renal failure (ARF), 64-66, 66t
Acute renovascular disease, 65
Acute rheumatic fever, 372, 373f
Acute tubular necrosis, 65

ADA deficiency, 345t, 353-354
Adenosine deaminase deficiency (ADA), 345t, 353-354
ADHD. *See* Attention deficit hyperactivity disorder
Adolescent(s). *See also* Adolescent medicine
 anemia in, 379
 anorexia nervosa in, 386-388
 bulimia nervosa in, 386-388
 dysfunctional uterine bleeding in, 383-384
 group A β-hemolytic streptococci in, 381-382
 hirsutism in, 384-386
 infectious mononucleosis in, 380-381
 males, reproductive health in, 382-383
 oligomenorrhea in, 384
 pelvic masses in, 388
 pregnancy in, 388-394
  cord blood banking in, 393-394
  initial laboratory profile in, 388-390
  mid-trimester screening in, 390
  pathologic conditions associated with, 391-393
  third trimester screening in, 391
 respiratory infections in, *Mycoplasma pneumoniae* and, 381
 secondary amenorrhea in, 384
 substance use among, 379-380
Adolescent medicine, 377-383. *See also* Adolescent(s)
 cholesterol screening in, 379
 gynecology, 383-386
  dysfunctional uterine bleeding, 383-384
  hirsutism, 384-386
  oligomenorrhea, 384
  secondary amenorrhea, 384
 hematology, 377-379, 378t
 lipid screening in, 379
 sickle cell screening in, 379
Adrenal biosynthetic defects, diagnosis of, molecular genetics in, 241
Adrenal cortex, 225-244
 diseases of, 236-241, 237t, 238f
  21-hydroxylase deficiency, 236-240. *See also* 21-Hydroxylase deficiency
Adrenal gland
 disorders of, 225-252
 function of, investigation of, 230-236
  basal tests in, 231-232
  dynamic tests in, 234-236
Adrenal medulla, 244-249
 function of, investigation of, 246-248, 247t
Adrenal steroids. *See* Steroid(s), adrenal
Adrenal tumors, steroid-producing, 241-242
Adrenarche, premature, 196
α_2-Adrenergic agonists, in psychiatric disorders, indications for and dosage of, 334t
β-Adrenergic blocking agents, for hypertension, 72
Adrenocortical disorders
 primary, pediatric, classification of, 237t
 secondary, pediatric, classification of, 237t
Adrenocortical hypofunction, 243-244
Adrenocorticotropic hormone (ACTH)
 adrenal steroid biosynthesis and, 229-230
 deficiency of, hypoglycemia due to, 293
Adrenoleukodystrophy, X-linked, 431t, 432
Adult hypolactasia, 122
Adult respiratory distress syndrome (ARDS), 38-39
 disorders associated with, 35, 36t
Agammaglobulinemia, X-linked, 345t, 346-347
Age
 as factor in diabetes mellitus, 277
 as factor in free T_4, 214, 215t
 as factor in growth retardation, 164t
 as factor in hematocrit, 5t
 as factor in IGF I and IGF II concentrations, 174t
 as factor in serum T_3, 211-213, 212t
 as factor in serum T_4, 211-213, 212t
 as factor in serum TSH values, 210, 210t
 as factor in THBR, 214, 215t
Age of onset, of puberty
 in females, 193
 in males, 194
Airway obstruction, upper, 33-35, 34t, 35t
Alanine aminotransferase, hemolysis effects on, 7t
Alaninemia, hyper-beta, 439t
Albumin
 in liver disease, 92
 in nutritional status, assessment of, 579-581, 580t
Alcaptonuria, 440t
Alcohol(s)
 clinical toxicology of, 556-558
 liver damage in older children due to, 103
Aldolase deficiency, 626
Aldosterone, biosynthesis of, inborn errors of, 241
Alkaline phosphatase, 91-92
 in tumor diagnosis and management, 491t, 494
Alymphocytosis, 345t
 of unknown origin, 353
Amenorrhea, secondary, in adolescents, 384
Amikacin
 described, 550t
 therapeutic drug monitoring of, 547
Amino acid(s), 208
 disorders of, 295, 436-445, 437t-442t
 essential, 583
 hemolysis effects on, 7t
 non-essential, 583
 profiles of, 583
 in proximal tubule, 52
Amino acid disorders, 436-445, 437t-442t. *See also specific diseases, e.g.,* Maple syrup urine disease
 defined, 436
 hyperphenylalaninemia, 436, 437t, 440t
 PKU, 436, 437t, 440t
 tyrosinemia, 437t, 440t, 443-444
α-Aminoadipic aciduria, 438t
Aminoglycoside(s), therapeutic drug monitoring of, 547
Aminoisobutyric acid, in tumor diagnosis and management, 491t, 501t

β-Aminoisobutyric aciduria, 439t
Amitriptyline
for migraine headaches, 319
therapeutic drug monitoring of, 549t
Ammonia
hemolysis effects on, 7t
in liver disease, 93
Analyte(s), status of, assessment of, 592t-593t
Analytical variation, 575
Analyzer(s), dead volume requirement for, 13, 13t
ANCA. *See under* Antineutrophil cytoplasmic antibody
Androgen(s)
adrenal, biosynthesis of, 232
secretion of, hypogonadotropism related to, 200-201
in sex differentiation, 184
Androgen insensitivity syndrome, in delayed puberty, 201t, 202
Androstenedione
in precocious puberty, 197, 197f
in puberty, 193
Anemia
in adolescents, 377-379
in chronic renal failure, 66
hemolytic, congenital Heinz body, 610
Aneurysm(s), giant, in Kawasaki syndrome, 137
Angiotensin converting enzyme (ACE) inhibitors, for hypertension, 72
Angiotensin II receptor antagonist, for hypertension, 72-73
Ankylosing spondylitis, juvenile, 368
Ankyrin
defects of, in hereditary spherocytosis, 620-621
in red cell membrane, 617
Anorexia nervosa, in adolescents, 386-388
Antibody(ies)
antineutrophil cytoplasmic, renal disease associated with, 63-64
antiperoxidase, 217
thyroid, 217
to T_3, 217
to T_4, 217
TSH receptor, 217
Antibody reactivity, in humoral immunity assessment, 341, 341t
Anticoagulant(s), for specimen collection, 8
Anticonvulsant(s)
for epilepsy, 306-315, 306t
therapeutic drug monitoring of, 543-544, 545t
toxicity of, clinical manifestations of, 544, 545t
Antidepressant(s)
in psychiatric disorders, indications for and dosage of, 334t
tricyclic
for ADHD, 330-331
for major depressive disorder, 333
Antigen(s)
in primary immunodeficiency disease evaluation, 342, 344
in tumor diagnosis and management, 491t, 496-497
tumor-associated, in tumor diagnosis and management, 491t, 497
Anti-inflammatory drugs, nonsteroidal (NSAIDs), for epilepsy, 319
Antineoplastic drugs, therapeutic drug monitoring of, 547-548
Antineutrophil cytoplasmic antibody (ANCA)—associated renal disease, 63-64
Antiperoxidase antibody (anti-TPO), 217
α1-Antitrypsin, fecal, in malabsorption evaluation, 119-120
α1-Antitrypsin deficiency
neonatal jaundice due to, 96-98, 96t
in older children, 101
Aplasia, thymic, 345t, 350-351
Apnea
contributors to, 29, 29f
obstructive, 28, 28f
Apnea of prematurity, 27-29, 28f, 29f
Apolipoprotein(s)
apo A-I, 459, 461t
decreased synthesis of, 474
increased catabolism of, 474
apo A-II, 459, 461t
apo A-IV, 459, 461t
apo B, 459-460, 461t
apo B-100, familial defective, 473
apo C, 461, 461t
apo CII, deficiency in, 470-471
apo E, 461, 461t
characteristics of, 459, 461t
cholesterol concentrations in, 468, 468t
concentration of, measurement of, 481
Apparent volume of distribution (Vd), 534
Arachidonic acid, metabolites of, 22, 23f
ARDS. *See* Adult respiratory distress syndrome
Arenal androgens, adrenal, biosynthesis of, 232
Arginine-insulin stimulation, growth hormone responses to, 175t
Argininemia, 438t, 441t, 447
Argininosuccinate lyase deficiency, 438t
Argininosuccinic aciduria, 447
Arrhythmia(s), 147-150, 148f
Arterial puncture, 4
Arthritis
psoriatic, juvenile, 369
rheumatoid, juvenile, 364
Ascorbate, assessment of, status of, laboratory tests for, 589t
L-Asparaginase, toxicity of, in tumor management, 506
Aspartate aminotransferase, hemolysis effects on, 7t
Aspartylglycosaminuria, 430t
Aspiration, suprapubic, 55
Aspirin, 553-554
Asthma, 37-38, 37t
bronchoconstriction in, factors precipitating, 37, 37t
Asymptomatic persistent proteinuria, 57
Ataxia telangiectasia, hereditary, 345t, 357-358
Atherosclerosis, coronary heart disease due to, 457
Atrium, right, venovenous catheter in, schematic of, 26f
Attention deficit hyperactivity disorder (ADHD), 327-331

Attention deficit hyperactivity disorder (ADHD) *(Cont.)*
clinical aspects of, 327-328
pathophysiology of, 328
with Tourette's syndrome, 321
treatment of, 328-331
Autoantibody(ies), insulin molecule—insulin, antibodies to, in diabetes mellitus, 275-276
Autoimmune chronic active hepatitis, 100
Autoimmune disorder, in delayed puberty, 203, 203t
Autoimmune disorders of childhood, 363-376. *See also* Rheumatic disorders
Azathioprine, following liver transplantation, 106
Azotemia
post-renal, 65-66
prerenal, 65

B cell(s), deficiencies of, 346-350
combined with T cell deficiencies, 345t, 352-359. *See also specific disorder*
immunophenotype in, 343t
common variable immunodeficiency, 345t, 348-349
hyper-IgM immunodeficiency syndrome, 345t, 347-348
IgA deficiencies, 345t, 349-350
IgG deficiencies, 345t, 350
immunophenotype in, 343t
transient hypogammaglobulinemia of infancy, 345t, 347
X-linked agammaglobulinemia, 345t, 346-347
Bacterial culture, urine, 55
Bacterial overgrowth, intestinal, 442t
Bacteriuria, significant, 54
Band 3
defects of, in hereditary spherocytosis, 621
in red cell membrane, 619
Bare lymphocyte syndrome, 345t, 356-357
Bartter syndrome, 74-75
Becker muscular dystrophy (BMD), mutation analysis in, 413-415, 414f, 415f
Benign transient hyperphosphatasemia, in older children, 105
Benzodiazepine(s)
for epilepsy, generalized seizures, 311-312
side effects of, 312
for status epilepticus, 315
Benzoylecgonine, abuse of, 564
Benzoylmethylecgonine, abuse of, 563-565
Bias, defined, 575
Bicarbonate, in proximal tubule, 50
Biliary atresia, liver transplantation for, 105
Biliary secretion, impaired, markers of, 85
Bilirubin
conjugated, 85, 86f
delta, 86-87
in diseased states, changes in, 88-90, 88t
hemolysis effects on, 7t
measurement of, 87-88
metabolism of, 85-87, 86f
inherited disorders of, 89-90
reagent strips for, 76
unconjugated, 86, 86f
Bilirubinemia, effects on specimen, 7-8
Binding proteins. *See* Protein(s), binding
Bioavailability, 534
Biochemical analysis, in primary immunodeficiency disease evaluation, 344
Biochemical phenotype, defined, 400
Biological markers
defined, 489
in tumor diagnosis and management, 489-501
alkaline phosphatase, 491t, 494
aminoisobutyric acid, 491t, 501t
antigens, 491t, 496-497
carrier proteins, 491-493, 491t
catecholamines, 491t, 498-500
CEA, 491t, 496
c-reactive protein, 491t, 500-501
creatine kinase, 495
cystathionine, 491t, 501t
enolase, 495-496
enzymes, 491t, 494-496
erythropoietin, 491t, 500
ferritin, 491t, 492-493
α-fetoprotein, 491-492
gangliosides, 491t, 497
growth factors, 491t, 500
HCG, 491t, 498
hormones, 491t, 497-500
hyaluronic acid, 491t, 501
interleukin-2 receptor, 491t, 497
lactate dehydrogenase, 491t, 494-495
β-2-microglobulin, 491t, 497
polyamines, 491t, 501
roles of, 490
storage proteins, 491-493, 491t
TAAs, 491t, 497
tDT, 491t, 496
thrombopoietin, 491t, 500
VMA, 499-500
Biotin, assessment of, status of, laboratory tests for, 589t
Biotin-responsive multiple carboxylase deficiency, 440t
Bleeding
intestinal, tests of, in malabsorption evaluation, 119-120
uterine, dysfunctional, in adolescents, 383-384
Blind loop syndrome, 116-117, 116-118
Blister(s), in porphyrias, 530, 530t
Blood. *See also under* Specimen(s)
occult, fecal, testing of, 119
volume of, in infants, 4, 5f
Blood collection, 1-4. *See also* Specimen(s), collection of
arterial puncture for, 4
procedure for, 2-3
site of, 2, 2f
skin puncture for, 2
venipuncture for, 3-4
Blood flow, intracardiac, abnormalities of, defects associated with, 128t, 130-131, 131t
Blood gases, collection of, 8
Blood pressure, normal, defined, 70
Bone(s), parathyroid hormone effects on, 254, 255f

Bone age, as factor in nighttime growth hormone concentration in normal children, 176f
Bone marrow transplantation, for congenital erythropoietic purpura, 521-522
Branched-chain α-ketoacid dehydrogenase deficiency, 295
Brancher deficiency, 433
Breast milk jaundice syndrome, 95
Bronchiolitis, 36
Bronchopulmonary dysplasia, 29-31
  cardiopulmonary dysfunction with, 30
  defined, 30
  developmental delays with, 30
  management of, 31
  natural history of, 30
  neurologic abnormalities with, 30
  pathophysiology of, 30-31
  risk factors for, 30
Bulimia nervosa, in adolescents, 386-388

Caffeine, therapeutic drug monitoring of, 547
Calcitonin
  disorders of, 257-258
  effects on organ systems, 254, 255f
Calcium
  assessment of, status of, laboratory tests for, 590t
  biochemistry of, 253-254
  disorders of
    clinical significance of, 258-267, 259t
    hypercalcemia, 259t, 260-261
    hyperparathyroidism, 265
    hyperphosphatemia, 259t, 262
    hypocalcemia, 258-260, 259t
    hypophosphatemia, 259t, 261-262
    neonatal hyperparathyroidism, 264-265
    neonatal hypoparathyroidism, 262-264
    nutritional causes of, 265-266
    rickets, 266-267
  metabolism of, disorders of, 253-271
  physiology of, 253-254
  reference values of, 267, 268t
  in renal diseases, 46-47
Calcium channel antagonists, for Tourette's syndrome, 323
Calcium channel blockers, for migraine headaches, 319
Canavan's disease, 442t
Cancer
  in children younger than 15 years, 489, 490f
  management of, 502-510. *See also specific drug and disorder*
  thyroid gland, 222
Candida extract, in primary immunodeficiency disease evaluation, 344
Candidiasis, chronic mucocutaneous, 345t, 351
Cannabinoid metabolites, abuse of, 563-564
Carbamazepine
  described, 550t
  for epilepsy, 306t
    partial and secondarily generalized seizures, 308-309
  mechanism of action of, 308
  side effects of, 308
  therapeutic drug monitoring of, 544, 545t, 549t
Carbamoyl phosphate synthetase, 438t, 445
Carbohydrate(s)
  absorption of, 111
  digestion of, 109t
  metabolism of, disorders of, 273-302. *See also specific disorder, e.g.,* Diabetes mellitus
    diabetes mellitus, 273-288
    hypoglycemic disorders, 288-298
Carbohydrate deficient glycoprotein syndrome (GDGS), 423, 431
Carbohydrate disorders, 432-435
Carcinoembryonic antigen (CEA), in tumor diagnosis and management, 491t, 496
Cardiomyopathy, 141-146
  causes of, 142-146, 142t-145t
  defined, 141
  differential diagnosis of, 142, 142t
  dilated, 141
  familial isolated, 145t, 146
  hypertrophic, 141
  inborn errors of metabolism and, 142, 143t
  malformation syndromes and, 144, 144t
  neuromuscular diseases and, 144, 145t
  restrictive, 141
Cardiovascular disorders, 127-155. *See also specific disorders, e.g.,* Congenital cardiovascular malformations
  acquired heart disorders, 136-150. *See also* Heart disease, acquired
  congenital cardiovascular malformations, 127-135
Cardiovascular malformations, congenital, 127-135. *See also* Congenital cardiovascular malformations
Carditis, manifestations of, 139, 139t
Carmustine (BCNU), toxicity of, in tumor management, 507
Carnitine, in nutritional status, assessment of, 585-586
Carnosinase deficiency, 439t
β-Carotene, for erythropoietic protoporphyria, 526
Carrier proteins, in tumor diagnosis and management, 491-493, 491t
Catch-up growth, 162
Catecholamine(s)
  biosynthesis of, 244-245, 245f
  catabolism of, 246f
  metabolism of, 245-246, 246f
  reference ranges for, 247, 247t
  in tumor diagnosis and management, 491t, 498-500
CD3 chain deficiencies, 345t, 356
CDGS. *See* Carbohydrate deficient glycoprotein syndrome
CEA. *See* Carcinoembryonic antigen
Cell(s)
  Leydig, 184
  Sertoli, 184

β-Cell(s), of islets of Langerhans, in diabetes mellitus, 274-275
Cell death abnormalities, 128t, 133, 133f, 133t
Central precocious puberty, 195, 195t
Cerebrospinal fluid (CSF), collection of, 9-10
Children, older, liver disease in, 100-105. *See also under* Hepatic disorders
Chloramphenicol, described, 550t
Chloride, in proximal tubule, 52
Cholecalciferol, assessment of, status of, laboratory tests for, 588t
Cholesterol
  apolipoprotein concentrations of, 468, 468t
  and coronary heart disease, 458
  lipid concentrations of, 467-468, 467t, 468t
  low density lipoprotein, estimation of, 480-481
  risk assessment chart for, 482, 482f
  testosterone from
    biosynthesis of, enzymes in, 190t
    biosynthetic pathway of, 184, 185f
  total, concentration of, measurement of, 477-478, 478t
Cholesterol screening, 474-475, 475t
  in adolescents, 379
Chorea, Sydenham's, 139, 139t
Choreoathetosis, 320
Chromium, assessment of, status of, laboratory tests for, 590t
Chromosome(s)
  chromosome 6, human, map of, 238f
  in sex differentiation, 182-183, 183f
Chronic mucocutaneous candidiasis, 345t, 351
Chronic renal failure, 66-69
Chronic tubulo-interstitial nephritis, 58
Circadian rhythm, ACTH and, 234
Cirrhosis, liver transplantation for, 105
Citrullinemia, 438t, 441t, 446
Clomipramine
  for obsessive-compulsive disorder, 326-327
  in psychiatric disorders, indications for and dosage of, 334t
Clonidine
  for ADHD, 330
  in psychiatric disorders, indications for and dosage of, 334t
  for Tourette's syndrome, 323
Cobalamin disorders, 439t
Cocaethylene (ethylbenzoylecgonine), abuse of, 564
Cocaine
  abuse of, 563-565
  liver damage in older children due to, 103
Colitis, ulcerative, 120
Common variable immunodeficiency, 345t, 348-349
Complete blood count (CBC), in cell-mediated immunity assessment, 341, 341t
Computed tomography (CT), in epilepsy, 304
Concanavalin A (ConA), in primary immunodeficiency disease evaluation, 342
Congenital cardiovascular malformations, 127-135
  abnormal targeted growth, 128t, 134, 134t
  cell death abnormalities, 128t, 133, 133f, 133t
  defects associated with abnormalities of intracardiac blood flow, 128t, 130-131, 131t
  ectomesenchymal tissue migration abnormalities, 128-130, 128t, 129f
  extracellular matrix abnormalities, 128t, 131-132, 131t, 132f
  genetic counseling for, 135
  pathogenetic classification of, 128-135, 128t, 129f
  situs and looping abnormalities, 134-135, 134t
Congenital erythropoietic porphyria, 515, 516t, 520-522, 522t
  biochemical findings in, 521, 522t
  clinical features of, 520-521
  described, 520
  enzyme deficiencies in, 519t
  inheritance of, 519t
  overproduction of heme precursors in, diagnostic patterns of, 522t
  prenatal diagnosis in, 522
  treatment of, 521-522
Congenital heart defects. *See also under* Congenital cardiovascular malformations
Congenital Heinz body hemolytic anemia, 610
Constitutional delay, in delayed puberty, 200
Contra-sexual precocious puberty, 196
Copper, assessment of, status of, laboratory tests for, 590t
Coproporphyria, hereditary. *See* Hereditary coproporphyria
Coronary heart disease
  atherosclerosis and, 457
  cholesterol and, 458
  costs related to, 457
  deaths due to, 457
  premature, lipids and lipoproteins and, 458. *See also under* Lipid(s); Lipoprotein(s)
  risk factors for, 457
Corticosteroid(s)
  for bronchopulmonary dysplasia, 31
  toxicity of, in tumor management, 506-507
Cortisol
  deficiency of, hypoglycemia due to, 293
  urinary steroid metabolites of, 231t
Counseling, genetic, for cardiovascular malformations, 135
"Crack," abuse of, 564
C-reactive protein, 374
  in tumor diagnosis and management, 491t, 500-501
Creatine kinase, in tumor diagnosis and management, 495

Creatinine, in renal diseases, 47-48, 48t
Creatinine kinase, hemolysis effects on, 7t
Crigler-Najjar syndrome, 88t, 89-90
Crohn's disease, 120
CSF. *See* Cerebrospinal fluid
CT. *See* Computed tomography
Cushing syndrome, 242-243
Cyanocobalamin, assessment of, status of, laboratory tests for, 589t
Cyclophosphamide, toxicity of, in tumor management, 505t, 507
Cyclosporine
following liver transplantation, 106
therapeutic drug monitoring of, 548-549
Cyproheptadine, for migraine headaches, 319
Cystathionine, in tumor diagnosis and management, 491t, 501t
Cystathioninuria, 439t
Cystic fibrosis, 121-122
mutation analysis in, 412-413
neonatal jaundice due to, 96t, 99
in older children, 101
Cystinosis, 75, 439t
Cystinuria, 439t, 445, 446f
Cytochrome P450scc, 184, 185f
Cytokine production, in primary immunodeficiency disease evaluation, 344
Cytotoxic T cell (CTL), function of, defects in, in primary immunodeficiency disease evaluation, 344

Dead volume requirements, for analyzers, 13, 13t
Debrancher enzyme deficiency, 433
Dehydroepiandrosterone (DHEA), in puberty, 193
Dehydroepiandrosterone sulfate (DHEA-S), in puberty, 193
Delayed puberty, 199-204
causes of, 199, 199t
classification of, 199, 199t
defined, 199
evaluation of, 203-204
11-Deoxycortisol, adrenal, biosynthesis of, 232
Deoxyhemoglobin S, polymerization and alignment of, 607-608, 607f
Dermatomyositis, juvenile, 366-368
Desipramine
for major depressive disorder, 332
in psychiatric disorders, indications for and dosage of, 334t
therapeutic drug monitoring of, 549t
Dexamethasone suppression tests, 234
Dextroamphetamine, in psychiatric disorders, indications for and dosage of, 334t
DHEA. *See* Dehydroepiandrosterone
DHEA-S. *See* Dehydroepiandrosterone sulfate
Diabetes mellitus, 273-288
type 1, 274-287
age as factor in, 277
antibodies in, 275-276
causes of, 274-275
climate effects on, 276-277
clinical presentation of, 277-278
complications of, long-term, surveillance for, 287
diagnosis of, 277-278
epidemiology of, 276-277, 277t
gender predilection for, 277
genetic susceptibility to, 276
hypoglycemia in, treatment of, 285-286
immune markers in, 275-276
incidence of, 276-277
management of, 278-287, 279t
metabolic factors in, 276
pathogenesis of, 274-275
psychosocial issues in, treatment of, 286
risk factors for, 276-277, 277t
treatment of
diet, 283-284
exercise, 284
insulin, 283
intensive, 286
monitoring metabolic control, 284-285
type 2, 287-288
types of, 273
Diabetic ketoacidosis
defined, 277
treatment of, 278-287, 279t
of early clinical course, 281
family education, 280-281
follow-up, 282-286
objectives of, 281-282
stabilization of hyperglycemia, 280-281
Dialysis, in chronic renal failure, 68-69
Diarrhea, types of, 115-116
Diazepam, for status epilepticus, 315
Diet, for diabetes mellitus, 283-284
DiGeorge syndrome, 345t, 350-351
Digoxin
described, 550t
therapeutic drug monitoring of, 544-546
toxicity of, 546
Dihydrolipoyl dehydrogenase deeficiency, 440t
Dihydropyrimidine dehydrogenase deficiency, 441t
1,25-Dihydroxy vitamin D, 256
2-Diphosphoglycerate (2-DPG), effects on binding of oxygen to hemoglobin, 604f, 605
Diphosphoglycerate mutase deficiency, 627
Disaccharidase deficiency tests, in malabsorption evaluation, 117-118
Disopyramide
described, 550t
therapeutic drug monitoring of, 549t
Distal tubule, in proximal tubule, 52-53
Diuretic(s), for hypertension, 72
Dopamine, effects on thyroid hormone measurements, 222
Double nucleation reaction, 607-608

Doxapram, therapeutic drug monitoring of, 547
DPG. *See* Diphosphoglycerate
Drug(s). *See also specific drug and* Therapeutic drug monitoring
absorption of, 538-539
of abuse, 563-565
among adolescents, 379-380
antineoplastic, therapeutic drug monitoring of, 547-548
bioavailability of, 534
concentration of
and clinical effect, relationship between, 537, 537f
free drug, 540-541
versus time profile for IV drug, 535f
versus time profile for orally administered drug, 536f
effects on thyroid hormone measurements, 222
elimination of
described, 534, 535f
protein binding effects on, 539-541
free, concentration of, 540-541
hyperinsulinism due to, 292-293
liver damage in older children due to, 102-103, 103t
measurement of, analytical procedures for, 543
metabolism of, 539
monitoring of
in chronic renal failure, 68
therapeutic, 533-550. *See also* Therapeutic drug monitoring
noncompliance with, 541
pharmacokinetics of, 534-535, 535f
plasma half-life of, 534, 535f
total body clearance of, 534
toxicity of, in tumor management, 504-507, 505t. *See also specific drug, e.g.,* Methotrexate
volume of distribution of, 534
Dubin-Johnson syndrome, 90
Duchenne muscular dystrophy, mutation analysis in, 413-415, 414f, 415f
Dysalbuminemia, familial, 211
Dysbetalipoproteinemia, 472-473
Dysfunctional uterine bleeding, in adolescents, 383-384
Dysgenesis, reticular, 345t, 355
Dyslipoproteinemia, familial, 469-474, 471t
Dystonia, 320
Dystrophin, multiple PCR analysis of, 415, 415f

Ebstein malformation, pathogenesis of, 133, 133f
ECMO
silicone membrane lung used in, schematic of, 24, 24f
for PPHN, 23-27, 24f-26f
venoarterial circuit of, 25f
Ectomesenchymal tissue migration abnormalities, 128-130, 128t, 129f
EDTA. *See* Ethylenediamine tetraacetic acid (EDTA)
Electrolyte(s)
disturbances of, 73-77
clinical management of, 74-76
pathophysiology of, 73-74
fecal, and osmolality, in malabsorption evaluation, 115-116
in renal diseases, 46-47
Electron transport, energy production by, 576
Electrophoresis
in lipoprotein separation, 477
protein, in humoral immunity assessment, 340, 341t
Elimination half-life, 534
Elliptocytosis, hereditary, 621-622. *See also* Hereditary elliptocytosis
Embden-Meyerhof pathway, energy production by, 576
Endocarditis, infective, 140-141
Endocrine disorders, neonatal jaundice and, 100
Endocrine system, effects on growth, 156-157, 157f, 161
Endogenous lipoprotein metabolism pathway, 463f, 464
disorders of, 471-472
Energy
production of, nutrients in, 576
quantitative assessment of, 576-578
requirements of, estimates of, 576-577
Enolase
deficiency of, 627
in tumor diagnosis and management, 495-496
Enteropathy(ies)
food-sensitive, 120
protein-losing, tests for, in malabsorption evaluation, 119-120
Environment, for specimen collection, 9
Enzyme(s)
deficiencies of, in porphyrias, 519, 519t
fecal, in malabsorption evaluation, 114
induction of, serum markers of, 91-92
release of, serum markers of, 91-92
serum, in malabsorption evaluation, 113-114
in tumor diagnosis and management, 491t, 494-496
Enzymopathy(ies), erythrocyte, 622-630. *See also* Erythrocyte enzymopathies
Epilepsy, 303-315. *See also* Seizure(s)
anticonvulsants for, 306-315, 306t
benzodiazepines for, 311-312
carbamazepine for, 308-309
clinical aspects of, 303-304
CT in, 304
diagnosis of, 304
ethosuximide for, 311
felbamate for, 312-313
fosphenytoin for, 308
gabapentin for, 313
generalized, treatment of, 310-312
lamotrigine for, 313-314
MRI in, 304
pathophysiology of, 304
phenobarbital for, 309
primidone for, 310
topiramate for, 314
treatment of, 305-315
laboratory's role in, 305-306, 306t
valproate for, 310-311
vigabatrin for, 314-315
Ergocalciferol, assessment of, status of, laboratory tests for, 588t

Erythema marginatum, 138
Erythrocyte enzymopathies, 622-630
aldolase deficiency, 626
diphosphoglycerate mutase deficiency, 627
enolase deficiency, 627
G6PD deficiency, 627-630, 628t
glucosephosphate isomerase deficiency, 625
hereditary defects in glycolytic pathway, 622-627
hexokinase deficiency, 625
LDH deficiency, 627
phosphofructokinase deficiency, 625-626
phosphoglycerate kinase deficiency, 626
pyruvate kinase deficiency, 623, 625
triosephosphate isomerase deficiency, 626
Erythrocyte sedimentation rate, 374
Erythropoietic protoporphyria, 515, 516t, 524-526
biochemical findings in, 525-526
causes of, 524
clinical features of, 524-525
described, 524
treatment of, 526
Erythropoietin, in tumor diagnosis and management, 491t, 500
Estradiol, in precocious puberty, 197, 197f
Ethanol, clinical toxicology of, 556-558
Ethosuximide
described, 550t
for epilepsy, 306t
generalized seizures, 311
mechanism of action of, 311
side effects of, 311
therapeutic drug monitoring of, 545t
Ethylbenzoylecgonine, abuse of, 564
Ethylene glycol, clinical toxicology of, 558-559
Ethylenediamine tetraacetic acid (EDTA), for specimen collection, 9
Evaporation, specimen, 4, 6f
Ewing's sarcoma, biological markers in, 491t
Exercise
for diabetes mellitus, 284
treadmill, growth hormone responses to, 175t
Exogenous lipoprotein metabolism pathway, 462-463, 462
disorders of, 469-471
External genitalia, 182
in sex differentiation, 184-185
Extracellular fluid (ECF) volume contraction, acute, 74
Extracellular matrix abnormalities, 128t, 131-132, 131t, 132f

Fabry disease, 427t
Failure to grow, biochemical investigation in, basis for, 163-169, 163t-167t, 168f
Familial combined hyperlipidemia, 471
Familial defective apolipoprotein B-100, 473
Familial dysalbuminemia, 211
Familial hypercholesterolemia, 473
Familial hypertriglyceridemia, 472
Familial hypoalphalipoproteinemia, 473-474
Familial isolated cardiomyopathy disorders, 145t, 146
Familial renal iminoglycinuria, 438t
Fanconi syndrome, renal, 75
Fat(s)
fecal, malabsorption of, 113
intake of, 475, 475t
malabsorption of, 113
Fatty acid(s)
disorders of, 295-296
essential, in nutritional status, assessment of, 583-585
Fatty acid disorders, 441t-442t, 451-453
Fatty stools, 112
Fecal α1-antitrypsin, in malabsorption evaluation, 119-120
Fecal electrolytes, and osmolality, in malabsorption evaluation, 115-116
Fecal enzymes, in malabsorption evaluation, 114
Fecal fat, malabsorption of, 113
Fecal occult blood, testing of, 119
Fecal pH, and sugars, in malabsorption evaluation, 118
Feces, collection of, 10
Felbamate
for epilepsy, 312-313
indications for, 312
mechanism of action of, 312
side effects of, 313
Female pseudohermaphroditism, 186, 187t
Ferber disease, 429t
Ferric chloride test, in metabolic disorders, 407t
Ferritin
in nutritional status, assessment of, 580t, 581
in tumor diagnosis and management, 491t, 492-493
Fertilization, in sex differentiation, 182
Fetal death *in utero,* 612
α-Fetoprotein, in tumor diagnosis and management, 491-492
Fever, rheumatic, 138-140, 139t
Fibronectin, in nutritional status, assessment of, 580t, 581
Fibrosis, cystic, 121-122
FK-506
following liver transplantation, 106-107
therapeutic drug monitoring of, 549
Flow cytometric immunophenotyping analysis, in primary immunodeficiency disease evaluation, 342, 343t
Fluoxetine, for obsessive-compulsive disorder, 327
Folic acid, assessment of, status of, laboratory tests for, 589t
Follicle stimulating hormone (FSH), in puberty, 192-193
Food-sensitive enteropathies, 120
Fosphenytoin
benefits of, 308
for epilepsy, partial and secondarily generalized seizures, 308
side effects of, 308

Free thyroxine (FT_4), 209, 213-216, 215t, 216t
 age-related values of, 214, 215t
Free thyroxine index (FT_4-I), 214
Friedewald equation, 480
FT_4. *See* Free thyroxine (FT_4)
Fucosidosis, 429t
Fumarase deficiency, 442t
Functional proteinuria, 57

Gabapentin
 for epilepsy, 313
 mechanism of action of, 313
 side effects of, 313
Galactosemia, neonatal jaundice due to, 96t, 98-99
Gamma-aminobutyric acid aminotransferase deficiency, 439t
Gamma-glutamyl transpeptidase (GGT), 91-92
Ganglioside(s), in tumor diagnosis and management, 491t, 497
G_{M1}-Gangliosidosis(es), 427t
G_{M2}-Gangliosidosis(es), 427t
Gastrointestinal system, schematic representation of, 107, 108f
Gaucher disease, 428t
Gender
 as factor in diabetes mellitus, 277
 as factor in IGF I and IGF II concentrations, 174t
 as factor in UTIs, 53
Gene(s), globin, genetic structure of, 600-603, 601t, 602f
Gene carriers, in acute porphyria, gene carriers and, 527
Generalized resistance of thyroid hormones, 222-223
Genetic(s), in diabetes mellitus, 276
Genetic counseling, for cardiovascular malformations, 135
Genetic metabolic disorders, 397-418, 419-456. *See also specific disorder, e.g.*, Inborn errors of metabolism
 amino acid disorders, 436-445, 437t-442t
 carbohydrate disorders, 432-435
 categories of, 421
 CDGS, 423, 431
 clinical manifestations of, 420
 diagnosis of, 416, 416t
 DNA diagnosis of, 408-416
 economic impact of, 420
 historical perspective of, 397-399
 inborn errors of metabolism, 401-405
 lysosomal storage diseases, 422-423, 424t-425t, 426f, 427t-430t
 maple syrup urine disease, 437t, 440t, 444
 mitochondrial disorders, 435-436
 mucopolysaccharidoses, 422, 424t-425t
 mutation analysis in, 409-410, 410f
 mutation in, biological basis of, 399-401
 in newborns, clinical features of, 403t
 numbers of, 419
 odors in patients with, 403, 403t
 organic acid disorders, 440t-441t, 447-450
 peroxisomal disorders, 431-432, 431t
 prevalence of, 419
 rhizomelic chondrodysplasia punctata, 431t, 432
 screening for, 406-408, 407t
 social impact of, 420
 suspected, laboratory evaluation of, 405-416
 urea cycle disorders, 438t, 441t, 445-447
 X-linked adrenoleukodystrophy, 431t, 432
 Zellweger syndrome, 431t, 432
Genetic sex, 182
Genital ridges, 182
Genitalia
 ambiguous, in newborn period, clinical and laboratory evaluation of, 186, 188-191, 189f, 190t, 192f, 193f
 external, 182
  in sex differentiation, 184-185
Gentamicin
 described, 550t
 therapeutic drug monitoring of, 547
Germ cell tumors, biological markers in, 491t
GFR. *See* Glomerular filtration rate
Gilbert's syndrome, 88t, 89
Globin chains, stability of, mutations affecting, 614-615
Globin genes, genetic structure of, 600-603, 601t, 602f
Globulin, thyroxine-binding, 211, 211t, 212t
Glomerular filtration rate (GFR), in renal diseases, 48-49
Glomerulonephritis, acute, 65
Glucagon, deficiency of, hypoglycemia due to, 293
Glucocorticoid(s)
 adrenal, biosynthesis of, 231-232
 effects on thyroid hormone measurements, 222
Gluconeogenesis, hepatic, disorders of, 294-295
Glucose, in proximal tubule, 50-51
Glucose-6-phosphate dehydrogenase (G6PD) deficiency, 599, 627-630, 628t
Glucosephosphate isomerase deficiency, 625
β-Glucuronidase, 425t
Glumerulonephritis, 62-63, 62t
Glutaric aciduria type I, 441t, 450, 451f
α-Glutathione-*S*-transferase, 91, 107, 107f
Glyceroluria, 442t
Glycogen storage diseases, 294-295, 433
Glycolipidosis(es), 423, 427t-430t
Glycolysis, energy production by, 576
Glycolytic pathway, 622-623, 624f
 hereditary defects in, 622-627
Glycoprotein(s), Tamm-Horsfall, 58
Glycoproteinoses, 423, 426f, 427t-430t
Goiter(s), 221

Gonadal differentiation, 182-184, 183f
46,XX Gonadal dysgenesis, in delayed puberty, 201-202, 201t
Gonadal steroids, in precocious puberty, 197, 197f
Gonadotropin(s), in precocious puberty, 197, 197f
Gonadotropin releasing hormone (GnRH), secretion of, release of inhibition of, in puberty, 192-193
Group A β-hemolytic streptococci infections, in adolescents, 381-382
Growth
 catch-up, 162
 endocrine control of, 156-157, 161
 glucocorticoids and, 162
 nutrition and, 156, 162
 paracrine control of, 157f, 161
 physiology of, 156-162, 157f
 pubertal, 162
 reference values related to, 173, 174t, 175t, 176f
 sex steroids and, 162
 skeletal, markers of growth hormone action and, 171
 targeted, abnormal, 128t, 134, 134t
 thyroid hormones and, 161-162
Growth disorders, 156-178. *See also specific disorder, e.g.,* Short stature
 biochemical investigation in, basis for, 163-169
 hormonal and biochemical investigation in, clinical significance of, 169-173, 174t, 175t, 176f
Growth factors, 157-159, 157f
 insulin-like, 160. *See also* Insulin-like growth factors
 in tumor diagnosis and management, 491t, 500
Growth hormone (GH), 157-159, 157f
 actions of, markers of, and skeletal growth, 171
 binding protein, 159, 171
 concentration of, nighttime, according to bone age and pubertal stage, 176f
 described, 191
 hormonal and biochemical investigation in, 170-171
 neuro-endocrine control of, 158-159
 receptors for, 159
 responses to treadmill exercise and arginine-insulin stimulation in normal boys and girls, 175t
 secretion of
  hormonal and biochemical investigation in, 169-171
  measurement of, 169-170
  patterns of, 159
 urinary, hormonal and biochemical investigation in, 170-171
Growth hormone (GH) assays, in growth hormone secretion evaluation, 169-171
Growth hormone (GH) deficiency, diagnosis of, 166-167, 168f
Growth hormone deficiency, hypoglycemia due to, 293
Growth hormone releasing hormone (GHRH), 158
Growth retardation
 abnormalities of growth hormone/IGFI axis and, 167t
 biochemical evaluation for, 165t
 causes of, age-related, 164t
Gulcocorticoid(s), effects on growth, 162
Günthers disease, 520-522, 522t. *See also* Congenital erythropoietic porphyria
Gynecology, adolescent, 383-386. *See also* Adolescent medicine, gynecology
Gynecomastia, 196

Hair, drugs of abuse effects on, 564-565
Half-life
 elimination, 534
 plasma, 534, 535f
Haloperidol
 in psychiatric disorders, indications for and dosage of, 334t
 for Tourette's syndrome, 322-323
Hartnup disorder, 437t
Hawkinsinuria, 437t, 440t
HCG. *See* Human chorionic gonadotropin
Headache(s)
 migraine, 315-319. *See also* Migraine headaches
 tension, and migraine headaches, relationship between, 316
Heart. *See also under* Cardiovascular
 defects of, congenital, 127-135. *See also* Congenital cardiovascular malformations
Heart disease, acquired, 136-150
 arrhythmias, 147-150, 148f
 cardiomyopathy, 141-146. *See also* Cardiomyopathy
 infective endocarditis, 140-141
 Kawasaki syndrome, 136-138
 myocardial infarction, 146-147
 myocardial ischemia, 146-147
 rheumatic fever, 138-140, 139t
Heel, blood sample from, 2, 2f
Hematin, for congenital erythropoietic purpura, 521
Hematocrit, by age, 5t
Hematological tests, in nutritional status, 587, 593
Hematology, adolescent, 377-379, 378t
Hematuria, 60-64
 defined, 60
 investigation of, 61-64, 62t
Heme
 biosynthesis of, 516-517, 517f
  biochemical genetics of, 519-520, 519t
  lead effects on, 559-560, 560f
  pathway of, 516, 517f
 precursors of
  metabolism of, 518, 518t
  overproduction of, 520, 522t
Hemoglobin(s)
 fetal hereditary persistence of, 616
 genetic structure of, 600-603, 601t, 602f
 structural variants of, 606
 synthesis of, 600-603, 602f
 unstable variants of, 610
 variants with altered oxygen affinities, 611

Hemoglobin dissociation curve, 602f
effects of pH, DPG, and temperature on binding of oxygen to hemoglobin, 604f
Hemoglobin H disease, 612
Hemoglobin molecule, assembly of, 603-605, 604f
Hemoglobinopathy(ies), 605-617
congenital Heinz body hemolytic anemia, 610
described, 605
hemoglobin variants with altered oxygen affinities, 611
laboratory diagnosis of, 616-617
molecular basis of, 600-617
sickling disorders, 606-610, 607f
structural hemoglobin variants, 606
thalassemia syndromes, 611-617. *See also* Thalassemia syndromes
unstable hemoglobin variants, 610
Hemolysis
of analytes, effects on specimen, 4, 7, 7t
bilirubin changes in, 88, 88t
neonatal jaundice due to, 95
Hemolytic anemia, congenital Heinz body, 610
Heparin, for specimen collection, 9
Hepatic disorders. *See also under* Liver
acute liver failure, 105
α1-antitrypsin deficiency, 101
benign transient hyperphosphatasemia, 105
bilirubin changes in, 88t, 89
biochemical changes in, 93-94, 93t
biochemical tests of, 81-107
cystic fibrosis, 101
drug-related, 102-103, 103t
hepatitis, 100
inborn errors of metabolism, 100-102
infection, 100
liver transplantation for, 105-107. *See also* Liver transplantation
lysosomal storage disorders, 100-101
neonatal jaundice, 94-100. *See also* Neonatal jaundice
in older children, 100-105
Reye's syndrome, 103-105, 104t
Wilson's disease, 101-102
Hepatic gluconeogenesis, disorders of, 294-295
Hepatic phosphorylase deficiency, 433
Hepatitis
autoimmune chronic active, in older children, 100
in older children, 100
Hepatoblastoma, biological markers in, 491t
Hepatocellular damage, tests of, 90-91
Hepatocyte(s), described, 81, 83f
Hepatoerythropoietic porphyria, 523-524
Hereditary coproporphyria, 516t
enzyme deficiencies in, 519t
homozygous, 528
inheritance of, 519t
overproduction of heme precursors in, diagnostic patterns of, 522t
Hereditary elliptocytosis, 621-622
common, 621-622
hereditary pyropoikilocytosis, 622
Southeast Asian ovalocytosis, 622
spherocytic, 622
Hereditary fructose intolerance, neonatal jaundice due to, 96t, 99
Hereditary pyropoikilocytosis (HPP), 622
Hereditary spherocytosis, 619-621
ankryn defects in, 620-621
band 3 defects in, 621
causes of, 620-621
described, 619
features of, 620
geographic predilection for, 619-620
osmotic fragility test in, 620
protein 4.2 defects in, 621
α-spectrin defects in, 620
Heroin, liver damage in older children due to, 103
Heterotaxy, 134-135, 134t
Hexokinase deficiency, 625
High density lipoprotein fractions, separation of, 479-480
Hirsutism, 196
in adolescents, 384-386
Histidinemia, 438t
Hodgkin's lymphoma, biological markers in, 491t
Homocarnosinosis, 439t
Homocystinuria, 439t, 444-445
Hormonal assays, in ambiguous genitalia evaluation, 191, 192f, 193f
Hormone(s), in tumor diagnosis and management, 491t, 497-500
Human chorionic gonadotropin (HCG), in tumor diagnosis and management, 491t, 498
Hunter syndrome, 424t
Hurler syndrome, 424t
Hurler-Scheie compound, 424t
Hyaline membrane disease. *See* Respiratory distress syndrome
Hyaluronic acid, in tumor diagnosis and management, 491t, 501
Hyaluronidase deficiency, 422-423
Hydrops fetalis, 612
3-Hydroxy-3-methylglutaric aciduria, 440t
3-Hydroxy,4-*N*-trimethylamino-butyric acid, in nutritional status, assessment of, 585-586
4-Hydroxybutyric aciduria, 442t
3-Hydroxyisobutyric aciduria, 441t
3-Hydroxyisobutyryl-CoA deacylase deficiency, 437t
11β-Hydroxylase deficiency, 240
21-Hydroxylase deficiency, 236-240
diagnosis of, 239
molecular pathology of, 238
prenatal diagnosis of, 240
screening in, 239-240
treatment of, 240
types of, 236-237
17α-Hydroxyprogesterone, adrenal, biosynthesis of, 233t
17-Hydroxyprogesterone, in precocious puberty, 197, 197f

3β-Hydroxysteroid dehydrogenase, oxosteroid isomerase deficiency, 240-241
Hyperapobetalipoproteinemia, 471-472
Hyper-beta-alaninemia, 439t
Hyperbilirubinemia
  conjugated, 96-100
  unconjugated, 95-96
Hypercalcemia, 259t, 260-261
Hypercalciuria, 64, 64t
Hypercholesterolemia
  defined, 474
  familial, 473
  management of, 481-483, 482f
Hyperglycinemia, nonketotic, 437t, 444
Hypergonadotropic hypogonadism
  in delayed puberty, 201-203, 201t, 203t
    with normal male external genitalia, 202-203, 203t
    with normal-appearing female external genitalia, 201-202, 201t
Hypergonadotropism, in delayed puberty, 204
Hyperhydroxyprolinemia, 438t
Hyper-IgM immunodeficiency syndrome, 347-348
Hyperinsulinism
  drug-related, 292-293
  hypoglycemia due to, 291-293
  transient neonatal, 291
Hyperlipidemia
  classification of, 469, 471t
  familial combined, 471
  primary *vs.* secondary, 469, 470t
Hyperlipoproteinemia, type V, 472
Hyperlysinemia, 437t
Hypermethioninemia, 439t
Hyperornithinemia-gyrate atrophy, 438t
Hyperornithinemia-hyperammonemia-homocitrullinuria (HHH) syndrome, 438t, 441t
Hyperoxaluria type I, 442t
Hyperoxaluria type II, 442t
Hyperparathyroidism
  neonatal, 264-265
  in older children, 265
Hyperphenylalaninemia, 436, 437t, 440t
Hyperphosphatasemia, benign transient, in older children, 105
Hyperphosphatemia, 259t, 262
Hyperprolinemia, 438t
Hypertension, renal disease and, 70-73, 71t
  causes of, 71-72, 71t
  investigation of, 70-72
  treatment of, 72-73
Hyperthyroidism, thyroid function tests in, 218-219, 219t
Hyperthyroxinemia, causes of, 213, 213t, 214t
Hyperthyroxinemic states, thyroid function tests in, 218, 219t
Hypertransfusion, for congenital erythropoietic purpura, 521
Hypertrichosis, in porphyrias, 530, 530t
Hypertriglyceridemia
  familial, 472
  management of, 483
Hyperventilation, for PPHN, 22
Hypoalphalipoproteinemia, familial, 473-474
Hypocalcemia, 258-260, 259t
Hypogammaglobulinemia
  acquired, 345t, 348-349
  transient, of infancy, 345t, 347
Hypoglycemia, 288-298
  abnormal fuel metabolism and, 294-296
  abnormal hormone secretion and, 291-293
  abnormal substrate availability and, 293-294
  ACTH deficiency and, 293
  amino acid disorders and, 295
  carbohydrate disorders and, 294-295
  causes of, 289-296
  cortisol deficiency and, 293
  defined, 289
  diagnosis of, 296-298, 297t
  fatty acid disorders and, 295-296
  glucagon deficiency and, 293
  growth hormone deficiency and, 293
  hyperinsulinism and, 291-293
  hypothyroidism and, 293
  inborn errors of metabolism and, 294-296
  ketotic, 293-294
  signs and symptoms of, 289
  in small-for-gestational-age infants, 296
  somatostatin deficiency and, 293
  surgery-related, 294
  treatment of, for diabetes mellitus, 285-286
Hypoglycemic disorders, 288-298. *See also under* Hypoglycemia
Hypogonadism
  hypergonadotropic, in delayed puberty, 201-203, 201t, 203t
  hypogonadotropic
    permanent, in delayed puberty, 200, 200t
    vs. hypergonadotropic hypogonadism, 199, 199t
Hypogonadotropic hypogonadism, *vs.* hypergonadotropic hypogonadism, 199, 199t
Hypogonadotropism
  androgen secretion—related, 200-201
  reversible, in delayed puberty, 200
Hypolactasia, adult, 122
Hypoparathyroidism, neonatal, 262-264
Hypophosphatemia, 259t, 261-262
Hypopituitarism, idiopathic, in delayed puberty, 204
Hypothalamic-pituitary-adrenal (HPA) axis, 234-235
Hypothyroidism
  hypoglycemia with, 293
  neonatal jaundice and, 95
  neonatal screening for, 220
  thyroid function tests in, 219
  treatment of, 220-221
  unsubstantiated, 221
Hypothyroxinemic states, thyroid function tests in, 218, 219t

Idiopathic hyperphosphatasemia of infancy, in older children, 105

Idiopathic hypopituitarism, in delayed puberty, 204
Ifosfamide, toxicity of, in tumor management, 505t, 507
IGF-1. *See* Insulin-like growth factor 1
Iminoglycinuria
familial renal, 438t
neonatal, 438t
Imipramine
described, 550t
for major depressive disorder, 332
in psychiatric disorders, indications for and dosage of, 334t
therapeutic drug monitoring of, 549t
Immune markers, in diabetes mellitus, 275-276
Immunoassays, drugs of abuse effects on, 565
Immunodeficiency diseases
classification of, 339
primary, 339-362
adenosine deaminase deficiency, 345t, 353-354
alymphocytosis of unknown origin, 345t, 353
B cell, 346-350. *See also specific disease and* B cell(s), deficiencies of
bare lymphocyte syndrome, 345t, 356-357
CD3 chain deficiencies, 345t, 356
chronic mucocutaneous candidiasis, 345t, 351
clinical presentation of, 340
common variable immunodeficiency, 345t, 348-349
DiGeorge syndrome, 345t, 350-351
evaluation of, 340-344, 341t-343t
advanced tests in, 340-344, 342t, 343t
flow cytometric immunophenotyping analysis in, 342, 343t
screening tests in, 340-341, 341t
in vitro lymphocyte proliferation assay in, 342
hereditary ataxia telangiectasia, 345t, 357-358
hyper-IgM immunodeficiency syndrome, 345t, 347-348
IgA deficiency, 345t, 349-350
IgG deficiencies, 345t, 350
Jak-3 deficiency, 353
laboratory diagnosis of, 340-344, 341t-343t
MHC class II deficiency, 345t, 356-357
Omenn's syndrome, 345t, 355
PNP deficiency, 345t, 354-355
reticular dysgenesis, 345t, 355
SCID, 345t, 352-357
T cell, 350-351
types of, 344-359
Wiskott-Aldrich syndrome, 345t, 358-359
X-linked agammaglobulinemia, 345t, 346-347
X-linked SCID, 345t, 352
ZAP-70 deficiency, 354
Immunoglobulin(s)
IgA deficiency, 345t, 349-350
IgG deficiencies, 345t, 350
in liver disease, 92-93
serum, quantitation of, in humoral immunity assessment, 340, 341t
Immunological tests, status of, 593-594
Immunometric assays (IMA), in TSH measurement, 209
Immunosuppression, following liver transplantation, 106
Immunosuppressive drugs, therapeutic drug monitoring of, 548-550, 549t, 550t
In vitro lymphocyte proliferation assay, in primary immunodeficiency disease evaluation, 342
Inborn errors of metabolism, 419
cardiomyopathies due to, 142, 143t
classification of, 404-405, 404t, 405t
clinical presentation of, 402-403, 403t, 404t
diagnosis of, 420-421
hypoglycemia due to, 294-296
laboratory approach to, 401-405
in older children, 100-102
pathogenesis of, 401-402
in Reye's syndrome-like illness, 104t
Incomplete precocious puberty, 196
Infant(s)
blood collection from, 2, 2f
blood volume in, 4, 5f
Infection(s). *See also specific type*
hepatitis in older children due to, 100
intestinal, 112-113
neonatal jaundice due to, 96
systemic and joint disorders associated with, 371-372
Infective endocarditis, 140-141
Inflammatory bowel disease, 120, 370
Inhaled nitric oxide (iNO), for PPHN, 23
Inherited disorders, neonatal jaundice due to, 96-99, 96t
Inherited genetic disorders, 397-418. *See also* Genetic metabolic disorders
Insulin, for diabetes mellitus, 283
Insulin hypoglycemia (stress) test, 235
Insulin molecule—insulin autoantibodies (IAA), antibodies to, in diabetes mellitus, 275-276
Insulin-like growth factors, 160
binding proteins, 160-161
hormonal and biochemical investigation in, 171-173
IGF-1
concentrations by age and gender, 174t
in nutritional status, assessment of, 581
significance of, 172-173
IGF-2, concentrations by age and gender, 174t
IGFBP-3, 173
serum levels of, age-related, 175t
Insulin-like growth factors assays, in insulin-like growth factor evaluation, 171-172
Intensive care unit (ICU), neonatal
respiratory distress syndrome in, 17
special needs of, 31-33

Interleukin-2 receptor, in tumor diagnosis and management, 491t, 497
Internal ducts, 182
in sex differentiation, 184-185
International League Against Epilepsy (ILAE), classification of epilepsy by, 304
Intestinal bacterial overgrowth, 442t
Intestinal bleeding, tests of, in malabsorption evaluation, 119-120
Intestinal disease
diagnostic tests for, 112
infections, 112-113
investigation of, 112-123
malabsorption, 113-120
Intestinal function, inherited disorders affecting, 122, 123t
Intestinal function tests, in malabsorption evaluation, 114-116, 115t
Intestinal tract, 107-112
absorption by
abnormal, 111-112
normal, 107-111, 108f, 109t, 110t
food-sensitive enteropathies, 120
inflammatory bowel disease, 120
inherited disorders, 121-122, 123t
pancreatic disease, 121
Intracardiac blood flow, abnormalities of, defects associated with, 128t, 130-131, 131t
Intra-individual variation, 574
Intrumentation, for specimen collection, 13, 13t
Iodide, 208
assessment of, status of, laboratory tests for, 590t
Iron
assessment of, status of, laboratory tests for, 590t
clinical toxicology of, 562-563, 563t
hemolysis effects on, 7t
total iron binding capacity, 563
Iron salts, 562-563, 563t
Ischemia, myocardial, 146-147
Islets of Langerhans, β-cells in, 274-275
Isoniazid, metabolism of, 539
Isopropanol, clinical toxicology of, 558-559
Isovaleric acidemia, 440t, 448-449

Jak-3 deficiency, 353
Jaundice, 94-100. *See also* Neonatal jaundice
obstructive, 96
physiological, 95
bilirubin changes in, 88t, 89
Juvenile ankylosing spondylitis, 368
Juvenile dermatomyositis, 366-368
Juvenile psoriatic arthritis, 369
Juvenile rheumatoid arthritis, 364

Kawasaki syndrome, 136-138
Ketoacidosis, diabetic
defined, 277
treatment of, 278-287, 279t. *See also* Diabetic ketoacidosis, treatment of
Ketone(s), reagent strips for, 76
Ketosis, 442t
Kidney(s), diseases of. *See* Renal diseases
Kidney transplantation, 69
for chronic renal failure, 69
Krabbe leukodystrophy, 428t
Krebs cycle, energy production by, 576
Kwashiorkor, 577

Laboratory
requirements of, 13, 13t
role in porphyria assessment, 528-530, 530t
services offered by, 14-16
Lactate dehydrogenase (LDH), 91
in tumor diagnosis and management, 491t, 494-495
Lactate dehydrogenase, hemolysis effects on, 7t
Lactate dehydrogenase (LDH) deficiency, 627
Lactic acidemia, 442t
Lactose breath test, in malabsorption evaluation, 118
Lactose tolerance test, in malabsorption evaluation, 118
Lamotrigine
for epilepsy, 313-314
mechanism of action of, 313
side effects of, 313-314
Laryngotracheobronchitis (LTB), *vs.* supraglottitis, 34-35, 35t
Laxative abuse tests, in malabsorption evaluation, 119
Lead, clinical toxicology of, 559-562, 560f
Lecithin cholesterol acyltransferase (LCAT), 459, 461t
Left heart defects, 130-131, 131t
Lennox-Gastaut syndrome, felbamate for, 312
Lepemia, effects on specimen, 7
Leucocyte esterase, 56
Leukodystrophy
Krabbe, 428t
metachromatic, 428t
Levo-thyroxine therapy, thyroid status evaluation in patients receiving, 220-221
Leydig cells, 184
Lidocaine, described, 550t
Liothyronine, 221
Lipid(s)
absorption of, 110-111
cholesterol concentrations in, 467-468, 467t
digestion of, 109t
metabolism of, disorders of, 457-487
diagnosis of, 474-481
management of, 481-483, 482f
screening for, 474-481
in nutritional status, assessment of, 583-585
screening for, in adolescents, 379
Lipoprotein(s)
characteristics of, 460t
cholesterol concentrations in, 467-468, 468t
classes of, 459, 460t
composition of, 458-462, 460t, 461t
defined, 458
density of, 459, 460t
electrophoretic separation of, 477
metabolism of
disorders of, 457-487
diagnosis of, 474-481
familial dyslipoproteinemia, 469-474, 471t

Lipoprotein(s) *(Cont.)*
management of, 481-483, 482f
primary *vs.* secondary hyperlipidemia, 469, 470t
screening for, 474-481
endogenous pathway in, 463f, 464
exogenous pathway in, 462-463, 462
low density lipoprotein receptor pathway in, 464, 465f
reverse cholesterol transport pathway in, 466-467, 466f
Lipoprotein lipase activity, deficiency in, 469-470
Lithium, for major depressive disorder, 333
Liver. *See also under* Bilirubin; Hepatic
architecture of, 81-82, 83f
described, 81-84
disorders of. *See* Hepatic disorders
excretion of, 85, 86f
function of
biochemical tests of, 84-93. *See also* Hepatic disorders
albumin, 92
ammonia, 93
bilirubin, 85-90
enzyme induction and release, 91-92
hepatocellular damage, 90-91
immunoglobulins, 92-93
dynamic tests of, 93
functional unit of, defined, 82
metabolic functions of, 81, 82f
Liver failure, acute, in older children, 105
Liver function tests (LFTs)
in liver transplant recipient, 107, 107f
types of, 84
Liver transplantation, 105-107
allograft function monitoring following, 107
complications following, 106
indications for, 105
recipients of, liver function tests in, postoperative changes in, 107, 107f
timing of, 106
Lomustine (CCNU), toxicity of, in tumor management, 507
Long-chain hydroxyacyl-CoA dehydrogenase deficiency, 441t
Looping abnormalities, 134-135, 134t
Lorazepam, for status epilepticus, 315
Low density lipoprotein cholesterol, estimation of, 480-481
Low density lipoprotein receptor pathway, 464, 465f
disorders of, 473
Lower airway disease, 35-39
ARDS, 38-39
asthma, 37-38, 37t
bronchiolitis, 36
causes of, 36t
Luteinizing hormone (LH), in puberty, 192-193, 198, 198f
Lyme disease, 372-374
Lymphoma(s)
Hodgkin's, biological markers in, 491t
non-Hodgkin's, biological markers in, 491t
Lysinuric protein intolerance, 437t, 441t
Lysosomal storage diseases, 422-423, 424t-425t, 426f, 427t-430t
in older children, 100-101

Macronutrient deficiency, 577
Magnesium
assessment of, status of, laboratory tests for, 590t
biochemistry and physiology of, 254
hemolysis effects on, 7t
in renal diseases, 47
Magnetic resonance imaging (MRI), in epilepsy, 304
Major depressive disorder, 331-333
clinical aspects of, 331-332
pathophysiology of, 332
treatment of, 332-333
Major histocompatibility complex (MHC) class II deficiency, 345t, 356-357
Malabsorption, 113-120
disaccharidase deficiency tests for, 117-118
fecal fat, 113
of food, 111-112
intestinal bleeding tests for, 119-120
intestinal function tests for, 114-116, 115t
laxative abuse tests for, 119
pancreatic function tests for, 113-114
protein-losing enteropathy tests for, 119-120
small bowel bacterial overgrowth tests for, 116-117
vitamin B_{12} absorption tests for, 119
Male pseudohermaphroditism, 186, 188f
"Male Turner syndrome," in delayed puberty, 202, 203t
Malformation syndromes, cardiomyopathies due to, 144, 144t
Malnutrition, protein-energy, 577-578
Malonyl-CoA decarboxylase deficiency, 441t
Manganese, assessment of, status of, laboratory tests for, 590t
Mannosidosis, 429t
Maple syrup urine disease (MSUD), 295, 437t, 440t, 444
Marasmus, 577
Maroteaux-Lamy syndrome, 425t
Maturity-onset diabetes in the young (MODY), 273
McArdle disease, 433-434
Meconium, drugs of abuse effects on, 564-565
Meconium aspiration syndrome (MAS), PPHN with, 21, 22t
Medium-chain acyl-CoA dehydrogenase (MCAD) deficiency, 295
prevalence of, 419
Medulla, adrenal, 244-249
function of, investigation of, 246-248, 247t
Menadione, assessment of, status of, laboratory tests for, 588t
Mephobarbital, for epilepsy, partial and secondarily generalized seizures, 309

3-Mercaptolactic-cysteine disulfiduria, 439t
6-Mercaptopurine
  therapeutic drug monitoring of, 548
  toxicity of, in tumor management, 505-506, 505t
Mesenchyme cushion, segmental formation of, mechanism for, 132f
Message processing, defects in, point mutations and, 614
Message stability, defects in, point mutations and, 613-614
Message transcription, defects in, point mutations and, 613
Metabolic disorders, genetic, 419-456. *See also* Genetic metabolic disorders
Metabolic stress, proteins and, 579, 580f
Metabolism, in diabetes mellitus, 276
Metachromatic leukodystrophy, 428t
Methanol, clinical toxicology of, 558-559
Methotrexate
  described, 550t
  gradient, from plasma to CSF during constant intravenous infusion, 508-509, 509f
  plasma disappearance curves in patients receiving six-hour infusions followed by leucovorin rescue, 509, 510f
  therapeutic drug monitoring of, 548, 549t
  toxicity of, in tumor management, 504-505, 505t
3-Methylcrotonyl-CoA carboxylase deficiency, 440t
5,10-Methylenetetrahydrofolate reductase deficiency, 439t
3-Methylglutaconic aciduria, 440t
Methylmalonic acidemia, 441t, 449
Methylphenidate
  for ADHD, 328-330
  in psychiatric disorders, indications for and dosage of, 334t
Methysergide, for migraine headaches, 319
Metyrapone test, 234-235
Mevalonic aciduria, 442t
Microalbuminuria, 60
β-2-Microglobulin, in tumor diagnosis and management, 491t, 497
Micronutrient status, assessment of, 586-587, 588t-591t
Migraine headaches, 315-319
  described, 315-316
  neurotransmitters in, 316
  pathogenesis of, 316
  pathophyisology of, 316
  and tension headaches, relationship between, 316
  treatment of, 317-319
Migratory polyarthritis, 138
Mineral(s), assessment of, status of, laboratory tests for, 590t-591t
Mineralocorticoid(s), adrenal, biosynthesis of, 232, 235-236
Mitochondrial disorders, 435-436
Mitogen(s), in primary immunodeficiency disease evaluation, 342
Mixed lymphocyte cultures (MLC), in primary immunodeficiency disease evaluation, 344
Molecular (DNA) phenotype, defined, 400
Mononucleosis, infectious, in adolescents, 380-381
Monosaccharide phosphates, accumulation of, 434
Morquio syndrome, 425t
Movement disorders, 320-324
MRI. *See* Magnetic resonance imaging
Mucolipidosis II, 430t
Mucopolysaccharidosis(es), 422, 424t-425t
  urinary, electrophoresis of, 422, 426f
Müllerian ducts, in sex differentiation, 184
Multiple acyl-CoA dehydrogenase deficiency, 442t
Multiple carboxylase deficiency, 440t, 449-450
Multiple drug resistance (MDR) cells, 548
Muscle phosphorylase deficiency, 433-434
Mutation(s)
  biological basis of, 399-401
  globin chain stability affected by, 614-615
  point
    alterations in protein translation due to, 614
    defects in message transcription, stability, and processing, 613-614
  thalassemia syndromes due to, 613-615
Mutation analysis
  in Becker muscular dystrophy, 413-415, 414f, 415f
  in cystic fibrosis, 412-413
  in Duchenne muscular dystrophy, 413-415, 414f, 415f
  in genetic metabolic disorders, 409-410, 410f
Mycoplasma pneumoniae, respiratory infections due to, in adolescents, 381
Myocardial infarction, 146-147
Myocardial ischemia, 146-147

Naratriptan, for migraine headaches, 318
Neimann-Pick disease, 428t
Neonatal ICU
  respiratory distress syndrome in, 17
  special needs of, 31-33
Neonatal iminoglycinuria, 438t
Neonatal jaundice, 94-100
  α1-antitrypsin deficiency and, 96-98, 96t
  causes of, 94t
  cystic fibrosis and, 96t, 99
  endocrine disorders and, 100
  galactosemia and, 96t, 98-99
  hemolysis and, 95
  hereditary fructose intolerance and, 96t, 99
  hypothyroidism and, 95
  infections and, 96
  inherited disorders and, 96-99, 96t
  Niemann-Pick Type C and, 96t, 99
  parenteral nutrition associated with, 99
  physiological jaundice, 95
  tyrosinemia Type 1 and, 96t, 98
  Zellweger's syndrome and, 96t, 99

Neonatal lupus syndrome, 365
Neonate(s)
hypothyroidism for, screening for, 220
jaundice in, 94-100. *See also* Jaundice
Nephritis
acute interstitial, 65
chronic tubulo-interstitial, 58
Nephrogenic diabetes insipidus, 75-76
Nephronophthisis, 58
Nephrotic syndrome, 59
Neural crest migration abnormalities, 128-130, 128t, 129f
Neuroblastoma(s), 249-250
biological markers in, 491t
screening for, 250
Neuroleptic(s), in psychiatric disorders, indications for and dosage of, 334t
Neurologic disorders, 303-324. *See also specific disorder, e.g.,* Epilepsy
choreoathetosis, 320
dystonia, 320
epilepsy, 303-315
migraine headaches, 315-319
movement disorders, 320-324
Tourette's syndrome, 320-324
Neuromuscular diseases, cardiomyopathies due to, 144, 145t
Neurotransmitters, in migraine headaches, 316
Newborn(s)
ambiguous genitalia in, clinical and laboratory evaluation of, 186, 188-191, 189f, 190t, 192f, 193f
hyperparathyroidism in, 264-265
hypoparathyroidism in, 262-264
metabolic disease in, clinical features of, 403t
metabolic screening in, 407-408
persistent pulmonary hypertension of, 21-27
respiratory disorders in, 18-33. *See also* Respiratory disorders, neonatal
Niacin, assessment of, status of, laboratory tests for, 589t
Nicotine, for Tourette's syndrome, 324
Niemann-Pick Type C, neonatal jaundice due to, 96t, 99
Nitric oxide (NO)
inhaled, for PPHN, 23
for PPHN, 21-22
Nitrite, urinary, 56
Nitrogen balance, protein and, 582
Nitroprusside, sodium, for hypertension, 73
Noncompliance, 541
Non-Hodgkin's lymphoma, biological markers in, 491t
Nonketotic hyperglycinemia, 437t, 444
Non-thyroidal illnesses, alterations in thyroid function in, 220
Noonan's syndrome, in delayed puberty, 202, 203t
Normotensive hyper-reninemic conditions, 73
Nortriptyline
for ADHD, 331
for major depressive disorder, 332-333
in psychiatric disorders, indications for and dosage of, 334t
5′-Nucleotidase (5NT), 91-92
Nutrient(s)
absorption sites for, 110, 110t
energy production from, 576
Nutrient levels, inter-individual, factors influencing, 573f, 573-574
Nutrition
effects on growth, 156, 162
parenteral, neonatal liver disease and, 99
Nutritional status
assessment of, 571-597
analytes measured in, reference ranges for, 592t-593t
energy status, 576-578
hematological tests in, 587, 593
immunological tests in, 593-594
laboratory, 572-575
biological variation in, 573-575, 573f
limitations of, 573-575, 573f
non-laboratory, 572t
carnitine in, assessment of, 585-586
essential fatty acids in, 583-585
laboratory indicators of, 587, 592t-593t, 593-594
lipids in, assessment of, 583-585
micronutrient, assessment of, 586-587, 588t-591t
proteins in, assessment of, 578-583. *See also under* Protein(s)

Obsessive-compulsive disorder (OCD), 325-327
clinical aspects of, 325
pathophysiology of, 325-326
with Tourette's syndrome, 321, 327
treatment of, 326-327
Obstructive apnea, 28, 28f
Obstructive uropathy, 65-66
Occult blood, fecal, testing of, 119
OKT3, following liver transplantation, 106
Oligomenorrhea, in adolescents, 384
Oligosaccharides, urinary, thin-layer chromatography of, 426f
Omenn's syndrome, 345t, 355
Organic acid(s), defined, 447
Organic acid disorders, 440t-441t, 447-450
Organic acidurias, 440t-442t
Ornithine carbamoyl transferase deficiency, 438t, 441t, 445-446
Orotic aciduria, 441t
Orthostatic proteinuria, 58-59
Osmolality, fecal electrolytes and, in malabsorption evaluation, 115-116
Osteodystrophy, renal, 67
Osteosarcoma, biological markers in, 491t
Ovalocytosis, Southeast Asian, 622
Over-feeding syndrome, 578
2-Oxoadipic aciduria, 441t
2-Oxoglutaric dehydrogenase deficiency, 442t
5-Oxoprolinuria, 442t
3-Oxothiolase deficiency, 441t

Pancreatic disease, 121
Pancreatic function tests, in malabsorption evaluation, 113-114
Pancreatic stimulation tests, in malabsorption evaluation, 114
Pancreatitis
acute, 121
chronic, 121
Pancreoluaryl test, in malabsorption evaluation, 114
PANDAS, 321
Pantothenic acid, assessment of, status of, laboratory tests for, 589t
Paracrine system, effects on growth, 157f, 161
Parathyroid hormone (PTH)
and calcium and phosphorus levels, 254, 255f
described, 254
disorders of, 254-256, 255f
effects on bone, 254, 255f
effects on organ systems, 254, 255f
reference values of, 267, 268t
Parathyroid-hormone—related peptides (PTHrPs), 255-256
Parenteral nutrition, neonatal liver disease and, 99
Partial testicular dysgenesis, in delayed puberty, 202-203, 203t
Patient phenotype, defined, 400
PBG-synthase deficiency
enzyme deficiencies in, 519t
inheritance of, 519t
overproduction of heme precursors in, diagnostic patterns of, 522t
PBG-synthase deficiency porphyria, 516t
Pediatric autoimmune neuropsychiatric disorders associated with streptococcal infections (PANDAS), 321
Pelvic masses, in adolescents, 388
Peptide(s), PTH-related, 255-256
Perimembranous ventricular septal defect, 130-131, 131t
Peripheral precocious puberty, 195-196, 195t
Permanent hypogonadotropic hypogonadism, in delayed puberty, 200, 200t
Permeability tests, in malabsorption evaluation, 115, 115t
Peroxisomal disorders, 431-432, 431t
Persistent hyperinsulinemic hypoglycemia of infancy (PPHI), 291-292
Persistent pulmonary hypertension of newborn (PPHN), 21-27
biochemical mediators of, 21-22
conditions associated with, 21, 22t
described, 21
diagnosis of, 21
ECMO therapy for, 23-27, 24f-26f
with meconium aspiration syndrome, 21, 22t
prevalence of, 21
treatment of, 22-23
pH
effects on binding of oxygen to hemoglobin, 604f, 605
fecal, and sugars, in malabsorption evaluation, 118
reagent strips for, 76
urine, in proximal tubule, 52
Phencyclidine (PCP), abuse of, 563-564
Phenobarbital
described, 550t
dosage of, 309
for epilepsy, 306t
partial and secondarily generalized seizures, 309
for migraine headaches, 319
side effects of, 309
for status epilepticus, 315
therapeutic drug monitoring of, 544, 545t
Phenolphthalein, screening tests for, 119
Phenotype(s)
biochemical, defined, 400
molecular, defined, 400
patient, defined, 400
Phenylethylmalonamide, therapeutic drug monitoring of, 544, 545t
Phenylketonuria (PKU), 436, 437t, 440t
prevalence of, 419
Phenytoin
described, 550t
effects on thyroid hormone measurements, 222
for epilepsy, 306t
dosage of, 307
partial and secondarily generalized seizures, 307
for migraine headaches, 319
side effects of, 307
for status epilepticus, 315
therapeutic drug monitoring of, 543-544, 545t, 549t
Pheochromocytoma(s), 248-249, 498-499
Phosphate(s), in proximal tubule, 51
Phosphofructokinase deficiency, 625-626
Phosphoglycerate kinase deficiency, 626
Phosphorus
assessment of, status of, laboratory tests for, 591t
biochemistry and physiology of, 254
disorders of, nutritional causes of, 265-266
hemolysis effects on, 7t
metabolism of, disorders of, 253-271
reference values of, 267, 268t
Photosensitivity, laboratory investigation of, 530
Phylloquinone, assessment of, status of, laboratory tests for, 588t
Phytohemagglutinin (PHA), in primary immunodeficiency disease evaluation, 342
Pimozide
in psychiatric disorders, indications for and dosage of, 334t
for Tourette's syndrome, 323
Pituitary aplasia, in delayed puberty, 204
Pituitary resistance to thyroid hormones (PRTH), 222-223
PKU. *See* Phenylketonuria
Plasma half-life, 534, 535f
Cis-Platinum, toxicity of, in tumor management, 505t, 506

PNP. *See* Purine nucleoside phosphorylase
Pokeweed mitogen (PWM), in primary immunodeficiency disease evaluation, 342
Polyamine(s), in tumor diagnosis and management, 491t, 501
Polyarthritis, migratory, 138
Polymerase chain reaction (PCR), in genetic metabolic disorders, 410-412
Pompe disease, 434
Porphyria(s)
acute, 526-528
gene carriers and, detection and management of, 527
homozygous forms of, 527-528
overt, 526
acute intermittent, 515, 516t. *See* Acute intermittent porphyria
autosomal dominant, acute, homozygous forms of, 527-528
blisters in, 530, 530t
causes of, 515-516
cutaneous, 520-526. *See also specific types, e.g.,* Congenital erythropoietic porphyria
blistering, 524
suspected, laboratory investigation of, 530, 530t
toxic, 523
described, 515
enzyme deficiencies in, 519, 519t
erythropoietic, congenital, 515, 516t. *See* Congenital erythropoietic porphyria
hepatoerythropoietic, 523-524
hypertrichosis in, 530, 530t
inheritance of, 519, 519t
laboratory investigation of, 528-530, 530t
PBG-synthase deficiency, 516t. *See* PBG-synthase deficiency porphyria
skin fragility in, 530, 530t
symptoms of, 515-516
types of, 515, 516t
variegate. *See* Variegate porphyria
Porphyria cutanea tarda, 515, 516t, 522-523
enzyme deficiencies in, 519t
inheritance of, 519t
overproduction of heme precursors in, diagnostic patterns of, 522t
Porphyrin, metabolism of, disorders of, 515-532. *See also under specific disorder and* Porphyria(s)
Post-renal azotemia, 65-66
Potassium
hemolysis effects on, 7t
in proximal tubule, 50
in renal diseases, 46
PPHN. *See* Persistent pulmonary hypertension of newborn
Prealbumin
in nutritional status, assessment of, 580t, 581
thyroxine-binding, 209
Pre-analytical variation, 574-575
Precocious puberty, 194-199
central, 195, 195t
contra-sexual, 196
described, 194
evaluation of, 196-199, 197f, 198f
incomplete, 196
peripheral, 195-196, 195t
Pregnancy, in adolescents, 388-394
Premature adrenarche, 196
Premature thelarche, 196
Prematurity
apnea of, 27-29, 28f, 29f
respiratory distress syndrome due to, 18
Prerenal azotemia, 65
Primidone
described, 550t
for epilepsy, partial and secondarily generalized seizures, 310
therapeutic drug monitoring of, 544, 545t, 549t
Procainamide
described, 550t
metabolism of, 539
therapeutic drug monitoring of, 549t
Progressive systemic sclerosis, 370-371
Prolidase deficiency, 438t
Propionic acidemia, 441t, 449
Propranolol
described, 550t
for migraine headaches, 318-319
side effects of, 318-319
therapeutic drug monitoring of, 549t
Protein(s)
absorption of, 111
binding
growth hormone, 159, 171
insulin-like growth factors, 160-161
carrier, in tumor diagnosis and management, 491-493, 491t
C-reactive, in tumor diagnosis and management, 491t, 500-501
digestion of, 109t
metabolic stress and, 579, 580f
metabolism of, injury effects on, 579, 580f
nitrogen balance and, 582
in nutritional status, assessment of, 578-583
renal, 58
retinol-binding, in nutrition status, assessment of, 580t, 581
somatic, 582
storage, in tumor diagnosis and management, 491-493, 491t
thyroxine-binding
abnormal serum concentration of, causes of, 211, 212t
binding of, causes of, 211, 212t
total, hemolysis effects on, 7t
in total body mass, 578
visceral, 579-582, 580t. *See also* Visceral proteins
Protein 4.1, in red cell membrane, 619
Protein 4.2
defects of, in hereditary spherocytosis, 621
in red cell membrane, 619
Protein binding, of drugs, 539-541
Protein electrophoresis, in humoral immunity assessment, 340, 341t

Protein translation, alterations in, point mutations in, 614
Protein-energy malnutrition, 577-578
Protein-losing enteropathy tests, in malabsorption evaluation, 119-120
Proteinuria, 57-59
asymptomatic persistent, 57
functional, 57
heavy, 59
low-grade, 57-59
orthostatic, 58-59
tubular, 58
Protoporphyria
enzyme deficiencies in, 519t
erythropoietic, 515, 516t
inheritance of, 519t
overproduction of heme precursors in, diagnostic patterns of, 522t
Proximal tubule
amino acids in, 52
bicarbonate in, 50
chloride in, 52
glucose in, 50-51
phosphate in, 51
potassium in, 50
in renal diseases, 49-53
sodium in, 49
titratable acid, 52
Pseudohermaphroditism
female, 186, 187t
male, 186, 188f
Psoriatic arthritis, juvenile, 369
Psychiatric disorders, 325-334
ADHD, 327-331
agents used in, indications for and dosage of, 334t
major depressive disorder, 331-333
obsessive-compulsive disorder, 325-327
Psychosocial issues, for diabetes mellitus, treatment of, 286
Psychostimulants, for Tourette's syndrome, 323
PTH. *See* Parathyroid hormone
Puberty
abnormal, growth disturbance in relation to, investigation for, 164t
abnormalities associated with, 192-204
adrenal androgens in, 193
biochemistry of, 192-194, 194t
delayed, 199-204. *See also* Delayed puberty
described, 181, 192
in females, 193, 194t
age of onset of, 193
growth at, 162
in males, 194, 194t
physiology of, 192-194, 194t
precocious, 194-199, 195t, 197f, 198f. *See also* Precocious puberty
sleep stages in, 198f
stage of, as factor in nighttime growth hormone concentration in normal children, 176f
Pulmonary surfactant, described, 18
Pure protein derivative (PPD), in primary immunodeficiency disease evaluation, 344
Purine nucleoside phosphorylase (PNP), deficiency of, 345t, 354-355
Pyridoxine, assessment of, status of, laboratory tests for, 588t-589t
Pyropoikilocytosis, hereditary, 622
Pyruvate carboxylase deficiency, 434
Pyruvate dehydrogenase, 435
Pyruvate kinase deficiency, 623, 625
Pyuria, defined, 56

Quantitation of serum immunoglobulins, in humoral immunity assessment, 340, 341t
Quinidine
described, 550t
therapeutic drug monitoring of, 549t

Radioactive thyroidal uptake, 218
Rapid response, 14
RBP. *See* Retinol-binding protein (RBP)
Red blood cell (RBC) disorders
biochemical basis of, 599-636
erythrocyte enzymopathies, 622-630
hemoglobinopathies, 605-617. *See also* Hemoglobinopathy(ies)
prevalence of, 599
red cell membrane defects, 617-622
Red cell membrane
defects of, 617-622
hereditary, 619-622
schematic model of, 618f
structure of, 617-619, 618f
Reference ranges, specimen-related, 12-13
Reference values, growth-related, 173, 174t, 175t, 176f
Reiter's syndrome, 369-370
Renal diseases, 45-80
ANCA-associated, 63-64
calcium in, 46-47
creatinine in, 47-48, 48t
electrolytes in, 46-47
evaluation of, methods of, 45-53
GFR in, 48-49
glumerulonephritis, 62-63, 62t
hematuria, 60-64
hypercalciuria, 64, 64t
magnesium in, 47
microalbuminuria, 60
potassium in, 46
proteinuria, 57-59
proximal tubule in, 49-53
renal tubular acidosis in, 53
renin angiotensin system and, 69-73, 70t
sodium in, 46
tubular function tests in, 49
urea in, 47
Renal failure
acute, 64-66
chronic, 66-69
Renal function, fetal, antenatal assessment of, 76-77
Renal osteodystrophy, 67
Renal proteins, 58
Renal transplantation, for chronic renal failure, 69
Renal tubular acidosis, in renal diseases, 53
Renal tubular disorders, 74-76
Renin, release of, factors influencing, 70t

Renin angiotensin system, renal disease and, 69-73, 70t
Reproductive disorders, 181-205. *See also* Puberty; Sexual differentiation
ambiguous genitalia in newborn period, clinical and laboratory evaluation of, 186, 188-191, 189f, 190t, 192f, 193f
in puberty, 192-204
sexual differentiation, 182-182
Resin T_3 uptake (RT_3U), by age, 214, 215t
Respiratory chain, energy production by, 576
Respiratory disorders, 17-44
bronchopulmonary dysplasia, 29-31
lower airway disease, 35-39
neonatal, 18-33. *See also specific disorder, e.g.,* Respiratory distress syndrome
apnea of prematurity, 27-29, 28f, 29f
PPHN, 21-27
respiratory distress syndrome, 18-21, 20t
upper airway disease, 33-35, 34t, 35t
Respiratory distress syndrome
in neonatal ICU, 17
in neonates, 18-21, 20t
biochemical defect in, 18-19
causes of, 18
presentation of, 18
prevention of, 19
treatment of, 19-19, 20t
Respiratory infections, *Mycoplasma pneumoniae* and, in adolescents, 381
Respiratory quotient (RQ), calculation of, 577
Restriction fragment length polymorphisms (RFLPs), in genetic disorders, 421
Reticular dysgenesis, 345t, 355
Retinol, assessment of, status of, laboratory tests for, 588t
Retinol-binding protein (RBP), in nutritional status, assessment of, 580t, 581
Reverse (RT_3), 216, 216t
Reverse cholesterol transport pathway, 466-467, 466f
disorders of, 473-474
Reverse T_3 (RT_3), 208
Reye's syndrome, 295
in older children, 103-105, 104t
Rheon, screening tests for, 119
Rheumatic disorders, 363
acute rheumatic fever, 372, 373f
inflammatory bowel disease, 370
juvenile ankylosing spondylitis, 368
juvenile dermatomyositis, 366-368
juvenile psoriatic arthritis, 369
juvenile rheumatoid arthritis, 364
Lyme disease, 372-374
neonatal lupus syndrome, 365
presentations of, patterns of, 363-364
progressive systemic sclerosis, 370-371
Reiter's syndrome, 369-370
SLE, 364-365
spondyloarthropathies, 368-370, 369t
systemic and joint disorders associated with infections, 371-372
vasculitis, 371
Rheumatic fever, 138-140, 139t
acute, 372, 373f
Rheumatoid arthritis, juvenile, 364
Rhizomelic chondrodysplasia punctata, 431t, 432
RIA, in TSH measurement, 209
Riboflavin, assessment of, status of, laboratory tests for, 588t
Rickets, 266-267
Right atrium, venovenous catheter in, schematic of, 26f
Right heart defects, 130-131, 131t
Risperidone, for Tourette's syndrome, 323-324
Rotor's syndrome, 90

Saccharopinuria, 437t
Salicylate(s)
clinical toxicology of, 552-556
poisoning by, nomogram for, 555, 555f
Sanfilippo syndrome, 424t
Sarcoma(s)
Ewing's, biological markers in, 491t
soft tissue, biological markers in, 491t
Sarcosinemia, 437t
Scheie syndrome, 424t
Schindler disease, 430t
SCID. *See* Severe combined immunodeficiency
Scintiscanning, thyroid, 218
Seizure(s). *See also* Epilepsy
categories of, 304
generalized
partial, treatment of, 306-310
secondarily, treatment of, 306-310
treatment of, 305-316
Selenium, assessment of, status of, laboratory tests for, 591t
Septo-optic dysplasia, in delayed puberty, 204
Sertoli cells, 184
Serum enzymes, in malabsorption evaluation, 113-114
Serum markers, of enzyme induction and release, 91-92
Serum thyroid binding, decreased, causes of, 213, 214t
Severe combined immunodeficiency, 352-357
types of, 352
X-linked, 345t, 352
Sex differentiation, described, 181
Sex steroids, effects on growth, 162
Sexual differentiation, 182-186
abnormal, 186
disorders related to, 186
biochemistry of, 182-185
differentiation of internal ducts and external genitalia in, 184-185
external genitalia in, 182
fertilization in, 182
formation of organs common to both sexes in, 182-184, 183f
genital ridges in, 182
gonadal differentiation in, 182-184, 183f
internal ducts in, 182
physiology of, 182-185

Short stature. *See also* Growth retardation
biochemical investigation in, basis for, 163-169, 163t-167t, 168f
causes of, 163t
routine evaluation of, 166t
Shwachman-Bodian syndrome, 121
Sialidosis, 430t
Sickle cell screening, in adolescents, 379
Sickling disorders, 606-610, 607f
SIDS (suddent infant death syndrome), 295
Signal transduction determination, in primary immunodeficiency disease evaluation, 344
Significant bacteriuria, 54
Situs defects, 134-135, 134t
Situs inversus otalis, 134-135, 134t
Skeletal growth, markers of growth hormone action and, 171
Skin, puncture of, for blood collection, 2, 2f
Skin fragility, in porphyrias, 530, 530t
SLE. *See* Systemic lupus erythematosus
Small bowel bacterial overgrowth tests, in malabsorption evaluation, 116-117
Sodium
in proximal tubule, 49
in renal diseases, 46
Sodium fluoride, for specimen collection, 9
Sodium nitroprusside, for hypertension, 73
Sodium valproate, liver damage in older children due to, 103
Soft tissue sarcomas, biological markers in, 491t
Somatic protein, 582
Somatostatin, 158
deficiency of, hypoglycemia due to, 293
Southeast Asian ovalocytosis, 622
Specialty testing, 14
Specific gravity, reagent strips for, 76
Specimen(s)
anticoagulant selection for, 8
bilirubinemia effects on, 7-8
collection of
blood, 1-4, 2f
CSF, 9-10
devices for, 8
EDTA in, 9
environment for, 9
feces, 10
heparin in, 9
laboratory instrumentation and methodology for, 13, 13t
sodium fluoride in, 9
urine, 10, 11t, 12f
evaporation of, 4, 6f
hemolysis effects on, 4, 7, 7t
interferences with, 4, 7-9
labelling of, 8
lipemia effects on, 7
microspecimens, centrifugation of, 9
reference ranges for, 12-13
transport of, 10
universal precautions with, 12
volume of, 4, 5f, 5t
α-Spectrin, defects of, in hereditary spherocytosis, 620
Spectrin, in red cell membrane, 617
Spherocytosis, hereditary, 619-621. *See also* Hereditary spherocytosis
Sphingomyelin, in respiratory distress syndrome, 19-21, 20t
Spondylitis, ankylosing, juvenile, 368
Spondyloarthropathy(ies), 368-370, 369t
SRY gene product, absent, conditions with, 187t
St. Vitus' dance, 139
"Stagnant loop" syndrome, 112
Stature
short, biochemical investigation in, basis for, 163-169, 163t-167t, 168f. *See also* Short stature
tall, biochemical investigation in, basis for, 169
Status epilepticus, treatment of, 315
Steatorrhoea, 112
Steroid(s)
adrenal
biosynthesis of, 225-229, 227f, 228t
control of, 229-230
catabolism of, 230, 231t
excretion of, 230, 231t
nomenclature of, 225, 226f
in precocious puberty, 197, 197f
structure of, 225, 226f
gonadal, in precocious puberty, 197, 197f
sex, effects on growth, 162
Steroid enzyme deficiencies, in delayed puberty, 201-202, 201t
Steroid hormone precursors, adrenal, biosynthesis of, 232
Stimulant(s), in psychiatric disorders, indications for and dosage of, 334t
Stool(s), fatty, 112
Storage proteins, in tumor diagnosis and management, 491-493, 491t
Streptococcal infections, group A β-hemolytic, in adolescents, 381-382
Streptolysin-streptodornase, in primary immunodeficiency disease evaluation, 344
Stress, metabolic, proteins and, 579, 580f
Substance abuse, 563-565
Substance use, among adolescents, 379-380
Sudden infant death syndrome (SIDS), 295
Sugar(s), fecal, pH and, in malabsorption evaluation, 118
Sulfite oxidase deficiency, 439t
Sumatriptan, for migraine headaches, 317-318
Supraglottitis, *vs.* laryngotracheobronchitis, 34-35, 35t
Suprapubic aspiration, 55
Surfactant
described, 18
for respiratory distress syndrome, 19, 20t
Surfactant deficiency, respiratory distress syndrome due to, 18

Surfactant protein B deficiency, congenital, 18-19
Surfactant replacement therapy, for respiratory distress syndrome, 19, 20t
Sweat test, in cystic fibrosis diagnosis, 122
Sydenham's chorea, 139, 139t
Systemic lupus erythematosus (SLE), 364-365
Systemic sclerosis, progressive, 370-371

T cell(s)
  cytotoxic, function of, defects of, in primary immunodeficiency disease evaluation, 344
  deficiencies of, 350-351
    chronic mucocutaneous candidiasis, 345t, 351
    combined with B cell deficiencies, 345t, 351-359. *See also specific disorder*
      immunophenotype in, 343t
    DiGeorge syndrome, 345t, 350-351
      immunophenotype in, 343t
T_3. *See* 3,5,3′-Triiodothyronine (T_3)
T_4. *See* 3,5,3′,5′-Thyroxine
TAAs. *See* Tumor-associated antigens
Tacrolimus (FK-506)
  following liver transplantation, 106-107
  therapeutic drug monitoring of, 549
Tall stature, biochemical investigation in, basis for, 169
Tamm-Horsfall glycoprotein (THG), 58
Tangier disease, 474
Targeted growth, abnormal, 128t, 134, 134t
tDT. *See* Terminal deoxynucleotidyl transferase
Telangiectasia, ataxia, hereditary, 345t, 357-358
Temperature, effects on binding of oxygen to hemoglobin, 604f, 605
Tension headaches, and migraine headaches, relationship between, 316
Terminal deoxynucleotidyl transferase (tDT), in tumor diagnosis and management, 491t, 496
Testes, "vanishing," 202, 203t
Testis determination
  conditions lacking, 186, 187t
  conditions with normal or partial, 186, 187t
"Testis determining factor" (TDF), 182-183, 183f
Testosterone
  from cholesterol
    biosynthesis of, enzymes in, 190t
    biosynthetic pathway of, 184, 185f
  in precocious puberty, 197, 197f
Tetanus toxoid, in primary immunodeficiency disease evaluation, 344
Tg. *See* Thyroglobulin
β-Thalassemia, 612-613
α-Thalassemia, 612
Thalassemia, described, 611
Thalassemia intermedia, 612
Thalassemia major, 613
Thalassemia syndromes, 611-617
  α-thalassemia, 612
  β-thalassemia, 612-613
  hereditary persistence of fetal hemoglobin, 616
  mutations causing, 613-615. *See also under* Mutation(s)
β-Thalassemia trait, 612
α-Thalassemia trait, 612
THBR. *See* Thyroid hormone binding ratio
Thelarche, premature, 196
Theophylline
  described, 550t
  metabolism of, 539
  therapeutic drug monitoring of, 546-547, 549t
Therapeutic drug monitoring, 533-550
  acetylsalicylic acid, 549t
  amikacin, 547
  aminoglycosides, 547
  amitriptyline, 549t
  analytical procedures for drug measurement in, 543
  anticonvulsant drugs, 543-544, 545t
  antineoplastic drugs, 547-548
  caffeine, 547
  carbamazepine, 549t
  cyclosporine, 548-549
  defined, 507
  desipramine, 549t
  digoxin, 544-546
  disopyramide, 549t
  doxapram, 547
  drug absorption in, 538-539
  drug metabolism in, 539
  free drug concentration in, 540-541
  general considerations in, 533-534
  gentamicin, 547
  imipramine, 549t
  immunosuppressive drugs, 548-550, 549t, 550t
  methotrexate, 549t
  noncompliance in, 541
  pharmacokinetic considerations in, 534-535, 535f
  phenytoin, 549t
  practical aspects of, 541-550, 542f, 545t, 549t, 550t
  primidone, 549t
  procainamide, 549t
  propranolol, 549t
  quinidine, 549t
  rationale for, 536-541, 537f
  requisition and report form for, 542f
  tacrolimus, 549
  theophylline, 546-547, 549t
  time of sampling in, 535-536, 536f
  tobramycin, 547
  in tumor management, 507-509, 509f, 510f
Thiamine, assessment of, status of, laboratory tests for, 588t
6-Thioguanine, toxicity of, in tumor management, 505-506, 505t
Thrombopoietin, in tumor diagnosis and management, 491t, 500
Thymic aplasia, 345t, 350-351
Thyroglobulin (Tg), 216, 217t
Thyroid antibodies, 217
Thyroid binding, decreased, causes of, 213, 214t

Thyroid function tests, 217-218
antibodies to T_4 and T_3, 217
applications of, 218-220, 219t
in Graves' disease, 218
in hyperthyroidism, 218-219, 219t
in hypothyroidism, 219
physiologic changes of, 209
radioactive thyroidal uptake, 218
scintiscanning, 218
thyroid antibodies, 217
ultrasonography, 218
Thyroid gland
cancer of, 222
disorders of, 207-224. *See also specific disorder, e.g.,* Hyperthyroidism
evaluation of, in patients receiving levo-thyroxine therapy, 220-221
function of, alterations in, in non-thyroidal illnesses, 220
structure of, 207
Thyroid hormone(s)
effects on growth, 161-162
homeostasis of, 207
measurements of, drug effects on, 222
resistance to, clinical syndromes of, 222-223
synthesis of, 208
transport of, 209
Thyroid hormone binding ratio (THBR), 209, 214, 215t, 216t
by age, 214, 215t
Thyroid-stimulating hormone (TSH), 207, 209-210, 210t
measurement of, 209
receptors for, antibodies against, 217
secretion of, 207-208
Thyroid-stimulating hormone (TSH) secretion, 158-159
Thyrotropin-releasing hormone (TRH), 207
Thyrotropin-releasing hormone (TRH) stimulation test, 210
3,5,3′,5′-Thyroxine (T_4), 207, 211-213, 212t-214t
age-related values for, 211-213, 212t
antibodies to, 217
secretion of, 208
transport of, 209
Thyroxine, free (FT_4), 213-216, 215t, 216t
Thyroxine-binding globulin (TBG), 211, 211t, 212t
Thyroxine-binding prealbumin (TBPA), 209
Thyroxine-binding proteins
abnormal serum concentration of, causes of, 211, 212t
binding of, causes of, 211, 212t
Titratable acid, in proximal tubule, 52
Tobramycin
described, 550t
therapeutic drug monitoring of, 547
α-Tocopherol, assessment of, status of, laboratory tests for, 588t
Topiramate
for epilepsy, 314
indications for, 314
side effects of, 314
Total body clearance, 534
Total energy expenditure (TEE), 576-577
Total iron binding capacity (TIBC), 563
Total lymphocyte count (TLC), in nutritional status, assessment of, 587, 593
Tourette's syndrome, 320-324
ADHD with, 321
clinical aspects of, 320-321
obsessive-compulsive disorder with, 321, 327
pathophyisology of, 321-322
treatment of, 322-324
Toxic cutaneous porphyria, 523
Toxicology
acetaminophen, 551-552, 553f
alcohol, 556-558
clinical, 551-565
ethylene glycol, 558-559
iron, 562-563, 563t
isopropanol, 558-559
lead, 559-562, 560f
methanol, 558-559
salicylates, 552-556
Trace elements, assessment of, status of, laboratory tests for, 590t-591t
Transdermal nicotine patch (TNP), for Tourette's syndrome, 324
Transferases, 91
Transferrin, in nutritional status, assessment of, 581
Transfusion medicine, 14
Transient hypogammaglobulinemia of infancy (THI), 345t, 347
Transient neonatal hyperinsulinism, 291
Transplantation
bone marrow, for congenital erythropoietic purpura, 521-522
liver, 105-107. *See also* Liver transplantation
renal, 69
Tricarboxylic acid cycle, energy production by, 576
Tricyclic antidepressants
for ADHD, 330-331
for major depressive disorder, 333
Triglyceride(s), concentration of, measurement of, 478-479
3,5,3′-Triiodothyronine (T_3), 207
age-related values for, 211-213, 212t
antibodies to, 217
reverse (RT_3), 208, 216, 216t
secretion of, 208
transport of, 209
L-Triiodothyronine sodium salt, 221
Triosephosphate isomerase deficiency, 626
TSH. *See* Thyroid-stimulating hormone
Tubular function tests, in renal diseases, 49
Tubular proteinuria, 58
Tubule(s)
distal, in proximal tubule, 52-53
proximal, 49-53. *See also* Proximal tubule
Tumor(s), 489-513. *See also specific types, e.g.,* Wilms' tumor
adrenal, steroid-producing, 241-242
CNS, biological markers in, 491t
germ cell, biological markers in, 491t

Tumor(s) *(Cont.)*
management of, 502-510
drug toxicity in
assessment of, 504-507, 505t
assessment ofdrug toxicity in. *See also specific drug, e.g.,* Methotrexate
tumor lysis syndrome, 502-504, 503f
therapeutic drug monitoring for, 507-509, 509f, 510f
Tumor lysis syndrome, management of, 502-504, 503f
Tumor markers, 489-501. *See also* Biological markers, in tumor diagnosis and management
Tumor-associated antigens (TAAs), in tumor diagnosis and management, 491t, 497
Turner syndrome
in delayed puberty, 201t, 202
male, 202-203, 203t
Tyrosinemia, 437t, 440t, 443-444
type 1, neonatal jaundice due to, 96t, 98

Ulcerative colitis, 120
Ultrasonography, thyroid, 218
Universal precautions, specimen-related, 12
Upper airway disease, 33-35, 34t, 35t
Upper airway obstruction, causes of, 33-34, 34t
Urea, in renal diseases, 47
Urea cycle disorders, 438t, 441t, 445-447
Urinalysis, 10, 11t
Urinary growth hormone, hormonal and biochemical investigation in, 170-171
Urinary nitrite, 56
Urinary tract disorders, 45-80
Urinary tract infections (UTIs), 53-57
diagnosis of, 54-56
gender predilection for, 53
localization of, 56-57
recurrence of, 53-54
Urine
for bacterial culture, 55
chemical analysis of, 76
collection of, 10, 11t, 12f
methods of, 54-55
bag sample, 55
catheter specimen, 55
mid-stream urine, 55
suprapubic aspiration, 55
osmolality of, calculation of, 53
preservation of, 10, 11t
volumes of, in normal pediatric population, 10, 12f
Urine net charge, 52-53
Urine osmolal gap, 53
Urine pCO_2, 53
Urine pH, in proximal tubule, 52
Urine tests, 10, 11t
Uropathy, obstructive, 65-66
Uroporphyrinogen decarboxylase deficiency disorders, 522-524
Uterine bleeding, dysfunctional, in adolescents, 383-384
UTIs. *See* Urinary tract infections

Valproate. *See* Valproic acid
Valproic acid
described, 550t
dosage of, 310
for epilepsy, 306t
generalized seizures, 310-311
mechanism of action of, 310
protein binding of, 540-541
side effects of, 311
therapeutic drug monitoring of, 544, 545t
Van Gierke disease, 433
Vanillylmandelic acid (VMA), in tumor diagnosis and management, 499-500
"Vanishing" testes, in delayed puberty, 202, 203t
Variation
analytical, 575
inter-individual, 573, 573f
intra-individual, 574
pre-analytical, 574-575
Variegate porphyria, 516t
enzyme deficiencies in, 519t
homozygous, 528
inheritance of, 519t
overproduction of heme precursors in, diagnostic patterns of, 522t
Vasculitis, 371
Vasodilation, for PPHN, 23
Venipuncture, for blood collection, 3-4
Verapamil, for migraine headaches, 319
Vigabatrin
for epilepsy, 314-315
side effects of, 314-315
Vincristine, toxicity of, in tumor management, 505t, 507
Virilization, 196
Visceral proteins
albumin, 579-581, 580t
ferritin, 580t, 581
fibronectin, 580t, 581
IGF-1, 581
in nutritional status, 579-582, 580t
prealbumin, 580t, 581
RBP, 580t, 581
transferrin, 581
Vitamin(s)
A, assessment of, status of, laboratory tests for, 588t
absorption of, 111
B_1, assessment of, status of, laboratory tests for, 588t
B_2, assessment of, status of, laboratory tests for, 588t
B_6, assessment of, status of, laboratory tests for, 588t-589t
B_{12}, assessment of, status of, laboratory tests for, 589t
C, assessment of, status of, laboratory tests for, 589t
D
assessment of, status of, laboratory tests for, 588t
disorders of, 256-257, 257f
effects on organ systems, 254, 255f
reference values of, 267, 268t
D_2, 256, 257f
D_3, disorders of, 256, 257f
E, assessment of, status of, laboratory tests for, 588t
K, assessment of, status of, laboratory tests for, 588t
status of, assessment of, laboratory tests for, 588t-589t
Vitamin B_{12} absorption tests, in malabsorption evaluation, 119